THE SIXTEENTH
MARCEL GROSSMANN MEETING

On Recent Developments in Theoretical and Experimental
General Relativity, Astrophysics and Relativistic Field Theories

PART D

THE SIXTEENTH
MARCEL GROSSMANN MEETING

On Recent Developments in Theoretical and Experimental
General Relativity, Astrophysics and Relativistic Field Theories

Proceedings of the MG16 Meeting
on General Relativity
Online, 5–10 July 2021

Editors

Remo Ruffini
University of Rome "La Sapienza", Rome, Italy
International Center for Relativistic Astrophysics Network (ICRANet), Pescara, Italy

Gregory Vereshchagin
International Center for Relativistic Astrophysics Network (ICRANet), Pescara, Italy

Series Editor

Remo Ruffini
University of Rome "La Sapienza", Rome, Italy
International Center for Relativistic Astrophysics Network (ICRANet), Pescara, Italy

NEW JERSEY • LONDON • SINGAPORE • BEIJING • SHANGHAI • HONG KONG • TAIPEI • CHENNAI

Published by

World Scientific Publishing Co. Pte. Ltd.

5 Toh Tuck Link, Singapore 596224

USA office: 27 Warren Street, Suite 401-402, Hackensack, NJ 07601

UK office: 57 Shelton Street, Covent Garden, London WC2H 9HE

Library of Congress Cataloging-in-Publication Data
Names: Marcel Grossmann Meeting on General Relativity (16th : 2021 : Online) | Ruffini, Remo, editor. | Vereshchagin, Gregory, editor.
Title: The sixteenth Marcel Grossmann meeting on recent developments in theoretical and experimental general relativity, astrophysics, and relativistic field theories : proceedings of the MG16 meeting on general relativity online, 5–10 July 2021 / editors: Remo Ruffini, University of Rome "La Sapienza", Rome, Italy, International Center for Relativistic Astrophysics Network (ICRANet), Pescara, Italy, Gregory Vereshchagin, International Center for Relativistic Astrophysics Network (ICRANet), Pescara, Italy.
Other titles: Proceedings of the MG16 meeting on general relativity online, 5–10 July 2021
Description: New Jersey : World Scientific, [2023] | Includes bibliographical references.
Identifiers: LCCN 2022047088 | ISBN 9789811269769 (set ; hardcover) | ISBN 9789811266584 (v. 1) | ISBN 9789811266591 (v. 2) | ISBN 9789811266607 (v. 3) | ISBN 9789811266614 (v. 4) | ISBN 9789811269776 (set ; ebook)
Subjects: LCSH: General relativity (Physics)--Congresses. | Gravitation--Congresses. | Quantum gravity--Congresses. | Cosmology--Congresses. | Astrophysics--Congresses.
Classification: LCC QC173.6 .M37 2021 | DDC 523.01--dc23/eng/20220929
LC record available at https://lccn.loc.gov/2022047088

British Library Cataloguing-in-Publication Data
A catalogue record for this book is available from the British Library.

Copyright © 2023 by Editors

All rights reserved.

This is an Open Access volume published by World Scientific Publishing Company. It is distributed under the terms of the Creative Commons Attribution-Non Commercial 4.0 (CC BY-NC) License. Further distribution of this work is permitted, provided the original work is properly cited.

For any available supplementary material, please visit
https://www.worldscientific.com/worldscibooks/10.1142/13149#t=suppl

Typeset by Stallion Press
Email: enquiries@stallionpress.com

Printed in Singapore

THE MARCEL GROSSMANN MEETINGS
Series Editor: REMO RUFFINI
Publications in the Series of Proceedings

Proceedings of the Sixteenth Marcel Grossmann Meeting on General Relativity
(Virtual Meeting, 2021)
Edited by G. Vereshchagin, R. Ruffini
World Scientific, 2022

Proceedings of the Fifteenth Marcel Grossmann Meeting on General Relativity
(Rome, Italy, 2018)
Edited by E.S. Battistelli, R.T. Jantzen, R. Ruffini
World Scientific, 2022

Proceedings of the Fourteenth Marcel Grossmann Meeting on General Relativity
(Rome, Italy, 2015)
Edited by M. Bianchi, R.T. Jantzen, R. Ruffini
World Scientific, 2017

Proceedings of the Thirteenth Marcel Grossmann Meeting on General Relativity
(Stockholm, Sweden, 2012)
Edited by K. Rosquist, R.T. Jantzen, R. Ruffini
World Scientific, 2015

Proceedings of the Twelfth Marcel Grossmann Meeting on General Relativity
(Paris, France, 2009)
Edited by T. Damour, R.T. Jantzen, R. Ruffini
World Scientific, 2012

Proceedings of the Eleventh Marcel Grossmann Meeting on General Relativity
(Berlin, Germany, 2006)
Edited by H. Kleinert, R.T. Jantzen, R. Ruffini
World Scientific, 2007

Proceedings of the Tenth Marcel Grossmann Meeting on General Relativity
(Rio de Janiero, Brazil, 2003)
Edited by M. Novello, S. Perez-Bergliaffa, R. Ruffini
World Scientific, 2005

Proceedings of the Ninth Marcel Grossmann Meeting on General Relativity
(Rome, Italy, 2000)
Edited by V.G. Gurzadyan, R.T. Jantzen, R. Ruffini
World Scientific, 2002

Proceedings of the Eighth Marcel Grossmann Meeting on General Relativity
(Jerusalem, Israel, 1997)
Edited by T. Piran
World Scientific, 1998

Proceedings of the Seventh Marcel Grossmann Meeting on General Relativity
(Stanford, USA, 1994)
Edited by R.T. Jantzen and G.M. Keiser
World Scientific, 1996

Proceedings of the Sixth Marcel Grossmann Meeting on General Relativity
(Kyoto, Japan, 1991)
Edited by H. Sato and T. Nakamura
World Scientific, 1992

Proceedings of the Fifth Marcel Grossmann Meeting on General Relativity
(Perth, Australia, 1988)
Edited by D.G. Blair and M.J. Buckingham
World Scientific, 1989

Proceedings of the Fourth Marcel Grossmann Meeting on General Relativity
(Rome, Italy, 1985)
Edited by R. Ruffini
World Scientific, 1986

Proceedings of the Third Marcel Grossmann Meeting on General Relativity
(Shanghai, People's Republic of China, 1982)
Edited by Hu Ning
Science Press – Beijing and North-Holland Publishing Company, 1983

Proceedings of the Second Marcel Grossmann Meeting on General Relativity
(Trieste, Italy, 1979)
Edited by R. Ruffini
North-Holland Publishing Company, 1982

Proceedings of the First Marcel Grossmann Meeting on General Relativity
(Trieste, Italy, 1975)
Edited by R. Ruffini
North-Holland Publishing Company, 1977

SPONSORS

International Center for Relativistic Astrophysics Network (ICRANet)
International Center for Relativistic Astrophysics (ICRA)

FREEDOM OF MOVEMENT FOR SCIENTISTS

The Marcel Grossmann Meetings were founded with the premise that scientists of all nations have a right to meet to exchange knowledge independent of national borders.

ACKNOWLEDGEMENTS

We acknowledge the outstanding job done before, during and after the meeting by the ICRANet/ICRA administrative and secretarial staff: Cristina Adamo, Silvia Latorre, Elisabetta Natale, and Cinzia di Niccolo. Finally this meeting and its proceedings could not have functioned without the dedicated IT support of the ICRANet system manager Gabriele Brandolini, with some temporary assistance from Domenico La Selva and Damiano Verzulli. We would like to thank Linda Kwan from World Scientific for valuable assistance during preparation of these proceedings.

ORGANIZING BODIES
OF THE SIXTEENTH MARCEL GROSSMANN MEETING

INTERNATIONAL ORGANIZING COMMITTEE

Blair David, Choquet Bruhat Yvonne, Damour Thibault, De Bernardis Paolo, Everitt C. W. Francis, Fryer Chris, Haensch Theodor, Henneaux Marc, Jones Christine, Kerr Roy, Kleinert Hagen, Kunz Jutta, Laemmerzahl Claus, Longair Malcolm, Mirabel Felix, Mirzoyan Razmik, Piran Tsvi, Rueda Jorge, Ruffini Remo (chair), Sasaki Misao, Sato Humitaka, Sunyaev Rashid, 't Hooft Gerard, Weinberg Steven, Yau Shing-Tung, Zhang Bing

LOCAL ORGANIZING COMMITTEE

Adamo Cristina, Bianco Carlo Luciano, Brandolini Gabriele A., di Niccolo Cinzia, Latorre Silvia, La Selva Domenico, Li Liang, Loppini Alessandro, Natale Elisabetta, Verzulli Damiano, Vereshchagin Gregory (chair), Wang Yu

INTERNATIONAL COORDINATING COMMITTEE

ALBANIA: Hafizi M. - ARGENTINA: Arguelles C., Scoccola C., Reula O., Romero G.E. - ARMENIA: Sahakyan N. - AUSTRALIA: Blair D., Ju L., Lun A., Manchester D., Melatos A., Quinn P., Scott S.M., Steele J.D. - AUSTRIA: Aichelburg P.C., Schindler S. - BELARUS: Kilin S., Prakapenia M., Siutsou I. - BELGIUM: Henneaux M. - BOLIVIA: Aguirre C.B. - BOSNIA: Pasic V. - BRAZIL: Barres de Almeida U., Coelho Goulart J., Dalmolin F.T., de Lima Rafael C.R., Guzzo M., Maia C., Malheiro M., Romero Filho C.A., Shellard R.C., Zen Vasconcellos C. - BULGARIA: Yazadjiev S. - CANADA: Singh D., Smolin L., Turok N. - CHILE: Bauer F., Bunster W.C., Giacomini A. - CHINA (MAINLAND): Cai R., Cai Y., Cao Z., Chang J., Chen J., Chen X., Dai Z., Feng L.-L., Han W., Jing Y., Li T.-P., Lin W., Lou Y.-Q., Luo J., Mei J., Tam T., Wang A., Wang Y., Wu X.-P., Wu Y.-L., Yuan Y.-F., Zhang B.-B., Zhang S.-N., Zhao G. - CHINA (TAIWAN): Chen Chiang-Mei, Chen Pisin, Lee Da-Shin, Lee Wo-Lung, Ni Wei-Tou - COLOMBIA: Bargueño de Retes P., Gonzalez G., Higuera Garzon M.A., Núñez L., Romano A.E., Valenzuela Toledo C.A., Zuluaga J.I. - CROATIA: Dominis Prester D., Karlica M., Milekovic M., Smolcic V., Smolic I., Suric T. - CUBA: Perez Martinez A., Pérez Rojas H. - CZECH REPUBLIC: Bicak J., Stuchlik Z. - DENMARK: Naselsky P. - ECUADOR: Contreras E. - EGYPT: Tawfik A.N., Wanas M.I. - ESTONIA: Einasto J., Saar E. - FINLAND: Poutanen J., Volovik G. - FRANCE: Brillet A., Buchert T., Chardonnet P., Coullet P., de Freitas Pacheco J.A., Deruelle N., Iliopoulos J., Lamanna G., Mignard F. - GEORGIA: Lavrelashvili George, Machabeli Giorgi - GERMANY: Biermann P., Blumlein J., Di Piazza A., Fritzsch H., Genzel R., Gilmozzi R., Hasinger G., Hehl F., Keitel C., Kiefer C., Mirzoyan R.,

Neugebauer G., Nicolai H., Renn J., Ringwald A., Ruediger A. - GREECE: Batakis N.A., Cotsakis S., Vagenas E.C. - HUNGARY: Fodor G., Levai P. - ICELAND: Bjornsson G., Jakobsson P. - INDIA: Chakrabarti S.K., Iyer B., Padmanabhan T., Souradeep T. - IRAN: Baghram S., Bavarsad E., Eslam Panah B., Firouzjahi H., Haghighat M., Mansouri R., Mashhoon B., Shakeri S., Sobouti Y., Taghi Mirtorabi M. - IRELAND: O'Murchada N. - ISRAEL: Milgrom M., Nakar E., Pe'er A., Piran T. - ITALY: Belinski V., Bianchi M., Bianco C.L., Cherubini C., Della Valle M., Falciano S., Filippi S., Haardt F., Menotti P., Merafina M., Pani P., Ricci F., Treves A., Vereshchagin G.V., Vitale S., Xue S.-S. - JAPAN: Fujimoto M.-K., Makishima K., Nakamura T., Sato K., Shibata M. - KAZAKHSTAN: Abishev M., Aimuratov Y., Boshkayev K., Mychelkin E.G., Spitaleri C. - KOREA (PYEONGYANG): Kim J.S. - KOREA (SEOUL): Kim S.P., Kim S.-W., Lee H.K., Lee H.-W., van Putten M. - KYRGYZSTAN: Gurovich V.Ts. - LIBYA: Gadri M. - MEXICO: Breton N., Cervantes-Cota J.L., Fraija Cabrera N.I., García-Diaz A.A., Macías Alvarez A., Mielke Eckehard W., Quevedo H., Rodriguez L.F. - NETHERLANDS: Slagter R. - NEW ZEALAND: Visser M., Wiltshire D. - NORWAY: Elgaroy O., Fonseca Mota D., Knutsen H. - PAKISTAN: Qadir A., Qamar S. - PERU: Vargas T. - POLAND: Belczynski K., Demianski M., Lewandowski Jerzy, Nurowski P., Sokolowski L. - PORTUGAL: Costa M., Da Silva A., Lemos J.P.S., Lobo F., Moniz P., Silva L.O. - ROMANIA: Visinescu M. - RUSSIA: Aksenov A., Arkhangelskaja I., Bisnovatyi-Kogan G., Blinnikov S., Chechetikin V.M., Cherepaschuk A.M., Khriplovich I., Lipunov V.M., Lukash V.N., Novikov I., Rudenko V.N., Starobinsky A.A. - SERBIA: Djordjevic G., Jovanovic P., Knezevic Z., Pankov-Hzvojevic M., Popovic L., Prodanovic T., Sijacki D., Simic S. - SLOVAKIA: Balek V. - SLOVENIA: Cadez A., Gomboc A., Zavrtanik D. - SOUTH AFRICA: Larena J., Maharaj S. - SPAIN: Elizalde E., Ibanez J., Perez M.J., Verdaguer E. - SWEDEN: Abramowicz M.A., Marklund M., Ryde F. - SWITZERLAND: Durrer R., Jetzer P. - TURKEY: Aliev A., Gurses M. - UKRAINE: Novosyadlyj B., Zaslavskii O., Zhuk A. - UNITED ARAB EMIRATES: Fernini I. - UNITED KINGDOM: Cruise A.M., Frenk Carlos S., Green M., Mavromatos N., Perry M., Willingale R. - USA: Abel T., Ashtekar A., Bardeen J., Carlstrom J., Cornish N., Dermer C., Fan X., Flanagan E., Fraschetti F., Fryer C., Incera V., Jantzen R.T. (chairperson), Kolb R., Laguna P., Lousto C., Madau Piero, Mathews Grant, Matzner Richard, Melia Fulvio, Mester John, Michelson Peter, Nordtvedt Kenneth, Parker Leonard, Pretorius F., Pullin J., Shapiro I., Shapiro S., Shoemaker D., Smoot G., Stiavelli M., Teukolsky S., van Nieuwenhuizen P., Zhang B. - UZBEKISTAN: Ahmedov B., Zalaletdinov R.M. - VATICAN CITY: Gionti G. - VENEZUELA: Fuenmayor E. - VIETNAM: Long H.N.

MARCEL GROSSMANN AWARDS

Sixteenth Marcel Grossmann Meeting

Institutional Awards

"for the creation of the world's best X-ray map of the entire sky, for the discovery of millions of previously unknown accreting supermassive black holes at cosmological redshifts, for the detection of X-rays from tens of thousands of galaxy clusters, filled mainly with dark matter, and for permitting the detailed investigation of the growth of the large-scale structure of the universe during the era of dark energy dominance".

S.A. LAVOCHKIN ASSOCIATION
- presented to its Designer General **Alexander Shirshakov**

MAX PLANCK INSTITUTE FOR EXTRATERRESTRIAL PHYSICS (MPE)
- presented to Professor **Peter Predehl**, Principal Investigator of eROSITA

SPACE RESEARCH INSTITUTE (IKI) OF THE RUSSIAN ACADEMY OF SCIENCES
- presented to Professor **Rashid Sunyaev**, Principal Investigator of SRG Observatory in Russia

Individual Awards

DEMETRIOS CHRISTODOULOU
"For his many lasting contributions to the foundation of mathematical physics including the dynamics of relativistic gravitational fields. Notably for: contributing in 1971, at the age of 19, to derive with Remo Ruffini the mass-energy formula of black holes as a function of their angular momentum, charge and irreducible mass. Christodoulou turned then to the study of partial differential equations and mathematical physics, to which he remained dedicated for the rest of his career. Highlights in this area include the theoretical discovery of the nonlinear memory effect of gravitational waves (Phys. Rev. Letters 1991), the monograph (1993) in collaboration with Sergiu Klainerman on the global nonlinear stability of the Minkowski spacetime, the monograph (2009) on the formation of black holes in pure general relativity by imploding gravitational waves, and the monographs (2007 and 2019) on the formation and further development of shocks in fluids."

GERARD 't HOOFT
"for his persistent devotion to the study of the quantum field theory boundary conditions at the black hole horizon".

TSVI PIRAN
"for extending Relativistic astrophysics across international frontiers, a true companion in the search for the deeper meaning of Einstein's great theory".

STEVEN WEINBERG
"for unwavering support for the MG meetings since their inception, a true companion in the search for the deeper meaning of Einstein's great theory".

Each recipient is presented with a silver casting of the TEST sculpture by the artist A. Pierelli. The original casting was presented to His Holiness Pope John Paul II on the first occasion of the Marcel Grossmann Awards.

15th Marcel Grossmann Meeting
July 2018, Rome, Italy

Institutional Awards

PLANCK SCIENTIFIC COLLABORATION (ESA)
"for obtaining important constraints on the models of inflationary stage of the Universe and level of primordial non-Gaussianity; measuring with unprecedented sensitivity gravitational lensing of Cosmic Microwave Background fluctuations by large-scale structure of the Universe and corresponding B-polarization of CMB, the imprint on the CMB of hot gas in galaxy clusters; getting unique information about the time of reionization of our Universe and distribution and properties of the dust and magnetic fields in our Galaxy"

- presented to Jean-Loup Puget, the Principal Investigator of the High Frequency Instrument (HFI)

HANSEN EXPERIMENTAL PHYSICS LABORATORY AT STANFORD UNIVERSITY
"to HEPL for having developed interdepartmental activities at Stanford University at the frontier of fundamental physics, astrophysics and technology"

- presented to Research Professor Leo Hollberg, HEPL Assistant Director

Individual Awards

LYMAN PAGE
"for his collaboration with David Wilkinson in realizing the NASA Explorer WMAP mission and as founding director of the Atacama Cosmology Telescope"

RASHID ALIEVICH SUNYAEV
"for the development of theoretical tools in the scrutinising, through the CMB, of the first observable electromagnetic appearance of our Universe"

SHING-TUNG YAU
"for the proof of the positivity of total mass in the theory of general relativity and perfecting as well the concept of quasi-local mass, for his proof of the Calabi conjecture, for his continuous inspiring role in the study of black holes physics"

14th Marcel Grossmann Meeting
July 2015, Rome, Italy

Institutional Award

EUROPEAN SPACE AGENCY (ESA)
"for the tremendous success of its scientific space missions in astronomy, astrophysics, cosmology and fundamental physics which have revolutionized our knowledge of the Universe and hugely benefited science and mankind"

- presented to its Director General Johann-Dietrich Woerner

Individual Awards

KEN'ICHI NOMOTO
"for heralding the role of binary systems in the evolution of massive stars"

MARTIN REES
"for fostering Research in black holes, gravitational waves and cosmology"

YAKOV G. SINAI
"for applying the mathematics of chaotic systems to physics and cosmology"

SACHIKO TSURUTA
"for pioneering the physics of hot neutron stars and their cooling"

FRANK C.N. YANG
"for deepening Einstein's geometrical approach to physics in the best tradition of Paul Dirac and Hermann Weyl"

T.D. LEE (award received by Yu-Qing Lou on behalf of Prof. T.D. Lee)
"for his work on white dwarfs motivating Enrico Fermi's return to astrophysics and guiding the basic understanding of neutron star matter and fields"

13th Marcel Grossmann Meeting
July 2012, Stockholm, Sweden

Institutional Award

ALBANOVA
for its innovative status as a joint institute established by Stockholm University and the Royal Institute of Technology and for fostering contributions to cosmology and astrophysics in the profound scientific tradition established by Oskar Klein.

- presented to the Rector of Stockholm University, Prof. Kåre Bremer.

Individual Awards

DAVID ARNETT
for exploring the nuclear physics and yet unsolved problems of the endpoint of thermonuclear evolution of stars, leading to new avenues of research in physics and astrophysics.

VLADIMIR BELINSKI and I.M. KHALATNIKOV
for the discovery of a general solution of the Einstein equations with a cosmological singularity of an oscillatory chaotic character known as the BKL singularity.

FILIPPO FRONTERA
for guiding the Gamma-ray Burst Monitor Project on board the BeppoSAX satellite, which led to the discovery of GRB X-ray afterglows, and to their optical identification.

12th Marcel Grossmann Meeting
July 2009, Paris, France

Institutional Award

INSTITUT DES HAUTES ÉSTUDES SCIENTIFIQUE (IHÉS)
for its outstanding contributions to mathematics and theoretical physics, and notably for having renewed basic geometrical concepts, and having developed new mathematical and physical aspects of spacetime.

- presented to Prof. Jean-Pierre Bourguignon

Individual Awards

JAAN EINASTO
for pioneering contributions in the discovery of dark matter and cosmic web and fostering research in the historical Tartu Observatory.

CHRISTINE JONES
for her fundamental contributions to the X-ray studies of galaxies and clusters tracing their formation and evolution and for her role in collaborations using clusters to study dark matter and in analyzing the effects of outbursts from supermassive black holes on the intracluster gas.

MICHAEL KRAMER
for his fundamental contributions to pulsar astrophysics, and notably for having first confirmed the existence of spin-orbit precession in binary pulsars.

11th Marcel Grossmann Meeting
July 2006, Berlin, Germany

Institutional Award

FREIE UNIVERSITÄT BERLIN

for the successful endeavor of re-establishing — in the spirit of the Humboldt tradition — freedom of thinking and teaching within a democratic society in a rapidly evolving cosmos

- presented to Dr. Dieter Lenzen, President of FUB

Individual Awards

ROY KERR

for his fundamental contribution to Einstein's theory of general relativity: "The gravitational field of a spinning mass as an example of algebraically special metrics."

GEORGE COYNE

for his committed support for the international development of relativistic astrophysics and for his dedication to fostering an enlightened relationship between science and religion.

JOACHIM TRUMPER

for his outstanding scientific contributions to the physics of compact astrophysical objects and for leading the highly successful ROSAT mission which discovered more than 200,000 galactic and extragalactic X-ray sources: a major step in the observational capabilities of X-ray astronomy and in the knowledge of our universe.

10th Marcel Grossmann Meeting
July 2003, Rio de Janeiro, Brazil

Institutional Award

CBPF (Brazilian Center for Research in Physics)
for its role as a teaching and research institution and as a place originating fundamental physics ideas in the exploration of the universe.

- presented to its founders Cesar Lattes, Josè Leite Lopez and Jayme Tiomno

Individual Awards

YVONNE CHOQUET-BRUHAT AND JAMES W. YORK, JR.
for separate as well as joint work in establishing the mathematical framework for proving the existence and uniqueness of solutions to Einstein's gravitational field equations.

YUVAL NE'EMAN
for his contributions to science, epistimology, mathematics and physics from subnuclear to space sciences.

9th Marcel Grossmann Meeting
July 2000, Rome, Italy

Institutional Award

SOLVAY INSTITUTES
for identifying and recording in discussions by the protagonists the crucial developments of physics and astrophysics in the twentieth century.

- presented to Jacques Solvay

Individual Awards

CECILLE AND BRYCE DEWITT
for promoting General Relativity and Mathematics research and inventing the "summer school" concept.

RICCARDO GIACCONI
for opening, five successive times, new highways for exploring the Universe.

ROGER PENROSE
for extending the mathematical and geometrical foundations of General Relativity.

8th Marcel Grossmann Meeting
June 1997, Jerusalem

Institutional Award

HEBREW UNIVERSITY
for its role as a cradle of Science and Humanities and for hosting the manuscripts of Albert Einstein.

- presented to M. Magidor, President of the Hebrew University of Jerusalem

Individual Awards

TULLIO REGGE
for his contributions to the interface between mathematics and physics leading to new fields of research of paramount importance in relativistic astrophysics and particle physics.

FRANCIS EVERITT
for leading the development of extremely precise space experiments utilizing superconducting technology to test General Relativity and the Equivalence Principle.

7th Marcel Grossmann Meeting
June 1994, Stanford, USA

Institutional Award

SPACE TELESCOPE SCIENCE INSTITUTE

for its critical role in the direction and operation of the Hubble Space Telescope, a truly unique international laboratory for the investigation and testing of general relativity in the context of modern astrophysics and cosmology.

- presented to Peter Stockman

Individual Awards

SUBRAHMANYAN CHANDRASEKHAR

for his contributions to the analysis of gravitational phenomena from Newton to Einstein and especially for leading the way to relativistic astrophysics with the concept of critical mass for gravitational collapse.

JIM WILSON

for having built on his experience in nuclear physics, thermonuclear reactions, and extensive numerical simulation to create a new testing ground for the novel concepts of relativistic astrophysics.

6th Marcel Grossmann Meeting
June 1991, Kyoto, Japan

Institutional Award

RITP

for keeping alive first in Hiroshima and them in Kyoto research in relativity, cosmology, and relativistic field theory and the development of a school of international acclaim.

- presented to Professor K. Tomita

Individual Awards

MINORU ODA

for participating in the pioneering work of the early sixties in X-ray astronomy and for his subsequent molding of an agile and diversified Japanese scientific space program investigating the deepest aspects of relativistic astrophysics.

STEPHEN HAWKING

for his contributions to the understanding of spacetime singularities and of the large scale structure of the Universe and of its quantum origins.

5th Marcel Grossmann Meeting
August 1988, Perth, Australia

Institutional Award

THE UNIVERSITY OF WESTERN AUSTRALIA
for its contributions to relativistic astrophysics.

- presented to the Vice Chancellor, Professor Robert Smith

Individual Awards

SATIO HAYAKAWA
for his contributions to research in gamma, X-ray and infrared radiation as well as cosmic rays.

JOHN ARCHIBALD WHEELER
for his contributions to geometrodynamics and Einstein's visions.

4th Marcel Grossmann Meeting
July 1985, Rome, Italy

Institutional Award

THE VATICAN OBSERVATORY
for its contributions to the origin and development of astrophysics.

- presented to His Holiness Pope John Paul II

Individual Awards

WILLIAM FAIRBANK
for his work in gravitation and low temperature physics.

ABDUS SALAM
for his work in unifying fundamental interactions.

Institutional Awards for the Spektrum-Roentgen-Gamma (SRG) mission

"for the creation of the world's best X-ray map of the entire sky, for the discovery of millions of previously unknown accreting supermassive black holes at cosmological redshifts, for the detection of X-rays from tens of thousands of galaxy clusters, filled mainly with dark matter, and for permitting the detailed investigation of the growth of the large-scale structure of the universe during the era of dark energy dominance".

S.A. LAVOCHKIN ASSOCIATION
- presented to its Designer General **Alexander Shirshakov**

MAX PLANCK INSTITUTE FOR EXTRATERRESTRIAL PHYSICS (MPE)
- presented to Professor **Peter Predehl**, Principal Investigator of eROSITA

SPACE RESEARCH INSTITUTE (IKI) OF THE RUSSIAN ACADEMY OF SCIENCES
- presented to Professor **Rashid Sunyaev,** Principal Investigator of SRG Observatory in Russia

On Tuesday June 29, 2021, the following 31 astro-ph appeared:

1. https://arxiv.org/abs/2106.14517
2. https://arxiv.org/abs/2106.14518
3. https://arxiv.org/abs/2106.14519
4. https://arxiv.org/abs/2106.14520
5. https://arxiv.org/abs/2106.14521
6. https://arxiv.org/abs/2106.14522
7. https://arxiv.org/abs/2106.14523
8. https://arxiv.org/abs/2106.14524
9. https://arxiv.org/abs/2106.14525
10. https://arxiv.org/abs/2106.14526
11. https://arxiv.org/abs/2106.14527
12. https://arxiv.org/abs/2106.14528
13. https://arxiv.org/abs/2106.14529
14. https://arxiv.org/abs/2106.14530
15. https://arxiv.org/abs/2106.14531
16. https://arxiv.org/abs/2106.14532
17. https://arxiv.org/abs/2106.14533
18. https://arxiv.org/abs/2106.14534
19. https://arxiv.org/abs/2106.14535
20. https://arxiv.org/abs/2106.14536
21. https://arxiv.org/abs/2106.14537
22. https://arxiv.org/abs/2106.14541
23. https://arxiv.org/abs/2106.14542
24. https://arxiv.org/abs/2106.14543
25. https://arxiv.org/abs/2106.14544
26. https://arxiv.org/abs/2106.14545
27. https://arxiv.org/abs/2106.14546
28. https://arxiv.org/abs/2106.14547
29. https://arxiv.org/abs/2106.14548
30. https://arxiv.org/abs/2106.14549
31. https://arxiv.org/abs/2106.14550

S.A. LAVOCHKIN ASSOCIATION
presented to its Designer General **Alexander Shirshakov**

Dr Alexander Shirshakov

S.A. Lavochkin Association created the Navigator space platform carrying German eRosita and Russian ART-XC X-Ray Telescopes, organized the launch of SRG Orbital X-Ray Observatory to the second Lagrangian point of the Sun-Earth system at a distance of 1.5 million km from the Earth and managed the observatory flight and the daily reception of its scientific data on Earth for 23.5 months.

Dr Alexander Shirshakov, Designer General of the S.A. Lavochkin Association, is specialized in design, manufacture, testing, launch and control of S/C for scientific purposes. Among those S/C launched, there are the «Radiostron» Astrophysical Observatory (2011) and the «Spektr-RG» space observatory (2019), while the planned S/C launches are «Luna-25» and «Exomars».

Dr Shirshakov started his career in 1973, working as an engineer of the State Unitary Enterprise «NPO named by S.A. Lavochkin» in Khimki (Russian Federation). Starting from 1989 he has played multiple roles within the Lavochkin Association, been appointed head of the group, head of the sector, head of department, deputy head of the complex, head of the branch, director of the center, deputy head of the Design Bureau, deputy General Designer and deputy General Director.

Dr Shirshakov is an editorial board Member of the reviewed edition of «Vestnik of Lavochkin Association». Since 2017, he is also member of the General Designer council. He has been awarded Honored Mechanical engineer of the Russian Federation as well as Agency-level award of the Russian Federal Space Agency.

MAX PLANCK INSTITUTE FOR EXTRATERRESTRIAL PHYSICS (MPE)
presented to Professor **Peter Predehl**, Principal Investigator of eROSITA

Professor Peter Predehl

eROSITA is the soft X-ray telescope on-board the Russian-German Spektr-RG mission which was successfully launched from Baikonur on July 13, 2019 and placed in a halo orbit around the L2 point. 30 years after ROSAT, eROSITA performs an all-sky survey with an unprecedented sensitivity, spectral and angular resolution. Clusters of galaxies are the largest collapsed objects in the Universe. Their formation and evolution is dominated by gravity, i.e. Dark Matter, while their large scale distribution and number density depends on the geometry of the Universe, i.e. Dark Energy. X-ray observations of clusters of galaxies provide information on the rate of expansion of the Universe, the fraction of mass in visible matter, and the amplitude of primordial fluctuations which are the origin of clusters of galaxies and the whole structure of the universe. eROSITA has been designed to detect at least 100.000 clusters of galaxies and to detect systematically more than 3 million obscured accreting Black Holes. eROSITA will also allow to study the physics of galactic X-ray source populations, like pre-main sequence stars, supernova remnants and X-ray binaries. The eROSITA telescope consists of seven identical Wolter-1 mirror modules. A novel detector system has been developed by MPE on the basis of the successful XMM-Newton pn-CCD technology. MPE is the scientific lead institute of eROSITA, responsible for the development of the instrument, the operation, the analysis software and data archive. Peter Predehl led this development as Principal Investigator of eROSITA and German lead scientist of the SRG mission for more than 15 years until the completion of the first of eight surveys in 2020. At this time eROSITA has already discovered more than 1 million X-ray sources, more than all X-ray observatories of the last 50 years together. This demonstrates that the design goals of the mission will easily be fulfilled.

SPACE RESEARCH INSTITUTE (IKI) OF THE RUSSIAN ACADEMY OF SCIENCES
presented to Professor **Rashid Sunyaev**

Professor Rashid Sunyaev

Space Research Institute (IKI) of the Russian Academy of Sciences was responsible for developing the overall concept and scientific program of the SRG Orbital observatory and played a leading role in developing the ART-XC telescope and the entire SRG observatory as part of the Russian space science program carried out by Roskosmos Corporation in the interests of the Russian Academy of Sciences.

During the flight to the L2 point of the Sun-Earth system, SRG with German (eRosita) and Russian (ART-XC named after Mikhail Pavlinsky) X-ray Telescopes aboard performed calibrations and long duration Performance Verification observations of a dozen of targets and deep fields. Starting in the middle of December 2019, the SRG scanned the whole sky three times. During these scans, SRG discovered two million point X-ray sources: mainly quasars, stars with hot and bright coronae, and more than 30 thousand clusters of galaxies. There is a competition and synergy in the search for clusters of galaxies between SRG and the ground-based Atacama Cosmology and South Pole Telescopes, which are searching for clusters of galaxies in microwave spectral band using Sunyaev-Zeldovich effect.

SRG provided the X-Ray map of the whole sky in hard and soft bands, the last is now the best among existing. The huge samples of the X-ray selected quasars at the redshifts up to $z = 6.2$ and clusters of galaxies will be used for well-known cosmological tests and detailed study of the growth of the large scale structure of the Universe during and after reionization. SRG/eRosita is discovering every day several extragalactic objects which increased or decreased their brightness more than 10 times during half of the year after the previous scan of the same one-degree wide strip on the sky. A significant part of these objects has observational properties similar to the Events of Tidal Disruption of a star orbiting in the vicinity of the supermassive black hole. ART-XC discovered a lot of bright galactic and extragalactic transients.

Rashid Sunyaev is the Principal Investigator of SRG mission in Russia, director-emeritus of the Max-Planck Institute for Astrophysics and Maureen and John Hendricks distinguished visiting professor of the Institute for Advanced Study, Princeton.

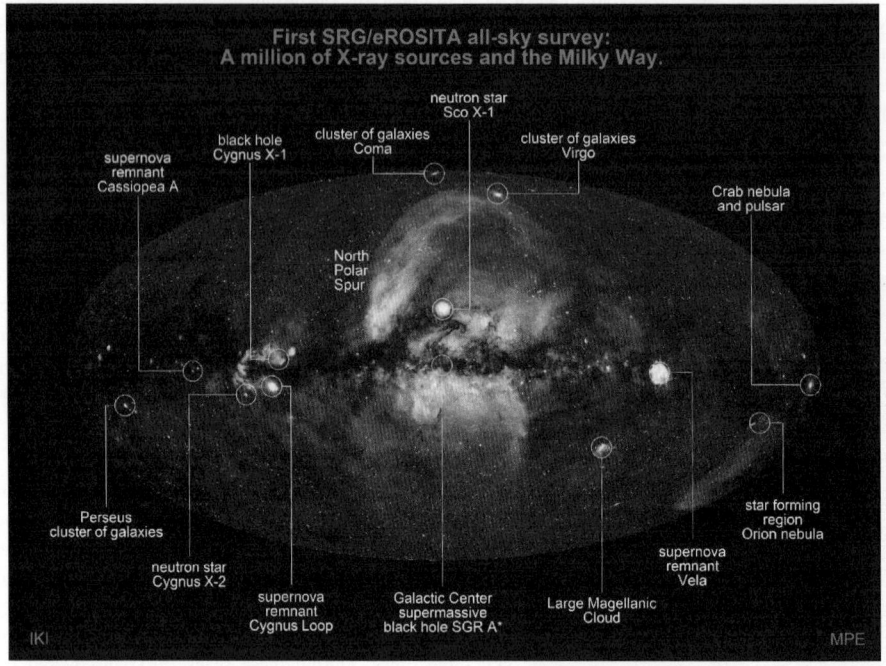

Individual Awards

Professor **DEMETRIOS CHRISTODOULOU**

"For his many lasting contributions to the foundation of mathematical physics including the dynamics of relativistic gravitational fields. Notably for: contributing in 1971, at the age of 19, to derive with Remo Ruffini the mass-energy formula of black holes as a function of their angular momentum, charge and irreducible mass. Christodoulou turned then to the study of partial differential equations and mathematical physics, to which he remained dedicated for the rest of his career. Highlights in this area include the theoretical discovery of the nonlinear memory effect of gravitational waves (Phys. Rev. Letters 1991), the monograph (1993) in collaboration with Sergiu Klainerman on the global nonlinear stability of the Minkowski spacetime, the monograph (2009) on the formation of black holes in pure general relativity by imploding gravitational waves, and the monographs (2007 and 2019) on the formation and further development of shocks in fluids."

Professor Demetrios Christodoulou

It was back in 1967 that Achille Papapetrou mentioned the case of the 16-year-old Demetrios Christodoulou to John Archibad Wheeler. Wheeler interviewed Demetrios in Paris and brought him immediately to Princeton where he was registered as an undergraduate at the university. After one year he entered the graduate school and started collaborating with me. At the time I was working with Wheeler on the effective potential approach to geodesics co-rotating and counter-rotating (see e.g. reference in The Classical Theory of Fields (Landau and Lifshitz, 1980) in the Kerr metric (later renamed as ISCO; see e.g. (Gravitation Misner, Thorne, Wheeler. 1973). In parallel, Frank Zerilli was working on the gravitational radiation emitted by the fall of a test particle in a Schwarzschild black hole (Zerilli 1970). From these limited conceptual arena Charles Misner and later Kip Thorne launched a program for the detection of gravitational waves on the Earth; see e.g. Misner 1974, Abbott et al. 2016, Abbott et al. 2017. See however Davis et al. 1972, Rodriguez et al. 2018 and J.A. Rueda et al. 2018.

A new approach started with the arrival of Demetrios: he was just creating mathematics following his needs. We identified the reversible and irreversible transformations of a Kerr black hole. Wheeler advanced a thermodynamic analogy. I addressed the need of identifying the concept of irreducible mass (from the Italian "irriducibile"), and was Demetrios's contribution to integrate, overnight, the differential equation for infinitesimal reversible transformations which led to the finite mass-energy formula of a Kerr black hole. That evening, while walking back home through IAS woods, I expressed to Wheeler the great relevance of the newly found formula by Demetrios and proposed to let Demetrios be the single author of this article, admiring his great mathematical talent. Wheeler agreed. The Editor of PRL objected since in that two pages article the Fig. 2 by Wheeler and myself was still unpublished. Actually that Fig. 2 followed a discussion I previously had with Penrose in Florence (Penrose 1961) which allowed us to present there, for the first time, a "Penrose Process". Some difficulties in achieving this process were obvious from the example in Fig. 2, which Roger later recognized himself (Penrose & Floyd 1971). The Editor finally agreed on our written request and the paper appeared on September 17, 1970 (Christodoulou, 1970). On January 1971 appeared my article with Johnny introducing the Black Hole (Ruffini & Wheeler, 1971), with the new physics we were developing in Princeton, including the concept of the "ergosphere". On march 1 1971 we submitted the mass formula of the Kerr Newmann metric, including the relation between the surface area of the horizon and the irreducible (Christodoulou & Ruffini, 1971). On March 11, 1971 the same results were independently confirmed by Steven Hawking, extending further the applicability of our equation (Hawking 1971).

The thesis was successfully discussed by a committee including Eugene Wigner (see Fig. 1), one of the closest collaborators of Albert Einstein and David Wilkinson (see Fig. 2), the head of the NASA WMAP mission, and Johnny and myself as supervisors. The new message was clear: Black Holes, far from being a sink of energy, were energy sources emitting "in principle" 50% of their mass energy, being extractable (Christodoulou & Ruffini, 1971).

Fig. 1 and Fig. 2: Demetrios during his thesis presentation with Eugene Wigner (Fig. 1) and David Wilkinson (Fig.2). Johnny and I were supervisors, ready to intervene in case of need, but no need of intervention was necessary! Wigner elaborated the aphorism of Niels Bohr "Interesting = wrong" in the most definite "very interesting if true = totally wrong".

Demetrios turned soon to the study of partial differential equations and mathematical physics, to which he dedicated for the rest of his career and results were published in four monographs: (Christodoulou and Klainerman 1994, Christodoulou 2007, Christodoulou 2009, Christodoulou 2019). In 1968, Johnny proposed to Demetrios the collapse of a "geon" composed of massless scalar field as a second topic for his thesis. It took almost forty years for him to solve this problem, extended by Demetrios to the focusing of gravitational waves leading to black hole formation (Christodoulou 2009).

Fig. 3: Prof. Remo Ruffini receiving the Cressy Morrison Award of the New York Academy of Sciences, 1972 for the discovery of the first Black Hole in our galaxy Cygnus X1.

A "long march" started on 12 December 1970 with the launch of the Uhuru satellite by Riccardo Giacconi. Early in 1971 an almost daily conversation with him and Herb Gursky at the Smithsonian Astrophysical Observatory, leading to the discovery of binary X-ray sources. This was soon followedby the announcement of Cygnus X1 identified as the first black hole in our galaxy (Ruffini 1973); see e.g. Gursky & Ruffini 1975, which contained as well the first publicannouncement of the Discovery of Gamma Ray burst, as well as Giacconi & Ruffini 1980, 2009; see Figs. 3 and 4).

Fig. 4: In the second row, from left to right, there are, among others: E. T. Newman, S. Chandrasekhar (Nobel 1983), R. Giacconi (Nobel 2002), R. Ruffini, A. Treves, A. Hewish (Nobel 1974), D. Arnett, J.H. Taylor (Nobel 1993), J. Wilson, R. Penrose (Nobel 2020), as well as J. Bahcall, T. Damour, T. Piran et al.

Today, after fifty years, this "long march" has reached a definite result: through the grandest observational multi-wavelength effort in the history of mankind, from space, ground and underground observatories, we are finally finding evidence that black holes are "alive" and their "extractable energy" in our mass formula (Christodoulou & Ruffini, 1971), is the energy source of the most energetic cosmological sources: gamma ray bursts (GRBs),the active galactic nuclei (AGNs) as well as the ultra-high energy cosmic rays (UHECRs) (Ruffini et al. 2021 and references therein). Their "inner engine", has three independent components: 1) a Kerr black hole which is neither in a stationary state nor in vacuum, 2) a background magnetic field aligned with the black hole rotation axis, and 3) an extremely diluted fully ionized plasma (Moradi et al. 2021).There is no role in this inner engine for ISCO. Indeed a new electro dynamical field equations describe the synchrotron radiation emitted close to the black hole horizon, they point to a discrete and repetitive emission of "blackholic quanta" in the MeV and in the GeV. The magnitudes and the emission time scales of these quanta, for M87 and GRB 130427A, are expressed as a function of the above three parameters (Rueda & Ruffini, 2021). A long lasting GeV emission with a luminosity decreasing as a temporal power law, allows for the first time in GRBs, the determination of the black hole mass and spin as well as their time evolution perfectly fulfilling our mass energy formula (Christodoulou & Ruffini, 1971): a long lasting emission process profoundly different from the traditional process of continued gravitational contraction.

Remo Ruffini

Professor GERARD 't HOOFT

"for his persistent devotion to the study of the quantum field theory boundary conditions at the black hole horizon".

Prof. Gerard 't Hooft has been a full Professor at the Utrecht University (the Netherlands), since 1977. Nowadays, he is an Emeritus Professor at that University. During his career, he has paid extended scientific visits to CERN (Geneva), Harvard, Stanford, Princeton and Duke University, NC. In 1999, together with M. Veltman, he received the Nobel Prize in Physics, awarded by The Royal Swedish Academy of Sciences, *"For elucidating the quantum structure of electroweak interactions in physics".*

Prof. 't Hooft's main subjects of research includes:

– Gauge Theories for the sub-atomic particles and forces, various aspects and ingredients of what is now called "The Standard Model of the sub-atomic particles: renormalizability, topological features such as magnetic monopoles and instantons, 1/N expansions.

– Theories for the quantization of the gravitational force and black holes: producing models for the quantum properties of a black hole, as derived from Standard Model and General Relativity alone; its topological features such as antipodal identification.

Professor Gerard 't Hooft

– Fundamental theories underlying quantum mechanics, in particular returning determinism and reality to the dynamics of the tiniest material entities in his universe.

Prof. 't Hooft has been awarded the Wolf Prize of the State of Israel (1982), the Pius XI Medal (Vatican City, 1983), the Lorentz Medal (KNAW Amsterdam, 1986) as well as the Spinoza Premium (Netherlands Organization for Scientific Research NWO, 1995).

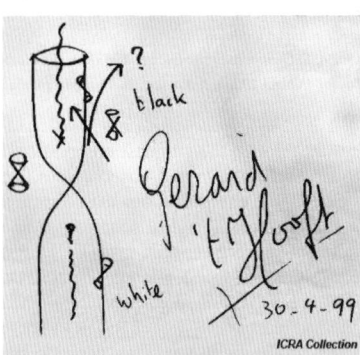

Fig. 2: The signature of Gerard 't Hooft on the wall of ICRA Room 301 (April 4, 1999).

A special event took place at ICRA on April 30, 1999. Prof. Ruffini invited Gerard 't Hooft to Rome to discuss a boundary condition for a quantum field on the black hole horizon, a topic Prof. Ruffini discussed in a previous article "Black-hole evaporation in the Klein-Sauter-Heisenberg-Euler formalism" with Thibault Damour (Phys. Rev. D 14, 332, 1976), but which needed to be examined in more detail. Prof. Ruffini planned to direct Gerard's attention to some specific aspects of this problem. Because we have traditionally been very attentive in spending ICRA travel funds, ICRA offered Gerard to come to Rome on a reduced fare weekend ticket arriving Friday and departing Monday. He had a great relaxing weekend together with Prof. Ruffini following his seminar, which among other things allowed Gerard to sign the wall in our ICRA Room (see Fig. 2), and during this splendid Rome spring weekend he also was able to find a missing factor of 2 in a formula in Prof. Ruffini's 1971 paper with Demetri Christodoulou on the black hole mass formula. The following October, Gerard received the Nobel prize, which meant that we could no longer get away with bringing him to Rome on a cheap ticket! Ever since Gerard has been in our MG IOC helping us with the preparation of the meetings. We are very happy to announce this MG16 Award to Gerard 't Hooft with the motivating phrase *"for his persistent devotion to the study of the quantum field theory boundary conditions at the black hole horizon".*

Remo Ruffini

Professor **TSVI PIRAN**

"for extending relativistic astrophysics across international frontiers, a true companion in the search for the deeper meaning of Einstein's great theory".

Professor Tsvi Piran

Tsvi Piran is the emeritus Schwartzmann professor at the Hebrew University of Jerusalem. He obtained his PhD in Physics, in 1976 from the Hebrew University working on the collisional Penrose process. Piran returned to the Hebrew University at 1981after being a post doc at Oxford and Texas and a long-term member at the IAS at Princeton. In 1982 he initiated and directed the first ever summer school on Gravitational Waves that took place at Les Houches. Piran was a visiting professor at Harvard, Columbia and New York and a Moore scholar at Caltech.

Piran's research deals with numerous aspects of relativistic astrophysics, ranging from the foundation of numerical relativity to modeling of observer relativistic phenomena and analytic work on the fate of gravitational collapse. Piran's research work focuses mostly on black holes and in particular on gamma-ray bursts. He was among the first to point out their cosmological origin and their association with merging neutron stars and heavy r-process nucleo synthesis. Piran's achievements were recognized in the 2019 EMET prize for Physics.

Professor **STEVEN WEINBERG**

"for unwavering support for the MG meetings since their inception, a true companion in the search for the deeper meaning of Einstein's great theory".

Professor Steven Weinberg. Photo courtesy of Matt Valentine.

Steven Weinberg is a member of the Physics and Astronomy Departments at The University of Texas at Austin. His research has covered a broad range of topics in quantum field theory, elementary particle physics and cosmology. He has been honored with numerous awards, including the Nobel Prize in Physics, the National Medal of Science, the Heinemann Prize in Mathematical Physics and in 2020, the Breakthrough Prize. He is a member of the US National Academy of Sciences, Britain's Royal Society, and other academies in the USA and abroad. The American Philosophical Society awarded him the Benjamin Franklin Medal, with a citation that said he is "considered by many to be the preeminent theoretical physicist alive in the world today." His books for physicists include *Gravitation and Cosmology*, the three-volume work *The Quantum Theory of Fields*, *Cosmology* and published in April of 2021, *Foundations of Modern Physics*. Educated at Cornell, Copenhagen, and Princeton, he also holds honorary degrees from sixteen other universities. He taught at Columbia, Berkeley, M.I.T., and Harvard, where he was Higgins Professor of Physics, before coming to Texas in 1982.

Fig. 1: Chuo Pei Yuan and Cheng Ning Yang at MG2 in Trieste, Italy (1979).

The Sixteenth Marcel Grossmann Meeting (MG16) is a very special one in many respects: it will take place during a pandemic and in spite of the many difficulties, we have decided not to postpone it but to organize it as a virtual meeting. As described on the MG series webpage, these meetings started in 1975 with the first meeting at the International Centre for Theoretical Physics (ICTP) in Trieste (Italy) that I organized with Nobel Prize winner Abdus Salam. A second meeting followed in 1979, with a significantly larger participation including Nobel Laurate Cheng Ning Yang and a Chinese delegation led by Chuo Pei Yuan (see Fig. 1), including Fang Li-Zhi who had accompanied me during my entire first visit to China in 1979. The first truly international MG meeting followed in 1982 in Shanghai (China):this represented an especially important step forward both for the meeting and for China. A multi-millennia *"motto"* in China, which was then proclaimed on banners everywhere, read *"Friends from all over the world are welcomed"*.

We were soon at an impasse over the participation of scientists from Israel, since no diplomatic relations existed between China and Israel at that time and the Israeli scientists were not to be allowed to attend the meeting. A long negotiation began. The boundary conditions were clearly set by Steven Weinberg, a member of the present MG16 IOC: no MG meetings on Einstein's theory of general relativity could occur without the participation of Israeli scientists. The intervention of Yuval Ne'emann, also a member of the MG IOC then as well as the Minister of Science of Israel (see Fig.2), proposed a compromise that would admit at least one Israeli scientist. I went to Beijing alone, meeting every morning for a week with 12 Chinese representatives led by Chuo Pei Yuan going over all possible options. I stayed in an isolated villa not far from Tiananmen Square, accompanied by the 3 volumes of Matteo Ricci (RI MA TO) to keep me company. No solution was in sight the entire week. At the last moment, just before my departure, an agreement was finally reached allowing two Israeli scientists into China. The historic compromise would admit Gerard Tauber and Tsvi Piran into China using a special ICRA travel document I had proposed for them to be able to participate in the meeting, accepted by the Chinese Ambassador in Rome. This modified the thousand-year Chinese *"motto"* to read *"Scientists from all over the world are welcomed"*. The event was extremely beneficial for China and signaled the truly international nature of the MG meetings.

Fig. 2: From right to left: Chaim Weizmann, President of Israel; Yuval Ne'emann, Minister of Science of Israel; R. Ruffini.

I kept on meeting Tauber in the years which followed (see Fig. 3). Soon after, Yuval Ne'emann visited China. The development of bilateral relations, including military cooperation and economical tights, grow exponentially until the establishment of normal diplomatic relations between Israel and China in 1992.

Fig. 3: From right to left: Arrigo Finzi, Remo Ruffini, Gerard Tauber and Konrad Bleuler.

Fig. 4: Albert Einstein, Hideki Yukawa and John. A. Wheeler with a handwritten dedication to Remo Ruffini "To Remo Ruffini, companion in the search for the deeper meaning of Einstein great theory. With warm regards, John Wheeler 5 April 1968".

Given their key role played in the foundations of the MG meetings, I am very happy to propose on behalf of the MG16 IOC, two special Marcel Grossmann Individual Awards: one to Steven Weinberg for *"for unwavering support for the MG meetings since their inception, a true companion in the search for the deeper meaning of Einstein's great theory"* and another one to Tsvi Piran, *"for extending Relativistic astrophysics across international frontiers, a true companion in the search for the deeper meaning of Einstein's great theory"*, in the words of John A. Wheeler's photo dedication to me (see Fig. 4).

Remo Ruffini

PREFACE

Since 1975, the Marcel Grossmann Meetings on Recent Developments in Theoretical and Experimental General Relativity, Gravitation, and Relativistic Field Theories have been organized in order to provide opportunities for discussing recent advances in gravitation, general relativity and relativistic field theories, emphasizing mathematical foundations, physical predictions and experimental tests. The objective of these meetings is to elicit exchange among scientists that may deepen our understanding of spacetime structures as well as to review the status of ongoing experiments aimed at testing Einstein's theory of gravitation either from the ground or from space. Previous meetings have been held in Trieste (MG1: 1975) and (MG2: 1979), Shanghai (MG3: 1982), Rome (MG4: 1985, MG9: 2000), Perth (MG5: 1988), Kyoto (MG6: 1991), Stanford (MG7: 1994), Jerusalem (MG8: 1997), Rio (MG10: 2003), Berlin (MG11: 2006), Paris (MG12: 2009), Stockholm (MG13: 2012), MG14 in 2015 and MG15 in 2018 both in Rome.

Due to the COVID-19 pandemic spreading in the last two years the decision was taken to organize the Sixteenth Marcel Grossmann meeting for the first time in history entirely online. Despite numerous challenges, related to the organization of large worldwide event, MG16 showed the strongest ever interest from the scientific community with a record-breaking number of almost 1200 registered participants and of more than 1000 speakers.

The traditional six-day schedule has been modified to account for different time zones of the speakers and each day the program of the meeting was divided in three blocks with the reference to the Central European Summer Time. The first block was starting at 06:30 in the morning, allowing comfortable time for speakers from Asia and Oceania. The second block was held in the daytime in Europe and Africa. The third block was starting in the afternoon and ending at 19:30 allowing accommodation of the speakers from the Americas. Each day the blocks of plenary sessions were interchanging with the blocks of about 30 parallel sessions each, making this one of the most intense MG meetings ever. All this was possible thanks to recent developments in communication technologies. The Indico open-source software was selected as a web platform for this meeting, while Zoom platform was adopted for the video-conferencing. The meeting was streamed on ICRANet YouTube channel.

The meeting started on Monday July 5 with the Award ceremony. The individual awards went to Demetrios Christodoulou, Tsvi Piran, Gerard 't Hooft and Steven Weinberg, while the Institutional Awards went to the S.A. Lavochkin Association, to the Max Planck Institute for Extraterrestrial Physics – MPE and to the Space Research Institute IKI of the Russian Academy of Sciences. Overall there were 54 plenary talks, 4 public lectures and 5 roundtables and about 90 parallel sessions. The plenary session "Events in Relativistics Astrophysics" on Monday have seen the contributions from Rashid Sunyaev, Michael Kramer, James Miller-Jones, Felix Mirabel. The public lectures were delivered by Razmik Mirzoyan, Asghar Qadir and Mohammad Bagheri. Plenary talks on Tuesday session "Black holes and the Quantum" by Juan Maldacena, Ahmed Almheiri, Gerard 't Hooft, Mihalis Dafermos, Sergiu Klainerman, Abhay Ashtekar and Frank Wilczek were bracketed by two roundtables on "New results from SRG/eRosita" with the participation of Andrea Merloni, Prof. Rashid Sunyaev, Alexander Lutovinov, Chandreyee Maitra, Esra Bulbul and "Solar neutrinos and Borexino" with the participation of Gianpaolo Bellini and Wick Haxton. Plenary talks on Wednesday in the session "Lambda CDM tensions" by George Efstathiou, Scolnic Daniel, Marc Kamionkowski, Wendy Freedman, Priya Natarajan and Licia Verde were followed by the roundtable "Precision cosmology" with the participation of Licia Verde, Marc Kamionkowski, Piero Rosati, and the public lecture by Francis Halzen. Two blocks of Thursday plenary sessions "Black holes in GRBs" and "Precision tests" included the talks by Roy Kerr, Yuan Ha, Lorenzo Amati, Elena Pian, Carlos Raúl Argüelles, Di Li, Jianglai Liu, Claus Lämmerzahl, Gerhard Heinzel and Ignazio Ciufolini and were followed by the roundtable "GRB 170817A and GRB 190829A" with the participation of Eleonora Troja, Liang Li, Rahim Moradi, Jorge Armando Rueda Hernandez. Two plenary blocks on Friday "Massive stars" and "Physics behind stellar collapse" included the talks by Selma de Mink, Norbert Langer, Jiri Bicak and Tomáš Ledvinka, Ivan De Mitri, Rahim Moradi and Giancarlo Cella. Finally, two plenary blocks on Saturday "Current and future missions" have seen the talks by Shuang-Nan Zhang, Weimin Yuan, Makoto Tashiro, Ruoyu Liu, Jean-Luc Atteia, Jim Hinton and Nicholas White and were followed by the roundtable "What is in our Galactic center" with the participation of Reinhard Genzel, Carlos Raúl Argüelles, Andreas Krut, Jorge Armando Rueda Hernandez, Eduar Becerra Vergara. The program of the meeting can be found at the official website http://www.icra.it/mg/mg16 and at ICRANet Indico website https://indico.icranet.org/event/1/.

These proceedings include about 400 papers containing the results presented at the Sixteenth Marcel Grossmann meeting. The plenary papers from the meeting have been published in International Journal of Modern Physics D as they were submitted. The table of contents includes also the links to YouTube videos with talks given at the meeting and cover plenary talks, public lectures, roundtables and all parallel sessions. The general link to the videos from MG16 is: https://www.youtube.com/watch?v=QFe1lsSid-o&list=PLr5RLbSWSonsaOnZukBDs0qsNIWM8AvRF.

As the editors we would like to express our gratitude to all the chairpersons of the parallel sessions at MG16, who peer-reviewed the papers submitted for these proceedings, as well as to the ICRANet secretariat office and in particular to Cinzia di Niccolo, Elisabetta Natale and Yasmina Di Domizio, as well as to ICRANet system manager Gabriele Brandolini for their help in preparation of this publication.

Remo Ruffini and Gregory Vereshchagin
November 2021

Contents

Publications in this Series	v
Sponsors and Acknowledgements	vii
Organizing Committees	ix
Marcel Grossmann Awards	xi
Preface	xxxvi

PART A
PLENARY SESSIONS

New results from testing relativistic gravity with radio pulsars
Michael Kramer 3

Dragging of inertial frames by matter and waves
Jiří Bičák and Tomáš Ledvinka 22

Probes of the progenitors, engines and physics behind stellar collapse
Chris L. Fryer 39

The observation of high-energy neutrinos from the cosmos: Lessons learned for multimessenger astronomy
Francis Halzen 59

The first results of PandaX-4T
Jianglai Liu on behalf of the PandaX Collaboration 85

XRISM: X-ray imaging and spectroscopy mission
Makoto S. Tashiro and the XRISM team 95

The SVOM mission
J.-L. Atteia, B. Cordier and J. Wei on behalf of the SVOM Collaboration 104

Quantum field theory with boundary conditions at the horizons
Gerard 't Hooft 133

The development of general relativity and the cosmological constant
Asghar Qadir 143

The irreducible mass of Christodoulou-Ruffini-Hawking mass formula
Yuan K. Ha 154

Reshaping our understanding on structure formation with the quantum nature of the dark matter
C. R. Argüelles, E. A. Becerra-Vergara, A. Krut et al. 164

First results of LHAASO
Ruo-Yu Liu for the LHAASO Collaboration 180

On the MG16 awards 2021
Remo Ruffini 196

The white dwarf binary merger model of GRB 170817A
J. A. Rueda, R. Ruffini, Liang Li et al. 217

PARALLEL SESSIONS

Accretion

• MHD Processes Near Compact Objects
Chairperson: Sergey Moiseenko
YouTube link: https://youtu.be/2WMTg06ZmV8

A semi-implicit multidimensional unstructured gas dynamical solver for astrophysical applications
Ilya A. Kondratyev and Sergey G. Moiseenko 242

Magnetized neutron stars propagating through a non-uniform ISM
O. D. Toropina, M. M. Romanova and R. V. E. Lovelace 255

Calculation of the kinetic coefficients of arbitrary degenerate electrons in magnetized dense matter
M. V. Glushikhina and G. S. Bisnovatyi-Kogan 264

Modeling of magnetic fields of accretion discs, using no-z- and RZ-approximations
M. V. Pashentseva and E. A. Mikhailov 272

• Accretion Discs and Jets
Chairpersons: Audrey Trova and Shokoufe Faraji
YouTube link: https://youtu.be/29Wj9RCVEKw

Limiting effects in tori clusters
D. Pugliese and Z. Stulchik 280

Hydrodynamical transport of angular momentum in accretion disks
in the presence of nonlinear perturbations due to noise
Subham Ghosh and Banibrata Mukhopadhyay 295

Properties of accretion disc models in the background quadrupole
Shokoufe Faraji 307

Magnetized tori around a uniformly accelerating black hole
Shokoufe Faraji and Audrey Trova 317

Multifrequency behaviour of high mass X-ray binaries
(Time lag between optical and X-ray outbursts)
Franco Giovannelli 321

Active Galactic Nuclei

• The Black Hole in M87
Chairpersons: Brian Punsly and Jorge Rueda
YouTube link: https://youtu.be/l1lTgksyJag

Rotation of the crescent image of M87* and polarization of its ESE hotspot
Krzysztof Nalewajko 339

Magnetic reconnection in jet-accretion disk systems
Chandra B. Singh, Elisabete M. de Gouveia Dal Pino,
Luis H. S. Kadowaki et al. 344

• Machine Learning in Astronomy: AGN, Transient Events, Cosmology and Others
Chairpersons: Rahim Moradi and Yu Wang
YouTube link: https://youtu.be/ErqrmMZQsBk

Exact fractal model of the universe and possible machine learning
methods for the verification of the fractality
A. A. Kirillov, E. P. Savelova and P. O. Vladykina 352

Estimating the photometric redshifts of galaxies and QSOs using
regression techniques in machine learning
A. Momtaz, M. H. Salimi and S. Shakeri 368

Deep learning in quasar physics
F. Rastegar Nia, M. T. Mirtorabi, R. Moradi, Y. Wang
and A. Vafaei Sadr 382

Cosmological density field emulation and gravitational wave inference
based on dimensionality reduction and supervised machine learning
Miguel Conceição, António da Silva and Alberto Krone-Martins 391

Unsupervised photometric detection of galaxy cluster candidates in
large surveys
Ana Carvalho, Alberto Krone-Martins and Antonio da Silva 409

• **Multiwavelength and Multi-Messenger Observations of Active Galactic Nuclei**
Chairpersons: Paolo Giommi and Narek Sahakyan

YouTube link: https://youtu.be/-Hyu2NQsExg

Time-dependent lepto-hadronic modeling of the emission processes in
blazar jets
S. Gasparyan, D. Bégué and N. Sahakyan 429

Multiwavelength study of high-redshift blazars
G. Harutyunyan and D. Israyelyan 445

Alternative Theories

• **Extended Theories of Gravity and Quantum Cosmology**
Chairpersons: Yi-Fu Cai and Wentao Luo

YouTube links: https://youtu.be/ADRr9DfV5zM
https://youtu.be/eOzpiC1cFkU
https://youtu.be/kYzJds_JIp8

Quantum gravity phenomenology from thermodynamics of spacetime
A. Alonso-Serrano and M. Liška 462

Gauge theory of gravity based on the correspondence between
the 1st and the 2nd order formalisms
David Benisty 479

$U(1)$ local strings in hybrid metric-Palatini gravity
Tiberiu Harko, Francisco S. N. Lobo and Hilberto M. R. da Silva 485

Inflationary supersymmetric FRLW quantum cosmology
N. E. Martínez-Pérez, C. Ramirez and V. M. Vázquez-Báez 499

Effective $f(R)$ actions for modified loop quantum cosmologies
Ana Rita Ribeiro, Daniele Vernieri and Francisco S. N. Lobo 517

Probing multiverse using gravitational wave observations
Moe Kukihara and Kazuhiro Hayama 531

Operator ordering ambiguity in observables of quantum cosmology
Harkirat Singh Sahota and Kinjalk Lochan 538

Decoupled quark stars in self-interacting Brans-Dicke gravity
M. Sharif and Amal Majid 548

Big-bounce in projectively invariant Nieh-Yan models: The Bianchi I case
*Flavio Bombacigno, Simon Boudet, Gonzalo J. Olmo
and Giovanni Montani* 561

Late time cosmology with derivatives of matter Lagrangian
Shahab Shahidi 576

On the semiclassical and quantum picture of the Bianchi I polymer dynamics
E. Giovannetti, G. Montani and S. Schiattarella 588

Quantum corrections to the Bianchi II transition under local rotational invariance
Sara F. Uria, David Brizuela and Ana Alonso-Serrano 597

- **Mathematical Problems of Relativistic Physics: Classical and Quantum**
Chairpersons: A. Shadi Tahvildar-Zadeh and Michael Kiessling
YouTube links: https://youtu.be/9Dr3M9Kb2jo
https://youtu.be/gMOykpapJ5A

The hypercomplex medium as storage of physical equations
Alexander P. Yefremov 605

The Maxwell-Bopp-Landé-Thomas-Podolsky-Einstein system for a static point source
Érik Amorim 619

On recent developments in the theory of relativistic dissipative fluids
V. Hoang 627

Adiabatic solutions in general relativity as null geodesics on the space of boundary diffeomorphisms
Emine Şeyma Kutluk 635

The point spectrum of the Dirac Hamiltonian on the zero-gravity Kerr-Newman spacetime
M. Kiessling, E. Ling and A. S. Tahvildar-Zadeh 648

Causal fermion systems: Classical gravity and beyond
Felix Finster 661

Newman-Penrose-Debye formalism for fields of various spins in pp-wave backgrounds
Aleksandr Kulitskii and Elena Yu Melkumova 679

Gravitational geometric phase
*Banibrata Mukhopadhyay, Tanuman Ghosh and
Soumya Kanti Ganguly* 689

Retarded potentials and radiation in odd dimensions
D. V. Gal'tsov and M. Khlopunov 699

Wave propagation in the anti-deSitter optical metric
D. García-Peláez and C. S. López-Monsalvo 713

New approaches to constrained dynamics and Hamilton-Jacobi
procedures in general relativity
D. Salisbury, J. Renn and K. Sundermeyer 719

Orientability of space from electromagnetic quantum fluctuations
N. A. Lemos and M. J. Rebouças 725

Essential self-adjointness of Dirac operators under the influence of
general-relativistic gravity
Michael K.-H. Kiessling, A. Shadi Tahvildar-Zadeh and Ebru Toprak 736

- **Wormholes, Energy Conditions and Time Machines**
  Chairpersons: Francisco Lobo and Diego Rubiera-Garcia

  YouTube links: https://youtu.be/tu_3Wqcd9Ys
  https://youtu.be/NqN1c-2fv8Y

Relic magnetic wormholes as possible source of toroidal magnetic
fields in galaxies
A. A. Kirillov and E. P. Savelova 743

Wormhole geometries induced by action-dependent Lagrangian theories
Ismael Ayuso, Francisco S. N. Lobo and José P. Mimoso 756

Gravitational lensing by wormholes in binary systems
S. Pietroni 774

Hyper-fast positive energy warp drives
E. W. Lentz 779

From black-bounce to traversable wormhole, and beyond
Alex Simpson 787

Tractor beams, pressor beams, and stressor beams within the context
of general relativity
Matt Visser, Jessica Santiago and Sebastian Schuster 808

A singularity theorem for evaporating black holes
E.-A. Kontou, B. Freivogel and D. Krommydas 822

Circularly symmetric thin-shell wormholes in F(R) gravity with
(2+1)-dimensions
Cecilia Bejarano, Ernesto F. Eiroa and Griselda Figueroa-Aguirre 831

Warp drive dynamic solutions considering different fluid sources
*Osvaldo L. Santos-Pereira, Everton M. C. Abreu and
Marcelo B. Ribeiro* 840

Symmetries and geometry of spacetime: Towards a new paradigm
Francisco Cabral, Francisco S. N. Lobo and Diego Rubiera-Garcia 856

- **Theories of gravity: Alternatives to the cosmological and particle standard models**
Chairpersons: Stefano Bellucci and Orlando Luongo

YouTube links: https://youtu.be/-aQcrYoQfBM
https://youtu.be/WsCwPb5OQhY
https://youtu.be/JMnrUfBgqVU
https://youtu.be/pPhZY-bbsew

Thermodynamics of scalar-tensor gravity: A new approach
Valerio Faraoni 876

Two body dynamics in a quadratic modification of general relativity
Soham Bhattacharyya 883

Alternatives to Λ: Torsion, generalized couplings, and scale invariance
C. J. A. P. Martins, C. M. J. Marques, C. B. D. Fernandes et al. 907

Model-independent test of scalar-tensor gravity theory by
reconstructing scalar mode of GW170817
Yuya Gushima and Kazuhiro Hayama 921

Cosmology in the novel scalar-tensor representation of $f(R,T)$ gravity
Tiago B. Gonçalves, João Luís Rosa and Francisco S. N. Lobo 932

On the interaction between electromagnetic, gravitational, and plasma
related perturbations on LRS class II spacetimes
P. Semrén 943

Condition for expansion-collapse duality between Einstein and
Jordan frames
Dipayan Mukherjee, H. K. Jassal and Kinjalk Lochan 958

The model of dark energy based on the quantum-mechanical uncertainty relation
Yu. V. Dumin 967

- **Conformal Dilaton Gravity and Related Issues**
Chairperson: Reinoud Jan Slagter

YouTube link: https://youtu.be/A3Ygi3YBs5A

Conformal dilaton gravity, antipodal mapping and black hole physics on a warped spacetime
R. J. Slagter 978

From neutrino masses to the full size of the universe — Some intriguing aspects of the tetron model
B. Lampe 999

Summary parallel session AT5
Reinoud Jan Slagter 1014

- **Horava-Lifshitz Gravity**
Chairperson: Anzhong Wang

YouTube links: https://youtu.be/vPT1dH1zITE
https://youtu.be/5z7zhpiDOpw

Boundary conditions for the Klein-Gordon field on Lifshitz spacetimes
Lissa de Souza Campos 1017

Dynamical system analysis of Bianchi-I spacetimes in $f(R)$ gravity
Saikat Chakraborty, Kazuharu Bamba and Alberto Saa 1026

Cosmological implications in modified Hořava-Lifshitz gravity
Abdul Jawad, Kazuharu Bamba and Farwa Khurshid 1038

Finite action principle and wormholes
Jan Chojnacki and Jan Kwapisz 1046

Strange quark stars in Hořava gravity
Grigoris Panotopoulos 1054

Shadows of Kerr-like black holes in $4D$ Einstein–Gauss–Bonnet gravity and constraints from EHT observations
Sushant G. Ghosh and Rahul Kumar Walia 1069

Wormhole interaction in 2d Hořava-Lifshitz quantum gravity
Jan Ambjørn, Yuki Hiraga, Yoshiyasu Ito and Yuki Sato 1084

Nature of singularities in vector-tensor theories of gravity
V. H. Satheeshkumar 1095

Hořava-Lifshitz and Einstein-Æther gravity in the light of Event
Horizon Telescope observations of M87*
Emmanuel N. Saridakis 1104

Hořava-Lifshitz gravity in $(3+1)$ dimensions coupled with anisotropic
matter and possible constraints from GRB 170817A
Tao Zhang and Fu-Wen Shu 1112

Summary of the parallel session AT6
Anzhong Wang 1119

- **Ghost-Free Models of Modified Gravity: Massive Gravity, Horndeski and DHOST Theories, Other Related Models; Their Properties and Solutions**

Chairpersons: Dmitry Gal'tsov and Michael Volkov

YouTube links: https://youtu.be/l8KHUPnT2D8
https://youtu.be/48OHIKpgNqs

Non-local R^2-like inflation, gravitational waves and Non-Gaussianities
K. Sravan Kumar 1124

Palatini kinetic scalar-tensor theory: Analytical and numerical solutions
D. V. Gal'tsov and D. S. Bushuev 1136

PART B

Black Holes: Theory and Observations/Experiments

- **Theoretical and Observational Studies of Astrophysical Black Holes**

Chairperson: Alexander Zakharov

YouTube links: https://youtu.be/fiv_MH-N2kw
https://youtu.be/GYoOb17GvE8

Reconstruction of a star motion in the vicinity of black hole from the
redshift of the electromagnetic spectrum
S. O. Komarov and A. K. Gorbatsievich 1151

Shadows of hairy Kerr black holes and constraints from M87*
Sushant G. Ghosh and Misba Afrin 1167

Displacement memory and BMS symmetries
Shailesh Kumar 1179

Physical black holes in semiclassical gravity
Sebastian Murk and Daniel R. Terno 1196

- **Black Hole Thermodynamics**
Chairperson: Hernando Quevedo

YouTube links: https://youtu.be/XmZDf5mrXQk
https://youtu.be/amseL2qykfk

Information recovery from evaporating rotating charged black holes
Zhi-Wei Wang, Samuel L. Braunstein and Saurya Das 1212

Black hole thermodynamics from entanglement mechanics
S. Mahesh Chandran and S. Shankaranarayanan 1223

Thermodynamics of charged black hole
M. Sharif and Amjad Khan 1238

Rindler trajectories and Rindler horizons in the Schwarzschild spacetime
Kajol Paithankar and Sanved Kolekar 1250

Linear growth of the two-point function for the Unruh state in $1+1$ dimensional black holes
Paul R. Anderson, Zachary P. Scofield and Jennie Traschen 1255

Stress-energy tensor for a quantized scalar field in a four-dimensional black hole that forms from the collapse of a null shell
Shohreh Gholizadeh Siahmazg, Paul R. Anderson, Raymond D. Clark and Alessandro Fabbri 1265

Microscopic model building for black hole membranes from constraints of symmetry
Swastik Bhattacharya and S. Shankaranarayanan 1275

Einstein-Maxwell-Dilaton-Axion mass formulas for black holes with struts and strings
Dmitri Gal'tsov, Gérard Clément and Igor Bogush 1291

- **Black Holes in Alternative Theories of Gravity**
Chairpersons: Jutta Kunz and Kamal Hajian

YouTube links: https://youtu.be/FRNGJKhiw7c
https://youtu.be/Tjfmuut1Eo0

Holography for rotating black holes in $f(T)$ gravity
Masoud Ghezelbash 1308

Infinitely degenerate exact Ricci-flat solutions in $f(R)$ gravity
Semin Xavier, Jose Mathew and S. Shankaranarayanan 1319

Universe in a black hole with spin and torsion
Nikodem Popławski 1327

Asymptotically flat black hole solution in modified gravity
Surajit Kalita and Banibrata Mukhopadhyay 1337

Shadow of a charged black hole surrounded by an anisotropic matter field
Javier Badía and Ernesto F. Eiroa 1343

Constraining modified gravity theories with physical black holes
Sebastian Murk 1351

Penrose suggestion as to pre-Planck-era black holes showing up in present universe data sets discussed, with a possible candidate as to GW radiation which may provide initial CMBR data
A. W. Beckwith 1359

Summary of the parallel session BH3
Kamal Hajian and Jutta Kunz 1372

Binaries

• Explosive Events Associated with Compact-Object Binary Mergers
Chairpersons: Chris Belczynski and Jorge Rueda

YouTube links: https://youtu.be/Dwq1ZU3gKrg
https://youtu.be/nw02ylI6R2M

Uncertainties in kilonova modeling
C. L. Fryer, C. J. Fontes, O. Korobkin et al. 1391

• Post-Newtonian and Post-Minkowskian Corrections for Binary Gravitating Systems
Chairperson: Johannes Bluemlein

YouTube link: https://youtu.be/wfiLG5r08yE

Tutti-Frutti method: Recent developments in the PN/PM/SF treatment of the gravitational two-body problem
Donato Bini and Andrea Geralico 1405

• Multichannel Studies of Nonstationary Relativistic Stars
Chairperson: Vladimir Lipunov

YouTube link: https://youtu.be/usn2PlU_qFA

GRB observations on cubesate satellites in the Universat–SOCRAT project
Sergey I. Svertilov, Michail I. Panasyuk, Vitaly V. Bogomolov et al. 1412

Multiwavelength observations of GRB160625B by MASTER,
Lomonosov, Konus-Wind and three stage collapse
V. M. Lipunov, V. A. Sadovnichy, M. I. Panasyuk et al. 1429

The role of the magnetic fields in GRB outflows
N. Jordana-Mitjans, C. G. Mundell, S. Kobayashi et al. 1449

MASTER optical observations of the blazar TXS0506+056 during the
IC170922A
V. M. Lipunov, K. Zhirkov, V. G. Kornilov et al. 1467

Boson Stars

• Scalar Fields in Cosmology
Chairpersons: Carlos Herdeiro and Alfredo Macias

YouTube links: https://youtu.be/SyLoguueGKk
https://youtu.be/f9nuo8Jvw-w

A short review on nonlinear perturbation theory of structure
formation for modified gravity
Jorge L. Cervantes-Cota and Alejandro Aviles 1474

Testing modified gravity theories with marked statistics
Alejandro Aviles 1494

Dark matter as condensed phase of generic bosons
Elías Castellanos and Jorge Mastache 1513

Cosmic Microwave Background

• Cosmic Backgrounds from Radio to Far-IR
Chairperson: Carlo Burigana

YouTube link: https://youtu.be/4e3Cj5wahck

New Planck tSZ map and its cosmological analysis
H. Tanimura, M. Douspis and N. Aghanim 1527

The CMB dipole: Eppur si muove
R. M. Sullivan and D. Scott 1532

High angular resolution Sunyaev Zel'dovich observations: The case of
MISTRAL
E. S. Battistelli, E. Barbavara, P. de Bernardis et al. 1542

Cosmological and astrophysical results exploiting magnification bias
with high-z sub-millimetre galaxies
L. Bonavera, M. M. Cueli and J. Gonzalez-Nuevo 1557

The impact of the Lorentz symmetry violation on the CMB polarization
Seddigheh Tizchang, Rohoollah Mohammadi and She-Sheng Xue 1571

Cosmic backgrounds from the radio to the far-infrared: Recent results and perspectives from cosmological and astrophysical surveys
Carlo Burigana, Elia Sefano Battistelli, Laura Bonavera et al. 1579

- **New Horizons in Cosmology with CMB Spectral Distortions**
Chairpersons: Jens Chluba and Andrea Ravenni

YouTube links: https://youtu.be/uBYLO4Smw3o
https://youtu.be/5oAPfzAe35k

CMB μT cross-correlations as a probe of PBH scenarios
Ogan Özsoy and Gianmassimo Tasinato 1609

Theoretical and numerical aspects of CMB spectral distortions from non-thermal energy injections
Sandeep Kumar Acharya, Jens Chluba and Abir Sarkar 1628

BISOU: A balloon project to measure the CMB spectral distortions
B. Maffei, M. H. Abitbol, N. Aghanim et al. 1633

Cosmic microwave background spectral distortions constraints on decaying dark matter particles and axion-like particles using *COBE/FIRAS* and *EDGES*
Boris Bolliet 1645

The COSmic Monopole Observer (COSMO)
S. Masi, E. Battistelli, P. de Bernardis et al. 1654

- **Status of the H_0 and σ_8 Tensions: Theoretical Models and Model-Independent Constraints**
Chairpersons: Joan Solà Peracaula and Adrià Gómez-Valent

YouTube links: https://youtu.be/VNWZ1Bzjus4
https://youtu.be/zEBOCwvetKE
https://youtu.be/nzgC7qV9H_Y

Measuring the Hubble constant H_0 from gravitational lensing
Liliya L. R. Williams 1672

Extra components consistency in the Hubble tension and BBN
Osamu Seto and Yo Toda 1686

Gravitational anomalies, axions and a string-inspired running vacuum model in Cosmology
Nick E. Mavromatos 1693

Early and not so early dark energy. What do cosmological observations tell us about them?
Adrià Gómez-Valent, Ziyang Zheng, Luca Amendola, Valeria Pettorino and Christof Wetterich 1713

Renormalized ρ_{vac} without m^4 terms
Cristian Moreno-Pulido and Joan Solà Peracaula 1733

BD-ΛCDM and running vacuum models: Theoretical background and current observational status
Javier de Cruz Pérez, Joan Solà Peracaula, Adrià Gómez-Valent and Cristian Moreno-Pulido 1752

Cosmological tensions: Hints for a new concordance model?
E. Di Valentino 1770

Solving both H_0 and σ_8 tensions in $f(T)$ gravity
Emmanuel N. Saridakis 1783

Precision Cosmology and Hubble tension in the era of LSS surveys
G. Fanizza 1792

• **Effects of Primordial Perturbations Enhancement: From Black Holes Formation to CMB Anomalies**
Chairpersons: Antonio Enea Romano and Krzysztof Turzynski
YouTube link: https://youtu.be/frjjONXbd1M

Primordial black holes arise when the inflaton falls
Keisuke Inomata 1803

Effects of the modification of gravity on the production of primordial black holes
Sergio Andrés Vallejo Peña 1809

Cosmic Strings

• **Cosmic Strings**
Chairpersons: Reinoud Jan Slagter and Batool Imtiaz
YouTube link: https://youtu.be/ZpaU82ZUHzM

$U(1)$ local strings in generalized hybrid metric-Palatini gravity
Hilberto M. R. da Silva, Tiberiu Harko, Francisco S. N. Lobo and João Luís Rosa 1820

New evidence of the azimuthal alignment of quasars spin vector in Large Quasar Groups and cosmic strings
R. J. Slagter 1835

Summary parallel session cosmic strings I
Reinoud Jan Slagter and Batool Imtiaz 1848

- **From Cosmic Strings to Superstrings**

Chairpersons: Carlos Martins and Ivan Rybak

YouTube link: https://youtu.be/LJFtV_4aSAg

Scaling solutions of wiggly cosmic strings
A. R. R. Almeida and C. J. A. P. Martins 1851

High resolution calibration of string network evolution
J. R. C. C. C. Correia and C. J. A. P. Martins 1871

Radiation from Global Cosmic Strings using adaptive mesh refinement
Amelia Drew and E. P. S. Shellard 1891

Analysing the scaling density of axion strings
A. Lopez-Eiguren 1898

Electroweak axion string and superconductivity
Yu Hamada, Yoshihiko Abe and Koichi Yoshioka 1912

Dark Energy and Large Scale Structure

- **Dark Energy and the Accelerating Universe**

Chairpersons: Alexei Starobinky and David Polarski

YouTube links: https://youtu.be/JZEPRS_rqbE
https://youtu.be/3aG_AT4UzWE
https://youtu.be/ZlTWquG-pFk

Hints for the $H_0 - r_d$ tension in uncorrelated Baryon Acoustic Oscillations dataset
Denitsa Staicova 1923

Observational constraints on nonlinear matter extensions of general relativity
E.-A. Kolonia and C. J. A. P. Martins 1935

Constraining the dark energy-dark matter interaction model using low-redshift observations
Archana Sangwan, Joseph P. J. and S. Shankaranarayanan 1948

On the evolution of inhomogeneous perturbations in the ΛCDM model and $f(R)$ modified gravity theories
T. Schiavone and G. Montani 1961

Soft dark energy and soft dark matter
Emmanuel N. Saridakis 1970

A simple parametrisation for coupled dark energy
Vitor da Fonseca, Nelson J. Nunes and Tiago Barreiro 1979

• **Cosmography with Gravitational Lensing**
Chairpersons: Claudio Grillo and Mimoza Hafizi
YouTube link: https://youtu.be/FXplIAvUDBM

A tale of two double quasars: Hubble constant tension or biases?
L. J. Goicoechea and V. N. Shalyapin 1990

Dark Matter

• **Interacting Dark Matter**
Chairpersons: Nikolaos Mavromatos
YouTube links: https://youtu.be/zOshKJlwD-Y
https://youtu.be/JR44dh2GYik

Dark energy and dark matter unification from dynamical space time: BBN constraints
D. Benisty 2005

Entropy and irreversible processes in gravity and cosmology
Llorenç Espinosa-Portalés and Juan García-Bellido 2013

LHC experiments for long-lived particles of the dark sector
Vasiliki A. Mitsou 2029

Constraining the interactions in the dark sector with cosmological data
Adrià Gómez-Valent, Valeria Pettorino and Luca Amendola 2050

Running vacuum interacting with dark matter or with running gravitational coupling. Phenomenological implications
Joan Solà Peracaula 2069

Dark matter properties from the Fornax globular cluster timing: Dynamical friction and cored profiles
D. Blas 2089

Growth of linear perturbations in a universe with superfluid dark matter
S. Banerjee, S. Bera and D. F. Mota 2101

Interacting dark sector in the late Universe: Mapping fields and fluids, and observational signatures
Joseph P. J. and S. Shankaranarayanan 2119

The role of self interactions in the cosmological evolution of warm dark matter
R. Yunis, C. R. Argüelles, D. López Nacir et al. 2127

Interaction energy between a charged medium and its electromagnetic field as a dark matter candidate
Mayeul Arminjon 2139

• **Dark Matter Searches with Liquid Xenon and Argon Detectors and Self Gravitating Systems and Dark Matter**
Chairpersons: Marco Merafina and Soroush Shakeri and She-Sheng Xue
YouTube link: https://youtu.be/H9oGYnGq9pI

The maximum mass of dilute axion stars
Pierre-Henri Chavanis 2149

A dark matter solution for the XENON1T electron excess and the galactic center 511 keV line
Yasaman Farzan 2174

Preliminary results of rich galaxy clusters' spatial distribution analysis on CfA2 Redshift Survey data: Compact objects or dark matter presence at redshift less 0.032
I. V. Arkhangelskaja, A. M. Galper, L. N. Khanh and D. N. Dorosheva 2189

• **Dark Matter: Beyond ΛCDM**
Chairpersons: Carlos Argüelles and Andreas Krut
YouTube links: https://youtu.be/hdKeo5L7pYE
https://youtu.be/i0IPHXzmV-s

Probing the nature of dark matter with Milky Way subhaloes
M. R. Lovell 2202

Addressing classical cosmological back-reaction with multiple scales
Yonadav Barry Ginat 2217

Imaging formation process for DM profiles
Omar de J. Cabrera-Rosas and Tonatiuh Matos 2222

The self-gravitating Fermi gas in Newtonian gravity and general relativity
Pierre-Henri Chavanis 2230

• **Dark Matter and Rare Processes**
Chairpersons: Carlos Rita Bernabei and Zurab Berezhiani
YouTube links: https://youtu.be/wheVrbETP_0
https://youtu.be/dVdZ4TIDxt0

The dark matter: DAMA/LIBRA and its perspectives
R. Bernabei, P. Belli, V. Caracciolo et al. 2252

Dark matter directionality approach
R. Bernabei, P. Belli, V. Caracciolo et al. 2272

Collapse models under test by high sensitivity γ-ray and X-ray measurements
C. Curceanu, Kristian Piscicchia, Massimiliano Bazzi et al. 2288

Leptophilic dark matter at linear colliders
P. S. Bhupal Dev 2296

DM6 session: Dark matter and rare processes
R. Bernabei and Z. Berezhiani 2316

- **The Nature of Galactic Halos**
  Chairpersons: Francesco De Paolis and Asghar Qadir
  YouTube link: https://youtu.be/qIwVnNxi0n0

Primordial black holes as dark matter candidates in the Galactic halo
Lindita Hamolli, Mimoza Hafizi, Francesco De Paolis and Achille A. Nucita 2319

Giant cosmic ray halos around M31 and the Milky Way
S. Recchia, S. Gabici, F. A. Aharonian and V. Niro 2335

A nearly complete census of intergalactic gas using the kinematic Sunyaev-Zel'dovich effect
Chaves-Montero, Jonás 2345

Searching for Intermediate Mass Black Holes in the Milky Way's galactic halo
A. Franco, A. A. Nucita, F. De Paolis, F. Strafella and M. Maiorano . . . 2352

Virial clouds evolution from the last scattering up to the formation of first stars
Noraiz Tahir, Asghar Qadir, Muhammad Sakhi and Francesco De Paolis 2360

Testing Weyl-modified gravity on M31 and Milky Way
Muhammad Bilal and Asghar Qadir 2365

PART C

Education

- **Teaching Einsteinian Physics to School Students**
  Chairpersons: David Blair and Matteo Luca Ruggiero
  YouTube links: https://youtu.be/W-WV6J8kprg
  https://youtu.be/UHYpwKQ09SU

Teaching relativity: A paradigm change
F. Herrmann and M. Pohlig 2371

Teaching relativity: Computer-aided modeling
F. Herrmann and M. Pohlig 2381

Solstices and Equinoxes in 1703 at the meridian line of St. Maria degli Angeli in Rome, and the stellar aberration of Sirius
Costantino Sigismondi and Silvia Pietroni 2388

Positional astrometry at arcsecond accuracy using historical instruments, with light equipment
Costantino Sigismondi and Lorenzo Ricciardi 2398

Daily, seasonal, and equinoctial solar paths on a school soccer field
Costantino Sigismondi 2411

Teaching relativity at the AstroCamp
C. J. A. P. Martins 2415

Sungrazing comets as General Relativistic gravitational probes
Silvia Pietroni and Costantino Sigismondi 2424

The three Summer solstice's markers of 1721 unveiled in the Basilica of Santa Maria degli Angeli in Rome
Costantino Sigismondi 2428

Einstein-First: Bringing children our best understanding of reality
A. Popkova, K. Adams, S. Boublil et al. 2438

Exact Solutions

• Exact Solutions in Four and Higher Dimensions
Chairpersons: David Blair and Matteo Luca Ruggiero
YouTube link: https://youtu.be/GHZUS5-4gVQ

Kundt spacetimes in the Einstein–Gauss–Bonnet theory
R. Švarc, J. Podolský and O. Hruška 2453

Exact decoupled solutions in curvature-matter coupled gravity
M. Sharif and Fizza Furqan 2464

Tolman-Oppenheimer-Volkov conditions beyond spherical symmetry
José P. Mimoso, Alan Maciel and Morgan Le Delliou 2479

A spherically symmetric stiff fluid spacetime in light of cosmic structure formation
Daniele Gregoris 2497

- **Exact Solutions (Including Higher Dimensions)**
Chairperson: Susan Scott

YouTube link: https://youtu.be/-hJjJvmmOew

Three-parameter solution for the null-surface formulation in
2+1 dimensions
Tina A. Harriott and J. G. Williams 2510

New exact stationary cylindrical anisotropic fluid solution of GR
M.-N. Célérier 2522

Early Universe

- **Quantum Fields**
Chairperson: Andrei Lebed

YouTube links: https://youtu.be/BLaTp0r0TkQ
https://youtu.be/ZifgaSDy5Vc

Hydrodynamic representation and energy balance for the Dirac and
Weyl fermions in curved space-times
Tonatiuh Matos, Omar Gallegos and Pierre-Henri Chavanis 2533

Breakdown of the Equivalence Principle for a composite quantum body
A. G. Lebed 2551

Extended DeWitt-Schwinger subtraction scheme, heavy fields and
decoupling
Antonio Ferreiro and Jose Navarro-Salas 2557

Renormalization and decoupling for the Yukawa model in curved
spacetime
Sergi Nadal-Gisbert, Antonio Ferreiro and José Navarro-Salas 2562

Trace anomaly and evaporation of spherical black holes
P. Meda 2573

On decay of the false Unruh vacuum
A. Shkerin 2587

Behaviour of noise kernel in de Sitter and FRW space-times
Ankit Dhanuka and Kinjalk Lochan 2600

Breaking Buchdahl: Ultracompact stars in semiclassical gravity
*Julio Arrechea, Carlos Barceló, Raúl Carballo-Rubio and
Luis J. Garay* 2608

Einstein anomaly with tensors of odd order in six dimensional curved space
Kohei Yamamoto and Satoshi Yajima 2619

Quantum memory and BMS symmetries
Sanved Kolekar and Jorma Louko 2623

- **Topological Methods, Global Existence Problems, and Spacetime Singularities**

Chairperson: Spiros Cotsakis

YouTube link: https://youtu.be/H8Itnc_C10c

Gravitational singularities, scattering maps for bouncing, and structure-preserving algorithms
Philippe G. LeFloch 2630

Brane-world asymptotics in a nonlinear fluid bulk
I. Antoniadis, S. Cotsakis and Ifigeneia Klaoudatou 2645

Primordial synchronization of Mixmaster spatial points
Spiros Cotsakis 2657

- **The Early Universe**

Chairperson: Stefano Ansoldi

YouTube links: https://youtu.be/m80hHWgOlFs
https://youtu.be/6tyaZ8MMVtw

Quintessential inflation from Lorentzian slow roll
David Benisty 2663

Condensed light, quantum black holes and L-CDM cosmology: Experimentally suggested and tested unified approach to dark matter, dark energy, cosmogenesis and two-stage inflation
Victor Borsevici 2672

Helical magnetic fields lead to baryogenesis
Ashu Kushwaha and S. Shankaranarayanan 2692

Polymer Quantization of the Isotropic Universe: Comparison with the Bounce of Loop Quantum Cosmology
G. Barca, E. Giovannetti, F. Mandini and G. Montani 2700

General relativistic evolution equations for density perturbations in open, flat and closed FLRW universes and the problem of structure formation
Pieter G. Miedema 2708

Constraining beyond ΛCDM models with 21cm intensity mapping
forecast observations combined with latest CMB data
M. Berti 2726

Entropy and irreversible processes in gravity and cosmology
Llorenç Espinosa-Portalés and Juan García-Bellido 2737

Fundamental Interactions and Stellar Evolution

• Why and How the Sun and the Stars Shine: The Borexino Experiment
Chairpersons: Giampaolo Bellini, Dmitry Naumov, Gioacchino Ranucci, Gemma Testera

YouTube links: https://youtu.be/hh5wDnM8miU
https://youtu.be/TG-HgBf7W4s
https://youtu.be/HLiis2LFeEs

Experimental detection of the CNO cycle
B. Caccianiga, N. Rossi, G. Testera et al. 2753

Borexino detector performances
A. Caminata, M. Agostini, K. Altenmüller et al. 2765

Study of antineutrinos from the Earth and the Cosmos with the
Borexino detector
Sandra Zavatarelli, M. Agostini, K. Altenmuller et al. 2774

Unveiling the engine of the Sun: Measurements of the pp-chain solar
neutrinos with Borexino
D. Guffanti, A. C. Re and O. Smirnov 2785

Electron neutrino survival probability in the energy range
200 keV–15 MeV
Marco Pallavicini on behalf of the Borexino Collaboration 2804

The relevance of pp-chain and CNO-cycle neutrino measurements for
solar physics
F. L. Villante and A. M. Serenelli 2815

Role of the CNO cycles in stars
A. Ianni 2835

Geoneutrino observation
Tadao Mitsui for the KamLAND Collaboration 2840

Synthesis of the session: Why and how the Sun and the stars shine
Gianpaolo Bellini 2845

- **Rotation in Stellar Evolution**
Chairperson: Georges Meynet

YouTube link: https://youtu.be/9LNoiwa0nv8

The internal rotation of low-mass stars from solar and stellar seismology
G. Buldgen and P. Eggenberger 2848

The rotation of supermassive stars
L. Haemmerlé 2865

Fast Transients

- **What Can We Learn from a Growing Sample of Fast Radio Bursts?**
Chairpersons: Duncan Lorimer, Victoria Kaspi and Bing Zhang

YouTube links: https://youtu.be/yo4n1SgfUrQ
https://youtu.be/NwGooPauhjU

Cosmology with high-redshift FRBs
A. Fialkov 2880

- **Non Standard Cosmological Probes**
Chairpersons: Duncan Lorimer, Victoria Kaspi and Bing Zhang

YouTube links: https://youtu.be/EEFUgiFeMck
https://youtu.be/Ryb15AINfMs

Closing the cosmological loop with the redshift drift
*C. J. A. P. Martins, C. S. Alves, J. Esteves, A. Lapel
and B. G. Pereira* 2890

Gamma-Ray Bursts as potential cosmological probes
L. Izzo 2906

Surface brightness fluctuations: The method and future applications
Michele Cantiello 2915

Preliminary results of analysis of Ia supernovae redshift distributions
on data of the Asiago Supernova and Open Supernova Catalogues
I. V. Arkhangelskaja 2930

- **Photospheric Emission in GRBs**
Chairpersons: Gregory Vereshchagin and Damien Bégué

YouTube links: https://youtu.be/ZifnzoUXIFc
https://youtu.be/n7vWAVhFXiU

Understanding prompt emission: Where do we stand?
Asaf Pe'er 2946

On explaining prompt emission from GRB central engines with
photospheric emission model
M. Bhattacharya and P. Kumar 2957

Monte Carlo simulations of photospheric emission in Gamma Ray Bursts
T. M. Parsotan and D. Lazzati 2972

The photosphere emission spectrum of hybrid relativistic outflow for
Gamma-Ray Bursts
Yan-Zhi Meng, Jin-Jun Geng and Xue-Feng Wu 2982

On diffusive photospheres in Gamma-Ray Bursts
G. V. Vereshchagin 2989

Summary of the parallel session GB3
G. V. Vereshchagin and D. Bégué 3002

- **High and Very High Energy Emission from Gamma-Ray Bursts**
  Chairpersons: Francesco Longo and Fabian Schüssler

YouTube links: https://youtu.be/ZUkLyyYowaM
https://youtu.be/zwN1mNVeUzA

Synchrotron and synchrotron self-Compton emission components in
GRBs detected at very high energies
Jagdish C. Joshi, Vikas Chand and Soebur Razzaque 3009

The VERITAS gamma-ray burst follow-up program
D. Ribeiro for the VERITAS Collaboration 3017

MAGIC view of Gamma-Ray Bursts at very high energies
A. Berti on behalf of the MAGIC Collaboration 3030

Prospects for VHE monitoring of gamma-ray bursts with SWGO
G. La Mura, U. Barres de Almeida, R. Conceição et al. 3041

Theoretical implications on the very high energy emission from
GRB 190114C
*D. Miceli, A. Berti, Z. Bosnjak et al. on behalf of the
MAGIC Collaboration* 3052

AGILE and GRBs: 13 years of observations
A. Ursi on behalf of the AGILE Team 3062

Searching for Gamma-Ray Bursts with the High-Altitude Water
Cherenkov (HAWC) observatory
K. L. Engel for the HAWC Collaboration 3074

- **Electromagnetic Counterparts of Compact Binary Mergers**
Chairpersons: Jonathan Granot and Paz Beniamini
YouTube link: https://youtu.be/AS7bwaT48us

CALET search for gamma-ray counterparts of gravitational wave events
Masaki Mori for the CALET Collaboration 3084

- **Unusual and New Types of Gamma-Ray Bursts**
Chairperson: Binbin Zhang
YouTube link: https://youtu.be/VrF0iU8Q6us

Off-axis jet scenario for early afterglow emission of low-luminosity Gamma-Ray Burst GRB 190829A
Yuri Sato, Kaori Obayashi, Ryo Yamazaki, Kohta Murase and Yutaka Ohira 3095

- **Gamma-Ray Burst Correlations: Observational Challenges and Theoretical Interpretation**
Chairpersons: Maria Giovanna Dainotti and Liang Li
YouTube links: https://youtu.be/gcEy2h6y1jg
https://youtu.be/m2pCT6RAmI0
https://youtu.be/GTCvcVhBjN4

GRB prompt phase spectra under backscattering dominated model
Mukesh Kumar Vyas, Asaf Pe'er and David Eichler 3101

Applying models of pulsar wind nebulae to explain X-ray plateaux following short Gamma-Ray Bursts
L. C. Strang and A. Melatos 3107

Searching for strange quark planets
Xu Wang, Yong-Feng Huang and Bing Li 3118

Probe the universe by using Gamma-Ray Bursts with X-ray plateaus
Fan Xu and Yong-Feng Huang 3124

A new perspective on cosmology through Supernovae Ia and Gamma Ray Bursts
B. De Simone, V. Nielson, E. Rinaldi and M. G. Dainotti 3130

Theory of plateau phase in Gamma-Ray Bursts
Asaf Pe'er 3141

Exploring the canonical behaviour of long Gamma-Ray Bursts using an intrinsic multi-wavelength afterglow correlation
S. R. Oates, J. L. Racusin, M. De Pasquale et al. 3150

- **GRB 170817A and Binary Models**
Chairpersons: Marica Branchesi and Giulia Stratta
YouTube link: https://youtu.be/FRBvkaLX5WU

Kilonova emission observed so far: A comparison with AT2017gfo
A. Rossi 3162

- **Binary-Driven Hypernovae of Type 1, 2 and 3**
Chairpersons: Carlo Luciano Bianco, Christian Cherubini and Simonetta Filippi
YouTube link: https://youtu.be/8IFLfget3C0

Neutrinos and gamma-ray production from proton-proton interactions in binary-driven hypernovae framework
S. Campion, J. D. Melon Fuksman and J. A. Rueda Hernandez 3172

General relativistic turbulence in spherically symmetric core-collapse supernovae simulations
L. Boccioli, G. J. Mathews and E. P. O'Connor 3184

Gravitational Waves

- **Sources of Gravitational Waves**
Chairperson: Andrew Melatos
YouTube links: https://youtu.be/Lr8b9nKsFm4
https://youtu.be/xuqJOXPDyVY
https://youtu.be/qzOrgojHsMg
https://youtu.be/KCJoWMd71pE

Mountain formation by repeated, inhomogeneous crustal failure in a neutron star
A. D. Kerin and A. Melatos 3194

Gravitational waves from neutrino mass generating phase transitions
Nobuchika Okada and Osamu Seto 3206

Efficiency of registration of chirp bursts and signals of collapsing stars by the Euro-Asian network of GW interferometers
V. N. Rudenko, S. L. Andrusenko, D. P. Krichevskiy and G. D. Manucharyan 3219

Joint analysis method on gravitational waves and low-energy neutrinos to detect core-collapse supernovae
O. Halim, C. Casentini, M. Drago et al. 3228

- **Mid-frequency Gravitational Waves (0.1–10 Hz): Sources and Detection Methods**
Chairperson: Wei-Tou Ni
YouTube link: https://youtu.be/sJ6A7a73Vxw

A cryogenic and superconducting inertial sensor for the Lunar Gravitational–Wave Antenna, the Einstein Telescope and Selene-physics
F. Badaracco, J. V. van Heijningen, E. C. Ferreira and A. Perali 3245

Space gravitational wave antenna DECIGO and B-DECIGO
S. Kawamura and the DECIGO working group 3254

Summary of the parallel session GW2
Dongfeng Gao, Wei-Tou Ni, Jin Wang et al. 3261

• **Numerical Relativity and Gravitational Wave Observations**
Chairperson: Nigel Bishop
YouTube links: https://youtu.be/eZPytAU4Zmk
https://youtu.be/th-3KqkxDnU

Salient features of the optimised PyCBC IMBH search
Koustav Chandra, Archana Pai, V. Villa-Ortega et al. 3277

Matter shells modifying gravitational wave signals
Monos Naidoo, Nigel T. Bishop and Petrus J. van der Walt 3286

Odd-dimensional gravitational waves from a binary system on a three-brane
D. V. Gal'tsov and M. Khlopunov 3301

Developments in numerical relativity and gravitational wave observations
Nigel T. Bishop 3309

High Energy

• **Very High Energy Gamma Rays**
Chairpersons: Razmik Mirzoyan and Alessandro De Angelis
YouTube link: https://youtu.be/jHM1RH20ZyM

Insights into the Galactic Center environment from VHE gamma-ray observations with ground-based facilities
C. Fruck 3316

The TAIGA experiment
M. Tluczykont, I. I. Astapov, A. K. Awad et al. 3324

Science perspectives of the Southern Wide-field Gamma-ray Observatory (SWGO)
K. L. Engel for the SWGO Collaboration 3343

• **Future Missions for High-Energy Astrophysics**
Chairpersons: Filippo Frontera and Shaolin Xiong
YouTube link: https://youtu.be/JgDsZX6RUkU

Laue lenses: Focusing optics for hard X/soft Gamma-ray astronomy
L. Ferro, M. Moita, P. Rosati et al. 3355

ASTENA: A mission concept for a deep study of the transient gamma-ray sky and for nuclear astrophysics
E. Virgilli, F. Frontera, P. Rosati et al. on behalf of the ASTENA Collaboration 3368

Polarimetric prospects of a new hard X-soft gamma-ray space mission for next decades
M. Moita, L. Ferro, F. Frontera et al. 3385

- **The SRG Mission: First Results from eROSITA and ART-XC**
  Chairperson: Andrea Merloni
  YouTube link: https://youtu.be/l0t1B716UcM

Prospect for WHIM detection in the cosmic web by *SRG/eROSITA*
H. Tanimura and N. Aghanim 3400

- **eXTP – Enhanced X-Ray Timing and Polarimetry Mission**
  Chairpersons: Marco Feroci and Fangjun Lu
  YouTube link: https://youtu.be/3d08eKmsImI

The role of eXTP in the multi-messenger astronomy era
G. Stratta and Gor Oganesyan 3403

- **Observations of HE and UHE Cosmic Rays**
  Chairpersons: Ivan De Mitri and Fabio Gargano
  YouTube link: https://youtu.be/l9DZyBMWO5c

CALET on the ISS: The first 5 years
Pier Simone Marrocchesi for the CALET Collaboration 3427

The fluxes of charged cosmic rays as measured by the DAMPE satellite
Paolo Bernardini on behalf of the DAMPE Collaboration 3442

Recent results from the Pierre Auger Observatory
E. Roulet for the Pierre Auger Collaboration 3449

The HERD space mission
F.C.T. Barbato on behalf of the HERD Collaboration 3455

PART D

History of Relativity

- **The "Fall and Rise" of Betelgeuse**
  Chairperson: Costantino Sigismondi
  YouTube link: https://youtu.be/VmbrE2gYmOM

The observation of the stars in daytime and near the horizon
Costantino Sigismondi and Paolo Ochner 3471

Fall and Rise of Betelgeuse: The summary of HR1 session
Costantino Sigismondi and Paolo Ochner 3475

Photometry of Betelgeuse at daylight
Otmar Nickel 3479

Evidence for dynamical changes in Betelgeuse using multi-wavelength data
Sneha Kachhara, Sandip V. George, Ranjeev Misra and G. Ambika 3485

The curious case of Betelgeuse
Jacco Th. van Loon 3494

Variable stars observed from city sites: The 2500 AAVSO-SGQ database
Costantino Sigismondi and Paolo Ochner 3501

Betelgeuse: An introductory course to observational astronomy
Costantino Sigismondi and Tiziana Pompa 3507

The meridian line of the Vatican obelisk to study the stellar aberration
Costantino Sigismondi and Lorenzo Ricciardi 3513

Betelgeuse, Sirius and the stars in the roman *Settecento*
Costantino Sigismondi 3519

- **History of Relativity, Gravitation and Cosmology**
Chairperson: Luis Crispino
YouTube link: https://youtu.be/RNbPUSp95PQ

On Einstein's last bid to keep a stationary cosmology
Salvador Galindo-Uribarri and Jorge L. Cervantes-Cota 3536

Jayme Tiomno: Relativity, gravity, cosmology, and the
Marcel Grossmann Meetings
William D. Brewer 3547

A look inside Feynman's route to gravitation
M. Di Mauro, S. Esposito and A. Naddeo 3563

Towards detecting gravitational waves: A contribution by
Richard Feynman
M. Di Mauro, S. Esposito and A. Naddeo 3576

Stellar gravitational collapse, singularity formation and theory breakdown
Kiril Maltsev 3596

The Hamilton-Jacobi analysis by Peter Bergmann and Arthur Komar
of classical general relativity
D. Salisbury 3626

- **Time and Philosophy in Physics**
Chairperson: Shokoufe Faraji

YouTube link: https://youtu.be/986v-V5JJEk

The passage of time and top-down causation
Barbara Drossel 3631

Explaining time's passage
Jonathan J. Dickau 3646

A glimpse to Feynman's contributions to the debate on the
foundations of quantum mechanics
M. Di Mauro, S. Esposito and A. Naddeo 3657

Summary of the parallel session HR3
Shokoufe Faraji 3671

Neutron Stars

- **Dense Matter in Compact Stars**
Chairpersons: Alessandro Drago and Jorge Rueda

YouTube links: https://youtu.be/U5Yr0oDVhqY
https://youtu.be/MvMDFh-1_bc

Massive compact stars in the two-families scenario
P. Char, A. Drago and G. Pagliara 3677

Quasi-universality of the magnetic deformation of neutron stars in
general relativity and beyond
J. Soldateschi, N. Bucciantini and L. Del Zanna 3684

Screening and elastic properties of the NS crust in the OCP
approximation
D. Barba González, C. Albertus Torres and M. A. Pérez-García 3703

Tidal deformability as a probe of dark matter in neutron stars
D. Rafiei Karkevandi, S. Shakeri, V. Sagun and O. Ivanytskyi 3713

Binary neutron star mergers with quark matter equations of state
Atul Kedia, Hee Il Kim, Grant Mathews and In-Saeng Suh 3732

Probing dense matter physics with transiently-accreting neutron stars:
The case of source MXB 1659-29
*Melissa Mendes, Andrew Cumming, Charles Gale and
Farrukh J. Fattoyev* 3736

• Compact Stars as Laboratories for Testing Strong Gravity
Chairpersons: Aurora Perez Martinez and César Augusto Zen Vasconcellos

YouTube link: https://youtu.be/C1KGecdNEfs

Vacuum properties and astrophysical implications
*A. Pérez Martínez, M. Pérez-Garcia, E. Rodríguez Querts
and A. Romero Jorge* 3756

Testing extended theories of gravity with GRBs
L. Mastrototaro 3762

• Pulsar Power in Physics and Astrophysics and Pulsars and Pulsar Systems at High Energies
Chairpersons: Andrea Possenti and Pak-Hin Tam

YouTube links: https://youtu.be/gAG29DZwUbM
https://youtu.be/ytdUBFrViHI

News and views regarding PSR J1757–1854, a highly-relativistic
binary pulsar
A. D. Cameron, M. Bailes, V. Balakrishnan et al. 3774

On the origin of the unique isolated X-Ray pulsar 1E 161348-5055
with 6.7 hr. spin period
V. Yu. Kim 3785

Advantages of including globular cluster millisecond pulsars in Pulsar
Timing Arrays
M. Maiorano, F. De Paolis, A. A. Nucita and A. Franco 3791

Searching for pulsars in globular clusters with the MeerKAT Radio
Telescope
F. Abbate on behalf of the MeerTIME/TRAPUM Collaboration 3799

Precision Tests

• Gravitational Lensing and Shadows
Chairpersons: Perlick Volker and Oleg Tsupko

YouTube links: https://youtu.be/6DXXWpMJ3IQ
https://youtu.be/F-K1gXn71_Y
https://youtu.be/B-V8r2HMztw

Gravitational lensing by rotating Simpson–Visser black holes
Sushant G. Ghosh and Shafqat Ul Islam 3812

Killing tensors in foliated spacetimes and photon surfaces
Igor Bogush, Kirill Kobialko and Dmitri Gal'tsov 3827

Decoding black hole metrics from the interferometric pattern of relativistic images
V. Bozza 3839

Symplectic evolution of an observed light bundle
N. Uzun 3844

Shadow of black holes with a plasma environment in 4D Einstein-Gauss-Bonnet gravity
Javier Badía and Ernesto F. Eiroa 3856

Aspects of neutrino mass hierarchy in gravitational lensing
Himanshu Swami 3865

Photon regions in stationary axisymmetric spacetimes and umbilic conditions
K. V. Kobialko and D. V. Gal'tsov 3874

Gravitational lensing by charged accelerating black holes
Torben C. Frost 3885

- **Experimental Gravitation**

Chairpersons: Angela di Virgilio and Claus Lammerzahl

YouTube link: https://youtu.be/mXcxztQ0nyk
https://youtu.be/tE3gIUBviTc

A manmade experiment aimed to clarify the gravity law in the Solar system
Alexander P. Yefremov and Alexandra A. Vorobyeva 3905

Gravitomagnetic field generation using high permittivity materials in superconducting magnetic energy storage devices
G. V. Stephenson 3910

Large ring laser gyroscopes: Geometry stabilization and laser control
U. Giacomelli, N. Beverini, G. Carelli et al. 3920

Dark gravitomagnetism with LISA and gravitational waves space detectors
A. Tartaglia, M. Bassan, G. Pucacco, V. Ferroni and D. Vetrugno 3929

Light rays in the Solar system experiments: Phases and displacements
Pravin Kumar Dahal and Daniel R. Terno 3942

The Ginger project – preliminary results
C. Altucci, F. Bajardi, A. Basti et al. 3956

• **Variation of the Fundamental Constants, Tests of the Fundamental Symmetries and Probes of the Dark Sector**
Chairpersons: Angela Victor Flambaum and Yevgeny Stadnik
YouTube links: https://youtu.be/NAZA-0tWHak
https://youtu.be/juhDGBJ12Lg
https://youtu.be/zxGgDP2sn60

Varying fundamental constants and dark energy in the ESPRESSO era
C. J. A. P. Martins 3963

• **Dragging is Never Draggy: MAss and CHarge Flows in GR**
Chairperson: Oldrich Semerak
YouTube link: https://youtu.be/ho31IgLNxu8

Testing the general relativistic nature of the Milky Way rotation curve with Gaia DR2
Mariateresa Crosta 3970

Spinning cylinders in general relativity: A canonical form for the Lewis metrics of the Weyl class
L. Filipe O. Costa, José Natário and N. O. Santos 3982

Magnetized black holes: The role of rotation, boost, and accretion in twisting the field lines and accelerating particles
Ondřej Kopáček and Vladimír Karas 3999

Spinning particle: Is Newton-Wigner the only way?
V. Witzany 4010

Gravitomagnetic resonance and gravitational waves
Matteo Luca Ruggiero and Antonello Ortolan 4019

Quantum Gravity

• **Loop Quantum Gravity**
Chairpersons: Marcin Kisielowski and Jerzy Lewandowski
YouTube links: https://youtu.be/VaLPseYWh9E
https://youtu.be/WFIgMqrQ07U

Studying the EPRL spinfoam self-energy
Pietropaolo Frisoni 4026

A spin foam framework for the black-to-white hole transition
Farshid Soltani 4045

Holographic properties of the bulk-to-boundary transmission of
information in regions of quantum space
Eugenia Colafranceschi 4062

- **Quantum Gravity Phenomenology**
Chairpersons: Giovanni Amelino-Camelia and Jerzy Kowalski-Glikman

YouTube links: https://youtu.be/vYnVb2zNl0o
https://youtu.be/icK8z80Hm-Y
https://youtu.be/svXLa0yhyYY

Minimal length discretization and properties of modified metric tensor
and geodesics
*Abdel Nasser Tawfik, Fady T. Farouk, F. Salah Tarabia
and Muhammad Maher* 4074

The structure of the multiverse from the entanglement entropy
Samuel Barroso Bellido 4082

Effective field theory from relativistic Generalized Uncertainty Principle
Vasil N. Todorinov, Saurya Das and Pasquale Bosso 4088

Stelle gravity as the limit of quantum gravity with maximal momentum
V. Nenmeli, S. Shankaranarayanan, V. Todorinov and S. Das 4107

Baryon asymmetry and minimum length
Saurya Das, Mitja Fridman, Gaetano Lambiase and Elias C. Vagenas ... 4114

On quantum gravity and quantum gravity phenomenology
Douglas Edmonds, Djordje Minic and Tatsu Takeuchi 4126

WKB approach to the gravity-matter dynamics: A cosmological
implementation
G. Maniccia and G. Montani 4146

Natural evidence for fuzzy sphere noncommutative geometry:
Super-Chandrasekhar white dwarfs
Surajit Kalita, T. R. Govindarajan and Banibrata Mukhopadhyay 4159

A model of polymer gravitational waves: Theory and some possible
observational consequences
*Angel Garcia-Chung, James B. Mertens, Saeed Rastgoo, Yaser Tavakoli
and Paulo Vargas Moniz* 4166

- **Loop Quantum Gravity: Cosmology and Black Holes**
Chairpersons: Jorge Pullin and Parampreet Singh

YouTube links: https://youtu.be/CAuAK31Ukho
https://youtu.be/JlYnEzRiRR0

Primordial power spectrum from a matter-ekpyrotic scenario in loop quantum cosmology *Bao-Fei Li, Sahil Saini and Parampreet Singh*	4178
The primordial power spectra in modified loop quantum cosmology *Bao-Fei Li, Javier Olmedo, Parampreet Singh and Anzhong Wang*	4188
Primordial perturbations in kinetically dominated regimes of classical and quantum cosmology *B. Elizaga Navascués, R. Jiménez-Llamas and G. A. Mena Marugán*	4193
Revisiting the Hamiltonian formalism of the Ashtekar–Olmedo–Singh black hole model *Alejandro García-Quismondo and Guillermo A. Mena Marugán*	4211
A comparison of different choices of clocks in a reduced phase space quantization in loop quantum cosmology with an inflationary potential using effective techniques *Kristina Giesel, Bao-Fei Li and Parampreet Singh*	4228
Initial conditions in LQC/mLQCs *Bao-Fei Li, Parampreet Singh and Anzhong Wang*	4234
Holonomy corrections in effective midisuperspace models *A. Alonso-Bardaji and D. Brizuela*	4239
Infrared signatures of quantum bounce in collapsing geometry *Harkirat Singh Sahota and Kinjalk Lochan*	4247
Effective black hole interior and the Raychadhuri equation *Keagan Blanchette, Saurya Das, Samantha Hergott and Saeed Rastgoo*	4256
Effect of loop quantization prescriptions on the physics of non-singular gravitational collapse *Kristina Giesel, Bao-Fei Li and Parampreet Singh*	4267
Summary of the parallel session QG3 *Jorge Pullin and Parampreet Singh*	4272

Strong Field

• **Strong Electromagnetic and Gravitational Field Physics: From Laboratories to Early Universe**
Chairpersons: Sang Pyo Kim and She-Sheng Xue

YouTube links: https://youtu.be/kexqTayqFiU
https://youtu.be/laymGp6x9Hg

Reliable equations of state of viscous strong and electroweak matter
A. Tawfik 4277

Neutral fermion pair production by Sauter-like magnetic step
T. C. Adorno, Zi-Wang He, S. P. Gavrilov and D. M. Gitman 4290

On the magnetic field screening in strong crossed electromagnetic field
S. Campion, J. A. Rueda Hernandez, S.-S. Xue and R. Ruffini 4306

Particle creation by strong fields and quantum anomalies
José Navarro-Salas 4317

Constraints on the non-minimal coupling of electromagnetic fields from astrophysical observations
Susmita Jana and S. Shankaranarayanan 4326

New partial resummation of the QED effective action
Silvia Pla and José Navarro-Salas 4337

Can a detector detect soft photons
Sanved Kolekar and Jorma Louko 4347

Breaking of the adiabatic invariance in the production of particles by strong fields
P. Beltrán-Palau, A. Ferreiro, J. Navarro-Salas and S. Pla ... 4352

Dynamics of relativistic electrons in non-uniform magnetic fields and its applications in quantum computing and astrophysics
Srishty Aggarwal and Banibrata Mukhopadhyay 4362

Validity of the semiclassical approximation in 1+1 electrodynamics: Numerical solutions to the linear response equation
Ian M. Newsome 4374

On Kerr black hole perfect MHD processes in Doran coordinates
C. Cherubini, S. Filippi, A. Loppini et al. 4387

Tadpole contribution to magnetic photon-graviton conversion
N. Ahmadiniaz, F. Bastianelli, F. Karbstein and C. Schubert .. 4393

- **The Effects of (Non)Linear Electrodynamics on the Properties of Astrophysical/Gravitational Compact Objects**
Chairperson: Seyed Hossein Hendi
YouTube link: https://youtu.be/SAIAXtQhavE

Correspondence of gamma radiation coming from GRBs and magnetars based on the effects of nonlinear vacuum electrodynamics
Tursynbek Yernazarov, Medeu Abishev and Yerlan Aimuratov 4401

Absorption of massless scalar waves by electrically charged regular black holes
Marco A. A. de Paula, Luiz C. S. Leite and Luís C. B. Crispino 4410

White Dwarfs

- **White Dwarf Explosions**
Chairpersons: Robert Fisher and María Pilar Ruiz Lapuente
YouTube links: https://youtu.be/ndaW6u2xuOo
https://youtu.be/IwjYaQaqJeI

Modeling Type Ia supernovae with explosions in white dwarfs near and below the Chandrasekhar mass
Friedrich K. Röpke, Florian Lach, Sabrina Gronow et al. 4420

Type Ia supernovae and their explosive nucleosynthesis: Constraints on progenitors
Shing-Chi Leung and Ken'ichi Nomoto 4427

Charged polarized white dwarfs with finite temperature as a possible source of type Ia supernovae
Sílvia P. Nunes, José D. V. Arbañil and Manuel Malheiro 4447

- **White Dwarfs, Magnetic Compact Stars and Nuclear Astrophysics**
Chairpersons: Manuel Malheiro and Jaziel Goulart Coelho
YouTube link: https://youtu.be/onicFElJQnA

CTCV J2056-3014 and other fast-spinning white dwarfs
C. V. Rodrigues, R. Lopes de Oliveira, A. Bruch et al. 4453

Gravitational waves from fast-spinning white dwarfs
M. F. Sousa, J. C. N. de Araujo and J. G. Coelho 4461

Highly magnetized white dwarfs: Implications and current status
B. Mukhopadhyay, M. Bhattacharya, A. J. Hackett et al. 4475

Electron captures and stability of white dwarfs
N. Chamel, L. Perot, A. F. Fantina et al. 4488

Massive hot white dwarfs: Consequences of finite temperature in the structure and on the onset of instabilities
Sílvia P. Nunes, José D. V. Arbañil and Manuel Malheiro 4508

A study of the infrared emission of SGR/AXPs in a disk scenario and its implications for their origin
Sarah Villanova Borges 4514

Particle acceleration and high energy emission in the white dwarf binaries AE Aquarii and AR Scorpii
P. J. Meintjes, S. T. Madzime, Q. Kaplan et al. 4522

Study the effects of anisotropy on the highly magnetized white dwarfs
Debabrata Deb, Banibrata Mukhopadhyay and Fridolin Weber 4532

List of Participants   4545

PART D

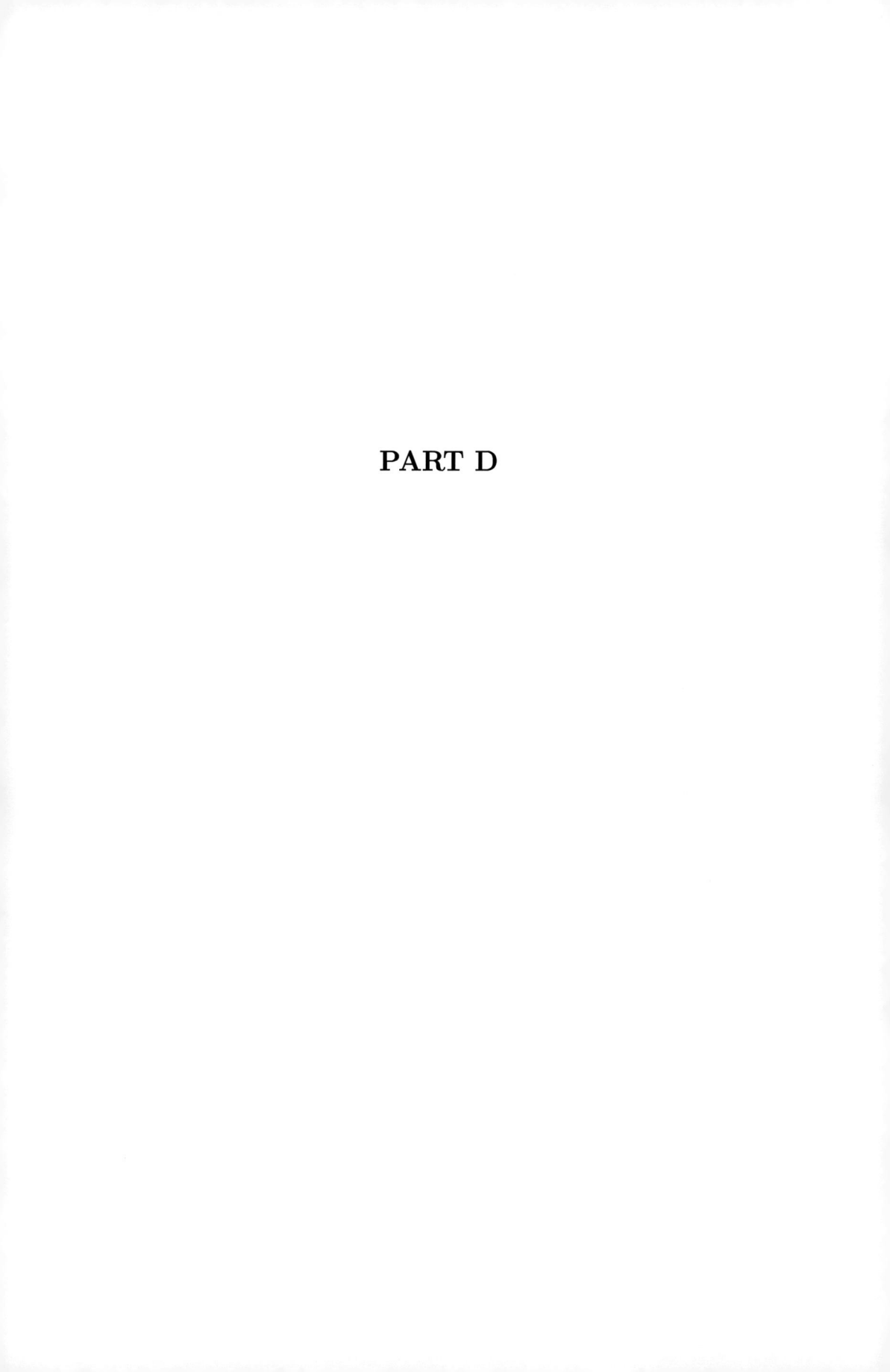

The observation of the stars in daytime and near the horizon

Costantino Sigismondi

ICRA, Sapienza University of Rome,
Rome, Italy
E-mail: sigismondi@icra.it
www.icra.it/solar

Paolo Ochner

Padova University and Asiago Astrophysical Observatory, Italy

Traditionally when a star was near the solar conjunction, its magnitude was not measured from groundbased observations. In this way the lightcurves of variable stars show yearly gaps of about two or three months each year. Some observations made in twilight and in daytime in Rome of Betelgeuse, Antares and Venus are described.

Keywords: Atmospheric seeing, Airmass extinction, Daytime astronomical observations of stars.

1. Introduction: Betelgeuse and its 2020 secondary minimum

On 31 march 2020 Betelgeuse's luminosity was again in its rising phase, after the deep minimum Worldwide discussed. The observations of this phase continued in the evening until April 2020, on a dark sky. By the end of April the star was entering in twilight visibility for Rome, and its luminosity measurement with Argelander's method become complicate. The sky background rised, and the Purkinje effect affected the perception of the stellar luminosity by naked eye. Moreover the airmass' extinction near the horizon is affected by the humidity, which is a variable effect with the season and with the meteorological local conditions. Air turbulence also complicates the signal to noise ratio of the star. The cases of Antares at the meridian at 21° of altitude at sunset and of Venus at the meridian in afternoon, both observed in Vatican, are also discussed.

2. Sky background, airmass and comparison stars

A bright star is visible through a telescope during the day, the conditions required are: clear sky and exact pointing. For Betelgeuse in twilight, near the Western horizon in end of May in Rome, a dried tree in the foreground was used to aim at the star's position with a monocular or a small Newtonian telescope of 76 mm mirror.

For measuring the stellar magnitude the usual comparisons stars were not visible: Aldebaran, red as Betelgeuse, was already set and Procyon, white and normally brighter than Betelgeuse, was not visible neither close to a landmark. Only Mercury, reddish, was bright and low enough to be seen and compared. γ Geminorum, white, also was detectable close to Betelgeuse and to another landmark.

These conditions allowed to verify that a "regular" $1/\sin$ cosecant law for the airmass extinction does not apply for the evening horizon in may in Rome.

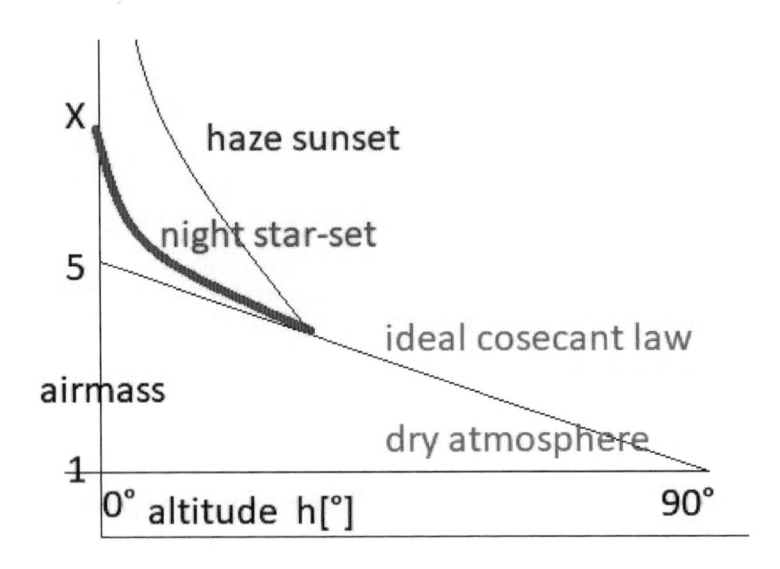

Fig. 1. Airmass extinction in dry atmosphere, night star set and haze sunset (as in end of August, in Rome). The deviation from the cosecant law are relevant below 15°.

Other experiences with sea sunsets showed strong departures from the cosecant law near the horizon in presence of humidity: the solar light can be extinct by an equivalent up to 30 airmasses of haze, or only by 5 airmasses in drier days. In the former situation the lower limb of the Sun disappears before reaching the horizon, while in the latter the Sun remains bright until the last glimpse of light.

2.1. *Atmospheric seeing*

Air turbulence is stronger in daytime, and large bubbles of hot air from locations close to the observer defocus the star. This fact complicates the visibility of the star on a bright sky background. Antares at the meridian, at 21° of altitude at sunset on 21 August 2021 was visible less than 50% of the duration of the observation, continuously disappearing and reappearing without having changed the focus of the telescope 10 × 42; only Venus, under clear sky, appeared steadily visible in daytime, through a monocular 7x18 on October 5, 2021. In other days of October 2021 the defocus affected also the observation of Venus.

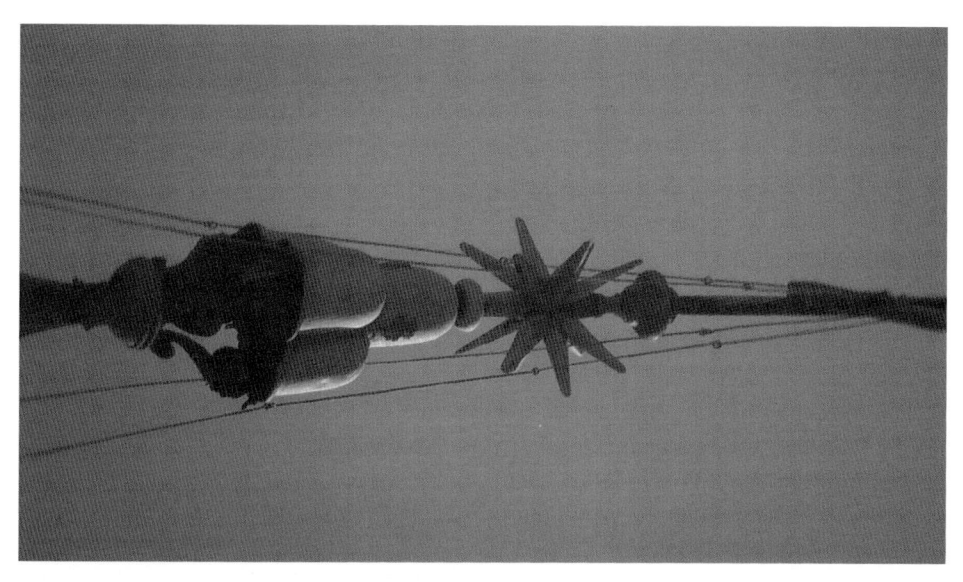

Fig. 2. A photo of Venus in daytime on October 5, 2021 at 16:10 local time, with the top of st. Peter's Obelisk in Vatican. In this photo Venus is below the center of the tridimensional star, as a bright point on the blue sky.

3. The early morning reappearances of Betelgeuse in September

My observations of Betelgeuse made in September from 2012 to 2021, and in general the first observations after the solar conjunction, showed a systematic increase of the perceived luminosity. Aldebaran, Procyon and Rigel are always used as comparison stars, and the airmass correction was carefully considered. The detector is my eye, and this systematic luminosity increasing, can be due to a physiological effect like the Purkinje's one, even if I applied the recommendation of not staring at the star. *Exempli gratia* on September 15, 2021 a careful observation, with the star "bracketed" with Aldebaran and Procyon and Rigel, yielded magnitude 0.27, 0.25 magnitudes brighter than V-band observations in AAVSO database for the same days. Moreover this luminosity is brighter than average maxima of Betelgeuse, which was nearly at the meridian on a starting twilight phase. Other September's luminous cases have to be attributed to the heavy haze at the Eastern horizon: either facing the Adriatic sea in Lanciano (265 m above sea level), either from the Asiago highland (1000 m). The clearness of the morning sky, and the low humidity dispersed in the atmosphere can be the responsible of such peculiar situation.

3.1. *Recovering airmass on the AAVSO-SGQ observations' catalogue*

The airmass of Betelgeuse during all these particular observations in September ranges from 2 to 3, and can be calculated on AAVSO-SGQ catalogue by selecting

SGQ as observer, in searching Alf Ori observations (and all the other variable stars observed).

The location of the observation is always reported in the notes, and the time is required by the application form. So the data for recomputing the airmass are made available.

4. Conclusions

The Argelander's method consists to bracket the luminosity of the star in study among two comparison stars. For Betelgeuse it is necessary to apply always the airmass corrections, because the angular distance of the comparison stars, usually Aldebaran and Procyon, produce artificial difference in luminosity.

The airmass correction can depart from the cosecant law near the horizon due to the haze (fig. 1).

Defocus effects of the air turbulence complicate this measurement. From Rome the magnitude of Betelgeuse has been measured as late as 31 May, in 2021. From the southern hemisphere in Australia Rod Stubbings could observe until the same date in 2021 and until 10 of June in 2020.

From Brasil, Florianopolis, Alexandre Amorim could observe from 8 July in the morning twilight.

The observations in V-band of Otmar Nickel were performed in daytime, during the solar conjunction, allowing a ungapped monitoring of the luminosity of this star.

References

1. C. Sigismondi, *Gerbertus* **13**, 65 (2020).
2. C. Sigismondi, ATel 13601 (2020), https://www.astronomerstelegram.org/?read=13601.
3. C. Sigismondi, Egress of Venus from St. Peter's obelisk (October 27, 2021), https://youtu.be/ZWTg8xSYiuU.
4. O. Nickel, *Photometry of Betelgeuse at daylight* MGM XVI Proceedings (2021).

Fall and Rise of Betelgeuse: The summary of HR1 session

Costantino Sigismondi

ICRA, Sapienza University of Rome,
Rome, Italy
E-mail: sigismondi@icra.it
www.icra.it/solar

Paolo Ochner

Padova University and Asiago Astrophysical Observatory, Italy

The occurrence of the deep minimum of Betelgeuse in 2020 has been object of a Worldwide debate, mainly on the public media. The session dedicated to Betelgeuse in the XVI Marcel Grossmann Meeting focused the many aspects of this debate, offering a good state of art of this subject, after and during an unprecedented observational effort from ground, airborne and from the space.

Keywords: Betelgeuse; Red giant; Variable stars.

1. Betelgeuse among the red giant variable stars

The special session HR1 *History of Relativity I* of the XVI Marcel Grossmann Meeting was dedicated to the Great Dimming of Betelgeuse, occurred from December 2019 to February 2020. This meeting gathered prominent scholars in this research field, and relevant representatives of the amateur astronomers who participated to the observational campaign of Betelgeuse (Wolfgang Vollmann from Vienna and Rod Stubbings from Australia).

The impact of Betelgeuse's dimming in the media, last year, is an index of how such an astronomical phenomenon can drive interest of the great public, and for how long, and why. One of the most recurrent issues was the supernova ending of its stellar history (because it was believed or announced to be imminent, as a consequence of the three months dimming... and this common mistake in the press, even specialized, was the reason why Relativistic Astrophysicists decided to clarify the nature of a potential gravitational collapse). Pre-supernova stages of supergiants are very poorly known, even for SN 1987A (Massimo Turatto, 2020 ICRANet Betelgeuse meeting), but a core-collapse event lasts only an hour, as recalled in the plenary session of this meeting (Chris Fryer).

In any case Betelgeuse ranks among the ten brightest stars in the sky, and it is variable, with amplitudes normally around 0.5 magnitudes from minimum to maximum, which become 1.0 magnitudes for the Great Dimming of 2020.

2. Observing Betelgeuse, the culture of mankind, and the didactic

Betelgeuse is part of the night sky culture of mankind, probably documented since Lascaux caves in the Pyrenees (Cro-Magnon civilization, 40000 years ago) and present in Greek mythology. Its dimming in 2020 has excited again the human fantasy, as well as an unprecedented observational campaign in all part of the spectrum.

Fig. 1. The Lascaux painting in the cave. The Taurus, at top center, is probably an Urus (Bos Primigenius). From this general view the detail of astronomical interest is shown below.

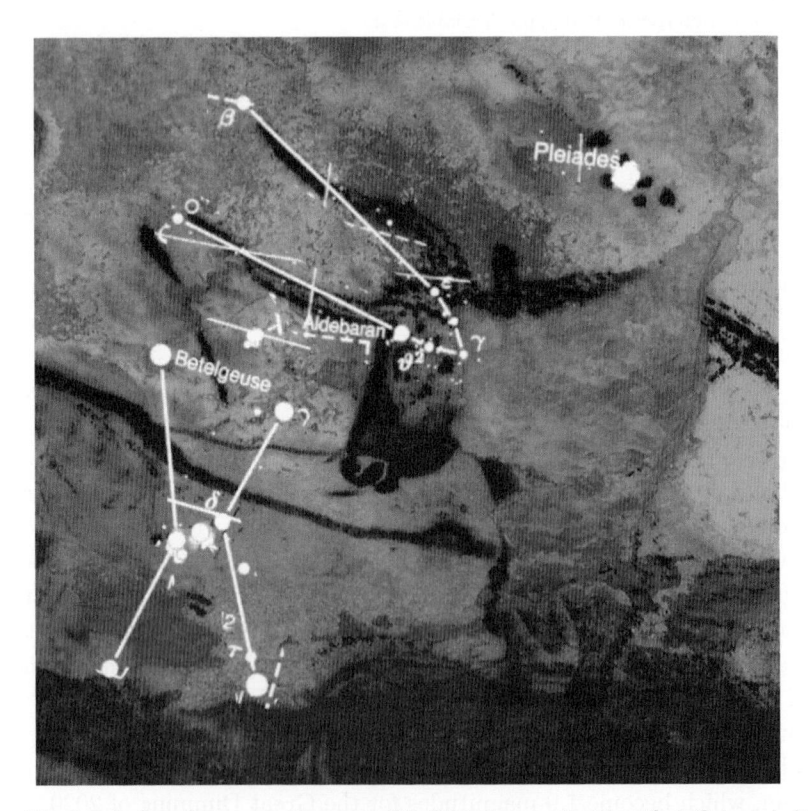

Fig. 2. The detail where Orion would appear. The Pleiades are also identified, Orion's belt is four point aligned in the previous global image. Andrea Dupree drawn our attention to this document.

This variability can be followed potentially by all, by applying some basic airmass correction to the reference stars and Betelgeuse itself (Costantino Sigismondi and Tiziana Pompa) even in twilight. The natural continuation of this approach, which is also didactic, is the daylight observations of Betelgeuse from ground, by Otmar Nickel, used to integrate the V and visual light curve of Betelgeuse obtained with the dark night sky. The search of peculiarities of "the painful shoulder"[4] of Orion is a natural way to approach this phenomenon, while the modern data on Betelgeuse magnitudes is less than two centuries (Sir John Herschel in 1837-41). How different is Betelgeuse from Antares and other red supergiant stars? In the timescales of stellar evolution how peculiar was this dimming? This provocation came from Jacco van Loon, the chairman of GAPS 2021, a 254-participants online meeting held in June 2021 on Red Supergiants.

3. Date of this meeting among the light curve of Betelgeuse

The date of this meeting occurred after a whole pulsational period (425 days) from the Great Minimum dated around 11 February 2020. This was the occasion to compare the Great Minimum with the following one, in order to verify the uniqueness of the 2020 event, or, conversely, its statistical fluctuation's nature. The light curves presented at this parallel session were all updated to the day before, thanks to the daytime and spacebased observations.

4. Time series analysis issues in the lightcurve of Betelgeuse

The time-series analysis of the light curve of Betelgeuse, to identify possible signatures of changes in the nature of the physical pulsations, has been the subject treated by Sandip V. George. The issue of new oscillation regime with period shorter than the main one of 425 days, seemed to appear from the preliminary light curves presented by Edward Guinan and Andrea K. Dupree: they exploited satellite and groundbased daytime measurements to follow the luminosity of the star during the months of solar conjunction.

5. ID card of Betelgeuse

The stellar parameters of Betelgeuse have been investigated in depth by Meridith Joyce by comparing observational data with synthetic data obtained with the best program of stellar evolution simulation, MESA. Mass, radius and distance have been reconsidered with this technique, while the measurements with astrometric satellites (from Hipparcos to GAIA) are affected by the asymmetry of the stellar surface of Betelgeuse. The opportunity to consider a recent merging history with a smaller companion was part of the presentation of Alexey Bobrick, concerning the dynamical history of Betelgeuse. The opportunity to observe Betelgeuse in the mid-infrared part of the spectrum from the stratosphere was presented by Graham

Harper, who showed that the variation of temperature on the photosphere of Betelgeuse, might be responsible for the dimming, more than "dust eclipses" produced by material ejections along the line of sight. Higher spatial resolution images obtained with the Hubble Space Telescope are confirming this issue, and the great hot and cold spots on the surface of the star are reflecting the convective cells on this supergiant, as the presentations of Edward Guinan and Andrea Dupree have shown from various perspectives.

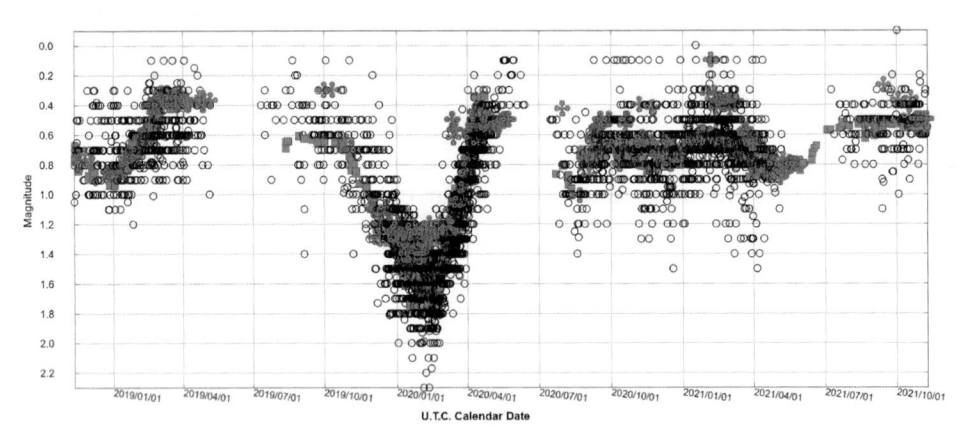

Fig. 3. The AAVSO light curve of Betelgeuse in the last three years (November 2018-2021). Evidenced in orange cross are 310 visual observations of the author. Note the green data in V-band during the Summer of 2021, by Otmar Nickel: they firstly cover completely the yearly gap during the solar conjunction. The visual data in the Summer 2020 are of Rod Stubbings from near Melbourne, Alexandre Amorim from Florianopolis and myself from Rome till end of May. The other V-band green data: 458 are of Wolfgang Vollmann who follows Betelgesue since 1976.

6. Perspectives

This session, held on July 8th, 2021, can be a reference for future studies on Betelgeuse and Red Giants in general, as well as an ideal introductory event to modern stellar variability, from naked eye observations to stellar interferometry techniques to airborne and space telescopes and satellite observations. The goal of having a good state-of-art meeting about Betelgeuse, its astrophysics and its observations, has been obtained.

References

1. Betelgeuse dimming: the state of the star International workshop (2020), http://icranet.org/index.php?option=com_content&task=view&id=1281.
2. GAPS 2021, IAU meeting 2021 https://gaps2021.wixsite.com/conference.
3. HR1 session of Marcell Grossmann Meeting 2021, https://youtu.be/VmbrE2gYmOM.
4. S. Wilk, JAAVSO **17**, 43, 1999 https://app.aavso.org/media/jaavso/1743.pdf.

Photometry of Betelgeuse at daylight

Otmar Nickel

zum Schollberg 11, 55129 Mainz, Germany
E-mail: otmar.nickel@web.de

In a backyard observatory in Mainz, Germany, several stars have been observed at daylight using a 250mm Newton telescope and a CCD camera. The sky background was measured on several days; values of 1.8 - 4.7 mag/arcsec2 were found at angles of 10°-100° distance to the Sun. Photometry of Betelgeuse was performed as a first attempt in 2020 with stacked images of Betelgeuse; it was improved in 2021 by using a neutral density filter (1 percent transmission) and measuring calibration and extinction coefficients on 4-8 bright reference stars. Photometry of Betelgeuse resulted in calculated errors of less than 0.05 mag from February to July 2021. It could be shown, that daylight observations of Betelgeuse can fill the observational gap with reliable magnitude data, when Betelgeuse is near to the Sun.

Keywords: Betelgeuse, photometry

1. Overview

Fig. 1 shows a light curve of Betelgeuse in the V-band, taken by many amateur astronomers with digital cameras (Kafka S, 2021). Unfortunately there are gaps in this curve, when Betelgeuse is near to the Sun, that means at a distance of less than about 30°. To fill these gaps there are 3 ways:
- Observations in twilight close to horizon (preferable in the southern hemisphere)
- Observations with space probes distant from earth (e.g. STEREO-A)
- Observations at daylight

In this paper I will report about daylight observations of Betelgeuse, which I have done this and the last year.

2. Equipment

The telescope of my observatory is a Newtonian telescope with 250 mm aperture on an equatorial mount. The mount is computer controlled with encoders in both axes. Images are acquired by a cooled CCD camera ATIK 460exm with a V filter and a neutral density filter (1 percent transmission), to reduce the light intensity. The camera is capable of exposures down to 1 ms. The front of the tube is prolonged with a cylindrical shade to reduce stray light from the Sun.

3. Sky brightness

The sky brightness can be measured in magnitudes per square arcsec; fig. 2 shows own measurements from 17 cloudless days (July to September 2020 and February to

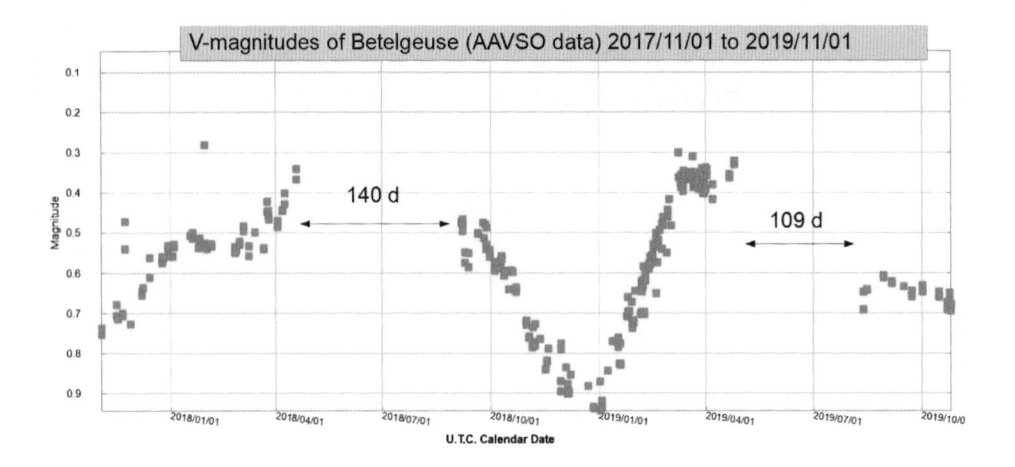

Fig. 1. Light curve of Betelgeuse 2017/11 to 2019/11 (AAVSO data)

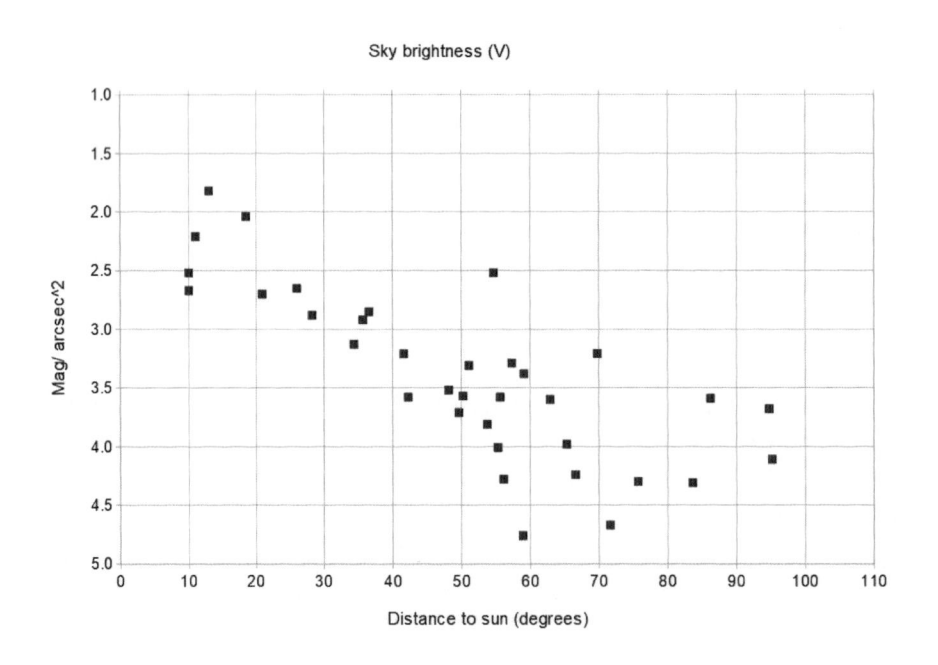

Fig. 2. Measured sky brightness versus solar angular distance

April 2021) at my observatory as graph. The sky brightness depends mainly on the angular distance to the Sun (which is shown here on the horizontal axis). Between 60 and 100 degrees the sky brightness seems to be stable, but here the scattering of data is very high, because other parameters (e.g. airmass and humidity) have more influence. It can be shown, that stars can be imaged with reasonable signal-to-noise ratio, if their brightness in magnitudes is at least in the order of the sky brightness in mag per square arcsec. Therefore stars up to 2 magnitudes could be observed near to the Sun.

4. Methods

To get images of a star at daytime with a reasonable signal-to-noise ratio, one has to record a large number of images with short exposure time and to add them together to a "stacked" image, as seen in fig. 3.

To evaluate the brightness of a star, first an instrumental magnitude has to be processed, which is proportional to the logarithm of pixel counts corrected by the sky background. The same procedure is done for one or more stars, whose magnitude is known to get a standardized magnitude by comparison.

I did first measurements of Betelgeuse (in 2020) with only 1 comparison star, namely Aldebaran (alpha Tau). To get the correct magnitude, it is necessary, to measure also the extinction of all stars used for the comparison. Therefore the method was improved in 2021 by using an ensemble of 4-8 reference stars with brightness of up to 2 magnitudes and measuring the extinction constant.

The standard magnitude V_{var} can be calculated by the following equation (Da Costa GS, 1992):

$$V_{var} = m_{inst} + T_v(B-V)_{var} + m_0 - k_v X_{var} \qquad (1)$$

where

m_{inst} = instrumental magnitude of variable
T_v = color transformation constant for V-Band
$(B-V)_{var}$ = color index of variable
m_0 = zero point (depending on sensitivity of the system)
k_v = extinction constant
X_{var} = airmass of the variable star

m_0 and k_v were determined for each measurement from the color corrected instrumental magnitudes of the ensemble of reference stars by linear regression.

5. Results

Fig. 4 shows the 2020 light curve of Betelgeuse with the results of my first attempts for daylight measurements (seen as crosses). The 3 red points are measurements of the STEREO-A space probe (Dupree A, et al, 2020). The errors of the daylight measurements were in the order of 0.07 mag.

Fig. 5 shows the 2021 light curve, again with my daylight measurements, seen as crosses. The gap of values could be relatively well filled with data, the errors were less than 0.05 mag, even at the closest distance of 16° to the Sun. There is a light

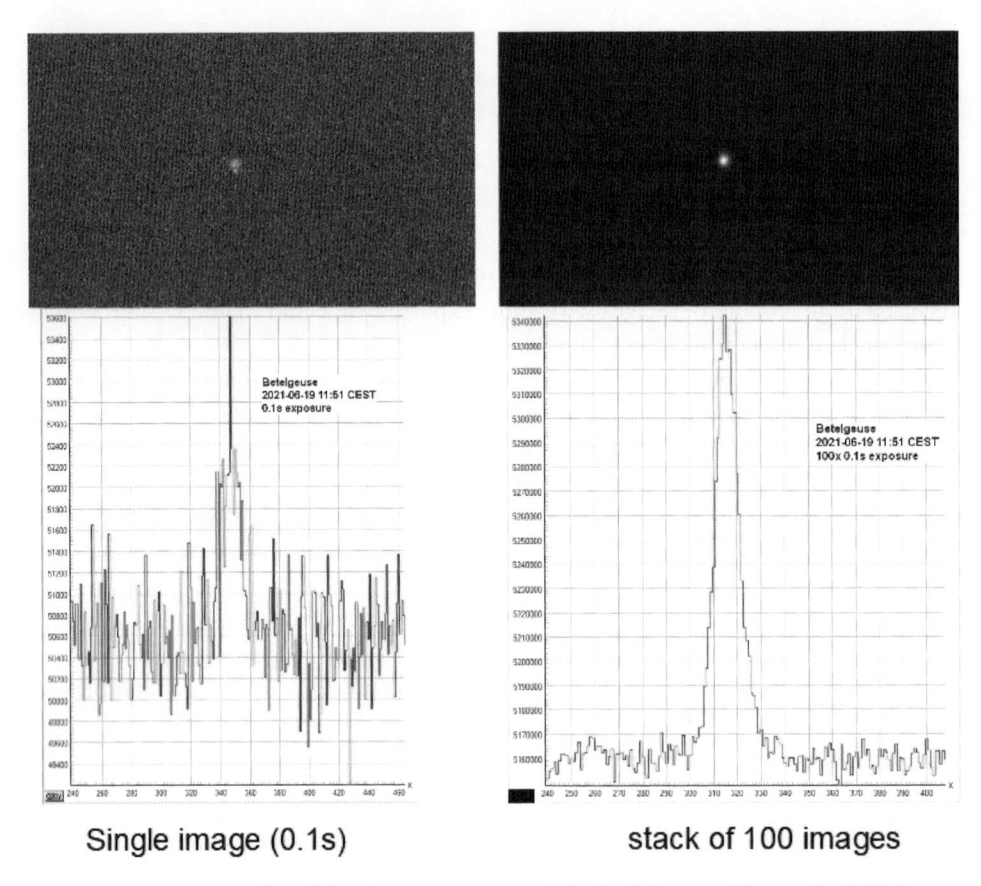

Fig. 3. Images and profiles of Betelgeuse near to sun, left: single image, right: stack of 100 images

systematic error of 0.02 magnitudes; the reason for that may be a slight error of the color transformation, which can be significant for Betelgeuse with its highly red color index.

The method was tested also on a star which comes even closer to the Sun than Betelgeuse: The V magnitude of Alpha Ari was measured on 6 days at a distance to the Sun of 35° down to 10°. The mean value of all measurements was 2.0 ±0.035, which is very close to the Hipparcos magnitude (2.01 mag).

6. Conclusions

- Measurements of the V magnitude of Betelgeuse are possible with astronomical cameras at daylight, even at closest distance to the Sun
- The method gives reliable results with an error of less than 0.05 mag (clear sky provided)

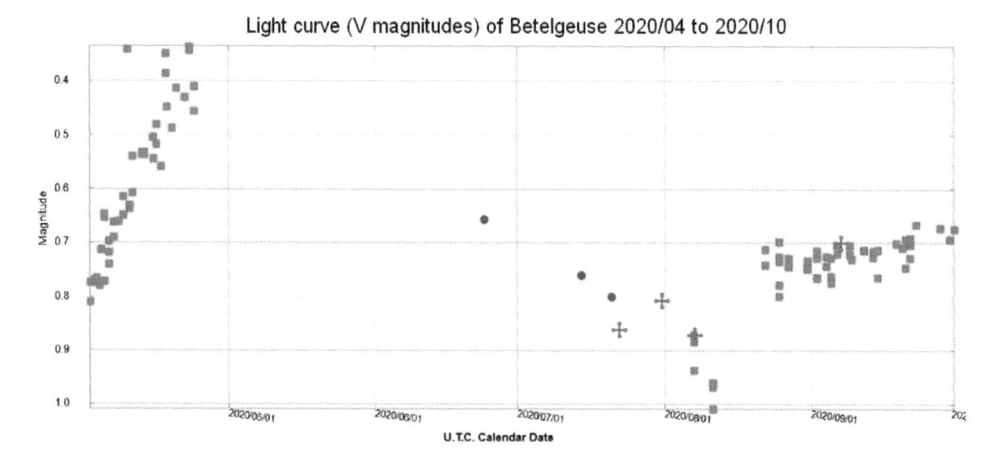

Fig. 4. Light curve of Betelgeuse 2020; green points: V mag data (AAVSO data base), crosses: daylight data, red dots: STEREO-A data

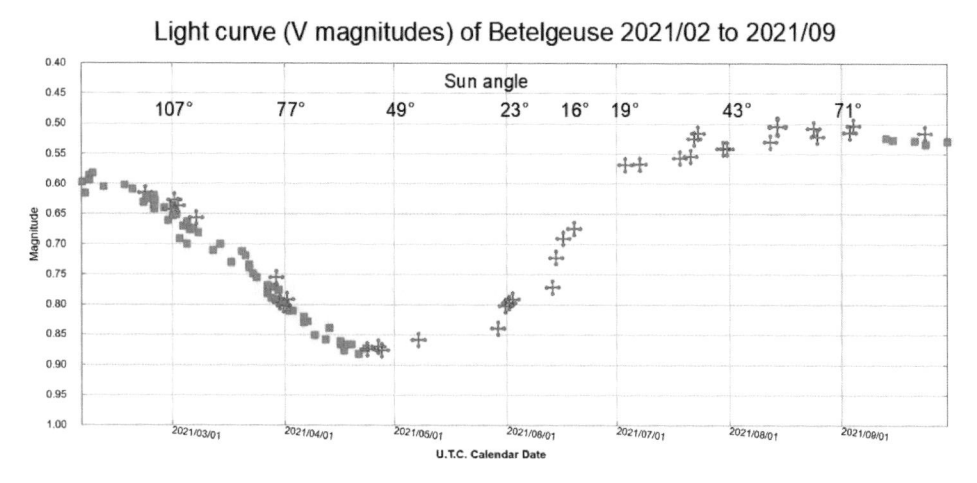

Fig. 5. Light curve of Betelgeuse 2021 (Kafka S, 2021); green points: V mag data (AAVSO data base), crosses: daylight data

- The solar conjunction gap of the light curve can be filled in the future, if the method is used also by other observers with suitable equipment.

Acknowledgements

The author would like to thank Prof. Sigismondi for the invitation to the MG16 meeting and for his help in preparing this paper.

References

1. Kafka, S., *Observations from the AAVSO International Database* (2021) `https://www.aavso.org`
2. Da Costa, GS, *Basic photometry techniques* in: Astronomical CCD Observing and Reduction Techniques **23**, 90 (1992)
3. Dupree, A and Guinan, E and Thompson, WT, *Photometry of Betelgeuse with the STEREO mission while in the glare of the Sun from Earth* The Astronomer's Telegram **13901** (2020)

Evidence for dynamical changes in Betelgeuse using multi-wavelength data

Sneha Kachhara

*Indian Institute of Science Education and Research (IISER) Tirupati,
Tirupati, India
E-mail: snehakachhara@students.iisertirupati.ac.in*

Sandip V. George

*Department of Computer Science, University College London, London WC1E 6BT,
United Kingdom
Interdisciplinary Center for Psychopathology and Emotion Regulation,
University Medical Center Groningen
University of Groningen, The Netherlands
E-mail: sandip.george@ucl.ac.uk*

Ranjeev Misra

*Inter University Center for Astronomy and Astrophysics (IUCAA) Pune,
Pune, India
E-mail: rmisra@iucaa.ac.in*

G. Ambika

*Indian Institute of Science Education and Research (IISER) Tirupati,
Tirupati, India
E-mail: g.ambika@iisertirupati.ac.in*

The reasons behind the Great Dimming and subsequent rising in the brightness of Betelgeuse between October 2019 and March 2020 still continues to baffle astronomers. It has been shown by George et al. (2020) that critical slowing down preceded the dimming event. This suggested that the dimming was as a result of the change in the nature of the nonlinear dynamics of the star. In this work we present additional evidence for dynamical changes in Betelgeuse prior to the Great Dimming event, using nonlinear time series analysis. We study the relations between the different bands in the photometry data collected from the Wing photometery (IR/near-IR) and Wasatonic observatory (V-band). We also analyse how the early warning signals studied previously changed during and after the Great Dimming.

Keywords: Critical slowing down, alpha orionis, recurrence quantification analysis, wing photometry.

1. Overview

The unprecedented dimming and subsequent brightening events in Betelgeuse between October 2019 and March 2020 have since been studied in extensive detail.[1–3] Three main hypotheses have been suggested as reasons for the dimming, namely changes in pulsation dynamics, star spots and a dust cloud. Combinations of these hypotheses have also been suggested as reasons for the dimming.[4,5] We will explore each of these explanations below, before explaining how the nonlinear dynamics of the light curve can contribute towards understanding the dimming.

The most prominent reason suggested for the Great Dimming observed in Betelgeuse has been the formation of a dust cloud. This has been put forward as an explanation by multiple authors. Measurements of effective temperature have suggested that no significant drop was observed during the dimming.[6] In addition, high angular resolution images showed a significant dimming in the southern hemisphere of Betelgeuse during the dimming event.[7] Observations from multiple wavelengths suggest that an outflow from the star itself, enhanced by pulsations, condensed around the southern hemisphere of the star.[4,5] It has also been suggested that the dimming could be explained by an ejection from the star that cools below 3000 K to form molecules, before condensing to dust.[8]

The dust hypothesis has been disputed as the sole reason for the dimming by a number of authors. Radiative transfer models using data from sub-millimeter wavelengths suggested that the dimming was a result of changes in the photosphere as opposed to external dust.[9] Further, observations during the dimming suggested that there was little change in the IR flux.[10] Moreover, Wing three-filter TiO and near-IR photometry found that the effective temperature during the dimming could be much lower than previously calculated, suggesting that the dimming observed in the visible spectrum could be due to photospheric motions.[11] Many of these authors proposed the presence of spots on the stellar surface as an alternative reason for the dimming of Betelgeuse.[9,12]

Finally, it has been suggested that the observed dimming was as a result of changes in pulsational dynamics.[11,13,14] Multiple authors have pointed out that the Great Dimming coincided with the minima of both the 430 days and 5.8 year periods.[11,15,16] However, the observed decrease in temperature in the star could not be explained by pulsational dynamics alone.[12]

Nonlinear time series analysis on the light curve of Betelgeuse prior to the major dimming event suggested that a critical slowing down was observed in the light curve well before the actual dimming occurred. When a nonlinear dynamical system undergoes a change of state, it often does so suddenly and with no change in the mean response. However, prior to many such changes in state (called a critical transition), multiple time series quantifiers called early warning signals (EWS) are shown to increase.[17] The presence of critical slowing down in Betelgeuse indicated that the star was about to undergo a change of state in its dynamical properties. It was suggested that the dimming phenomenon was the change of state itself or occurred as a result of it.[14] This work suggested that the reasons behind the dimming could be explained by studying the light curve before the Great Dimming occurred.

In this paper we explore the dynamical properties of Betelgeuse in greater detail, by studying how they changed before, during and after the Great Dimming. We do this by analysing Wing three-filter TiO and V band photometry measured at the Wasatonic Observatory[11,18] and V/Vis data from the American Association of Variable Star Observers (AAVSO).[19] We first gain further evidence for a dynamical change in Betelgeuse by studying the multiwavelength Wing data. We then study changes in the linear correlations between the wavelengths and study how they changed over the period leading up to the dimming. Finally we study how the quantifiers studied by George et al.[14] changed in the AAVSO light curve, in the period leading up to, during and after the Great Dimming.

2. Analysis

2.1. *Wing Three-filter and V-band Photometry*

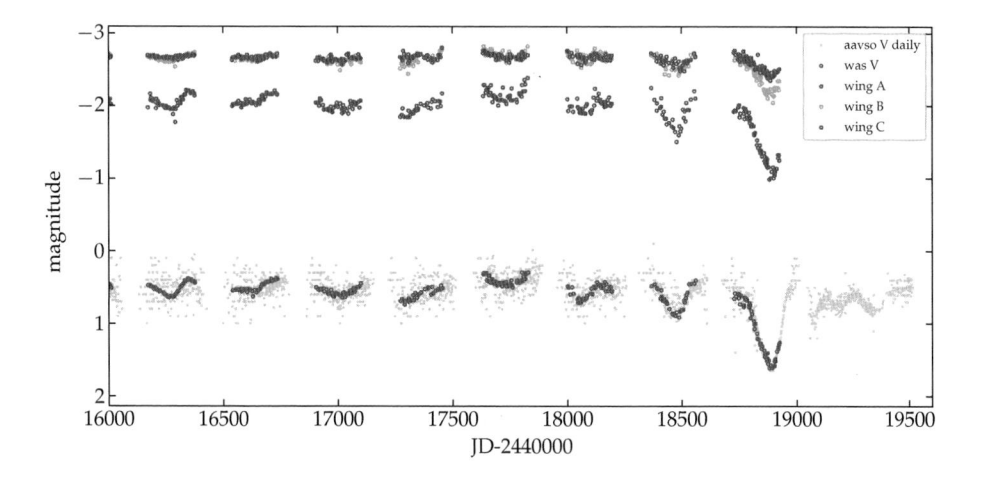

Fig. 1. Variation of intensity in Betelgeuse, as captured in Vis/V band AAVSO data (grey), V-band photometry from Wasatonic laboratory (blue), and Infrared Wing three-filter (A: green, B: orange, C: red) data.

Wing photometry consists of an eight band measurement of electromagnetic radiation from an astronomical source, initially developed for studying M supergiant stars.[20] Later, a simplified three-filter system was proposed that measures infrared magnitude, color and spectral type for a star.[21] In this study, photometric data (IR/near-IR) from three Wing filters,[21] and a wideband V filter collected by the Wasatonic observatory, are analyzed. The V-band filter is centered around 5550 Å. The Wing A filter is dominated by the TiO 7190 Å. The Wing B and C filters are continuum bands centered around 7500 Å and 10240 Å respectively. More information about the data may be found in Harper et al. (2020).[11]

We first calculate the cross-correlations (see figure 2 (a)), using Person Correlation Coefficient among data from different bands in a sliding window fashion with a window size = 300 points. The V-band and A band are already known to exhibit strong correlation,[11] but we find that this correlation decreases prior to dimming. It is interesting that this trend starts much before the actual dimming episode, hinting towards a prolonged process. Moreover, we find this trend to be simultaneous in all pairs of data.

We then employ nonlinear time series analysis techniques to analyze the multivariate data. Building on dynamical systems theory, our techniques assume the existence of a state space representation for the data. Since dynamical features of the source are intimately related to the topological properties in state space, its quantification can yield valuable information.

One of these helpful properties is recurrence: the tendency of a system to visit the neighborhoods of previously occupied states. Recurrence is a prominent feature of deterministic dynamics and can be easily captured in terms of Euclidean distances among points on the attractor (trajectories) in state space.[22] When presented in matrix form, it is known as the Recurrence matrix (R). A 2-dimensional visual representation of R is known as the recurrence plot (RP). Statistical measures on RP, collectively known as the Recurrence Quantification Analysis (RQA), reveal subtle characteristics of the dynamics at play. Changes in some of these RQA measures may serve as EWS for a system close to a dynamical transition.[23] For the multivariate data, we make use of Recurrence Rate (RR) to study dynamical features of the Betelgeuse light curve.

We analyze recurrence properties of the data in the same sliding window fashion, keeping distance threshold constant at 0.1 for calculation of RP. We do this separately for each band, and present the results for RR (fraction of points in the recurrence matrix) in figure 2 (b). Again, we find an increasing trend in all wavelengths. Interestingly, the trend is most consistent for IR bands. Further, it corresponds well to the correlation indicated in figure 2 (a). This indicates that if there is a dynamical process at play, it may not be a peripheral phenomenon. Similar variation across bands hints at the possibility of change at the stellar scale, probably in the pulsation dynamics.

These results agree well with EWS observed in the AAVSO data,[19] reported previously.[14] However, the length of available data limits an extensive analysis, at this point in time.

2.2. Beyond the Great Dimming

In this section we present results on how the nonlinear parameters of the light curve changed after the Great Dimming, using V band data from the AAVSO.[19] In George et al. (2020),[14] we reported signatures of dynamical transitions in this data in the form of critical slowing down. We reported an increase in multiple EWS including the autocorrelation at lag 1 (ACF(1)), variance and recurrence based measures in the data leading up to the dimming. The increase in these quantifiers indicated

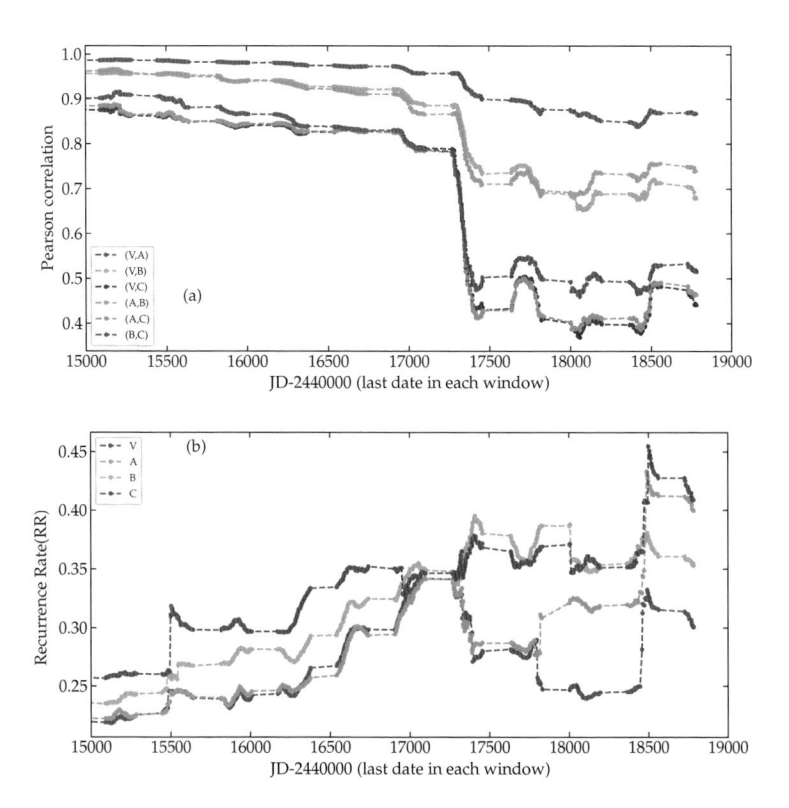

Fig. 2. (a) Cross-correlation between pairs of data from different bands calculated in a sliding window fashion upto (but not including) dimming. (b) Recurrence Rate (RR) obtained with fixed recurrence threshold = 0.1, for each band. Window size = 300.

that a critical transition was imminent. It was assumed that the Great Dimming occurred as a result of this critical transition. In the present paper we go beyond the Great Dimming and analyse how the EWS changed since.

2.2.1. *Autocorrelation and Variance*

To do this we initially bin the data from 1990 onwards into 10 day bins, and calculate the ACF(1) and variance in windows of size 300. This is presented in figure 3.1. Both the ACF(1) and Variance show an increase leading up to the dimming, a sharp rise when the Great Dimming occurred, and a slow reduction after the dimming ended. In figure 3.2 we select an area around the dimming, bin the data into 5 day bins and choose a window size of 40 points. The data again shows the same trends, with a rise leading up to the dimming, a sharp rise during the Great Dimming and a fall since. With the smaller window and bin size, the error on the quantifiers increases (changing approximately as $\frac{1}{\sqrt{n}}$).

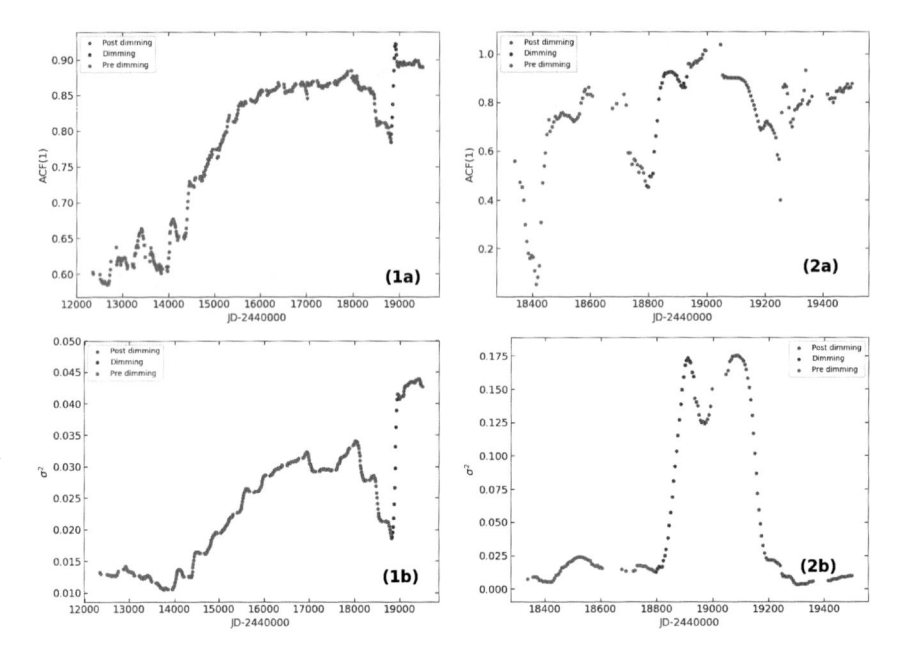

Fig. 3. Variation in the (a) Autocorrelation at lag 1 and (b) Variance calculated from the light curve of Betelgeuse upto the dimming (red), during the dimming (blue) and post dimming (green). The left panels (figures 1a and 1b) show the variation from 1990 onwards using a window size of 300 points on data binned every 10 days. The right panels zoom into a region around the dimming, with data binned every 5 days with a window size of 40.

2.2.2. Recurrence Measures

We then analyze AAVSO data in terms of recurrence measures as well. For this, we fix the recurrence rate (RR) as 0.1, and calculate Determinism (DET) and Laminarity (LAM) in the same sliding window fashion. We find a consistent rise in these measures prior to dimming, followed by a sudden dip and subsequent rise (see figure 4 (a) and (b)). We also present typical recurrence plots for two windows near dimming episode (one prior and one including dimming) in figure 4 (c) and (d) respectively as a visual aid. Clearly, the sudden drop in brightness affects the structure of the RP, and the recurrence measures reflect it. However, it is interesting to see the rise prior to dimming, possibly caused by dynamical factors (details discussed in George et al.[14]). The trend in post dimming behaviour seems in agreement which could be verified with future observations in the coming years.

3. Discussion

We presented the nonlinear analysis on two datasets measuring the brightness of Betelgeuse before, during and after the Great Dimming of 2019-20. We conducted a multivariate time series analysis of the data from Wing-IR photometry and the

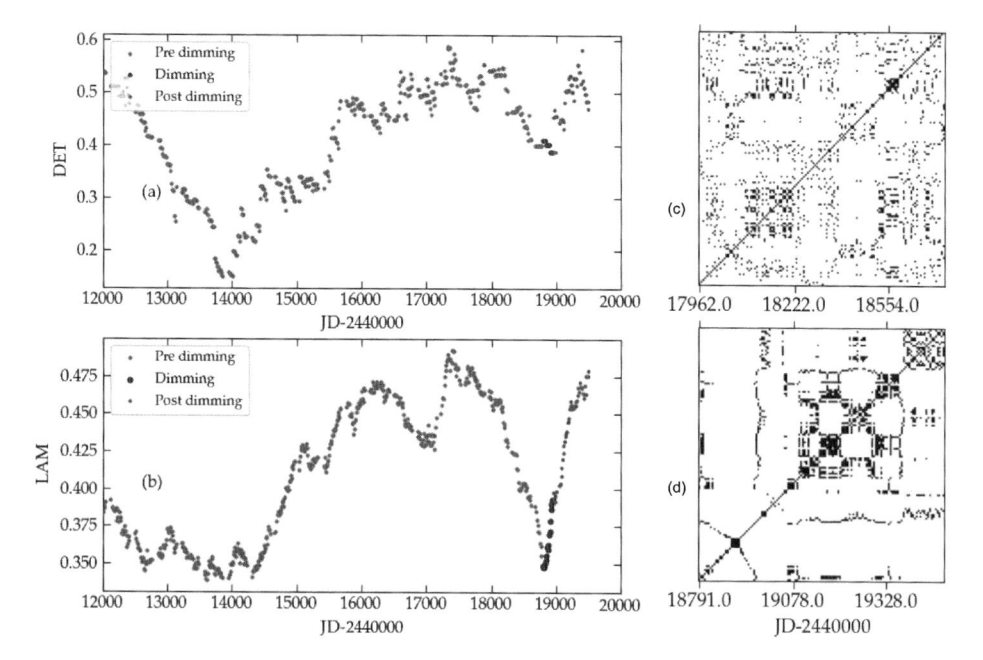

Fig. 4. Recurrence measures (a) Determinism (DET) and (b) Laminarity (LAM) calculated from the light curve of Betelgeuse upto the dimming (red), during (blue), and post dimming (green). The left panels (figures a and b) show the variation from 1990 onwards using a window size of 300 points on data binned every 10 days. The right panels (figures c and d) show typical recurrence plots for prior and during dimming respectively. The recurrence rate was fixed at 0.1.

V band photometry from Wasatonic laboratory. We show that prior to the dimming, the cross correlations and individual recurrence measures vary considerably. Our results suggest that a change in the dynamics of Betelgeuse commenced in advance of the Great Dimming of 2019-20. We also analyse early warning signals in AAVSO light curve for the period including and after the Great Dimming. While not conclusive, we see evidence that the values of the early warning signals have reduced since the Great Dimming.

Our results make a strong case that the dynamics of Betelgeuse underwent significant changes leading up to the Great Dimming. Variable stars are known to undergo changes in their nonlinear properties as they evolve.[24–26] In this study we observe that the recurrence properties, cross correlations and early warning signals change prior to the Great Dimming. In addition, Betelgeuse is known to exhibit multiple frequencies in its light curve, including a short period, thought to be driven by the κ mechanism, a long period thought to be convection driven[27] and a recently detected overtone of the short period.[11,28] It is possible that the pulsational dynamics of Betelgeuse, including the birth of new periods may have preceded the Great Dimming, and these need to be examined in detail.

Taken together with the study on the light curve of Betelgeuse by George et al. (2020),[14] our results seem to indicate that the Great Dimming was not an isolated incident, and to understand the reasons for the dimming, we must consider changes in the dynamics before it.

Acknowledgments

We acknowledge Dr. Graham Harper for useful discussions, and Richard Wasatonic and Prof. Edward Guinan for the multi wavelength data used in this study. We acknowledge with thanks the variable star observations from the AAVSO International Database contributed by observers worldwide and used in this research. SVG acknowledges financial support from the European Research Council (ERC) under the European Union's Horizon 2020 research and innovative programme (ERC-CoG-2015; No 681466 awarded to M. Wichers). SK acknowledges financial support from the Council of Scientific and Industrial Research (CSIR), India.

References

1. E. F. Guinan, R. J. Wasatonic and T. J. Calderwood, The fainting of the nearby red supergiant betelgeuse, *The Astronomer's Telegram* **13341**, p. 1 (2019).
2. E. F. Guinan, R. J. Wasatonic and T. J. Calderwood, Updates on the "fainting" of betelgeuse, *The Astronomer's Telegram* **13365**, p. 1 (2019).
3. C. Sigismondi, Rapid rising of betelgeuse's luminosity, *The Astronomer's Telegram* **13601**, p. 1 (2020).
4. A. K. Dupree, K. G. Strassmeier, L. D. Matthews, H. Uitenbroek, T. Calderwood, T. Granzer, E. F. Guinan, R. Leike, M. Montargès, A. M. Richards et al., Spatially resolved ultraviolet spectroscopy of the great dimming of betelgeuse, *The Astrophysical Journal* **899**, p. 68 (2020).
5. Kravchenko, K., Jorissen, A., Van Eck, S., Merle, T., Chiavassa, A., Paladini, C., Freytag, B., Plez, B., Montargès, M. and Van Winckel, H., Atmosphere of betelgeuse before and during the great dimming event revealed by tomography, *A&A* **650**, p. L17 (2021).
6. E. M. Levesque and P. Massey, Betelgeuse just is not that cool: Effective temperature alone cannot explain the recent dimming of betelgeuse, *The Astrophysical Journal Letters* **891**, p. L37 (2020).
7. M. Montargès, E. Cannon, E. Lagadec, A. de Koter, P. Kervella, J. Sanchez-Bermudez, C. Paladini, F. Cantalloube, L. Decin, P. Scicluna et al., A dusty veil shading betelgeuse during its great dimming, *Nature* **594**, 365 (2021).
8. B. Davies and B. Plez, The impact of winds on the spectral appearance of red supergiants, *Monthly Notices of the Royal Astronomical Society* (2021).
9. T. E. Dharmawardena, S. Mairs, P. Scicluna, G. Bell, I. McDonald, K. Menten, A. Weiss and A. Zijlstra, Betelgeuse fainter in the submillimeter too: An analysis of jcmt and apex monitoring during the recent optical minimum, *The Astrophysical Journal Letters* **897**, p. L9 (2020).
10. R. Gehrz, J. Marchetti, S. McMillan, T. Procter, A. Zarling, J. Bartlett and N. Smith, Betelgeuse remains steadfast in the infrared, *The Astronomer's Telegram* **13518**, p. 1 (2020).

11. G. M. Harper, E. F. Guinan, R. Wasatonic and N. Ryde, The photospheric temperatures of betelgeuse during the great dimming of 2019/2020: No new dust required, *The Astrophysical Journal* **905**, p. 34 (2020).
12. S. Alexeeva, G. Zhao, D.-Y. Gao, J. Du, A. Li, K. Li and S. Hu, Spectroscopic evidence for a large spot on the dimming betelgeuse, *Nature communications* **12**, 1 (2021).
13. E. F. Guinan and R. J. Wasatonic, The continued unprecedented fading of betelgeuse, *The Astronomer's Telegram* **13410**, p. 1 (2020).
14. S. V. George, S. Kachhara, R. Misra and G. Ambika, Early warning signals indicate a critical transition in betelgeuse, *Astronomy & Astrophysics* **640**, p. L21 (2020).
15. J. R. Percy, What's up with betelgeuse?, *Journal of the Royal Astronomical Society of Canada* **114** (2020).
16. C. Sigismondi, Betelgeuse 2020 dimming: getting the minimum, *Gerbertvs, International Academic Publication on History of Medieval Science* **13**, 39 (2020).
17. M. Scheffer, J. Bascompte, W. A. Brock, V. Brovkin, S. R. Carpenter, V. Dakos, H. Held, E. H. Van Nes, M. Rietkerk and G. Sugihara, Early-warning signals for critical transitions, *Nature* **461**, 53 (2009).
18. G. M. Harper, E. Chambers, W. D. Vacca, H. Wiesemeyer, D. Fadda, C. deWitt, R. Wasatonic, A. M. S. Richards, N. Ryde, C. Fischer, M. J. Richter, E. F. Guinan, R. Minchin, U. U. Graf and S. Colditz, Sofia upgreat/fifi-ls emission line observations of betelgeuse during the great dimming of 2019/2020, *The Astronomical Journal* **Accepted** (2021).
19. S. Kafka, Observations from the AAVSO International Database (2021).
20. N. White and R. Wing, Photoelectric two-dimensional spectral classification of m supergiants, *The Astrophysical Journal* **222**, 209 (1978).
21. R. F. Wing, Three-color narrow-band photoelectric photometry of red variables, *Journal of the American Association of Variable Star Observers (JAAVSO)* **21**, 42 (1992).
22. N. Marwan, M. C. Romano, M. Thiel and J. Kurths, Recurrence plots for the analysis of complex systems, *Physics reports* **438**, 237 (2007).
23. N. Marwan, S. Schinkel and J. Kurths, Recurrence plots 25 years later—gaining confidence in dynamical transitions, *EPL (Europhysics Letters)* **101**, p. 20007 (2013).
24. J. R. Buchler and G. Kovacs, Period doubling bifurcations and chaos in w virginis models, *The Astrophysical Journal* **320**, L57 (1987).
25. R. Szabó, Z. Kolláth, L. Molnár, K. Kolenberg, D. Kurtz, S. Bryson, J. Benkő, J. Christensen-Dalsgaard, H. Kjeldsen, W. Borucki *et al.*, Does kepler unveil the mystery of the blazhko effect? first detection of period doubling in kepler blazhko rr lyrae stars, *Monthly Notices of the Royal Astronomical Society* **409**, 1244 (2010).
26. S. V. George, R. Misra and G. Ambika, Fractal measures and nonlinear dynamics of overcontact binaries, *Communications in Nonlinear Science and Numerical Simulation* **80**, p. 104988 (2020).
27. R. B. Stothers, Giant convection cell turnover as an explanation of the long secondary periods in semiregular red variable stars, *The Astrophysical Journal* **725**, p. 1170 (2010).
28. M. Joyce, S.-C. Leung, L. Molnár, M. Ireland, C. Kobayashi and K. Nomoto, Standing on the shoulders of giants: new mass and distance estimates for betelgeuse through combined evolutionary, asteroseismic, and hydrodynamic simulations with mesa, *The Astrophysical Journal* **902**, p. 63 (2020).

The curious case of Betelgeuse

Jacco Th. van Loon

Lennard-Jones Laboratories,
Keele University, ST5 5BG, UK
E-mail: j.t.van.loon@keele.ac.uk
www.astro.keele.ac.uk/~jacco

Betelgeuse is the nearest red supergiant, one of the brightest stars in our sky, and statistically speaking it would be expected to be "typical". Yet it exhibits many features that seem "curious", to say the least. For instance it has a high proper motion. It rotates fast. It has little dust. It dimmed unexpectedly. Is any of these, and other, phenomena atypical, and taken together does it make Betelgeuse atypical? This is important to know, because we need to know whether Betelgeuse might be a prototype of red supergiants in general, or certain subclasses of red supergiants, since we can study it in such great detail. It is also important to know as it may be a link to understanding other, apparently atypical cases such as supernova 1987A, and maybe even such exotica as Thorne-Żytkov objects. Studying this question in itself helps us understand how we deal with rarity and coincidence in understanding the Universe we live in.

Keywords: Red supergiants – stellar variability – dust formation – supernova progenitors – Philosophy of Science – Betelgeuse.

1. Prologue

Not far in the sky from the most famous supernova remnant, the Crab Nebula, the most famous red supergiant, Betelgeuse, has been a familiar sight for peoples in either hemisphere. Distinctively orange, and one of the brightest lights on the nightly celestial firmament, its prominent position in the corner of arguably the most iconic constellation, Orion, Betelgeuse commands our attention and this in itself makes it special. This perspective aims to challenge the uniqueness and surprising behaviour of many a favourite star, and what it tells us about us. It could be seen as a more philosophical sequel to the Paris 2012 workshop on Betelgeuse.[1]

2. Is Betelgeuse typical?

It's got to be, right? Surely, as the nearest example of a red supergiant, Betelgeuse must be ordinary? This is because the chances are favourable for a draw of one from among many to be drawn from the most common.

While this may often be true, and hence unremarkable and thus unnoticed, it is not always the case, as is expected when considering many draws from samples that do include rare examples. (The basis for many false associations, let alone causal relationships.) For instance, the first supernova witnessed by naked eye for three centuries, and the best studied, supernova 1987A wasn't! It had been expected to have been a star like Betelgeuse to have exploded, and yet it was all but. (Though they may have much more in common than at first sight.[1])

We are not placed in a typical red supergiant environment. While within a Bubble created by multiple supernovæ, we are not currently situated in a spiral arm. So perhaps Betelgeuse is typical for this particular environment, but not necessarily for red supergiants that are largely found in the denser, more actively star-forming regions of a spiral galaxy such as the spectacular H II regions in the prominent spiral arms several times more distant, or the even more distant massive clusters near the Galactic Centre.

But all things considered, Betelgeuse does not stand out in either luminosity, temperature, mass-loss rate or dust content – in fact it looks like a fairly commonly identified SN II-P progenitor![2] (But this may partly be a selection bias of the progenitor identification strategies.)

3. Is Betelgeuse atypical?

Just like most people look similar – four limbs, a head with a pair of eyes and ears and a nose upfront – when inspected more closely individual traits set us apart. This doesn't make each specimen a species, and in the end, we have much more in common than differentiates us, both in terms of the way we look and the way we behave.

Among Betelgeuse's perplexities count its location at some distance from sites of recent star formation, its large space motion, and a picture-perfect bow shock.[3] Upon close inspection, it spins at a baffling rate[4,5] and also is super-nitrogenous.[6]

And then came the 'Great Dimming'.[7] (Which may have nothing or all to do with the above.) A drop in brightness by half relegated Betelgeuse to the realm of much more inconspicuous stars, but sent alarm bells ringing with fears – or excitement – for its imminent luminous demise.

But none have been scrutinised as much as Betelgeuse. Brief late phases of underrepresented stars at birth, red supergiants themselves are rare, so few are seen up as close as Betelgeuse. It is not how well we know Betelgeuse, but how poorly we know the other red supergiants that defines its curiousness.

4. Our one-sided view of Betelgeuse

Because of the attention it has recently received, we shall first unpick how rare is Betelgeuse's Great Dimming, before we return to its full portfolio of properties.

By our very own nature as observers and thinking minds, and our position in the Universe, we suffer from anthropocentric bias: just because *we* didn't see it before, or elsewhere, doesn't make it rare per se. The 20th-century artist Pablo Picasso exposed this imperfect picture by recovering what is hidden from view in a form referred to as "cubism". But how do we do that in reality? Do we know it? Do we infer it? Or do we ignore it? If you look out into a field and see what looks like a black lamb, what do you conclude? That:

- lambs are black?
- lambs exist that are black?
- lambs exist of which at least one side is black?
- apparitions exist that look like lambs of which at least one side is black?

Despite well-known examples of non-isotropy in astronomy (cf. exoplanet transits, γ-ray bursts, pulsars) it is too often overlooked.

Betelgeuse forms dust clouds episodically, as convection cells cause dark spots[8] that induce cooler circumstellar conditions where dust can form,[9] likely in an already cooler parcel of lifted gas.[10] In the case of Betelgeuse this is exacerbated because Betelgeuse is on the cusp between a warm chromosphere and dusty wind.[11] Counting the number of dust clouds and considering their projected distances from Betelgeuse, a dust cloud forms about once every five years!

Imagine Betelgeuse were cubic and we only faced one side at a time (compare a standard die), then we'd only see one in every six events randomly happening on one of its sides. (In reality the polar and equatorial regions may display different behaviour especially in the case of a rapidly spinning Betelgeuse.) This means we *may* have had a Great Dimming *on our side* once every few decades (cf. the visual lightcurve[12]), but we *certainly* missed Great Dimmings happening *on another side*!

It is tempting to expect a dust cloud to form at every minimum in the ~ 2000 day cycle. But that depends on whether this periodicity represents radial pulsation (in which case it is true) or convectional modulation – in which case the five-yearly cloud would always be in front, though other clouds would be forming more frequently throughout, above cool convection cells not seen by us, hence being in tension with observational evidence. It is more likely that a dust cloud forms at a pulsational minimum but only above a cool convection cell (the latter causing the ~ 400-day cycle, but again that's our biased perspective, there could be a cool convection cell *somewhere* on the surface at all times). In fact, forming at some height above the surface, such dust cloud is less likely to be seen directly in front of the star than the convection cell is – at one stellar radius above the surface this chance is already diminished by a factor four. (Note that even the cloud purported to have caused the Great Dimming did not cover the entire face of Betelgeuse.[7]) The Great Dimming might have been our treat, but bread and butter for Betelgeuse.

Previous dimmings have been disputed, but it is not outrageous if of a few expected *chance* occurrences (as opposed to *predicted* events) just one has materialised. A century is not a very long time span in the life of a star, even that of a red supergiant (one pro mille!), and Betelgeuse may have exhibited many more dimmings, and may exhibit many more to come. Our Sun has arguably been more dramatic, as we know it so well: the sunspot cycle is a fairly regular rythm of activity, but we are still astounded by the Maunder Minimum of the late-17th and early-18th centuries – what if the telescope had only been invented a century later? (We would never have known.)

5. How common are anomalies?

If Betelgeuse ought to be common for being the nearest red supergiant, then so should be Antares for being only the second-nearest red supergiant. But as we argued, this is not a given. It would be much less likely, though, if both Betelgeuse *and* Antares were special. This then begs the question: is Betelgeuse different from Antares?

Antares has similar luminosity, temperature, convection,[13] mass loss, (low) dust content and lightcurve (with similar dimmings). Like Betelgeuse, it produces discrete dust clouds.[14,15] But Antares is a *slow* rotator and is accompanied by a hot star (on a sufficiently wide orbit not to be directly affected by it). How different does that make them?

Imagine stars are characterised by five features, that each have a 1:10 chance of being anomalous (imagine a ten-sided die). Then 1:2 stars are expected to be anomalous. Every other star. So a star is just as likely to be common as it is to be anomalous, despite the majority of stars to be common in any given feature. It should not come as a surprise if both Betelgeuse and Antares had some properties that are rare among the general population of red supergiants. This is what makes individual people distinctive.

Imagine another scenario, where a penguin among other penguins in a colony is distinguished by:

- the colour of its coat: blue (as opposed to brown).
- the texture of its coat: smooth (as opposed to fluffy).
- the colour of its cheeks: yellow.
- the colour of the underbill: orange.

Does that make this individual penguin anomalous in four ways? Most definitely not! It is anomalous in just one way: being an adult (surrounded by infants)!

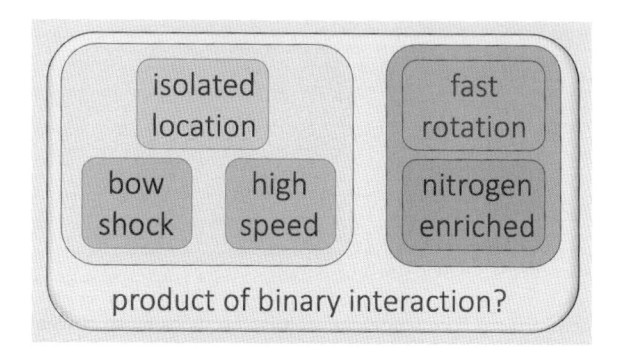

Fig. 1. Betelgeuse has various characteristics which have been treated as peculiarities. Irrespective of whether these are indeed oddities at all, they can be reduced to fewer characteristics – possibly just one – for which there may well be a totally reasonable – if not banal – explanation.

Returning to the curious case of Betelgeuse, its isolated location, high speed and bow shock are all related, and so may be its fast rotation and nitrogen enrichment – both can be reconciled into one: binary interaction (Fig. 1). And a common one at that: 10–40 per cent of massive stars will be affected by a companion.[16–18]

Then which is more special: Betelgeuse or Antares? Neither – both cases are expected equally: the result of binary interaction (Betelgeuse) and multiple but unaffected (Antares). The nearby Universe thus seems to be living up to expectations remarkably well!

6. How to find out how common is Betelgeuse?

Moving onwards, if we want to find out what red supergiants typically look like, how they generally evolve, and how and why some may deviate from the norm, we will not succeed in this by studying Betelgeuse harder and longer, but by statistical studies of samples of other red supergiants, such as:

- lightcurve studies based on sparse and/or time-limited data but for large samples in nearby galaxies ('Great Dimmings' may be seen in other galaxies, too[19]).
- nitrogen abundance measurements and their link with rotation.
- radial velocity monitoring and spectral energy distributions, to determine binary fractions.
- three-dimensional space motion studies in conjunction with rejuvenation scenarios, to determine past binary interactions.
- interferometric size measurements in relation to the location on the Hertzsprung–Russell Diagram, and mass (loss) measurements from seismology.

Fig. 2. What draws your eye? The white canvas that occupies most of what you're looking at? Or the black dot offset from the centre, which only covers a tiny fraction of your view? We are drawn to the exceptional, not the norm.

7. Epilogue

The take-away message from this discussion is that when making inferences we need to account for biases. We tend to look for the distinctive, not the common. For instance, when we look at a white panel with a black dot (Fig. 2) our attention is drawn to the dot even though it occupies much less space than the rest of the canvass. Just as we occupy ourselves with the few per cent of baryonic Universe, preferentially in its condensed forms, leaving the vastness of space largely neglected. If we saw less of the canvass, we might have missed the black dot altogether, but if we saw more we might find out black dots to be rather common!

Acknowledgements

I'd like to thank Costantino Sigismondi for organising the Betelgeuse session at the 16th Marcel Grossmann meeting and for inviting me to speak.

References

1. J. Th. van Loon, Betelgeuse and the Red Supergiants, in Betelgeuse Workshop 2012, eds. P. Kervella, T. Le Bertre and G. Perrin, EAS Publications Series, Vol. 60, pp. 307–316 (2013).
2. S. J. Smartt, Observational Constraints on the Progenitors of Core-Collapse Supernovæ: The Case for Missing High-Mass Stars, *Publications of the Astronomical Society of Australia* **32**, 16 (2015).
3. L. Decin, N. L. J. Cox, P. Royer, *et al.*, The enigmatic nature of the circumstellar envelope and bow shock surrounding Betelgeuse as revealed by Herschel. I. Evidence of clumps, multiple arcs, and a linear bar-like structure, *Astronomy and Astrophysics* **548**, A113 (2012).
4. H. Uitenbroek, A. K. Dupree and R. L. Gilliland, Spatially Resolved Hubble Space Telescope Spectra of the Chromosphere of α Orionis, *The Astronomical Journal* **116**, 2501 (1998).
5. P. Kervella, L. Decin, A. M. S. Richards, G. M. Harper, I. McDonald, E. O'Gorman, M. Montargès, W. Homan and K. Ohnaka, The close circumstellar environment of Betelgeuse. V. Rotation velocity and molecular envelope properties from ALMA, *Astronomy and Astrophysics* **609**, A67 (2018).
6. D. L. Lambert, J. A. Brown, K. H. Hinkle and H. R. Johnson, Carbon, nitrogen and oxygen abundances in Betelgeuse, *The Astrophysical Journal* **284**, 223 (1984).
7. M. Montargès, E. Cannon, E. Lagadec, *et al.*, A dusty veil shading Betelgeuse during its Great Dimming, *Nature* **594**, 365 (2021).
8. X. Haubois, G. Perrin, S. Lacour, *et al.*, Imaging the spotty surface of Betelgeuse in the H band, *Astronomy and Astrophysics* **508**, 923 (2009).
9. P. Kervella, G. Perrin, A. Chiavassa, S. T. Ridgway, J. Cami, X. Haubois and T. Verhoelst, The close circumstellar environment of Betelgeuse. II. Diffraction-limited spectro-imaging from 7.76 to 19.50 μm with VLT/VISIR, *Astronomy and Astrophysics* **531**, A117 (2011).

10. P. Kervella, T. Verhoelst, S. T. Ridgway, G. Perrin, S. Lacour, J. Cami and X. Haubois, The close circumstellar environment of Betelgeuse. Adaptive optics spectro-imaging in the near-IR with VLT/NACO, *Astronomy and Astrophysics* **504**, A115 (2009).
11. J. Th. van Loon, M.-R. L. Cioni, A. A. Zijlstra and C. Loup, An empirical formula for the mass-loss rates of of dust-enshrouded red supergiants and oxygen-rich Asymptotic Giant Branch stars, *Astronomy and Astrophysics* **438**, 273 (2005).
12. M. Joyce, S.-C. Leung, M. László, M. Ireland, C. Kobayashi and K. Nomoto, Standing on the Shoulders of Giants: New Mass and Distance Estimates for Betelgeuse through Combined Evolutionary, Asteroseismic, and Hydrodynamic Simulations with MESA, *The Astrophysical Journal* **902**, 63 (2020).
13. K. Ohnaka, G. Weigelt and K.-H. Hofmann, Vigorous atmospheric motion in the red supergiant star Antares, *Nature* **548**, 310 (2017).
14. K. Ohnaka, Imaging the outward motion of clumpy dust clouds around the red supergiant Antares with VLT/VISIR, *Astronomy and Astrophysics 568*, A17 (2014).
15. E. Cannon, M. Montargès, A. de Koter, L. Decin, M. Min, E. Lagadec, P. Kervella, J. O. Sundqvist and H. Sana, The inner circumstellar dust of the red supergiant Antares as seen with VLT/SPHERE/ZIMPOL, *Monthly Notices of the Royal Astronomical Society* **502**, 369 (2021).
16. H. Sana, S. E. de Mink, A. de Koter, N. Langer, C. J. Evans, M. Gieles, E. Gosset, R. G. Izzard, J.-B. Le Bouquin and F. R. N. Schneider, Binary Interaction Dominates the Evolution of Massive Stars, *Science* **337**, 444 (2012).
17. S. E. de Mink, H. Sana, N. Langer, R. G. Izzard and F. R. N. Schneider, The Incidence of Stellar Mergers and Mass Gainers among Massive Stars, *The Astrophysical Journal* **782**, 7 (2014).
18. J. J. Eldridge, E. R. Stanway, L. Xiao, L. A. S. McClelland, G. Taylor, M. Ng, S. M. L. Greis and J. C. Bray, Binary Population and Spectral Synthesis Version 2.1: Construction, Observational Verification, and New Results, *Publications of the Astronomical Society of Australia* **34**, 58 (2017).
19. J. E. Jencson, D. J. Sand, J. E. Andrews, N. Smith, J. Pearson, J. Strader, S. Valenti, E. R. Beasor and B. Rothberg, An Exceptional Dimming Event for a Massive, Cool Supergiant in M51, *The Astrophysical Journal* **submitted** (arXiv:2110.11376).

Variable stars observed from city sites: The 2500 AAVSO-SGQ database

Costantino Sigismondi

*ICRA, Sapienza University of Rome,
Rome, Italy
E-mail: sigismondi@icra.it
http://www.icra.it/solar*

Paolo Ochner

Padova University and Asiago Astrophysical Observatory, Italy

The observations of Betelgeuse since Christmas 2011 were started either to study the star and to contribute to observational astronomy from urban contexts, with high level of light pollution, using the naked eye. Since then 811 observations to November 9, 2021 have been made and communicated to the AAVSO international database. Antares and also other interesting long-period variable stars like VY CMa, RS Oph (recurrent nova), V766 Cen and several novae and SN2014J are part of the 2.5 K database of visual observations, obtained with the Argelander method applied to naked eye or telescopic observations. It is an invitation for the young generations, to contribute to these studies with careful and feasible observations, which require a reduction for airmass extinction of the variable star and of the comparison stars, when they are not on the same narrow field of view. The possibility to deduce the airmass by reading the notes (containing the location of the observation) of all the AAVSO-SGQ catalogue is finally presented as a point of force of my observations.

Keywords: Mira, Betelgeuse; Eta Carinae; VY Canis Majoris; RS Ophiuchi, Antares; V766 Cen, Novae, SN2014J

1. Theory and observations in history of astronomy

I observe variable stars since 1997, I have started with Mira. The "candidacy" of Mira Ceti as Betlehem Star because it is close to the position of the Jupiter-Saturn triple conjunction of 6-7 b.C. was conceived by me at the Pontifical University of Lateran and the study was continued in Yale (2001-2004) with Dorrit Hoffleit. Maxima correlation function ruled out Mira for having two consecutive bright maxima, but this property was confirmed in the "oldest" Myra-type: R Leonis, R Hydrae and χ Cygni, from their almost four-century-long lightcurves. To a bright maximum normally a dim one follows, as the correlation function of their consecutive maxima shows. These studies were supported by historical and personal visual observations. Since 2011 I observe two first magnitude variable stars, with airmass correction to reach 0.01 magnitudes accuracy with naked eye.

AAVSO observer Sebastian Otero first claimed this accuracy, as for his first data on Nova Centauri 2013, observed also by me from Porto Alegre and Rio de Janeiro.

Betelgeuse's 811 observations in 10 years, include the deep minimum of 2020.

My SGQ contributions to AAVSO-database, paralleled with Betelgeuse's V-band measurements, help to define the "personal equations" present in all 25M visual observations before CCD era (1911-on) going back to 1893 for Betelgeuse.

2. Light curves completeness

The temporal extension of lightcurves is crucial to understand the stellar behaviour. With respect to Betelgeuse, more complicate cases are Antares and Aldebaran, less variable and with distant comparison stars. The Southern hypergiants VY CMa, low in the roman horizon, V766 Cen and Eta Carinae from South America in 1999, 2003 and 2013-2014 have been also monitored with binoculars or small telescopes. Delta Scorpii (Be binary star, whose system was at periastron in 2011) has also been studied from Rio de Janeiro, since 2011. Concluding: my 2.5K direct visual observations in nearly 25 years are data and experience useful to understand and simulate the accuracy of the World largest visual observations database for variable stars, the AAVSO one.

3. Betelgeuse among the long-period variable star

Betelgeuse is indeed the brightest variable star, but not the bigger one. Roughly the pulsational periods are proportional to the mass of the star through the relation that we found in the harmonic oscillators between the elastic force and the frequency and the mass: $K \times x = F = m\omega^2 \times x$.

Then $\omega = \sqrt{K/m}$. This physical assumption is very simple, and basic; it not fulfills all observational details nowadays available, but is a good starting point to interpret the difference of 9 years of observations of Betelgeuse with the ones of Antares.

The oscillation of Betelgeuse is evident and its main period is visible, while Antares shows either an oscillation and a rising trend.

Eta Carinae in 15 years (from 1999 to 2014) also showed a rising trend, while V766 Cen and VY CMa have been measured only for a short period, below one month, and other observers or future observations will allow to detect a trend.

4. Betelgeuse and Antares: Airmass correction and trends

From 2011 to 2021 Antares in the AAVSO database has been observed 619 times by 13 persons (only 3 with more than 10 observations). In the same time interval Betelgeuse has been observed nearly 14000 times by 360 observers. Not necessarily more observations are better, because of the "personal equations", or the systematic effect of each observer can experience for the Purkinje effect (physiological and slightly different from one individual to another), or the airmass extinction not applied when the comparison stars are far apart from the star.

The data of all the observers fill completely a full magnitude range for these reasons.

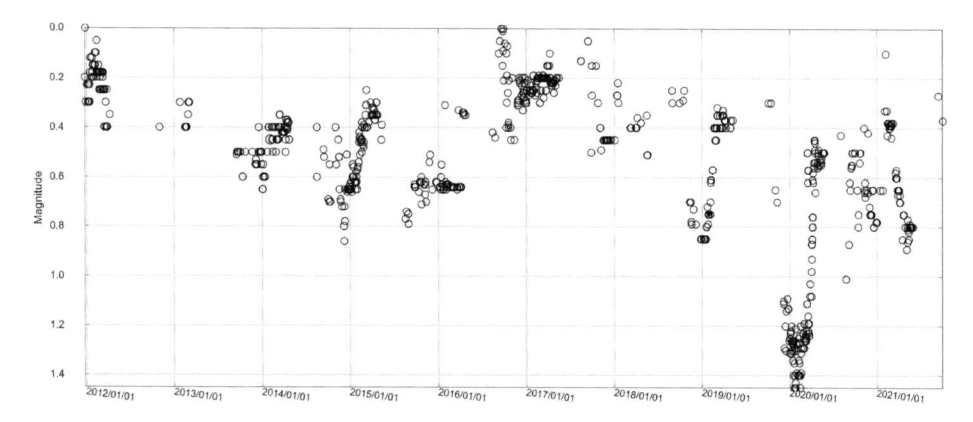

Fig. 1. The observations of Betelgeuse from 2011 to 2021 by Costantino Sigismondi, SGQ AAVSO observer.

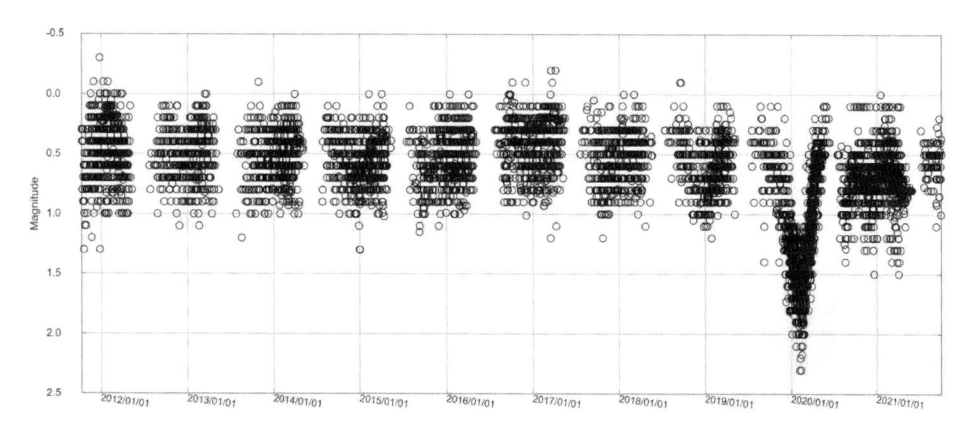

Fig. 2. All visual observations of Betelgeuse from 2011 to 2021 by the AAVSO observers: the oscillations are less evident, only the one during the deep minimum is clear. This was because Betelgeuse was at the meridian during this phase, around midnight, and its altitude was nearly constant night after night. The magnitude of the minimum from all data has a wide uncertainty. Only few visual data, still the majority for Betelgeuse, are corrected for the airmass: this is the cause of such uncertainties. The yearly gap due to solar conjunction is the most clear feature.

In the case of Betelgeuse I suppose that the airmass extinction is not applied by the majority of the observers, so I select only the obervers that I know personally as applying that correction.

Antares is a more Southern star (less observers in the Southern hemisphere), and even more separated by the comparison stars, then its measurements are more complicate. The amplitude of its variability is smaller than Betelgeuse's. These difficulties may explain the rather low number of observations available: 4% with respect to Betelgeuse. The oscillation I have detected are not clearly distinct from a yearly period, which seems related to the altitude above the horizon of the star

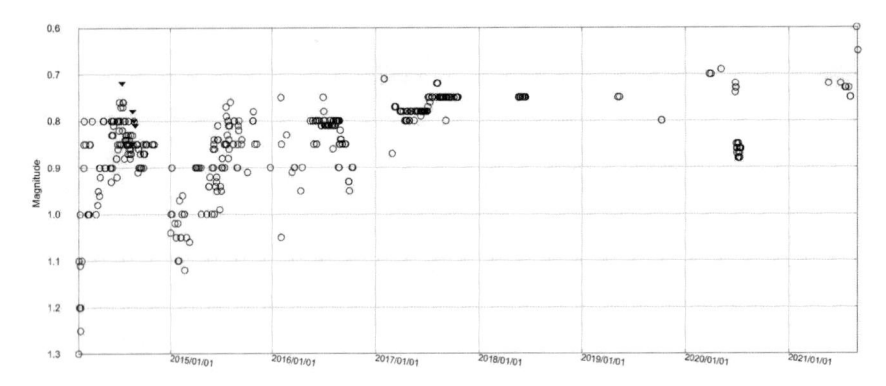

Fig. 3. The observations of Antares from 2014 to 2021 by Costantino Sigismondi, SGQ AAVSO observer.

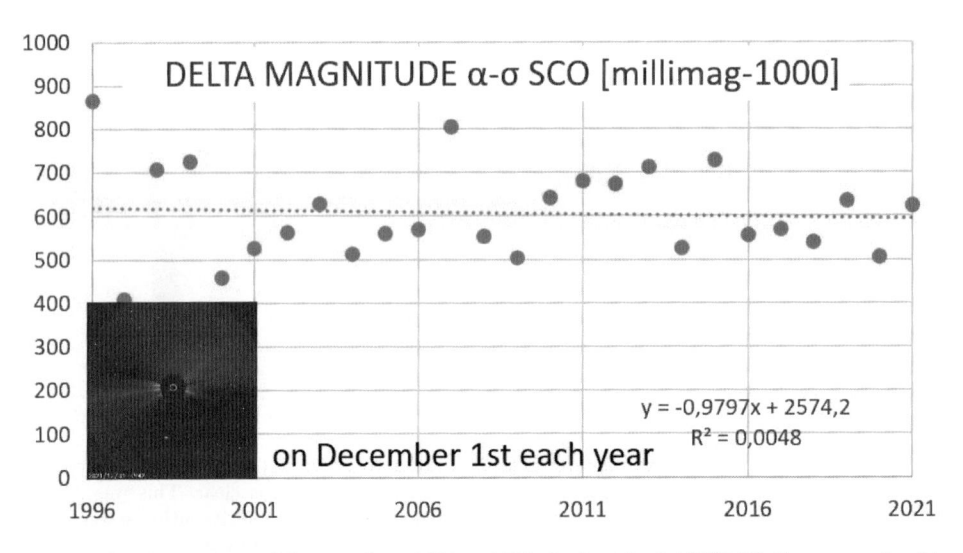

Fig. 4. The observations of Antares from 1996 to 2021 obtained by LASCO C3 Coronograph with the differential photometry made with σ Scorpii. The icon shows the image of Dec 1st, 2021.

observed at a given evening hour, and not to the star itself. The trend of the increase of the luminosity is more evident from these data.

As Betelgeuse, Antares presents rather rapid changes of luminosity during its period of visibility. No trend over the 2.5 decades can be guessed by either the visual data and the sampling each 1st of December, made with the SOHO LASCO C3 Coronograph, which includes for some days a year Antares in its field of view. That Coronograph could show stars of 5th magnitude under low activity of the solar corona. Antares is nearly saturated with this instrument, because it shows a lateral photons' spilling.

5. Recovering airmass on the AAVSO-SGQ observations' catalogue

The airmass of all variable stars can be calculated on AAVSO-SGQ catalogue by selecting SGQ as observer, in searching Alf Ori observations (and all the other variable stars observed).

The location of the observation is always reported in the notes, and the time is required by the application form. So the data for recomputing the airmass are made available.

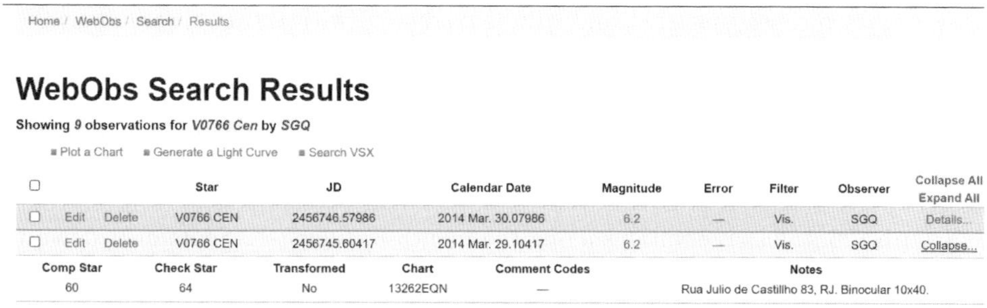
Home / WebObs / Search / Results

WebObs Search Results

Showing *9* observations for *V0766 Cen* by *SGQ*

Plot a Chart · Generate a Light Curve · Search VSX

☐			Star	JD	Calendar Date	Magnitude	Error	Filter	Observer	Collapse All Expand All
☐	Edit	Delete	V0766 CEN	2456746.57986	2014 Mar. 30.07986	6.2	—	Vis.	SGQ	Details...
☐	Edit	Delete	V0766 CEN	2456745.60417	2014 Mar. 29.10417	6.2	—	Vis.	SGQ	Collapse...

Comp Star	Check Star	Transformed	Chart	Comment Codes	Notes
60	64	No	13262EQN	—	Rua Julio de Castillho 83, RJ. Binocular 10x40.

Fig. 5. Example on V766 Centauri of the information contained in the notes: RJ is the city, Rio de Janeiro, and the address allows to have from google maps the geographical coordinates of the observation. From the time the altitude h° in the sky of the star is obtained, yielding the airmass with the cosecant law 1/sin(h°)

6. Conclusions and Perspectives: The quality of SGQ observations

The luminosity of Betelgeuse allowed to study that star in each condition from urban sites, namely for my observations Paris, Rome, Rio de Janeiro, Warsaw, without very dark skies neither without the possibility to be well screened from the light directed toward my eyes. The oscillations at the main period of 1.2 years are clearly detected.

More complicate has been the study of **Antares** which is farther from its comparison stars than Betelgeuse, and which is closer to the horizon for all the European cities. The oscillation of Antares is ranging from 1.16 to 0.88 according to the General Catalgue of Variable Stars 5.1, but my observations of the Summer 2021 found it around the magnitude 0.70 ± 0.05, at its maximum since 7 years. For Antares the comparison with Saturn was useful in the last years, and the planet has also a "light-curve" due to the geometrical change of the rings' plane. The small oscillations of Antares are not clearly detected for the aforementioned difficulties: at the horizon there are more obstacles and the atmospheric extinction is not linear with the cosecant of the altitude $1/sin(h^{\circ})$. In the General Catalogue of Variable Stars 5.1 the is no value for the oscillating period of Antares. It is classified as LC variable, and according to wikipedia it means: *A slow irregular variable (ascribed the GCVS types L, LB and LC) is a variable star that exhibit no or very poorly defined* periodicity in their slowly changing light emissions. These stars have often been little-studied, and once more is learnt about them, they are reclassified into other categories such as semiregular variables. A long period study on the variability of Antares has conducted by me following a 2014 study on Delta Scorpii, with the SOHO C3 coronograph. The next datum from SOHO C3 will be available 15 days after the closure of these proceedings, on December 1st 2021. This measure will be interesting since in the summer 2021 Antares has shown the brightest luminosity of the last 7 years. The two datasets of **Eta Carinae** in 1999 and in 2013-4 allow to see its slow rising. The other hypergiant **V766 Cen** and **VY CMa** have been observed for a short time slot, and will be compared with future observations. For them the differential magnitude has been estimated with stars in the same or near the telescopic field of view, being them not visible to the naked eye. Actually Eta Carinae could be visible with the naked eye, but not in the city lights. To observe it from Rio de Janeiro (Copacabana seaside with a strong illumination in 2003 and Observatorio Nacional in 2013) I had to use a small telescope. The recurrent nova **RS Oph** (2021, 24 observations along the month 8 August-12 September down to magnitude 9 with a 76 mm telescope, fig. 5), other Novae in Sagittarius from 2015 to 2018 and the SN 2014J are part of this personal database of 2564 high quality visual observations to date (9 November 2021), available to the science community.

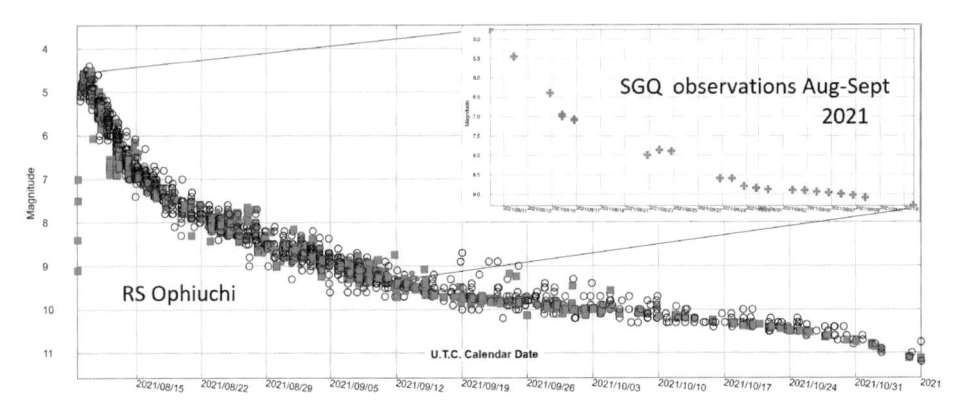

Fig. 6. The AAVSO light curve of RS Oph with the SGQ contributions evidenced in orange. They are compared with the V-band observations, and they are in very good agreement.

References

1. Antares in the General Catalogue of Variable Stars (2021), http://www.sai.msu.su/gcvs/cgi-bin/search.cgi?search=Alf+Sco.
2. C. Sigismondi, AAVSO-SGQ database (insert SGQ in the observers' code) https://app.aavso.org/webobs/search/.
3. Curt Renz, Saturn Stellar Magnitude https://www.curtrenz.com/saturn.html.
4. C. Sigismondi, et al. (2014) *Photometry of Delta Scorpii from 1996 to 2013 using SOHO LASCO C3 coronograph* - https://arxiv.org/abs/1410.8492.

Betelgeuse: An introductory course to observational astronomy

Costantino Sigismondi

*ICRA, Sapienza University of Rome,
Rome, Italy
E-mail: sigismondi@icra.it
http://www.icra.it/solar*

Tiziana Pompa

Liceo Galilei, Pescara, Italy

Betelgeuse is the brightest variable star in the sky, with a pulsational main period of 14 months and typical magnitude variation of 0.5 magnitudes. In 2020 its deep dimming was of one whole magnitude, particularly evident to each attentive observer. The technique of airmass correction to detect the stellar signal from the atmospheric extinction treats the naked eye observations as the digital astronomical observations. Harlow Shapley said in 1930s "theories come and go, while a good observation stands forever" and he spoke about naked eye observations, nowadays they are less considered in science mainly because of philosophical reasons concerning the subjectivity of knowledge and the deceit of the senses, while the knowledge of the eye physiology and of data reduction could recover the correct relationship between the human being and the Universe.

Keywords: Betelgeuse; Red giant; Variable stars, Atmospheric Extinction, Quadrant.

1. General Overview on observing Betelgeuse

According to Dorrit Hoffleit (1907-2007) director of the Maria Mitchell Observatory and astronomer at Yale University, Mira is the educational star. But it requires the use of a telescope at its minimum, and a binocular for its maximum phase, to spot it in city lights. Betelgeuse is a semiregular variable star of first magnitude, in the most famous constellation in the sky, visible from both hemispheres because it is on the celestial equator. It is visible (to the naked eye) for nine months a year. Its magnitude estimate, according to the Argelander method, requires other first magnitude stars, separated by several degrees, at rather different airmasses.

Procyon, Aldebaran, Pollux, Castor as well as γ Geminorum, Regulus, Denebola, Mars and even Mercury have been used as comparison stars, and their airmass corrections included.

Since January 2019 we steered a project in schools to observe and measure the light curve of Betelgeuse. We observed Betelgeuse and its comparison stars with a special colored quadrant where the angular height in sight corresponds to the airmass exctinction with respect to the zenit. The schools were the Lyceum Morgagni and Ferraris in Rome and Ostia and the Lyceum Galilei in Pescara.

☐	Edit	Delete	ALF ORI	2458869.58333	2020 Jan. 21.08333	1.40	—	Vis.	SGQ	Details...
☐	Edit	Delete	alf Ori	2458869.30556	2020 Jan. 20.80556	1.45	—	Vis.	SGQ	Details...
☐	Edit	Delete	alf Ori	2458866.35764	2020 Jan. 17.85764	1.29	—	Vis.	SGQ	Collapse...

Comp Star	Check Star	Transformed	Chart	Comment Codes	Notes
Bet Gem mv=1.16	Alf Gem mv=1.58	No	Tirion2000.0/Simbad	—	Pescara, front sea 7th floor, Betelgeuse dimming meeting. Naked eye with airmass correction.

☐	Edit	Delete	ALF ORI	2458866.27431	2020 Jan. 17.77431	1.35	—	Vis.	SGQ	Collapse...

Comp Star	Check Star	Transformed	Chart	Comment Codes	Notes
et Gem mv=1.16	Alf Gem mv=1.58	No	Tirion2000.0/Simbad	UL	Pescara, ICRANet, Betelgeuse dimming meeting. Naked eye with airmass correction.

☐	Edit	Delete	alf Ori	2458866.22014	2020 Jan. 17.72014	1.45	—	Vis.	SGQ	Collapse...

Comp Star	Check Star	Transformed	Chart	Comment Codes	Notes
et Gem mv=1.16	Alf Gem mv=1.58	No	Tirion2000.0/Simbad	UL	Pescara, ICRANet, Betelgeuse dimming meeting. Naked eye with airmass correction.

☐	Edit	Delete	ALF ORI	2458865.35764	2020 Jan. 16.85764	1.30	—	Vis.	SGQ	Details...
☐	Edit	Delete	ALF ORI	2458864.42500	2020 Jan. 15.92500	1.26	—	Vis.	SGQ	Details...
☐	Edit	Delete	ALF ORI	2458863.39583	2020 Jan. 14.89583	1.28	—	Vis.	SGQ	Details...
☐	Edit	Delete	ALF ORI	2458862.26042	2020 Jan. 13.76042	1.40	—	Vis.	SGQ	Details...

Fig. 1. The observations made during the meeting of 2020 during the Great Dimming.

The great dimming of Betelgeuse was then observed and measured to the nearest 0.01 magnitude at naked eye (fig. 1).

These observations have been sent to AAVSO, as contributes of students to citizen science. Similar operations have been realized with the students of the Astrophysics Laboratory, Sapienza University of Rome. Summer vactions' homework are "offered" by Antares, a first magnitude stars greatly separated by its more suitable comparison stars. Recently Saturn worked as reference, but a planet is not a constant standard candle. The introduction to photometry, colorimetry and spectrometry with these naked-eye cases is complete and historically meaningful.

2. Colorimetry: From the spectrum to the Newton's disk

The color of the stars is something lost in city environment, because lost is the visibility of the sky in general, owing to the artificial light directed toward our eyes and toward the sky. Betelgeuse is clearly a red star, and it can be noticed by comparing it with Procyon or Rigel, normally used as comparison stars for magnitude's estimates, or Sirius, that are rather close to Betelgeuse.

The Newton's disk for solar spectrum has been replicated for Betelgeuse with red-yellowish tonalities.

The connection between the color of the star and the its temperature can be done by noticing the percentage of color of a given wavelength, as represented in the Newton's disk. Basically the Wien's law is represented with the apple pie diagram: the largest sector corresponds to the wavelength of the maximum intensity in the spectrum.

3. Betelgeuse the brightest long-period variable star

Among the variable stars Betelgeuse is indeed the brightest, and the most simple one to be detected thanks to its location in Orion, near the celestial equator. This

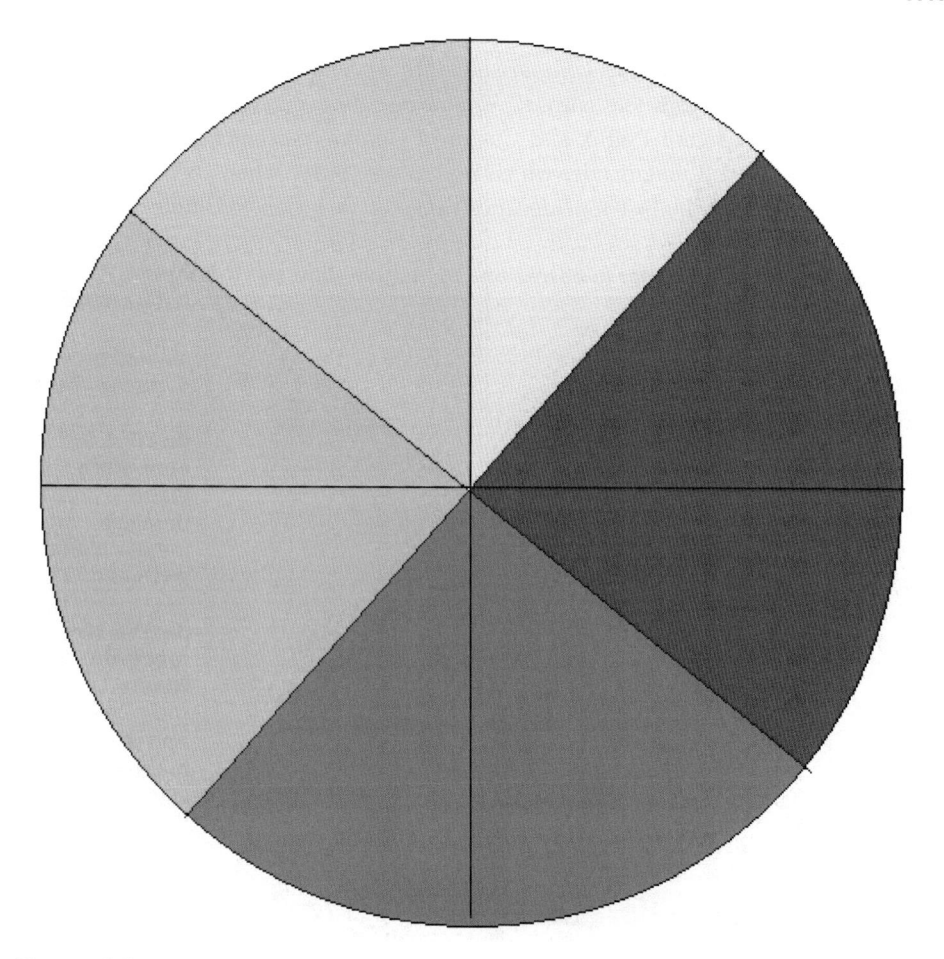

Fig. 2. Colorimetry: the Newton's disk of Betelgeuse as realized by 14 years old students in 2020.

position makes Betelgeuse popular either from the Northern and the Southern hemispheres. The period of main oscillation is 1 year and two months, and the secondary modulating period is almost six years. In a reasonable space of time achievable by a school class program, the star can be followed from a maximum through the following minimum to the next one maximum, i.e. a complete oscillation. This allows the students to familiarize with the oscillating nature of such phenomenon, and primarily with the fact that among the "fixed" stars something changes and within a factor of two in intensity (2.512 times for a whole magnitude gap from minimum to maximum) even if the star is a supergiant as Betelgeuse is.

4. The quadrant for the airmass correction

Hanging a weight on the top right corner of the quadrant in figure 3, the thread shows the magnitude's correction and the corresponding angular altitude of the star. The brighter stars used as comparison stars with the Argelander's method are reported near the bottom left corner: Aldebaran, Procyon, Rigel, Spica, Regulus and Deneb. There are not Pollux and Castor of Gemini, neither Bellatrix in Orion, stars dimmer than 1.2 magnitude, which in January 2019, when the quadrant was designed, were out of the last four-decades range of variation of Betelgeuse.

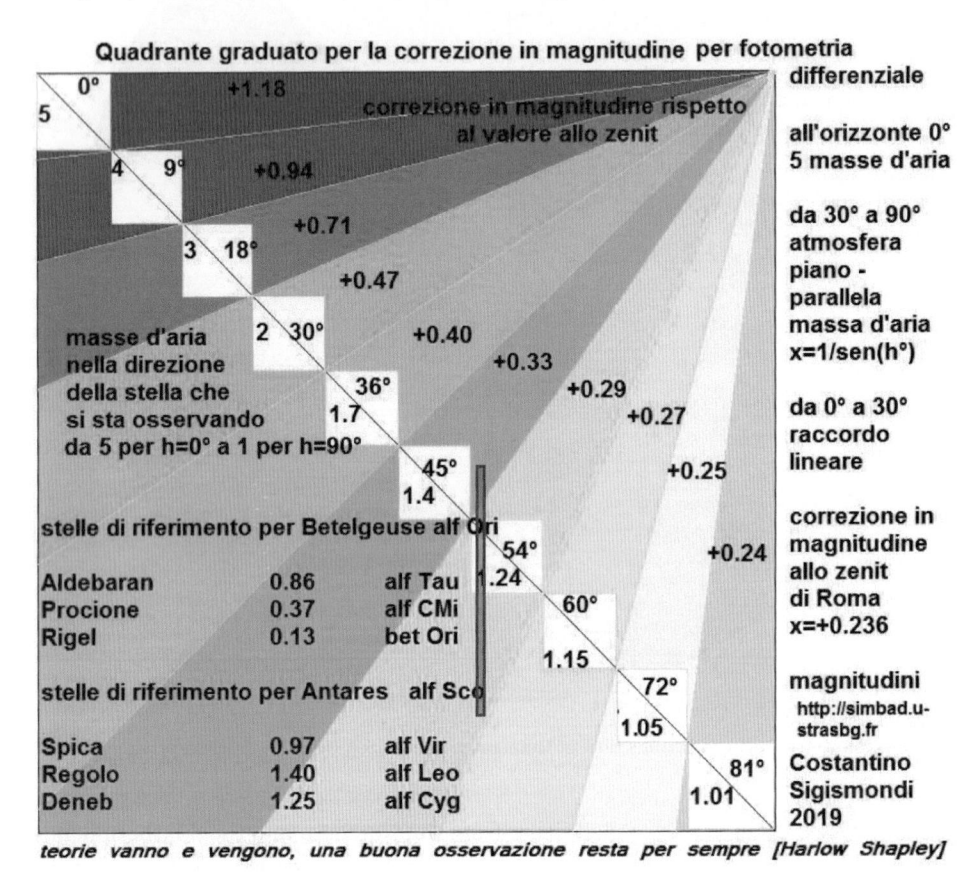

Fig. 3. The quadrant prepared for the observations of Betelgeuse for the students of the Morgagni Lyceum in Rome and the Galilei Lyceum in Pescara.

5. Data reduction

It is not obvious for a young student that an astronomical observation, or an experiment in general, require a data treatment, to be presented or to be analyzed to obtain science results. In particular an observation with naked eyes seems something really far from the data analysis concept. While a light-curve shows the intrinsic "behaviour" of a star, and it is exactly what we want to observe and measure, a single observation made with the naked eye seems a static datum. The difference in altitude of the stars determines a different atmospheric extinction acting on them,

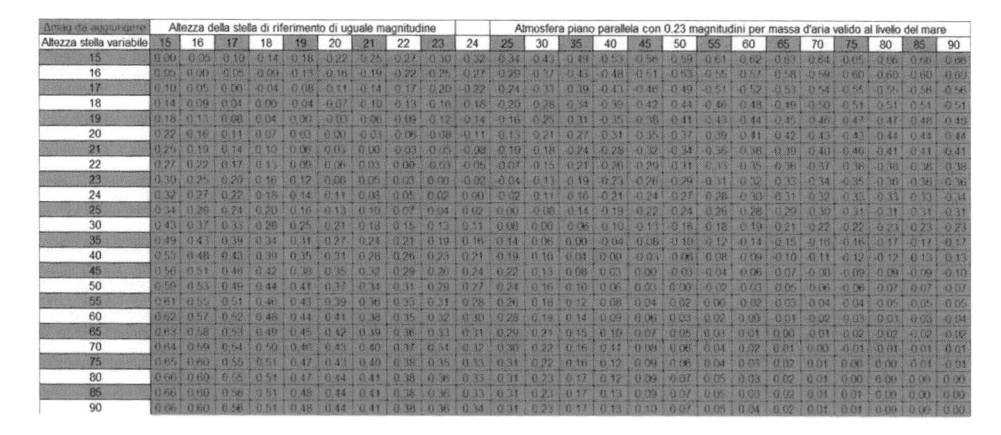

Fig. 4. The airmass table for Rome with $\Delta Mag = 0.236/sin(h)$.

Fig. 5. The quadrants realized for the special event of the Betelgeuse Deep Minimum Meeting of January, 17th 2020.

and this computation has to be done for each of the observed stars: Betelgeuse and the two bracketing comparison stars (Aldebaran and Procyon, usually). This operation generate a system of two first order equations in the incognita *magnitude* of the variable star. The solution of such system is a range of magnitudes for the variable star, hopefully as narrow as 0.05 or 0.02 magnitudes. The data reduction can be made also by using Stellarium 0.20.2, ad higher versions, where an extinction's model is implemented. With respect to Betelgeuse Stellarium airmass fails below 10° and our quadrant is more reliable.

6. Conclusions and Perspectives

Betelgeuse is a good "student star" or the "educational star" following Dorrit Hoffleit. She was applying such definition for Mira Ceti (from 2nd magnitude to 9th) but the students were College students with an astronomical telescope available. Betelgeuse requires attention indeed, but it is visible always to the naked eye. It is visible also from the light-polluted cities, and the observations can be done from their home, as homework, rather easily from September-November before sunrise to April-May after sunset, and nearly all night long in between. The possibility to participate to AAVSO observational campaigns, with a real citizen science contribution can stimulate the most interested students to pursue the way of a scientific career in astronomy.

References

1. Betelgeuse dimming: the state of the star International workshop (2020), `http://icranet.org/index.php?option=com_content&task=view&id=1281`.
2. `http://www.aavso.org`.
3. C. Sigismondi, Quadrante per Magnitudini (2019) `https://docs.google.com/document/d/1UDJIOmdYZnBEAK4pDzdCWjEoGVBqjjbp1gL9HvrmbiY/edit?usp=sharing`.
4. `http://www.stellarium.org`.

The meridian line of the Vatican obelisk to study the stellar aberration

Costantino Sigismondi

ICRA, Sapienza University of Rome,
Rome, Italy
E-mail: sigismondi@icra.it
www.icra.it/solar

Lorenzo Ricciardi

University of Rome 3,
Rome, Italy

The first evidence of the stellar aberration come out from telescopic meridian observations, including daytime ones. The distance in ecliptic longitude between the star and the Sun has to change from 180° to 90° to have the maximum effect in the delay of the transit, with respect to a constant sidereal day of 23h 56m 04.09s. We present the measurements of meridian transits of Antares and Ras Alhague during the Summer 2021, at the meridian line of St. Peter's square, whose gnomon is the Vatican obelisk. The possibility to observe such transits in daylight has been also verified with Antares (21 August, 2021) and Venus (October 2021). The geometry of the instrument and its configuration is ideal to introduce students to the observations of this special relativistic effect, from an experimental point of view. The transits observed from the same position, the Scorpio zodiacal disk, from October 16 to November 11, 2021 permitted to scan the axis of the obelisk and the one of the uppermost cross, finding an offaxis of (16±3) mm West for the upper pyramid and a further deviation of (5 ± 3) mm West of the cross.

Keywords: Vatican obelisk; Meridian line; Stellar Aberration; Ecliptic longitude; Sidereal day.

1. The Vatican obelisk and the meridian line of St. Peter's square

The Egyptian obelisk was carried in Rome by Emperor Caligola and set on the Vatican Circus. It was the only one which survived along the middle ages, considered the witness of the martyrdom of the apostle St. Peter. Pope Sixtus V and the architect Domenico Fontana moved it in front of the Basilica of St. Peter in 1586 with the special design to emulate and surpass the Augustus' obelisk mentioned by Plinius the Elder in his Naturalis Historia. The Dominican astronomer Egnazio Danti who also worked at the Gregorian Reformation of the Calendar (1582) drafted the project of a meridian line, which would have been the largest in the World, his untimely death on 22nd October 1586, 40 days after the translation of the obelisk, delayed this work of 230 years. Only in 1817 Cardinal Peter Maccarani, with the astronomer rev. Filippo Luigi Gigli, realized the line in granite, 7cm wide and 70 meter's long from Cancer to Capricorn. The characteristics of such line are measured and reported in this paper, they have been used as zero calibration of the instruments in the measurements of the Earth's rotation period.

2. The stellar aberration

Published in 1727 as a discovery of a new motion of the fixed stars, by the Royal Astronomer James Bradley, the stellar aberration moves the stars around an ellipse. The ecliptic longitude of the Sun determines the longitude's aberration amount for a given star: it is maximum ± 20.62 arcsec if the star is on the ecliptic plane, and with the Sun in conjunction or opposition, it is zero in both quadratures. Out of the ecliptic plane a latitude component appears, which equals the longitudinal one at the ecliptic pole, where γ Draconis, the star observed by James Bradley, it is located. We observed Antares between 130° to 100° from the Sun and Ras Alhague in evening, twilight and sunset conditions; the aberration is proportional to the difference of the cosine of such angles or 47% of the 20.62 arcsec, i.e. 9 arcsec. A difference in 9 arcsec is corresponding to 0.6 s in transit time, with respect to a constant sidereal day. In 30 days, as the duration of this series of observations, it corresponds to a drift in the duration of the sidereal day of +0.023 s/day.

The aberration value of 9 arcsec corresponds to twice the parallax maximum estimated error of 4.5 arcsec (corresponding to 2 mm on the meridian line at 92 m from the gnomon on the Capricorn's disk).

2.1. Reducing the parallax error

A mirror located in the center of the meridian line, always in the same point, is aimed with the monocular at its center. The top of the obelisk is at 92 meters of distance, and an error of pointing of ±2 mm is possible, this yield a maximum angular uncertainty of ±4.5 arcsec.

3. The observations at the meridian line of obelisk's occultations: A differential measure

The inclination coefficient 235.872 s = 3 m 55.872 s is the difference with 24 hours of the measured average sidereal day. The event measured is the disappearance of Antares behind the obelisk, called *first contact* behind the obelisk.

The figure 1 represents the linear fit of the UTC transit times observed with a monocular as ingress and egress time behind the obelisk, as seen from the same point of the end of the meridian line next to the Capricorn sign. The average sidereal day is 23h 56m 04.128s ±0.02, which is +0.038 ±0.02 s larger than the standard value for it. The special relativistic effect +0.0207 s is within a sigma from our result.

These measurements are made all from the same place of the meridian line, near the black star of the Capricorn's disk for Antares and Venus (in afternoon meridian transit during its Eastern solar elongation) and near the black star of Virgo's disk for Ras Alhague, so they are differential. Systematic deviations along the meridian line do not affect them.

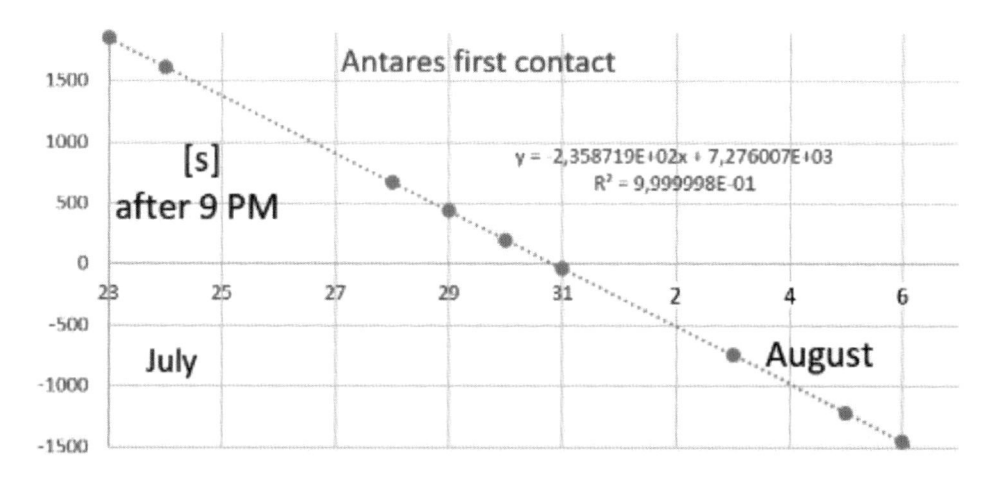

Fig. 1. The average sidereal day from 23 July (Sun $\lambda = 121°$) to 21 August 2021 (Sun $\lambda = 149°$). Antares has $\lambda = 250°$. In this timespan the ecliptic elongation of Antares from the Sun ranges from $\lambda = 129°$ to $\lambda = 101°$. The difference of the cosines is 0.2, multiplied by 20.6 arcsec, the aberration constant, yields 9 arcsec, which in time is 0.6 s. In the 29 days of this plot the theoretical value is is 0.0207 s/day, and the measured one is 0.038±0.02 s/day.

4. Local deviations from the North of the meridian line

A general astrometric recognition of the meridian line has been done on the zodiacal disks, obtaining the following deviations with respect to the axis of the obelisk.

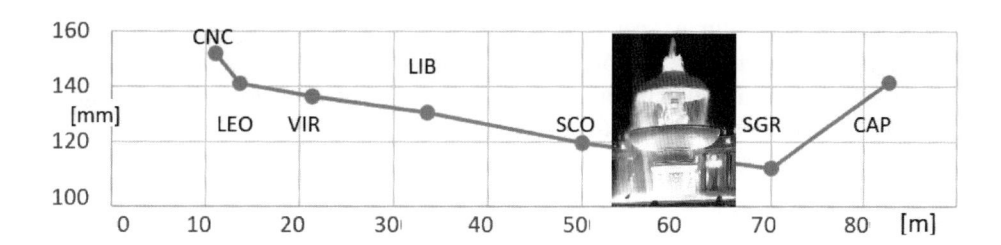

Fig. 2. Deviations in mm from the obelisk's axis along the line.

The cross on top of the obelisk is not aligned with its axis, being slightly west. The cross has been probably used for aligning the Capricorn with the Summer signs. They are at the same westward distance from the obelisk axis, being aligned with the celestial North within 2 mm along 71 meters, which corresponds to 6 arcseconds: the top of the technology of 1817.

5. Orthogonality of the cross over the obelisk

After calibrating the meridian line with respect to the North, it is possible to calibrate the gnomon (the obelisk with the cross) with respect to the vertical of its axis.

Fig. 3. The Southern face of the obelisk in full Sun: on the top the dark Southern arm if the cross is slightly on the left from the obelisk's axis.

The technique consists in measuring the difference between the observed transit and the calculated one, and transforming it into linear distances with the local velocity of the shadow. A series of observations made from October 16 to November 11, 2021 has been made to verify the orthogonality of the cross above the obelisk, and its symmetry axis. The Sun, as seen from the star of the Scorpio's marble zodiacal disk, started to pass behind the top of the cross, and it scanned all the features (cross, star, mounts, pyramid and the uppermost sections of the monolith). The instant in which the Sun passed through their symmetry axis was compared with the transit time calculated with the ephemerides. After many verifications in St. Maria degli Angeli meridian line to the nearest arcsecond, the ephemerides of Stellarium 0.20.2 have been used for St. Peter's square meridian line. The final result of this study has an uncertainty of ± 3 mm, due to the location of the telescope or of the camera, in case of direct vision, on the marble disk.

With respect to the symmetry axis of the obelisk:

- the axis of the obelisk from the point is defined (10 and 11 November)
- the star is 16.5 mm West of the axis (20 October)
- the middle part of the cross is further 10 mm West (18 October)
- the uppermost part of the cross is further 5 mm West (16 October)

Being the errorbar ± 3mm the cross can be vertical as well as slightly inclined. The four tyrants have the function of stabilization during windy days. On 14 october, a windy day, the oscillations of the cross have been detected. The cross

Fig. 4. The Sun at noon on November 10, 2021, as seen from the Scorpio's black star.

is 90 mm wide and the oscillation were 5 mm - 10 mm. All the structure on top of the obelisk is 5 meter high, then the oscillations are small. The orthogonality of the whole structure verified from 64 m, has an angular accuracy of $\pm\ 10''$.

6. Discussion and conclusions

The measurement of the length of the sidereal day with a fixed star is not a simple experiment. It is necessary to have a fixed instrument and a very low parallax. The Vatican obelisk was the fixed reference frame used for this experiment, and the parallax was reduced by observing from the center of the granite meridian line of St. Peter's square. A mirror was used to aim at the same point of the line, to reduce the parallax down to 4 arcsec. The final result over 31 days on Antares from 21 July to 21 August 2021 allowed to detect the contribution of Special Relativity as stellar light aberration within less than a sigma (0.02 s) of the predicted theoretical value of the average sidereal day: 23h 56m 04.138 s ±0.02 s, 0.0273 s larger than the aberrated value.

An extremely good result obtained with such historical instrument, the obelisk-meridian line of St. Peter's in the Vatican. A monocular, a mirror and a UTC synchronized watch and an audio-recorder has been a light equipment to perform such an experiment. The didactic value of this experience is paramount.

The deviation of the line from North and of the obelisk with the uppermost cross with the vertical are measured with a few millimeters accuracy, by comparing the transit's timings with the ephemerides.

References

1. J. Bradley, *Phil. Trans.* **35**, 637-661 (1727-1728).
2. C. Sigismondi, Venus transit of October 27, 2021 at the vatican obelisk. https://drive.google.com/drive/u/2/folders/1ugl5TkhzQnE9qJcfJgx2BkiNnUIfKRAX.

Betelgeuse, Sirius and the stars in the roman *Settecento*

Costantino Sigismondi

ICRA, Sapienza University of Rome,
Rome, Italy
E-mail: sigismondi@icra.it
http://www.icra.it/solar

Betelgeuse was reported as a magnitude "1-" in the Almagest of Ptolemy (150 AD), while it is of first magnitude star in the Uranometria of Bayer (1603). The latter with the stellar catalogue of Philippe de la Hire were used to include in 1701 the stars in the Great Meridian Line of St. Maria degli Angeli by Francesco Bianchini (1662-1729). For Sirius and Arcturus a series of star were positioned on the floor of the Basilica in correpondence with their positions up to two hours before their meridian transit, with 15 minutes of interval in the case of Sirius. Other stars in the floor represent the motion of the Sun on 20 August 1702 and in the Equinoxes, so that since two hours before the meridian transit it was possible to see how the Sun approached the Celestial Equator. Their astrometrical calibration with the Sun along the year is here published for the first time: for some of the stars the timing accuracy of their location is within a few seconds, as well as their distance from the pinhole, while in other cases it may reflect the "quantization" due to the terracotta bricks on the former floor of the Basilica. Because of the precession and proper motion the position of Sirius on the line changed from 1701 to 2021, and it has taken into account in this analysis. The black marble stars of the Vatican obelisk meridian line (1817), are calibrated with respect to the 3D star on top of the obelisk, by projecting the Sun behind it through a 7×18 prismatic monocular.

Keywords: Betelgeuse; Stellar Variability, History of Astronomy, Meridian Line, Santa Maria degli Angeli, Vatican obelisk, Rome, Francesco Bianchini (1662-1729).

1. Positional astronomy in 1700 in Rome

During the *Settecento* in Rome the research in astronomy was dedicated to Celestial Mechanics,[1] as in the other Eurpean Countries. In the various observatories present in Rome (the Jesuits at the Collegio Romano, the Dominicans at Minerva, Bianchini in St. Maria degli Angeli) the measure of their geographical coordinates with lunar eclipses was performed and compared with the other European cities. A lunar occultation was firstly observed by Giovanni Battista Audiffredi at Minerva, the one of Spica, with evidence of multiple nature of this stellar system. This observation was realized in view of a better knowledge of the lunar orbit. Francesco Bianchini (1669-1729) in St. Maria degli Angeli observed also three lunar eclipses in 1703 in order to verify the lunar theory in the Gregorian Calendar, and we used them to recover the UTC of the solar meridian transits. The coordinates of the stars used to measure the solar longitude were taken from the Catalogue of Philippe de la Hire (1700), of the Observatory of Paris. Bianchini placed 22 stars on the marble of the meridian line st. Maria degli Angeli, and Bellatrix, the western shoulder of Orion, or γ Orionis and Betelgeuse, the oriental one, are reported with their magnitude in figure 4. Two of the stars have been found in the wrong place: both of the Northern hemisphere, placed in the Southern hemisphere. The reason was a misreading of the coordinates in the book of Philippe de la Hire, like if that work was hurried, without any time for revision. Other stars have been placed with an extreme care and precision, like for Sirius.

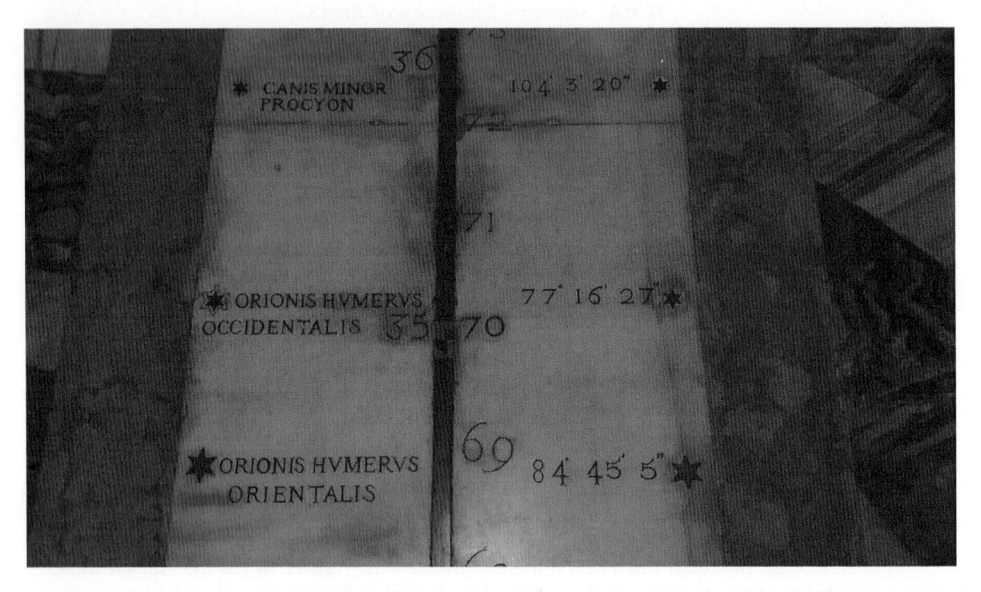

Fig. 1. Procyon, Bellatrix (occidentalis) and Betelgeuse (orientalis) on the meridian line of St. Maria degli Angeli, with their magnitude. Bellatrix is smaller than Betelgeuse. 35° is the zenithal distance of Bellatrix, $70 = 100 \times tan 35°$.

2. Magnitudes and stellar positions in St. Maria degli Angeli

Bianchini wanted to represent the zodiacal signs with the corresponding constellations of the Atlas of Johannes Bayer, the Uranometria (1603). Francesco Tedeschi realized the marble *tarsie* and Bianchini provided the magnitude's scale according the Catalogue. Also on the meridian line the magnitudes were attributed according to that Catalogue, not being stellar variability still recognized as a general property of the stars.

The position of Sirius on the meridian line is the one of 1700 "precessioned" to 1701. The precession was the only one motion of the celestial sphere to be known at that time. The proper motion was discovered by Edmund Halley on Arcturus' coordinates few years later in 1718. The stellar aberration, which is annual, was discovered by James Bradley in 1727 on γ Draconis.

If we compute the position of Sirius with the coordinates of today, applying the precession down to 1701 we do not found its position on the meridian line, because of its proper motion in declination of 1.211 arcsec/year Southwards, which

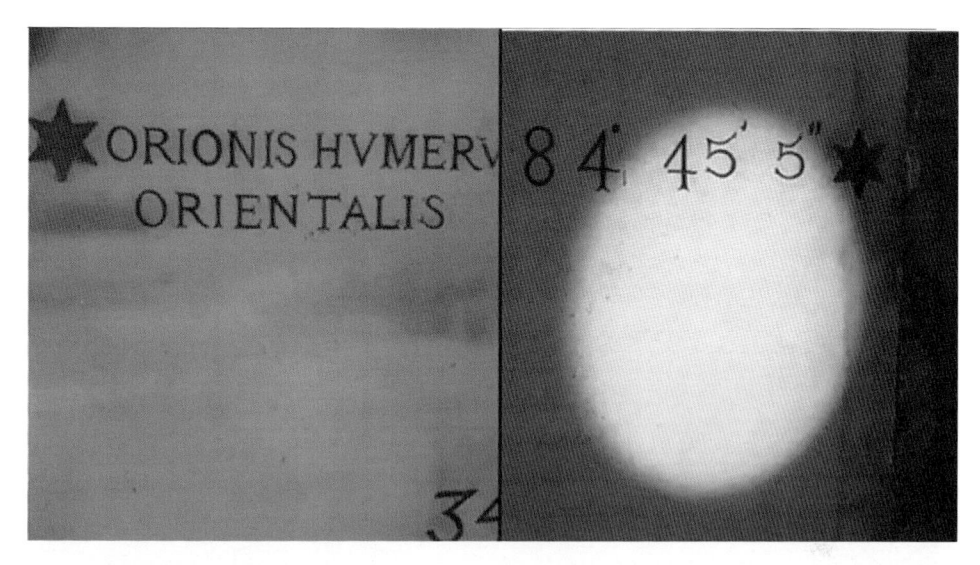

Fig. 2. The Sun passing over the position of Betelgeuse in the spring of 2018. The ecliptic longitude 84°45′5″ of 1701 is reported on the meridian line, in correspondence of its declination 34° is the zenithal angle of the Northern limb of the Sun at the moment of the photo.

Fig. 3. The star of the celestial North pole in the Basilica of St. Maria degli Angeli.

in 320 years totalized 387 arcsec, i.e. 0.68 centesimal parts or 137 mm towards the Capricorn sign.

The positions of the stars of series of Sirius, on the hyperbola of Sirius' path on the floor of the main hall, the original roman hall of 30 meters of heigth, have been placed to mark each 15 minutes the approach of Sirius to the meridian line.

Fig. 4. The ellipse of 2100 orbit of the Polaris, around the North Celestial Pole.

Fig. 5. The constellation of Leo at the meridian line of St. Maria degli Angeli, represented with its stars and corresponding magnitudes, according to the Uranometria (1603).

Excepted the star of -2 hours, which is absent without signs of effraction, all other stars are placed within 10 seconds of accuracy, from the actual time of meridian transit. This verification has been realized on February 5 and November 8 2021 by observing the Sun transiting on the same path. Knowing the instant declination of the Sun, also the distance from the pinhole's vertical has been verified.

As example I report the observations of the star 1 hour 45 minutes, 45 and 30 minutes before the meridian transit on November 8th 2021.

- first contact 10:08:12 – 11:08:10 – 11:22:34.5
- last contact 10:09:42 – 11:09:40 – 11:24:02
- star inside for 01:30 – 01:30 – 01:27.5

The conjunction was respectively at 10:08:57, 11:08:55 and 11:23:18.5 and the solar meridian transit occurred at 11:54:04, then with an advance respectively of 1h45m07s 45m09s and 30m40s. The time difference was -7, -9, and -40 seconds. The 30 minutes-before star shows a wrong position in timing (azimuth) but a correct position in declination (distance from the pinhole's projection) since the duration of the timing is nearly constant (90 s) or compatible with the motion in declination of the Sun during 1h 15 min of 0.86 arcminutes.

Moreover the solar transit lasted 2 m 21 s, and the transit over the star 1 m 30 s, this meant that the center of the star was separated by the solar one by 33 s (see fig.1).

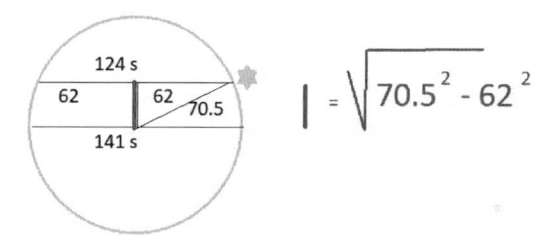

$$l = \sqrt{70.5^2 - 62^2}$$

Fig. 6. The theorem of Pitagora can be applied on the solar ellipse, because the properties of its chords are preserved in the projection on the floor of the Basilica. The data are of the meridian transit of 7 Novembre 2021: 141 s is the transit's duration and 124 s is the time of Sirius star inside the solar moving ellipse on the floor.

By using the same technique to the ten stars of Sirius all over the floor of the Basilica we found the stars with azimut (timing) errors of 7 to 40 seconds, or 5 cm to 16 cm, while the declination (distance from the pinhole's vertical point) is correct, since the duration of the contacts of the solar limb with the stars is constant.

The azimuthal dimension of 14 cm, is compatible with the presence of terracotta bricks on the ancient floor of St. Maria degli Angeli, the one realized by Michelangelo.

3. Equinoctial line and Papal path of 20 August 1702

It seems like the stars, originally, were all placed at the center of the closest terracotta bricks, placed with the long side parallel to the main hall of the Basilica. Another way of describing that fact is that 11 bricks were prepared with a star in

Fig. 7. The Sun on the meridian line at Sirius' declination on November 7th 2021. The star is included in the solar image. It transit lasted 141 s and the "time of flight" of Sirius was 84 s.

Fig. 8. The solar image "climbs" the column of Vanvitelli on November 7th 2021.

the middle, and later they were used to substitute the selected bricks by the actual path of Sirius. The stars of the Celestial Equator show an alignment not exactly perpendicular to the meridian line, by two arcminutes, or 11 mm over 20 meters, the timings are accurate. It may reflect the use of a "paleo" meridian line which

Fig. 9. The star of Sirius on the marble *Imetto* of the meridian line.

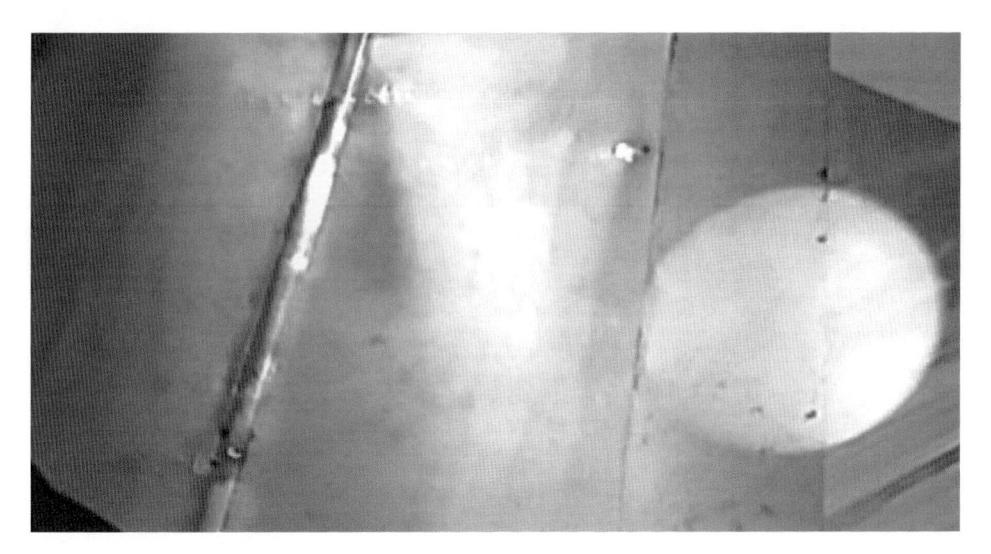

Fig. 10. The Sun four minutes before the meridian transit of 8 November: its position with respect to Sirius' star is nearly tangent. With respect to 7 Nov 2021 the Sun is 16.5′ more South, about 50% of its diameter. This image, with the one of figure 6, account for this fact precisely, being a differential measure. The Sun moves perpendicularly to the brass line.

was better aligned with the North than the present one, modified after the intervent of Giacomo Filippo Maraldi, an astronomer of Cassini's observatory visiting Rome when Bianchini was tracing the Great Gnomon. He had his own observing place in the Tower of Biscia in Palazzo Venezia, from which he transmitted the visual signal to S. Maria degli Angeli. The boreal line, 6 meters long and a few months "older" than the Great Line, was used by Bianchini only to measure the latitude of the pinhole, and later abandoned, but it was better aligned to the North than the Great one. This would explain the 2 arcminutes of shift of the Equator, materialized by the alignment of four stars placed each 30 minutes before the meridian transit.

For the stars of the papal path the accuracy on their location is slightly better than of Sirius, but always a few cm of difference with respect to the theoretical positions are found.

Fig. 11. One of the stars of the solar phat of August 20, 1702, when the pope Clement XI visited the meridian line. Photo of August 19, 2021.

4. Marble disks in St. Peter's square in 1817

Their location on the meridian line is connected with the top features of the obelisk. The marble is really of fine quality, offering a very good reflection to the projected image through a telescope. Also the chromatic aberration is well visible.

Fig. 12. The star of Scorpio on the meridian line of St. Peter's square. The line was realized in 1817, the director of the works and committent was Cardinal Pietro Maccarani, head of the Fabric of St. Peter. The art of marble *tarsie* was still at its apogee. Photo of 20 October 2021.

5. Conclusions and Perspectives

The stars of St. Maria degli Angeli described in this text are important to understand the technology used to place them, owing their astronomical significance. The verification of their positions requires still more observations, because on 5 February and 8 November 2021 not all stars were measured. Better data are available for 19 August 2021 for the stars of the papal visit. Has Bianchini placed the stars, and

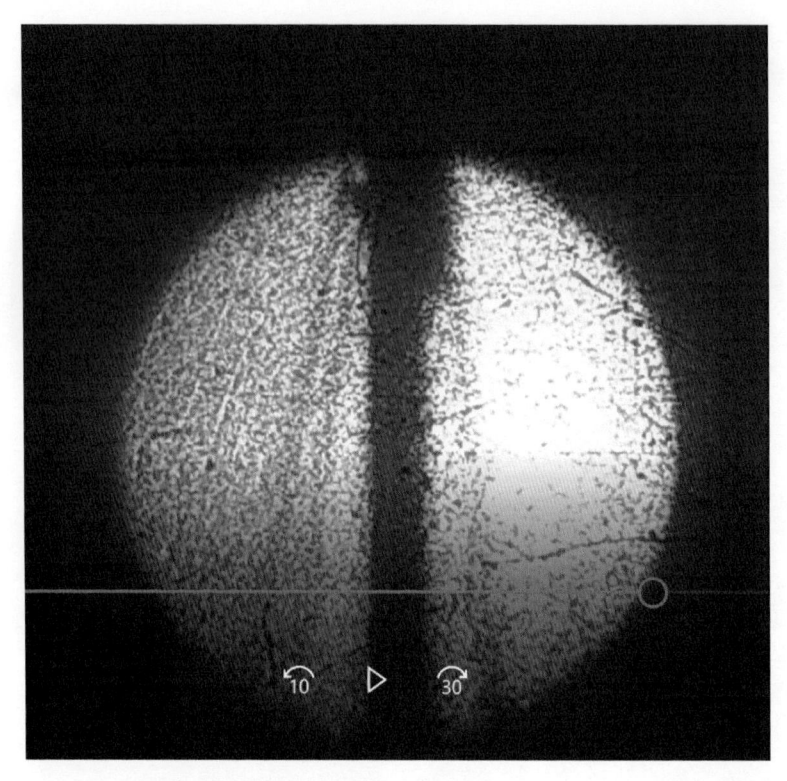

Fig. 13. The Sun projected on the Scorpio marble on October 18, 2021, at the meridian transit: the central part of the uppermost cross is visible.

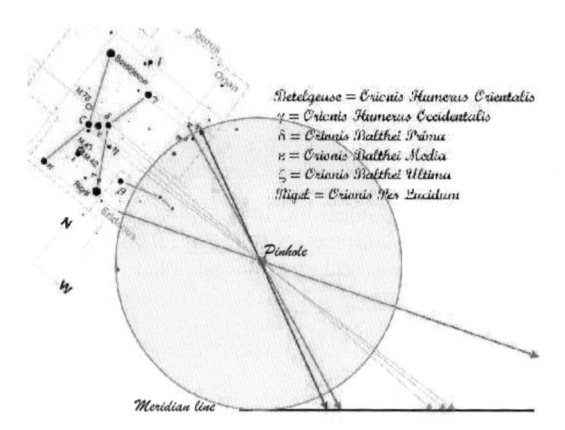

Fig. 14. The projection of the stars of Orion along the meridian line through the pinhole.

Fig. 15. A star on the floor of St. Peter's Basilica.

Vanvitelli left them in the same place? Has Bianchini placed the stars of Sirius in the center of the bricks and then changed only the relevant ones? Or was continuous the position of the stars on the floor of the Basilica since the inauguration of the meridian line in 1702?

In the Vatican the stars on the meridian line of St. Peter's square and the stars on the obelisk belong to different centuries: nineteenth and sixteenth one. Pope Sixtus V placed some obelisks in the squares of Rome (Laterano and Piazza del Popolo and St. Peter's square) as well as the one of St. Maria Maggiore. On the top of these obelisks a three-dimensional star is always present. It is like the crossing point of all the direction, a geodetic point near each relevant point of the Urbs. Sixtus V was the ruler of the urbanistic of Rome, and its plan is effective still nowadays. I presented here the observations in St. Peter's square made with a small telescope, like the one that Bianchini used in the Basilica of St. Maria degli Angeli to observe the stars transiting through the window over the pinhole. The sidereal period of the Earth's rotation was recovered to the nearest $1/100$ s, by using the vatican obelisk

Fig. 16. Before and after the solar meridian transit, as seen from Scorpio on November 10, 2021.

Fig. 17. The ghost image of the Sun behind the three-dimensional star superimposed to the obelisk's profile, and its nearly 100 m-long shadow at 10:40 AM on November 18, 2021. Both the Sun and its halo are overexposed, and only the ghost image holds the solar position's information.

Fig. 18. The Sun projected near the Scorpio's star (left Oct 20, 2021, -20 s transit's advance) and Sagittarius' star (right: Nov 18, 2021, -27.8 s). The connection between the star and the solar occultation by the three-dimensional star above the obelisk is not given by the dates reported on the zodiacal disk, but there is a 3-5 days anticipation, due also to the concave shape of the square.

Fig. 19. The dimension of the solar image projected on November 18, 2021 compared with 0.50 euro. The mini-telescope has 7 x magnification, with respect to a pinhole image. This image was projected at 300 mm of distance from the telescope's objective. The pinholhe image would have sized 3 mm (always 1 to 100 the ratio diameter:focal length of the solar image). Then the image is 21 mm of transverse diameter. The meridional diameter is rather 2 times the transverse one.

as sighting reference. This technique has been adapted also to hazy days, when the image cannot be projected to the marble: a direct vision of the obelisk is realized as in fig. 16. The calibration of the line with respect to the celestial North, and of the obelisk and the uppermost cross with respect to the vertical axis of symmetry of the obelisk is another fine technique, to inspect the details of the wonderful manufacture of about two millenia B. C. the obelisk from Heliopolis, dedicated to the Sun healer from blindness. Art, religion and science are profoundly entangled in this approach to the stars in the roman *Settecento*.

Fig. 20. The comparison between the direct image (overexposed halo) and the ghost image, on November 17, 2021 behind the Northern fountain's water. The top of the obelisk, as seen from the meridian black star is visible, also in the left-down pane, where the Sun's halo saturates most of the image, and some water's droplets appear black. The instant of the meridian transit was chosen for this screenshot, as the green ghost image shows, being divided into two equal parts by the top cross. The meridian transit occurred at 11:54:41, 28 s before the ephemerides' one at 11:55:09. The use of the small telescope allowed to reach always a timing accuracy better than one second. The offaxis angle of the telescope was evaluated by the motion of the projected image in term of the solar angular diameter of 32.4′ entering the Sagittarius. The lens is placed on the meridian line axis within 0.5 mm. The transit lasted 2 min 16 s, $\varnothing_\odot = 32' \ 05''$, $16''$ less for Nov 18.

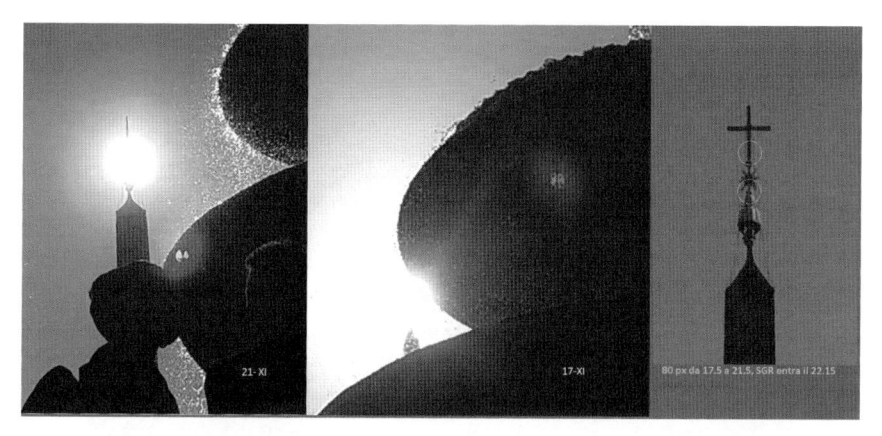

Fig. 21. The Sun filmed from the Sagittarius' black star on November 17 (center) and 21st (left). The position of the Sun is reported on the cross on 17 November and below the 3-D star on 21st. The red circle is where the ingress in Sagittarius occurred on 22.15 November 2021.

Fig. 22. The Sun at 12:07:40 of 4 December 2021, 8 minutes after the meridian transit. The yellow empty disk represents the position of the Sun at the meridian, and the red one the position at the Winter solstice of December 21, 2021. The photo is taken from the zodiacal marble disk of the Capricorn, on the black star. The alignment between the Sun at the solstice and the 3-dimensional star is confirmed as in the other austral zodiacal signs of Scorpio and Sagittarius.

Fig. 23. The principle of the shadow's motion perpendicular to the meridian line around the meridian transit has been used to draw this image: the red line and circle are used to predict the position of the Sun 25 minutes later at the meridian transit: the Sun disappears at the ground level at the two extremes of the meridian diameter. Then the Sagittarius' marble disk has been located in the sole point were the Sun could illuminated all the disk's meridian diameter at the ingress of Sagittarius. The photo is of Sunday 21 November 2021, 16 hours before the ingress of the Sun into Sagittarius, and 30 minutes before the papal Angelus.

References

1. C. Sigismondi, *Meridiani e Longitudini a Roma* Sapienza University of Rome, 2006 and Biblioteca Casanatense 2005. https://rosa.uniroma1.it/rosa03/semestrale_di_geografia/article/view/15345, https://casanatense.beniculturali.it/?p=75.
2. C. Sigismondi, *Lo Gnomone Clementino* Gerbertus **7** 1, 80, 2014.
3. C. Sigismondi, *Lo Gnomone Clementino: Astronomia Meridiana in Chiesa dal '700 ad oggi* https://arxiv.org/ftp/arxiv/papers/1106/1106.2498.pdf 2016.
4. M. Catamo and C. Lucarini, *Il Cielo in Basilica* Arpa-Agami, Roma, 2012.

5. C. Sigismondi, *Sirius' path in the Basilica*: 5 feb https://drive.google.com/drive/u/2/folders/1vRCHMT0ueVmARxydUVbmabzSQEjAzB_v 8 nov https://drive.google.com/drive/u/2/folders/1z9uP-3qODZAbKV0wK0Rwl FhRPxedHqw4.
6. C. Sigismondi, Meridian transits in St. Peter's square in November 2021 from Sagittarius' disk 17 nov https://drive.google.com/drive/u/2/folders/1qS8Xrg0dz1Mt91oEdHLdMhnRPZ7il11K 18 nov https://drive.google.com/drive/u/2/folders/1S5Ovd6cQTfcVzmYkUVCvlz8g7T2So9Pw 20 nov https://drive.google.com/drive/u/2/folders/1N5XLETPkApu7SE9e2ngdS-_KyJninrbw 21 nov https://drive.google.com/drive/u/2/folders/1g3N5pBNTVwDL26ei_zTql1hklcq_rnyc.
7. Papa Francesco, *La mia idea di arte* 37-42 Mondadori, Milano 2016.

On Einstein's last bid to keep a stationary cosmology

Salvador Galindo-Uribarri* and Jorge L. Cervantes-Cota[†]

Departamento de Física, Instituto Nacional de Investigaciones Nucleares,
Carretera México Toluca Km. 36.5, Ocoyoacac, C.P. 52750, Edo. Mex., México
* E-mail: salvador.galindo@inin.gob.mx
[†] E-mail: jorge.cervantes@inin.gob.mx

It is commonly known that the steady-state model of the universe was proposed and championed in a series of influential papers around mid-twenty century by Fred Hoyle, Hermann Bondi, and Thomas Gold. In contrast it is little known that, many years before, Albert Einstein briefly explored the same idea; that is of a "dynamic steady state" universe. In 1931 during his first visit to Caltech, Einstein tried to develop a model where the universe expanded and where matter was supposed to be continuously created. This latter process was proposed by him to keep the matter density of the universe constant. However, Einstein shortly abandoned the idea. The whole event has already been described and analyzed by C. O'Raifeartaigh and B. McCann in 2014. It is the purpose of this brief note to point out what might have prompted Einstein to consider a continuous creation of matter and the prevailing circumstances at that time that drove Einstein's intent.

Keywords: History of Physics; Cosmology; Einstein.

1. Introduction

The first relativistic model of the cosmos is due to Einstein. His model entailed the idea of a universe both isotropic and homogeneous on the largest scales (idea known as "Cosmological Principle"). At that time, it was the accepted view that the universe was stationary. This was not unreasonable since relative velocities of stars are small. To achieve a stationary universe, Einstein added in 1917 to his original field equations, the so-called cosmological constant "λ" to counterbalance the effects of gravity and attain a static universe[1]:

$$G_{\mu\nu} - \lambda g_{\mu\nu} = -\kappa \left(T_{\mu\nu} - \frac{1}{2} g_{\mu\nu} T \right). \tag{1}$$

Einstein showed that the value of the constant he introduced was proportional to the mean mass density ρ of the universe and inversely proportional to the square of R, its radius of curvature,

$$\lambda = \frac{\kappa \rho}{2} = \frac{1}{R^2}. \tag{2}$$

The introduction of λ in the original field equations was accepted by the early few practitioners of General Relativity as convenient to keep the current standard view at the time, of a static universe.

However, Einstein was uneasy with his forced introduction of the λ constant. Several of his papers show his uneasiness. For instance, in a 1919 publication Einstein stated:

"...the general theory of relativity requires that the universe be spatially finite. [This] requires the introduction of a new universal constant λ, standing in a fixed relation to the total mass of the universe (or respectively, to the equilibrium density of matter). This is gravely detrimental to the formal beauty of the theory".[2]

It was not until 1931 that Einstein at long last dropped off λ from his field equations. During those days, Einstein was visiting professor in Pasadena California attending an invitation made by Robert Andrews Millikan to spend a short season at Caltech (from late December 1930 to early March 1931). Soon after his arrival to California he discussed Hubble's redshift measurements and its implications with Mount Wilson Observatory astronomers.

Today there is still a justified widespread view that Einstein discarded the cosmological constant immediately after he was satisfied of the validity of Hubble's evidence for a non-static universe. This rendered λ in his field equations, redundant. In April of that same year, Einstein submitted for publication, a paper to the Sitzungsberichte der Preussischen Akademie der Wissenschaften where he rejected his cosmological term as superfluous and no longer justified. In his own words, "theoretically unsatisfactory".[3]

But the view that Einstein dropped off λ just before his meetings with the Mount Wilson astronomers (in early Jan 1931) is not strictly exact. In the interval between his arrival to California and his 1931 Sitzungsberichte paper (April 1931), he made a last effort to model a "dynamic steady state" universe, keeping λ in his field equations. This was serendipitously discovered in 2013 by Cormac O'Raifeartaigh in an unpublished Einstein's manuscript kept in the Albert Einstein Archives (AEA) maintained by the Hebrew University of Jerusalem.[4] The first translation into English of the manuscript, contents and its analysis, has been already covered in 2014 by his discoverer Cormac O'Raifeartaigh and his colleague Bruce McCann.[5] In addition, the manuscript contents were also commented in a note added in proof by Harry Nussbaumer and later also reviewed by him.[6,7]

2. A significant finding

The discovery by O'Raifeartaigh of the unpublished manuscript showing a model still using the lambda constant, came as a great surprise to everyone. From the moment Einstein arrived at Caltech it seemed that he had already accepted a non-static universe. Various reports in the local press affirm this. And consequently, people supposed that Einstein had already scrapped the constant from his field equations as unnecessary.

As a celebrity, during his visit to California, Einstein's activities and sayings were reported daily by the press. In Jan 3 the New York Times (NYT) reported that during an interview given the previous day Einstein stated: "New observations by Hubble and Humason (astronomers at Mount Wilson) concerning the red shift of light in distant nebulae make the presumptions near that the general structure of the universe is not static".[8] The next following month the NYT (Feb 5) another front-page story, informed that Einstein delivered a lecture the previous day (Feb 4) where he no longer held to the model of "Stable universe".[9]

On January 15, Einstein attended a welcome dinner in his honor at "The Athenaeum", a club house for the California Institutes Associates (a group of promoters of southern California scientific and scholarly research). The dinner was attended by around 200 guests among them a selected group of astronomers that had collaborated with their own research in testing relativity.[10] The final dinner speech was delivered by one of them, Walter S Adams, director of Mount Wilson. Adams had verified Einstein's prediction of gravitational redshift.[11] During his speech Adams highlighted the problem of the "nature and structure of the universe" and he announced that:

"Professor Einstein is now inclined to consider the most promising line of attack on the problem to be based on theories of a non-static universe, the general equations of which have been developed so ably by Dr. Richard Chase Tolman, of the California institute of technology".[12]

Despite the multiple examples that can be cited, affirming Einstein's alleged intention to follow a non-static approach, the 2014 discovery by O'Raifeartaigh of the manuscript, revealed that Einstein temporarily followed a different scheme in his unpublished document.

3. The manuscript

The unpublished manuscript is entitled "Zum kosmologischen Problem", that is located in the Albert Einstein Archives (AEA) (draft, 1931. Doc [2-112]). It is a signed, four-page handwritten manuscript by Einstein on American paper. Assigned by AEA to January or February 1931.

The cosmological model depicted in the manuscript was not previously detected given that the first words of its title are identical to those of Einstein's 1931 Sitzungsberichte paper (April 1931). For this reason, it was assumed to be a draft of the latter publication.

The manuscript has already been extensively analyzed by O'Raifeartaigh and colleagues[13] and in the here cited papers by Nussbaumer, so we shall limit ourselves to giving a succinct description of its contents based on those publications.

4. The model in the manuscript

In the manuscript Einstein explores a solution to his field equations retaining λ that could be compatible with Hubble's observations; to be precise an expanding universe in which the density of matter does not change over time. Einstein starts his analysis by choosing the metric of flat space expanding exponentially (De Sitter metric):

$$ds^2 = -e^{\alpha t}(dx_1^2 + dx_2^2 + dx_3^2) + c^2 dt^2. \tag{3}$$

So, the distance between two points increases over time as $e^{\alpha t/2}$, and he remarks: "one can thus account for Hubbel's [sic] Doppler effect by giving the masses (thought of as uniformly distributed) constant co-ordinates over time".

In his calculations he finds that α^2 (representing the expansion of the universe) is related to its overall density ρ as,

$$\alpha^2 = \frac{\kappa}{3}\rho. \tag{4}$$

That is, ρ determines the expansion. Since the redshift measurements at the time suggested that the universe expansion is constant, so he concluded that the density must be constant as well.

In the final part of his manuscript, Einstein proposes that the density of matter remains constant by supposing a continuous formation of matter in empty space. He then observes that: "For the density to remain constant, new particles of matter must be continually formed within that volume from space."

At the end of the manuscript, he associates the cosmological constant with an energy of space: "by setting the λ-term, space itself is not empty of energy". Consequently, the continuous creation of matter becomes associated to the λ cosmological constant.

Einstein's "dynamic steady state" universe simultaneously incorporated the observed expansion of the universe together with a new paradigm, namely of an expanding universe that maintained its isotropy and spatial homogeneity the same as it always has and always will (later dubbed the perfect cosmological principle) by means of the continuous creation of matter.

The "dynamic steady state" model was so compelling to set aside. However, Einstein didn't submit his manuscript for publication. O'Raifeartaigh and colleagues detected the possible reason why Einstein gave up publishing it.[13] He must have noticed on revision, that his model contained a flaw. Once the error is corrected the model leads to the trivial solution $\rho = 0$, that is an empty universe of matter. Therefore, he promptly abandoned this attempt.

We must ask now what it was that attracted Einstein to consider the possibility of a universe where there is a continuous creation of matter. To find a possible answer we shall consider the reception at that time, of an expanding universe as opposed to prevailing static views.

5. Universe's age and Earth's age tension

Towards the beginning of the 1930s the main objection to the interpretation of the Hubble constant as the indicator of the universe expansion was that it's measured value implied a younger universe than that of Earth's accepted age.

Before 1930's, scientific estimates of the age of the Earth dated from mid-19th century, from Helmholtz-Kelvin gravitational contraction ages,[14] passing through those resting on geology (i.e., the amount of salt in the oceans, sediments) and - after a fierce debate between geologist and physicists[15] - finally deferred to an age based on early-20th century radioactive dating.[16] This produced by the 1930's, an estimate of the universe age of around 4 billion years.[17]

In 1931, at the time Einstein was visiting Caltech, the matter of determining the age of the earth was not entirely resolved to the extent that the National Research Council decided to appoint a committee to investigate to settle the question.[18]

On the other hand, the cosmological age of the universe based on the universe expansion, was estimated by taking the reciprocal of the value of the Hubble constant (Hubble's time). Hubble first evaluation of his eponymous constant was of around 500 kilometers per second per megaparsec. This implied a universe's age of about two billion years, which was in a tense contradiction with the estimated age of the Earth, as just mentioned, of about four billion years. As consequence, such mismatch created room for doubt, Einstein himself included. Some critics questioned that the observed nebulae redshifts, were in fact a manifestation of the Doppler's effect. Such was the panorama that reigned in the early 30s.

This incongruity raised two possible explanations: on the one hand Hubble constant value was wrong, or on the other hand, Doppler's shift needed a novel interpretation, as it is said today "perhaps new physics".

As it is well known, the Hubble constant estimation involved measurement of distance and velocity of a variable star (a Cepheid) belonging to a galaxy in question. This involved monitoring the apparent brightness of the Cepheid variable to obtain its period. Then, using Shapley's Cepheid calibration, its absolute brightness was established and consequently the distance to the galaxy where the Cepheid was located. At that time there was little doubt on the correctness of Shapley's calibration. Also, measurement of recession velocity of galaxies even in those days, was straightforward. Spectral recordings had already achieved good accuracy. So, Hubble's constant value was in little doubt. Eventually, some astronomers pointed out that Cepheid's calibration could be slightly inaccurate as the apparent star's luminosity could be diminished by interstellar media and that had to be accounted for. It must be remembered that It was not until mid-1940's that Walter Baade identified two Cepheid types and made a major correction to Shapley's calibration and thus to Hubble's value.[19] Now we know that the problem was on the way off value of Hubble's constant at that time.

On the second possibility, that the incongruity between the ages of the earth and the universe had its origin in an erroneous interpretation of the observed redshift, Fritz Zwicky gave in 1929 an alternative explanation. Zwicky, a resident scholar at Caltech, suggested the concept of "tired light".[20] This was a hypothetical redshift mechanism where photons lost energy over time through interactions with other particles in their trajectories through a static universe. So, the more distant objects would appear redder than more nearby ones. It is pertinent to mention that the term "tired light" was not used by Zwicky but later coined to refer to this concept by Caltech cosmologist Richard Tolman in the early 1930s in relation to the so called Tolman Surface Brightness Test.

6. Earlier dynamic stationary state cosmologies

Zwicky was not alone. There was also an academic minority that put forward similar ideas to Zwicky's explanation even before his 1929 suggestion. All these "tired light" propositions had in common the assumption that photons heading earthward, somehow interchanged with the intergalactic medium, part of their energy, thus red shifting their frequencies.

"Tired light" was championed by the few enthusiasts of steady state cosmologies. Its appeal as we shall see resides on the fact that it circumvents the standard interpretation of the redshift as an indicator of galaxy recession and thus safeguards their view of a static universe.

The Nobel laureate Walther Nernst and William Duncan Macmillan, a well-known Chicago professor, were leading advocates of a steady-state universe. What these had in common is that they presuppose the universe as eternal, self-preserving structure in which matter and radiation are constantly been transformed into one another to keep the universe in a stationary balanced state thus avoiding a heat-dead of the universe. A cosmic destiny they both abhorred.

MacMillan's supposes in his own version of "tired light": "That there is a leakage of energy from the photon [...] due perhaps to an inherent instability in the photon, or, possibly, [due] to collisions with other photons". He concludes therefore: "it is evident that the frequency [of the photon] declines with the energy, and the lines of the spectrum are shifted toward the red".[21]

In addition, he considers that the "evaporated" energy from the photon continues to exist as abundant radiant energy of "very low frequency". A kind of primitive version of the modern CMB radiation (but the latter being Black Body radiation). Then he puts forward the possibility that perhaps the "evaporated" energy "disappears into the fine structure of space and reappears eventually in the structure of the atom". In other words, he proposes a mechanism of matter creation.

Another notable hypothesis was that of the Nobel laureate, Walther Nernst, who suggested that some photons are partially absorbed by the luminiferous æther (which he accepts to exist).[22] In his 1928 essay "Phyco-Chemical Considerations in Astrophysics", Nernst outlines the notion of matter creation in his stationary universe:

"I may therefore hold fast to the hypothesis uttered by me that, just as the principle of the stationary condition of the cosmos demands that the radiation of the stars be absorbed by the luminiferous æther, so also finally the same thing happens with mass, and that, conversely, strongly active elements are continually being formed from the æther, though naturally not in amounts demonstrable to us,..."[23].

It is worth noticing that both, MacMillan and Nernst, claim energy transfer occurs by an unknown process yet to be discovered.

The "tired light" proposal did not vanish into oblivion as alternative explanation to redshift been caused by recessional motion. As late as 1935, Edwin Hubble himself and Richard Tolman (both at Caltech during Einstein's several yearly visits) investigated the possibility that "tired light" might be an alternative interpretation of redshift.

They did that comparing the surface brightness of galaxies as a function of their redshift (applying the so called "Tolman Surface Brightness Test"[24]). According to Tolman Test, the relationship between surface brightness of a galaxy and its redshift differs in the case of a static universe from that of an expanding one. In a coauthored publication they explored this possibility.[25] In their joint paper and to simplify their analysis, they employed Einstein's static model of the universe: ... "combined with the assumption that the photons emitted by a nebula [a galaxy] lose energy on their journey to the observer by some unknown effect, which is linear with distance, and which leads to a decrease in frequency, without appreciable transverse deflection". In short, they employed Einstein's model plus "tired light". As result of their analysis, they conceded: "Until further evidence is available, both the present writers wish to express an open mind with respect to the ultimately most satisfactory explanation of the nebular red-shift" ..."They both incline to the opinion, however, that if the red-shift is not due to recessional motion, its explanation will probably involve some quite new physical principles".

7. On Einstein's arrival at Caltech

Up until now, we have seen that in the late 1920s and early 1930s, Hubble's law was commonly interpreted as a demonstration that the universe was truly expanding. However, there was still the problem of reconciling the age of the universe with that of the earth. This inconsistency, in addition to raising a reasonable doubt about the interpretation of the redshift, gave rise to the credibility of the theories of a stationary universe. For some, the appeal of a universe without evolving through time resided in that such universe has no beginning and no end, so it converts the "age of the universe" as a senseless question issue, consequently eliminating the earth-universe ages paradox.

Attempting to develop a stationary cosmological model was indeed an attractive motivation for Einstein, since it would avoid his well-known aversion to a universe that has a beginning and reinforce his well-known paradigm of a static universe. But adopting such an idea required reliable and robust observational evidence of the continuous creation of matter.

As we will see below, fresh "evidence" (that turned out to be illusory) of the continuous creation of matter emerged just as Einstein arrived at Caltech. This came from Millikan (Einstein host at Caltech) so it must have seemed reliable to Einstein. We must remember that Millikan received the Nobel prize partly for experimentally verifying Einstein's photoelectric equation.

8. Birth cries of atoms

On the 1st of February 1931, during Einstein's stay at Caltech, a paper by Millikan and his collaborator H. Cameron appeared in Physical Review. Its title was "A more accurate and more extended cosmic-ray ionization-depth curve, and the present evidence for atom-building".[26] This paper contained what it would seem to be the experimental evidence Einstein needed, that is, observational evidence of continuous matter creation. In our opinion, it was this publication what encouraged Einstein to use the continual creation of matter hypothesis in his unpublished manuscript. So, Einstein made his last bid to keep a stationary cosmology.

Millikan's 1931 paper is the apogee of a series of publications on cosmic rays where he explores their composition and origins. But, before we comment on this publication it is convenient to recall very briefly Millikan's research on cosmic rays. During the early 20's he and his collaborators made a series of observations on board of balloons, high altitude peaks, and different geographical locations, at various latitudes and in the depths of lakes proving in his 1926 publication that cosmic rays were of extraterrestrial origin.[27] Millikan believed that his measurements proved that the primary cosmic rays were energetic photons. He also stated that cosmic rays, "...must arise from nuclear changes of some sort..." but far more energetic than any radioactive change thus far on record".

In the same 1926 paper he suggested that cosmic rays probably came from among the following three nuclear processes: a) The capture of an electron by the nucleus of a light atom, b) the formation of helium out of hydrogen, or c) some new type of "nuclear change", such as the condensation of radiation into atoms.

Regarding third suggestion he made above, we must emphasize that Millikan here raises the creation of matter from the "condensation of radiation into atoms." this idea was not his, as he himself stated in a note written by him for the journal Science in 1930.[28] In the note he recalls having in 1915 discussions on the "running down of the universe" (i.e., when the universe has reached a state of maximum entropy) at the University of Chicago with his then colleague William Duncan Macmillan (of whom we have already commented) where the issue of atom building was discussed. Millikan recalls,

"In our conversations at Chicago W. D. Macmillan constantly held out for the view that a still further step forward should be taken and that the idea of "running down of the universe" should be given up by the assumption that atom building went on in space by the condensation of radiation into atoms. He discussed his idea in detail with me in the year 1915, and in July, 1918 he published it in full".[29]

In 1928 Millikan and Cameron found that incoming cosmic rays could be grouped into three independent energy bands centered at 26, 110, and 120 (MeV).[30] They argued that these bands are produced by the release of photons when eventually a "sudden union" (i.e., fusion) between atoms occur. To support their assertion, they observed that the center of the bands agreed respectively with 26 MeV (which is just about the mass defect of helium), 110 MeV (which is close to the mass defect of oxygen and nitrogen) and 220 MeV (to that of silicon.) So, their inference was that the three photon bands reaching the earth must be generated by the "sudden union" of: 4 hydrogen atoms fused to form helium, 14 to form nitrogen, 16 to form oxygen and 28 to form silicon". Secondary electrons, they claimed, were produced in the atmosphere by Compton scattering of gamma rays. Millikan believed that space was filled with a tenuous gas of electrons and protons (the latter he called "positive electrons"). So, to get around the "running down of the universe" he assumed that "These building stones [protons and electrons] are continuously being replenish throughout the heavens by the condensation with the aid of some as yet wholly unknown mechanism of radiant heat into positive and negative electrons".

Millikan supposed discovery of the continuous formation of matter went beyond the scientific sphere provoking the attention of among the scientific and the lay publics. In a statement made by Millikan to the press, cosmic rays were "birth cries of atoms, a Millikan phrase that achieved a good deal of currency".[31]

Regarding Millikan's 1931 publication the one which appeared on print just at the time Einstein was hosted by Millikan, this was basically a continuation of his 1928 paper including revised energy calculations that further bolstered his tenacious ideas. A short time later Arthur Holly Compton showed that not all cosmic rays were photons, but at least a large part of them consists of charged particles. This led to a debate between the two Nobel laureates. The debate went on for some time with Compton at the winning side but that's another story.

9. Final comments

Einstein before long abandoned the idea of keeping the λ constant in his field equations. In his next publication, the 1931 Sitzungsberichte paper, he does not make use of the constant anymore.[3] At the end of the paper Einstein adds some remarks about the age of the universe problem, which was quite severe without the use of the λ constant. Today we know that the problem was on the way off value of Hubble's constant at that time. Einstein signals two possible errors that may be occurring in the initial approach to the problem. First, he insinuates that the matter distribution might be inhomogeneous and that a homogeneity approximation may be illusional. Then he adds that in astronomy one should be cautious with large extrapolations in time. His first comment is surprising as it seems to indicate some reservations on the cosmological principle.

The next following winter (1931-1932), Einstein was back in Caltech for a second stay where he met De Sitter. Together they formulated a model today known as the Einstein-de Sitter universe, assuming a flat space with no cosmological constant and with an expansion velocity asymptotically approaching zero in the infinite future.[32]

This became the standard model up to the mid-1990s. This was the Einstein's last intent to produce a cosmological model.

Acknowledgments

JLCC acknowledges support by CONACyT project 283151.

References

1. A. Einstein (1917). Kosmologische Betrachtungen zur allgemeinen Relativitätstheorie. Sitz. König. Preuss. Akad. 142-152. Or 'Cosmological considerations in the general theory of relativity' CPAE 6 (Doc. 43).
2. A. Einstein (1919). Spielen Gravitationsfelder im Aufbau der materiellen Elementarteilchen eine wesentliche Rolle? Sitz. König. Preuss. Akad. 349-356. Or 'Do gravitation fields play an essential part in the structure of the elementary particles of matter?' CPAE 7 (doc.17).
3. A. Einstein (1931). Sitzungsber. Preuss. Akad. Wiss. 235-37.
4. C. O'Raifeartaigh (2014). Einstein's steady-state cosmology. Physics World, 27(09), 30.
5. C. O'Raifeartaigh and B. McCann, (2014). Einstein's cosmic model of 1931 revisited: An analysis and translation of a forgotten model of the universe. Eur. Phys. J. H 39 (2014) 63-85, e-Print: 1312.2192 [physics.hist-ph].
6. H. Nussbaumer (2014). Einstein's conversion from his static to an expanding universe. EPJ-H, Eur. Phys. J. H. Vol. 39, 37-62, DOI: 10.1140/epjh/e2013-40037-6. http://arxiv.org/abs/1311.2763.
7. H. Nussbaumer (2018). Einstein's aborted attempt at a dynamic steady-state universe. Acta Historica Astronomiae, 64, 463-477.
8. New York Times, p. 1 (Jan. 3, 1931).
9. New York Times, p. 1 and 17 (Feb. 5, 1931).
10. A. C. Balch, Professor Einstein at the California Institute of Technology. Science, 73, 375-379 (1931).
11. W. S. Adams (1925). The relativity displacement of the spectral lines in the companion of Sirius. Proceedings of the National Academy of Sciences of the United States of America, 11(7), 382.
12. R. A. Millikan and W. S. Adams, The reason and the results of Dr. Einstein's visit to the California Institute of Technology. Science 73380-381, (1931).
13. C. O'Raifeartaigh, B. McCann, W. Nahm, and S. Mitton (2014). Einstein's exploration of a steady-state model of the universe. The European Physical Journal H, 39(3), 353-367.
14. J. D. Burchfield (1990). Lord Kelvin and the Age of the Earth. University of Chicago Press.
15. H. Hellman and H. Hellman (1998). Great feuds in science: Ten of the liveliest disputes ever. New York: Wiley.
16. C. Lewis (2002). The Dating Game: One man's search for the Age of the Earth. Cambridge University Press.
17. L. Badash (1968). Rutherford, Boltwood, and the age of the earth: The origin of radioactive dating techniques.
18. The Age of the Earth. Bulletin of the pp. 487. Washington, D.C. (1931). Geological Magazine, 68(11), 523-525. doi:10.1017/S0016756800098459 academy of science.

19. W. Baade (1944). The resolution of Messier 32, NGC 205, and the central region of the Andromeda nebula. ApJ 100 137-146.
20. F. Zwicky (1929). "On the Redshift of Spectral Lines Through Interstellar Space". Proceedings of the National Academy of Sciences. 15 (10): 773-779.
21. W. D. MacMillan (1932). Velocities of the spiral nebulae. Nature, 129(3246), 93-93.
22. W. Nernst (1928). Physico-chemical considerations in astrophysics. Journal of the Franklin Institute, 206(2), 135-142.
23. W. Nerst (1928) ibid ref.[22], p 141.
24. R. C. Tolman (1930). On the estimation of distances in a curved universe with a non-static line element. Proceedings of the National Academy of Sciences of the United States of America, 16(7), 511.
25. E. Hubble and R. C. Tolman (1935). Two methods of investigating the nature of the nebular redshift. The Astrophysical Journal, 82, 302.
26. R. A. Millikan and G. H. Cameron (1931). A more accurate and more extended cosmic-ray ionization-depth curve, and the present evidence for atom-building. Physical Review, 37(3), 235.
27. R. A. Millikan and G. H. Cameron (1926). High frequency rays of cosmic origin III. Measurements in snow-fed lakes at high altitudes. Physical Review, 28(5), 851.
28. R. A. Millikan (1930). Remarks on the history of cosmic radiation. Science, 71(1851), 640-641.
29. W. D. MacMillan (1918). On stellar evolution. The astrophysical journal, 48, 35.
30. R. A. Millikan and G. H. Cameron (1928). The origin of the cosmic rays. Physical review, 32(4), 533.
31. D. J. Kevles (1979). Robert A. Millikan. Scientific American, 240(1), 118-125. p 122.
32. A. Einstein and W. de Sitter (1932). On the relation between the expansion and the mean density of the Universe. PNAS, 18, 213-214.

Jayme Tiomno: Relativity, gravity, cosmology, and the Marcel Grossmann Meetings

William D. Brewer

Fachbereich Physik, Freie Universität Berlin,
14195 Berlin, F.R. Germany
E-mail: william.brewer@fu-berlin.de
www.users.physik.fu-berlin.de/~wbrewer/index.html

Jayme Tiomno belonged to the 'founder's generation' of physicists in Brazil. He began working in relativity theory early in his career, at a time when it was not at all 'fashionable', through the influence of his early mentor, Mario Schenberg in São Paulo. When he went to graduate school in Princeton, in February 1948, his advisor there, John Wheeler, gave him a project in General Relativity, even though this was more than 4 years before Wheeler's 'turn' from nuclear and particle physics to field theory and gravitation.

Tiomno and Wheeler however soon discovered their mutual interest in meson decays, and Tiomno's Masters and PhD theses were on topics from particle physics, which remained his major field of interest for the following 20 years, during which he collaborated with Abdus Salam, among others. Only when he returned to Princeton in 1971, a refugee from the oppressive dictatorship in Brazil, did he again begin working in gravitation and field theory, having missed the 'golden age' initiated in part by Wheeler's group.

At the IAS, Tiomno experienced a renaissance of his interest in field theory, working with Remo Ruffini and others. He continued this work in the 1980's after he was able to return to the CBPF in Rio de Janeiro (which he had helped to found). His participation in the Marcel Grossmann Meetings was limited but significant.

Keywords: Physics Brazil; History of Physics; Marcel Grossmann Meetings; General Relativity; Gravitation

1. Introduction

Jayme Tiomno was born in Rio de Janeiro on April 16, 1920, the son of Russian-Jewish immigrants who had arrived in Brazil about 10 years earlier. There was nothing in his background that might suggest that he would become an eminent theoretical physicist. But his parents both valued education and saw to it that he and his siblings (an older brother, a twin sister, and two younger sisters) were all able to attend college. In the year of his birth, on Sept. 7, the Brazilian national holiday, the *Universidade do Rio de Janeiro* (URJ) was founded as the first real university in Brazil (as a collection of faculties and institutes combined from existing institutions).

After his childhood and youth spent in small cities in Minas Gerais, Tiomno's family returned in 1934 to Rio, where Jayme completed his *curso complementar* in medicine and then began studying medicine in 1938 at the *Universidade do Brazil* (UB – as the URJ was now called). In early 1939, Jayme was enrolled by his brother for Natural History at the *Universidade do Distrito Federal* (UDF), a newer research university founded in the capital in 1935 by Anisio Teixeira, an eminent educator who was at the time Director of Education of the Federal District.

Fig. 1. (a) Jayme Tiomno, 1941. (b) Tiomno, Wheeler, Ruffini, 2001 (c) Mario Schenberg, 1937.

Tiomno qualified for the physics course, but was unable to study at the UDF because it was closed by the Vargas regime. Its physics curriculum was incorporated into the *Faculdade Nacional de Filosofia* (FNFi) and moved to the UB. Tiomno later had to decide between medicine and physics, and he chose the latter, graduating in 1941. Figure 1 shows Tiomno at age 21, when he graduated from the FNFi, and also 60 years later, with his Princeton mentor John Wheeler and his later collaborator Remo Ruffini, at Wheeler's 90th birthday in 2001; and Tiomno's first graduate mentor, Mario Schenberg, about the time Tiomno began his university career.

Tiomno entered military service, and was able to do some research with his mentor, the experimentalist Joaquim da Costa Ribeiro, and complete his *licenciatura* (teaching certificate) during the War. However, his real interest lay in theory, inspired by his Italian professor of theoretical physics, Luigi Sobrero (a former assistant of Levi-Cività), and after the War, he obtained a fellowship to do graduate research at the Universidade de São Paulo (USP), in the department founded by Gleb Wataghin, under Wataghin's star pupil, the theoretician Mario Schenberg. The photo in Fig. 2 shows Tiomno's professors Sobrero and Costa Ribeiro as well as the teaching assistants in physics at the FNFi in May, 1942. Many of them later became noted scientists.

Tiomno spent most of 1946 at USP, studying hard to catch up in modern physics, to which he had hardly been exposed at the FNFi. After his fellowship ended, he returned to Rio in early 1947, but was then offered an assistantship with Mario Schenberg at USP, where he went in mid-year of 1947. He worked with Schenberg on formulating gravitation in Minkowski space, his introduction to relativity. The project was completed but never published, partly because relativity, and especially non-Einsteinian interpretations of gravitation, were hard to publish in 1948, and

Fig. 2. The teaching staff in physics at the FNFi, 1942. From left: Paulo Alcântara Gomes, Elisa Frota-Pessôa, Jayme Tiomno, Joaquim da Costa Ribeiro, Luigi Sobrero, Leopoldo Nachbin, José Leite Lopes, and Mauricio Matos Peixoto.

partly due to Schenberg's political difficulties, which forced him to go into exile in Europe in the following years.

Tiomno, in the meantime, on the recommendations of Schenberg and José Leite Lopes, was granted a fellowship for graduate work at Princeton by the U.S. State Department. He had to leave Brazil abruptly in early February 1948 to meet the starting deadline for his fellowship. In Princeton, he joined the group of John Archibald Wheeler, already a well-known theoretician, working in nuclear and particle physics. Nevertheless, Wheeler started Tiomno on a project involving point particles in GR (and eventually their gravitational-radiative damping). Tiomno was frustrated with the project and received little help from Wheeler (and from Einstein). Wheeler had already suggested this topic to Leopold Infeld, who in 1949 published the result with his assistant Alfred Schild.[1] By then, Tiomno and Wheeler had turned their interest to the pion-muon decay chain, and Tiomno spent the next 20 years working mainly in particle physics, apart from two collaborative projects with David Bohm – one a conformally-invariant formulation of the Dirac theory, which Tiomno only completed 12 years later; the other the inclusion of spin into Bohm's deterministic version of quantum mechanics (1955).

Fig. 3. John Wheeler and Jayme Tiomno in Princeton, Summer 1948.

When Wheeler (Fig. 3) left on sabbatical in June, 1949, Tiomno, with his fresh MSc degree, collaborated with Chen Ning Yang and David Bohm on weak-interaction physics and on relativistic quantum mechanics. He then began his PhD thesis work with Eugene Wigner as mentor. He finished his thesis in September 1950 and returned to São Paulo on October 10.

While still at Princeton, Tiomno also met Richard P. Feynman and Cécile Morette, and invited both to visit the newly-founded *Centro Brasileiro de Pesquisas Físicas* (CBPF) in Rio, which he had helped to plan and implement. He later also encouraged Bohm to apply (successfully) for the vacant chair of Advanced Physics in São Paulo (vacated by Gleb Wataghin when he returned to Italy in 1949). The young David Bohm is shown in Fig. 4, about the time that he completed his undergraduate studies.

Fig. 4. David Bohm, around 1940.

Figure 5 is a photo of a meeting at Princeton in early 1949, where several young Brazilian physicists conferred about the newly-founded CBPF in Rio, and met the Japanese theoretician Hideki Yukawa, on sabbatical in Princeton at the time. More information on Tiomno's life and career can be found in our recent biography.[2]

2. The development of gravitation, General Relativity and cosmology research after 1950

Modern gravitational physics dates from the early 20th century. Lorentz, Poincaré, Fitzgerald and others had speculated about applying the principle of relativity to electromagnetism (Maxwell theory). Albert Einstein realized the significance of those speculations and formulated his Special Relativity in 1905. Ten years later, with the help of Marcel Grossmann, he completed his General Theory of Relativity (GR), the modern theory of gravitation. After the early period from 1915–1925, when solutions to Einstein's field equations were found (e.g. by K. Schwarzschild, 1916: gravitational singularity; A. Einstein, 1917: closed, static universe; W. de Sitter, 1917: zero-density universe; A. Friedmann, G. Lemaître, 1924/27: expanding

Fig. 5. A group of young Brazilians, together with Hideki Yukawa (behind, center), in Princeton, early 1949. César Lattes (behind, left), José Leite Lopes (below, center) and Jayme Tiomno (below, right) were the chief founders of the CBPF (Brazilian Center for Physics Research, Rio de Janeiro), which began operations about this time. At the upper right is Walter Schützer, and at lower left is Hervasio de Carvalho.

universe), Einstein began working on a unified theory of gravity and electromagnetism, and active work on GR decreased after about 1928. Some of the early contributors to GR theory are shown in Fig. 6.

In the period 1935–1955, Einstein published with N. Rosen, L. Infeld, B. Hoffmann, P. Bergmann, W. Pauli, V. Bargmann, and E.G. Strauss on some details of GR theory, and some other authors – notably J.R. Oppenheimer et al. (1939: collapse of stellar remnants) and K. Gödel (1949: stationary rotating homogeneous universe with timelike loops) also made important contributions. But only in the early 1950's did the 'great revival' of GR and its applications to relativistic astrophysics and cosmology begin, stimulated initially by J.A. Wheeler and his school (Princeton, University of Maryland, Caltech), and independently by Bryce DeWitt and Cécile Morette DeWitt (University of North Carolina, University of Texas), and in England by D.W. Sciama, C. Isham, R. Penrose, and S. Hawking (in London and Cambridge), and in the USSR by Y. Zel'dovitch, I. Novikov, and R. Sunyaev.

Fig. 6. (a) Karl Schwarzschild, ca. 1910. (b) Willem de Sitter. (c) Georges Lemaître.

Tiomno's interest in field theory and GR was rekindled in 1966/67, when he spent a year as Associate of the ICTP (International Centre for Theoretical Physics) in Trieste (founded in 1964 by Abdus Salam, with Tiomno's active participation). While there, he reconnected with two Argentine physicists whom he had known earlier, in Rio and in London: Juan José Giambiagi and Carlos Guido Bollini. Their joint papers, especially 'A Linear Theory of Gravitation' (1970), mark Tiomno's revived interest in gravitation theory. Giambiagi, Tiomno and Bollini are shown in Fig. 7 while at the ICTP in 1966/67, and also shown are Jayme Tiomno with his wife Elisa Frota-Pessôa in Trieste at the same time. That interest was intensified during his stay in Princeton in 1971/72, after his blacklisting in Brazil by the military dictatorship. There, he interacted with Wheeler's now flourishing school. In the years 1972–75, he published 13 articles on gravitation and field theory. In addition to his two more senior collaborators, Remo Ruffini and Leonard Parker, his coauthors included the younger physicists C.V. Vishveshwara, Marc Davis, Jeffrey M. Cohen, Frank J. Zerilli, Robert M. Wald, and Reinhard A. Breuer. Many of those publications dealt with radiation – both electromagnetic and gravitational – from particles orbiting or falling into black holes; but they also included speculations on pulsars and the balance of forces on particles near black holes, as well as the possibility and properties of gravitational 'synchrotron radiation'. Figure 8 shows Tiomno and Elisa in Princeton in 1971, and also Tiomno's farewell letter to Wheeler upon leaving Princeton in June, 1972.

The text of Tiomno's letter to Wheeler when he left Princeton reads: *"We are leaving tomorrow, looking forward to a vague possibility of remaining in Rio. We were much pleased with our stay in Princeton. I have profited much from it and started a new phase of my career. Even the disagreeable dispute with a colleague has had a positive result to stress my friendship with you and to make me recover from the difficulty of writing papers. Here are some of them, which would not exist*

Fig. 7. (a) J.J. Giambiagi, J. Tiomno, C.G. Bollini, ICTP 1966. (b) Jayme Tiomno and Elisa Frota-Pessôa, ICTP 1966.

without your decisive help. Elisa joins me in sending regards to Janette and hoping we shall see you soon, somewhere . . . Jayme. PS. I have also sent a set of preprints to Goldberger."

We can only speculate on the precise details of the 'dispute' mentioned; it was probably a conflict over the publication of an article written jointly by Breuer, Ruffini, Tiomno and Vishveshwara (which appeared later in Phys. Rev. D. See Ref. 1 for more details).

After returning to Brazil in mid-1972, Jayme and Elisa were confronted with their continued blacklisting by the military dictatorship, which considered them to be 'subversive' (a charge which verges on the ridiculous, in retrospect). They could not even work at the private foundation CBPF, which they had helped to found and establish. Finally (after a Papal dispensation), they were given the opportunity to work at the Catholic University (PUC) in Rio de Janeiro, albeit with limited privileges. They remained there until after the Amnesty in 1979, and then still refused to beg for reinstatement to their university positions. Jayme finally rejoined the 'reformed' CBPF at the end of 1980; it was now an independent laboratory of the national science research funding agency CNPq. There, he became an honored and very active member of the faculty, retiring as 'Researcher emeritus' in 1992. For more information on the development of relativity and gravitation research after their 'rennaissance' in the 1950's, see the references.[3–5]

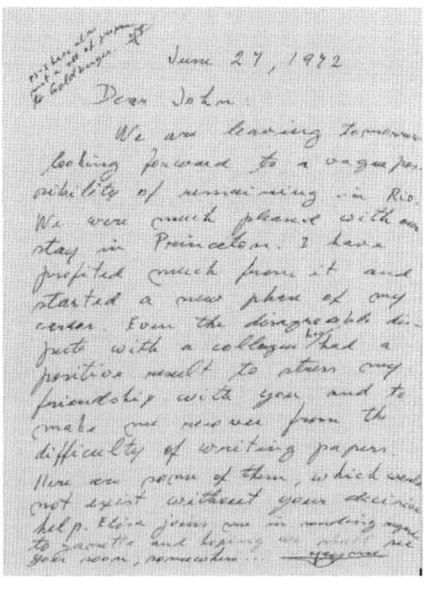

Fig. 8. (a) Tiomno and Elisa, Princeton 1971. (b) Tiomno's 'farewell letter' to Wheeler, June 1972.

3. Tiomno's Scientific Work

Like Wheeler's scientific career, Tiomno's lifework can be divided into three distinct periods, although not so sharply:

– The first was his early work on relativity and particle physics, which extended from 1947 through about 1967. Highlights of this period were his work on the Weak Interaction (initially called the 'Universal Fermi Interaction', a term coined by Tiomno and C.N. Yang in 1949); his work on S-matrix theory and causality (with Walter Schützer; see Fig. 5); his prediction of the K* meson (with N. Zagury and A.L.L. Videira); and work on hyperons and global symmetry (with Abdus Salam).
– The second period began in the late 1960's and extended to around 1981. It was characterized by a shift in interest toward field theory, gravitation and cosmology, and was stimulated by collaborations with Giambiagi and Bollini as well as with his Princeton colleagues in 1971/72.
– The third period might be called his "eclectic phase", after he had returned to the CBPF in 1980, when he was involved in numerous projects relating to particle physics, Special Relativity, General Relativity, field theory, gravitation and cosmology, ending with his interest in relativistic rotating systems in the mid-1990's.

In the following, we give some selected examples of Tiomno's publications from the 1970's to the mid-1980's, as an illustration of the variety and the relevance of his work in his second and third periods.

3.1. *Some Selected Publications, 1970-1985*

(1) 'A Linear Theory of Gravitation', in: Lettere al Nuovo Cimento **3**, 65 (1970) (with C.G. Bollini and J.J. Giambiagi).

(2) 'Equivalence of Lorentz Transformations and Foldy-Wouthuysen Transformation for Free Spinor Fields', in: Physica **53**, 581–601 (1971).

(3) 'Electromagnetic Field of a Particle Moving in a Spherically-Symmetric Black-Hole Background', in: Lettere al Nuovo Cimento **3**, 211 (1972) (with R. Ruffini and C.V. Vishveshwara).

(4) 'Can Synchrotron Gravitational Radiation Exist?', in: Physical Review Letters **28**, 1352 (1972) (with Marc Davis, R. Ruffini and F. Zerilli).

(5) 'Pulses of Gravitational Radiation of a Particle Falling Radially into a Schwarzschild Black Hole', in: the Physical Review **D5**, 2932 (1972) (with Marc Davis and R. Ruffini).

(6) 'Maxwell Equations in a Spherically Symmetric Black-Hole Background', in: Lettere al Nuovo Cimento **5**, 851–855 (1972).

(7) 'Pair-Producing Electric Fields and Pulsars', in: the Astrophysical Journal **178**, 809 (1972) (with L. Parker).

(8) 'Polarization of Gravitational Synchrotron Radiation', in: Lettere al Nuovo Cimento **4**, 857 (1972) (with R.A. Breuer and C.V. Vishveshwara).

(9) 'Balancing of Electromagnetic and Gravitational Forces and Torque Between Spinning Particles at Rest', in: the Physical Review **D7**, 356 (1973).

(10) 'Gyromagnetic Ratio of a Massive Body', in: the Physical Review **D7**, 998 (1973) (with J.M. Cohen and R.M. Wald).

(11) 'Electromagnetic Field of Rotating Charged Bodies', in: the Physical Review **D7**, 992 (1973).

(12) 'Charged point particles with magnetic moments in General Relativity', in: Revista Brasileira de Física **8**, 350 (1978) (with Ricardo M. Amorim).

(13) 'On the relation between fields and potentials in non-abelian gauge fields', in: Revista Brasileira de Física **9**, 1 (1979) (with J.J. Giambiagi and C.G. Bollini).

(14) 'Singular potentials and analytic regularizations in classical Yang-Mills Equations', in: Journal of Math. Phys. **20**, 1967 (1979) (with C.G. Bollini and J.J. Giambiagi).

(15) 'Gauge field copies', in: Phys. Letters **83B**, 185 (1979) (with J.J. Giambiagi and C.G. Bollini).

(16) 'Wilson Loops and Related Strings for the instanton and its variational derivatives', in: Il Nuovo Cimento **59**, 412 (1980) (with C.G. Bollini and J.J. Giambiagi).

(17) 'Wilson Loops in Kerr Gravitation', in: Letters to Il Nuovo Cimento **81**, 13 (1981) (with C.G. Bollini and J.J. Giambiagi).

(18) 'Geodesic Motion and Confinement in Gödel's Universe', in: the Physical Review **D27**, 779 (1983) (with M. Novello and I.D. Soares).

(19) 'Gödel-type metric in Einstein-Cartan Spaces', in: Contributed Papers to the 10th International Conference on General Relativity and Gravitation, p. 507 (1983) (with A. Teixeira and J. Duarte).
(20) 'Homogeneity of Riemannian Spacetimes of Gödel type', in: the Physical Review **D28**, 1251 (1983) (with M. Rebouças).
(21) 'Pseudoscalar Mesons and Scalar diquarks—decay constants', in: Il Nuovo Cimento **81A**, 485 (1984) (with I. Bediaga, E. Predazzi, A.F.S. Santoro and M.H.G. Souza).
(22) 'Gravitational coupling of scalar and fermionic fields to matter vorticity: Microscopic asymmetries', in: Revista Brasileira de Física, Suppl. **14**, 372 (1984) (with I.D. Soares).
(23) 'Lifetimes in a quark-diquark system', in: Lettere al Nuovo Cimento **42**, 92–96 (1985) (with A.F.S. Santoro, I. Bediaga, M.G.H. Souza and E. Predazzi).
(24) 'On Experiments to detect possible failures of Relativity Theory', in: Foundations of Physics **15**, No. 9, pp. 945–961 (1985) (with W. Rodrigues).
(25) 'Gluon and qq mixing: [1440] system', in: Zeitschrift f. Physik **C30**, 493 (1985) (with A.C.B. Antunes, F. Caruso and E. Predazzi).
(26) 'Experiments to Detect Possible Weak Violations of Special Relativity', in: Physical Review Letters **55**, 143 (1985) (with A.K.A. Maciel).

Of special note are the publications that Tiomno himself listed as particularly important when he was nominated in 1995 for the Physics Prize of the Third-World Academy of Sciences (TWAS - an organization founded by Abdus Salam to complement the work of the ICTP). These include Items 1, 4, 9, 14, 16, 19, and 26 in the above list – and they illustrate how his interest in gravitation and field theory developed over the years.

4. ICRA and the MG Meetings. MG-X

The first international conference series to be initiated for the newly-revived field of General Relativity and Gravitation carried exactly that name – GR-1 was held at Chapel Hill, NC/USA in January 1957. It was organized by Bryce and Cécile (Morette) DeWitt, who had obtained positions at the University of North Carolina. In fact, it had a predecessor, a conference organized in Bern, Switzerland and held in July 1955 to celebrate the 50th anniversary of the initial publication of (Special) Relativity theory. It is often called 'GR-0', while later conferences in the series are listed as 'GR-1' etc. GR-2 took place in a former palace in Royaumont, near Paris, a location that was suggested by Cécile Morette DeWitt. Tiomno attended it, since he was in Europe at the end of his sabbatical year in London, 1958/59. This conference series continues today, now at three-year intervals, and GR-23 is scheduled for July 2022 in Beijing. Figure 9 shows Tiomno and Elisa in Paris in June 1959, at the end of their London stay, when he attended the Royaumont conference (GR-2). Tiomno also later published a paper in the proceedings of GR-10 (Item 19 in the above list).

Fig. 9. Jayme Tiomno and Elisa Frota-Pessôa in Paris, June 1959 (at the west end of the *Pont d'Iena*).

Another conference series was started in Dallas, TX/USA in 1963. It is called the 'Texas Symposia on Relativistic Astrophysics', and its initial motivation was to consider the newly-discovered Quasars in the light of relativity theory. This was the first time that the term 'Relativistic Astrophysics' was used publicly. An amusing account of the genesis of these conferences, which continue today at (usually) two-year intervals (the 31st is planned for December 2021 in Prague), was given by Engelbert L. Schucking, one of the original organizers from 1963, in *Physics Today* (August 1989, pp. 46-52).

In 1975, two of Tiomno's former collaborators, Abdus Salam and Remo Ruffini, founded the conference series 'Marcel Grossmann Meetings (on Recent Developments in Theoretical and Experimental General Relativity, Gravitation, and Relativistic Field Theories)', which should be familiar to the audience of this talk. Ruffini was at the time still officially at the Institute for Advanced Study in Princeton, but was on leave in 1975 as a visitor to the University of Western Australia (Nedlands) and the University of Kyoto in Japan. The following year, he accepted a faculty position at the University of Catania, Sicily. Abdus Salam had been Head of the Department of Theoretical Physics at Imperial College London since 1957 (where Tiomno was one of the first visiting scientists, in the academic year 1958/59), and he became Director of the ICTP Trieste after its founding in 1964. The Centre offered a good platform for hosting the MG conferences, and the first two were held there in 1975 and 1979. MG-III, held in Shanghai in 1982, established the three-year interval still continued today. It was the result of the friendship between Remo Ruffini, who became Professor of Physics at his *alma mater*, the University of Rome 'La Sapienza' in 1978, and a Chinese visitor, Fang Li Zhi, whom he hosted in the late 1970's (cf. MG-XVI Awards Ceremony, Part 2). Later conferences in the series have been held in many cities on most of the continents.

Given his association with their founders and his own work in field theory, gravitation and cosmology, it was natural that Jayme Tiomno would have an interest in those meetings. But Tiomno, in spite of his close connection with the two founders of the MG conference series, did not attend the earlier MG meetings, both in Trieste; they took place during the 'leaden years' in Brazil, when he may not have been free to travel, and he had also not done any new, relevant research since leaving Princeton in 1972. By the time of MG-III, held in Shanghai/China in 1982, Remo Ruffini invited Mario Novello, from Tiomno's DRP Department at the CBPF, to participate in the meeting. Tiomno himself did not however attend the MG-III meeting; it was far from Brazil and perhaps difficult for him to obtain a visa.

Fig. 10. (a) Tiomno, Elisa and Mario Novello, 1991. (b) Tiomno with his last collaborator, Ivano Soares, in 1997.

In 1985, Ruffini and Abdus Salam, together with several other prominent scientists, founded the ICRA organization (International Center for Relativistic Astrophysics), based in Rome and Pescara, Italy (ICRANet). By 1985, Tiomno's time had come, and he gave an invited paper on the LET–SRT controversy at MG-IV, held that year for the first time in Rome. Remo Ruffini and Abdus Salam were no doubt pleased to give him the opportunity to experience an MG conference, and Novello's enthusiasm also played an important role in convincing him to attend. After the meeting in Rome, Tiomno resumed his contacts with his former collaborators, and in 1994, the year of MG-VII, held in Stanford/CA, USA, he was a member of the 'Committee of the Americas', part of the international coordinating committee for the conference; but he again did not attend the meeting itself—by then, as *researcher emeritus*, he was reducing his overseas travel and participation in conferences, and encouraging some of his former students and collaborators to actively take over those functions, including Mario Novello and Marcelo Rebouças, among others.

Prior to the MG-X Meeting planned for 2003, the Brazilian physicists offered to host the conference at the CBPF, and Mario Novello served as chairman of its local organizing committee. At that meeting, the Institutional Award, presented at each conference to an outstanding institution in research and teaching, was given to the CBPF 'for its role as a teaching and research institution and as a place originating fundamental physics ideas in the exploration of the universe', and presented to its founders, César Lattes, José Leite Lopes, and Jayme Tiomno, who were all present.

Fig. 11. (a) José Leite Lopes, Tiomno, and Remo Ruffini at the prize ceremony, MG-X, 2003. (b) Leite Lopes and Tiomno at MG-X in Rio, 2003.

That same year, ICRANet, the international networking arm of ICRA, was officially chartered. Ruffini needed at least three states to create it, and at the time, he had just two: the Vatican and Armenia. Brazil's membership in ICRANet was also prepared at the 2003 Meeting, and Mario Novello later became its representative for Brazil (a post now occupied by Ulisses Barres de Almeida of the CBPF). Brazil formally agreed to join in 2005, and its membership was finalized in 2011.

Thus, although Jayme Tiomno himself was not strongly engaged in these meetings, his influence continues to be felt in them through the *Centro* that he helped to found, and through his former students and collaborators, who are actively involved in them, both scientifically and organizationally.

5. Conclusions

The three major strands of fundamental physics in the 20th century have wound their way through the decades, producing many offshoots and sometimes seeming to fuse into a single strand. They each experienced periods of hectic activity and rapid progress, and longer periods of relative neglect and apparent stagnation.

Particle physics reached its preliminary climax in the late 1970's with the formulation of the Standard Model of Particle Physics (combining the electroweak unified theory with quantum chromodynamics to describe three of the four fundamental interactions (weak, strong, electromagnetic); however leaving gravity out of the picture). In the intervening 40 years, the SMPP has been completed and perfected, but although no one really believes it to be the 'last word' on the microscopic world, the predicted 'new physics' beyond the SMPP has failed to appear, both experimentally and theoretically.

Gravitational physics has also produced the Standard Model of Cosmology (based on GR), and it has been enriched by many new discoveries and technical advances. But the SMC leaves many open questions and unsolved problems: dark matter, dark energy, inflation; and its fundamental constant, the Hubble constant, is currently the subject of conflicting measured values.

Fundamental quantum mechanics has given rise to a number of important offshoots: quantum optics, quantum information, quantum computing; but the interpretation of quantum mechanics is still elusive, as is its combination with gravity – quantum gravity.

Jayme Tiomno contributed significantly to all three of those major strands. But also, and for him more importantly, he contributed to the establishment and improvement of physics education and research in his native country, Brazil. This was his most serious goal during his long lifetime, and he made major contributions to its present success. The lesson to be learned from his lifelong efforts is that serious and honest work often leads to unexpected and lasting successes, even though it faces drastic obstacles and may appear hopeless at the time.

Acknowledgments

The author thanks Prof. Alfredo Tiomno Tolmasquim for much effort in the preparation of our joint book, reference,[2] upon which much of this article is based. Readers should consult it for many more references to original sources. Thanks are due also to Prof. Luis Carlos Bassalo Crispino, who was chairman of the session of MG-XVI where this paper was presented.

References

1. Leopold infeld and Alfred Schild, 'On the Motion of Test Particles in General Relativity', Rev. Mod. Phys. **21**, 408 (1949).
2. '*Jayme Tiomno: A Life for Science, A Life for Brazil*', William Dean Brewer and Alfredo Tiomno Tolmasquim, Springer/Nature, Cham/CH, June 2020; ISBN 978-3-030-41010-0.
3. Alexander Blum, Roberto Lalli, and Jürgen Renn, *Isis* **106**, No. 3, 598-620 (2015).
4. Alexander Blum and Dieter Brill, *ArXiv*:1905.05988v1 (2019).
5. '*Building the General Relativity and Gravitation Community During the Cold War*', Roberto Lalli, Springer, 2017; ISBN 973-3-319-54654-4.

A look inside Feynman's route to gravitation

M. Di Mauro

*Dipartimento di Matematica, Università di Salerno, Via Giovanni Paolo II,
Fisciano (SA), 84084, Italy
E-mail: madimauro@unisa.it*

S. Esposito* and A. Naddeo[†]

*INFN, Sezione di Napoli, C. U. Monte S. Angelo, Via Cinthia,
Napoli, 80125, Italy
* E-mail: sesposit@na.infn.it
[†] E-mail: anaddeo@na.infn.it*

In this contribution we report about Feynman's approach to gravitation, starting from the records of his interventions at the Chapel Hill Conference of 1957. As well known, Feynman was concerned about the relation of gravitation with the rest of physics. Probably for this reason, he promoted an unusual, field theoretical approach to general relativity, in which, after the recognition that the interaction must be mediated by the quanta of a massless spin-2 field, Einstein's field equations should follow from the general properties of Lorentz-invariant quantum field theory, plus self-consistency requirements. Quantum corrections would then be included by considering loop diagrams. These ideas were further developed by Feynman in his famous lectures on gravitation, delivered at Caltech in 1962-63, and in a handful of published papers, where he also introduced some field theoretical tools which were soon recognized to be of general interest, such as ghosts and the tree theorem. Some original pieces of Feynman's work on gravity are also present in a set of unpublished lectures delivered at Hughes Aircraft Company in 1966-67 and devoted primarily to astrophysics and cosmology. Some comments on the relation between Feynman's approach to gravity and his ideas on the quantum foundations of the fundamental interactions are included.

Keywords: Gravitation; Quantum field theory; Loop diagrams.

1. Introduction: A timeline

Among the many scientific interests that Feynman had in the 1950s and in the 1960s, a prominent place was taken by the understanding of the relation of gravitation to the rest of physics,[a] and in particular the assessment of its consistency with the uncertainty principle.[b] Feynman likely began to seriously think about gravity in

---

[a] "Next we shall discuss the possible relation of gravitation to other forces. There is no explanation of gravitation in terms of other forces at the present time. It is not an aspect of electricity or anything like that, so we have no explanation. However, gravitation and other forces are very similar, and it is interesting to note analogies." (Ref. 1, Vol. 1, Sec. 7-7); "My subject is the quantum theory of gravitation. My interest in it is primarily in the relation of one part of nature to another." (Ref. 2, p. 697).

[b] "...it would be important to see whether Newton's law modified to Einstein's law can be further modified to be consistent with the uncertainty principle. This last modification has not yet been completed." (Ref. 1, Vol. 1, Sec. 7-8).

the early 1950s, just after completing his work on quantum electrodynamics. This was attested by Murray Gell-Mann[3] in a paper written for a Physics Today special issue devoted to Feynman's legacy,[c] as well as by Bryce S. DeWitt,[4] in a letter to Agnew Bahnson written in November 1955.[5] Feynman's efforts began in a period in which general relativity, after a stagnation which lasted about thirty years, was gradually emerging as a mainstream research area, giving rise to a process known as the *renaissance* of general relativity.[6]

A crucial event to consider, in order to reconstruct Feynman's approach to gravitation, is the 1957 Chapel Hill conference[4] on *The Role of Gravitation in Physics*, which was also pivotal to the renaissance of general relativity. At that conference, the gravitational physics community delineated the tracks along which subsequent work would develop in the subsequent decades. The main threads were the following[7]: classical gravity, quantum gravity, and the classical and quantum theory of measurement (as a bridge between the previous two topics). In that conference Feynman's work on gravity, of which nothing had been published yet, was presented for the first time, and put on paper in the records.[4] In fact these written records testify that by the time of the conference he had already deeply thought, and performed computations, about each of the above listed three topics, focusing in particular on classical gravitational waves, on the arguments in favor of quantum gravity from fundamental quantum mechanics, and finally on quantum gravity itself. Thus, in this contribution, we take as starting point for our reconstruction Feynman's interventions at Chapel Hill and follow the development of his work in the subsequent years, until the late sixties, where he apparently lost interest in the subject.

The ultimate goal of Feynman's work was the development of a quantum field theory of gravitation, which led him to face deep conceptual as well as mathematical issues, such as divergent integrals and the lack of unitarity beyond the tree level approximation. This task accompanied Feynman for some years, as stated in a letter[8] he wrote to Viktor F. Weisskopf in 1961 ("As you know, I am studying the problem of quantization of Einstein's General Relativity. I am still working out the details of handling divergent integrals which arise in problems in which some virtual momentum must be integrated over"), as well as reported by William R. Frazer[9] in a short summary of the talks given at the La Jolla conference, later in the same year.[d] A first comprehensive account of Feynman's results on quantum gravity can

---

[c]Indeed here Gell-Mann remembered his visit to Caltech during the Christmas vacation of 1954-55, the discussions with Feynman about quantum gravity, and the fact that Feynman "had made considerable progress".

[d]The International Conference on the Theory of Weak and Strong Interactions was held in June 14-16, 1961, at the University of California, San Diego, in La Jolla. Here, Geoffrey F. Chew gave his celebrated talk on the S-matrix,[10] while an afternoon session was devoted to the theory of gravitation, where Feynman reported on his work on the renormalization of the gravitational field, and recognized non-unitarity as the main difficulty, which was shared also by Yang-Mills theory.

be found in the talk he gave in 1962 at the Warsaw conference,[e] whose written version was later published as a regular paper in Acta Physica Polonica.[2] Further details were given by Feynman much later, in a couple of papers[11,12] published in 1972 in the Festschrift for John A. Wheeler's 60th birthday,[13] which were written in a period in which he was already deeply absorbed in the study of partons and strong interactions.

Among the main sources which contribute to offer a clear account of Feynman's work on gravity issues, it is mandatory to include the famous Caltech Lectures on Gravitation,[14] delivered in 1962-63 and aimed to advanced graduate students and postdocs. Finally, there is some unpublished material, included in two sets of lectures, given in the 1960s at the Hughes Aircraft Company, which only recently have been made available on the web.[f] In particular, the 1966-67 set of lectures,[16] which were devoted to astronomy, astrophysics and cosmology, contains an introductory treatment of general relativity, with an emphasis on applications to the main subjects. While sharing many similarities with the above quoted Caltech lectures,[14] the Hughes treatment offers to the attentive reader several original points. In those same years Feynman had succeeded in finding a new derivation of Maxwell's equations,[17,18] and a generalization of this approach to gravity is suggested (but not pursued) in several places in the Hughes lectures on astrophysics, as well as in the set of lectures given in the following year and devoted to electromagnetism.[19]

After outlining the main steps and sources which helped us to reconstruct the full development of Feynman's work on gravitation,[g] in this contribution we focus on two key issues: the formulation of quantum gravity as a quantum field theory of a massless spin-2 field, the graviton, in whole analogy with quantum electrodynamics, which is the content of Section 2, and the unitarity and renormalization issues arising beyond the tree level approximation, presented in Section 3. Our concluding remarks close the paper.

2. Gravity as a quantum field theory

Feynman's strategy in approaching gravity was firstly outlined at Chapel Hill conference in a series of critical comments (Ref. 4, pp. 272-276), in which a non-geometric and field theoretical line of attack is put forward. His starting point was an hypothetical, counterfactual situation, in which scientists would discover the principles of Lorentzian quantum field theories before general relativity.[h] The main concern in

---

[e]The International Conference on General Relativity and Gravitation was held in Jabłonna and Warsaw in July 25-31, 1962, with Leopold Infeld as the chairman of the local organizing committee. The discussion focused on three main topics: the general properties of gravitational radiation, the quantization of gravity and the exact solutions of the Einstein field equations.
[f]See Ref. 15 for a brief account of Feynman's involvement in teaching at the Hughes Aircraft Company.
[g]See Ref. 20 for a comprehensive account of this work.
[h]In fact, in Ref. 4, p. 273, Feynman said: "Instead of trying to explain the rest of physics in terms of gravity I propose to reverse the problem by changing history. Suppose Einstein never existed [...]".

such a situation would then be to include a new force, the gravitational one, in the framework of quantum field theory. This approach would be later completed in the first part of the Caltech lectures.[14] Feynman's reasoning was the following: on the basis of the general principles of quantum field theory and of experimental results it is possible to conclude that gravity, as any other force, has to be mediated by exchanges of a virtual particle, which in this case is a massless neutral spin-2 quantum, the graviton. Thus, by constructing a Lorentz invariant quantum field theory of the graviton[i] and by imposing certain consistency requirements, full general relativity should be recovered. Clearly, by following the same procedure for the spin-1 case Maxwell's equations are obtained (in this case it is much simpler, being the theory linear). Such an approach testifies his ideas about fundamental interactions as manifestations of underlying quantum theories,[18] which were expressed by him several times, for example in the Hughes Lectures[19]:

> I shall call conservative forces, those forces which can be deduced from quantum mechanics in the classical limit. As you know, Q.M. is the underpinning of Nature (Ref. 19, p. 35).

Let us describe the steps in more detail. First of all, one has to establish the spin of the mediating quantum. Both in the Caltech[14] and in the 1966-67 Hughes lectures,[16] the choice of a spin-2 mediator was justified by the observation that energy, which is the source of the gravitational force, grows with the velocity. The same observation ruled out the possibility of a spin-0 field, because the associated charge would decrease with the velocity. This result can be traced back to an old argument by Einstein (never published but recalled in Ref. 26, pp. 285-290), according to which the vertical acceleration of a body would depend on its horizontal velocity, and in particular would be zero for light, making light deflection impossible. Once the spin of the graviton is established, one can easily construct the linearized theory of the associated field, which is a massless spin-2 field. Nonlinearity then comes into play because the graviton has to couple with anything carrying energy-momentum, then also with itself, and this coupling must be universal. The resulting nonlinear theory is general relativity. General covariance and the geometric interpretation of general relativity are finally recovered as a byproduct of the gauge invariance of the theory[j]. For Feynman, this was only half of the whole story. In fact, by pushing calculations beyond tree level, quantum gravity effects would be taken into account. This was Feynman's ultimate goal, i.e. obtaining a quantum theory of gravity, which in this approach amounts to the quantization of another field.

---

[i]The linear theory for a massless spin-2 field and its massive counterpart was completely worked out by Markus Fierz and Wolfgang E. Pauli in Ref. 21, on the basis of a previous work by Paul A. M. Dirac,[22] while iterative arguments similar to Feynman's ones were later put forward by Suraj N. Gupta[23] and Robert H. Kraichnan[24] in an attempt to generate infinite nonlinear terms both in the Lagrangian and in the stress-energy tensor. See for details Ref. 25.
[j]See Ref. 14, p. 113.

Let us describe how Feynman sketched the above procedure at the Chapel Hill conference (Ref. 4, pp. 272-276). In whole analogy with electrodynamics, he wrote down the following action:

$$\int \left(\frac{\partial A_\mu}{\partial x_\nu} - \frac{\partial A^\nu}{\partial x^\mu}\right)^2 d^4x + \int A_\mu j^\mu d^4x + \frac{m}{2}\int \dot{z}_\mu^2 ds + \frac{1}{2}\int T_{\mu\nu} h^{\mu\nu} d^4x$$
$$+ \int (\text{second power of first derivatives of } h), \quad (1)$$

where $h_{\mu\nu}$ is the new field associated with the graviton, i.e. a symmetric second-order tensor field, which satisfies second order linear equations of the kind:

$$h^{\mu\nu,\sigma}{}_{,\sigma} - 2\bar{h}^\mu{}_\sigma{}^{,\nu\sigma} = \bar{T}^{\mu\nu}, \quad (2)$$

where the *bar* operation is defined on a generic second rank tensor $X_{\mu\nu}$ as:

$$\bar{X}_{\mu\nu} = \frac{1}{2}(X_{\mu\nu} + X_{\nu\mu}) - \frac{1}{2}\eta_{\mu\nu} X^\sigma{}_\sigma. \quad (3)$$

The equations of motion for particles also follow from the above action:

$$g_{\mu\nu}\ddot{z}^\nu = -[\rho\sigma,\mu]\dot{z}^\rho \dot{z}^\sigma, \quad (4)$$

where $g_{\mu\nu} = \eta_{\mu\nu} + h_{\mu\nu}$, $\eta_{\mu\nu}$ is the Minkowski metric, and $[\rho\sigma,\mu]$ are the Christoffel symbols of the first kind.

However, when the field $h_{\mu\nu}$ is coupled to the matter according to Eq. (4), the corresponding stress energy tensor $T_{\mu\nu}$ does *not* obey to a conservation law, leading to a consistency problem. This happens at variance with electromagnetism, where Maxwell equations guarantee conservation of the current j^μ. Instead here $T_{\mu\nu}$ does not take into account the effect of gravity on itself, which requires nonlinearity.[k] Thus a suitable $T_{\mu\nu}$ has to be found in order to satisfy the condition $\partial_\nu T^{\mu\nu} = 0$. The solution to this consistency issue[l] can be obtained by adding to the action a nonlinear third order term in $h_{\mu\nu}$, which leads to the following equation for $T_{\mu\nu}$:

$$g_{\mu\lambda} T^{\mu\nu}{}_{,\nu} = -[\rho\nu,\lambda]T^{\rho\nu}. \quad (5)$$

One can then go on to higher order approximations, until the procedure converges. But finding the general solution of Eq. (5) is a really difficult task in the absence of a standard procedure. Feynman's idea was to look for an expression for the $T_{\mu\nu}$, and hence for the action, that is invariant under the following infinitesimal transformation of the whole tensor field $g_{\mu\nu}$:

$$g'_{\mu\nu} = g_{\mu\nu} + g_{\mu\lambda}\frac{\partial A^\lambda}{\partial x^\nu} + g_{\nu\lambda}\frac{\partial A^\lambda}{\partial x^\mu} + A^\lambda \frac{\partial g_{\mu\nu}}{\partial x^\lambda}, \quad (6)$$

where the 4-vector A^λ is the generator. This is a geometric transformation in a Riemannian manifold with metric, hence one can say that geometry gives the metric

---
[k]Feynman noticed that nonlinearity was necessary in order to explain the precession of the perihelion of Mercury (as discussed in Ref. 14, p. 75).
[l]See for details Refs. 4, p. 274 and 14, pp. 78-79.

$g_{\mu\nu}$. As such, in Feynman's approach geometry comes into play at the end and not at the beginning. By working out calculations, the full nonlinear Einstein gravitational field equations are obtained.

Lectures 3-6 of Feynman's graduate course on gravitation (Ref. 14) contain all the details of the above procedure. Interestingly, a proof is also given of the ability of this field theory based formalism to reproduce key physical effects of curved spacetime geometry. For instance, in Lecture 5 (Ref. 14, pp. 66-69) it is shown that, in the action of a scalar field, the time dilation $t \to t' = t\sqrt{1+\epsilon}$ exactly reproduces the effect of a constant weak gravitational field described by the tensor $g_{44} = 1+\epsilon$, $g_{ii} = -1$, $i = 1, 2, 3$. Incidentally such an effect plays a pivotal role in producing the right result for the precession of Mercury's perihelion. Before moving to applications, Feynman devoted some lectures to the discussion of the usual geometric approach to gravity and of its link with the field theory based approach (Ref. 14, Lectures 7-10):

> Let us try to discuss what it is that we are learning in finding out that these various approaches give the same results (Ref. 14, p. 112).

Despite advocating one approach over another, Feynman was in fact intrigued by the double nature of gravity, which has both a geometrical interpretation and a field interpretation, and in Section 8.4 of Ref. 14 he recognized how an explanation may be provided by gauge invariance. Indeed a viable procedure may be established in order to obtain the invariance of the equations of physics under space dependent variable displacements. This amounts to looking for a more general Lagrangian, to be obtained by adding to the old one new terms, involving a gravity field. The net result is a new picture of gravity, as the field corresponding to a gauge invariance with respect to displacement transformations.

Summing up, Feynman succeeded in obtaining the full nonlinear Einstein equations by means of a consistency argument applied to a Lorentz invariant quantum field theory of the graviton. According to John Preskill and Kip S. Thorne,[25] it is likely that he was completely unaware of the earlier work by Gupta[23] and Kraichnan,[24] which as mentioned had been developed along a similar line of attack, but was still incomplete. So he would have developed his approach independently, besides getting more complete results. A Lorentz-invariant field theoretical approach to gravity would have been later pursued also by Steven Weinberg,[27,28] albeit quite different from Feynman's one,[m] as well as by Stanley Deser.[29–32] Indeed Deser's approach, while being similar to Feynman's one, was more elegant and general and led to completion the whole program started with Kraichnan and Gupta. Finally, a rigorous and general analysis of the relation between spin-2 theories and general covariance was carried out by Robert M. Wald.[33]

---

[m]Weinberg's approach relied on the analyticity properties of graviton-graviton scattering amplitudes, and it was quite more general, since Weinberg actually proved that a quantum theory of a massless spin-2 field can only be consistent if this field universally couples to the energy-momentum of matter, hence the equivalence principle has to be obeyed.

3. Fighting with loops: The renormalization of gravity

After obtaining the Einstein-Hilbert action and the full nonlinear Einstein gravitational field equations, Feynman's efforts were mainly directed towards discussing quantum field theory issues beyond the tree level approximation, i.e. loop diagrams, unitarity and renormalization.

To the best of our knowledge, these issues were publicly addressed for the first time by Feynman in 1961 at the already mentioned La Jolla conference,[9] where nonlinearity was recognized as the very source of difficulty within both gravitation and Yang-Mills theories. Indeed the sources of the gravitational field are energy and momentum, and the gravitational field carries energy and momentum itself. In the same way, the source of a Yang-Mills field is the isotopic spin current, and the Yang-Mills field carries isotopic spin itself. This means that both the gravitational field and the Yang-Mills field are self-coupled, resulting in nonlinear field theories. A difficulty that nonlinearity brings about is the fact that loop diagrams seem to clash with unitarity.

As recalled in the introduction, Feynman's results on quantum gravity can be found in a report of the talk given at the 1962 Warsaw conference, later published in Acta Physica Polonica,[2n] with many details discussed much later in the two 1972 Wheeler Festschrift papers.[11,12]

Also in this case Feynman followed his original strategy, leaving aside quantization of space-time geometry, constructing a quantum field theory for the graviton, and working out results at different perturbative orders. Since the goal was the quantum theory, the Einstein equations and the corresponding Lagrangian were assumed as a starting point, rather than derived from scratch. The theory was coupled to a scalar field, and perturbative calculations up to the next to leading order were pursued. This implied the inclusion of loop diagrams, which make quantum corrections to enter the game. In Feynman's own words:

> I started with the Lagrangian of Einstein for the interacting field of gravity and I had to make some definition for the matter since I'm dealing with real bodies and make up my mind what the matter was made of; and then later I would check whether the results that I have depend on the specific choice or they are more powerful (Ref. 2, p. 698).

The metric was split in the following way:

$$g_{\mu\nu} = \delta_{\mu\nu} + \kappa h_{\mu\nu}; \qquad (7)$$

where the Minkowski metric is here denoted by $\delta_{\mu\nu}$ and κ is a dimensionful coupling constant. Substituting (7) and expanding, the Lagrangian for gravity coupled with

---

[n] As pointed out by Trautman in some recently published memories (34, p. 406), the text of Feynman's plenary lecture became available too late to be included in the proceedings, therefore it was published only in 1963 as a regular paper.

a scalar field can be cast in the form:

$$L = \int \left(h_{\mu\nu,\sigma}\overline{h}_{\mu\nu,\sigma} - 2\overline{h}_{\mu\sigma,\sigma}\overline{h}_{\mu\sigma,\sigma}\right) d\tau + \frac{1}{2}\int \left(\phi_{,\mu}^2 - m^2\phi^2\right) d\tau \tag{8}$$

$$+ \kappa \int \left(\overline{h}_{\mu\nu}\phi_{,\mu}\phi_{,\nu} - m^2\frac{1}{2}h_{\sigma\sigma}\phi^2\right) d\tau + \kappa \int (hhh) \, d\tau + \kappa^2 \int (hh\phi\phi) \, d\tau + \ldots$$

where the bar operation has been defined in (3) and a schematic notation has been adopted for the highly complex higher order terms. The first two terms are simply the free Lagrangians of the gravitational field and of matter, respectively. Before considering radiative corrections the classical solution of the problem was worked out, which involved the variation of Eq. (8) with respect to h and, then, to ϕ, giving rise to the following equations of motion with a source term:

$$h_{\mu\nu,\sigma\sigma} - \overline{h}_{\sigma\nu,\sigma\mu} - \overline{h}_{\sigma\mu,\sigma\nu} = \overline{S}_{\mu\nu}(h,\phi), \tag{9}$$

$$\phi_{,\sigma\sigma} - m^2\phi = \chi(\phi, h). \tag{10}$$

A close inspection revealed that Eq. (9) was singular, so that Feynman was forced to resort to the invariance of the Lagrangian under the transformation:

$$h'_{\mu\nu} = h_{\mu\nu} + 2\xi_{\mu,\nu} + 2h_{\mu\sigma}\xi_{\sigma,\nu} + \xi_\sigma h_{\mu\nu,\sigma}, \tag{11}$$

ξ_μ being arbitrary. This meant that the source $S_{\mu\nu}$ had to be divergenceless in order to make Eq. (9) consistent. Finally, by making the gauge choice $\overline{h}_{\mu\sigma,\sigma} = 0$, the law of the gravitational interaction of two systems by means of the exchange of a virtual graviton was obtained. Feynman then went on computing other processes, such as an interaction vertex coupling two particles and a graviton and the gravitational analog of gravitational Compton effect (i.e. with a graviton replacing the photon).

After these preliminary calculations, Feynman went to the next to leading order approximation, thus encountering diagrams with closed loops:

> However the next step is to take situations in which we have what we call closed loops, or rings, or circuits, in which not all momenta of the problem are defined (Ref. 2, pp. 703-704).

He realized that working out closed loop diagrams required the solution of a number of conceptual issues, and he succeeded in showing that any diagram with closed loops can be expressed in terms of sums of on shell tree diagrams, which is the content of his celebrated tree theorem (which was treated in detail in Ref. 11). Further details on the statement of the tree theorem and, in particular, on the nature of the proof for the one-loop case were given by Feynman in the discussion section (Ref. 2, pp. 714-717), while answering some related questions by DeWitt. But the main problem to face in carrying out one-loop calculations was the lack of unitarity, due to the presence of contributions arising from the unphysical longitudinal polarization states of the graviton, which did not cancel as they should. Following a suggestion by Gell-Mann,[o] Feynman considered the simpler Yang-Mills case (his results in this case were summarized in Ref. 12) and found the same pathological behavior:

> But this disease which I discovered here is a disease which exist in other theories. So at least there is one good thing: gravity isn't alone in this difficulty. This observation that Yang-Mills was also in trouble was of very great advantage to me. [...] the Yang-Mills theory is enormously easier to compute with than the gravity theory, and therefore I continued most of my investigations on the Yang-Mills theory, with the idea, if I ever cure that one, I'll turn around and cure the other (Ref. 2, p. 707).

The solution to this issue was obtained by expressing each loop diagram as a sum of trees and then computing the trees. This worked even if the process of opening a loop by cutting a graviton line implies the replacement of a virtual graviton with a real transverse one. Finally, in order to guarantee gauge invariance the sum of the whole set of tree diagrams corresponding to a given process has to be taken.

The same results, according to Feynman, could be obtained by direct integration of the closed loop. In the last case a mass-like term has to be added to the Lagrangian to avoid singularity but at the price of breaking gauge invariance. At the same time a contribution has to be subtracted, which is obtained by making a ghost particle (with spin-1 and Fermi statistics) to go around the loop and artificially coupled to the external field. In this way both unitarity and gauge invariance would be restored. This procedure was worked out also for Yang-Mills theory, but in that case the ghost particle has spin-0.[12]

Once successfully solved the one-loop case, Feynman's efforts pointed toward a further generalization of the above procedure to two or more loops:

> Now, the next question is, what happens when there are two or more loops? Since I only got this completely straightened out a week before I came here, I haven't had time to investigate the case of 2 or more loops to my own satisfaction. The preliminary investigations that I have made do not indicate that it's going to be possible so easily gather the things into the right barrels. It's surprising, I can't understand it; when you gather the trees into processes, there seems to be some loose trees, extra trees (Ref. 2, p. 710).

But, in Feynman's words, preliminary attempts seem to suggest that novel difficulties enter the game when dealing with two or more loops, as also mentioned in the last of his published Lectures on Gravitation (Ref. 14, Lecture 16, pp. 211-212). Here, once again, he recognized in the lack of unitarity of some sums of diagrams the main source of the observed pathological behavior and pointed out that a similar

---

[o] "I suggested that he try the analogous problem in Yang-Mills theory, a much simpler nonlinear gauge theory than Einsteinian gravitation." (Ref. 3, p. 53).

feature was shared also by Yang-Mills theory. Finally, while hinting at the problem of finding ghost rules for high order diagrams, he argued in favor of the non-renormalizability of gravity as a consequence of these difficulties:

> I do not know whether it will be possible to develop a cure for treating the multi-ring diagrams. I suspect not – in other words, I suspect that the theory is not renormalizable. Whether it is a truly significant objection to a theory, to say that it is not renormalizable, I don't know (Ref. 14, Lecture 16, pp. 211-212).

It is not clear whether Feynman was suggesting a link between non-unitarity and non-renormalizability issues. But in any case Feynman's results played a prominent role in the development of gauge theory and quantum gravity. Feynman's rules for ghosts were later generalized to all orders by DeWitt,[35–37] while Ludvig D. Faddeev and Viktor N. Popov[38] derived them in a much simpler way, by means of functional integral quantization, setting the standard for all subsequent work in the field. In particular, DeWitt proved that Yang-Mills theory and quantum gravity are in fact unitary at two[35] and arbitrarily many loops.[36,37] However, while Yang-Mills theory was later shown to be renormalizable (cf. Refs. 39-42), gravity presented divergences which could not be renormalized (cf. Refs. 43-46), confirming Feynman's suspect. It should be mentioned that, in subsequent years, modified theories of gravity, characterized by an action quadratic in the curvature, have been put forward. Unlike ordinary general relativity, these theories are renormalizable but not unitary.[47]

It is worth mentioning that, unlike most of his contemporaries, Feynman did not think about non-renormalizability as a signature of inconsistency of a theory, as also recalled by Gell-Mann,[p] and claimed by Feynman himself in one of his last interviews, given in January 1988:

> The fact that the theory has infinities never bothered me quite so much as it bother others, because I always thought that it just meant that we've gone too far: that when we go to very short distances the world is very different; geometry, or whatever it is, is different, and it's all very subtle (48, p. 507).

In fact, within the modern view on quantum field theory, which was developed in 1970s, non-renormalizability is considered only a signature of the fact that the theory loses its validity at energies higher that a certain scale. Nevertheless, one has an *effective field theory*, which works and can be useful to make predictions under that scale (interesting historical discussions can be found in Refs. 49 and 50). This is true also for gravity.[51] But, as remembered by John P. Preskill in a recent talk

---

[p] "He was always very suspicious of unrenormalizability as a criterion for rejecting theories" (Ref. 3, p. 53).

(Ref. 52, slide 37), although he anticipated this view, apparently Feynman was not really at ease with it:

> I spoke to Feynman a number of times about renormalization theory during the mid-80s (I arrived at Caltech in 1981 and he died in 1988). I was surprised on a few occasions how the effective field theory viewpoint did not come naturally to him". [...] Feynman briefly discusses in his lectures on gravitation (1962) why there are no higher derivative terms in the Einstein action, saying this is the "simplest" theory, not mentioning that higher derivative terms would be suppressed by more powers of the Planck length.

As a further remark, let us notice that in the last years Feynman's tree theorem has spurred a renewed interest in researchers working in the context of advanced perturbative calculations and generalized unitarity (cf. Refs. 53-57).

4. Concluding remarks

In this paper we focused on Feynman's contributions to the research in quantum gravity, starting from his interventions at Chapel Hill conference in 1957 and ending with the Wheeler festschrift papers. His approach was field theoretical rather than geometric, reflecting his strong belief in the unity of Nature, which is quantum at the deepest level. Quantization of gravity, according to him, simply had to be considered as the quantization of another field, the spin-2 graviton field. In this way full general relativity would be recovered at leading order, while the inclusion of loop diagrams brought into the picture a bunch of new difficulties. In this respect, Feynman's struggle against loops, while succeeding at one-loop order, failed with two- and higher-loop diagrams. Nevertheless, his results triggered further efforts and some tools he developed, such as the tree theorem, have recently become of widespread use among people working on scattering amplitudes.

References

1. R. P. Feynman, R. B. Leighton and M. Sands, *The Feynman Lectures on Physics* (Addison-Wesley, Reading, MA, 1963).
2. R. P. Feynman, Quantum theory of gravitation, *Acta Phys. Polon.* **24**, 697 (1963).
3. M. Gell-Mann, Dick Feynman - The guy in the office down the hall, *Phys. Today* **42**, 50 (1989).
4. C. DeWitt-Morette and D. Rickles, *The Role of Gravitation in Physics*, Report from the 1957 Chapel Hill Conference (Edition Open Access, 2011).
5. Letter from Bryce DeWitt to Agnew Bahnson, dated 15 November 1955, as cited in,[4] p. 25.
6. A. S. Blum, R. Lalli and J. Renn, The renaissance of General Relativity: How and why it happened, *Annalen der Physik* **528**, 344 (2016).
7. P. G. Bergmann, Summary of the Chapel Hill Conference, *Rev. Mod. Phys.* **29**, 352 (1957).
8. R. P. Feynman, unpublished letter to Victor F. Weisskopf, February 1961; in *Richard P. Feynman Papers*, California Institute of Technology Archives, Box 3, Folder 8.

9. W. R. Frazer, Theory of Weak and Strong Interactions, *Physics Today* **14**(12), 80 (1961).
10. G. F. Chew, *S-matrix theory of strong interactions: A lecture note and reprint volume*, Frontiers in physics series (W. A. Benjamin, New York, 1961).
11. R. P. Feynman, Closed loop and tree diagram, in Ref.[13].
12. R. P. Feynman, Problems in quantizing the gravitational field and the massless Yang-Mills field, in Ref.[13].
13. J. R. Klauder (ed.), *Magic Without Magic - John Archibald Wheeler. A Collection Of Essays In Honor Of His 60th Birthday* (Freeman, San Francisco, 1972).
14. R. P. Feynman, F. B. Morinigo, W. G. Wagner and B. Hatfield, *Feynman Lectures on Gravitation* (Addison-Wesley, Reading, MA, 1995).
15. M. Di Mauro, S. Esposito and A. Naddeo, When Physics Meets Biology: A Less Known Feynman, *Transversal Int. J. Hist. Sci.* **4**, 163 (2018).
16. R.P. Feynman, *Astronomy, Astrophysics, and Cosmology*, lectures at Hughes Aircraft Company, Notes taken and transcribed by John T. Neer, 1966-67.
17. R. De Luca, M. Di Mauro, S. Esposito and A. Naddeo, Feynman's different approach to electromagnetism, *Eur. J. Phys.* **40**, 065205 (2019).
18. M. Di Mauro, R. De Luca, S. Esposito and A. Naddeo, Some insight into Feynman's approach to electromagnetism, *Eur. J. Phys.* **42**, 025206 (2021).
19. R.P. Feynman, *Electrostatics, Electrodynamics, Matter-Waves Interacting, Relativity*, lectures at Hughes Aircraft Company, Notes taken and transcribed by John T. Neer, 1967-68.
20. M. Di Mauro, S. Esposito and A. Naddeo, A road map for Feynman's adventures in the land of gravitation, *Eur. Phys. H* **46**, 22 (2021).
21. M. Fierz and W. Pauli, On relativistic wave equations for particles of arbitrary spin in an electromagnetic field, *Proc. Roy. Soc. Lond. A* **173**, 211 (1939).
22. P. A. M. Dirac, Relativistic wave equations, *Proc. Roy. Soc. Lond. A* **155**, 447 (1936).
23. S. N. Gupta, Gravitation and Electromagnetism, *Phys. Rev.* **96**, 1683 (1954).
24. R. H. Kraichnan, Special-Relativistic Derivation of Generally Covariant Gravitation Theory, Phys. Rev. **98**, 1118 (1955).
25. J. Preskill and K. S. Thorne, Foreword to Ref.[14].
26. A. Einstein, Notes on the Origin of the General Theory of Relativity, in *Ideas and Opinions*, translated by Sonja Bargmann, (Crown, New York, 1954).
27. S. Weinberg, Derivation of gauge invariance and the equivalence principle from Lorentz invariance of the S- matrix, *Phys. Lett.* **9**, 357 (1964).
28. S. Weinberg, Photons and gravitons in perturbation theory: Derivation of Maxwell's and Einstein's equations, *Phys. Rev.* **138**, B988 (1965), B988.
29. S. Deser, Self-interaction and gauge invariance, *Gen. Rel. Grav.* **1**, 9 (1970).
30. D. G. Boulware and S. Deser, Classical General Relativity Derived from Quantum Gravity, *Annals Phys.* **89**, 193 (1975).
31. S. Deser, Gravity From Self-interaction in a Curved Background, *Class. Quant. Grav.* **4**, L99 (1987).
32. S. Deser, Gravity from self-interaction redux, *Gen. Rel. Grav.* **42**, 641 (2010).
33. R. M. Wald, Spin-2 Fields and General Covariance, *Phys. Rev. D* **33**, 3613 (1986).
34. A. Trautman and D. Salisbury, Memories of my early career in relativity physics, *Eur. Phys. J. H* **44**, 391 (2019).
35. B. S. DeWitt, Theory of radiative corrections for non-abelian gauge fields, *Phys. Rev. Lett.* **12**, 742 (1964).
36. B. S. DeWitt, Quantum Theory of Gravity. 2. The Manifestly Covariant Theory, *Phys. Rev.* **162**, 1195 (1967).

37. B. S. DeWitt, Quantum Theory of Gravity. 3. Applications of the Covariant Theory, *Phys. Rev.* **162**, 1239 (1967).
38. L. D. Faddeev and V. N. Popov, Feynman Diagrams for the Yang-Mills Field, *Phys. Lett. B* **25**, 29 (1967).
39. G. 't Hooft, Renormalization of Massless Yang-Mills Fields, *Nucl. Phys. B* **33**, 173 (1971).
40. G. 't Hooft, Renormalizable Lagrangians for Massive Yang-Mills Fields, *Nucl. Phys. B* **35**, 167 (1971).
41. G. 't Hooft and M. J. G. Veltman, Regularization and Renormalization of Gauge Fields, *Nucl. Phys. B* **44**, 189 (1972).
42. G. 't Hooft and M. J. G. Veltman, Combinatorics of gauge fields, *Nucl. Phys. B* **50**, 318 (1972).
43. G. 't Hooft and M. J. G. Veltman, One loop divergencies in the theory of gravitation, *Ann. Inst. H. Poincare Phys. Theor. A* **20**, 69 (1974).
44. M. H. Goroff and A. Sagnotti, Quantum gravity at two loops, *Phys. Lett. B* **160**, 81 (1985).
45. M. H. Goroff and A. Sagnotti, The Ultraviolet Behavior of Einstein Gravity, *Nucl. Phys. B* **266**, 709 (1986).
46. A. E. M. van de Ven, Two loop quantum gravity, *Nucl. Phys. B* **378**, 309 (1992).
47. K. S. Stelle, Renormalization of Higher Derivative Quantum Gravity, *Phys. Rev. D* **16**, 953 (1977).
48. J. Mehra, *The Beat of a different drum: The Life and science of Richard Feynman* (Oxford University Press, Oxford, 1994).
49. S. Weinberg, On the Development of Effective Field Theory, *Eur. Phys. J. H* **46**, 6 (2021).
50. S. Weinberg, Effective field theory, past and future, *Int. J. Mod. Phys. A* **31**, 1630007 (2016).
51. C. P. Burgess, Quantum gravity in everyday life: General relativity as an effective field theory, *Living Rev. Rel.* **7**, 5 (2004), and references therein.
52. J. Preskill, *Feynman after 40*, Talk given at APS April Meeting, 16 April 2018, http://theory.caltech.edu/~preskill/talks/APS-April-2018-Feynman-4-3.pdf.
53. R. Britto, Loop Amplitudes in Gauge Theories: Modern Analytic Approaches, *J. Phys. A* **44**, 454006 (2011).
54. I. Bierenbaum, S. Catani, P. Draggiotis and G. Rodrigo, Feynman's Tree Theorem and Loop-Tree Dualities, *PoS* **LC2010**, 034 (2010).
55. S. Caron-Huot, Loops and trees, *JHEP* **05**, 080 (2011).
56. M. Maniatis, Application of the Feynman-tree theorem together with BCFW recursion relations, *Int. J. Mod. Phys. A* **33**, 1850042 (2018).
57. M. Maniatis, Application of Britto-Cachazo-Feng-Witten recursion relations and the Feynman-tree theorem to the four-gluon amplitude with all plus helicities, *Phys. Rev. D* **100**, 096022 (2019).

Towards detecting gravitational waves: A contribution by Richard Feynman

M. Di Mauro

Dipartimento di Matematica, Università di Salerno,
Fisciano, 84084, Italy
E-mail: madimauro@unisa.it

S. Esposito* and A. Naddeo†

INFN, Sezione di Napoli, C. U. Monte S. Angelo, Via Cinthia,
Napoli, 80125, Italy
* E-mail: sesposit@na.infn.it
† E-mail: anaddeo@na.infn.it

An account of Richard Feynman's work on gravitational waves is given. Feynman's involvement with this subject can be traced back to 1957, when he attended the famous Chapel Hill conference on the Role of Gravitation in Physics. At that conference, he presented in particular the celebrated sticky bead argument, which was devised to intuitively argue that gravitational waves must carry energy, if they exist at all. While giving a simple argument in favor of the existence of gravitational waves, Feynman's thought experiment paved the way for their detection and stimulated subsequent efforts in building a practical detecting device. Feynman's contributions were systematically developed in a letter to Victor Weisskopf, completed in February 1961, as well as in his Caltech Lectures on Gravitation, delivered in 1962-63. There, a detailed calculation of the power radiated as gravitational radiation was performed, using both classical and quantum field theoretical tools, leading to a derivation of the quadrupole formula and its application to gravitational radiation by a binary star system. A comparison between the attitudes of Feynman and of the general relativity community to the problems of gravitational wave physics is drawn as well.

Keywords: History of physics; History of relativity; Gravitational waves.

1. Introduction

The contributions of Richard P. Feynman to physics notoriously touched all four fundamental interactions of Nature. His first breakthrough occurred in the theory of electromagnetism, with his version of covariant quantum electrodynamics that earned him the 1965 Nobel prize,[1] which was developed by him between the late 1940s and the early 1950s. A few years later, Feynman's interest had focused on another fundamental interaction, namely gravity. Feynman first mentioned this new interest of his to Murray Gell-Mann, who much later recalled:

> We first discussed it when I visited Caltech during the Christmas vacation of 1954-55 [...] I found that he had made considerable progress.[2]

In view of this statement,[a] it is conceivable that Feynman's interests were directed towards gravity some time before 1954, probably shortly after completing his work on quantum electrodynamics. While working also on other subjects, most notably condensed matter physics and the theory of weak interactions,[5] Feynman nurtured his interest in gravity at least until the second half of the 1960s. In these fifteen years, he gave several contributions to the both classical and quantum gravity, some of which would later be recognized as pivotal for the field. The first public contribution to gravity was given by Feynman at the Chapel Hill conference in 1957,[4] where he took active part to many of the numerous discussion sessions. After that, records of his later work are documented by several published and unpublished sources. For detailed historical accounts of Feynman's contributions to gravitational physics, see Refs. 6 and 8.

In this paper, we focus on Feynman's work on gravitational waves. As well-known, at Chapel Hill Feynman proposed a simple and intuitive thought experiment in favor of the existence of gravitational waves. This "sticky bead" argument presumably contributed to inspiring the pioneering experimental efforts by Joseph Weber. In fact, Feynman's qualitative argument was supported and extended by detailed calculations, several results of which were presented at Chapel Hill as well. While the original calculations are presumably lost, Feynman included a detailed description of an updated version of them in a letter he wrote to Viktor F. Weisskopf in early 1961.[9] These updated computations were also included in the famous graduate lectures on gravitation he delivered at Caltech in the academic year 1962-63.[7] They show that Feynman had addressed most of the contemporary theoretical problems of the subject, showing that gravitational waves carry energy, and that they can be detected by suitable instruments; moreover, he computed in detail the energy radiated by binary self-gravitating systems. Feynman's comments clearly show that he regarded his results as compelling (and probably somewhat straightforward as well, since he did not publish them) solutions to the above mentioned issues. Indeed, in his subsequent work on gravity, Feynman did not deal with gravitational waves any more, focusing instead on quantum gravity.

The paper is organized as follows. In Sect. 2 we briefly sketch the history of gravitational waves prior to Feynman's engagement with them, highlighting the theoretical problems which were the concern of scientists in the 1950s and 1960s. In Sect. 3 we briefly introduce the historical context in which the Chapel Hill conference took place and we summarize Feynman's contributions to it. In Sect. 4 we examine the letter to Weisskopf, and the parts of the Lectures on Gravitation which discuss gravitational waves. We close this section with a summary of Feynman's solutions to the theoretical issues in gravitational wave research. In Sect. 5 we give some comments on Feynman's work on gravitational waves, in particular in connection with his general views on gravity and on fundamental interactions in general.

---

[a]This was confirmed by Bryce S. DeWitt, who declared: "Even by 1955 Feynman claimed to have spent a great deal of effort on the problem of gravitation".[3]

In Sect. 6 we outline some contemporary and later developments, and in particular we describe the solutions to the theoretical issues that are currently accepted by the scientific community. Sect. 7 is devoted to conclusions.

2. Brief history of gravitational waves up to the 1950s

The main open problem concerning gravitational waves, when Feynman tackled them, was their very existence as physical entities.[b] In fact, general relativity enjoys general covariance, which means that coordinate systems have no intrinsic meaning. While very elegant and powerful, this symmetry also poses great difficulties, which have kept haunting general relativity practitioners since the earliest days of the theory. Namely, it is not easy to distinguish between real physical phenomena and mere artifacts due to a bad coordinate choice, hence invariant characterizations are needed. One of the earliest examples is the Schwarzschild singularity,[11] which occurs in the spherically symmetric solution found by Karl Schwarzschild. In fact, the metric describing this solution in spherical coordinates displays a singularity on a surface located at a given value of the radial coordinate. This singularity is now well-known to be apparent, and it is removed by choosing a different coordinate system,[12] but it took more than forty years to really understand what this meant. Two other, strictly linked examples, are given by the definition of energy in general relativity, and by gravitational waves themselves. When Albert Einstein first showed in 1916[13] that the gravitational field equations he had written down the year before[14] predict in the weak field limit the existence of wave-like excitations, and when in 1918[15] he corrected a major mistake in his 1916 paper, finding his celebrated quadrupole formula describing the leading-order energy emission through gravitational radiation, he chose a particular coordinate system, in which his equations looked formally analogous to the equations of electromagnetism. Einstein immediately recognized that some of the wave solutions he had found were spurious, and could be eliminated by a coordinate change (they were flat space in curved coordinates), while the remaining ones were not spurious, and carried energy according to his formula.

2.1. The question of the existence of gravitational waves

A weak point in Einstein's derivation was spotted and corrected by Sir Arthur S. Eddington,[16] namely, the fact that Einstein's choice of coordinates explicitly contained the speed of light, hence the propagation speed of gravitational waves may have been inadvertently put in by hand by the German physicist. Eddington improved and extended Einstein's work, giving a more rigorous proof of the fact that some of Einstein's solution were not coordinate artifacts, they carried energy and they propagated with the speed of light. Finally, Eddington rederived the

---

[b]For details on the history of gravitational waves, with a focus on the theoretical side, we refer to Ref. 10.

quadrupole formula, correcting a minor error by Einstein (an overall factor of 2), and applied it to the computation of energy radiated away by a rigid rotator. However, in complaining about the lack of an invariant way of distinguishing physical from spurious waves, Eddington referred to the latter in a very suggestive way, stating that, being coordinate artifacts, they propagate with the "speed of thought" (Ref. 17, p. 130). This generated a misunderstanding according to which Eddington attributed this characteristic to gravitational waves in general, thus questioning their very existence. Indeed, doubts concerning the existence of gravitational waves did not stop bothering the scientists working in general relativity for a long time. Another problem was posed by the fact that, unlike electromagnetism, gravitation is described by a highly nonlinear theory, while gravitational waves had been found only in the linearized approximation. The possibility thus existed that gravitational waves were in fact only artifacts of the linearized theory, meaning that there is no solution to the full gravitational field equations describing gravitational fields propagating as waves. This point of view was shared for some time by Einstein himself, after in 1937 he had tried with Nathan Rosen to find plane wave solutions to the full gravitational field equations.[18] Indeed, the two physicists found singularities in their solutions, and interpreted them as obstructions to the existence of propagating solutions to the equations.[c] After a well-known incident with a referee,[20] Einstein finally realized that the singularities he had found were coordinate artifacts, and that in fact he and Rosen had found an exact solution to his field equation, which enjoyed cylindrical symmetry. This was one of the first solutions to the full theory describing gravitational waves.[d] However, the question of the physical effects ascribable to these waves was still unclear, since it seemed that they did not carry energy, as still argued by Rosen himself in 1955 (Ref. 22, pp. 171-174), and anyway the Einstein-Rosen solution was non-physical, since its source was not localized. What was needed was an exact solution describing waves radiating from a localized center, which was still unavailable at the time. In any case, the fact that even Einstein himself had doubted that gravitational waves could exist certainly contributed to making them a neglected field of study for twenty more years.

A very important breakthrough occurred in 1956, when Felix A. E. Pirani managed to give an invariant characterization of gravitational radiation, in terms of spacetime curvature rather than energy,[23,24] giving in fact birth to the modern popular description of gravitational waves as propagating ripples of curvature. This work was performed in the context of Pirani's investigations of the physical meaning of the Riemann curvature tensor, based on the geodesic deviation equation[25] and on the classification of curvature tensors in terms of their principal null directions.[26] In particular, using the geodesic deviation equation, Pirani showed that the passage of a gravitational wave should modify the proper distance between test particles,

---

[c] Einstein mentioned this in a letter to Max Born (Ref. 19, letter 71).
[d] Actually, Einstein and Rosen had rediscovered a solution first found by Guido Beck in 1925.[21]

as an effect of the variation of the curvature. Thus, a measurable effect could be ascribed at least in principle to gravitational waves.

2.2. *The question of energy loss*

The issue of existence was not the only one which was at stake in gravitational wave physics in the 1950s. Even taking existence for granted, indeed, there was a problem concerning gravitational radiation by self-gravitating systems, such as binary stars. The first applications by Einstein and Eddington involved rigid bodies such as rotators, which can be considered to be kept together by the electromagnetic interaction, while a bound state kept together by gravity itself is beyond the reach of the linearized approximation, which was the only context in which gravitational energy radiation had been studied. In fact, many physicists even doubted that gravitational waves were radiated at all by such a system. And even if radiation did occur, it was unclear whether the Einstein quadrupole formula, which had been obtained in the linearized theory, correctly described the resulting energy loss. The issue had been addressed for the first time in 1941 by Lev D. Landau and Evgenij M. Lifshitz, in the first edition of their textbook,[27] where the binary system was treated by using the post-Newtonian approximation, and energy loss was computed by applying the quadrupole formula. However, there was no consensus about the correctness of their calculation, and the question was still open in the 1950s.

2.3. *Summary of the open problems*

From what we said above, it emerges that the situation concerning gravitational wave research was far from clear in the 1950s, with many basic theoretical problems and no hope of experimental guidance. We may summarize the main issues at stake as follows:

(1) The actual existence of gravitational waves as physical entities, their speed of propagation and their energy conveying;
(2) The existence of gravitational waves as solutions to the full nonlinear gravitational field equations;
(3) The radiation of gravitational waves by self-gravitating systems and the correctness of the quadrupole formula in describing the energy loss.

3. The Chapel Hill conference

As we saw, before the 1950s research on gravitational waves was carried out by only a handful of pioneers. This lack of interest was in fact not only the result of the doubts expressed by Einstein and also attributed to Eddington. The whole field of general relativity remained dormant for thirty years, from the mid-1920s to the mid-1950s, after an initial burst of activity. During this period, later baptized "low-watermark" phase,[28–30] general relativity was considered by most physicists to be a rather esoteric and heavily mathematical subject, with tenuous relations with the physical world.

Around the mid-1950's, things began to change, and gravity slowly regained a prominent place in physics. Pivotal to this change of attitude, which was dubbed the "renaissance" of general relativity,[31–33] was the organization of a series of international conferences entirely devoted to the subject. The renaissance of general relativity was characterized by the fact that physicists began studying the theory in a less speculative fashion than before, by focusing on its physical implications, and by developing dedicated, i.e. intrinsically general relativistic methods. That was also a time where researchers from other fields, most notably particle and field theory, began to be interested on gravitation and to apply their methods to it. One of them was of course Feynman, who started working on gravity just in this period, and it was in one of these conferences, namely the one (organized by DeWitt and his wife Cécile DeWitt-Morette) at the University of North Carolina at Chapel Hill in January 1957,[4] that he first announced his results in the field, as we anticipated in the introduction. In his many contributions to the discussions at Chapel Hill, he clearly delineated his attitude towards gravity, and presented a host of results he had already obtained. Besides the arguments on favor of the existence of gravitational waves, which we discuss in the following subsections, Feynman sketched a proposal for a field-theoretical approach to classical gravity. His view, shared by other particle physicists, was indeed that gravity had to be regarded as a fundamental interaction like all the others, and hence it had to be described by a field theory, which would also encode quantum corrections to the classical theory. Indeed, within a few years, he managed to derive the field equations of general relativity (as summarized in Ref. 7), and he attacked the problem of quantum gravity, from this perspective.[6,8] Finally, the Chapel Hill conference is notably one of the few occasions where Feynman expressed his views about foundational quantum issues, which were inspired by the problem of the quantization of gravity.[4,6,8,34]

3.1. *The sticky bead argument*

Feynman presented his famous sticky bead argument in a session devoted to discussing the necessity of gravity quantization (in which he also proposed a thought experiment in order to argue in favor of that). In fact, Feynman had arrived a day later at the conference[e], skipping the session devoted to gravitational waves. However, further discussion of gravitational waves in sessions devoted to quantum gravity was not off-topic, since the existence of these waves is of course very important for the quantization of the theory. Thus, in the middle of a discussion about whether the gravitational field had to be quantized even in the absence of gravitational waves, Feynman proposed a simple physical argument in favor of their existence (Ref. 4, p. 260 and pp. 279-281). He argued that if gravitational waves

---

[e]An amusing and well-known recollection of his arrival in North Carolina can be found in Ref. 35.

exist, they must carry energy and this, together with the existence of these waves as solutions of the linearized theory, was enough for him to be confident in their existence. He expressed this intuitive feeling with the words: "My instincts are that if you can feel it, you can make it" (Ref. 4, p. 260). Feynman's reasoning was detailed in an expanded version of his remarks, included in the records of the conference[4]:

> I think it is easy to see that if gravitational waves can be created they can carry energy and do work. Suppose we have a transverse-transverse wave generated by impinging on two masses close together. Let one mass A carry a stick which runs past touching the other B. I think I can show that the second in accelerating up and down will rub the stick, and therefore by friction make heat. I use coordinates physically natural to A, that is so at A there is flat space and no field [...]. Then Pirani at an earlier section gave an equation for the motion of a nearby particle. (Ref. 4, p. 279).

The result by Pirani is of course that obtained in Refs. 23 and 24 (which indeed had been presented earlier at the conference, cf. Ref. 4, p. 141), stating that the displacement η of the mass B (measured from the origin A of the coordinate system) in the field of a gravitational wave satisfies the following differential equation:[f]

$$\ddot{\eta}^a + R^a_{0b0}\eta^b = 0, \qquad (a,b = 1,2,3) \tag{1}$$

R being the Riemann curvature tensor at the point A. Feynman continued:

> the curvature tensor [...] does not vanish for the transverse-transverse gravity wave but oscillates as the wave goes by. So, η on the RHS is sensibly constant, so the equation says the particle vibrates up and down a little (with amplitude proportional to how far it is from A on the average, and to the wave amplitude.) Hence it rubs the stick, and generates heat. (Ref. 4, p. 279)

The upshot is that the stick absorbs energy from the gravitational wave, which means that the latter carries energy and is able to do work.

3.2. *Feynman's theoretical detector*

In connection with the device he considered, Feynman went on considering a possible gravitational wave detector in which there are four, rather than two test masses, which oscillate as shown in Figure 1.

This thought device was used to compute how much energy gravitational waves would carry. The device was described by Feynman as follows:

> If I use 4 weights in a cross, the motions at a given phase are as in the figure (Fig. 1). Thus a quadrupole moment is generated by the wave. Now the

---

[f]This follows from the geodesic deviation equation (Ref. 4, p. 141; Refs. 23 and 24).

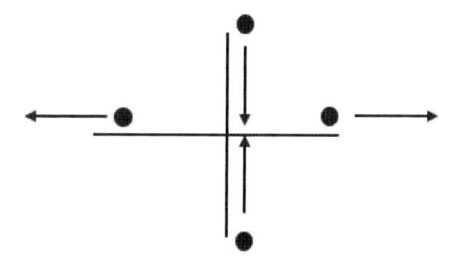

Fig. 1. Scheme of Feynman's gravitational wave detector.

question is whether such a wave can be generated in the first place. First since it is a solution of the equations (approx.) it can probably be made. Second, when I tried to analyze from the field equations just what happens if we drive 4 masses in a quadrupole motion of masses like the figure above would do - even including the stress-energy tensor of the machinery which drives the weights, it was very hard to see how one could avoid having a quadrupole source and generate waves. Third my instinct is that a device which could draw energy out of a wave acting on it, must if driven in the corresponding motion be able to create waves of the same kind. [...] If a wave impinges on our "absorber" and generates energy - another "absorber" placed in the wave behind the first must absorb less because of the presence of the first, (otherwise by using enough absorbers we could draw unlimited energy from the waves). That is, if energy is absorbed the wave must get weaker. How is this accomplished? Ordinarily through interference. To absorb, the absorber parts must move, and *in moving generate a wave* which interferes with the original wave in the so-called forward scattering direction, thus reducing the intensity for a subsequent absorber. In view therefore of the detailed analysis showing that gravity waves can generate heat (and therefore carry energy proportional to R^2 with a coefficient which can be determined from the forward scattering argument). I conclude also that these waves can be generated and are in every respect real. (Ref. 4, p. 280, emphasis in the original)

In this quote, Feynman's point of view about the existence of gravitational waves is evident: since they exist as solutions of the field equations (albeit in the linearized approximation), they carry energy, and they can be generated (in fact, the detector generates secondary waves), then they must be a real phenomenon.

3.3. *Binary systems*

Within the discussion (Ref. 4, p. 260), Feynman also quoted a result concerning the calculation of the energy radiated by a self-gravitating two-body system in a circular orbit. This result shows that he had addressed also this issue, performing detailed calculations. The quoted result is:

$$\frac{\text{Energy radiated in one revolution}}{\text{Kinetic energy content}} = \frac{16\pi}{15}\frac{\sqrt{mM}}{m+M}\left(\frac{u}{c}\right)^5, \qquad (2)$$

where m and M are the masses of the two bodies, and u is their relative velocity. In the case of the Earth-Sun system, this formula describes as expected a tiny effect, leading to a huge order of magnitude (about 10^{26} years) for the lifetime of the motion of the Earth around the Sun. Despite the smallness of the effect, this is a definite prediction. Feynman stated to have performed a full analysis of this problem some time before (Ref. 4, p. 280), but he only quoted the result, without presenting his computations. Fortunately, Feynman reported a version of them four years later, in the letter written to Victor F. Weisskopf,[9] to which we now turn.

4. The letter to Weisskopf and the sixteenth lecture on gravitation

As anticipated, a complete and systematic description of Feynman's computations on gravitational waves can be found in a letter he wrote to Weisskopf in February 1961,[9] to answer a question that the Austrian physicist had asked him in the fall of 1960, concerning the reality of gravitational radiation. The letter was so detailed that it was subsequently included in the material distributed to the students attending the Caltech lectures in 1962-63. Indeed, the sixteenth lecture of that course (the last one in the published version[7]) dealt with gravitational waves, and reproduced part of the computations showed in the letter itself, with additional interesting comments.

The computations that Feynman reported in the letter and in the lectures were surely related to those he had performed before the Chapel Hill conference, but included several improvements that Feynman had conceived meanwhile. Indeed, at the end of the letter, he recalled the conference, claiming that

> It was this entire argument used in reverse that I made at a conference in North Carolina several years ago to convince people that gravity waves must carry energy. [...] Only as I was writing this letter to you did I find this simpler argument from the Lagrangian (Ref. 9, p. 14).

What Feynman meant by "argument used in reverse" and by "simpler argument from the Lagrangian" will be clear by the end of this section.

The most striking fact about the computations is that they are performed adopting a quantum point of view, treating general relativity as a quantum field theory, and then considering the classical limit:

> My view is quantum mechanical, but the classical limits are easily derived. (Ref. 9, p. 6)

Only later the same computation is repeated from the usual, classical point of view, in the framework of linearized gravity. As we saw, in fact, in that period Feynman was struggling with the quantization of gravity, building on the field theoretical viewpoint that he had advocated at Chapel Hill. In the beginning of 1961, he had recognized that loop diagrams in the theory present major difficulties, but he was still far from a solution (later in the same year he would report on his progress at the La Jolla conference[36]). However, he could safely study classical gravity by applying his field theoretical methods to tree diagrams, which are the only ones relevant to the classical limit (while loop diagrams describe quantum corrections). This is what he did in the letter,[g] claiming that:

> I am studying the problem of quantization of Einstein's General Relativity. I am still working out the details of handling the divergent integrals which arise in problems in which some virtual momentum must be integrated over. But for cases of radiation, without the radiation corrections, there is no difficulty. (Ref. 9, p. 1)

The "radiation corrections" Feynman was referring to are of course what are usually called radiative corrections, i.e. higher order corrections to the processes, which include the troublesome loop diagrams. In fact, in the Lectures Feynman adopted this point of view in studying many other problems in classical gravity:

> All other problems in the theory of gravitation[h] we shall attack first by the quantum theory; in order to obtain the classical consequences on macroscopic objects we shall take the classical limits of our quantum answers. (Ref. 7, p. 163)

The field theoretical methods that Feynman used are intrinsically perturbative. Feynman explicitly discussed the validity of this approximation, and of the linearized approximation he used in the classical computation, stating that this is a natural and obvious choice in view of the extreme weakness of the gravitational interaction. He stated in fact that:

> I won't be concerned with fields of arbitrary strength [...]. I am surprised that I find people objecting to an expansion of this kind, because it would be hard to find a situation where numerically a perturbation series is more justified! (Ref. 9, p. 1)

which is confirmed in the Lectures:

> There needs to be no apology for the use of perturbations, since gravity is far weaker than other fields for which perturbation theory seems to make extremely accurate predictions. (Ref. 7, p. 207)

---

[g]A conceptually analogous calculation was performed in 1936 by Matvei Bronstein,[37] who derived the quadrupole formula with the correct factor of 2 by computing the emission coefficients of transverse gravitons.

[h]Here Feynman was referring to all problems, apart from that of a spherical mass distribution and cosmology.

From these quotations, it is evident that Feynman considered the contemporary debate around the existence of gravitational waves in the full nonlinear theory of general relativity, as opposed to the linearized theory, to be pointless, since the perturbative/linearized theory would furnish an excellent approximation in most cases of interest.[i]

4.1. *The quantum computation*

To perform his computation, Feynman started from linearized gravity, which from his point of view was the linear theory of a massless charged spin-2 quantum field coupled to matter. For simplicity, he considered scalar (spin-0) matter, and he computed the probabilities for single graviton emission in several processes involving matter particles, in the low energy limit. The result is that the probability of emission of a graviton with frequency ω in the solid angle $d\Omega$ is (Ref. 9, p. 7; Ref. 7, p. 214):

$$P = a^2 \frac{d\Omega}{4\pi} \frac{d\omega}{\omega} \frac{\lambda^2}{4\pi^2}, \qquad (3)$$

where a is a kinematical factor and λ is the gravitational coupling constant (which is proportional to the square root of Newton's constant G).

Feynman knew that the probabilities of radiation of massless quanta become universal in the low energy limit, i.e. the probability of emission of a soft quantum in an interaction is independent of the spin of the interacting quanta (hence the choice of scalar matter implies no loss of generality), and most importantly of the kind of interaction which is involved. This happens because the low-energy limit is equivalent to the long-wavelength limit, in which the physics is insensitive to short-distance details. In particular, soft graviton emission occurs, with the same probability, also when matter quanta interact gravitationally. Since classical radiation is related to soft quantum emission, the implication is that masses accelerating under the reciprocal gravitational interactions must emit gravitational radiation as any other accelerating mass:

> Although this was worked out for spin zero particles, the result, as $\omega \to 0$, is the same for all, spin 1/2, photons, etc. It is correct for collisions irrespective of the kind of force. For example, Schiff asked me if two masses under their mutual gravitation can radiate. The answer is certainly yes. (Ref. 9, p. 7)

According to Feynman, these results proved that self-gravitating system must radiate gravitational waves. This view was confirmed in the Lectures:

---

[i]He also acknowledged the fact that the problem was at the moment of purely academic interest, stating that "the most "practical" thing to do is to go to zero order and forget the whole problem altogether" (Ref. 9, p. 1).

> As far as the radiation is concerned, the exact nature of the over-all scattering process is not important. I emphasize the last point because there are always some theorists who go about mumbling some mystical reasons to claim that the radiation would not occur if the scattering is gravitational - there is no basis for these claims; as far as we are concerned, radiation of gravity waves is as real as can be; the sun-earth rotation must be a source of gravitational waves. (Ref. 7, p. 215).

Thus the issue of gravitational radiation by self-gravitating systems was considered solved by Feynman. We emphasize that his quantum point of view was pivotal to that conclusion, since his reasoning relied on a well-known result of quantum field theory, namely the universality of soft graviton emission. Once again, Feynman showed some annoyance towards the physicists who continued to have doubts, while the solution was so clear to him.

4.2. *The classical computation and the quadrupole formula*

In the second part of the letter, Feynman switched to a classical computation, which was considered to be more appropriate for macroscopic objects, such as celestial bodies:

> for the motion of big objects such as planets and stars it may be more consistent to work in the classical limit. (Ref. 7, p. 215)

The classical computation was developed in close analogy with electrodynamics, taking into account that in the case of gravitation the source is a tensor $S_{\mu\nu}$ rather than a vector J_μ. The differential equation which has to be solved to find classical gravitational waves is (in the notation of Ref. 7):

$$\Box^2 \overline{h}_{\mu\nu} = \lambda S_{\mu\nu}, \qquad (4)$$

where $h_{\mu\nu}$ is the field describing deviations of the metric from the flat Minkowski metric and the bar operation is defined as:

$$\overline{h}_{\mu\nu} = \frac{1}{2}(h_{\mu\nu} + h_{\nu\mu}) - \frac{1}{2}\eta_{\mu\nu} h^\sigma{}_\sigma. \qquad (5)$$

$\Box^2$ is the usual, flat-space, d'Alembertian operator. As well-known, the above equation corresponds to the linearized Einstein equations in the de Donder gauge $\partial^\mu \overline{h}_{\mu\nu} = 0$. When all quantities are periodic with a given frequency ω, the solution at a point 1 located at a distance from the source much greater than the linear dimensions of the source itself (which is the region where $S_{\mu\nu}$ is expected to be large):

$$\overline{h}_{\mu\nu}(\vec{r}_1) = -\frac{\lambda}{4\pi r_1} e^{i\omega r_1} \int d^3\vec{r}_2 S_{\mu\nu}(\vec{r}_2) e^{-i\vec{K}\cdot\vec{r}_2}, \qquad (6)$$

with $|\vec{r}_1| \gg |\vec{r}_2|$ as stated. This approximation holds for nearly all cases of astronomical interests, where wavelengths are much longer than the system's dimensions, such as for instance binary stars and the Earth-Sun system. Finally, Feynman assumed that the motions of matter in the source were slow, so that he could resort to the post-Newtonian approximation. This is where the computations in the last section of Lecture 16 of the Caltech Lectures (Ref. 7, pp. 218-220) stopped, while in the letter Feynman went on computing the power radiated by the above waves in the quadrupole approximation which, for a periodic motion of frequency ω, read (Ref. 9, p. 11):

$$\frac{\text{mean energy radiated}}{\text{sec.}} = \frac{1}{5} G \omega^6 \sum_{ij} \left| Q'_{ij} \right|^2, \tag{7}$$

where $Q'_{ij} = Q_{ij} - \frac{1}{3}\delta_{ij}Q_{kk}$, $Q_{ij} = \sum_a m_a R_i^a R_j^a$ is the quadrupole mass moment, and the root mean square average is taken. The result (7) was then shown to agree with the quantum mechanical probability (3) computed in the first part of the letter (after suitable averaging). To strengthen this result, Feynman had considered earlier (Ref. 9, p. 10) an analogous comparison for the case of electromagnetism, finding again perfect correspondence.

Feynman then applied his formulas to the case of a circularly rotating double star (Ref. 9, p. 12), promptly recovering the result (2). In sum, Feynman's classical computation was analogous to that performed earlier by Landau and Lifshitz. However, his treatment was simpler, since he managed by using a very ingenious method for computing the energy density, which essentially exploits the fact that for classical transverse plane waves the linearized gravity Lagrangian reduces to that of the harmonic oscillator. This spared him formal complications such as the cumbersome energy-momentum pseudo-tensor, which was used by Landau and Lifschitz. This is in fact the "simpler argument from the Lagrangian" which he referred to in the end of the letter.

The above treatment was then supplemented with a thorough analysis of the effects of a gravitational wave impinging on a device made of two test particles placed on a rod with friction, in this way providing a more complete description of the working principle of the gravitational wave detector previously introduced at Chapel Hill. A second absorber, made of four moving particles in a quadrupole configuration, as in Figure 1, was also considered, and shown to be able to absorb energy from a gravitational wave acting on it. The oscillating device was shown to re-radiate waves with the same energy content. Apparently, at Chapel Hill, Feynman had derived the expression for the radiated energy (which was then applied to the binary system case) from the detailed study of the quadrupolar detector, either because at that time he did not know how to extract the definition of energy from the gravitational Lagrangian, or because the existing methods were considered to be too cumbersome by him. In the letter, instead, Feynman found a simple way of taking the opposite route (from this we can understand why Feynman claimed that the argument at Chapel Hill had been "used in reverse"), since the quadrupole formula was derived in general from the linearized Einstein equations and then applied to the detector case.

Thus, Feynman had shown that gravitational waves carry energy, and he had computed how much, also in the case of a binary star, satisfactorily addressing both the first and the third of the above issues. At the end of Lecture 16 of Ref. 7, Feynman commented again on the energy content of gravitational waves:

> What is the power radiated by such a wave? There are a great many people who worry needlessly at this question, because of a perennial prejudice that gravitation is somehow mysterious and different - they feel that it might be that gravity waves carry no energy at all. We can definitely show that they can indeed heat up a wall, so there is no question as to their energy content. The situation is exactly analogous to electrodynamics (Ref. 7, p. 219).

and in the letter, while recalling the Chapel Hill conference he commented:

> I was surprised to find a whole day at the conference devoted to this question, and that "experts" were confused. That is what comes from looking for conserved energy tensors, etc. instead of asking "can the waves do work?" (Ref. 9, p. 14).

These two quotes again display Feynman's annoyance towards the relativity community. The fact that relativists kept arguing about these problems without reaching an agreement, and that they privileged sophisticated formal tools to plain physical thinking, definitely disturbed Feynman, who repeatedly expressed his annoyance, and may have contributed to his loss of interest in the subject.

4.3. *Feynman's answer to the three issues*

The detailed study of Feynman's work on gravitational waves reveals what he thought the solutions to the issues listed in Sect. 2 should be, at least from a theoretical point of view, pending the ultimate experimental verification. In summary, these were:

(1) Feynman's thought experiments and calculations clearly show that gravitational waves exist and that they carry energy, while the fact that they propagate with the speed of light is a consequence of the fact that they emerged from massless quanta, i.e. the gravitons;
(2) Since gravity is so weak, it makes perfect sense to study gravitational waves using the linearized approximation;
(3) Gravitationally-bound system emit gravitational radiation as any other bound system, and the energy loss is described by the quadrupole formula in the approximations valid in most situations of interest.

5. Comments on Feynman's attitude towards gravity and gravitational waves

As emphasized, Feynman's approach to gravitational waves, and to gravitation in general, was much closer in spirit to particle physics than to general relativity. In fact, Feynman preferred a field theoretical approach over the geometrical one which had become the standard one among relativists. In his opinion, indeed, the latter approach divided gravity from other fundamental interactions, preventing the investigation of the relation of gravitation with the rest of physics, and also posing great obstacles towards its quantization.

A second motivation which underlies Feynman's choice of using quantum field theoretical methods for investigating classical gravitational radiation and other problems in classical gravity, was his belief that quantum mechanics underlies Nature at the most fundamental level, with the forces we observe at the macroscopic level emerging from quantum interactions in the classical limit. This is most clearly expressed by him in some unpublished lectures:

> I shall call conservative forces, those forces which can be deduced from quantum mechanics in the classical limit. As you know, Q.M. is the underpinning of Nature... (Ref. 38, p. 35)

Feynman recognized that the main problem with gravity was the fact that general relativity had received only a handful of experimental confirmations, while the subjects of gravitational waves and quantum gravity were confined to pure theory. These subjects were being investigated by the relativity community by resorting to sophisticated mathematics, in the hope that rigor could be a substitute for empirical evidence. Feynman had a different point of view. To him, the best way to proceed was to try to extract physical predictions from the theory *as if* these were easily accessible experimentally. This viewpoint was strongly advocated by him at Chapel Hill in some critical comments:

> There exists, however, one serious difficulty, and that is the lack of experiments. [...] so we have to take a viewpoint of how to deal with problems where no experiments are available. There are two choices. The first choice is that of mathematical rigor. [...] The attempt at mathematical rigorous solutions without guiding experiments is exactly the reason the subject is difficult, not the equations. The second choice of action is to "play games" by intuition and drive on. Take the case of gravitational radiation. [...] I think the best viewpoint is to pretend that there are experiments and calculate. In this field since we are not pushed by experiments we must be pulled by imagination. (Ref. 4, pp. 271-2)

and shortly after

> The real challenge is not to find an elegant formalism, but to solve a series of problems whose results could be checked. This is a different point of view. Don't be so rigorous or you will not succeed. (Ref. 4, p. 272)

This is in fact the viewpoint that Feynman adopted in his investigations of gravitational waves, but also in his work on quantum gravity.[8]

6. Contemporary and subsequent developments

When the Chapel Hill conference took place, the time was ripe for the existence of gravitational waves to be accepted by most physicists. Thus, the work of Pirani, and Feynman's sticky bead argument, managed to convince people that gravitational waves belong to the realm of physical phenomena, and suggested ways to investigate their physical effects. In fact, an argument similar to Feynman's was conceived independently by a leading relativist, Hermann Bondi, who was also present at Chapel Hill. This is referred to by several of Bondi's remarks at the conference, such as the following one, made after Pirani's talk (Ref. 4, p. 142): "Can one construct in this way an absorber for gravitational energy by inserting a $d\eta/d\tau$ term, to learn what part of the Riemann tensor would be the energy producing one, because it is that part that we want to isolate to study gravitational waves?". The absorber of gravitational energy is just a more formal description of the "stickiness" of Feynman's sticky-bead. Shortly after the conference, Bondi published his variant of the sticky-bead device,[39] although unlike Feynman he did not succeed in relating the intensity of the gravitational wave to the amount of energy carried by it. Inspired by these discussions, another participant to the conference, Joseph Weber, soon undertook his lifetime effort to experimentally detect gravitational waves[40]; Weber built his famous resonant bar detector in 1966[41] and even announced the first experimental detection of gravitational waves coming from the center of the Milky Way in 1969.[42] While this finding was later disproved, Weber's works triggered all the subsequent research on the detection of gravitational waves, which culminated in the monumental detections by the LIGO-Virgo collaboration in 2016.[43] Among all the physical results that this brought about, the confirmation came that gravitational waves move with the speed of light.[44]

Thus, it may be said that the first issue, that of the existence and physical effects of gravitational waves, was solved after Chapel Hill, with agreement among the scientific community. The same cannot be said of the other two issues. The relativity community reached an agreement on the status of gravitational waves in the full nonlinear theory only some years later, thanks to the rigorous work performed in that framework by Bondi, Pirani, Ivor Robinson and Andrzej Trautman, among others. In particular, Robinson and Trautman found exact solutions to the equations of general relativity describing waves radiated from bounded sources.[45] Furthermore, in the sixties, Bondi, Rainer W. Sachs, Ezra T. Newman and Roger Penrose,[46–50] gave a satisfactory definition of the energy radiated at infinity as gravitational radiation by an isolated gravitating system in an asymptotically flat spacetime. Thus, the modern theoretical characterization of gravitational waves had emerged by the late 1960s.

The last issue took still longer to be settled, since it crucially involved the problem of motion in general relativity and the issue of radiation reaction, whose foundations were still quite shaky.[51] The doubts concerning whether binary systems radiated gravitational energy were fought by crucial empirical input, which came in the mid-1970s with the discovery of the first binary neutron star.[52,53j] This did not immediately settle the quadrupole formula controversy yet,[54] but it prompted many efforts towards its resolution. The confirmation of came when Thibault Damour[55] showed that there was quantitative agreement between the emission rate computed from the quadrupole formula and observations. In fact, it is only in the final stages of the merging of compact objects that higher (mass and current) momenta need to be included (see e.g. Ref. 56 and references therein).

7. Conclusions

In the above pages, we have described the work performed by Richard Feynman in the physics of gravitational waves. We have seen how his attitude towards physics, and towards fundamental interactions, shaped this work, and how he managed to give sound and substantially correct answers to the main theoretical problems of the time. Feynman's physical intuition and sound calculations convinced him early on of the existence of gravitational waves and gravitational radiation. His work contributed to the settlement of the issue, and played a role in triggering the first experimental efforts towards their detection. Feynman did not share the theoretical concerns of most relativists, who continued to argue about other issues, until rigorous solutions and/or experimental input were available, and considered those arguments pointless, harshly criticizing them. This may have been contributed to his loss of interest in the subject, starting from the late 1960s, when he began to be involved to the only fundamental interaction to whose understanding he had not contributed yet, that is, the strong interaction.[5] But that is another story.

Acknowledgments

The authors would like to thank the staff of the Caltech archives for providing them a copy of Feynman's letter to Weisskopf.[9]

---

[j]In fact, so far, all direct and indirect evidence for gravitational waves has come from binary systems, which hence are the only confirmed sources.

References

1. R. P. Feynman, The development of the space-time view of quantum electrodynamics, *Science* **153**, no. 3737, 699 (1966).
2. M. Gell-Mann, Dick Feynman-The Guy in the Office Down the Hall, *Phys. Today* **42**, 50 (1989).
3. Letter from Bryce DeWitt to Agnew Bahnson, dated 15 November 1955, cited in Ref. 4, p. 25.
4. C. DeWitt-Morette and D. Rickles, *The Role of Gravitation in Physics*, Report from the 1957 Chapel Hill Conference (Edition Open Access, Berlin, 2011).
5. J. Mehra, *The Beat of a different drum: The Life and science of Richard Feynman*, (Oxford University Press, Oxford, 1994).
6. J. Preskill and K. S. Thorne, Foreword to Ref. 7.
7. R. P. Feynman, F. B. Morinigo, W. G. Wagner and B. Hatfield, *Feynman Lectures on Gravitation*, (Addison-Wesley, Reading, MA, 1995).
8. M. Di Mauro, S. Esposito and A. Naddeo, A road map for Feynman's adventures in the land of gravitation, *Eur. Phys. J. H* **46**, no.1, 22 (2021), [arXiv:2102.11220 [physics.hist-ph]].
9. R. P. Feynman, unpublished letter to Victor F. Weisskopf, February 1961; in Richard P. Feynman Papers, California Institute of Technology Archives, Box 3, Folder 8.
10. D. Kennefick, *Traveling at the speed of thought: Einstein and the quest for gravitational waves* (Princeton University Press, Princeton, 2007).
11. K. Schwarzschild, Über das Gravitationsfeld eines Massenpunktes nach der Einsteinschen Theorie (On the gravitational field of a mass point according to Einstein's theory), *Sitzungsber. Preuss. Akad. Wiss. Berlin (Math. Phys.)*, **1916**, 189 (1916), [arXiv:physics/9905030 [physics]].
12. M. D. Kruskal, Maximal extension of Schwarzschild metric, *Phys. Rev.* **119** (1960), 1743-1745.
13. A. Einstein, Näherungsweise Integration der Feldgleichungen der Gravitation (Approximate Integration of the Field Equations of Gravitation), *Sitzungsber. Preuss. Akad. Wiss. Berlin (Math. Phys.)* **1916**, 688 (1916).
14. A. Einstein, Die Feldgleichungen der Gravitation (The Field Equations of Gravitation), *Sitzungsber. Preuss. Akad. Wiss. Berlin (Math. Phys.)* **1915**, 844 (1915).
15. A. Einstein, Über Gravitationswellen (On Gravitational Waves), *Sitzungsber. Preuss. Akad. Wiss. Berlin (Math. Phys.)* **1918**, 154 (1918).
16. A. S. Eddington, The propagation of gravitational waves, *Proc. Roy. Soc. Lond.* A **102**, 268 (1922).
17. A. S. Eddington, *The Mathematical Theory of Relativity*, 2nd edn. (Cambridge University Press, Cambridge, 1960).
18. A. Einstein and N. Rosen, On Gravitational waves, *J. Frank. Inst.* **223**, 43 (1937).
19. A. Einstein and M. Born, *The Born-Einstein Letters: Friendship, Politics, and Physics in Uncertain Times* (MacMillan, New York, 2005).
20. D. Kennefick, Einstein versus the *Physical Review*, Physics Today **58**, 9, 43 (2005).
21. G. Beck, Zur Theorie binärer Gravitationsfelder (The Theory of binary gravitational fields), *Z. Phys.* **33**, 713 (1925).
22. A. Mercier and M. Kervaire (eds.), *Fünfzig Jahre Relativitätstheorie* (Birkhäuser, Basel, 1956).
23. F. A. E. Pirani, On the Physical significance of the Riemann tensor, *Acta Phys. Pol.* **15**, 389 (1956), reprinted in *Gen. Rel. Grav.* **41**, 1215 (2009).
24. F. A. E. Pirani, Invariant formulation of gravitational radiation theory, *Phys. Rev.* **105**, 1089 (1957).

25. J. L. Synge, On the deviation of geodesics and null-geodesics, particularly in relation to the properties of spaces of constant curvature and indefinite line-element, *Annals Math.* **35**, 705 (1934).
26. A. Z. Petrov, Klassifikacya prostranstv opredelyayushchikh polya tyagoteniya, *Uch. Zapiski Kazan. Gos. Univ.* **114 (8)**, 55 (1954) English translation: Classification of spaces defined by gravitational fields, *Gen. Rel. Grav.* **32 (8)**, 1665 (2000).
27. L. D. Landau and E. M. Lifshitz, *The Classical Theory of Fields,* first English edition, Addison-Wesley, Cambridge, 1951.
28. J. Eisenstaedt, La relativité générale à l'étiage: 1925-1955, *Arch. Hist. Exact Sci.* **35**, 115 (1986).
29. J. Eisenstaedt, Trajectoires et impasses de la solution de Schwarzschild, *Arch. Hist. Exact Sci.* **37**, 275 (1987).
30. J. Eisenstaedt, The low water mark of general relativity, 1925-1955, in D. Howard, J. Stachel (eds.), *Einstein and the History of General Relativity*, (Birkhäuser, Basel, 1989), pp. 277-292.
31. C. M. Will, *Was Einstein Right? Putting General Relativity to the Test*, (Oxford University Press, Oxford, 1986).
32. C. M. Will, *The renaissance of general relativity*, in P. C. W. Davies (ed.), *The New Physics*, (Cambridge University Press, Cambridge, 1989).
33. A. S. Blum, R. Lalli and J. Renn, *The Renaissance of General Relativity in Context*, *Einstein Studies* **16** (Birkhäuser, Cham, 2020).
34. H. D. Zeh, Feynman's interpretation of quantum theory, *Eur. Phys. J. H* **36**, 63 (2011).
35. R. P. Feynman, *Surely You're Joking, Mr. Feynman! - Adventures of a curious character* (W.W. Norton & Co., New York, 1985).
36. W. R. Frazer, Theory of Weak and Strong Interactions, *Phys. Tod.* **14**(12), 80 (1961).
37. M. P. Bronstein, Quantentheories schwacher Gravitationsfeldern (Quantum theory of weak gravitational fields), *Physikalische Zeitschrift der Sowietunion* **9**, 140 (1936), English translation by M. A. Kurkov, edited by S. Deser, *Gen. Relativ. Grav.* **44**, 267 (2012).
38. R. P. Feynman, *Electrostatics, Electrodynamics, Matter-Waves Interacting, Relativity*, lectures at the Hughes Aircraft Company, Notes taken and transcribed by J. T. Neer, 1967-68.
39. H. Bondi, Plane gravitational waves in general relativity, *Nature* **179**, 1072 (1957).
40. J. Weber, Detection and Generation of Gravitational Waves, *Phys. Rev.* **117**, 306 (1960).
41. J. Weber, Observation of the Thermal Fluctuations of a Gravitational-Wave Detector, *Phys. Rev. Lett.* **17**, 1228 (1966).
42. J. Weber, Evidence for discovery of gravitational radiation, *Phys. Rev. Lett.* **22**, 1320 (1969).
43. B. P. Abbott et al. [LIGO Scientific and Virgo], Observation of Gravitational Waves from a Binary Black Hole Merger, *Phys. Rev. Lett.* **116**, 061102 (2016) [arXiv:1602.03837 [gr-qc]].
44. B. P. Abbott et al. [LIGO Scientific, Virgo, Fermi-GBM and INTEGRAL], Gravitational Waves and Gamma-rays from a Binary Neutron Star Merger: GW170817 and GRB 170817A, *Astrophys. J. Lett.* **848**, L13 (2017), [arXiv:1710.05834 [astro-ph.HE]].
45. I. Robinson and A. Trautman, Spherical Gravitational Waves, *Phys. Rev. Lett.* **4**, 431 (1960).
46. H. Bondi, M. G. J. van der Burg and A. W. K. Metzner, Gravitational waves in general relativity. 7. Waves from axisymmetric isolated systems, *Proc. Roy. Soc. Lond. A* **269**, 21 (1962).

47. R. K. Sachs, Gravitational waves in general relativity. 8. Waves in asymptotically flat space-times, *Proc. Roy. Soc. Lond. A* **270**, 103 (1962).
48. R. K. Sachs, Gravitational radiation, In *Relativity, Groups and Topology*, C. DeWitt and B. S. DeWitt eds. (Gordon and Breach, New York, 1964) pp. 521-562.
49. E. Newman and R. Penrose, An Approach to gravitational radiation by a method of spin coefficients, *J. Math. Phys.* **3**, 566 (1962).
50. R. Penrose, Zero rest mass fields including gravitation: Asymptotic behavior, *Proc. Roy. Soc. Lond. A* **284**, 159 (1965).
51. J. Ehlers, A. Rosenblum, J. N. Goldberg and P. Havas, Comments on Gravitational Radiation Damping and Energy Loss in Binary Systems, *Astrophys. J. Lett.* **208**, L77 (1976).
52. R. A. Hulse and J. H. Taylor, Discovery of a pulsar in a binary system, *Astrophys. J. Lett.* **195**, L51 (1975).
53. J. Taylor, L. Fowler, P. McCulloch, Measurements of general relativistic effects in the binary pulsar PSR1913 + 16. *Nature* **277**, 437 (1979).
54. D. Kennefick, The binary pulsar and the quadrupole formula controversy, *Eur. Phys. J. H* **42** (2017) no.2, 293-310.
55. T. Damour, Gravitational radiation reaction in the binary pulsar and the quadrupole formula controversy, *Phys. Rev. Lett.* **51**, 1019 (1983).
56. L. Blanchet, Gravitational Radiation from Post-Newtonian Sources and Inspiralling Compact Binaries, *Living Rev. Rel.* **17**, 2 (2014), [arXiv:1310.1528 [gr-qc]].

Stellar gravitational collapse, singularity formation and theory breakdown

Kiril Maltsev

Heidelberg Institute for Theoretical Studies,
Schloss-Wolfsbrunnenweg 35, 69118 Heidelberg, Germany
E-mail: kiril-maltsev@h-its.org
www.h-its.org

Department of Physics and Astronomy, University of Heidelberg,
Im Neuenheimer Feld 226, 69120 Heidelberg, Germany
www.uni-heidelberg.de

We review three definitions (missing point(s) unsteadiness, infinite quadratic curvature invariant, and geodesic incompleteness) of what a gravitational singularity is, and argue that prediction of a gravitational singularity is problematic for General Relativity (GR), indicating breakdown of Lorentzian geometry, only insofar as it concerns the infinite curvature singularity characterization. In contrast, the geodesic incompleteness characterization is GR's innovating hallmark, which is not meaningfully available in Newtonian gravity formulations (locally infinite density field, and locally infinite gravitational force) of what a gravitational singularity is. It is the continuous, non-quantized, nature of Lorentzian geometry which admits gravitational contraction be continued indefinitely. The Oppenheimer-Snyder 1939 analytical solution derives formation of a locally infinite curvature singularity *and* of incomplete geodesics, while Penrose's 1965 theorem concerns formation of incomplete (null) geodesics only. We critically examine the main physical arguments against gravitational singularity formation in stellar collapse, with scope restriction to decades spanning in between Schwarzschild's 1916 solution and Penrose's 1965 singularity theorem. As the most robust curvature singularity formation counter-argument, we assess Markov's derivation of an upper bound on the quadratic curvature invariant $R_{\mu\nu\lambda\delta}R^{\mu\nu\lambda\delta} \leq \frac{1}{\ell_P^4}$ from a ratio of natural constants $\hbar$, c and G, in connection with Wheeler's grounding of the premise that the Planck scale ℓ_P is ultimate.

Keywords: Geodesic incompleteness; Infinite curvature; Schwarzschild incompressible fluid; Einstein-Rosen bridge; ISCO; Chandrasekhar mass; TOV mass; Core collapse; Compact stars; Oppenheimer-Snyder collapse; Singularity theorems; Curvature bound; Theory breakdown.

1. Characterization of a gravitational singularity

Over the period of over hundred years, the idea that gravitational singularity formation, predicted by General Relativity, is physical - representing a genuine feature of reality - was iteratively regarded with skepticism. The scientific community's doubts at times were based on mere conceptual reservation and reluctance to accept a novel paradigm, while at other times had justification by strong physical argument. In Sec. (1), we will outline how (not) to conceive what a gravitational singularity in General Relativity is, and compare two contrasting interpretational views: realism and anti-realism about singularity formation. We will provide a simple field-theoretical argument in favour of the interpretation of the prediction of curvature divergence as an indication of theory breakdown in Sec. (1.3). The goal of the subsequent Sections (2) and (3) is to explore some of the main arguments that have historically (with a scope restriction to 1916-1965) been advocated as preclusions to gravitational singularity formation in stellar collapse, and to assess their relevance for the present.

1.1. *Coordinate vs. geometric singularity*

A first important propaedeutic worth a recall is the demarcation between a coordinate singularity and a geometric singularity. Let $(\mathcal{M}, g_{\mu\nu})$ be an ordered pair, with $\mathcal{M}$ a manifold, associated with a spacetime, and $g_{\mu\nu}$ a Lorentzian metric with signature $(-, +, +, +)$, defined on the manifold $\mathcal{M}$ and associated with geometric properties of the spacetime. A coordinate singularity indicates the limit of applicability of a coordinate chart to represent a metric tensor $g_{\mu\nu}$. The line element $(ds^2 = g_{\mu\nu}\,dx^\mu\,dx^\nu)$ of the single-parameter (M, associated with mass) Schwarzschild metric in the Schwarzschild spherical coordinate chart $(x^0, x^1, x^2, x^3) = (ct, r, \theta, \phi)$ reads

$$ds^2 = -\left(1 - \frac{2GM}{r}\right) dt^2 + \left(1 - \frac{2GM}{r}\right)^{-1} dr^2 + r^2 g_\Omega. \tag{1}$$

As $r \to 2GM$, the radial component $g_{rr} \to \infty$ while the temporal component $g_{tt} \to 0$. Yet, the Gullstrand-Painlevé, the Kruskal-Szekeres and the Eddington-Finkelstein coordinates are examples of coordinate systems for which the Schwarzschild metric, when transformed onto another coordinate chart $(ds'^2 = g'_{\mu\nu}\,dx'^\mu\,dx'^\nu)$, is regular at the Schwarzschild boundary (which, in Schwarzschild coordinates, locates at the $r = 2GM$ two-sphere) of the set of nested round spheres. To illustrate, the line element in Eddington-Finkelstein coordinates (v, r, θ, ϕ) reads

$$ds^2 = -\left(1 - \frac{2GM}{r}\right) dv^2 \pm 2\,dv\,dr + r^2 g_\Omega \tag{2}$$

where a tortoise coordinate $r^* = r + 2GM\,ln|\frac{r}{2GM} - 1|$ is introduced, satisfying $\frac{dr^*}{dr} = \left(1 - \frac{2GM}{r}\right)^{-1}$, to define the time-advanced ingoing (for $v = t + r^*$) and time-retarded outgoing (for $v = t - r^*$) coordinates, respectively. Representation of the Schwarzschild metric in Eddington-Finkelstein coordinates shows curves to be extendible beyond the Schwarzschild boundary. According to the Principle of General Covariance, coordinate systems play no role in the formulation of fundamental laws of physics; they only have a descriptive-representational role. No observer, and therefore no coordinate system is privileged over another, yet the capability of physical representation by one coordinate chart may break down while others do not: an illucidating GR-independent example is the failure of representation of the North (at $\theta = 0$) and of the South Pole (at $\theta = \pi$) by spherical coordinates, while their representation is regular in cartesian coordinates. In GR, changing a coordinate chart implies a re-definition of the coordinate axes relative to a proper inertial frame. While the introduction of a new coordinate chart allows to transform away the apparent singularity at the Schwarzschild boundary $r = 2GM$, the central metric field irregularity at $r = 0$ persists in the maximally extended Schwarzschild spacetime. The Kretschmann scalar curvature invariant is a coordinate-independent measure that allows to identify a curvature singularity in the geometry of the metric field. It is defined as full contraction of the Riemann tensor with itself, summing over all of its components:

$$K = R_{\mu\nu\lambda\rho}R^{\mu\nu\lambda\rho}. \qquad (3)$$

Its evaluation on the Schwarzschild metric yields $K = \frac{48G^2M^2}{r^6}$, which is finite at the Schwarzschild boundary $r = 2GM$, but divergent at $r = 0$.

1.2. Missing point(s) unsteadiness, infinite quadratic curvature invariant, or geodesic incompleteness?

Calculation of the Kretschmann scalar is one method to tell apart a genuine singularity in the geometry of the metric field from a mere coordinate singularity pertinent to a coordinate representation of the metric. There has, however, been debate over what the appropriate definition of a gravitational singularity is, which appropriately characterizes it physically. In particular, as summarized and cross-examined in Ref. 1, three different main conceptions (all of which have sub-classes) have been proposed:

(1) missing point(s) unsteadiness,
(2) infinite curvature, and
(3) path inextendibility.

Missing point(s) unsteadiness. The conception that a gravitational singularity is a missing point, or a set of missing points, on the spacetime manifold, suggests that a spacetime is singular if it contains a 'hole'.[2] Then, the metric field $g_{\mu\nu}$ is discontinuous at a point $p \notin \mathcal{M}$ or a set of points $\{p_i\} \notin \mathcal{M}$, which have been removed from the $\mathcal{M}$ spacetime manifold, akin to a tear in a piece of cloth. Conceptually, a missing point on the spacetime manifold suggests the absence of spacetime itself at that point. The motivation for this singularity characterization stems from the fact that derivative operators, such as the Riemann tensor, are locally ill-defined at points at which the metric field $g_{\mu\nu}$ is discontinuous - at points that lie outside of its domain. The demand that the metric is continuous and differentiable everywhere formalizes into the requirement of non-degeneracy: $det(g_{\mu\nu}) \neq 0$. The condition is fulfilled if all the components of both the covariant $(g_{\mu\nu})$ and the contravariant $(g^{\mu\nu})$ metric tensor are regular. Then, a (removable) gravitational singularity violates the steadiness condition for any choice of coordinate chart: the missing point, or points, on the spacetime manifold give rise to the impossibility of its smooth local extension, and thereby to unsteadiness in the gravitational field. This historically original notion of a gravitational singularity has been deployed in the works of Schwarzschild, Einstein, Hilbert, and contemporaries.

The missing point(s) singularity definition suggests that the singular spacetime manifold could be 'patched' by the appendage of the boundary that embeds the singularity. The main burden to accepting this notion of singularity is that the boundary construction in the neighbourhood of the singularity turns into the location problem[1]: there is no Lorentz-covariant location of the missing point(s) on the spacetime manifold, which would be coordinate- and therefore observer-independent. Assuming that there are no more additional dimensions to the spacetime, there is no way of imagining it being embedded in a larger topological space, with respect to which one could identify the locations of the subspace point(s) to be missing out.

Infinite quadratic curvature invariant. There are many sub-classes to definitions of a gravitational singularity in terms of an infinite curvature pathology. They differ in choice of the curvature tensor and of the divergence criterion. One of the curvature singularity classes is identified by the Kretschmann scalar, a quadratic curvature invariant defined with the Riemann tensor. It is used as an indicator of the presence of a local curvature singularity, when $K \to \infty$. A local observer is then subject to tidal forces that arise from the differences in "strength" of the gravitational field between two neighbouring points in space-time, and the curvature singularity manifests in its growth without bound. However, a well-behaved quadratic curvature invariant does not imply that all other local curvature measures are regular: there are examples of space-times where the quadratic Riemann curvature invariants are vanishing but the Ricci curvature tensor $R_{\mu\nu}$ diverges.[3] Again others, such as the conformal Misner singularities, where curvature scalars are well-behaved but the Riemann tensor evaluated with some local tetrad is divergent. Yet the advantage of curvature tensor *products* over curvature tensors is the former's coordinate-independence.

A problem with a local curvature singularity characterization, even if defined by virtue of curvature tensor products, is that it is incomplete: there are examples of well-defined space-times in which the state of motion of the observer is decisive in determining the physical response, as the putative singularity is traversed: whether or not an object is rotating about its axis, or subject to proper acceleration in the direction of motion, determines whether the object gets torn into pieces by infinite tidal forces, or whether it survives the cross-over.[4] In the latter example, the curvature pathology arises for a non-rotating observer resting on a geodesic, and an improved local gravitational singularity definition needs be reformulated accordingly. However, even this extension of the singularity definition is insufficiently precise, given a number of counter-examples: a point in spacetime may be well-defined for an observer travelling on a complete geodesic and experiencing well-behaved tidal forces all the way along, while this same point exhibits a curvature pathology for an observer travelling on an incomplete geodesic.[3] Finally, therefore, the most general gravitational singularity definition that aims to invoke a locally infinite curvature invariant needs to confess that the curvature pathology arises locally along a curve that is incomplete. This raises the question whether infinite curvature is even a necessary feature of a gravitational singularity, rather than an inessential singularity property, since the formation of an incomplete path may entail but does not require a curvature pathology. The relation between curvature divergence and geodesic incompleteness remains a delicate problem that still seeks its resolution in Lorentzian differential geometry, but for which there seem to be two options:

(1) a gravitational singularity is defined by geodesic incompleness (or, more generally, path inextendibility) alone. It does not imply divergence of any local curvature measure, which is an additional feature, realized in some singular spacetimes but not in others.
(2) a gravitational singularity is defined by geodesic incompleteness concurring with a locally divergent quadratic curvature invariant; curvature divergence endows geodesic incompleteness with a physical (and local) characterization.

Important conclusions can be drawn from comparison of the curvature singularity characterization in Einstein's gravity theory to the Newtonian gravity theory counterpart. The formulation of the Raychaudhuri-Komar singularity theorem[a] in the framework of Newton-Cartan gravity,[8] a geometrized tensor reformulation of Newtonian gravity theory suggests that

- in Newtonian gravity[b], curvature divergence (as measured by the geometrized Poisson equation $R_{\mu\nu}\xi^\mu\xi^\nu = 4\pi\rho$ where ξ^μ is an arbitrary time-like vector) arises as consequence of a locally (infinite density) pathology in the stress-energy field, which is source of the gravitational field, while

---

[a] The Raychaudhuri-Komar singularity theorem[5,6] predicts formation of an infinite matter density singularity from generic conditions. It applies to a perfect fluid (described by the stress-energy tensor in the form of eq. (11)), whose timelike ($u^\mu u_\mu = -1$) velocity field u^μ is geodesic and non-rotational. If the derivative of the divergence $\theta \equiv \nabla_\mu u^\mu$ along the geodesic congruence is positive (negative) at an instant of time and the convergence condition $R_{\rho\nu}u^\rho u^\nu \geq 0$ holds, then the energy density ρ of the fluid diverges in the infinite past (future) along every integral curve of u^μ. The above mentioned modern formulation of the theorem is taken from Ref. 7.

[b] The key difference is the following: while in Newtonian gravity a gravitational force field singularity may arise only as consequence of a pathological infinite energy density matter state, Einstein's gravity theory allows for formation of gravitational singularities in a vacuum ($T_{\mu\nu} = 0$), analytically as solutions to the vacuum Einstein Field Equations. A generic example is the collision of two plane gravitational waves ($R_{\mu\nu} = 0$) in an otherwise flat background. Tipler's general plane-wave singularity theorem[9] proves the collision spacetime be future null geodesically incomplete. In addition, in the collision region of the 'sandwiched' GWs, under certain conditions (which depend on polarization of the colliding GWs) a curvature singularity may form at the focused point, or a coordinate singularity instead, along with a Killing-Cauchy horizon.[10–12]

- geodesic incompleteness is a pathology in the gravitational field itself, independent of pathology or non-pathology of a matter state. This singularity characterization is not meaningfully available in Newtonian gravity theory.[c]

This distinction reminds of the interest to enquire not only about how a singularity is defined, but also how it is generically formed under physical conditions.

Geodesic incompleteness. The definition of a gravitational singularity in terms of geodesic incompleteness is the least problematic and most widely accepted singularity characterization. In contrast to a complete geodesic that is continued indefinitely, an incomplete path has a finite affine length parameter (which is proper time τ, for a time-like vector field). One of the ways to formalize geodesic completeness reads as follows:

A spacetime is singular if it contains an incomplete causal geodesic γ : $[0, a) \to \mathcal{M}$ such that there is no extension $\gamma' : \mathcal{M} \to \mathcal{M}'$ for which $\gamma' \circ \gamma$ is extendible.[13]

The demand for unique geodesics that do not cross implies that the causal geodesic is not well-defined beyond the affine length a, at which the affine parameter converges. A relativistic spacetime $(\mathcal{M}, g_{\mu\nu})$ is timelike ($\gamma^\mu \gamma_\mu = -1$), null ($\gamma^\mu \gamma_\mu = 0$), or spacelike ($\gamma^\mu \gamma_\mu = +1$) geodesically incomplete if it entails an incomplete timelike, null, or spacelike geodesic, respectively. The example of the Taub-NUT space-time shows that a space-time can be time-like complete but null-incomplete, and vice versa.[14] Geodesic incompleteness implies that the worldline of a freely falling observer terminates, with no possibility of further extension.[d] A background presupposition of path inextendibility is that the spacetime in the theory is *maximally extended* and that it does not form a subset of a larger dimensional, more extensive geometry into which the manifold (e.g., a four-dimensional spacetime) is embedded.

1.3. Theory breakdown?

Singularity realism vs. anti-realism. The above mentioned three gravitational singularity definitions in General Relativity are conceptually quite distinct pathologies in the geometry of the gravitational field, and do not imply one another: missing point(s) unsteadiness singularity suggests the (local) absence of spacetime itself,

---

[c]See Ref. 8 for an opposing view. According to our assessment, the author confounds the geodesic incompleteness characterization of a gravitational singularity in Newton-Cartan gravity with that of the missing point(s) unsteadiness.

[d]In Refs. 1, 15, 16 a more inclusive *b-incompleteness* criterion is advocated as gravitational singularity definition. According to b-incompleteness, the inextendible path can but does not need be a geodesic: A maximal spacetime is singular if and only if it contains an inextendible path of a generalized affine length. Since every incomplete geodesic is b-incomplete, the geodesic incompleteness characterization is sufficient for the argument of this paper.

while an infinite quadratic curvature invariant suggests that tidal forces become infinite at a point in space-time, which itself may be well-defined on the manifold. Geodesic incompleteness suggests the finitude of worldlines in a spacetime, which nevertheless may be well-defined and endowed with well-behaved finite quadratic curvature invariants at any point on the manifold.

The predictions of gravitational singularities by General Relativity can, for each of the singularity classes separately, be physically interpreted in one of the two ways: either as

(1) a theory deficiency, or as
(2) opening up a profoundly novel viewpoint of properties of space-time geometry.

The stance of singularity realism is supported by arguments such as the empirical success of General Relativity as the predictive theory, and the reasoning that the prediction of -say- geodesic incompleteness does not prima facie logically imply any contradiction or internal inconsistency within the gravitation theory. The realist stance is also inclined to accept a gravitational collapse singularity as part of the definition of a Black Hole.

In contrast, the stance of singularity anti-realism is supported by lessons learnt from the pre-history of radical theory changes in physics, which teach us to only partially confess to the belief in some statements made by the current best physical theory, but not in others. Of particular concern are the prior experiences with singularities, in ray optics, in phase transition hydrodynamics, in Newtonian N-body gravitational dynamics, in Maxwellian electromagnetism and in other subfields of physics[e], all of which nail down the appearance of a *divergent quantity* as an artifact of the mathematical model that is deployed. Anti-realism about gravitational singularities in GR is supported by the mathematical ill-definition and non-differentiability of geometrical quantities, as far as the infinite curvature characterization is concerned. The relevance of the argument is demonstrated below upon the example of the electromagnetic interaction potential between two fermionic charges.

Theory change: The case of Electromagnetism. In classical electromagnetism, the Coulomb potential between two point masses carrying electromagnetic charges q_1 and q_2 reads

$$V(r) = -\frac{1}{4\pi\epsilon}\frac{q_1 q_2}{r}, \qquad (4)$$

where r is the relative distance between the point masses. For vanishing distance $r \to 0$, the interaction potential $V(r)$ diverges. The physics of the electromagnetic interaction is, however, inappropriately described by the classical Maxwellian field theory at small relative distances at scale of order of magnitude of the de Broglie wavelengths of the charged particles. Here, effects of their quantum nature become non-negligible, and Quantum Electrodynamics takes over as descriptive theory

---

[e]See Ref. 19 for a brief discussion of some of the above mentioned examples.

instead: the basic interaction potential between two fermion charges Q_1 and Q_2 in Minkowski space-time $\eta_{\mu\nu}$ and the relative wave-vector **k** turns into the integral

$$V(r) = -\frac{-g^2\hbar c Q_1 Q_2}{4\pi} \frac{1}{(2\pi)^3} \int d^3k \, e^{\frac{i\mathbf{k}\cdot\mathbf{r}}{\hbar}} \frac{4\pi\eta_{\mu\nu}}{k^2}. \quad (5)$$

The upshot from this comparison is that the prediction of a singularity qua divergency in the interaction potential marks the limits of an empirically adequate applicability of a theory: it arises as an artifact of the theory description at coarse-grained scale. Similarly, General Relativity is a classical field theory that describes the phenomenology of gravitation at a macroscopic scale at which principles of classical physics apply. However, gravitational collapse - which is central subject of this work- involves processes in the strong gravity regime at microscopic scales $\delta r \to 0$, at which GR is not tested as gravitation theory, and hence lacks the basis for trust in its predictions.

2. Singularities in the interior Schwarzschild metric (1916–1939)

2.1. *Schwarzschild's incompressible fluid model, and Einstein's singularity resolution attempts*

Infinite pressure requirement. In his first 1916 paper,[20] Schwarzschild derives an analytical solution to the gravitational field *exterior* to a gravitating point mass, completing earlier work of approximated solutions found by Einstein. Eq. (1) is a simplified writing of the metric due to Droste[21] who found the same solution independently, that renounces from redundant variable transformations, and where the radial coordinate r is defined as a radial measure away[f] from the point mass M. In contrast, in his second 1916 publication[22] he calculates[g] the gravitational field *inside and outside* of, not a point mass, but of a static non-rotating spherically symmetric incompressible fluid. The externally measured radius of the fluid sphere is given by $P_a = \sqrt{\frac{3}{\varkappa\rho_0}} \sin\chi_a$, and internal properties of the fluid are supposed to give rise to an inner pressure source $P(r)$. In order to calculate the pressure distribution, Schwarzschild proceeds by imposing a Hydrostatic Equilibrium (HE) condition and the vanishing pressure boundary condition $P(P_a) = 0$ onto the fluid. From there, he finds an analytic expression to the pressure gradient $P(\chi) = \rho_0 \left(\frac{2\cos\chi_a}{3\cos\chi_a - \cos\chi} - 1\right)$ be proportional to the density and to $v = \frac{2}{3\cos\chi_a - \cos\chi}$ which Schwarzschild refers

---

[f] Note that a covariant measure of spatial distance between two nested spheres at r_1 and r_2 is obtained from the proper distance $\varrho = \int_{r_1}^{r_2} dr \sqrt{g_{rr}}$.

[g] The line element of the interior Schwarzschild solution in the original coordinates used by Schwarzschild takes the non-trivial form:

$$ds^2 = \left(\frac{3\cos\chi_a - \cos\chi}{2}\right)^2 dt^2 - \frac{3}{\varkappa\rho_0}(\chi^2 + \sin^2 d\theta^2 + \sin^2\chi \sin^2 d\theta \, d\phi^2). \quad (6)$$

Schwarzschild derives a metric with two independent parameters (χ_a and ρ_0) associated with internally measured radius and density of the incompressible fluid, respectively. Here, $\varkappa = 8\pi k^2$ where k is the Gaussian gravitation constant.

to as the *"naturally measured light velocity"*.[22] After a critical matter concentration threshold[h] is surpassed, v, and thereby also the pressure, diverge at the center ($\chi = 0$). There, the gravitational field becomes infinite, and introduces a discontinuity into metric $g_{\mu\nu}$. From his calculation follows the requirement of an infinite pressure at the center of the sphere in order to maintain its HE, which he evaluates as physically unacceptable, and as a breakdown of the incompressible constant density fluid model. He summarizes his finding as follows:[i]

> *"In the center of the sphere ($\chi = 0$) the speed of light and pressure become infinite, as soon as $\cos \chi_a = 1/3$, and as the fall velocity has become equal to $\sqrt{8/9}$ of the (naturally measured) speed of light. Therewith a limit of concentration is given, beyond which the sphere of incompressible fluid may not exist. Applying our equations to $\cos \chi_a < 1/3$, one would obtain unsteadiness already above the center of the sphere [...]. Over these solutions, which indeed are physically meaningless, since they result in infinite pressure in the center, one can pass over to the limiting case of a mass concentrated at a point [...]. For an externally measuring observer follows (...) that the sphere of given gravitational mass $\alpha/2k^2$ may have no smaller externally measured radius than $P_a = \alpha$."*[22]

The Newtonian central singularity counterpart, and pragmatism on the "impassible barrier". In Droste's coordinates, Schwarzschild's analytical 1916 solution entailed the prediction of two irregularities: the central singularity at the center of the incompressible fluid sphere ($r = 0$), and at the Schwarzschild coordinate singularity at $r_S = 2GM$ - above the center of the sphere but beneath the internal radius of the incompressible fluid. Both irregularities were perceived as troublesome by contemporaries, however, the Schwarzschild singularity has historically been assessed as the major problem. Coordinate transformations of the type of eq. (2) to eliminate the unsteadiness at the Schwarzschild surface have been under development, yet their significance was not fully clarified until the work of Lemaitre (1932); but various other considerations of how to handle with the prediction of irregularities in the metric field were brought forward instead. The central $r = 0$ singularity has likely not been considered as a threat to General Relativity for the reason that it already occurred in the gravitational potential $\phi(r) = -\frac{GMm}{r}$ between two gravitating point masses M and m in Newtonian gravity. The Schwarzschild singularity, however, was novel and predicted to occur in the deep interior of stars that soon were modelled by Schwarzschild's ideal fluid ansatz: for instance, the Schwarzschild radius of the Sun amounts to roughly

---

[h]The critical matter concentration threshold is obtained from applying the condition $\cos \chi_a = \frac{1}{3}$ to the externally measured radius $P_a = \sqrt{\frac{3}{\kappa \rho_0}} \sin \chi_a$, from which follows $P_a = \alpha$ for a point mass and $P_a = \frac{9}{8}\alpha$ for an incompressible fluid sphere. $\alpha/2k^2$ is the gravitational mass.
[i]Translation from the German original into English by the author K. M.

3 km, far below the Sun's radius of about 0.7 million km. Eddington called the Schwarzschild surface the *"magic circle"*, and conjectured that no particles inside a star may penetrate this *"impassible"*[2] barrier. Reason is that, as Droste remarked in Ref. 21, the penetration would take an infinitely long time ($g_{tt} \to 0$), or as Einstein put it, *"a clock kept at this place would go at the rate zero"*[23] but nothing could develop without time, according to this line of reasoning.

Observation of stars was at that time period based solely on their surface properties[j], and traced on the Hertzsprung-Russell diagram. Since the prediction of the Schwarzschild singularity thereby escaped any empirical test, the prevailing logical positivist attitude to science, which assumed that any empirically unverifiable statement is meaningless, is likely to have fostered a less concerned view of the Schwarzschild singularity: no stars had been known to have a physical radius smaller than $2GM$, thus the Schwarzschild singularity appeared tolerable so long as it did not produce any falsifiable predictions. Nevertheless, during the Paris conference (1922), Hadamard contemplated the possibility of the Schwarzschild surface surpassing the physical radius of a star. Einstein conceived this scenario as a threat to the theory of General Relativity, and aimed to disprove the possibility of the "Hadamard catastrophe" on physical grounds.

The innermost stable circular orbit. Einstein was guided by an understanding of Mach's principle as implying that the metric field is determined by its matter-energy content, for *"inertia originates in a kind of interaction between bodies"*.[24] Guided by Mach's principle, he interpreted a singularity in the gravitational field as an indication of a pathological matter state that gives rise to it. Hence, he aimed to prove that while stellar matter is source of the gravitational field, it is impossible to accumulate matter neither at their center of mass at $r = 0$, nor at the Schwarzschild surface $r = r_S$, where the singularities were supposed to arise. Then -according to his line of reasoning- irregularities in the metric field are unphysical, so long as they are not occupied by matter, which originates the properties of the gravitational field. In his 1939 paper, Einstein's goal was to demonstrate that this holds true in an allegedly more realistic model of stellar matter than Schwarzschild's perfect fluid ansatz. He starts the paper with an expansion of the argument brought forward by Schwarzschild himself, pointing at the inadequacy of incompressible fluid assumption:

> *"The concept of an incompressible liquid is not compatible with relativity theory as elastic waves would have to travel with infinite velocity. It would be necessary, therefore, to introduce a compressible liquid whose equation of state excludes the possibility of sound signals with a speed in excess of*

---

[j]Asteroseismology, the study of stellar interior structure through their global oscillation modes, which are excited in the interior and induce structural imprints onto photometric observables, had not yet been developed at that time.

the velocity of light. But the treatment of any such problem would be quite involved; besides, the choice of such an equation of state would be arbitrary within wide limits, and one could not be sure that thereby no assumptions have been made which contain physical impossibilities."[23]

Instead, Einstein proposes another model: a spherically symmetric self-gravitating many-body system composed of non-interacting point particles of equal unit mass. For this system, Einstein calculates the interior gravitational field and equations of motion, and finds the innermost stable circular orbit (ISCO) to lie above the Schwarzschild radius in GR, in contrast to the treatment of the same many-body system in Newtonian gravity, which does not yield any lower bound on the radius of the ISCO. Orbits of a radius tighter than the Schwarzschild radius, as he finds, require orbital velocities that exceed the speed of light, which is prohibited by the principles of relativity theory. From there, he concludes that the irregularities in the metric field at $r = r_S$ and at $r = 0$ are physically irrelevant, because these regions do not get populated by particles in the self-gravitating many-body system.

Einstein's calculations were correct and insightful in their own right, however he draw false conclusions from them. With his background premise that all test particle orbits always remain stable, he excluded possibility of unstable orbits, such as an inspiral. A more cautious conclusion would have been that there are no *stable* particle orbits within a certain distance away from the Schwarzschild radius. A spiral-like particle trajectory, of orbital velocity smaller than the speed of light yet beneath the innermost stable orbital radius, is not impeded from arising by Einstein's calculation: Einstein's calculation shows that an orbit radius lower than r_S cannot be circularly stable.

The Einstein-Rosen bridge. Einstein was even ready to sacrifice the original version of the gravitational field equations for the sake of doing away gravitational singularities in the Schwarzschild metric. At the same time, he was opportunist[25] about turning the prediction of field singularities into a solution to the problem of particle representation and of particle motion in General Relativity. With regard to the latter problem, he saw the logical independence of the geodesic law from the field equations as a weakness of GR. One of his approaches to a remedy was to derive the geodesic law from application of the covariant conservation law $\nabla_\nu T^{\mu\nu} = 0$ to the Einstein Field Equations (EFE) at the limiting case of matter-free space ($T^{\mu\nu} = 0$). From there would follow that, "*[i]f one assumes that matter is arranged in narrow 'world tubes', one obtains from this by an elementary consideration the theorem that the axes of those 'world tubes' are geodesic lines (in the absence of electromagnetic fields). This means: the law of motion is a consequence of the field law.*".[26] With regard to the former problem, Einstein assessed the representation of matter by the stress-energy tensor as phenomenological approximation, as a crude substitute of known (quantum) properties of matter. Instead, singularities in the gravitational field, seemingly problematic at first, opened up a novel approach to resolve another problem. His proposal was the representation of elementary particles by pole singularities in an empty gravitational field:

> "All attempts to represent matter by an energy-momentum tensor are unsatisfactory and we wish to free our theory from any particular choice of such a tensor. Therefore we shall deal here only with gravitational equations in empty space, and matter will be represented by singularities of the field."[27]

In this approach unifying particle representation and motion, particles in GR are represented by localized pole singularities in the metric fields $g_{\mu\nu}$, which outside the singularities are regular elsewhere and satisfy the source-free ($T_{\mu\nu} = 0$) EFE, while particle geodesics are represented as displacements of pole singularities in and by the gravitational field obeying the source-free EFE. This approach was a stepstone toward a unified field theory Einstein was questing for, yet Einstein presumed that the total field (obtained from what he refers to as the *"completed field equations"*), unifying the gravitational field and the matter field, would eliminate singularities:

> "[...] one will have to say that the field of a material particle may the less be viewed as a pure gravitational field the closer one comes to the position of the particle. If one had the field equation of the total field, one would be compelled to demand that the particle themselves would everywhere be describable as singularity free solutions of the completed field-equations."[28]

The prediction of singularities in solutions to the EFE fostered his view that GR is a preliminary, not the final field theory. The belief in the singularity representation of particles was further shaken Silberstein's argument[29] that, due to the existence of a *static* axisymmetric solution to the field equations representing two pole singularities, either the field equations are wrong, or the problem of motion cannot be treated with it, or particles cannot be represented as singularities. Reason is that the two particles so represented are, in Silberstein's construction, immobile and not accelerated in each other's gravitational field. Influenced by Silberstein's argument, in Einstein's 1935 paper with his student Rosen,[30] the authors present a formalism that casts the representation of a particle from the point mass singularity representation at the origin of the Schwarzschild metric onto a non-singular particle representation obtained from a topological bridge construction connecting two asymptotically flat regions of spacetime. To get there, Einstein and Rosen proceed by two essential steps. First, they modify the source-free EFE by transforming the Ricci tensor (which equals $R_{\mu\nu} = R^\lambda_{\mu\nu\lambda} = g^{\lambda\rho} R_{\rho\mu\nu\lambda} = 0$ in the source-free field) to the tensor density

$$R_{\mu\nu} \to R^*_{\mu\nu} = g^2 R_{\mu\nu} \qquad (7)$$

where g is the determinant of the metric field $g_{\mu\nu}$. The effect it had in their study of the flat Minkowski metric in Rindler coordinates is that the irregularity condition $g = 0$, since the new field equations have no denominators in g and do not result in 'divide by zero' divergences. Hence, Einstein & Rosen's move was to make the unsteadiness singularity condition $det(g_{\mu\nu}) = 0$ itself irrelevant, by the mutilation of the source-free field equations. Second, Einstein & Rosen perform a coordinate transformation, $u^2 = r - 2GM$, which shifts the Schwarzschild singularity down to the origin of the coordinate system, thereby transforming away the entire central region $r \in [0, 2GM[$ and, therewith, the central singularity. They interpret the line element ds^2 resulting from the spherically symmetric solution to the mutilated field equations as describing a spacetime with two congruent sheets (at $u < 0$, and at $u > 0$) cross-connected by a "bridge" at $u = 0$ (hence $r = 2GM$). Despite that g vanishes at the shifted $u = 0$ origin, the unsteadiness singularity condition is invalidated by the mutilated EFE for an empty gravitational field:

> "The whole field consists of two equal halves, separated by the surface of symmetry $x_1 = 0$, such that for the corresponding points (x_1, x_2, x_3, x_4) and $(-x_1, x_2, x_3, x_4)$ the g_{ik} are equal. As a result we find that, although we are permitting the determinant g to take the value 0 (for $x_1 = 0$), no change of sign of g and in general no change in the 'inertial index' of the quadratic form occurs."[30]

Electrically neutral[k] particles are henceforth described by topological ripples in the singularity-free solution of the new source-free field equations, for which the problem of particle representation and motion coincides. While the topological bridge construction extends the spacetime region from $u > 0$ onto another $u < 0$ (and vice versa), it has later shown to be non-traversable.[31] What remains problematic in the Einstein-Rosen argument is the assessment of whether a spacetime is singular or not in coordinates in which the Schwarzschild metric is not maximally extended. The maximally extended Schwarzschild metric is given by the Kruskal-Szekeres spacetime,[32] which analogously allows for a topological bridge construction connecting two spherically symmetric halves. However the crucial difference to the Einstein-Rosen calculation is that, in the Kruskal-Szekeres spacetime, the symmetric halves are glued together at the $r = 0$ line. In consequence, gravitational singularity formation is not avoided, since the Kretschmann scalar diverges at $r = 0$ in the maximally extended Kruskal-Szekeres spacetime.

---

[k] The authors move on to consider the case of a charged particle. To account for the electromagnetic charge, they solve the mutilated field equations with a $T^{\mu\nu}$ source term that represents the Maxwell electromagnetic field. Here they introduce a second modification to the EFE, consisting in the change of sign (from positive to negative) of the stress-energy tensor $T^{\mu\nu}$ on the right-hand side of the EFE for the sake of again obtaining the topological bridge as solution to the metric field from the unified treatment of gravitation and electromagnetism. The change of sign, on the other hand, forces Einstein & Rosen to concede the possibility of negative stress-energy.[25]

2.2. Chandrasekhar's mass limit vs. Eddington's equilibrium hypothesis

In 1926 Eddington published seminal work[33] on the theory of internal structure, energy generation, radiation transfer and evolution of stars, which remained the primary source of reference for generations of astrophysicists (although the process of nuclear fusion as the dominant supply source of stellar inner energy was not clarified until work of Bethe & Bloch (1939)). Henceforth, the scientific community was equipped with more realistic models of stellar matter, which allowed to address the *astrophysical* viability of the prediction of gravitational singularities in stars modelled by the Schwarzschild ideal hydrodynamics ansatz. The 'standard model' of stellar structure assumed contributions to the Equation of State (EOS) $P = P(\rho, T)$ from classical ideal gas pressure $P \propto \rho T$ and from the Stefan-Boltzmann law of black body radiation pressure $P \propto T^4$ as the main pressure sources that counterbalance gravitational contraction of the star and maintain HE of the perfect fluid in its interior. This 'standard model' was an adequate approximation for most types of observed stars, but not for the faint White Dwarf stars. Based on comparison of observed stellar bolometric luminosity and total mass tuples, Milne (1930) suggested that in order for a steady equilibrium state to always hold, the classical ideal gas law must break down beyond a critical core luminosity L_c, at which he argued that the matter configuration in the White Dwarf star must condense to a quantum degenerate gas.[34]

Breakdown of the (polytropic) Equation of State. Chandrasekhar's achievement consisted in the calculation of an upper mass limit[35, 36] for mechanical stability of an electron degenerate White Dwarf star, beyond which the Pauli pressure of electrons is not sufficent to counterbalance collapse of the star under the weight of the nuclei it is composed of. In his calculation, Chandrasekhar models the electrons by a quantum ideal Fermi gas, which respect the Pauli Exclusion Principle (a maximum of two electrons, with anti-aligned spins in the 'up' and 'down' states, are allowed to occupy the same classical phase space cell) and whose energy levels are occupied up to the Fermi energy maximum according to Fermi-Dirac quantum statistics. The Pauli degeneracy pressure relates to electron density ρ_e by the polytropic EOS law $P(r) = K\rho(r)^\gamma$, which is independent of temperature, and where the adiabatic index equals $\gamma = 5/3$ (non-relativistic degeneracy) or $\gamma = 4/3$ (special relativistic degeneracy). The electron density itself is dependent on nuclear composition and density of the White Dwarf, and the parameter K takes this into account. Chandrasekhar works with a simple White Dwarf model composed solely of protons and electrons. In a Newtonian gravity treatment, Chandrasekhar proceeds by imposing the HE condition

$$\frac{dP(r)}{dr} = -\frac{Gm(r)}{r^2}\rho(r) \qquad (8)$$

where $m(r)$ is the shell mass up to radius r, obtained from the volume integral over the total density profile $\rho(r)$. He further assumes that the density distribution peaks in the center ($r = 0$) of the White Dwarf. From there he follows that there is an upper limit to total mass M, for any given density gradient $\rho(r)$, at which electron degeneracy pressure is still sufficient to maintain HE. As the star contracts under its own gravity, electrons need to speed up in their motion in order to retain the necessary phase space volume that is required to accomodate all of the electron states in accord with the Pauli principle. He finds that, as *all* the electrons inside the White Dwarf attain relativistic degeneracy, the polytropic index (and thereby also the pressure) decreases, and at a critical Chandrasekhar mass (which, in general, depends on nuclear composition of the star, and for which the solar mass unit $\odot$ is commonly used) the internal radius of the White Dwarf tends to zero:

> "*We are bound to assume therefore that a state must come beyond which the equation of state (...) is not valid, for otherwise we are led to the physically inconceivable result that for $M = 0.92 \odot \beta^{-\frac{3}{2}}, r_1 = 0$, and $\rho = \infty$.*"[37]

Chandrasekhar's fluid ansatz was different from Schwarzschild's in that Schwarzschild calculated the resulting pressure required to sustain HE for any incompressible fluid of given density and radius, while Chandrasekhar instead assumed a relativistic electron degeneracy pressure source to calculate the maximum mass that still maintains the fluid's HE, as function of a specified matter density gradient that peaks in the center. However both the authors arrive at the compatibility of their solution equations with the formation of a singular density ($\rho \to \infty$) point mass, and both suggest to dismiss this conclusion under sacrifice of the scope of validity of their respective solution equations: Schwarzschild's turn was to suggest that the assumption of the incompressible fluid breaks down, while Chandrasekhar's turn instead was to argue that it is not the general framework of the perfect fluid ansatz itself but the polytropic EOS employed therein what breaks down[1]. The Chandrasekhar mass limit improved an earlier upper mass limit estimate

---

[1] Apart from dismissing the scope of validity of the polytropic EOS, another turn is to reject the presumption that the HE condition continues to be valid as the Chandrasekhar mass is approached. Neither Schwarzschild nor Chandrasekhar question the appropriateness of the HE condition in the aforementioned works *before* the critical mass concentration limit is reached. To anticipate, as is known today from a more realistic treatment of matter in electron degenerate stellar cores, nuclear and particle interactions may trigger hydrodynamic instabilities and the energy release that power explosions as the Chandrasekhar mass is approached. Thermonuclear reactions inside a White Dwarf, composed of -for example- a degenerate Carbon-Oxygen core that is surrounded by an outer shell of mainly Helium ions, under certain yet not well understood conditions[38] (one possible progenitor mechanism is the accretion of hot matter onto the White Dwarf from a companion star) ignite a deflagration or detonation before the Chandrasekhar mass limit is attained, which unbinds (thermonuclear runaway energy release from Carbon fusion is one of the possible explosion mechanisms) the star in a Type 1a Supernova, and leaves no remnant behind. In more massive stars, an (effective) Chandrasekhar mass limit indeed sets the condition for onset of stellar core collapse (CC), onward of which the HE assumption becomes an inappropriate constraint on the physics: violent Neutron Star formation is one of the outcomes of CC, after -according to current

by Stoner (1930) who assumed a constant density fluid. With the theoretical model of gravitational implosion ($r_1 \to 0$) of a sufficiently massive White Dwarf star, he demonstrated that (Newtonian) gravitational singularity formation is not merely a mathematical curiosity but a possible outcome of stellar evolution that connects to stellar progenitor models.

The final equilibrium conjecture. Driven by views of a philosophy of science which exclude the possibility of gravitational implosion, Eddington vehemently dismissed Chandrasekhar's mathematically rigorous calculation of an upper mass limit for mechanical stability of a White Dwarf star. During the meeting of the astronomical society, he expressed concerns about the relativistic degeneracy formula deployed by Chandrasekhar, suggesting that quantum degeneracy is lifted when relativistic effects become important:

> *"The formula is based on a combination of relativity mechanics and non-relativity quantum theory, and I do not regard the offspring of such a union as born in lawful wedlock (...) There is no such thing as relativistic degeneracy!"* [39]

Instead, he conjectured that when the nuclear energy supply is exhausted, the star reaches a final stable equilibrium state at which radiation pressure compensates further gravitational contraction:

> *"The star has to go on radiating and radiating and contracting and contracting until, I suppose, it gets down to a few km radius, when gravity becomes strong enough to hold in the radiation, and the star can at last find peace."* [39]

His argument was heuristic and not grounded upon an elaborated theoretical final equilibrium model, but it was influential enough to prevent Chandrasekhar's work from receiving a wider attention.

2.3. Tolman-Oppenheimer-Volkoff mass limit vs. unexplored Equation of State effects

(More) compact stars. The discovery of the neutron[40] in 1932 opened up new directions in nuclear stellar astrophysics. But even prior to its discovery, Landau

---

'standard' CC Supernova models- a neutrino-driven convection-enhanced explosion has ejected a significant fraction of mass from the collapsing core. The explosive mass ejection allows the stellar post-collapse remnant find a new HE state at ultra-dense matter conditions, which -in the simplest treatment- is again modelled by a polytropic Equation of State: HE is now sustained by neutron degeneracy pressure of a quantum ideal gas composed of neutrons.

presented a model[m] of a more compact stellar core, taking form of a *"gigantic nucleus"*,[41] composed of a stable matter configuration at which the protons and electrons still co-exist at densities even greater than the limiting $\rho_c \propto 10^{12} \frac{g}{cm^3}$ assumed in the original Chandrasekhar mass White Dwarf. While Landau did not explicitly invoke a neutron composition in his stellar core model, he anticipated the idea that stable matter configurations at even higher densities than the White Dwarf do exist, and still are adequately approximated by a polytropic EOS, taking degeneracy pressure into account. Few years later, in 1934 the astronomers Baade and Zwicky suggested the explosive transformation of an ordinary star into a Neutron Star as an explanation of observations of supernova transients.

> *"If super-novae are giant analogues to ordinary novae, we may expect that ionized gas shells are expelled from them at great speeds. If this assumption is correct, part of the cosmic rays should consist of protons and heavier ions. [...] We have tentatively suggested that the super-nova process represents the transition of an ordinary star into a neutron star. If neutrons are produced on the surface of an ordinary star they will 'rain' down towards the center if we assume that the light pressure on neutrons is practically zero. This view explains the speed of the star's transformation into a neutron star."*[42]

The details of the nuclear physics involved therein, in particular the transition of the protons, bounded together by the strong nuclear force, into neutrons by virtue of undergoing Electron Capture, were developed in subsequent years by Hund (1936) and by Gamow (1937).[43] Because of the half-integer spin of the neutrons, Pauli pressure of the neutron ideal Fermi gas, rather than of the electron gas, is responsible for maintaining stability of the compact star, withstanding further gravitational contraction. Oppenheimer & Serber (1938) re-estimated the upper mass limit for a stable degenerate neutron core modelled by a polytropic EOS, but corrected the result of Landau, which posed too tight constraints on nuclear binding energy.[44]

Unexplored EOS effects. A treatment of degenerate neutron cores in General Relativity followed soon hereafter: it was based on Tolman's solution ansatz to the interior Schwarzschild field of a spherically symmetric static matter distribution[45, 46]:

$$ds^2 = e^\nu dt^2 - \frac{1}{1 - \frac{2Gm(r)}{r}} dr^2 + r^2 g_\Omega \tag{10}$$

---

[m] He arrives at the important formula

$$M_0 = \frac{3.1}{m^2} \left(\frac{\hbar c}{G}\right)^{3/2} \tag{9}$$

where M_0 is the limiting mass that is sufficient to maintain the (Newtonian) HE, and the parameter m is the mass of a nuclear ion per one electron. For a degenerate White Dwarf core, $m \simeq 2m_p$ where m_p is the proton rest mass, and from there follows the well-known $M_0 \simeq 1.44 M_\odot$ Chandrasekhar limit.

where $m = m(r) = \int_0^r dr' 4\pi r'^2 \rho(r')$ is the volume integral over energy density up to the radial coordinate r, and where the coefficient $v = v(r)$ obtained from the fluid's EOS. Oppenheimer & Volkoff (1939) adopted this ansatz for their calculation of the gravitational field inside neutron cores,[47] which they assumed to have density $\rho(r)$, isotropic pressure $P(r)$, be at rest ($u^\mu = 0$) and under the absence of mechanical stresses. Under these assumptions, the stress-energy tensor of the perfect fluid

$$T^{\mu\nu} = \left(\rho(r) + \frac{P(r)}{c^2}u^\mu u^\nu - P(r)g^{\mu\nu}\right) \quad (11)$$

simplifies, with $T_1^1 = T_2^2 = T_3^3 = -P$ and $T_4^4 = \rho$ remaining as the only non-vanishing diagonal components. Plugging them and Tolman's metric ansatz into the EFE $R_{\mu\nu} - \frac{1}{2}Rg_{\mu\nu} = \frac{8\pi G}{c^4}T_{\mu\nu}$, they derive a general relativistic HR condition, which -in a modern reformulation of the solution equations- reads

$$\frac{dP(r)}{dr} = -\frac{Gm(r)}{r^2}\rho(r)\left(1 + \frac{P(r)}{\rho(r)c^2}\right)\left(1 + \frac{4\pi r^3 P(r)}{m(r)c^2}\right)\left(1 - \frac{2Gm(r)}{rc^2}\right)^{-1}. \quad (12)$$

In the general relativistic HE, both the stress-energy field *and* the gravitational field are stationary. The solution to the TOV equation (12) requires the supply of an EOS $P = P(\rho, T)$, which reduces to $P = P(\rho)$ if temperature-independent (as in the polytropic case), and which coincides with Schwarzschild's 1916 solution to the interior field if the constant density assumption $\rho(r) = \rho_0$ is made. In their calculation of the upper mass limit to general relativistic stability, Oppenheimer & Volkoff model the neutron core by a variant of a more realistic polytropic EOS than Landau's, which however only takes into account Fermi degeneracy pressure of the neutron gas, and neglects contributions to the EOS from thermal energy and internal particle interaction forces. Under these assumptions, they derive a general relativistic upper mass limit $M_{TOV} \leq \frac{3}{4}M_\odot$. At the same time, they comment on solutions to the field equations for greater core masses:

> *"For masses greater than $\frac{3}{4}M_\odot$ there are no static equilibrium solutions. (...) There would then seem to be only two answers possible to the question of the 'final' behaviour of very massive stars: either the equation of state we have used so far fails to describe the behaviour of highly condensed matter that the conclusions reached above are qualitatively misleading, or the star will contract indefinitely (...) although more and more slowly, never reaching true equilibrium."*[47]

The Tolman-Oppenheimer-Volkoff mass limit is seen as a first general relativistic (albeit rather coarse, given a simplistic treatment of matter in the neutron core) demarcation between a Neutron Star vs. Black Hole final fate of core collapse. As an alternative to complete gravitational collapse, the authors trace out a similar argument to Chandrasekhar's, namely that the EOS used in their calculation might become inadequate at more extreme matter conditions[n] and that yet unknown pressure sources (which not necessarily need to arise from fermionic degeneracy pressure) might be responsible for restoring HE of the star. In that case, the TOV condition eq. (12), and resulting mass limit, needs be re-evaluated with a yet unexplored EOS, in place of the polytropic ansatz which accounts for fermionic degeneracy pressure.

3. Oppenheimer-Snyder collapse (1939–1965)

3.1. *Indefinite gravitational contraction*

After Oppenheimer and Volkoff established the upper mass limit for stability of a neutron core in 1939, Oppenheimer and his student Snyder that same year sought for solutions to the EFE for the case that the TOV mass limit is exceeded by polytrope fluid models of mass $M > M_{TOV} = 0.75\, M_\odot$, beyond neutron star densities ($\rho_c \propto 10^{15} \frac{g}{cm^3}$). Their result is that they do not find any stable matter states that allow for *stationary* solutions to the field equations for $g_{\mu\nu}$ that would respect the TOV equilibrium condition. Instead, under the idealizing assumption of vanishing pressure $P(r) = 0$, they find an analytical *evolved* solution to the gravitational field, describing gravitational collapse of freely falling matter henceforth simply modelled as dust. They reformulate Tolman's ansatz to the interior Schwarzschild metric (eq. (10)) in a coordinate system that is co-moving ($u^\mu = 0$) with the collapsing matter. As result, the stress-energy tensor again takes the simple form of eq. (11), but -given the zero pressure assumption- the only non-vanishing component is the density $T_4^4 = \rho$. The gravitational contraction of the star is continued indefinitely: as the continued spherically symmetric gravitational contraction shrinks the sphere of dust down to asymptotically zero, the central density diverges, local measures of

---

[n] When taking a leap further ahead into the future, the reliance of compact star models on developments in nuclear and particle physics becomes evident: after the postulation of the subnuclear quark particles[48,49] as constituents of hadronic matter and therefore of nucleons in 1964, Ivanenko & Kurdgelaidze in 1965 constructed a simple Quark Star model.[50] With the discovery of the theoretical description of the constituents of matter at a higher energy scale, a novel model for HE, sustained by degeneracy pressure of the constituent fermions, becomes conceivable. The Quark Star model assumes that the quarks constituting the neutron, bound together by the strong interaction at coupling strength $\alpha_s(k^2)$ that logarithmically decreases with scale, at high enough temperatures undergo a deconfinement phase transition to asymptotic freedom. The deconfinement of quarks justifies application of, once again, the quantum ideal Fermi gas model. The free quarks collectively reach a stable subnuclear HE configuration sustained by degeneracy pressure of the fermionic quark gas. Whether or not Quark Stars exist in nature is an unresolved scientific enquiry, especially in light of the fact that according to more recent, state-of-art models of Neutron Stars, the EOS of their (possibly deconfined and quark degenerate) cores is not well understood.[51]

The lower the mass, the lower does the quark degeneracy pressure need to be in order to maintain HE. Putatively, Quark Stars are therefore physically reasonable mimickers of very *low* mass Black Hole, but not of intermediate mass, massive, and supermassive Black Hole candidates. It is unlikely that the degeneracy pressure from any of the established fermions known in today's Standard Model of elementary particle physics is sufficient for the corresponding exotic compact star to act as supermassive Black Hole mimicker. However, certain models of compact Boson Stars open up new directions for physical speculation.

curvature diverge, and incomplete geodesics form.º The admission of the formation of a point mass singularity by the solution equations has been found before in the perfect fluid models of Schwarzschild, Chandrasekhar, Landau and Oppenheimer & Volkoff. What is remarkable^p about the Oppenheimer & Snyder solution is that, along with the curvature singularity (which is, by virtue of the EFE, consequence of a locally divergent stress-energy field), their calculations also predict geodesic incompleteness.

Non-vanishing pressure and mass loss effects. The Oppenheimer-Snyder type dust collapse model fulfills the conditions for the Raychaudhuri-Komar singularity theorem to apply, which implies formation of an infinite density point mass provided that the Weak Energy Condition (see Sec. (3.3)) holds: the Oppenheimer-Snyder collapse assumes a perfect fluid, which is irrotational, and geodesic (the absence of proper acceleration is consequence of the $P = 0$ assumption). From an infinite density point mass, the EFE imply a *curvature* singularity. Though what is more, the authors affirm their belief in the validity of the solution equations even for the case of non-zero pressure $P \neq 0$:

> *"We believe that the general features of the solution obtained in this way give a valid indication even for the case that the pressure is not zero, provided that the mass is great enough to cause collapse (...) Of course, actual stars would collapse more slowly than the example which we studied analytically because of the effect of the pressure of the matter, of radiation, and of rotation."*[52]

At the same time, they enumerate a number of physical mechanisms that could prevent a star from surpassing the TOV mass limit, after all of its thermonuclear internal energy resources have been exhausted:

(1) the fission of the star into fragments by its rotation,

ºSetting the proper time τ of a local observer co-moving with the collapsing matter of the outermost dust shell in relation with the coordinate time measured by a distant observer t outside the collapsing star, and taking the asymptotic limit $t \to \infty$, they find that proper time of a time-like geodesic converges to a finite $\tau \to \tau_0$. As the collapsing star shrinks beneath its Schwarzschild radius, time-like geodesics become space-like. The authors calculate the asymptotic space-like configuration of the gravitational field inside the collapsing star: the temporal component $g_{tt} \to 0$ vanishes while the radial component g^{rr} reaches a finite configuration in the interior $r < r_S$ except at $r = 0$ where it becomes infinite. In addition, a coordinate singularity develops at $r = r_S$.
PThe authors also anticipate the idea that the two-sphere $r = r_S$ constitutes an event horizon, preventing an escape from the collapsing star and isolating it from any causal interaction with the exterior:

> *"After this time τ_0 an observer comoving with the matter would not be able to send a light signal from the star; the cone within which a signal can escape has closed entirely."*[52]

(2) photon radiation pressure blowing off outer mass layers,
(3) significant enough mass radiation.

From the perspective of modern astrophysical stellar evolution models of the late pre-collapse evolutionary stages, the above mentioned effects are unlikely to be strong enough to be a general argument preventing implosion of a physically realistic massive core.[q]

3.2. *The Landau-Wheeler arguments, and Boson Stars*

Landau pointed out in his 1932 and 1938 papers that a compression of fermions, over course of stellar gravitational collapse, to a point mass, with all fermions occupying the same phase space cell, leads to violation of fermionic quantum statistics,[41,56] which prohibits occupation of the same quantum state by more than one fermion. The formation of a point mass singularity is further complicated by other quantum principles. In particular, the Heisenberg uncertainty principle, according to which position and momentum of a particle cannot both be precisely constraint at the same time. Energy compactness considerations, advocated by Wheeler, according to which a quantum particle of given rest-mass energy is not allowed to localize at scales smaller than its Compton wavelength in order to be well-defined. Wheeler confronted Oppenheimer at the Solvay Conference (1958) to argue on heuristic grounds that the collapsing (fermionic) nuclear matter must dissolve into electromagnetic, gravitational and/or neutrino radiation.[57] In a way, his opposition to Oppenheimer's result was akin to Eddington's to Chandrasekhar's work, in that Wheeler took up Eddington's idea that radiation becomes held in the star, which though still maintains its final equilibrium. But Wheeler went further with an elaborated model of a *Geon* as a HE candidate. In 1955, a decade before the stationary

---

[q](1): According to more recent computer simulations of rotating core collapse that deploy a polytrope EOS,[53] the infalling matter is indeed fragmented into an inner core contracting subsonically and an outer core contracting supersonically. The centrifugal force has the effect of deforming the inner core, and reducing the available gravitational energy to 'push' the outer core into an explosion. Rotation therefore has impact on the fate of the collapsing core regarding whether it explodes or not, but is not an implosion preventing mechanism that generalizes. (2): The high energy photon radiation in the hot stellar core leads to photo-disintegration of heavy nuclear ions (mostly iron group elements), which a more realistic massive core is composed of. Therefore, the photo-disintegration facilitates rather than prevents gravitational collapse, for it occurs at the price of taking away internal energy from the star: thermal radiation pressure contributes to the total pressure that maintains HE, and photo-disintegration has the overall effect of reducing it.[54] (3): Stellar winds in late phase massive star evolution do significantly contribute to mass loss, however the mass radiation mostly takes away mass from the envelope rather than from the core of the star, which -due to its greater compactness- is stronger bound gravitationally. Mass ejection from the core is strong enough only in the case of a CC Supernova explosion, signalling the violent birth of a proto-Neutron Star. However, a successful launch of an explosion is only one of the possible outcomes of stellar CC, along with a Failed Supernova, a Weak Supernova that precedes Black Hole formation by fallback of ejected matter onto the proto-Neuton Star, and the direct quiescent Black Hole formation.[55]

Newman-Kerr electrovacuum solution was found, Wheeler presented a solution to the EFE describing a spherically symmetric confined classical radiation field. His idea was that radiation is trapped in form of standing waves in closed circular toroid tracks of radius of the Geon, and collectively arranges to form stable macroscopic objects.[58] These Geon configurations were supposed to consist of either of trapped electromagnetic waves or of trapped gravitational waves, held together by their own self-gravity in a stable equilibrium state. Since their reduced wavelength is negligibly small compared to the radius, the Geon decay rate is negligible over long time scales. By proposing a non-singular bosonic HE alternative to gravitational implosion, Wheeler further elaborated not only Eddington's but also Landau's argument. Though the transition of fermionic mass-energy to bosonic states in a collapsing star still remained a conjecture, without a specified generic transition mechanism. Alas, his model -as well as variants thereof- turned out to be unstable: a small equilibrium perturbation to the confined radiation field leads to onset of its implosion.[r]

Following a different approach in line with Wheeler's *Geometrodynamics* research program, Wheeler together with his student Fuller returned to the idea of a non-singular Einstein-Rosen bridge connecting two symmetrical regions of an empty spacetime, and studied Wormhole solutions in the maximally extended Kruskal-Szekeres metric, with an introduced minimum proper circumference at the connecting "throat" in order to obtain a singularity-free metric.[31] But it was found that these suffer from qualitatively the same problem as Geon models, namely that Wormholes in 4-dimensional, general relativistic spacetime are unstable against equilibrium perturbations in a dynamic problem (which results in shrinkage of circumference of the throat down to zero, and divergence of curvature invariants after finite proper time), unless even higher-dimensional space-time or quantum theoretical considerations are taken into account that stabilize the topological bridge.

---

[r]However, when a complex scalar field φ is considered instead of the electromagnetic field, the equation of motion for the complex scalar field (the Klein-Gordon equation) admits stable geon-like soliton solutions, stabilizing as a Boson Star. Their gravitational field is sourced by the self-gravity of the bosonic waves, which are dispersed in accordan with the Klein-Gordon equation, satisfying the laws of Bose-Einstein quantum statistics: bosonic particles of mass μ confined within an object of size $2R$ possess a proper velocity $v \propto (2R\mu)^{-1}$. It is the Heisenberg uncertainty pressure of the bosons which provides the pressure (along with a self-interaction term, which adds either a positive or a negative contribution to pressure, depending on the nature of the self-scattering potential $V(\varphi)$) to counterbalance contraction and maintain HE. However, given a limitation by the finite internal radius, and thereby the proper velocity of the Bosons, there is a maximum mass to stability of a Boson Star, $M_{BS} \propto \frac{m_P^2}{\mu}$ (whose precise value is determined from specific boson star models), beyond which the Heisenberg uncertainty pressure is insufficient to withstand gravitational collapse (m_P is the Planck mass).[59] It therefore seems not implausible that Boson Stars, even if they exist, are only an intermediate stable configuration state, before gravitational collapse of the compact Boson Star occurs if it has become sufficiently massive.

3.3. The Khalatnikov-Lifshitz asymmetry argument, and Penrose's 1965 theorem

The Oppenheimer & Snyder paper convinced Landau about the reality of complete gravitational collapse of matter, but not of the irregularities in the metric field by the formation of singularities (referring to all three notions defined in Sec. 1). As one of the leading figures of the Soviet school assessed the prediction of gravitational singularities in collapsing stars as well as in Early Universe Cosmology to be the major unsolved problem of theoretical physics, his judgement would shape the thinking of a generation of Soviet theorists. The Landau school accepted the reality of gravitational collapse sooner than the Wheeler school, and would endow it with the name "Frozen Star", grounded upon effects at the Schwarzschild boundary, apparent to an external observer, rather than interior singularity hallmarks.[s] Doubting singularity formation as physically viable, Khalatnikov and Lifshitz in the early 60s advocated that in any physically realistic stellar gravitational collapse scenario, the condition of spherical symmetry, inherent in the Schwarzschild metric, would be violated.[60] In realistic asymmetric collapse, they argued that nonlinearity effects would dominate the interaction between gravitational field and matter, resulting in chaotic dynamics and impeding formation of the central singularity. Instead, they interpreted the central singularity as an artifact prediction that arises from the imposed spherical symmetry condition in the Oppenheimer-Snyder collapse.

Penrose's work on the singularity theorem[61] historically was motivated as a counter to the Khalatnikov-Lifshitz argument. The theorem states that, provided that a set of conditions are fulfilled, the production of geodesic incompleteness singularities is generic to General Relativity theory, independent of spherical symmetry assumptions:

> *The question has been raised as to whether this singularity is, in fact, simply a property of the high symmetry assumed. The matter collapses radially inwards to the single point at the center, so that a resulting space-time catastrophe there is perhaps not surprising. Could not the presence of perturbations which destroy the spherical symmetry alter the situation drastically? [...] It will be shown that, after a certain critical condition has been unfilled, deviations from spherical symmetry cannot prevent space-time singularities from arising.*[61]

---

[s]Characteristics of the Frozen Star definition are

- the infinite gravitational redshift of light signals, down to zero, emitted from the Schwarzschild boundary, and
- the illusory coordinate singularity effects that, as measured in coordinate time of a distant external observer, it takes infinitely long for the outermost coontracting stellar surface to collapse under the star's Schwarzschild boundary; as well as the infinite gravitational time delay of a test object asymptotically approaching the Schwarzschild boundary from outside but never reaching it.

Penrose starts off with three premises (geodesic completeness, the weak energy condition, and the causality condition) and shows that they lead to a contradiction, provided that a closed future-directed trapping surface, which is not necessarily spherically symmetric, has formed. The resolution of the contradiction requires that one of the premises is refuted. If one holds onto the latter two conditions, then the geodesic completeness assumption needs be rejected. Put differently, the conditions that need be fulfilled in order for the singularity theorem to apply are

- *Weak Energy Condition*: $R_{\mu\nu}\hat{\gamma}^\mu\hat{\gamma}^\nu \geq 0$, strictly speaking a geometrical condition that demands the convergence of null-like and time-like vector fields γ.[t]
- *Causality Condition*: the spacetime has an initial Cauchy hypersurface, and by global hyperbolicity is time-orientable (no closed null-like or time-like curves).
- *Boundary Condition*: formation of a closed future-trapped surface.

Assuming that the above conditions are satisfied throughout the entire course of stellar gravitational collapse, Penrose's theorem guarantees formation of incomplete null geodesics[u]. For the case of a collapsing star modelled by the Schwarzschild ansatz, the outermost trapped surface forms at $r_b = r_S$ where r_b is the outer boundary of the spherically symmetric collapsing star. Under which generic conditions a trapping surface forms, and whether it is reasonable to assume that the weak energy and causality conditions apply throughout the entire course of gravitational core collapse, are separate research questions that require further investigation, going beyond the scope of this work.

The geodesic incompleteness singularity theorem is independent of the EFE. Therefore, it applies to any theory of gravity, e.g. $f(R)$ theories, formulated using the framework of Lorentzian geometry, that satisfies the stated causality, energy and boundary conditions. The Penrose theorem does not state 'where' in space-time the incomplete geodesics locally form. Moreover, the theorem makes no statement about local curvature divergence. The lack of a physical characterization of geodesic incompleteness formation is by some (e.g. Landau & Lifschitz in Ref. 62) seen as weakness of the theorem - the theorem does not exemplify the reasons for which the geodesic incompleteness occurs: whether or not the path inextendibility is due to

---

[t]In GR, the Ricci tensor $R_{\mu\nu}$ is related to $T_{\mu\nu}$ by the EFE, which gives the geometrical condition a conceptual interpretation in terms of energy related physical quantities.
[u]A key tool used in the formulation and proof of the singularity theorems is the focusing effect of the Raychaudhuri equation. The equation describes the divergence behaviour of a congruence family of geodesics. The divergence of a congruence is defined as the derivative of the logarithm of the determinant of the congruence volume. Raychaudhuri's equation then describes the evolution of geodesic congruences. The closed trapping surface condition implies that light rays emitted in opposite directions orthogonal to a closed space-like 2-sphere converge. Null geodesics include the entire boundary of the proper future: when they converge from opposite sides, there is no more future boundary. The congruence volume of parallel null geodesics reaches zero within finite affine length. Consequence is the generic prediction that the relativistic spacetime $(\mathcal{M}, g)$ is not future null geodesically complete.

curvature divergence, is left open. The latter fact can, however, instead be seen as a strength of the theorem, in that it allows to treat the geodesic incompleteness and infinite curvature singularity notions apart from one another: the Penrose theorem does not need to relate geodesic incompleteness to any pathological mass-energy or curvature state in order to apply.

3.4. *The Planck-Wheeler length, and Markov's curvature bound*

Curvature fluctuations at Planck scale. Together with his students Harrison and Wakano, Wheeler in 1958 mapped out, in a research study that combines theoretical and numerical work, a catalogue of the endpoints of stellar thermonuclear evolution for a wide range of stellar masses.[57] The catalogue played a pivotal role in his later conviction that along with the White Dwarf and Neutron Star compact remnant endpoints of stellar evolution, the complete gravitational collapse as predicted by the Oppenheimer & Snyder model, although it makes crude approximative assumptions, is a possible outcome of evolution of massive stars. Along with exclusion of alternatives to complete gravitational collapse, the decisive role[64] for Wheeler's conviction was played by computer simulations of CC, in particular those of Colgate & White (1966),[63] which adopted more realistic EOS models of stellar matter, and thereby undermined Wheeler's earlier objection that the Oppenheimer-Snyder collapse model is physically unreasonable. Wheeler's updated stance on the issue of the final fate was that mass-energy disappears, as it gets torn into pieces by the divergent tidal forces at the center of mass. The complete gravitational collapse results in a gravitating vacuum ($T_{\mu\nu} = 0$), which he later called *"mass without mass"*, or *"disembodied mass"*.[65] However, with regard to the prediction of curvature singularity formation as part of the final fate, Wheeler expressed mistrust in GR as the appropriate theory of gravity at smallest scales. His conviction was that the Planck length $\ell_P = \sqrt{\frac{\hbar G}{c^3}}$ is the minimum scale at which space is resolved in an ultimate theory of gravity, and at which he expected space to exhibit *"quantum foam"*[66] of random curvature fluctuations, including microscopic wormholes. Whether or not a gravitational singularity forms over course of unhalted implosion would then be assessed by a successor theory, after the *"fiery marriage"* of quantum theory and gravitation. The important point he raised is that -while he accepted reality of gravitational collapse- the curvature singularity might be an artifact prediction that arises neither because a yet unexplored pressure source has not been taken into account, nor because of idealization, but because the theory of gravity itself breaks down.

Maximal energy density. Aiming at the same goal (the theoretical preclusion of curvature singularity formation) but following a different line of argument, Markov in 1947 first stated the conditions under which there arises an upper limiting bound to curvature,[67] an idea he would explore and elaborate further over the subsequent decades (see e.g. Refs. 68, 69) His proposal was that a limiting quadratic curvature invariant

$$R_{\mu\nu\lambda\delta}R^{\mu\nu\lambda\delta} \leq \frac{1}{\ell_P^4} \qquad (13)$$

is consequence of a maximal density $\rho_q = \frac{c^5}{G^2\hbar} \simeq 10^{94}\frac{g}{cm^3}$ of mass-energy that is permitted to occur in nature. The limiting energy density, a construction from the ratio of the three natural constants c, $\hbar$ and G of special relativity (SR), quantum theory (QT) and gravitation, remains a conjecture. Though he gives a motivation for it, from consideration of the underlying principles of the theories that provide the limiting constraints: from SR, that the propagation velocity of any signal cannot exceed c (a principle held so sacred by Einstein); and from QT, that the action cannot be less than $\hbar$ (a condition which is violated in classical physics). At the same time, Markov highlights that it is the nonlinearity in the differential gravitational field equations coupling stress-energy to measures of curvature, which needs to supply the energy cut-off to avoid UV divergences and the renormalization problem of quantum field theory.[v]

4. Conclusions

The decades spanning in between Schwarzschild's analytical 1916 solution to the EFE and Penrose's 1965 singularity theorem produced a rich pool of thought about the nature of gravitational singularities, and about the viability of their physical realization in stellar gravitational collapse. The examination of the arguments in favour or against realism on singularity formation requires to take into account considerations from differential geometry, stellar astrophysics, and history of science. We have investigated a long list of singularity formation counter-arguments and, while telling the three gravitational singularity notions apart, came to the following conclusions:

- Geodesic incompleteness is an innovative (as it is not available in Newtonian gravity), the most general and a non-local singularity characterization, which is compatible with but does not require divergence in any curvature quantities, and which does not prima facie contradict principles neither of general relativity nor of quantum theory. Prediction of geodesic incompleteness by Penrose's theorem therefore does not indicate breakdown of GR.

---

[v] As the maximal density limit is reached, he argues that a phase transition of matter-energy into a de Sitter vacuum takes place. The latter conjecture has been be elaborated by Gliner and Sakharov in 1966, with applications to singularity resolution in Cosmology: the negative pressure $P = -\rho < 0$ obeyed by the false vacuum $T_{\mu\nu} = \Lambda g_{\mu\nu}$ introduces a repulsive term into the field equations and violates, by virtue of the EFE with Λ included on the right-hand side, the weak energy condition. With the unclarified nature of Λ, the de Sitter phase transition is a non-singular albeit speculative outcome of gravitational collapse, whose investigation goes beyond the scope of this work.

- An infinite quadratic curvature invariant is not a trustworthy prediction of GR, because it is a local singularity characterization evaluating properties of the gravitational field down at microscopic scales below the Planck length, while GR is a phenomenological theory of gravity. A microscopic theory of gravity theory, perhaps a unified field theory Einstein and Wheeler were questing for, would reconcile the physics of the gravitational field itself with principles of quantum theory. In addition, there are several sub-classes of infinite curvature singularities, which are problematic in their own right.
- Curvature singularity avoidance is achieved in general not by introduction of a yet unexplored speculative EOS which either appropriately describes mass-energy at extreme conditions and restores HE in a collapsing star, or implies a phase transition that introduces a repulsive term by virtue of the EFE (even if there are such remedies, GR would still allow for analytic solutions to EFE with singular curvature, which remains problematic), but by modification of the gravitation theory itself. Markov's bound on the quadratic curvature invariant is consequence of a limiting mass-energy density conjecture, from which it is derived. However, theoretical work has shown that -under certain conditions- curvature singularities form in GR even from a vacuum spacetime, as in the case of colliding gravitational waves, independent of matter. We therefore propose to retain Markov's conclusion (eq. 13) but to reverse the logic: a limiting density of both stress-energy and of gravitational energy is consequence of a bound on the quadratic curvature invariant. The curvature bound needs be introduced from first principle quantization considerations, which GR -as a macroscopic theory- does not itself supply from within the gravity theory.
- Curvature divergence signals the breakdown of Lorentzian geometry, independent of the EFE: the continuous nature of Lorentzian geometry permits gravitational contraction in Oppenheimer-Snyder collapse be continued indefinitely, without that a limiting scale is ever reached. GR does not cure a problem it itself inherits from Newtonian gravity: since in either theory measures of distance are non-quantized, a curvature pathology in GR is permitted to occur in GR for the same reason that allows for infinite force in Newtonian gravity. If quantum theory is not well-defined at scales smaller than the Planck length, it is not evident why GR should be. In addition, it is the lowest scale at which Lorentz symmetry applies. ℓ_P therefore is a natural unit measure for quantization of the quadratic curvature invariant, which can only be achieved by a quantizing tessellation of Lorentzian geometry in units of Planck length and Planck time. Assuming that physics at scales below the Planck scale is meaningless, the curvature bound ($R_{\mu\nu\lambda\delta}R^{\mu\nu\lambda\delta} = \frac{1}{\ell_P^4}$ limit) impedes formation of any energy density singularity in any inertial frame, because it makes space contraction to a point an impossibility.

Acknowledgments

The author is grateful to Tushar Menon, Erik Curiel, Fritz Roepke, Fabian Schneider, Dennis Lehmkuhl, Roger Penrose, Martin Lesourd and Juliusz Doboszewski for discussions on related topics, and to Siobhan Roberts for the motivation to write. The work of K. M. is supported by the Klaus Tschira Foundation.

References

1. E. Curiel, The Analysis of Singular Spacetimes, *Philosophy of Science* **66**, S119 (sep 1999).
2. J. Earman and J. Eisenstaedt, Einstein and Singularities, *Studies in History and Philosophy of Science Part B: Studies in History and Philosophy of Modern Physics* **30**, 185 (jun 1999).
3. S. W. Hawking, G. F. R. Ellis and R. K. Sachs, The Large Scale Structure of Space-Time, **27**, 91 (apr 1974).
4. G. F. R. Ellis and B. G. Schmidt, Singular space-times, **8**, 915 (nov 1977).
5. A. Raychaudhuri, Relativistic Cosmology. I, **98**, 1123 (may 1955).
6. A. Komar, Necessity of Singularities in the Solution of the Field Equations of General Relativity, **104**, 544 (oct 1956).
7. J. M. M. Senovilla and D. Garfinkle, The 1965 Penrose singularity theorem, *Classical and Quantum Gravity* **32**, p. 124008 (jun 2015).
8. J. O. Weatherall, What Is a Singularity in Geometrized Newtonian Gravitation?, *Philosophy of Science* **81**, 1077 (dec 2014).
9. F. J. Tipler, Singularities from colliding plane gravitational waves, *Phys. Rev. D* **22**, 2929 (dec 1980).
10. U. Yurtsever, Structure of the singularities produced by colliding plane waves, *Physical Review D* **38**, 1706 (sep 1988).
11. T. Wang, J. Fier, B. Li, G. Lü, Z. Wang, Y. Wu and A. Wang, Singularities of plane gravitational waves in Einstein's general relativity, *General Relativity and Gravitation* **52** (feb 2020).
12. K. Q. Abbasi, I. Hussain and A. Qadir, Probing Szekeres' colliding sandwich gravitational waves, *The European Physical Journal Plus* **136** (may 2021).
13. C. J. Clarke, *The analysis of space-time singularities*, no. 1 (Cambridge University Press, 1993).
14. C. W. Misner, Taub-Nut Space as a Counterexample to almost anything, in *Relativity Theory and Astrophysics. Vol.1: Relativity and Cosmology*, ed. J. Ehlers 1967, p. 160.
15. B. Schmidt, A new definition of singular points in general relativity, *General relativity and gravitation* **1**, 269 (1971).
16. J. Earman, *Bangs, crunches, whimpers, and shrieks: Singularities and acausalities in relativistic spacetimes* (Oxford University Press, 1995).
17. R. Geroch, What is a singularity in general relativity?, *Annals of Physics* **48**, 526 (1968).
18. J. K. Beem, Some examples of incomplete space-times, *General Relativity and Gravitation* **7**, 501 (jun 1976).
19. I. Stewart, Physical infinity, in *Infinity: A Very Short Introduction*, (Oxford University Press, mar 2017) pp. 91–102.

20. K. Schwarzschild, Über das Gravitationsfeld eines Massenpunktes nach der Einsteinschen Theorie, *Sitzungsberichte der Königlich Preußischen Akademie der Wissenschaften Berlin*, 189 (1916).
21. J. Droste, The field of a single centre in Einstein's theory of gravitation, and the motion of a particle in that field, *Ned. Acad. Wet., SA* **19**, p. 197 (1917).
22. K. Schwarzschild, Über das Gravitationsfeld einer Kugel aus inkompressibler Flüssigkeit nach der Einsteinschen Theorie, *Sitzungsberichte der königlich preußischen Akademie der Wissenschaften zu Berlin*, 424 (1916).
23. A. Einstein, On a Stationary System With Spherical Symmetry Consisting of Many Gravitating Masses, *The Annals of Mathematics* **40**, p. 922 (oct 1939).
24. A. Einstein, Letter to Ernst Mach. Zurich, 25 June, reported at pag. 544 of. CW Misner, KS Thorne, and JA Wheeler, Gravitation (1973).
25. J. Eisenstaedt, Dark Bodies and Black Holes, Magic Circles and Montgolfiers: Light and Gravitation from Newton to Einstein, *Science in Context* **6**, 83 (1993).
26. A. Einstein and J. Grommer, Allgemeine Relativitätstheorie und Bewegungsgesetz, *Albert Einstein: Akademie-Vorträge: Sitzungsberichte der Preußischen Akademie der Wissenschaften 1914–1932*, 2 (1927).
27. A. Einstein and L. Infeld, On the motion of particles in general relativity theory, *Canadian Journal of Mathematics* **1**, 209 (1949).
28. M. Black, A. Einstein and P. A. Schilpp, Autobiographical Notes, *Journal of Symbolic Logic* **15**, p. 157 (1949).
29. L. Silberstein, Two-centers solution of the gravitational field equations, and the need for a reformed theory of matter, *Physical Review* **49**, p. 268 (1936).
30. A. Einstein and N. Rosen, The Particle Problem in the General Theory of Relativity, *Physical Review* **48**, 73 (jul 1935).
31. R. W. Fuller and J. A. Wheeler, Causality and Multiply Connected Space-Time, *Phys. Rev.* **128**, 919 (oct 1962).
32. M. D. Kruskal, Maximal Extension of Schwarzschild Metric, *Phys. Rev.* **119**, 1743 (sep 1960).
33. A. S. Eddington, *The Internal Constitution of the Stars*, 1926).
34. C. R. Almeida, Stellar equilibrium vs. gravitational collapse, *The European Physical Journal H* **45**, 25 (feb 2020).
35. S. Chandrasekhar, The Maximum Mass of Ideal White Dwarfs, *The Astrophysical Journal* **74**, p. 81 (jul 1931).
36. S. Chandrasekhar, XLVIII.The density of white dwarf stars, *The London, Edinburgh, and Dublin Philosophical Magazine and Journal of Science* **11**, 592 (feb 1931).
37. S. Chandrasekhar and E. A. Milne, The Highly Collapsed Configurations of a Stellar Mass, *Monthly Notices of the Royal Astronomical Society* **91**, 456 (mar 1931).
38. W. Hillebrandt, M. Kromer, F. K. Röpke and A. J. Ruiter, Towards an understanding of Type Ia supernovae from a synthesis of theory and observations, *Frontiers of Physics* **8**, 116 (april 2013).
39. January 11 Meeting of the Royal Astronomical Society, *The Observatory* **58**, 33 (1935).
40. J. Chadwick, Possible Existence of a Neutron, *Nature* **129**, 312 (feb 1932).
41. L. D. Landau, On the theory of stars, *Phys. Z. Sowjetunion* **1**, p. 152 (1932).
42. W. Baade and F. Zwicky, Remarks on Super-Novae and Cosmic Rays, *Physical Review* **46**, 76 (jul 1934).
43. D. G. Yakovlev, P. Haensel, G. Baym and C. Pethick, Lev Landau and the concept of neutron stars, *Physics-Uspekhi* **56**, p. 289 (2013).
44. J. R. Oppenheimer and R. Serber, On the Stability of Stellar Neutron Cores, *Physical Review* **54**, 540 (oct 1938).

45. R. C. Tolman, Effect of Inhomogeneity on Cosmological Models, *Proceedings of the National Academy of Sciences* **20**, 169 (mar 1934).
46. R. C. Tolman, Static Solutions of Einstein's Field Equations for Spheres of Fluid, *Physical Review* **55**, 364 (feb 1939).
47. J. R. Oppenheimer and G. M. Volkoff, On Massive Neutron Cores, *Physical Review* **55**, 374 (feb 1939).
48. G. Zweig, *An SU(3) model for strong interaction symmetry and its breaking. Version 2*, in *Developments in the quark theory of hadrons. Vol. 1. 1964 - 1978*, eds. D. B. Lichtenberg and S. P. Rosen 2 1964, pp. 22–101.
49. M. Gell-Mann, A schematic model of baryons and mesons, *Physics Letters* **8**, 214 (feb 1964).
50. D. D. Ivanenko and D. F. Kurdgelaidze, Hypothesis concerning quark stars, *Astrophysics* **1**, 251 (1967).
51. J. M. Lattimer and M. Prakash, Neutron Star Structure and the Equation of State, *The Astrophysical Journal* **550**, 426 (mar 2001).
52. J. R. Oppenheimer and H. Snyder, On Continued Gravitational Contraction, *Physical Review* **56**, 455 (sep 1939).
53. S. Yamada and K. Sato, Numerical study of rotating core collapse in supernova explosions, *The Astrophysical Journal* **434**, p. 268 (oct 1994).
54. R. Kippenhahn, A. Weigert and A. Weiss, *Stellar Structure and Evolution* (Springer Berlin Heidelberg, 2012).
55. A. Heger, C. L. Fryer, S. E. Woosley, N. Langer and D. H. Hartmann, How Massive Single Stars End Their Life, **591**, 288 (jul 2003).
56. L. Landau, Origin of Stellar Energy, *Nature* **141**, 333 (feb 1938).
57. B. K. Harrison, M. Wakano and J. A. Wheeler, Matter-energy at high density: End point of thermonuclear evolution, *La structure et évolution de l'univers*, 124 (1958).
58. J. A. Wheeler, Geons, *Physical Review* **97**, 511 (jan 1955).
59. L. Visinelli, Boson Stars and Oscillatons: A Review (September 2021).
60. E. M. Lifshitz and I. M. Khalatnikov, Investigations in relativistic cosmology, *Advances in Physics* **12**, 185 (april 1963).
61. R. Penrose, Gravitational Collapse and Space-Time Singularities, *Physical Review Letters* **14**, 57 (jan 1965).
62. L. D. Landau, and E. Lifshitz, *The Classical Theory of Fields: Volume 2* (Butterworth-Heinemann, 1975).
63. S. A. Colgate and R. H. White, The Hydrodynamic Behavior of Supernovae Explosions, *The Astrophysical Journal* **143**, p. 626 (mar 1966).
64. S. Furlan, John Wheeler Between Cold Matter and Frozen Stars: The Road Towards Black Holes (2021).
65. J. A. Wheeler, The lesson of the black hole, *Proceedings of the American Philosophical Society* **125**, 25 (1981).
66. J. A. Wheeler, On the nature of quantum geometrodynamics, **2**, 604 (dec 1957).
67. M. Markov, O Predelnom Lambda-Protsesse, *Zhurnal eksperimentalnoi i teoreticheskoi fiziki* **17**, 848 (1947).
68. M. Markov, Supplement of the Progress of Theoretical Physics, Commemoration Issue for 30th Anniversary of Meson Theory by Dr, *H. Yukawa*, p. 85 (1965).
69. M. Markov, Limiting density of matter as a universal law of nature, *ZhETF Pisma Redaktsiiu* **36**, 214 (1982).

The Hamilton-Jacobi analysis by Peter Bergmann and Arthur Komar of classical general relativity

D. Salisbury
Physics Department, Austin College,
Sherman, Texas 75090, USA
E-mail: dsalisbury@austincollege.edu
www.austincollege.edu

Peter Bergmann initiated in 1966 an application of Hamilton-Jacobi techniques to general relativity. Little had been done by this time on extending this analysis to gauge theories. He proved that when, as in the case of Einstein's theory, the phase space generator of evolution consisted of a linear combination of constraints, the Hamilton principal function must be independent of spacetime coordinates. Also the Hamilton Jacobi equations that determined this functional of the 3-metric retained their form under phase space functionals that were invariant under the action of the spacetime diffeomorphism group. Komar followed up beginning in 1967 with a series of papers in which he proved that a complete solution of the Hamilton Jacobi equations was determined by a commuting set of diffeomorphism invariants. These invariants thereby labeled equivalence classes of solutions of Einstein's equations under the action of the full four-dimensional diffeomorphism group. Furthermore, this set satisfied canonical commutation relations with another invariant set. The hope and expectation was that these invariants could be promoted to quantum operators in a quantum theory of gravity. This framework will be contrasted with J. A. Wheeler's geometrodynamical program in which the only underlying covariance group is spatial diffeomorphisms. The full spacetime diffeomorphism symmetry is replaced by the notion of 'multi-fingered' time. A related dispute concerning the 'sandwich conjecture' will be discussed, relevant to the functional integral approach to quantum gravity. Two three geometries cannot determine a corresponding four geometry if they lie in distinct four dimensional diffeomorphism equivalence classes.

Keywords: Hamilton-Jacobi equations; geometrodynamics; quantum gravity.

1. Introduction

The following is a brief historical overview of work on a Hamilton-Jacobi approach to general relativity that was undertaken by Peter Bergmann and Arthur Komar in the 1960's and 1970's. A more detailed initial version, discussing both the relation of their research to previous and concurrent approaches, and to later progress, appears in Ref. 1. A further revision and expansion is in progress. The emphasis throughout their investigations was on the full four-dimensional diffeomorphism covariance of Einstein's theory. This lead to a divergence with the geometrodynamical approach of John Wheeler and company where only the spatial covariance is fully respected.

2. Bergmann's initial Hamilton-Jacobi analysis of general relativity

It is not widely recognized that it was Peter Bergmann who pointed out to Peres prior to the publication of his groundbreaking paper in Ref. 2 that his S appearing as an argument in the four general relativistic constraint equations should be interpreted "as the Hamilton-Jacobi functional for the gravitational field." Of course the following are now identified as the Wheeler-DeWitt equations,

$$\mathcal{H}_\mu \left(g_{ab}, \frac{\delta S}{\delta g_{cd}} \right) = 0, \quad (1)$$

where the $\mathcal{H}_\mu \left(g_{ab}, p^{cd} \right)$ are the secondary constraints in general relativity. Bergmann proved in Ref. 3 that in a theory in which the Hamiltonian is constrained to vanish S could not depend explicitly on the time. The argument applied equally well to spatial dependence, as noted first in Ref. 4. Thus $S = S[g_{ab}(\vec{x})]$. Bergmann also showed that the Hamilton-Jacobi equations were form invariant under canonical transformations generated by diffeomorphism invariants. The fact that the numerical value of S is altered under the action of $\mathcal{H}_0$ presented a puzzle. The question arose whether this could this be inconsistent with the accepted notion of 'frozen time'.

3. Komar's isolation of solution equivalence classes

Komar observed in Ref. 4 that although there were only four Hamilton-Jacobi equations the principal function S delivered $6 \times \infty^3$ expressions for the momenta,

$$p^{ab}(\vec{x}) = \frac{\delta S}{\delta g_{ab}(\vec{x})}, \quad (2)$$

and therefore the $p^{ab}(\vec{x})$ are not uniquely determined. Two additional constraints needed to be imposed, with $A = 1, 2$,

$$\alpha_A^0 \left[g_{ab}(\vec{x}), \frac{\delta S}{\delta g_{cd}(\vec{x})} \right] - \alpha_A(\vec{x}) = 0. \quad (3)$$

From the fact that

$$\frac{\delta \alpha_A^0}{\delta g_{ab}} + \frac{\delta \alpha_A^0}{\delta p^{cd}} \frac{\delta^2 S}{\delta g_{cd} \delta g_{ab}} = 0, \quad (4)$$

and similarly for the $\mathcal{H}_\mu$ it follows that

$$\{\mathcal{H}_\mu, \alpha_A^0\} = \frac{\delta^2 S}{\delta g_{ab} \delta g_{cd}} \left(-\frac{\delta \mathcal{H}_\mu}{\delta p^{ab}} \frac{\delta \alpha_A^0}{\delta p^{cd}} + \frac{\delta \mathcal{H}_\mu}{\delta p^{cd}} \frac{\delta \alpha_A^0}{\delta p^{ab}} \right) = 0. \quad (5)$$

In other words, the α_A^0 must be diffeomorphism invariants (and they must also commute with each other.)

The constant values of $\alpha_A^0 \left[g_{ab}(\vec{x}), p^{cd}(\vec{x}) \right]$ identify equivalence classes under the action of the spacetime diffeomorphism group. In Ref. 5 he showed that there existed invariant functionals β_0^A that were canonically conjugate to the α_A^0. However, as formulated at this stage by Komar, one cannot yet obtain solutions of Einstein's equations by setting $\beta^A(\vec{x}) = \frac{\delta S}{\delta \alpha_A(\vec{x})}$. One still requires a temporal coordinate - like the 'intrinsic' q^0 that appears in the free particle action.

In Ref. 5 he showed that there existed invariant functionals β_0^A that were canonically conjugate to the α_A^0. However, as formulated at this stage by Komar, one cannot yet obtain solutions of Einstein's equations by setting $\beta^A(\vec{x}) = \frac{\delta S}{\delta \alpha_A(\vec{x})}$. One still requires a temporal coordinate - like the 'intrinsic' q^0 that appears in the free relativistic particle action, with increment given by

$$dS_p = p_\mu dq^\mu, \qquad (6)$$

with constraint $p^2 + m^2 = 0$. This can be compared to vacuum general relativity where the non-vanishing contribution to the increment in the action takes the form

$$dS_{gr} = \int d^3x \, p_{ab} dg^{ab}, \qquad (7)$$

with constraints $\mathcal{H}_\mu = 0$.

In the particle case one can choose the 'intrinsic time' $t = q^0$ as the evolution parameter and also solve for p_0 resulting in

$$dS_p = -\left(\vec{p}^2 + m^2\right)^{1/2} dt + p_a dq^a. \qquad (8)$$

This yields the complete Hamilton principal function

$$S_p(q^a, t; \alpha^b) = -\left(\vec{\alpha}^2 + m^2\right)^{1/2} t + \alpha_a q^a. \qquad (9)$$

The analogue of the gravitational α_0^A in this case is p^a. The analogue of the canonical conjugate β_B^0 would be the reparameterization constant $q^a - p^a q^0/p^0$. The general solution is obtained from

$$\beta^a = \frac{\partial S_p}{\partial \alpha^a}$$

Bergmann and Komar, Ref. 6, had explicitly recognized this type of emergence of intrinsic time evolution. Earlier, Komar in Ref. 7 had proposed that intrinsic curvature-based coordinates could be constructed using Weyl curvature scalars. He and Bergmann in Ref. 8 proved that these scalars depended only on g_{ab} and p^{cd}. The question naturally arise as to why Bergmann and Komar did not proceed with the use of intrinsic coordinates in their Hamilton-Jacobi treatment. A Bergmann quote in Ref. 9 from 1971 is revealing: "Although intrinsic coordinates lead, in principle, to a complete set of observables in general relativity, their defects, of which the most glaring is their deviation from Lorentz coordinates, render this procedure illusory. It appears preferable to retain coordinates that are approximately, or asymptotically Lorentzian and hence not to destroy one's intuition." Thus in spite of prolonged occupation with a Hamiltonian formulation of the the underlying general covariance of general relativity, Bergmann still seemed to have ceded undue importance to the more familiar Poincaré symmetry of conventional field theory.

However, as shown in Ref. 10 it is in principle possible to carry out a canonical change of variable in the non-vanishing increment dS_{GR} to intrinsic spacetime coordinates $x^\mu = X^\mu(g_{ab}, p^{cd})$, analogous to the parameter choice $t = q^0$ in the free relativistic particle model. This is a corrected version of Refs. 11 and 12. Current work with Kurt Sundermeyer and Jürgen Renn is in preparation. One makes a canonical change of variables such that

$$dS_{gr} = \int d^3x\, p^{ab} dg_{ab}$$
$$= \int d^3x \left(\pi_\mu dX^\mu + p^A dg_A + \frac{\delta G}{\delta g_{ab}} dg_{ab} + \frac{\delta G}{\delta g_A} dg_A + \frac{\delta G}{\delta X^\mu} dX^\mu \right). \quad (10)$$

One must find a generator $G[g_{ab}, X_A, g_B]$ such that $p_{ab} = \frac{\delta G}{\delta g_{ab}}$. Then

$$dS'_{gr} := d(S_{gr} - G) = \int d^3x \left(\pi_\mu dX^\mu + p^A dg_A \right). \quad (11)$$

Next choose the X^μ as intrinsic coordinates, i.e., set $x^\mu = X^\mu$. Finally, one eliminates the canonical conjugates to X^μ, π_ν, by solving the constraints. Then we have the resulting intrinsic Hamilton-Jacobi equation

$$\pi_0 \left[g_A, \frac{\delta S'_{gr}}{\delta g_B}, x^\mu \right] + \frac{\partial S'_{gr}}{\partial x^0} = 0. \quad (12)$$

From the complete solutions $S'_{gr}[g_A, x^\mu; \alpha_B]$ one can obtain the full set of physically distinct solutions of Einstein's equations from

$$\beta^A = \frac{\delta S'_{gr}}{\delta \alpha_A}. \quad (13)$$

4. Contrast with geometrodynamics

The contrast of this program with Wheeler's geometrodynamics cannot be overstated. The multifingered time approach assumed that the full four-dimensional diffeomorphism symmetry had been lost. States should be labeled by the $2 \times \infty^3$ diffeomorphism invariants $\alpha_A(\vec{x})$, and not by three-geometries.

References

1. D. Salisbury, Observables and Hamilton-Jacobi approaches to general relativity. I. Early history, *arXiv:2106.10774[gr-qc]* (2021).
2. A. Peres, On Cauchy's problem in general relativity - II., *Il Nuovo Cimento* **26**, 53 (1962).
3. P. G. Bergmann, Hamilton-Jacobi and Schrödinger theory in theories with first-class Hamiltonian constraints, *Physical Review* **144**, 1078 (1966).
4. A. B. Komar, Hamilton-Jacobi quantization of general relativity, *Physical Review* **153**, 1385 (1967).
5. A. B. Komar, Hamilton-Jacobi version of general relativity, *Physical Review* **170**, 1195 (1968).
6. P. G. Bergmann and A. B. Komar, Status report on the quantization of the gravitational field, in *Recent Developments in General Relativity*, ed. L. Infeld (Pergamon Press, 1962) pp. 31–46.
7. A. B. Komar, Construction of a complete set of independent observables in the general theory of relativity, *Physical Review* **111**, 1182 (1958).

8. P. G. Bergmann and A. B. Komar, Poisson brackets between locally defined observables in general relativity, *Physical Review Letters* **4**, 432 (1960).
9. P. G. Bergmann, Hamilton-Jacobi theory with mixed constraints, *Annals of the New York Academy of Sciences* **172**, 571 (1971).
10. D. Salisbury, J. Renn and K. Sundermeyer, Restoration of four-dimensional diffeomorphism covariance in canonical general relativity: An intrinsic Hamilton-Jacobi approach.
11. D. Salisbury, J. Renn and K. Sundermeyer, Restoration of four-dimensional diffeomorphism covariance in canonical general relativity: An intrinsic Hamilton-Jacobi approach, *arXiv:1508.01277v6* (2021).
12. D. Salisbury, J. Renn and K. Sundermeyer, Erratum. Restoration of four-dimensional diffeomorphism covariance in canonical general relativity: An intrinsic Hamilton Jacobi approach, *International Journal of Modern Physics A* **33**, p. 1892001 (2018).

The passage of time and top-down causation

Barbara Drossel

*Institute of Condensed Matter Physics, Technical University of Darmstadt,
Hochschulstr. 6, 64289 Darmstadt, Germany
E-mail: drossel@fkp.tu-darmstadt.de*

It is often claimed that the fundamental laws of physics are deterministic and time-symmetric and that therefore our experience of the passage of time is an illusion. This talk will critically discuss these claims and show that they are based on the misconception that the laws of physics are an exact and complete description of nature. I will argue that all supposedly fundamental deterministic and time-symmetric laws have their limitations and are supplemented by stochastic and irreversible elements. In fact, a deterministic description of a system is valid only as long as interactions with the rest of the world can be ignored. The most famous example is the quantum measurement process that occurs when a quantum system interacts with a macroscopic environment such as a measurement apparatus. This environment determines in a top-down way the possible outcomes of the measure- ment and their probabilities. I will argue that more generally the possible events that can occur in a system and their probabilities are the result of top-down influences from the wider context. In this way the microscopic level of a system is causally open to influences from the macroscopic environment. In conclusion, indeterminism and irreversibility are the result of a system being embedded in a wider context.

Keywords: Indeterminism, irreversibility, contextual emergence, top-down causation, nonreductionism

1. Introduction

The success of physics at explaining, calculating and controling processes in nature has led to the widespread belief that the equations of physics describe accurately how the state of a system changes with time under the influence of the various physical forces. Even more, many physicists think that the properties of the fundamental equations of physics are also properties of nature. Since these equations are deterministic, it is concluded that nature also is deterministic, with the time development being completely determined by the initial state and the fundamental laws. Furthermore, these laws are invariant under changing the direction of time. Based on this, many physicists think that the perceived direction of time is merely a consequence of very special initial conditions of the universe, and that all processes in nature could in principle also run backwards in time. Einstein is the most prominent scientist who considered the irreversible passage of time as an illusion since the present contains already the future, as it is fixed by the deterministic laws of physics and the initial conditions.

The implications of this understanding of physics are immense. It follows in particular that our experience of being agents that can act in the "now" and thus bring about future developments is also an illusion. And if everything is fully determined by the laws of physics, this contradicts our experience that our decisions are driven by non-physical causes such as values and logic and purpose.

While many philosophers of science buy the bold claims made by physicists, others are more skeptical. Indeed, there are many reasons to be skeptical. Physics as a science is always an approximate and incomplete description of nature and not a direct image of what goes on in nature. And many physicists not working with supposedly 'fundamental' physics such as quantum physics, but in condensed matter physics or soft matter physics, are aware of these limitations of the basic physical theories at describing nature. Instead of deriving the properties of their systems starting from the many-particle Schrödinger equation (which would be the fundamental equation for an object that consists of a huge number of atoms), they write down simpler models and effective theories that capture more directly the phenomenon to be described. These theories are often even in logical contradiction with the supposed fundamental theory, as explained in the following quote by Nobel laureate Anthony Leggett[1]:

> No significant advance in the theory of matter in bulk has ever come about through derivation from microscopic principles. [...] I would confidently argue further that it is in principle and forever impossible to carry out such a derivation. [...] The so-called derivations of the results of solid state physics from microscopic principles alone are almost all bogus, if 'derivation' is meant to have anything like its usual sense. Consider as elementary a principle as Ohm's law. As far as I know, no-one has ever come even remotely within reach of deriving Ohm's law from microscopic principles without a whole host of auxiliary assumptions ('physical approximations'), which one almost certainly would not have thought of making unless one knew in advance the result one wanted to get, (and some of which may be regarded as essentially begging the question). This situation is fairly typical: once you have reason to believe that a certain kind of model or theory will actually work at the macroscopic or intermediate level, then it is sometimes possible to show that you can 'derive' it from microscopic theory, in the sense that you may be able to find the auxiliary assumptions or approximations you have to make to lead to the result you want. But you can practically never justify these auxiliary assumptions, and the whole process is highly dangerous anyway: very often you find that what you thought you had 'proved' comes unstuck experimentally (for instance, you 'prove' Ohm's law quite generally only to discover that superconductors don't obey it) and when you go back to your proof you discover as often as not that you had implicitly slipped in an assumption that begs the whole question. [...] I claim then that the important advances in macroscopic physics come

essentially in the construction of models at an intermediate or macroscopic level, and that these are logically (and psychologically) independent of microscopic physics. Examples of the kind of models I have in mind which may be familiar to some readers include the Debye model of a crystalline solid, the idea of a quasiparticle, the Ising or Heisenberg picture of a magnetic material, the two-fluid model of liquid helium, London's approach to superconductivity .... In some cases these models may be plausibly represented as 'based on' microscopic physics, in the sense that they can be described as making assumptions about microscopic entities (e.g. 'the atoms are arranged in a regular lattice'), but in other cases (such as the two-fluid model) they are independent even in this sense. What all have in common is that they can serve as some kind of concrete picture, or metaphor, which can guide our thinking about the subject in question. And they guide it in their own right, and not because they are a sort of crude shorthand for some underlying mathematics derived from 'basic principles.'

The goal of this paper is to show that the claim that nature is at its most fundamental level reversible and deterministic is wrong. First, I want to explain that the time-reversible and deterministic nature of the supposedly fundamental physical equations are in fact idealizations that hold only under very specific conditions. In particular, the studied objects must be carefully isolated from interacting with the rest of the world. By taking a closer look at the areas of physics that are supposedly based on these fundamental equations, I will point out instances where indeterministic and irreversible additional elements are added to the theory when needed. This shows that the programme of deriving everything *only* from the fundamental equations is never realized in practice. I will furthermore argue that indeterminism and irreversibility are closely related, as the first implies the second.

The central part of my paper will focus on the influence of the environment and on top-down effects. By looking at what happens in a quantum measurement, we will see that the environment determines the possible events and their probabilities. This will lead us to a more general discussion of how stochasticity and irreversibility are the result of top-down effects from the context. A consequence of this is a contextually emergent view of nature, where not everything is controlled bottom-up by microphysics but there are also top-down influences from the surrounding context - even from without physics. This prepares the conclusion that while physics underlies everything that happens in nature, it does not determine everything.

2. Irreversibility and indeterminism in the 'fundamental' theories of physics

The following considerations show that no theory that was once or is now thought to be fundamental can do without adding irreversible elements.

2.1. *Classical mechanics*

Classical mechanics is based on Newton's law

$$m\frac{d^2\vec{x}}{dt^2} = \vec{F}(\vec{x}). \quad (1)$$

This law is deterministic as the position $\vec{x}$ and velocity $\vec{v} = d\vec{x}/dt$ at a given moment in time determine the future time evolution of $\vec{x}$ and $\vec{v}$. The law is invariant under time reversal as a change of the sign of t does not change the law. Consequently, when a time evolution of $\vec{v}$ and $\vec{x}$ has occurred from time $t = 0$ to $t = t_f$, the reverse time evolution takes place when starting at time t_f and inverting the velocity $\vec{v}$. When applying Newton's law to many particles that interact via mutual forces, the same conclusions are obtained. Due to its impressive success at unifying Kepler's laws of planetary motion and Galileis laws for falling bodies, Newton's theory was considered for a long time an exact and comprehensive description of the physical world, but there have always been cautious voices pointing out its limitations, see.[2,3] Only with the advent of the theory of relativity and quantum mechanics did it become clear to everybody that this view is wrong. Sometimes I wonder why physicists still make this mistake to believe that their most recent theories are exact and universal....

Back to classical mechanics: Even before the mentioned developments in the 20th century, it was clear that classical mechanics cannot do without irreversible elements: When comparing the equations to reality, one needs to include friction. For instance, a pendulum that swings freely under the influence of gravity will eventually come to rest as friction reduces the swinging amplitude with time. When including friction, Newton's law becomes

$$m\frac{d^2\vec{x}}{dt^2} = \vec{F}(\vec{x}) - \eta\frac{d\vec{x}}{dt} \quad (2)$$

with a friction term proportional to the velocity, the strength of which is determined by the friction coefficient η. Even the apparently so perpetual motion of the planets on their orbits is slowed down by friction due to tidal forces.

Classical mechanics also knows stochasticity. As explained so well by Gisin,[4,5] determinism is valid only if position and velocity have infinite precision. But physics is always limited to a finite number of bits when measuring and calculating the motion of objects. For chaotic systems, the time evolution of which depends extremely sensitively on the initial values, this means in practice that prediction of the future time evolution becomes impossible beyond a certain time horizon. There are good reasons to conclude that this indeterminism is not just a matter of our limited abilities, but an inherent feature of nature, see also.[5-7]

If we accept that chaotic systems are inherently stochastic, the irreversible nature of friction is coupled to stochasticity on the atomic level of description: Viewed microscopically, the slowing down of the pendulum is due to collisions of the pendulum with the randomly moving molecules in the air. However, the motion of the atoms is not deterministic since it is chaotic when described by Newton's laws.

2.2. Classical electrodynamics

Classical electrodynamics is governed by Maxwell's four equations,

$$\nabla \cdot \vec{E} = 4\pi \varrho \tag{3}$$

$$\nabla \times \vec{E} = -\frac{1}{c}\frac{\partial \vec{B}}{\partial t} \tag{4}$$

$$\nabla \cdot \vec{B} = 0 \tag{5}$$

$$\nabla \times \vec{B} = \frac{4\pi}{c}\vec{j} + \frac{1}{c}\frac{\partial \vec{E}}{\partial t} \tag{6}$$

These equations are again deterministic as an initial configuration of the electric and magnetic fields $\vec{E}$ and $\vec{B}$ and of the charge and current density distributions ϱ and $\vec{j}$ determine the future evolution of the fields, and using Newton's equation for the motion of the charges under the influence of the fields they also determine the time evolution of the charge and current densities.

The equations are also time reversible: When reversing the direction of time and that of currents and magnetic fields, Maxwell's equations remain unchanged. So for each time evolution there is an equally realistic reversed time evolution (as nature knows of no preferred orientation for currents or magnetic fields).

However, there is an important subfield of electrodynamics where the time reversal invariance is broken: This is the emission of radiation from accelerated charges. Using the electrostatic potential ϕ and the magnetic vector potential $\vec{A}$ instead of $\vec{E}$ and $\vec{B}$, the emitted radiation takes the form

$$\phi(\vec{r},t) = \int d^3r' \frac{\varrho\left(\vec{r}',t - \frac{|\vec{r}-\vec{r}'|}{c}\right)}{|\vec{r}-\vec{r}'|}, \tag{7}$$

$$\vec{A}(\vec{r},t) = \frac{1}{c}\int d^3r' \frac{\vec{j}\left(\vec{r}',t - \frac{|\vec{r}-\vec{r}'|}{c}\right)}{|\vec{r}-\vec{r}'|}. \tag{8}$$

This means that the potentials (and consequently the fields) at a position $\vec{x}$ at time t are determined by the motion of the charges at earlier times $t - \frac{|\vec{r}-\vec{r}'|}{c}$, which is simply the time electromagnetic radiation takes to propagate with the velocity of light from the point of origination $\vec{r}'$ to the point of measurement $\vec{r}$. All electromagnetic fields thus have localized sources in the temporal past.[8]

When explaining the reasons why emission of radiation is described by the retarded solutions, one has to resort to microscopic stochasticity: Radiation emitted by localized sources is absorbed by walls etc. The reverse process would be that different walls conspire to emit radiation that converges from all directions to a localised sink where it is completely absorbed and turned into motion of electrical charges. However, this 'conspiracy' is argued to be impossible as the atoms of the walls perform random thermal motion and therefore emit incoherent thermal radiation and not radiation that is correlated over large spatial scales. The thermal motion of the wall atoms is considered to be stochastic.

There is a second way how stochasticity enters electrodynamics: When trying to describe what happens at the atomic scale when light is emitted, one needs to resort to a quantum version of electrodynamics, which is quantum electrodynamics and describes the emission of light in terms of the stochastic emission of energy quanta (each containing an energy $\hbar\omega$ with ω being the frequency) from the source. And this brings us to the next section, which deals with quantum mechanics.

2.3. *Quantum mechanics*

The basic equation of nonrelativistic quantum mechanics for one particle is the Schrödinger equation

$$i\hbar\frac{\partial}{\partial t}\Psi(\vec{x},t) = \hat{H}\Psi(\vec{x}) \tag{9}$$

with the Hamilton operator

$$\hat{H} = \frac{\hat{p}^2}{2m} + V(\vec{x}). \tag{10}$$

Here, the first term is the kinetic energy, and the second the external potential. Given the initial state $\psi(\vec{x},0)$, the state at other times t are given by the relation

$$\Psi(\vec{x},t) = e^{-i\hat{H}t/\hbar}\,\Psi(\vec{x},0) \tag{11}$$

if the potential $V(\vec{x})$ is not explicitly time dependent.

This equation is deterministic. This means that the initial state, combined with the Hamiltonian determines the future time evolution. It is also invariant under time reversal: The time-reversed Schrödinger equation is solved by the complex conjugate wave function Ψ^*, and this does not affect the observables as they are calculated from expressions that contain products of Ψ and Ψ^*. All this holds also for the many-perticle version of the Schrödinger equation.

However, quantum mechanics is incomplete without a rule for how to calculate the outcome of a measurement. And this rule says that out of all possible measurement outcomes of an observable, one of them (let us call the corresponding state ϕ_n) is chosen stochastically with a probability that is given by $|\langle\phi_n|\Psi\rangle|^2$. This process is irreversible, as the reverse process (that the measurement apparatus or photographic plate returns to the pre-measurement state and emits the particle that has been absorbed during measurement) is not observed in nature. In this way, quantum mechanics includes from the onset irreversibility and stochasticity. There are a number of interpretations of quantum mechanics that attempt to explain away this dichotomy between the Schrödinger equation and the measurement process by describing also all the atoms of the measurment device by quantum mechanics, usually invoking decoherence in one way or another[9]; however, to many people these interpretations remain unsatisfactory as they cannot really explain why in a single run of an experiment only one of the possible outcomes is observed.[10,11] In one way or another, stochasticity kreeps into any interpretation. It does so even in Bohmian mechanics, where all stochasticity of the future time evolution is contained in the random features of the initial state.

2.4. *Quantum field theory*

The theory that is often considered the most fundamental one is quantum field theory, which is a relativistic theory for many particles and has several building blocks that take into account the different types of interactions and particles. It is a combination of the Glashow-Salam-Weinberg model for the electroweak interaction and of quantum chromodynamics for the strong interaction. Just as for nonrelativistic quantum mechanics, this theory includes two parts. Unitary time evolution according to a Hamilton operator is only applied between preparation and measurement of particles. The measurement outcome (e.g. of a scattering experiment or particle collision experiment) is again described by a probability that is calculated in a similar way as above. This means that everything written above for nonrelativistic quantum mechanics applies also to quantum field theory.

2.5. *Thermodynamics*

Thermodynamics is considered fundamental only by some scientists. But these scientists argue that thermodynamics might be even more fundamental than the other fields of physics. The most famous quotation in this direction is by Sir Arthur Eddington (From his book *The Nature of the Physical World*[12]):

> The law that entropy always increases holds, I think, the supreme position among the laws of Nature. If someone points out to you that your pet theory of the universe is in disagreement with Maxwell's equations - then so much the worse for Maxwell's equations. If it is found to be contradicted by observation - well, these experimentalists do bungle things sometimes. But if your theory is found to be against the Second Law of Thermodynamics I can give you no hope; there is nothing for it but to collapse in deepest humiliation.

Einstein had a similarly high opinion of thermodynamics:

> A law is more impressive the greater the simplicity of its premises, the more different are the kinds of things it relates, and the more extended its range of applicability. [...] It is the only physical theory of universal content, which I am convinced, that within the framework of applicability of its basic concepts will never be overthrown.

Now, the second law of thermodynamics is about the irreversibility of nature: All processes run in the direction in which the entropy of the universe increases. The relations of thermodynamics can be obtained also from a microscopic description, which is that of statistical physics. But statistical physics is not deterministic, as it is based on probabilities for the different possible microscopic states a system can take. This means that we have again a link between irreversibility and stochasticity in this field of physics.

3. A reversible, deterministic theory cannot give irreversibility

It is often argued that a 'fundamental' microscropic theory that is deterministic and reversible, such as classical mechanics or quantum mechanics, can give rise to irreversibility. Even textbooks on statistical mechanics often make this claim and use arguments based on coarse-graining. In this section, I will demonstrate that the 'derivations' of irreversibility from a microscopic reversible and deterministic theory all employ additional assumptions that are not part of the theory. They all invoque stochasticity or randomness in one way or another and are therefore not truly deterministic. As soon as stochasticity is employed, irreversibility follows naturally. The first subsection will argue that stochasticity leads to irreversibilty, and the second subsection will show how stochasticity is smuggled into the derivations of the second laws of thermodynamics from classical mechanics.

3.1. *Stochasticity gives irreversibility*

In the previous section, we have seen that irreversible processes are always coupled to stochasticity when considered on the atomic level, for instance when friction is described in terms of atomic collisions or when the approach to thermodynamic equilibrium is described by stochastic transitions between different microscopic states. More general considerations suggest that irreversibility and stochasticity are indeed intimately connected: Progress of time is perceived via changes. These changes occur in the form of events. Whenever one of a set of possible events occurs, the open future becomes the definite past. Thus, events are both irreversible and stochastic. There are several theories that are based on such events constituting the fabric of spacetime itself on the Planck scale.[13,14] But we need not know the most fundamental level in order to see that any stochastic event is also irreversible. This is because once the event has occurred the state prior to this event cannot be retrodicted. For a quantum measurement, e.g., the outcome does not allow to reconstruct the incoming wave function. A stochastic event itself is a step by which an indeterminate future gives way to a definite outcome. Against this, it is sometimes argued that probabilities can also be applied backwards for retrodiction. Yes, but this is qualitatively different: probabilities used in retrodiction are either Bayesian probabilities that are based on incomplete knowledge of the past, or they are frequencies in an ensemble of events. In principle, the past that precedes a given event is fixed in either case. In contrast, the future is not fixed if stochasticity is real and not merely apparent.

3.2. The hidden assumption in so-called 'derivations' of the Second Law from classical mechanics

In the following, I will use classical mechanics to demonstrate that additional assumptions are smuggled in when irreversibility is 'derived' from a reversible deterministic theory. A similar type of argument can be made for the supposed derivations of the Second law from a many-particle Schrodinger equation.[6] In both cases, the additional arguments are randomness of initial conditions and of statistical independence of degrees of freedom. The main ideas behind the 'derivations' of the Second Law from classical mechanics are as follows:

(i) A gas is modelled as a conservative mechanical system of $N \simeq 10^{23}$ small balls with hard-core repulsion, enclosed in a container of volume V with perfectly reflecting walls. Since energy does not change during time evolution, the trajectory of this mechanical system in $6N$-dimensional phase space stays within the $6N-1$-dimensional energy shell in which the initial state is placed. (ii) It is generally assumed, even though this is not proven, that the dynamics of this system is ergodic. This means that a "typical" trajectory approches each point of the energy shell with arbitrary precision ϵ if enough time has passed. Or, equivalently, an initially small and compact phase-space volume of dimension $6N$ (representing an ensemble of very similar initial conditions) will become stretched and folded to the extent that eventually some part of it will be in every small volume of size ϵ^{6N-1} in the energy shell. (iii) The vast majority of cells of size ϵ^{6N-1} correspond to macrostates with maximum entropy, which have (among other properties) an even distribution of density over the entire volume. (iv) Therefore, if starting in one of the few cells that correspond to a low-entropy initial state, after sufficiently long time the state of the system will 'almost certainly' be in a cell of maximum entropy.

Of course, each of these steps could be discussed in depth, in particular the starting assumption of infinite-precision phase space points and infinite-precision trajectories. I will focus on the last step and accept all preceding ones for the sake of brevity. In this last step, additional assumptions creep in: The last step is based on the assumption that the trajectory taken by the system is a 'typical' trajectory, or, equivalently, that among all the possible initial states that lie within the initial energy-shell volume element, the true initial state is a randomly chosen one. This is an assumption of randomness of the initial state. The laws of classical mechanics would not be violated if all particles of the gas would gather in irregular time intervals in some corner of the container. Among all possible initial states that agree with each other within a desired degree of precision, there would be particular initial states that show such an atypical behavior. We therefore have to introduce the additional assumption that the 'true' initial state is not such an 'atypical' one that leads to unexpected low-entropy future states. This is somewhat similar to what one does in electrodynamics when ruling out spatially localized sources of radiation that lie in the future.

Instead of postulating random initial conditions, one could equivalently argue that the initial state is not fixed with infinite precision but only with finite precision, and that randomness comes in as the time evolution of the system proceeds and more and more bits that were not fixed initially become relevant for fixing the ongoing time evolution. In my view there are many reasons to prefer this latter perspective, and it has been defended most forcefully by Nicolas Gisin.[5]

But there is more to stochasticity than that it is always added to 'deterministic' theories when real-world problems are addressed. Stochasticity depends on context. The next section focuses on this issue.

4. Stochasticity is context dependent

We have seen above that whenever the environment of a system is included irreversibility comes in: In mechanical systems, the environment causes friction. In electrodynamics, considering the emission of radiation means that there is an environment into which this radation can be emitted. In quantum mechanics, the interaction of a quantum particle with the rest of the world, which is here represented by a measurment device, causes the irreversible measurement event. Thermodynamics is a very interesting field of science from this point of view as it is a prime example of the environment determining what happens in a system: The environment imposes the temperature and the chemical potential. The environment performs changes on the system (such as pushing a piston or connecting a hot and a cold object) the effect of which is calculated in thermodynamics problems.

It is usually not acknowledged that stochasticity also requires a context. Karl Popper emphasized it in his paper "The propensity interpretation of probability",[15] where he argues that probabilities are defined only when the conditions under which the experiment is to be repeated are specified. Probabilities are thus defined relative to a setup in which the event of interest occurs. Popper justifies the propensity view by the findings of quantum mechanics. Indeed, the "fundamental" stochastic event is a quantum event. Its standard example is a measurement. Let us take for illustrative purposes the Stern-Gerlach experiment. It is the simplest quantum measurement as the observable to be measured is a spin-1/2, with only two measurement results, which we denote as $|+\rangle$ and $|-\rangle$. The measurement device measures the spin with respect to direction chosen by the experimenter. Let this direction be the positive z direction. If the incoming particles have not been polarized such that they point in the z direction, both measurement outcomes $|+\rangle$ and $|-\rangle$ are possible, and their probabilities depend on the preparation procedure. Now, the experimenter could have chosen to measure the spin with respect to another direction, for instance the x direction. In this case the possible measurement results would be again $|+\rangle$ and $|-\rangle$, but now these two results signify an orientation parallel or antiparallel to the direction of the x axis and no longer to the z axis. In general, the probabilities for the two measurement results are also different compared to a measurement in z direction.

This example demonstrates that the possible events and their probabilities are not an intrinsic property of the quantum particle but the combined effect of the way how the quantum particle has been prepared and of the measurement device. Had the experimenter chosen to measure position or energy instead of spin, the possible results and their probabilities would again have been different. Had the experimenter decided not to perform any measurement, the quantum particle would have remained in the state generated by the preparation procedure.

Now, quantum measurements are just one class of quantum mechanical events by which a quantum particle undergoes an irreversible, stochastic transition and exchanges energy with a macroscopic, finite-temperature object (which is a classical object). There need not be an experimenter, the particle could interact with the rest of the world in a different way. Examples are nuclear fusion reactions in the core of the sun or the emission of photons into space from the warm surface of the earth. Again, the fact that these events happen and their probabilities depend on the context.

So far, not many models for quantum measurement take this context explicity into account. Many authors, however, speak in a more general sense of quantum contextuality.[16,17] The Copenhagen interpretation of the measuremeent process makes an explicit distinction between classical objects (the measurment setup) and quantum objects, but does not detail how this difference arises. More explicit considerations of how the context is involved in a quantum measurement are advanced by Ellis[18] and more recently by Drossel and Ellis.[11]

This insight that there is a top-down effect from the environment or the larger spatial scale to the quantum particle leads us to the next section where we introduce the concepts of contextual emergence and top-down causation.

5. Contextual emergence and top-down causation

Physics is viewed by many people as a reductionistic science where the properties of an object are derived from its parts and their interactions. Consequently, those theories that deal with the most microscopic objects (i.e., particle physics and quantum field theory) are considered to be the most fundamental ones and to describe, at least in principle, everything that occurs on larger scales. But this is a one-sided view that ignores the various ways in which the context or the larger structure influences what happens at a smaller scale. To understand this better, it is useful to think of nature as a hierarchy of objects, with the objects on the lower level being the parts of the objects on the next hierarchical level. For instance, one can build the hierarchy Elementary particle - Atom - Crystal - Earth - Solar system - Galaxy - Universe; or, choosing a hierarchy that involves us humans: Elementary particle - Atom - Molecule - Cell - Organ - Individual - Society.

Now, describing an object in terms of its parts and their interaction is practised successfully by all scientists. For instance, describing the conducting properties of a metal, physicists build a model of electrons performing collisions with the lattice defects and the lattice vibrations (the so-called phonons) of the metal. Or, when exploring the cycle of growth and division of a biological cell, scientists describe this process by a network of molecular interactions and reactions. This success of the reductionist procedure often veils the view for the top-down influences that are equally important: The metal block provides the environment for lattice vibrations to exist, and the temperature of the metal block determines how many phonons of which frequency are present. The lattice structure of the metal determines what the conduction bands of the metal look like and thus strongly affects the way how electrons can propagate in the material. The wider context, such as the connection to a power supply is the prerequisite for conduction happening at all. Similarly, the growth and division of cells is regulated by mechanical and chemical cues from the embedding tissue to which the cell belongs. Furthermore, the cell depends on a continuous supply of nutrients and building material from its environment. For any other system of the hierarchies mentioned above, we can similarly list a variety of top-down influences of the whole on its parts. This topic of top-down causation is discussed extensively by George Ellis in his book "How can physics underlie the mind".[19]

All this means that reduction, successful as it is, is only part of the story. The complement of reduction is emergence: while reduction considers how the whole can be explained in terms of its parts, the concept of emergence considers the qualitatively new properties of the whole, which are not properties of the parts. One distinguishes between different concepts of emergence. Proponents of weak emergence hold that the emergent properties, even though they appear surprising and qualitatively different from the properties of the parts, can ultimately be fully accounted for by the properties of the parts. For a physicist this means that the theory describing the parts and their interactions contains at least implicitly all the phenomena observed in the whole. It is closely associated with a reductionist view. In contrast, proponents of strong emergence hold that the emergent properties are explained only partially by the parts and their interactions and cannot be fully reduced to them. The notion that captures best the type of strong emergence that occurs in physics is that of contextual emergence. It emphasizes that the existence of the parts and their properties depend on the context, the boundary conditions, etc. Until know, strong (or contextual) emergentists are a minority among physicists. The reductionist paradigm prevails despite the many good reasons to question it.

With this understanding of contextual emergence and top-down causation, we will gain a deeper understanding of how indeterminism enables our experience of the passage of time and of being agents.

6. Indeterminism and top-down causation

It is often argued that indeterminism is of no help at justifying free will and agency. The reason given is that stochasticity is completely random in the sense that random events are not influenced by anything else and can therefore not be part of a conscious act or decision - which is not random but follows logical reasoning or is based on values. However, our discussion of the quantum measurement process above has shown that stochastic events are not completely random. On the contrary, the possibility of these events and the nature of these events is set by the context. This is not appreciated very often. Karl Popper made the interesting suggestion that chance at the lower level is necessary for top-down causation from the higher level,[20] and he has been criticized for it.[21] But I think that he is right, and so do others.[7] Only when the entities at the lower level are not fully controlled by the microscopic laws can they respond to the higher level.

In biological systems, the influence of the environment on the types of stochastic events and their effects is evident at all levels: Let us take gene expression. The process by which transcription factors bind to the promoter region of a gene and enable transcription has many random elements, as diffusion and binding of transcription factors is subject to thermal noise. However, the context determines which transcription factors are activated at all. For instance, when I experience joy, this triggers the discharge of endorphins, which in turn stimulates the production of further endorphines via gene expression. On a larger timescale, evolution has shaped the transcription factors that we possess and the affinities to the different genes, resulting in the binding and dissociation rates that characterize the stochastic dynamics in our cells.

As another example, consider the brain. The neurons in our brain fire "randomly". At the same time, this electric activity reflects the brain activity, for instance while I formulate the text of this paper and type it. There is a wider context that influences the stochastic events in the brain: The past experiences have shaped the connection patterns and the strengths of the synapses of our neural network, and this in turn affects how activity propagates through the network and which neurons or groups of neurons are triggered by which others. Although there is randomness in the individual firing events of neurons, and on a more microscopic level in the opening and closing of ion channels, the frequency of firing and the neurons involved and the temporal sequence of which regions become active and which output neurons pass the signal on (for instance to my fingers while I am typing) is not random at all. Somehow it even reflects my creative activity while I develop my arguments for this text.

The constructive role of randomness in biological systems is discussed in more depth in several review articles.[22–24]

7. Conclusions

The view of physics that I have defended in this article is very different from the reductionist view that is propagated in many textbooks. The main problem with that view is that theories are applied far beyond their range of applicability. Any physical theory is an approximation and not an exact description of the physical processes of interest. And by no means it is a complete description of everything that is going on in the physical world. I have argued that even though the supposedly fundamental theories are deterministic and time-reversible, these theories are in practice supplemented by irreversible and stochastic features. There is no reason to assume that irreversibility and stochasticity are only apparent. Such a claim is based on ideology and not on evidence. I have argued that irreversibility and stochasticity enter when the influence of the environment on a system is taken into account. This focused the attention on the often-neglected topics of emergence and top-down causation. It is the context that sets the stage for the possible events that can happen in the system, and the context also influences the probabilities of these events.

It follows that our experience of time flowing and us being agents that can influence what happens is not contradicted by physics. Physics enables everything and underlies everything, but it does not determine everything. On the contrary, physics appears to be sufficiently complex to allow even life and consciousness to function on a material platform.[19] This bears some resemblence to Turing machines in computational science, which are complex enough to allow for any possible type of calculation.

Top-down influences come in different shapes. Top-down causation from the wider material context is easier to understand but is only part of the story. In particular the two biological examples of Section 6 illustrate that there is also an influence from the nonmaterial world of ideas, rationality, goals and desires on the activity of our genes and neurons. It may well be that physics will never find an access to describing these influences. The goal of my paper is far more modest, namely to make the case that physics cannot rule out that these influences are present. Physics is not causally closed and does not encompass everything that happens in our world.

To conclude, we should not let naive interpretations of the laws of physics constrain our view of reality. On the contrary, we should trust our most immediate experiences that are the basis for us being capable of thinking and acting, and based on these we should critically examine those simplistic metaphysical claims.

References

1. A. J. Leggett, On the nature of research in condensed-state physics, *Foundations of Physics* **22**, 221 (1992).
2. M. van Strien, Was physics ever deterministic? the historical basis of determinism and the image of classical physics, *The European Physical Journal H* **46**, 1 (2021).
3. F. Del Santo, Indeterminism, causality and information: Has physics ever been deterministic?, in *Undecidability, Uncomputability, and Unpredictability*, (Springer, 2021) pp. 63–79.
4. N. Gisin, Indeterminism in physics, classical chaos and bohmian mechanics: Are real numbers really real?, *Erkenntnis*, 1 (2019).
5. N. Gisin, Real numbers are the hidden variables of classical mechanics, *Quantum Studies: Mathematics and Foundations* **7**, 197 (2020).

6. B. Drossel, On the relation between the second law of thermodynamics and classical and quantum mechanics, in *Why More Is Different*, (Springer, 2015) pp. 41–54.
7. F. Del Santo and N. Gisin, Physics without determinism: Alternative interpretations of classical physics, *Physical Review A* **100**, p. 062107 (2019).
8. S. Weinstein, Electromagnetism and time-asymmetry, *Modern Physics Letters A* **26**, 815 (2011).
9. W. H. Zurek, Decoherence, einselection, and the quantum origins of the classical, *Reviews of modern physics* **75**, p. 715 (2003).
10. M. Schlosshauer, Decoherence, the measurement problem, and interpretations of quantum mechanics, *Reviews of Modern Physics* **76**, p. 1267 (2005).
11. B. Drossel and G. Ellis, Contextual wavefunction collapse: An integrated theory of quantum measurement, *New Journal of Physics* **20**, p. 113025 (2018).
12. A. Eddington, *The nature of the physical world: The Gifford Lectures 1927* (BoD–Books on Demand, 2019).
13. M. Cortês and L. Smolin, Quantum energetic causal sets, *Physical Review D* **90**, p. 044035 (2014).
14. R. D. Sorkin, Spacetime and causal sets, *Relativity and gravitation: Classical and quantum*, 150 (1990).
15. K. R. Popper, The propensity interpretation of probability, *The British journal for the philosophy of science* **10**, 25 (1959).
16. P. Grangier and A. Auffèves, What is quantum in quantum randomness?, *Philosophical Transactions of the Royal Society A: Mathematical, Physical and Engineering Sciences* **376**, p. 20170322 (2018).
17. G. Jaeger, Quantum contextuality and indeterminacy, *Entropy* **22**, p. 867 (2020).
18. G. F. Ellis, On the limits of quantum theory: Contextuality and the quantum–classical cut, *Annals of Physics* **327**, 1890 (2012).
19. G. Ellis, *How can physics underlie the mind?: Top-down causation in the human context* (Springer Heidelberg, 2016).
20. K. R. Popper and J. C. Eccles, *The Self and Its Brain: An Argument for Interactionism* (Springer Heidelberg Berlin, 1977).
21. T. O'Connor and H. Y. Wong, Emergent properties, in *The Stanford Encyclopedia of Philosophy*, ed. E. N. Zalta (Metaphysics Research Lab, Stanford University, 2015) Summer 2015 edn.
22. R. Noble and D. Noble, Harnessing stochasticity: How do organisms make choices?, *Chaos: An Interdisciplinary Journal of Nonlinear Science* **28**, p. 106309 (2018).
23. K. Wiesenfeld and F. Moss, Stochastic resonance and the benefits of noise: from ice ages to crayfish and squids, *Nature* **373**, 33 (1995).
24. L. S. Tsimring, Noise in biology, *Reports on Progress in Physics* **77**, p. 026601 (2014).

Explaining time's passage

Jonathan J. Dickau

Independent Researcher, ISGRG member
Poughkeepsie, New York 12603, USA
E-mail: jonathan@jonathandickau.com
www.jonathandickau.com

The way we experience time is in the accumulation of experiences and events that happen in the moment, and then are behind us. Since the time of Anaximander at least; philosophers have tried to explain both the nature of time and its origin or basis. In modern times; scientists are the ones exploring the domain of time, so now *they* attempt to explain the nature and basis of time – with varying degrees of success. This is complicated because explanations from Classical Physics or Relativity are different from, and incompatible with, answers from Quantum Mechanics, so we hope Quantum Gravity theories will help resolve this. Recent advances in Mathematics hold promise for a unified basis explaining both the thermodynamic and quantum-mechanical time arrows in a way that consistently informs our Philosophy. However; we may need to explore beyond the island of familiar Maths, to reconcile the divergent pictures of how and why time passes.

Keywords: Origin of time; passage of time; basis of time; Philosophy of time; Physics of time.

1. Introduction

While we imagine time is a single entity; the reality of time is more complex and more interesting. As far back as Anaximander[1]; philosophers have tried to make sense of that complexity, and his analogy of stepping into a moving stream actually comes very close to the reality we observe, since things keep moving while events are happening. So the simplest realities of life are governed by a rule that assures most decisions will be complex instead of simple. Coupling Plato's observation "time is the image of eternity[2]" with the insight that space is a projection of infinity can help us make sense of his deeper message. But then; we see glimpses into quantum gravity from the ancient Greek philosophers. Rovelli's book "Reality is Not What it Seems[3]" wonderfully recounts insights from those individuals that extend to topics including quantum gravity and the nature of time. While I agree with his view that we find the seeds of quantum gravity and the birth of atomism among ancient philosophers; we differ somewhat on whether time is fundamental or primordial on that basis. The resolution involves both cosmology and quantum gravity. So this paper explores how recent developments in Mathematics might have a deeper relevance than was previously appreciated to advance our understanding of time. I will discuss the examples cited above in greater detail and offer unique insights from my own research.[4,5]

Already in 1922, concluding a debate with Bergson; Einstein said "There is no such thing as the time of the philosopher.[6]" So for some it is a dead issue. But the debate goes on in the Physics community and among modern philosophers, over the consequences of how physical theory affects our understanding of time. This debate centers on the sharply differing views of time in Relativity and Quantum Mechanics. And there is strong evidence both views must be true. So if the traditional outlook is that time is a single entity for all; that view is broken. But this emphasizes the need to create new ways to conceptualize what we have learned in Physics and incorporate it into our Philosophy.[7] And yet; Anaximander's ancient view of time as a stream which continues to flow even as you are stepping in it remains enlightening in modern times. So there is hope for reconciling Physics with Philosophy, and knowledge that by developing quantum gravity theories; we gain a better philosophical understanding of time. I think the reverse is also true; it is easier to choose or develop better approaches to quantum gravity, by understanding the Philosophy of time better. Prevailing QG theories share many features and predictions with considerable common ground to explore.[8] So I examine ideas of Connes,[9] Longo,[10] Gisin,[11] as well as Drossel and Ellis,[12] on the emergence of time from quantum gravity, with some unique insights on wavefunction collapse from Dieter Zeh,[13] and a discussion of the possibility of global asymmetry as it applies to whether time is primordial or fundamental.[14]

2. What Is There to Explain?

If we had a better understanding of the extreme micro- and macro-scale in Physics; time would not be an enigma at all. But from my view; people are unaware they live in the 'Goldilocks zone' on an island of comfortable norms. The realm of familiar Maths is perfectly sufficient for exploring anything anywhere on the island; so who could want more? Theoretical Physics seeks the origins of events of our current surface-layer reality in deeper layers or causal elements further back in time. But if we cut ourselves off from the possibility those origins are higher-dimensional; we omit some probable realities that solve standing problems in Physics. This is because evolutive properties arise unavoidably when the underlying or governing algebra is non-commutative or non-associative. Time's passage may thus be caught up in how higher-order spaces are reduced in dimension through cosmological transitions to obtain a cosmos with familiar properties, such as the one we inhabit. Evolution arises automatically if the dimensions are high enough, as any system's degrees of freedom approach infinity; so it becomes almost certain that a space or its underlying algebra will evolve, or is self-evolving, once certain initial conditions are met. This involves a unit of minimum uncertainty or action, and at least a modicum of energy; but physicists observe that these conditions are handily met at the Planck scale. One might question creating something from nothing, but we are uncertain absolute nothing ever existed. So there is little argument, about reasons for time to move inexorably forward, if we assume the universe started from variations or variability and moved toward conditions.

And yet; people ask "what can cause numbers to change on their own or physical parameters change of their own accord?" It seems more reasonable to accept that virtual particles can pop in and out of existence in pairs, rather than that objects and spaces are evolving processes. But to explain time; we may need to accept that everything evolves on its own, unless it is otherwise constrained. To understand why time passes; I suggest we start with the assumption that objects and spaces are not necessarily static or fixed, and could be inherently time-evolving. This is precisely what Alain Connes proposed, when in 2000 he emphatically wrote "Noncommutative measure spaces evolve with time![15]" This result is based largely on the findings of Tomita[16] and Takesaki[17] studying modular Hilbert algebras, but Connes has generalized that work to create a new kind of differential geometry. This methodology is more nearly universal than people are aware of, however. Even if some of his ideas are not verified by current evidence; his line of reasoning is not falsified thereby, because intrinsic time evolution undeniably arises in higher-d Maths. This idea or the broader context it suggests provides a framework for a more realistic yet more flexible view of time. In this view time is, at its root, inherently or automatically progressing; originating from the dynamism of intrinsic evolution of forms and spaces in higher dimensions because the non-commutativity and/or non-associativity of their underlying algebra induces algebraic and geometric directionality and/or sequentiality.

This approach offers a unified basis for the quantum-mechanical and thermodynamic arrows of time that resolves some paradoxes or quandaries. If we see time in the tendency for objects and spaces to evolve automatically, once the degrees of freedom are high enough; we have a way to unite the Math and the Physics of time that resolves the paradox of differing time arrows from various models. This is perhaps a more major advancement than has been appreciated to this point. It restores seeing time as an accumulation of experiences or events that occur and are then behind us in a view of Quantum Mechanics where Heisenberg's uncertainty or 'unsharp measure' is due to spacetime being non-commuting. All interactions or observations accumulate because quantum-mechanical reality is like Anaximander's stream. But if we assume the evolution of the early cosmos was higher-dimensional too; we can extend intrinsic time to canonical time evolution in the initial origin at the Planck time through the inflationary period at least until baryogenesis, and likely continuing to play a part until decoupling or recombination occurred, or at a 5-d $\to$ 4-d boundary[18,19] that is seen as a black hole $\to$ white hole transition[20,21] in some theories. Time evolves from higher-d spaces through cosmological transitions, in these models. The Aikyon theory of Singh[22,23] employs Connes' intrinsic time and the octonions to explain both cosmic origins and particle physics without such transitions, but affirms other aspects of my present work. So we now examine a proposed basis for these varied ideas.

3. Explaining What We Observe

Great successes in Physics assume what we observe is built and can be explained from the bottom up, from the smallest components or the simplest applicable formulas, but there is another way to explain what we see, where nature employs top-down methods taking advantage of higher-order and higher-dimensional mathematical forms, as well. If we allow a broader spectrum of possibilities at the cosmos' origin, by assuming that both bottom-up and top-down strategies are at work at the same time; a picture emerges where dimensionality has an upper and lower limit at the outset of geometrogenesis, which later converges toward a single value.[24] This lets emergent forms be shaped by higher-d figures like the Monster Group and E_8, during the earliest phases of cosmological evolution, even while they are being built from lower-d components. From this radically top-down outlook, even when coupled with causal structure theories of quantum gravity; the conventional view using bottom-up reasoning is inside-out, and we need a view where we see the universe from the outside-in, to fully understand it. The disparity is partly due to the way most people have learned Maths, where the simplest elements are taught first and advanced ideas are derived from the simplicities. However; we know there are patterns that emerge in complex structures from which simple rules can be derived.

This dichotomy is called additive vs. formant synthesis. In the one case; you add bits of clay to make a sculpture or individual harmonic tones to create the desired waveform, while in the other you chip bits away from the outside or remove some overtones from a more complex waveform, to obtain the desired shape. Here I propose that nature has utilized and always uses both methods to shape the cosmos. It builds larger and more complex forms using smaller pieces, but it also pares physical reality down from a palette of possible forms, and borrows structure from more complex forms to create simpler ones. In this way; nature can employ the full range of Mathematics and exploit the true organizing power of what resides in higher dimensions. But the outside-in view is difficult to obtain on the island of common Maths where mathematical structures are built from the bottom-up, rather than inherited from orderly patterns in higher-level structure. To gain *that* view we need to look beyond the familiar island where features like commutativity and associativity can be taken for granted, and explore the unfamiliar expanse of non-commutative and non-associative algebras and geometry. Luckily mathematicians have already charted a lot of the content that exists in higher-d spaces, and we are learning how some of it works to shape the laws of Physics. A clear example is found in the normed division algebras, and in the reduction of the octonions to the quaternions, the complex numbers, and the reals.

$$\mathbb{O} \supset \mathbb{H} \supset \mathbb{C} \supset \mathbb{R} \tag{1}$$

The octonions are the most general number type, 8-dimensional with one real and seven imaginary parts but are non-associative; the quaternions are 4-d with three imaginary parts but are non-commutative; the complex numbers have one real and one imaginary part, but are well-behaved; and only the reals encode a constant value. Imaginary numbers encode variation or the freedom to vary by a specified amount in a certain direction or orientation. Though they are the granddaddy of familiar types, the octonions are thought to be weird and difficult.[25] Viewing the imaginary dimensions as rotations; the octonions reduce to the quaternions if 4 of their 7 axes are fixed, that reduce to the complex numbers if 2 of the remaining 3 are fixed, and if the last rotation is halted, only the real-numbered value remains. The octonion algebra itself is a reduction because 480 possible multiplication tables before choosing a starting place and direction reduce to 16, 8 left- and 8 right-handed algebras.[26] And once any table is chosen, we must employ only that one table thereafter. Each step in any octonion calculation thus proceeds from optiony toward specificity.

$$Smooth \supseteq Top \supseteq Meas \qquad (2)$$

$$Gas \supseteq Liquid \supseteq Solid \qquad (3)$$

In the relations above; we see this pattern of moving from variability or variations to definite conditions as a more general bridge between the fields of Math and Physics that needs to be further explored. Moving from left to right; we see that acquiring a surface or boundary makes a space or object topological, or indicates a phase change from a gas to a liquid state. Then having a fixed metric makes objects or spaces measurable, or indicates the transition or phase change to the solid state. This reflects the sensibility of the earlier expression where applying successive constraints to the octonions eventually gets us to the real numbers. We observe that evolutive properties arising from directionality in higher-d Maths project onto or influence what comes after, such that things tend to evolve from highly variable states toward specific conditions and discrete possibilities. One might question the applicability of this line of reasoning to real-world Physics or everyday life. It certainly has a place for answering questions in early universe Cosmology, in Quantum Gravity, and the underpinnings of Quantum Mechanics. But the actual footprint of non-commutative and non-associative algebra and geometry is scarcely known. That is why it is important for today's Physics researchers to look into evolutive properties that arise in these Maths, as a possible source or root cause for the evolution of time.

The idea that spaces with certain properties have a built-in time evolution is neither well-known nor well-understood, except among a handful of ardent researchers in this arena. But when Tomita[27] opened that door, by discovering intrinsic evolution in modular Hilbert algebras; Connes and others were quick to apply that notion to a broader class of objects and spaces. To walk through that door, we must go beyond the island of familiar Maths and embrace the idea that non-commutativity and non-associativity are more of a blessing than a curse to Physics,[28] because they assure directed evolution. But we must first accept that if reality is quantum-mechanical, non-commutative ordering factors automatically arise due to Heisenberg uncertainty making the space we live in non-commutative. Notably; this issue also arises in Relativity[29] as factor-ordering problems sometimes, when applying the equivalence principle. However, it happens often. Cycles of action must be undertaken in a specific sequence both when doing octonion algebra and with common tasks like painting or baking,[30] where a process of ratcheting accumulation happens in both cases. So the demands of additional rules of order and sequence one must learn to use non-commutative and non-associative algebras are not unnatural or onerous, and in fact represent the same laws of directional evolution all natural processes must follow.

$$\delta: \to \text{Aut}(M) \qquad (4)$$

Connes[31] uses the above expression, where $\text{Out}(M) = \text{Aut}(M)/\text{Int}(M)$ the quotient group of automorphisms of M by its normal subgroup of inner automorphisms, to show how modular or Tomita flow gives rise to intrinsic time evolution. He emphatically asserts that non-commutative spaces evolve with time and this is greatly expanded in recent work by Longo,[32] showing why non-commutative spaces must evolve, and explaining the basis for time's emergence in detail. Non-commutativity is enough to assure time will evolve, and we undeniably live in a space that is non-commutative. The background state of physical reality is not what Classical Physics would imagine a vacuum to be, a static space absent of contents. We can point to quantum uncertainty or virtual particles to explain this, but time's directionality can also be seen to result from residing in a higher-d spacetime instead of 3-d space plus time. Longo extends Connes' arguments to a more robust connection between quantum mechanics and thermodynamics using the language of operator algebras, and shows how time emerges as a result. But he sees this as resulting from wavefunction collapse, and I do not see emergent time as dependent upon that feature. Here I remind the reader of an outside-in view offered by Dieter Zeh[33] suggesting that the global wavefunction is more real or fundamental than particles or quantum transitions, and persists while we measure. But recent work by Peter Morgan,[34] using the Koopman-von Neumann formalism, suggests we can choose between collapse and no-collapse models depending on the context, so long as we talk about subsequent measurements rather than states.

Things go from possibility toward actuality. However; this dynamism does not depend on properties arising in higher-d spaces and hyper-complex algebras or from infinities, as in the above examples, so higher-d attributes are not essential for top-down mechanisms to work. Gisin[35] points out that even real numbers, which are commonly viewed as fixed quantities, are only fixed by a process of determination. From an intuitionist view; the exact or precise value of a quantity is not known before it is determined in a process. So if there is a specific real number with a large number of digits; we may not find out what extended values are for a long time, and information on what is beyond a given point is no better than random data. This is like a stochastic background in the realm of the indeterminate, which influences our view of time. Gisin speaks to this issue[36] and also has novel ideas about wavefunction collapse.[37] This work informs the Contextual Collapse model of Drossel and Ellis,[38] a top-down approach which treats the quantum measurement problem in detail, where measurement is by nature a multi-stage process. Their work addresses shortcomings in decoherence theory and other models, which they handle individually, concluding that a robust description includes both Quantum and Classical elements because any physical measurement unavoidably includes a mix of both, depending on the context. They further extend the conversation to how quantum measurements are a special case, projections of the wavefunction; of a larger class they call events which are ubiquitous in nature.

4. What Kind of Philosophy Is Best for Physics?

Is there a single best Philosophy of Physics? While some would argue that learning Philosophy is a side trip for those learning Physics; that in itself is a Philosophy about how Science is done. So it is unavoidable that the two are interwoven. This is aptly illustrated by Rovelli[39] in his paper arguing that Philosophy and Physics need each other, contrasting the schools of Isocrates and Plato. While Isocrates taught that practical skills and their application should be cultivated; Plato advocated the quest for knowledge of how or why things work, and how they came to be as they are. While Plato was among the first to be called a philosopher; we put both in that category in modern times, and their teachings are seen as two competing schools of Philosophy. Aristotle argued that general theory supports practice, and one can argue that both approaches are needed to make progress in some areas. But the debate about which philosophy is best goes on today, writ large on the face of politics. This influences funding for all areas of Science, depending on the philosophy of the prevailing political party. This split is seen to be connected to our perception of time, in that liberals have a more forward-facing view, being focused on creating a better future, while conservatives tend to focus on preserving the legacy and traditions of our past, which is more rearward-facing. Here again; people fiercely debate which philosophy is correct, or benefits us most, rather than seeing that both viewpoints are needed.

If asked what kind of Philosophy is best for Physics; I would advise people to seek an inclusive or encompassing view of reality. We need to be explorers, unafraid to look beyond the boundaries, if we want to make important discoveries or developments. And we must be wary of information silos that present a self-consistent but wrong-headed view of the world. The incorrect usage of the word recombination persists in astrophysics, for example, to describe what happens at the horizon of last scattering during decoupling; even though early-universe cosmology tells us nuclei and electrons never were combined into atoms before then. This illustrates how skilled scholars work on an island of familiar and comfortable norms, with fierce pressure to remain within the bounds of their area of specialization. The self-consistent view within the silo is often reinforced by walls that are polished mirror smooth. An outsider and generalist like myself gets a different view from others when attending quantum gravity lectures, for example, because the common ground stands out as starkly as the differences between approaches, and I have no need for a clear winner. I think all of the current lines of research inform us in useful ways, and are not mutually-exclusive. But we should not stop exploring or seeking other options to explore, just because we have some viable explanations for gravity on the table.

So the ideal Philosophy for Physics always leaves the door open to learning more about what we think we know, discovering something new or unexpected, and so on. We are unavoidably inside a construction that is the cosmos, and further limited because we can see only what is within the Hubble radius. We are on the inside, looking out at the larger cosmos. This is why I advocate seeking the outside-in view of Math and Physics, as a radical extension of the top-down view, and as a possible cure for the view that making things from the bottom-up cannot only create all form but aptly explains all we see. A basic fact about explorers is needing somewhere to explore. Perhaps we need to get off-planet to obtain the perspective we need for the outside-in view beyond our limitations. Or maybe we only need to seek that perspective from higher ground philosophically. To see a circle in its entirety; one must be off the page, in the 3rd dimension. Likewise; to draw that circle, one must be in a dimension one higher than the surface on which you are drawing. If this as a general pattern; there is always a need to discern what the structure we are living in would look like from one dimension higher. But the block universe of General Relativity, of spacetime as seen from the outside, is a severe limitation. So we need to frame other constructs that give us better scaffolding for our ideas of the view from out there. And that is the main thrust of this paper; to inspire others who might help to create that structure.

When entertaining questions about Philosophy and Physics; one cannot forget the way Mathematics always makes its way onto the scene. Plato brought to light the notion of a mathematical ideal or archetype which is projected onto physical reality. We now have a much more sophisticated notion of how that works, but the idea persists to this day. I think we need to be hyper-dimensional Platonists, with a guide to the Atlas of Lie Groups[40] in every College library where they teach higher-level Math and Physics subjects. In this way; we will speed up the process of discovery fueled by what we know. But we need to introduce some ideas at an earlier age, so tomorrow's young people will have the benefit of what we as adults already know. This is what David Blair[41] seeks to do with the "Einstein First" program, which teaches advanced concepts based on our latest knowledge, and then works that back into the structure of what students have already learned. This allows young people to benefit from the understanding of their elders, in a context that is not intimidating for teachers with a limited knowledge of Relativity. We should attempt to do the same with other areas of Mathematics and Physics so the next generation will have the benefit of what we have learned. This might not be possible if we teach things solely from the bottom-up view. What if we had young people building Zome models[42] of E_8 instead? At least we need to give kids a chance to see what these figures look like, at Science Centers and Math Museums.

The nexus of Philosophy and Physics must be strong, for either topic to provide useful information. This means it is incumbent on the organizers of events and publications to provide a context for insightful contributions that forge a stronger connection between what appear to be separated views, or to push the envelope of developments on the outskirts. The 16th Marcel Grossmann conference was exemplary on both of these fronts, in its spirit of cooperation, openness, and inclusivity. The organizers deliberately included minority views and off-limits topics in both the choice of plenary speakers and in the various breakout sessions. So people were encouraged to look outside of their silos somewhat, and to explore what is beyond the island of comfortable mainstream assumptions. During MG16; a Philosophy of Physics approaching the ideal was observed. But in the world at large; there is a lot of progress to be made forging connections to support a higher ideal. What we see now is a world that largely ignores the advice of both philosophers and physicists, in favor of following popular icons. There is much to do, if we want the ideas that enlighten physicists to be meaningful for everyone, but things being discovered in Physics have a meaning that unavoidably affects all equally. There is no point to arguing Physics is devoid of meaning. Therefore our Philosophy must include the notion that Physics is relevant.

We owe much of our current understanding to the philosophers of ancient Greece, not least the notion of atomism with indivisibly small bits or increments in the cosmos or the way it is constructed, as was well-explained in Rovelli's book.[43] Leucippus likely brought the seed of this idea to Democritus from Anaximander's school. But we can see that atomism applied to Plato's comment that time is the projected image of eternity, shows up as every atom in the stream of Anaximander having a duration or persistence in time. This is observed as a half-life, when examining the same phenomenon in nuclear or sub-atomic Physics, due in part to the relativistic effects of time dilation. But here I note that parcels of space needed to have persistence in time already for those particles to exist. That is why it is important to continue our exploration of quantum gravity theories and try to understand the cosmological context for these theories in a broader way. So physicists should see it as a responsibility to build bridges between the philosophically disconnected islands of thought, by applying a Philosophy of Physics that supports our common endeavor to learn the secrets of the cosmos. Encouraging students as well as researchers to explore beyond what is known is important, and willingness to question our own boundaries is an important first step. We must be ready to leave the world of comfortable norms behind, when examining cosmic origins, to fully understand how things got to be the way they are now.

References

1. Anaximander, (c. 611-546 BC).
2. Plato, *Timaeus* 37d (c. 360 BC).
3. C. Rovelli, *Reality is not What it Seems — the Journey to Quantum Gravity* (Allen Lane, 2016).
4. J. J. Dickau, Gravitation by Condensation, in *Fundamental Physics and Physics Education Research*, eds. B. G. Sidharth, J. C. Murillo, M. Michelini, C. Perea (Springer, Cham., 2020) https://doi.org/10.1007/978-3-030-52923-9_7.
5. J. J. Dickau, The Intrinsic Time of Alain Connes and Evolutive Properties in higher-d Algebras, *Prespacetime Jour.*, **12**, 3, pp. 283–299 (2020).
6. A. Einstein, quote from a debate with Henri Bergson (1922).
7. C. Rovelli, Physics Needs Philosophy. Philosophy Needs Physics, *Found. Phys.*, **48**, 5, pp. 481–491 (2018).
8. J. J. Dickau, Confluence of Theories, *Prespacetime Jour.*, **11**, 4, pp. 346–351 (2020).
9. A. Connes, A View of Mathematics, unpublished essay, pg. 16, which now part of the *UNESCO Encyclopedia of Life Support Services* (2004).
10. R. Longo, The Emergence of Time, *Expositiones Mathematicae*, **38**, 2, pp. 240–258, (2020) https://doi.org/10.1016/j.exmath.2020.01.005, arXiv:1910.13926.
11. N. Gisin, Mathematical languages shape our understanding of time in physics, *Nature Physics*, **16**, pp. 114–116, (2020) https://doi.org/10.1038/s41567-019-0748-5, arXiv:2002.01653.
12. B. Drossel and G. F. R Ellis, Contextual Wavefunction Collapse: An integrated theory of quantum measurement, *New Jour. Phys.*, **20**, 113025, arXiv:1807.08171 (2018).
13. H. D. Zeh, There are no quantum jumps, nor are there particles!, *Phys. Lett. A*, **172**, 4, pp. 189–192 (1993).
14. D. Schleicher and D. Dudko, Core Entropy of Quadratic Polynomials, *Arnold Math Jour.*, **6**, pp. 333–385, arXiv:1412.8760 (2020).
15. A. Connes, *Noncommutative Geometry Year 2000*, in *Visions in Mathematics: GAFA 2000 Special volume, Part II*, pp. 481–559, Birkhäuser Basel, arXiv:math/0011193 (2000).
16. M. Tomita, Quasi-standard von Neumann algebras, unpublished preprint (1967).
17. M. Takesaki, Tomita's Theory of Modular Hilbert Algebras and its Applications, *Lect. Notes Math*, Vol. 128 Springer-Verlag, Berlin-New York (1970).
18. G. Dvali, G. Gabadadze, and Porrati, 4D Gravity on a Brane in 5D Minkowski Space, *Phys. Lett. B*, **485**, 1–3 pp. 208–214, arXiv:hep-th/0005016 (2000).
19. C. de Rham, et al. Cascading Gravity: Extending the Dvali-Gabadadze-Porrati Model to Higher Dimension, *Phys. Rev. Lett.*, **100**, 251603 (2008).
20. R. Pourhasan, N. Afshordi, and R. Mann, Out of the White Hole: a holographic origin for the Big Bang, *Jour. of Cosmo. and Astroparticle Phys.*, **2014**, arXiv:1309.1487; (2014).
21. N. Poplawski, Radial motion into an Einstein–Rosen bridge, *Phys. Lett. B*, **687**, 2–3, pp. 110–113, arXiv:0902.1994 (2010).
22. T. P. Singh, Octonions, trace dynamics and non-commutative geometry: A case for unification in spontaneous quantum gravity, *Z. Naturforschung A*, **75**, 12, pp. 1051–1062, arXiv:2006.16274; (2020).
23. T. P. Singh, Trace dynamics and division algebras: towards quantum gravity and unification, *Z. Naturforschung A*, **76**, 2, 131–162, arXiv:2009.05574 (2021).
24. J. J. Dickau, Bimetric Convergence, *Prespacetime Jour.*, **11**, 4, pp. 294–304 (2020).
25. J. C. Baez, The octonions, *Bull. Am. Math Soc.*, **39**, pp. 145–205, arXiv:math/0105155 (2002).

26. R. Lockyer, 16 Octonion Algebras – 30 Aliases – 480 Representations, preprint, (2010) can be found at: http://www.octospace.com/files/16_Octonion_Algebras_-_480_Representations.pdf.
27. M. Tomita, ibid Ref. 16 (1967).
28. P. C. Kainen, *An octonion model for physics*; in *Proceedings of 4th Intl. Conf. on Emergence, Coherence, Hierarchy, and Organization (ECHO IV)*, Odense, Denmark (2000) found at: http://faculty.georgetown.edu/kainen/octphys.pdf and also at: https://www.researchgate.net/publication/2472211_An_Octonion_Model_for_Physics.
29. C. W. Misner, K. S. Thorne, and J. A. Wheeler, *Factor-ordering problems in the Equivalence Principle*, chap. 16, sec. 3, pp. 388–392 in: *Gravitation*, W.H. Freeman and Co., New York (1973).
30. J. J. Dickau, Painting, Baking and Non-Associative Algebra, *Prespacetime Jour.*, **11**, 3, pp. 265–268 (2020).
31. A. Connes, ibid Ref. 15 (2000).
32. R. Longo, ibid Ref. 10 (2020).
33. H. D. Zeh, ibid Ref. 13 (1993).
34. P. W. Morgan, The collapse of a quantum state as a signal analytic sleight of hand, preprint, arXiv:2101.10931 (2021).
35. N. Gisin, ibid Ref. 11 (2020).
36. N. Gisin, *Time Really Passes, Science Can't Deny That*, in *Time in Physics* eds. R. Renner and S. Stupar, Springer, pp. 1–15, arXiv:1602.01497 (2017).
37. N. Gisin, *Collapse. What Else?* in *Collapse of the Wavefunction* Ed. Shan Gao, Cambridge Uni. Press, pp. 207–224, arXiv:1701.08300 (2018).
38. B. Drossel and G. F. R Ellis, ibid Ref. 12 (2018).
39. C. Rovelli, ibid Ref. 3 (2018).
40. *Atlas of Lie Groups and Representations*, (2007) with much explanatory material found at: http://www.liegroups.org/.
41. D. Blair, *The Einstein-First Project*, (2021) much information found at: https://www.einsteinianphysics.com/.
42. D. A. Richter, *Gosset's Figure in 8 Dimensions, A Zome Model*, found at: http://homepages.wmich.edu/~drichter/gossetzome.htm which is constructed from Zometools, found at: https://www.zometool.com/.
43. C. Rovelli, ibid Ref. 7 (2016).

A glimpse to Feynman's contributions to the debate on the foundations of quantum mechanics

M. Di Mauro

Dipartimento di Matematica, Università di Salerno, Via Giovanni Paolo II,
Fisciano (SA), 84084, Italy
E-mail: madimauro@unisa.it

S. Esposito* and A. Naddeo†

INFN, Sezione di Napoli, C. U. Monte S. Angelo, Via Cinthia,
Napoli, 80125, Italy
*E-mail: sesposit@na.infn.it
† E-mail: anaddeo@na.infn.it

The broad debate on foundational issues in quantum mechanics, which took place at the famous 1957 Chapel Hill conference on *The Role of Gravitation in Physics*, is here critically analyzed with an emphasis on Richard Feynman's contributions. One of the most debated questions at Chapel Hill was whether the gravitational field had to be quantized and its possible role in wave function collapse. Feynman's arguments in favor of the quantization of the gravitational field, based essentially on a series of gedanken experiments, are here discussed. Then the related problem of the wave function collapse, for which Feynman hints to decoherence as a possible solution, is discussed. Finally, another topic is analyzed, concerning the role of the observer in a closed Universe. In this respect, Feynman's many-worlds characterization of Everett's approach at Chapel Hill is discussed, together with later contributions of his, including a kind of Schrödinger's cat paradox, which are scattered throughout the 1962-63 Lectures on Gravitation. Philosophical implications of Feynman's ideas in relation to foundational issues are also discussed.

Keywords: Gedanken experiment; Wave function collapse; Many-worlds.

1. Introduction: The Chapel Hill conference

Richard Feynman's most famous contribution in quantum theory is undoubtedly his celebrated path integral approach.[1] His contributions to the debate on interpretational issues are instead much less well known.[2,3] The first such contributions took place in the wide discussions which characterized the 1957 Chapel Hill conference,[4] whose title was: *The Role of Gravitation in Physics*. The Chapel Hill conference, which played a key role in triggering the so called *Renaissance* of general relativity[5] was of capital importance in establishing the future research lines in the field. Broadly, the main tracks were[6]: classical gravity, quantum gravity, and the classical and quantum theory of measurement (as a link between the previous two topics). In particular, foundational quantum issues were widely discussed by researchers attending the conference. The main motivation for addressing them came from the fundamental question of whether the gravitational field had to be quantized, like other fundamental fields, or not. As its title declares, the ambitious goal of the conference was the merging of general relativity with the rest of physics and, especially, with the world of elementary particle physics, which was ruled by quantum mechanics, hence it was (and it still is, of course) very important to understand physics in regimes where both gravity and quantum mechanics become important. This was clearly stated by Peter G. Bergmann in the opening session of the second half of the conference, which was in fact focused on problems within the quantum domain (Ref. 4, p. 165):

> Physical nature is an organic whole, and various parts of physical theory must not be expected to endure in "peaceful coexistence." An attempt should be made to force separate branches of theory together to see if they can be made to merge, and if they cannot be united, to try to understand why they clash. Furthermore, a study should be made of the extent to which arguments based on the uncertainty principle force one to the conclusion that the gravitational field must be subject to quantum laws: (a) Can quantized elementary particles serve as sources for a classical field? (b) If the metric is unquantized, would this not in principle allow a precise determination of both the positions and velocities of the Schwarzschild singularities of these particles?

The answer to these questions was expected to lead to a novel perspective on the ordinary notions of space and time, by introducing uncertainty relations for quantities such as distances and volumes. Physicists hoped that, as a result, the divergences which plagued quantum field theory would get suppressed by the gravitational field. Along with the formal discussion on the main approaches to the quantization of the gravitational field (namely the canonical, the functional integral and the covariant perturbative approaches), which would have been developed in the following decades, a lot of time was devoted to conceptual issues, especially in discussion sessions. A broad debate arose on the problem of quantum measurement, the main conceptual question being:

> What are the limitations imposed by the quantum theory on the measurements of space-time distances and curvature? (Ref. 4, p. 167)

or, equivalently

> What are the quantum limitations imposed on the measurement of the gravitational mass of a material body, and, in particular, can the principle of equivalence be extended to elementary particles? (Ref. 4, p. 167)

As the editors of the written records of the conference[4] emphasized, an answer to the above questions could not be simply found in dimensional arguments, since the

Planck mass does not set a lower limit to the mass of a particle whose gravitational field can be measured. Indeed, a simple argument shows that the gravitational field of *any* mass can in principle be measured, thanks to the "long tail" of the Newtonian force law (Ref. 4, pp. 167-8).

The great part of the discussions of interest to us here developed in Section VIII of the conference (Ref. 4, pp. 243-60), where the focus was mainly on the contradictions eventually arising in the logical structure of quantum theory if gravity quantization is not assumed, but in fact many even more foundational issues for quantum physics in general were touched as well. Feynman greatly contributed to these discussions, proposing several gedanken experiments in order to argue in favor of the necessity of gravitational quantization, and hinting to decoherence as a viable solution to the problem of wave function collapse. His contributions in fact triggered a wide debate on the quantum measurement problem and on the existence and meaning of macroscopic quantum superpositions. Further, in the subsequent session of the conference, which was the closing one (Ref. 4, pp. 263-278), he gave a "many-worlds" characterization of Hugh Everett III's relative state interpretation of quantum mechanics,[7] which had just been described for the first time by Everett's advisor, John A. Wheeler. It is interesting to notice that, in fact, the Chapel Hill conference was one of the few places where Feynman was directly involved in discussions about the foundations and interpretation of quantum mechanics.[2]

The Chapel Hill discussions played a pivotal role in triggering subsequent research on foundational issues, mainly on the quantum measurement problem and on the various possible interpretations of quantum mechanics, with an emphasis on the consequences of Everett's one. In this respect it is worth mentioning further contributions by Feynman, who despite not being often involved with foundational quantum issues, nonetheless kept thinking deeply on them also in the following years, especially when working on gravity, as hinted for example in a letter written in 1961 to Viktor Weisskopf[8]:

> How can we experimentally verify that these waves are quantized? Maybe they are not. Maybe gravity is a way that quantum mechanics fails at large distances.

as well as in several suggestions and considerations scattered throughout his 1962-63 graduate lectures on gravitation.[9]

In this paper, we historically and critically analyze Feynman's contributions to the debate about the foundations of quantum mechanics and gravity, with an emphasis on the Chapel Hill discussions, which constitute the main source about his thoughts on the matter. In particular, Section 2 deals with the problem of the quantization of the gravitational field while in Sections 3 and 4 the focus is on wave function collapse following a measurement and on Everett's relative state interpretation of quantum mechanics. Finally our concluding remarks are summarized in Section 5.

2. Quantization of the gravitational field: Gedanken experiments

In this Section we report on Feynman's arguments in favor of the quantization of the gravitational field. As a matter of fact, Feynman believed that nature cannot be half classical and half quantum and shared Bergmann's general ideas, as recalled by himself in some concluding remarks made at the end of the conference:

> The questions raised in the last three days have to do with the relation of gravity to the rest of physics. We have gravity - electrodynamics - quantum theory - nuclear physics - strange particles. The problem of physics is to put them all together. The original problem after the discovery of gravity was to put gravity and electrodynamics together since that was essentially all that was known. Therefore, we had the unified field theories. After quantum theory one tries to quantize gravity (Ref. 4, p. 272).

In particular, for Feynman gravity, like the other fundamental interaction that we experience at the macroscopic, classical level, i.e. electromagnetism, has a quantum foundation (see e.g. Refs. 10–12). Coherently with this, he developed an approach to quantum gravity (whose first hints were given at Chapel Hill, cf. Ref. 4, pp. 271-276) which was characterized by being fully quantum from the beginning.[9,13]

Feynman's arguments in favor of the quantization of gravity were totally different from the usual dimensional arguments, which rely on the assumption that gravity has to dominate over all other interactions at the Planck scale. According to him quantum effects involving gravity should be subject to probing without invoking such high scales. He provided further evidence to support this claim by putting forward thought experiments designed to show that, if quantum mechanics is required to hold for objects massive enough to produce a detectable gravitational field (the opposite would require a modification of quantum mechanics), then the gravitational field has to be quantized, in order to avoid contradictions. This view supported the hope that quantization of the metric would help taming the divergences present in quantum field theory and, in this way, it was relevant also for the theory of elementary particles. Let us thus retrace the discussion in more detail.

Section VIII began with Thomas Gold stating that, in the absence of phenomena not explainable by classical gravity, the only way to argue in favor of quantization of gravity is the presence of logical contradictions, of which he was not convinced (Ref. 4, pp. 243-244). Bryce S. DeWitt pointed out that difficulties may arise in the presence of quantized matter fields depending on the choice of the quantum expectation value of the stress-energy tensor as the source of the gravitational field (Ref. 4, p. 244). Indeed a measurement may change this expectation value, which implies a change of the gravitational field itself. The classical theory of gravitation is valid because fluctuations are negligible at the scale where gravitational effects become sizeable. At this point Feynman put forward his first thought experiment, which was a variant of the two-slit diffraction experiment, in which a mass indicator has been put behind the two-slit wall. Within a space-time region whose linear dimensions are of order L in space and L/c in time, the uncertainty on the gravitational potential (divided by c^2 so that it is dimensionless and thus homogeneous to a metric) is in general $\Delta g = \sqrt{\frac{\hbar G}{c^3 L^2}} = \frac{L_P}{L}$, where $L_P = \sqrt{\frac{\hbar G}{c^3}}$ is the Planck length.[a] The order of magnitude of the potential generated by a mass M within the spatial part of the considered region is $g = \frac{MG}{Lc^2}$, which implies $\Delta g = \frac{\Delta M G}{Lc^2}$. A comparison with the previous general expression gives a mass uncertainty $\Delta M = \frac{c^2 L_P}{G} \approx 10^{-5}$ grams, if the time of observations is less than L/c. On the other side, by allowing an infinite time, M would be obtained with infinite accuracy. This option, according to Feynman, could not take place for a mass M fed into the two-slit apparatus, so that the apparatus will not be able to uncover the difficulty unless M is at least of order 10^{-5} grams. Thus he concluded that

> Either gravity must be quantized because a logical difficulty would arise if one did the experiment with a mass of order 10^{-4} grams, or else [...] quantum mechanics fails with masses as big as 10^{-5} grams (Ref. 4, p. 245).

Subsequent discussions moved on more formal matters such as the meaning of the equivalence principle in quantum gravity, with Feynman contrasting Helmut Salecker's suggestion of a possible violation of the equivalence principle in the quantum realm. Then a further remark by Salecker himself brought the participants' attention back to the topical issue, the necessity of gravitational quantization. In particular, as explained by an Editor's note (see Ref. 4, p. 249), Salecker hinted to the possibility to build up an action-at-a-distance theory of gravitation in whole analogy to the electromagnetic case, with charged quantized particles acting as a source of a unquantized Coulomb field. At this stage Frederik J. Belinfante proposed the quantization of both the static part and the transverse part of the gravitational field (the last one describing gravitational radiation) as a way to circumvent difficulties related to the choice of the expectation value of the stress energy tensor as the source of the gravitational field. As noticed by Zeh,[2] Belinfante's proposal reflects his ideas on the ontology of quantum mechanics, which point toward an epistemic rather than ontic interpretation of the wave function:

> "There are two quantities which are involved in the description of any quantized physical system. One of them gives information about the general dynamical behavior of the system, and is represented by a certain operator (or operators). The other gives information about our knowledge of the system; it is the state vector [...] the state vector can undergo a sudden change if one makes an experiment on the system. The laws of nature therefore unfold continuously only as long as the observer does not bring extra knowledge of his own into the picture." (Ref. 4, p. 250).

---

[a] This follows from an argument given by Wheeler in Ref. 4, pp. 179-180, involving a path integral for the gravitational field.

Belinfante's description used the Heisenberg picture, at variance with Feynman who reasoned in terms of wave functions as dynamical objects. Indeed, according to Belinfante "the wave function [...] must change for reasons beyond the system's physical dynamics. He does not refer to ensembles of wave functions or a density matrix in order to represent incomplete knowledge" (Ref. 2, p. 65).

Feynman promptly replied with his second gedanken experiment, a Stern-Gerlach experiment with a gravitational apparatus. More in detail, he considered a spin-1/2 particle going through a Stern-Gerlach apparatus and then crossing the first or the second of two counters (denoted as 1 and 2, respectively), each one connected by means of a rod to an indicator. He took the indicator as a little ball with a diameter of 1 cm, going up or down depending on the position of the object, at counter 1 or 2, respectively. Quantum mechanics, as underlined by Feynman, provides in principle an amplitude for the ball up and an amplitude for the ball down[b]. However, the ball is chosen to be macroscopic, so as to be able to produce a detectable gravitational field, which in turn can move a probe ball. In other words a channel between the object and the observer is established via the gravitational field. This ideal experiment led Feynman to infer the following conclusion about gravity quantization:

> Therefore, there must be an amplitude for the gravitational field, provided that the amplification necessary to reach a mass which can produce a gravitational field big enough to serve as a link in the chain does not destroy the possibility of keeping quantum mechanics all the way. There is a bare possibility (which I shouldn't mention!) that quantum mechanics fails and becomes classical again when the amplification gets far enough, because of some minimum amplification which you can get across such a chain. But aside from that possibility, if you believe in quantum mechanics up to any level then you have to believe in gravitational quantization in order to describe this experiment (Ref. 4, p. 251).

A subsequent answer to a question by Hermann Bondi[c] further highlighted, according to Zeh (Ref. 2 p. 67), Feynman's position against the epistemic interpretation of the wave function:

> I don't really have to measure whether the particle is here or there. I can do something else: I can put an inverse Stern-Gerlach experiment on and bring the beams back together again. And if I do it with great precision, then I arrive at a situation which is not derivable simply from the information that there is a 50 percent probability of being here and a 50 percent probability of

---

[b]Zeh[2] points out how Feynman's description of the measurement process is very close to the standard measurement and registration device proposal by John von Neumann.[14]

[c]"What is the difference between this and people playing dice, so that the ball goes one way or the other according to whether they throw a six or not?" (Ref. 4, p. 252).

being there. In other words, the situation at this stage is not 50-50 that the die is up or down, but *there is an amplitude* that it is up and an amplitude that it is down – a complex amplitude – and as long as it is still possible to put those amplitudes together for interference you have to keep quantum mechanics in the picture. (Ref. 4, p. 252, our emphasis)

3. Wave function collapse

The aim of this Section is to highlight Feynman's ideas about the quantum measurement problem. Indeed, from the last sentence of the last quote, one can infer a clear reference to the problem of wave function collapse, as well as a hint to decoherence as a possible solution. A further suggestion can be found in a subsequent remark:

Well, it's a question of what goes on at the level where the ball flips one way or the other. In the amplifying apparatus there's already an uncertainty - loss of electrons in the amplifier, noise, etc. - so that by this stage the information is completely determined. Then it's a die argument. You might argue this way: Somewhere in your apparatus this idea of amplitude has been lost. You don't need it any more, so you drop it. The wave packet would be reduced (or something). Even though you don't know where it's reduced, it's reduced. And then you can't do an experiment which distinguishes *interfering* alternatives from just plain odds (like with dice). (Ref. 4, p. 252, our emphasis)

According to Feynman, wave packet reduction occurs somewhere in his experimental apparatus thanks to the amplifying mechanism, so that a huge amount of amplification (via the macroscopic gravitational field of the ball) may be effective in changing amplitudes to probabilities. Then he wondered about the possibility to devise an experiment able in principle to avoid the wave packet reduction due to the amplification process. Subsequent criticism by Leon Rosenfeld and Bondi further stimulated Feynman's intuition. So he was led to envisage a sort of quantum interference in his experiment, driven by the gravitational interaction between macroscopic balls, which could be described by means of a quantum field with suitable amplitudes taking a value or another value, or to propagate here and there. But, as Bondi suggested, any irreversible element should be removed, such as for instance the possibility of gravitational links to radiate. Probably, this is another point in which a further hint to the role of decoherence in destroying quantum interference can be recognized, even if in Bondi's and Feynman's words a reference is made only to classical irreversibility.[2] In fact the meaning of decoherence, its origin and its role in smearing out phase relations as well as in triggering the transition to classicality, were still unclear in the late 1950s[d]. The discussion went on with Feynman arguing that quantum interference might eventually take place with a mass of macroscopic

---

[d]For a historical and research account on decoherence, see Ref. 15 and references therein.

size, say about 10^{-5} gram or 1 gram, and hinting to the possible role of gravity in destroying quantum superpositions. In his words:

> There would be a *new principle*! It would be *fundamental*! The principle would be: – *roughly*: *Any piece of equipment able to amplify by such and such a factor* (10^{-5} *grams or whatever it is*) *necessarily must be of such a nature that it is irreversible*. It might be true! But at least it would be fundamental because it would be a new principle. There are two possibilities. Either this principle – this missing principle – is right, *or* you can amplify to any level and still maintain interference, in which case it's absolutely imperative that the gravitational field be quantized... *I believe*! *or* there's another possibility which I have't thought of (Ref. 4, pp. 254-255, emphasis in original).

The same ideas would have been pursued later by Feynman in his Lectures on Gravitation,[9] where he considered "philosophical problems in quantizing macroscopic objects" and hinted to the possibility of a failure of quantum mechanics induced by gravity:

> I would like to suggest that it is possible that quantum mechanics fails at large distances and for large objects. Now, mind you, I do not say that I think that quantum mechanics *does* fail at large distances, I only say that it is not inconsistent with what we do know. If this failure of quantum mechanics is connected with gravity, we might speculatively expect this to happen for masses such that $\frac{GM^2}{\hbar c} = 1$, of M near 10^{-5} grams, which corresponds to some 10^{18} particles (Ref. 9, pp. 12-13).

Within the same set of lectures (Ref. 9, p. 14), the possibility is recognized that amplitudes may reduce to probabilities for a sufficiently complex object, thanks to a smearing effect on the evolution of the phases of all parts of the object. Such a smearing effect could have a gravitational origin. A similar idea is expressed in the end of the letter to Weisskopf,[8] as already mentioned in the Introduction. This shows how Feynman was open-minded with respect to all possibilities, despite his strong belief in the quantum nature of reality.

The debate on gravity quantization here highlighted and, in particular, Feynman's deep insights, triggered subsequent research on the possibility of a gravity-induced collapse of wave function, as a viable solution to the measurement problem in quantum mechanics.[16–25] The idea is attractive since gravity is ubiquitous in nature, and gravitational effects depend on the size of objects, so it has been greatly developed in the subsequent years up to the present day. Along this line of thinking, Roger Penrose suggested that a conflict emerges when a balanced superposition of two separate wave packets representing two different position of a massive object is considered.[22,23] In his words (see Ref. 26, p. 475): "My own point of view is that as soon as a *significant* amount of space-time curvature is introduced, the rules of quantum linear superposition must fail". Clearly the conflict is the result of putting together the general covariance of general relativity and the quantum mechanical superposition principle. By assuming in each space-time the validity of the notions of stationarity and energy, and by taking the difference between the identified time-translation operators as a measure of the ill-definiteness of the final superposition's energy, the decay time for the balanced superposition of two mass distributions can be estimated:

$$t_D = \frac{\hbar}{\Delta E_{grav}}. \tag{1}$$

Here ΔE_{grav} is the gravitational self-energy of the difference between the mass distributions of each of the two locations of the object. This means that massive superpositions would immediately undergo collapse. The same idea led Penrose to introduce the so called Schrödinger-Newton equation,[24] which governs a peculiar non-linear evolution of the center-of-mass wave function. Its soliton-like dynamics is the result of a competition between a partial shrinking due to the non-linear term and a partial spreading due to the usual dynamical term.

More recently, other collapse models(called *dynamical* collapse models) have been put forward,[27–30] where the collapse of the wave function is induced by a different mechanism, i.e. the interaction with a random source such as an external noise source.

From the experimental side, a lot of proposals have been made as well, mainly aimed to explore a parameter range where both quantum mechanics and gravity are significant. For instance it has been possible to create a quantum superposition state with complex organic molecules with masses of the order $m = 10^{-22}$ kg.[31,32] Recent experimental proposals involve matter-wave interferometers,[33–35] quantum optomechanics[36–39] and magnetomechanics.[40] Today a major challenge is, on one hand, to design viable experiments at the interface between the quantum and classical worlds, while on the other hand to reveal and discriminate gravity-induced decoherence from environmental decoherence in such experiments. However, despite such a huge theoretical and experimental effort, a definite answer to the quantum measurement problem as well as to the problem of the emergence of classical from the quantum world is still lacking.

4. The role of the observer in a closed Universe

In this Section we deal with the issue of the role of the observer in a closed Universe, as emerged from discussions carried out in the closing session of Chapel Hill conference. Here Wheeler gave the first public presentation of Everett's relative-state interpretation of quantum mechanics,[7,41] as follows:

> General relativity, however, includes the space as an integral part of the physics and it is impossible to get outside of space to observe the physics. Another important thought is that the concept of eigenstates of the total

energy is meaningless for a closed Universe. However, there exists the proposal that there is one "universal wave function". This function has already been discussed by Everett, and it might be easier to look for this "universal wave function" than to look for all the propagators (Ref. 4, p. 270).

Feynman promptly replied by characterizing of Everett's approach as "many-worlds":

The concept of a "universal wave function" has serious conceptual difficulties. This is so since this function must contain amplitudes for all possible worlds depending on all quantum-mechanical possibilities in the past and thus one is forced to believe in the equal reality of an infinity of possible worlds (Ref. 4, p. 270).

The same idea will be presented some years later in the Lectures on Gravitation (Ref. 9, pp. 13-14), where Feynman also discussed the role of the observer in quantum mechanics. The Schrödinger's cat paradox allowed him to illustrate the difference between the results of a measurement carried out by an external as well as an internal observer. While the external observer describes his results by an amplitude, with the system collapsing into a well-defined final state after the measurement, according to the internal observer the results of the same measurement are given by a probability. Clearly the absence of an external observer leads to a paradox, which is much more effective when considering the whole Universe as described by a complete wave function. This Universe wave function is governed by a Schrödinger equation and implies the presence of an infinite number of amplitudes, which bifurcate from each atomic event. In other words, according to Feynman, the Universe is constantly spitting into an infinite number of branches, as a result of the interactions between its components. Here the key observation is that interactions play the role of measurements. As a consequence, an inside observer knows which branch the world has taken, so that he can follow the track of his past. Feynman's conclusion brings into play a conceptual problem:

Now, the philosophical question before us is, when we make an observation of our track in the past, does the result of our observation become real in the same sense that the final state would be defined if an outside observer were to make the observation (Ref. 9, p. 14)?

A further discussion of the meaning of the wave function of the Universe is carried out later in the Lectures on Gravitation (Ref. 9, pp. 21-22). Here Feynman restated his "many-worlds" characterization of Everett's approach with reference to a "cat paradox on a large scale", from which our world eventually could be obtained by a "reduction of the wave packet". Concerning this reduction, he wondered about the relation between Everett's approach and collapse mechanisms of whatever origin. Perhaps it may be relevant to quote a comment by John P. Preskill, within a talk about the Feynman legacy, given at the APS April Meeting (cf. Ref. 42, slide 29):

> When pressed, Feynman would support the Everett viewpoint, that all phenomena (including measurement) are encompassed by unitary evolution alone. According to Gell-Mann, both he and Feynman already held this view by the early 1960s, without being aware of Everett's work[e]. However, in 1981 Feynman says of the many-worlds picture: "It's possible, but I am not very happy with it".

Historically, Everett's proposal[7] was the first attempt to go beyond the Copenhagen interpretation in order to apply quantum mechanics to the Universe as a whole. To this end, the well known separation of the world into "observer" and "observed" has to be superseded by promoting the observer to be part of the system, while the usual quantum rules are still effective in measuring, recording or doing whatever operation. Quantum fluctuations of space-time in the very early Universe have also to be properly taken into account. On the other hand, this proposal lacks an adequate description of the origin of the quasi-classical realm as well as a clear explanation of the meaning of the branching of the wave function.

Everett's work has been further developed by many authors[43–48] and its more recent generalization is known as *decoherent histories approach to quantum mechanics of closed systems*. A characterizing feature of this formulation is that neither observers nor their measurements play a prominent role. Furthermore the so called *retrodiction*, namely the ability to construct a history of the evolution of the Universe towards its actual state by using today's data and an initial quantum state, is allowed. The process of prediction requires to select out decoherent sets of histories of the Universe as a closed system, while decoherence in this context plays the same role of a measurement within the Copenhagen interpretation. Decoherence is a much more observer-independent concept and gives a clear meaning to Everett's branches, the main issue being to identify mechanisms responsible for it. In particular, it has been shown that decoherence is frequent in the Universe for histories of variables such as the center of mass positions of massive bodies.[49]

5. Concluding remarks

In this paper we have retraced Feynman's thoughts on foundational issues in quantum mechanics. Such ideas were rarely expressed by him, who mainly linked his name to his masterful application of thus theory, but they clearly emerged whenever he focused on the problem the interface of quantum mechanics and gravity, with the ensuing great conceptual questions. These problems, such as that of the collapse of the wave function, of macroscopic superpositions and of observers which are parts of the observed system itself, are of course not limited to the gravitational

---

[e]We do not agree that Feynman was not aware of Everett's work in the 1960s, since he commented on it at Chapel Hill in 1957.

realm, but lie at the very heart of quantum physics. Despite much progress having been achieved since Feynman's times, part of which had been anticipated by him and other participants to the Chapel Hill conference, much work still needs to be done, before his most famous remark[50] "I think I can say that nobody understands Quantum Mechanics" can be considered to be no longer true.

References

1. R. P. Feynman, Space-time approach to non-relativistic quantum mechanics, *Rev. Mod. Phys.* **20**, 367 (1948).
2. H. D. Zeh, Feynman's interpretation of quantum theory, *Eur. Phys. J. H* **36**, 63 (2011).
3. M. Di Mauro, S. Esposito and A. Naddeo, A road map for Feynman's adventures in the land of gravitation, *Eur. Phys. H* **46**, 22 (2021).
4. C. DeWitt-Morette and D. Rickles, *The Role of Gravitation in Physics*, Report from the 1957 Chapel Hill Conference (Edition Open Access, 2011).
5. A. S. Blum, R. Lalli and J. Renn, The renaissance of General Relativity: How and why it happened, *Annalen der Physik* **528**, 344 (2016).
6. P. G. Bergmann, Summary of the Chapel Hill Conference, *Rev. Mod. Phys.* **29**, 352 (1957).
7. H. Everett III, "Relative state" formulation of quantum mechanics, *Rev. Mod. Phys.* **29**, 454 (1957).
8. R. P. Feynman, unpublished letter to Victor F. Weisskopf, February 1961; in *Richard P. Feynman Papers*, California Institute of Technology Archives, Box 3, Folder 8.
9. R. P. Feynman, F. B. Moriniго, W. G. Wagner and B. Hatfield, *Feynman Lectures on Gravitation* (Addison-Wesley, Reading, MA, 1995).
10. R. De Luca, M. Di Mauro, S. Esposito and A. Naddeo, Feynman's different approach to electromagnetism, *Eur. J. Phys.* **40**, 065205 (2019).
11. M. Di Mauro, R. De Luca, S. Esposito and A. Naddeo, Some insight into Feynman's approach to electromagnetism, *Eur. J. Phys.* **42**, 025206 (2021).
12. R. P. Feynman, *Electrostatics, Electrodynamics, Matter-Waves Interacting, Relativity*, lectures at Hughes Aircraft Company, Notes taken and transcribed by John T. Neer, 1967-68.
13. R. P. Feynman, Quantum theory of gravitation, *Acta Phys. Polon.* **24**, 697 (1963).
14. J. von Neumann, *Mathematische Grundlagen der Quantenmechanik (Mathematical foundations of quantum mechanics)* (Springer, Berlin, 1932), Chap. 6.
15. W. H. Zurek, Decoherence, einselection, and the quantum origins of the classical, *Rev. Mod. Phys.* **75**, 715 (2003).
16. F. Károlyházy, Gravitation and quantum mechanics of macroscopic objects, *Il Nuovo Cimento A* **42**, 390 (1966).
17. A. Frenkel, Spontaneous localizations of the wave function and classical behavior, *Found. Phys.* **20**, 159 (1990).
18. A. Frenkel, A Tentative Expression of the Károlyházy Uncertainty of the Space-Time Structure Through Vacuum Spreads in Quantum Gravity, *Found. Phys.* **32**, 751 (2002).
19. L. Diosi, Gravitation and quantum mechanical localization of macroobjects, *Phys. Lett. A* **105**, 199 (1984).
20. L. Diosi, Models for universal reduction of macroscopic quantum fluctuations, *Phys. Rev. A* **40**, 1165 (1989).

21. L. Diosi, Notes on certain Newton gravity mechanisms of wavefunction localization and decoherence, *J. Phys. A: Math. Gen.* **40**, 2989 (2007).
22. R. Penrose, *Gravity and state-vector reduction*, in *Quantum Concepts in Space and Time*, eds. R. Penrose and C. J. Isham, (Clarendon Press, Oxford, 1986), p. 129.
23. R. Penrose, On gravity's role in quantum state reduction, *Gen. Rel. Grav.* **28**, 581 (1996).
24. R. Penrose, Quantum computation, entanglement and state reduction, *Phil. Trans. R. Soc. Lond. A* **356**, 1927 (1998).
25. R. Penrose, *The Road to Reality: A Complete Guide to the Laws of the Universe* (Jonathan Cape, London, 2004).
26. R. Penrose, *The emperor's new mind: Concerning computers, minds, and the laws of physics* (Oxford University Press, Oxford, 1989).
27. G. C. Ghirardi, R. Grassi and A. Rimini, Continuous spontaneous reduction model involving gravity, *Phys. Rev. A* **42**, 1057 (1990).
28. G. C. Ghirardi, A. Rimini and T. Weber, Unified Dynamics for Microscopic and Macroscopic Systems, *Phys. Rev. D* **34**, 470 (1986).
29. P. Pearle, Ways to describe dynamical state-vector reduction, *Phys. Rev. A* **48**, 913 (1993).
30. A. Bassi and G. C. Ghirardi, Dynamical reduction models, *Phys. Rept.* **379**, 257 (2003).
31. S. Gerlich, S. Eibenberger, M. Tomandl, S. Nimmrichter, K. Hornberger, P. J. Fagan, J. Tuxen, M. Mayor and M. Arndt, Quantum interference of large organic molecules, *Nat. Commun.* **2**, 263 (2011).
32. S. Eibenberger, S. Gerlich, M. Arndt, M. Mayor and J. Tuxen, Matter-wave interference of particles selected from a molecular library with masses exceeding 10 000 amu, *Phys. Chem. Chem. Phys.* **15**, 14696 (2013).
33. I. Pikovski, M. Zych, F. Costa and C. Brukner, Universal decoherence due to gravitational time dilation, *Nat. Phys.* **11**, 668 (2015).
34. M. Zych, F. Costa, I. Pikovski and C. Brukner, Quantum interferometric visibility as a witness of general relativistic proper time, *Nat. Commun.* **2**, 505 (2011).
35. Y. Margalit, Z. Zhou, S. Machluf, D. Rohrlich, Y. Japha and R. Folman, A self-interfering clock as a "which path" witness, *Science* **349**, 1205 (2015).
36. S. Bose, K. Jacobs and P. L. Knight, Scheme to probe the decoherence of a macroscopic object, *Phys. Rev. A* **59**, 3204 (1999).
37. W. Marshall, C. Simon, R. Penrose and D. Bouwmeester, Towards quantum superpositions of a mirror, *Phys. Rev. Lett.* **91**, 130401 (2003).
38. F. Maimone, G. Scelza, A. Naddeo and V. Pelino, Quantum superpositions of a mirror for experimental tests for nonunitary Newtonian gravity, *Phys. Rev. A* **83**, 062124 (2011).
39. O. Romero-Isart, A. C. Pflanzer, F. Blaser, R. Kaltenbaek, N. Kiesel, M. Aspelmeyer and J. I. Cirac, Large Quantum Superpositions and Interference of Massive Nanometer-Sized Objects, *Phys. Rev. Lett.* **107**, 020405 (2011).
40. H. Pino, J. Prat-Camps, K. Sinha, B. P. Venkatesh and O. Romero-Isart, On-chip quantum interference of a superconducting microsphere, *Quantum Sci. Technol.* **3**, 25001 (2018).
41. S. Osnaghi, F. Freitas and O. Freire Jr., The origin of the Everettian heresy, *Stud. Hist. Phil. Mod. Phys.* **40**, 97 (2009).
42. J. Preskill, *Feynman after 40*, Talk given at APS April Meeting, 16 April 2018, http://theory.caltech.edu/~preskill/talks/APS-April-2018-Feynman-4-3.pdf.

43. M. Gell-Mann and J. B. Hartle, Classical equations for quantum systems, *Phys. Rev. D* **47**, 3345 (1993).
44. R. B. Griffiths, *Consistent Quantum Theory* (Cambridge University Press, Cambridge, 2002).
45. R. Omnes, *Interpretation of Quantum Mechanics* (Princeton University Press, Princeton, 1994)
46. M. Gell-Mann and J. B. Hartle, *Quantum Mechanics in the Light of Quantum Cosmology*, in *Complexity, Entropy, and the Physics of Information*, ed. W. H. Zurek, SFI Studies in the Sciences of Complexity, Vol. VIII, (Addison Wesley, Reading, MA, 1990).
47. P. C. Hohenberg, An Introduction to consistent quantum theory, *Rev. Mod. Phys.* **82**, 2835 (2010).
48. J. B. Hartle, *The Quantum Mechanics of Closed Systems*, in *Directions in General Relativity*, eds. B. L. Hu, M. P. Ryan and C. V. Vishveshwara, Volume 1, (Cambridge University Press, Cambridge, 1993).
49. E. Joos and H. D. Zeh, The emergence of classical properties through interaction with the environment, *Zeit. Phys. B* **59**, 223 (1985).
50. R. P. Feynman, *The Character of Physical Law* (MIT Press, Boston, MA, 1967).

Summary of the parallel session HR3

Shokoufe Faraji

University of Bremen, Center of Applied Space Technology and Microgravity (ZARM), 28359 Germany

This is the summary of the parallel session entitled "Time and Philosophy in Physics", chaired by Shokoufe Faraji in the sixteenth Marcel Grossmann Meeting. This parallel session aimed to discuss open issues related to Time and fundamental laws from different perspectives in a complementary point of view.

Keywords: Time in Physics, Time in Philosophy; passage of Time; fundamental laws

1. Introduction

It is astonishing that we can understand the Universe in the way we study it. However, concurrently celebrating the achievements of science, we should respect its limits and not claim more than it can actually achieve or attain, where by pushing its limits, complex philosophical issues may arise. However, the concern is about when theories are applied beyond their range of applicability. Since the visible Universe may not give us enough information to characterize the laws of physics completely, thus we need a more comprehensive framework that not only incorporates science but can also go beyond the limits.

Therefore, for example the questions on the domain of validity of the fundamental laws of physics and the nature of existence of infinities are sound viable. However, maybe above all, the nature of Time and the order present in nature is the greatest secret in the Universe.[1-5]

2. The passage of Time and top-down causation

This is reported by Prof. Barbara Drossel.

There is a common underlying agreement among many physicists to consider the properties of the fundamental equations of physics are also properties of nature. Therefore, since these equations are deterministic, it is concluded that nature is also deterministic. Besides, the Time evolution is completely determined by the initial state and the fundamental laws. Furthermore, these laws are invariant under changing the direction of Time. However, any physical theory is an approximation and not an exact description of the physical processes of interest. And by no means it is a complete description of everything that is going on in the physical world. Even a deterministic and Time-reversible fundamental theory is in practice supplemented by irreversible and stochastic features. In conclusion, the irreversibility and stochasticity enter when the influence of the environment on a system is taken into account, which is related to emergence and top-down causation and microsystems are causally open to influences from the macroscopic environment.

3. Temporal asymmetry and causality

This is reported by Prof. Wayne Myrvold.

The temporal asymmetry between past and future permeates virtually every aspect of the world of our experience. As far as we know, it has no counterpart in the laws of fundamental physics. One option is to trace this asymmetry to a fact about the early state of the universe, either taken as a contingent, unexplained fact, or as a consequence of some physical principle. However, there is an alternate route to explaining temporally asymmetric phenomena, according to how work on the process of equilibration is done. This does not involve any hypothesis about the past, rather it is founded on conditions that we can apply at any Time, closely related to the concept of causality.[6] In fact, temporal asymmetry enters our explanations because the very notion of what it means to explain something is temporal asymmetry. To sum up, the conceptions of casual order and temporal order are not independent and in fact they are two sides of the same coin.

Therefore, the absence of temporally asymmetry in the fundamental laws is no obstacle to explaining that asymmetry. What is invoked is a temporal asymmetry in the very notion of explanation.

4. Temporal ordering in Philosophy and Physics

This is reported by Prof. Norman Sieroka.

Time and temporal order are one of the oldest and most eminent concepts in both philosophy and physics. One of the main aims of philosophy is to coordinate the human experience in structural analysis and comparison. For this, one needs to acknowledge the differences in types of Time and Time scales. Then we realize many issues about Time are issues about the ordering of events both within and across different types and scales.[7]

From the philosophical point of view, mainly there are two different types of temporal orderings. The first one, the presentism or possibilism perspective; events being characterized by the present, past or future, and try to focus on mental states and experience; however, this view may have trouble in physics if simultaneity is not absolute. The second view is Eternalism; the ordering relation is only about events being earlier or later and focuses on physical states, and there is no vital distinction between past, present and future. However, it seems the second one to be of importance to physics.

To sum up, the relation between these two orderings and their inner dynamics can be interesting in the context of the interaction between philosophy and physics. Besides, investigation of the notion of an *event* seems fundamentally essential in both areas.

5. Time in Quantum Gravity: A false problem

This is reported by Prof. Carlo Rovelli.

There are several problems of Time in Physics that are related to each other. Indeed, always a lot of confusion comes from mixing problems that are distinct one from another. In particular, an extensive discussion of Time in Quantum Gravity was caused in the 60th by the Wheeler-de Witt equation, which at first sight suggests Time is frozen and there is no evolution. However, dealing with Time in General Relativity is a slightly different than in non-relativistic Physics.[8] The difficulty for developing Time in General Relativity is to struggle with the meaning of the coordinates. In fact, coordinates in non-relativistic field Theory are measurable by rods and clocks; in contrast to General Relativity, there is nothing physical attached to coordinates. In fact, all possible versions of Time in General Relativity is a quantity that is locally dependent on the Gravitational field. This means the entire formulation of dynamics as evolution in Time does not fit within the scope of General Relativity. In fact, instead of conceptualizing the evolution of physical variables evolving with respect to a variable, we are forced to consider the evolution of a variable with respect to one another. So by this perception, the relativistic dynamics is not frozen in Quantum Gravity and simply described in a different language. Thus, we can predict the relation among a number of variables, and there is no mystery about *emergence of Time* in Quantum Gravity. In fact, many tentative quantum gravity theories, from the Wheeler-de Witt equation to Loop Quantum Gravity, do not specify a Time variable, and yet they are predictive. Of course, this view has substantial consequences, for example, there are some indications that the Time might be discrete.

6. The issue of Time in Fundamental Physics

This is reported by Prof. Abhay Ashtekar.

The Notion of Time in fundamental physics has undergone radical revisions over centuries dramatically.[9] However, new observational windows continually open up in the process. In particular, issues at the forefront of cosmology and quantum gravity pose new conceptual and technical challenges. The same is true in particle Physics, GPS systems or Quantum Information Theory.

A pleasing feature is coming together from physical and operational ideas, fundamental concepts from General Relativity, the associated Hamiltonian constraint, and a post-Pauli understanding of how one should think of Time in Quantum Mechanics. In fact, in Quantum Mechanics, the focus is on the extended system by considering the clock. In Quantum Gravity, there is no such thing as Time in Quantum mechanics, and the extended system kinematics is already contained the dynamical variables of General Relativity.

However, it does not mean *everything is understood and well-controlled*. Many refinements, extensions and technical issues are still open; however, there is no conceptual roadblock to this understanding.

7. Time in General Relativity and Quantum Mechanics

This is reported by Prof. Claus Laemmerzahl.

The nature of Time is characteristic of the underlying theory. Within the formalism of General Relativity, it is possible to define or characterize a distinguished clock and Time operationally, and this is the so-called standard clock providing proper Time. In addition, within Quantum Mechanics, it is possible to define a clock and the corresponding Time. This clock is an atomic clock, and it provides Time in the unit of the second. It can be proven with high precision that both clocks are compatible though they are based on entirely different notions.[10] Based on such standard clocks, we define Special Relativity effects such as the gravitational redshift, gravitational Time delay and gravitomagnetic clock effect. This compatibility breaks down in strong gravitational fields and also in generalized theories of gravity.

It would be of some interest to study the relativistic two-body problem and another Time scale from chirp. In addition, studying a bound system in an external gravitational field like the Earth-Moon system in the field of the Sun, seems necessary to our understanding.

8. Time's passage

This is reported by Janathan Dickau.

The way we experience Time is in the accumulation of experiences and events that happen in the moment. On the one hand, philosophers have tried to explain both the nature of Time and its origin. On the other hand, the meaning of Time in different areas of physics like in Classical and Quantum Mechanics, and Relativity are different. So we hope for example Quantum Gravity theories will help resolve this issue. Recent advances in Mathematics also hold promise for a unified basis explaining both the thermodynamic and quantum-mechanical Time arrows in a consistent way. It is important to continue our exploration of quantum gravity theories and try to understand the cosmological context for these theories in a broader way. So physicists should see it as a responsibility to build bridges between the philosophically disconnected islands of thought, by applying a Philosophy of Physics that supports our common endeavor to learn the secrets of the cosmos.

9. A glimpse of Feynman's contributions to the debate on the Foundations of Quantum Mechanics

This is reported by Dr. Adele Naddeo.

One of the most debated questions in the famous 1957 Chapel Hill conference on "The Role of Gravitation in Physics" was whether or not the gravitational field has to be quantized.[11] Feynman proposed several gedanken experiments in order to argue in favor of the necessity of gravitational quantization, and hinting to decoherence as a viable solution to the problem of wave function collapse.[12] Feynman believed that nature cannot be half classical and half quantum; therefore, we had the unified field theories. After quantum theory one tries to quantize gravity!

Another issue was related to the limitations that quantum quantum theory may impose on the measurements of space-time distances and curvature. However, since the Planck mass does not set a lower limit to the mass of a particle whose gravitational field can be measured, so the gravitational field of any mass can in principle be measured.

Feynman also discussed the role of the observer in quantum mechanics. The Schrödinger's cat paradox allowed him to illustrate the difference between the results of a measurement carried out by an external as well as an internal observer.[13] While the external observer describes his results by an amplitude, according to the internal observer the results of the same measurement are given by a probability. In other words, according to Feynman, the Universe is constantly spitting into an infinite number of branches, as a result of the interactions between its components. As a consequence, an inside observer knows which branch the world has taken, so that he can follow the track of his past. However, in 1981 Feynman says of the many-worlds picture: *It's possible, but I am not very happy with it.*

10. Conclusion

Physics enables everything and underlies everything, but it does not mean it determines everything.[5] Perhaps the world is much more complicated than can be explained only by science. Thus, we should trust our most immediate experiences, new conceptual and technical challenges. In fact, they are the basis and guides for being capable of thinking and acting. Based on these, we could critically examine and take care of metaphysical claims and our ultimate questions like: does the world covered by science describe the whole reality? What about underlying assumptions and axioms in cosmology? What about all the philosophical issues related to "the interpretation of quantum mechanics," "measurement Problem," and the ontological character of quantum states? Why does the Universe have such a unique structure that life can exist?

References

1. R. Penrose, *The road to reality: A complete guide to the laws of the universe* (Vintage, London, 2005).
2. G. F. Ellis, Physics in the real universe: Time and spacetime, *General relativity and gravitation* **38**, 1797 (2006).
3. G. Auletta, G. F. Ellis and L. Jaeger, Top-down causation by information control: From a philosophical problem to a scientific research programme, *Journal of The Royal Society Interface* **5**, 1159 (2008).
4. J. Birriel, Fashion, faith, and fantasy in the new physics of the universe fashion, faith, and fantasy in the new physics of the universe by roger penrose, published by princeton university press (sept. 27, 2016), 520 pages. isbn-10:0691119791, *The Physics Teacher* **56**, 482 (10 2018).
5. G. Ellis, *How can physics underlie the mind?: Top-down causation in the human context* (Springer Heidelberg, 2016).

6. W. Myrvold and J. Christian, *Quantum Reality, Relativistic Causality, and Closing the Epistemic Circle* 01 2008.
7. N. Sieroka, Philosophie der zeit, *Nova acta Leopoldina: Abhandlungen der Kaiserlich Leopoldinisch-Carolinisch Deutschen Akademie der Naturforscher* **425**, 23 (12 2020).
8. C. Rovelli, Time in quantum gravity: An hypothesis, *Phys. Rev. D* **43**, 442 (Jan 1991).
9. A. Ashtekar, Time in Fundamental Physics, *arXiv e-prints*, p. arXiv:1312.6322 (December 2013).
10. V. Perlick, Characterization of standard clocks by means of light rays and freely falling particles, *Gen. Relativ. Gravitation* (1987).
11. C. M. Dewitt and D. Rickles, *The role of gravitation in physics : report from the 1957 chapel hill conference* (2011).
12. M. Di Mauro, S. Esposito and A. Naddeo, A road map for Feynman's adventures in the land of gravitation, *European Physical Journal H* **46**, p. 22 (December 2021).
13. H. D. Zeh, Feynman's interpretation of quantum theory, *European Physical Journal H* **36**, 63 (July 2011).

Massive compact stars in the two-families scenario

P. Char*, A. Drago† and G. Pagliara†

Space Sciences, Technologies and Astrophysics Research (STAR) Institute, Université de Liège, Bât. B5a, 4000 Liège, Belgium

†*Dipartimento di Fisica e Scienze della Terra, Università di Ferrara, Via Saragat 1, 44122 Ferrara, Italy and INFN Sezione di Ferrara, Via Saragat 1, 44122 Ferrara, Italy*

We review the two-families scenario of compact stars. Under the hypothesis that strange quark matter is the ground state of dense matter one can infer the existence of two separated branches of stars: hadronic stars and quark stars. While the first branch is populated by very compact and light stars, the second branch can be populated by very massive stellar objects. A possible confirm to this scenario derives from the gravitational waves detections GW170817 and GW190814, the first one suggesting the existence of stars with radii as small as 11km for $M \sim 1.4 M_\odot$ and the second one suggesting the existence of a compact star with a mass above $2.5 M_\odot$.

Keywords: Compact stars, Binary mergers

1. Introduction

The opening of the Gravitational Waves (GWs) astronomy has already led to some important and new measurements of the structure of neutron stars (NSs) and constraints on the population and mass distribution of neutron stars binaries[1] and neutron star - black hole (BH) binaries.[2] There are two merger events on which we want to focus here: GW170817[3] and GW190814.[4] The first one has being unambiguously associated to a NS-NS merger and it is the first example of multimessenger astronomy since, in this case, also the electromagnetic counterparts GRB170817A and AT2017gfo have been detected. With a total mass of $2.74 M_\odot$, this event is associated to the merger of two NSs with a mass around $1.37 M_\odot$ and thus far below the two solar mass limit observed through pulsar timing measurements, see e.g.[5]. Interestingly by combining the constraints on the tidal deformability obtained from the GW signal and the properties of the electromagnetic signals, a precious constraint on the structure of NSs has been found: the radius of the $1.4 M_\odot$ mass NS $R_{1.4} = 11.0^{+0.9}_{-0.6}$km at 90% credible interval.[6] Such a small radius suggests a quite soft equation of state for dense nucleonic matter and one can predict a maximum mass m_{max} value of $\sim 2.3 M_\odot$.

On the other hand, GW190814 has been produced by the merger of a $23 M_\odot$ BH and a compact object with mass in the range $2.5 - 2.67 M_\odot$. The nature of the low mass companion is unclear, it could be the lightest BH or the heaviest NS ever discovered. By assuming that it is indeed a NS, one would get a very strong constraint on the equation of state: only very stiff equations of state could lead to such massive compact stars, see e.g.[7]. Thus, a tension emerges between the constraints obtained from GW170817 and GW190814.

The two-families scenario[8-14] proposes a solution to this tension based on the hypothesis of coexistence of hadronic stars (HS) and quark stars (QS) the first being very compact and the second being very massive. In the following we will review this scenario outlining the differences with respect to the standard one family scenario and other astrophysical scenarios with two separated branches of compact stars.

2. Modelling the equation of state and structure of compact stars

The equation of state of dense matter is rather uncertain and indeed NSs are considered in nuclear and particle physics as natural laboratories for matter at extremely high densities, order of ten times the nuclear saturation density n_s. There are however a few theoretical arguments that suggest, qualitatively, what could happen if matter is compressed (in NSs by gravity) above n_s. First, the increase of the baryon chemical potential must lead, at some unknown density, to the appearance of new baryons, namely hyperons or delta resonances. The appearance of new degrees of freedom is necessary accompanied by a softening of the equation of state. The value of the threshold density for the emergence of these degrees of freedom and how much the equation of state is softened due to their appearance depend on the details of the theoretical modelling of the equation of state. With the present knowledge one cannot exclude that NSs in which also hyperons and delta resonance (called hadronic stars, HSs) form could be as massive as $2M_\odot$, see for instance[15] where also kaon condensates are considered in the computation of the equation of state. If the maximum mass of NSs $M_{max} \sim 2.6 M_\odot$, it is difficult to explain such a massive object in terms of a HS (at the moment there are no calculations showing that HS could be so massive). Thus, the threshold for the formation of hyperons and delta would be above the central density n_c reached in NSs. For $m_{max} = 2.6 M_\odot$ it has been found in[16] that $n_c \leq 4.5 n_s$, one would thus conclude that no new degrees of freedom are produced up to $4.5 n_s$. Such a possibility could be realised if an extremely strong hyperon-hyperon repulsion is assumed as e.g. in the calculations of.[17] Here we will adopt the most common result that hyperons and/or delta resonance appear in dense matter already at about twice n_s.[18] The resulting softening, if no ad hoc repulsion term between hyperons is added (see e.g.[19]), is such that M_{max} for HSs could be as low as $1.6 M_\odot$. Moreover radii as small as 10km are obtained for the most massive configurations. Thus very compact objects are interpreted as being HSs, we will discuss one example of mass-radius relation within this scenario later on.

How to explain then the existence of massive NSs, with masses possibly as high as $2.6 M_\odot$? Since in the two-families scenario massive stars are QSs, the equation of state of quark matter must be rather stiff. Let us consider the simple constant speed of sound (CSS) equation of state for which the pressure p and the energy

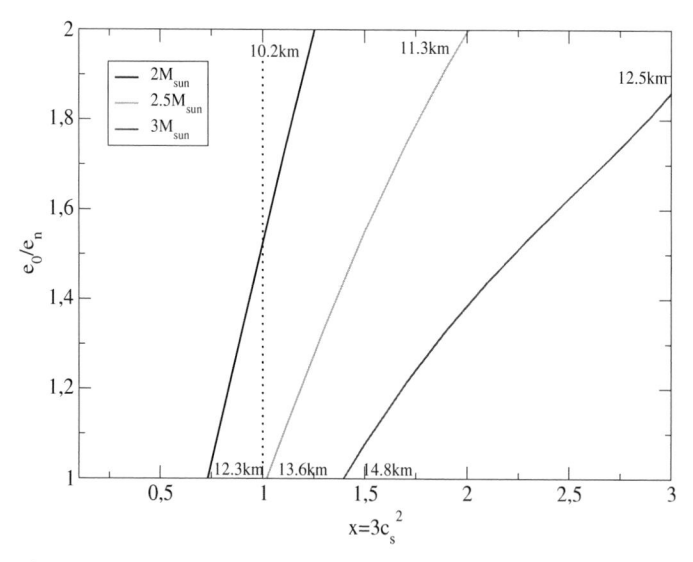

Fig. 1. Lines of constant $m_{\max}$ in the e_0-x plane. The vertical dashed line indicates the conformal limit, $c_s^2 = 1/3$.

density e are related by the relation: $p = c_s^2(e - e_0)$ where e_0 is the energy density at zero pressure and c_s is the (constant) speed of sound. The stiffness is regulated by e_0 and c_s: the larger the value of c_s and/or the smaller the value of e_0, the stiffer the equation of state. Indeed, by solving the TOV equations by adopting such an equation of state one can show, through numerical calculations, that $m_{\max}$ as function of e_0 and c_s can be described by the following parametrization: $m_{max}(x,e_0) = (e_s/e_0)^{1/2}(0.11+3.27x-1.04x^2+0.13x^3)$ where $x = c_s^2/(1/3)$ and e_s is the energy density of nuclear matter $e_s \sim 150$ MeV/fm^3, see.[20] For c_s the upper bound is 1, namely the causal limit whereas the lower bound for e_0 can be taken at $e_0 = e_s$, namely by assuming that strange quark matter has an energy density at $p = 0$ not smaller than the one of nuclear matter.

In Fig. 1 we display the constant maximum mass curves in the x - e_0 plane. As one can notice, if one sets $c_s = 1/3$, namely to its asymptotic value as predicted by perturbative QCD (the so called conformal limit), one can reach values for $m_{\max}$ as high as $\sim 2.5 M_\odot$ if e_0 is set to e_s. Thus for $c_s = 1/3$ one could touch the lower limit for the low mass companion of GW190814. Small deviations from the conformal limit would allow to easily reach its upper limit, namely $2.67 M_\odot$. It is interesting to also discuss the radii of massive compact stars. For a fixed value of maximum mass, the radius of $m_{\max}$ decreases for increasing values of c_s (and e_0). For instance for $m_{\max} = 2 M_\odot$, $r_{\max}$ ranges from 12.3km (for $x = 0.7$) to 10.2 (for $x = 1.2$) km. Interestingly, the analysis of the NICER data on PSR J0740+6620, provides $R = 12.35 \pm 0.75$ km for $M = 2.08 \pm 0.07 M_\odot$.[21] In our scenario, and under the hypothesis that $m_{\max}$ is actually $\sim 2 M_\odot$, one would infer that c_s needs to be close to the conformal limit in order to explain the radius of PSR J0740+6620.

This is at odd with the so-called twin-stars scenario where a strong first order phase transition is assumed to occur from nucleonic matter to quark matter. The necessary softening associated with the phase transition must be compensated by large values of c_s ($c_s \sim 1$) in order to explain the existence of massive stars, see e.g.[22].

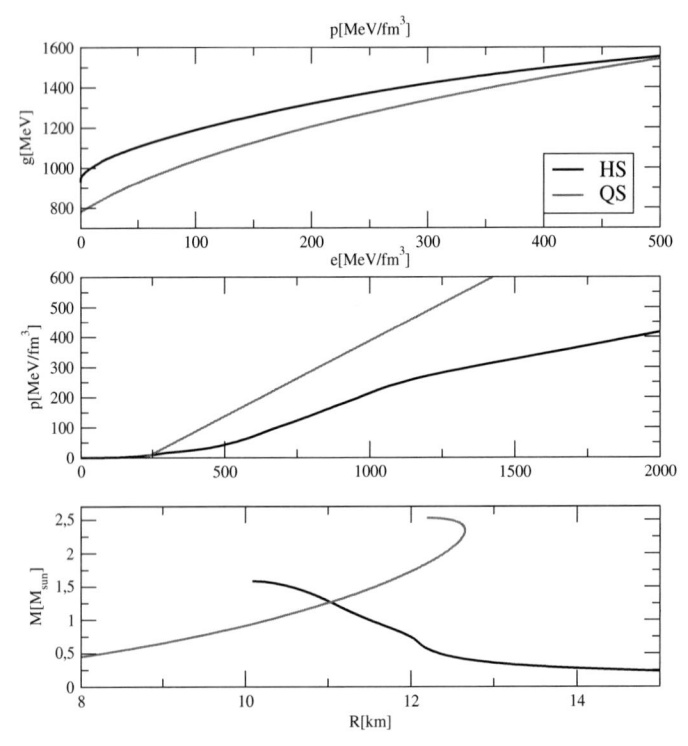

Fig. 2. Upper panel: Gibbs potential g as a function of the pressure for hadronic and quark matter. The phase with the lowest g is thermodynamically preferred. Middle panel: relation between pressure and energy density for hadronic and quark matter. Lower panel: mass-radius relations for HSs and QSs.

An important point when discussing the possibility of separated branches of compact stars is the thermodynamical consistency of the equations of state. In the two-families scenario, the branch of QSs is populated via the conversion of a HS. The conversion itself, to start, needs a specific condition on the thermodynamical variable of the two phases, namely at the same pressure (and same temperature) the new phase must have a smaller Gibbs potential according to the second principle of thermodynamics. To compute the Gibbs potential $g = (e+p)/n$ we need to first compute the baryon density in the CSS model as a function of the pressure. By using the relation $p = n^2 \frac{\partial(e/n)}{\partial n}$ one can show that:

$$n = n_0 \left(\frac{p(1+c_s^2) + c_s^2 e_0}{c_s^2 e_0} \right)^{\frac{1}{1+c_s^2}} \quad (1)$$

where n_0 is the baryon density at zero pressure. In Fig. 2, upper panel we show the comparison between the Gibbs potential of a hadronic equation of state, SFHo-HD taken from[13] and a CCS equation of state of quark matter with $c_s^2 = 0.5$, $e_0 = 1.5 e_s$ and $n_0 = 1.8 n_s$. The Gibbs potential of the quark phase is below the one of the hadronic phase at least up to very large values of the pressures (~ 500 MeV/fm^3) that are not reached within the HSs branch (for which the maximum central pressure is ~ 330 MeV/fm^3 for this specific example). This means that quark matter can be nucleated from hadronic matter, the only necessary condition being the amount of strangeness in the hadronic phase. In,[13] we have estimated that the critical mass of HSs allowing for nucleation varies in the range $1.5 - 1.6 M_\odot$. In the middle panel of Fig. 2, we display the relation between pressure and energy density for the two equations of state. One can notice that the quark matter equation of state is stiffer in the $p - e$ plane and thus leads to larger maximum masses. Although the quark equation of state is stiffer than the hadronic one, is anyway preferred (once the nucleation and the conversion process start) due to its smaller Gibbs potential. Finally in the lower panel, we display the mass radius curve of HSs and QSs. In this specific example, the quark equation of state leads to a maximum mass of $2.5 M_\odot$ and this could potentially explain the nature of the low mass companion of GW190814 as being a QS. At the same time, the HSs branch is populated by very compact stars, as small as 10km. The event GW170817 is interpreted in our scenario as a merger of a HS and a QS. The computed average tidal deformability, $\tilde{\Lambda}$, is in agreement with the constraints obtained from the GW signal, see.[13]

3. Conclusions

We have reviewed the two-families scenario proposed in.[8] In this scenario two brances of compact stars exist, HSs which could be very compact and QSs which could be very massive. This scenario can therefore explain why certain sets of data (both on GW and EM signals) suggest small radii ($R < 11$km) and other sets of data suggest large masses, as large as $2.5 M_\odot$. The coexistence of these branches is possible because the quark matter equation of state can be rather stiff (in the $p - e$ plane) while being thermodynamically preferred with respect to the hadronic matter equation of state (in the $g - p$ plane). Interestingly, the two branches separate for values of mass of $\sim 1.6 M_\odot$ at variance with other scenarios with separated branches, as e.g. the twin stars scenario, in which the new branch opens up at $\sim 2 M_\odot$,[22]

In the two-families scenario the specific process of conversion of a HS into a QS has been extensively studied, see[23–25]: basically it is a combustion process which could be very fast (with time scales of the order of ms) due to hydrodynamical instabilities. The new stellar object has a larger radius with respect to the progenitor HS as studied in detail in Ref.[26]. In the twin-stars scenario instead, the formation of a hybrid star is triggered by a mechanical instability with respect to the gravitational collapse. It has to be shown that from a $2 M_\odot$ star (where the twin branch starts) one can form a much lighter ($M \sim 1.6 M_\odot$) and compact ($R \sim 10$ km) star (see[22]) preventing the collapse to a BH.

Finally, another difference between the two-families scenario and the twin stars scenario concerns the value of the speed of sound of quark matter: it can stay below or quite close to the conformal limit ($c_s^2 = 1/3$) in the former while it must be set to the causal limit ($c_s^2 = 1$) in the latter. In this case one should find out a physical mechanism that allows to match the pQCD results at asymptotic densities according to which c_s^2 must tend again to $1/3$.

References

1. B. P. Abbott *et al.*, GW190425: Observation of a Compact Binary Coalescence with Total Mass $\sim 3.4 M_\odot$, *Astrophys. J. Lett.* **892**, p. L3 (2020).
2. R. Abbott, Observation of Gravitational Waves from Two Neutron Star-Black Hole Coalescences, *ApJL*, **915**, p. L5 (2021).
3. B. Abbott *et al.*, GW170817: Observation of Gravitational Waves from a Binary Neutron Star Inspiral, *Phys. Rev. Lett.* **119**, p. 161101 (2017).
4. R. Abbott *et al.*, GW190814: Gravitational Waves from the Coalescence of a 23 Solar Mass Black Hole with a 2.6 Solar Mass Compact Object, *Astrophys. J. Lett.* **896**, p. L44 (2020).
5. P. Demorest, T. Pennucci, S. Ransom, M. Roberts and J. Hessels, Shapiro Delay Measurement of A Two Solar Mass Neutron Star, *Nature* **467**, 1081 (2010).
6. C. D. Capano, I. Tews, S. M. Brown, B. Margalit, S. De, S. Kumar, D. A. Brown, B. Krishnan and S. Reddy, GW170817: Stringent constraints on neutron-star radii from multimessenger observations and nuclear theory (2019).
7. F. Fattoyev, C. Horowitz, J. Piekarewicz and B. Reed, GW190814: Impact of a 2.6 solar mass neutron star on nucleonic equations of state (7 2020).
8. A. Drago, A. Lavagno and G. Pagliara, Can very compact and very massive neutron stars both exist?, *Phys. Rev.* **D89**, p. 043014 (2014).
9. A. Drago, A. Lavagno, G. Pagliara and D. Pigato, The scenario of two families of compact stars, *Eur. Phys. J.* **A52**, p. 40 (2016).
10. A. Drago and G. Pagliara, Merger of two neutron stars: predictions from the two-families scenario, *Astrophys. J. Lett.* **852**, p. L32 (2018).
11. G. Wiktorowicz, A. Drago, G. Pagliara and S. Popov, Strange quark stars in binaries: formation rates, mergers and explosive phenomena, *Astrophys. J.* **846**, p. 163 (2017).
12. G. F. Burgio, A. Drago, G. Pagliara, H. J. Schulze and J. B. Wei, Are Small Radii of Compact Stars Ruled out by GW170817/AT2017gfo?, *Astrophys. J.* **860**, p. 139 (2018).
13. R. De Pietri, A. Drago, A. Feo, G. Pagliara, M. Pasquali, S. Traversi and G. Wiktorowicz, Merger of compact stars in the two-families scenario, *Astrophys.J.* **881**, p. 122 (2019).
14. I. Bombaci, A. Drago, D. Logoteta, G. Pagliara and I. Vidaña, Was GW190814 a Black Hole–Strange Quark Star System?, *Phys. Rev. Lett.* **126**, p. 162702 (2021).
15. V. B. Thapa, M. Sinha, J. J. Li and A. Sedrakian, Massive Δ-resonance admixed hypernuclear stars with antikaon condensations, *Phys. Rev. D* **103**, p. 063004 (2021).
16. C. Drischler, S. Han, J. M. Lattimer, M. Prakash, S. Reddy and T. Zhao, Limiting masses and radii of neutron stars and their implications, *Phys. Rev. C* **103**, p. 045808 (2021).

17. D. Lonardoni, A. Lovato, S. Gandolfi and F. Pederiva, Hyperon Puzzle: Hints from Quantum Monte Carlo Calculations, *Phys. Rev. Lett.* **114**, p. 092301 (2015).
18. A. Drago, A. Lavagno, G. Pagliara and D. Pigato, Early appearance of delta isobars in neutron stars, *Phys. Rev.* **C90**, p. 065809 (2014).
19. S. Weissenborn, D. Chatterjee and J. Schaffner-Bielich, Hyperons and massive neutron stars: vector repulsion and SU(3) symmetry, *Phys. Rev.* **C85**, p. 065802 (2012), [Erratum: Phys. Rev. C90, no. 1, 019904 (2014)].
20. S. Traversi, P. Char, G. Pagliara and A. Drago, Speed of sound in dense matter and two families of compact stars (2 2021).
21. M. C. Miller *et al.*, The Radius of PSR J0740+6620 from NICER and XMM-Newton Data, *Astrophys. J. Lett.* **918**, p. L28 (2021).
22. J.-E. Christian and J. Schaffner-Bielich, Confirming the existence of twin stars in a NICER way (9 2021).
23. A. Drago, A. Lavagno and I. Parenti, Burning of an hadronic star into a quark or a hybrid star, *Astrophys. J.* **659**, 1519 (2007).
24. G. Pagliara, M. Herzog and F. K. Röpke, Combustion of a neutron star into a strange quark star: The neutrino signal, *Phys. Rev. D* **87**, p. 103007 (2013).
25. A. Drago and G. Pagliara, Combustion of a hadronic star into a quark star: The turbulent and the diffusive regimes, *Phys. Rev. C* **92**, p. 045801 (2015).
26. A. Drago and G. Pagliara, Why can hadronic stars convert into strange quark stars with larger radii, *Phys. Rev. D* **102**, p. 063003 (2020).

Quasi-universality of the magnetic deformation of neutron stars in general relativity and beyond

J. Soldateschi*, N. Bucciantini and L. Del Zanna

Dipartimento di Fisica e Astronomia, Università degli Studi di Firenze, and INFN - Sezione di Firenze, Via G. Sansone 1,
I-50019 Sesto F. no (Firenze), Italy
*E-mail: jacopo.soldateschi@unifi.it

INAF - Osservatorio Astrofisico di Arcetri, Largo E. Fermi 5,
I-50125 Firenze, Italy

Neutron stars harbour extremely powerful magnetic fields, leading to their shape being deformed. Their magnetic deformation depends both on the geometry - and strength - of their internal magnetic field and on their composition, encoded by the equation of state. However, both the details of the internal magnetic structure and the equation of state of the innermost part of neutron stars are mostly unkown. We performed a study of numerical models of magnetised, static, axisymmetric neutron stars in general relativity and in one of its most promising extensions, scalar-tensor theories. We did so by using several realistic equations of state currently allowed by observational and nuclear physics constraints, considering also those for strange quark stars. We show that it is possible to find simple relations among the magnetic deformation of a neutron star, its Komar mass, and its circumferential radius in the case of purely poloidal and purely toroidal magnetic configurations satisfying the equilibrium criterion in the Bernoulli formalism. These relations are quasi-universal, in the sense that they mostly do not depend on the equation of state. Our results, being formulated in terms of potentially observable quantities, could help to understand the magnetic properties of neutron stars interiors and the detectability of continuous gravitational waves by isolated neutron stars, independently of their equation of state. In the case of scalar-tensor theories, these relations depend also on the scalar charge of the neutron stars, thus potentially providing a new way to set constraints on the theory of gravitation.

Keywords: Neutron stars; magnetic deformation; scalar-tensor theories.

1. Introduction

The most compact material objects in the known Universe are neutron stars (NSs), which are also known to harbour extremely powerful magnetic fields, especially in the sub-class known as magnetars[1–4]: the surface magnetic field of NSs has been found to be in the range 10^{8-12}G for radio and γ-ray pulsars,[5–7] while estimates in magnetars reach 10^{15}G.[8,9] While the surface and magnetospheric magnetic fields of NSs can be probed through many different methods,[10,11] their internal magnetic field remains mostly unknown, both in its strength and geometry. Predictions expect that values up to 10^{16}G and 10^{17-18}G could be reached inside magnetars and newly-born proto-NSs, respectively.[12–14] On the other hand, while it is known that neither purely poloidal nor purely toroidal magnetic configurations are stable[15,16] and mixed configurations are more favoured,[17–19] the extact magnetic field geometry in the interior of NSs is less clear. Fortunately, these magnetic fields present potentially observable effects to the structure of NSs: they can modify the torsional oscillations of NSs,[20,21] their cooling properties[22,23] and their deformation.[24,25]

In this scenario, another unknown regarding the internal structure of NSs enters the game: the equation of state (EoS) of NSs remains mostly unconstrained. Recent observational results rejected the validity of many EoS: the observation of very massive NSs [e.g. the most massive NS known to date, with a mass potentially reaching $\sim 2.28 M_\odot$[26]]; the limits on the stiffness of NSs[27,28] obtained by the first observation of gravitational waves (GWs) emitted by a binary NS merger[29]; the results of the NICER telescope[30,31] on the possible NSs radii. However, this uncertainty is further enhanced by the effect that the strong magnetic field buried inside NSs exherts on their composition, for example determining the presence of exotic particles or the existence of a superconducting phase.[32–36] For these reasons, understanding and constraining the interplay between the magnetic field of NSs and their EoS is fundamental in order to improve our knowledge of these objects.

Other than observations in the electromagnetic domain, GWs can help to probe the inner structure of NSs. Of particular importance are continuous GWs (CGWs), which are emitted, for example, by a time-varying deformation. Such scenario can happen e.g. in the case of magnetically-deformed NSs whose magnetic axis is not aligned with their rotation axis.[25,37,38] Since magnetic fields found in regular pulsars are too low to cause a significant deviation from spherical symmetry,[24] newly-born proto-NSs and millisecond magnetars are the most promising sources of CGWs,[39] along with millisecond pulsars which possess a superconducting core.[38]

While the problem of the inner composition and magnetic field of NSs is an interesting problem on its own, it is deeply intertwined with the long-standing quest for the definitive theory of gravity. Even if general relativity (GR) remains the best theory to model the gravitational interaction, it has long been known that our understanding of gravity through GR presents some issues on the galactic and cosmological scales.[40] While one possibility is to introduce a dark sector,[41,42] another path is to introduce modification to GR, leading to alternative theories of gravity.[43] Among the possible alternatives to GR, scalar-tensor theories (STTs) - in which gravity is mediated also by a scalar field non-minimally coupled to the spacetime metric - have gathered a strong interest because of their simplicity, because they derive from some suggested theories of quantum gravity,[44] in general they satisfy the weak equivalence principle, and they are free of the issues affecting other alternatives to GR.[45–47] Of great importance in the development of STTs was the discovery of a non-perturbative strong field effect, exhibited in some of these theories, named 'spontaneous scalarisation',[48] which leads to strong deviations from GR in the vicinity of compact material objects (i.e. NSs), while it remains unconstrained in the weak-field limit. The presence of a scalar field leads to an enrichment of the physics of NSs, for example by causing the emission of additional modes of

GWs[49,50] or by modifing the mass-radius relation of NSs, the binary NS merger dynamics,[51] the frequency of NS normal modes,[52] their tidal and rotational deformation,[53,54] their magnetic deformation[55–57] and the light propagation properties in their vicinity.[58] While massless STTs have been mostly ruled out by observations,[59–61] STTs with a massive scalar field are still viable.[62–64] As anticipated, part of the phenomenology of STTs is degenerate with the EoS of NSs, for example concerning the mass-radius relation or their deformabilities. For such reason, disentangling their roles is important in order to have a more informative interpretation of observations.

In the following we assume a signature $\{-,+,+,+\}$ for the spacetime metric and use Greek letters μ, ν, λ, ... (running from 0 to 3) for 4D spacetime tensor components, while Latin letters i, j, k, ... (running from 1 to 3) are employed for 3D spatial tensor components. Moreover, we use the dimensionless units where $c = G = M_\odot = 1$, and we absorb the $\sqrt{4\pi}$ factors in the definition of the electromagnetic quantities. All quantities calculated in the Einstein frame (E-frame) are denoted with a bar ($\bar{\cdot}$) while all quantities calculated in the Jordan frame (J-frame) are denoted with a tilde ($\tilde{\cdot}$).

2. Neutron stars in general relativity

The spacetime metric in the case of static, axisymmetric configurations can be well approximated[65,66] using the conformally flat condition (CFC).[67,68] Then, for spherical-like coordinates $x^\mu = [t, r, \theta, \phi]$, the line element is

$$g_{\mu\nu}dx^\mu dx^\nu = -\alpha^2 dt^2 + \psi^4 \left[dr^2 + r^2 d\theta^2 + r^2 \sin^2\theta d\phi^2\right], \quad (1)$$

where $g_{\mu\nu}$ is the spacetime metric, with determinant g, $\alpha(r,\theta)$ is the lapse function and $\psi(r,\theta)$ is the conformal factor. The energy-momentum tensor for a magnetised ideal fluid is[69,70]

$$T^{\mu\nu} = (\rho + \varepsilon + p) u^\mu u^\nu + p g^{\mu\nu} + F^\mu_{\ \lambda} F^{\nu\lambda} - \frac{1}{4} F^{\lambda\kappa} F_{\lambda\kappa} g^{\mu\nu}, \quad (2)$$

where ρ is the rest mass density, ε is the internal energy density, p is the pressure, u^μ is the four-velocity and $F^{\mu\nu}$ is the Faraday tensor. The 3+1 formalism[71,72] can be used to recast the equations in a more computationally-friendly way; under these assumptions, the Einstein equations for the metric become two Poisson-like equations, one for ψ and one for $\alpha\psi$.[19]

As for the magnetohydrodynamics (MHD) quantities, using the pseudo-enthalpy h, related to the pressure and density by $d \ln h = dp/(\rho + \varepsilon + p)$, Euler's equation becomes the 'generalised Bernoulli integral',[19]

$$\ln\left(\frac{h}{h_c}\right) + \ln\left(\frac{\alpha}{\alpha_c}\right) - \mathcal{M} = 0, \quad (3)$$

where $\mathcal{M}$ is the magnetisation function and h_c and α_c are the values of h and α at the centre of the star, respectively (having assumed $\mathcal{M}_c = 0$). The magnetisation function in the case of a purely poloidal magnetic field is assumed to be $\mathcal{M} = k_{\mathrm{pol}} A_\phi$, where k_{pol} is the poloidal magnetisation constant and A_ϕ is the ϕ-component of the vector potential, computed by solving the relativistic Grad-Shafranov equation. For a purely toroidal magnetic field, we instead use $\mathcal{M} = -k_{\mathrm{tor}}^2 (\rho + \varepsilon + p)\mathcal{R}^2$, where k_{tor} is the toroidal magnetisation constant and $\mathcal{R}^2 = \alpha^2 \psi^4 r^2 \sin^2 \theta$. In the first case, the poloidal components of the magnetic field are found through the Grad-Shafranov equation[66,73] for A_ϕ; in the second case, the toroidal component is proportional to $(\rho + \varepsilon + p)\mathcal{R}^2/\alpha$. Finally, the EoS closes the system of equations. We describe the EoS we used in Sect. 5. For a more detailed description of the equilibrium formalism the reader is referred to Refs. 55–57.

3. Scalar-tensor theories in a nutshell

The action of massless STTs in the J-frame, according to the 'Bergmann-Wagoner formulation',[74–76] is

$$\tilde{S} = \frac{1}{16\pi} \int \mathrm{d}^4 x \sqrt{-\tilde{g}} \left[\varphi \tilde{R} - \frac{\omega(\varphi)}{\varphi} \tilde{\nabla}_\mu \varphi \tilde{\nabla}^\mu \varphi \right] + \tilde{S}_{\mathrm{p}} \left[\tilde{\Psi}, \tilde{g}_{\mu\nu} \right], \quad (4)$$

where $\tilde{g}$ is the determinant of the spacetime metric $\tilde{g}_{\mu\nu}$, $\tilde{\nabla}_\mu$ its associated covariant derivative, $\tilde{R}$ its Ricci scalar, $\omega(\varphi)$ is the coupling function of the scalar field φ, and $\tilde{S}_{\mathrm{p}}$ is the action of the physical fields $\tilde{\Psi}$. In the E-frame, the action is obtained by making the conformal transformation $\bar{g}_{\mu\nu} = \mathcal{A}^{-2}(\chi)\tilde{g}_{\mu\nu}$, where $\mathcal{A}^{-2}(\chi) = \varphi(\chi)$ and χ is a redefinition of the scalar field in the E-frame, related to φ by $\mathrm{d}\chi/\mathrm{d}\ln\varphi = \{[\omega(\varphi) + 3]/4\}^{1/2}$. In the E-frame, the scalar field is minimally coupled to the metric: Einstein's field equations retain their usual form in the E-frame, but the energy-momentum tensor is now the sum of the one describing the fluid and electromagnetic fields and of the scalar field one. On the other hand, the scalar field is minimally coupled to the physical fields in the J-frame: the MHD equations in the J-frame have the same expression as in GR. In addition to the metric and MHD equations, in STTs we have an additional equation to solve for the scalar field. In the E-frame it is

$$\Delta \chi = -4\pi \bar{\psi}^4 \alpha_{\mathrm{s}}(\chi) \mathcal{A}^4 \tilde{T} - \partial \ln\left(\bar{\alpha}\bar{\psi}^2\right) \partial \chi, \quad (5)$$

where $\Delta = f^{ij} \hat{\nabla}_i \hat{\nabla}_j$ and $\hat{\nabla}_i$ are, respectively, the 3D Laplacian and nabla operator of the flat space metric f_{ij}, $\partial f \partial g = \partial_r f \partial_r g + (\partial_\theta f \partial_\theta g)/r^2$, $\alpha_{\mathrm{s}}(\chi) = \mathrm{d}\ln\mathcal{A}/\mathrm{d}\chi$ and $\tilde{T} = 3\tilde{p} - \tilde{\varepsilon} - \tilde{\rho}$ is the trace of the J-frame energy momentum tensor of the fluid and electromagnetic fields. We used an exponential coupling function $\mathcal{A}(\chi) = \exp\{\alpha_0 \chi + \beta_0 \chi^2/2\}$.[48] The α_0 parameter regulates the effects of the scalar field in the weak-field limit, while the β_0 parameter controls spontaneous scalarisation. We chose $\alpha_0 = -2 \times 10^{-4}$ and $\beta_0 \in [-6, -4.5]$. The most recent observational constraints to date require that, for massless scalar fields, $|\alpha_0| \lesssim 1.3 \times 10^{-3}$ and $|\beta_0| \gtrsim 4.3$[61]; in the case of massive scalar fields, lower values of β_0 are allowed,[77] as long as the screening radius is smaller than the separation of the binary NSs whose observation confirmed the absence of dipolar GWs.[78,79] We emphasise that results found in a massless STT regarding the internal structure of a NS are also valid for STTs containing a screening effect as long as the screening radius is larger than the NS radius; as such, our results regarding the magnetic deformation of NSs are valid also in the case of a massive scalar field, with a mass such that its screening radius is larger than the NS radius but lower than the binary separation. For a more detailed description of the formulation of STTs within the 3+1 formalism the reader is referred to Refs. 55–57.

4. The magnetic deformation of polytropic neutron stars

We now focus on the case of static NSs in the weak magnetic field regime, where the magnetic deformation of the star is well approximated by a perturbative approach; this was shown to happen for $B_{\max} \lesssim 10^{17}$G,[80,81] where $B_{\max} = \max[\sqrt{B_i B^i}]$ and B_i are the components of the magnetic field. We focus only on the range of masses corresponding to stable configurations. All the results shown are computed using the XNS code,[19,55–57,66,80,82] which solves the coupled equations for the metric, scalar field, and MHD structure of a NS under the assumptions of stationarity and axisymmetry, adopting conformal flatness and maximal slicing.

In Newtonian gravity[83,84] and in GR,[16,66] in the limit of weak magnetic fields, the quadrupole deformation e of a magnetised NS can be expressed as a linear function of $B_{\max}^2$.[66] Equivalently, instead of using $B_{\max}^2$ one can parametrise e also in terms of $\mathcal{H}/W$, where $\mathcal{H}$ is the magnetic energy of the NS, defined in the J-frame as

$$\tilde{\mathcal{H}} = \pi \int \mathcal{A}^3 \tilde{B}_i \tilde{B}^i \sqrt{\tilde{\gamma}} \mathrm{d}r \mathrm{d}\theta , \qquad (6)$$

W being its binding energy.

In STTs, we found that $\bar{e}$ still has a linear trend with $\tilde{B}_{\max}^2$ (or $\tilde{\mathcal{H}}/\bar{W}$), but with coefficients that depend more strongly on the baryonic mass M_0 (which is the same in the J-frame and in the E-frame) than in GR; the strength of this dependence is related to the value of β_0. In the limit $\tilde{B}_{\max} \to 0$, keeping fixed M_0 and β_0:

$$|\bar{e}| = c_\mathrm{B} \tilde{B}_{\max}^2 + \mathcal{O}\left(\tilde{B}_{\max}^4\right), \quad |\bar{e}| = c_\mathrm{H} \frac{\tilde{\mathcal{H}}}{\bar{W}} + \mathcal{O}\left(\frac{\tilde{\mathcal{H}}^2}{\bar{W}^2}\right), \qquad (7)$$

where $c_\mathrm{B} = c_\mathrm{B}(M_0, \beta_0)$ and $c_\mathrm{H} = c_\mathrm{H}(M_0, \beta_0)$ are the 'distortion coefficients', and $\tilde{B}_{\max}$ is normalised to 10^{18}G.

The coefficients c_B and c_H as functions of M_0, for various β_0, are shown in Fig. 1, in the case of NSs endowed with a purely toroidal or a purely poloidal magnetic field and described by the POL2 EoS $\tilde{p} = K_\mathrm{a} \tilde{\rho}^{\gamma_\mathrm{a}}$, with $\gamma_\mathrm{a} = 2$ and $K_\mathrm{a} = 110$ in dimensionless units. The black line represents GR, which corresponds to $\alpha_0 = \beta_0 = 0$. The other lines stand for $\beta_0 = \{-4.5, -4.75, -5.0, -5.25, -5.5, -5.75, -6.0\}$ and $\alpha_0 = -2 \times 10^{-4}$. The effect of scalarisation is visible in the distinctive change in the slope as the scalarised sequences depart from the GR one. The more negative

β_0 is, the more enhanced are the modifications with respect to GR. At a fixed M_0, scalarised NSs have lower distortion coefficient and quadrupole deformation than the GR models with the same mass for most of the scalarisation range. We found that, in the the ranges $1.2 \leq M_0/M_\odot \lesssim 2.4$ and $-6 \leq \beta_0 \leq -4.5$, the distortion coefficients are well approximated by a combination of power laws of the baryonic mass M_0, the J-frame circumferential radius $\tilde{R}_c$ and the E-frame scalar charge $\bar{Q}_s$.[55] In particular

$$c_B \approx c_1 M_{0;1.6}^\alpha R_{10}^\beta \left[1 - c_2 Q_1^\gamma M_{1.6}^\delta R_{10}^\rho\right], \tag{8}$$

where $M_{0;1.6}$ is M_0 in units of $1.6 M_\odot$, R_{10} is $\tilde{R}_c$ in units of 10km, Q_1 is $\bar{Q}_s$ in units of $1 M_\odot$, $[c_1, \alpha, \beta, c_2, \gamma, \delta, \rho] = [0.16, -2.22, 4.86, 0.87, 1.32, -1.27, -2.21]$ in the toroidal case and $[c_1, \alpha, \beta, c_2, \gamma, \delta, \rho] = [0.077, -1.99, 5.80, 1.38, 1.22, -0.86, -3.49]$ in the poloidal case. The coefficient c_H in the toroidal cases is similar to that in the poloidal case; in fact, it is possible to find a functional form over the entire mass range that holds for both magnetic configuartions with an accuracy of few percents:

$$c_H \approx 0.5 + \mathcal{F}(M_0)\mathcal{T}(M_0, \bar{Q}_s, \tilde{R}_c) \times \begin{cases} 0.65 \text{ for toroidal}, \\ 1.02 \text{ for poloidal}, \end{cases} \tag{9}$$

where $\mathcal{F}(M_0)$ does not depend explicitly on the scalar field and described the role of the equation of state, $\mathcal{T}(M_0, \bar{Q}_s, \tilde{R}_c)$ represents the correction due to the presence of scalarisation, and the last numerical factor differentiates the oblate from the prolate geometry, which depends on the magnetic field configuration. We found that:

$$\mathcal{F}(M_0) = 4.98 - 1.95 M_{0;1.6}, \tag{10}$$

$$\mathcal{T}(M_0, \bar{Q}_s, \tilde{R}_c) = 1 - \frac{1.90}{R_{10}^{2.45}} \left(\frac{Q_1}{M_{0;1.6}}\right)^{1.3}. \tag{11}$$

5. Selection of equations of state

The results shown in Sect. 4 are found using a simple polytropic law which, while allowing us to compare our results to previous studies,[16,19] is not allowed by observations. For this reason, we further computed the distortion coefficients for a selection of EoS allowed by observational and nuclear physics constraints.[57] In particular, we selected 13 different EoS that span a diverse range of calculation methods and particle contents. All EoS we used, except the polytropic one, are chosen to satisfy the lates constraints: they reach a maximum mass of at least $\sim 2.05 M_\odot$,[85] satisfy various nuclear physics constraints,[86] are not too stiff,[87] and give the NS a radius between $\sim$10km and $\sim$14km for $1.4 M_\odot$ mass models[88,89]. We chose 6 EoS which contain only $npe\mu$ particles (APR,SLY9,BL2,DDME2,NL3$\omega\rho$,SFH), 2 EoS containing also hyperons (DDME2-Y,NL3$\omega\rho$-Y), 2 EoS containing an uds quark matter domain treated with the Nambu-Jona-Lasinio model (BH8, BF9), 2 EoS containing an uds quark matter domain treated with the MIT bag model or perturbative QCD (SQM1, SQM2), as well as the POL2 EoS.

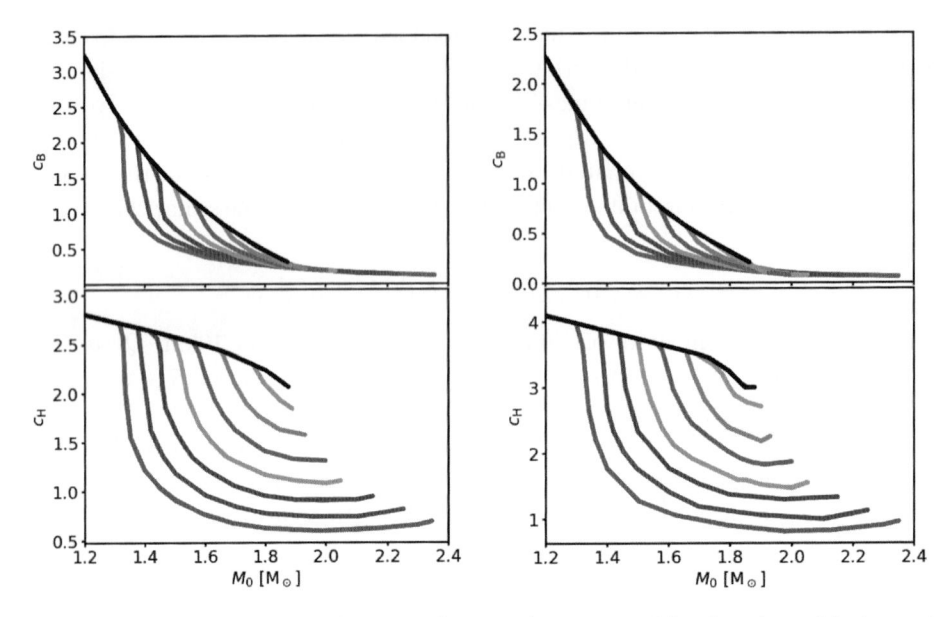

Fig. 1. Distortion coefficients c_B (top panels) and c_H (bottom panels) as functions of the baryonic mass M_0 of models with a purely toroidal magnetic field (left panels) and with a purely poloidal magnetic field (right panels), for various value of β_0: from $\beta_0 = -6$ (magenta curve) to $\beta_0 = -4.5$ (light blue curve) increasing by 0.25 with every line. The black curve corresponds to GR. Adapted from Soldateschi et al., A&A, 645, A39 (2021).

In Fig. 2 we plot the Komar mass $\bar{M}_k$ against the circumferential radius $\tilde{R}_c$ for models of un-magnetised, static NSs computed with the described EoS. The left panel refers to GR, while the right panel to STT with $\beta_0 = -6$. From the left panel of Fig. 2 we see that the NS radii have values ranging from $\sim$10km to $\sim$14km for most EoS, excluding the less compact SQM2 and especially the POL2 EoS. The maximum masses are around $\sim$2-2.2$M_\odot$ for most EoS, except for the NL3$\omega\rho$ and the POL2 EoS.

6. Quasi-universal relations for the magnetic deformation of neutron stars

We computed the distortion coefficients in Eq. 7 for the EoS described in Sect. 5, as well as another distortion coefficient:

$$|\bar{e}| = c_s \tilde{B}_s^2 + \mathcal{O}\left(\tilde{B}_s^4\right), \tag{12}$$

where $\tilde{B}_s$ is the magnetic field calculated at the pole of the NS, at the surface, normalised to 10^{18}G. The coefficients c_B and c_H contain quantities that are not directly accessible by observations, because they require to know the details of the internal structure and magnetic field geometry of NSs. On the other hand, c_s may prove to be more useful to compare our results to observations. This last coefficient is

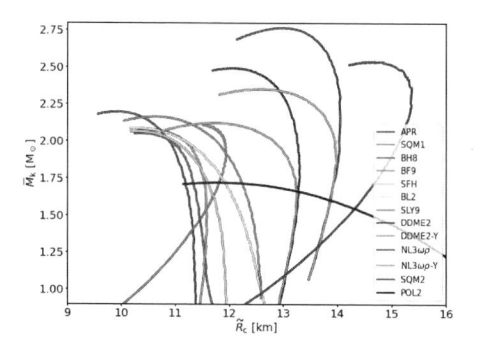

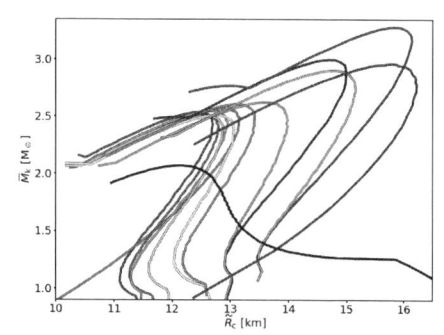

Fig. 2. Komar mass $\bar{M}_k$ against circumferential radius $\tilde{R}_c$ for un-magnetised, static models of NSs computed with the EoS described in Sect. 5 in GR (left plot) and in STT with $\beta_0 = -6$ (right plot). The EoS are color-coded, and ordered in the legend, according to the compactness $C = M_k/R_c$ calculated at $M_k = 1.4 M_\odot$ in GR: red for the highest compactness and blue for the lowest compactness. Adapted from Soldateschi et al., ArXiv e-prints (2021), arXiv:2106.00603v2 [astro-ph.HE].

defined only for configurations endowed with a poloidal magnetic field (the toroidal one being hidden under the surface).

We found that c_B, c_H and c_s are similar for all standard EoS (i.e. all EoS except SQM1, SQM2 and POL2) as functions of the Komar mass.[57] For this reason, we chose to consider the dependence also on another potentially observable quantity, namely the circumferential radius $\tilde{R}_c$, to understand whether the spread among the various EoS could be further reduced. We used the 'principal component analysis' (PCA) technique to find the best-fit relation between $c_{B,H,s}$, $\bar{M}_k$ and $\tilde{R}_c$. We found the following formulas approximating $c_{B,H}$ in GR to a satisfying level of accuracy for all standard EoS (thus the name 'quasi-universal relations'):

$$c_B^{PCA} = \begin{cases} 0.13^{+0.03}_{-0.02} R_{10}^{5.45} M_{1.6}^{-2.41} \text{ for poloidal,} \\ \\ 0.25^{+0.03}_{-0.03} R_{10}^{5.03} M_{1.6}^{-2.07} \text{ for toroidal,} \end{cases} \quad (13)$$

$$c_H^{PCA} = \begin{cases} 5.77^{+0.04}_{-0.06} - 0.77 R_{10} - 4.14 M_{1.6} - 0.27 M_{1.6}^2 + \\ \quad +0.07 R_{10}^2 + 2.28 M_{1.6} R_{10} \text{ for poloidal,} \\ \\ 7.02^{+0.05}_{-0.07} - 5.22 R_{10} - 2.76 M_{1.6} - 0.12 M_{1.6}^2 + \\ \quad +1.92 R_{10}^2 + 1.51 M_{1.6} R_{10} \text{ for toroidal,} \end{cases} \quad (14)$$

where $M_{1.6} = \bar{M}_k/1.6 M_\odot$. Moreover, we found that, in GR, c_s is well-approximated by the following relation:

$$c_s^{PCA} = 2.97^{+0.12}_{-0.23} R_{10}^{4.61} M_{1.6}^{-2.80} . \quad (15)$$

The coefficient c_s computed using Eq. 15 is plotted against the value computed with formula Eq. 12 in Fig. 3 (top left plot), together with the error of the approximation (bottom left plot). The dashed black line is a reference $c_s = c_s^{\text{PCA}}$ bisecting line, which represents a perfect approximation. The superscript and subscript in the first coefficient of Eq. 15 are the values defining the purple and magenta lines bounding the magenta shaded area in Fig. 3, top left plot. The dark blue line, bounding the shaded blue area, marks the 90th percentile of the errors (the bounds containing 90% of the results). The corresponding values of these errors are showed with lines of the same colour in the bottom left plot. The approximation c_s^{PCA} holds with a very small error, under a few percents. Moreover, we found that the quasi-universal relations for c_B hold with a slightly larger error, around $\sim 10\%$. The approximation for c_H is even more accurate, with an error that is mostly under $\sim 1\%$. Moreover, we found that performing $c_H^{\text{PCA}} \to 5/3 c_H^{\text{PCA}} - 0.9$ allows one to use the coefficients found in the toroidal case also in the poloidal configurations with a $\sim 2\%$ error.

Applying the quasi-universal relations derived in the case of standard EoS, Eqs. 13-14-15, to the polytropic models computed with the POL2 EoS, leads to larger errors, especially in the case of c_B. We refer the reader to Ref. 57 for more details.

In the case of STTs, we find quasi-universal relations for $\Delta c_B = |c_B - c_B^{\text{GR}}|$, $\Delta c_H = |c_H - c_H^{\text{GR}}|$ and $\Delta c_s = |c_s - c_s^{\text{GR}}|$, where $c_B^{\text{GR}}, c_H^{\text{GR}}$ and c_s^{GR} are the relations found in the GR case: Eqs. 13-14-15 respectively. In this case, we also allowed the dependence of the distortion coefficients on the scalar charge $\bar{Q}_s$. We found the following quasi-universal relations:

$$\Delta c_B^{\text{PCA}} = \begin{cases} 0.03^{+0.05}_{-0.03} R_{10}^{8.23} M_{1.6}^{-5.08} Q_1^{2.60} \text{ for poloidal,} \\ \\ 0.06^{+0.09}_{-0.05} R_{10}^{5.96} M_{1.6}^{-3.52} Q_1^{1.95} \text{ for toroidal,} \end{cases} \quad (16)$$

$$\Delta c_H^{\text{PCA}} = \begin{cases} 1.96^{+0.17}_{-0.18} R_{10}^{0.72} M_{1.6}^{-1.96} Q_1^{1.54} \text{ for poloidal,} \\ \\ 1.49^{+0.26}_{-0.17} R_{10}^{0.75} M_{1.6}^{-1.81} Q_1^{1.55} \text{ for toroidal,} \end{cases} \quad (17)$$

$$\Delta c_s^{\text{PCA}} = 0.92^{+0.20}_{-0.27} R_{10}^{4.77} M_{1.6}^{-4.50} Q_1^{1.71}. \quad (18)$$

The quasi-universal relation in Eq. 18 is plotted against the corresponding value Δc_s, computed through formula Eq. 12, in Fig. 3 (top right plot). The bottom right plot displays the relative error of the quasi-universal relation. The dashed line is a reference $\Delta c_s = \Delta c_s^{\text{PCA}}$ bisecting line, which would be a perfect approximation. We can see that the approximation for c_s holds with an error that is around 10%. Moreover, we found that the quasi-universal relations for Δc_B hold with an error of

~ 50%. The approximation for Δc_H is more accurate, with a relative error of just a few percents. Similarly to what we found in the GR case, performing $c_H^{PCA} \to 3/2 c_H^{PCA} - 0.2$ allows us to use the coefficients found in the toroidal case in the poloidal geometry with a ~ 10% error.

Using Eq. 16 for models computed using the POL2 EoS, errors in approximating Δc_B remain of the same magnitude in the poloidal case, while they increase by ~ 20% in the toroidal case. Instead, Eq. 17 holds also for the POL2 EoS, at the expense of an error reaching a few tens of percents for the approximation of Δc_H, as in the case of approximating Δc_s using Eq. 18 for polytropic models computed using the POL2 EoS.

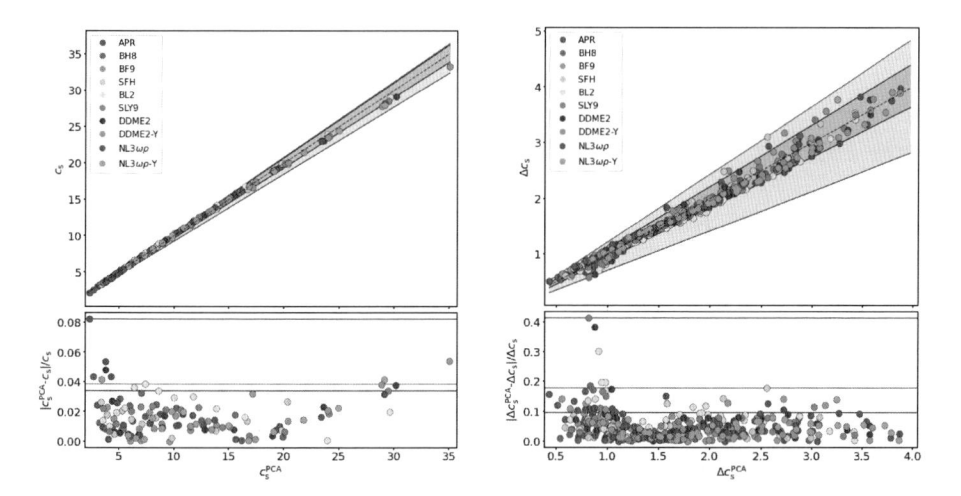

Fig. 3. Top left plot: distortion coefficient c_s, calculated according to Eq. 12 in GR, versus its approximation c_s^{PCA} calculated with the quasi-universal relation in Eq. 15. Top right plot: Difference Δc_s between the distortion coefficient c_s, calculated according to Eq. 12 in STT with $\beta_0 \in \{-6, -5.75, -5.5, -5\}$, and the GR quasi-universal relation in Eq. 15. This is plotted versus its approximation Δc_s^{PCA}, calculated with the quasi-universal relation in Eq. 18. The corresponding relative deviations from the PCA are given in the bottom plots. The dashed lines are $c_{B,H} = c_{B,H}^{PCA}$ and $\Delta c_s = \Delta c_s^{PCA}$, respectively. The magenta shaded areas comprise all data points and the purple and magenta lines represent the upper and lower bounds of Eq. 15 and Eq. 18, respectively; the dark blue lines bounding the shaded blue area mark the 90th percentile error region. The EoS are color-coded, and ordered in the legend, according to the compactness $C = M_k/R_c$ calculated at $M_k = 1.4 M_\odot$ in GR: red for the highest compactness and blue for the lowest compactness. Adapted from Soldateschi et al., ArXiv e-prints (2021), arXiv:2106.00603v2 [astro-ph.HE].

As in the case of the POL2 EoS, we incur in larger errors if we apply the quasi-universal relations we found to the case of the SQM1 and SQM2 EoS. In GR, c_B^{PCA} is a factor ~ 0.4 − 0.8 lower than c_B. The maximum error for approximating c_H with Eq. 14 increases to ~ 8 − 12% in the case of SQM1, and ~ 5% (~ 40%) for purely poloidal (toroidal) magnetic fields in the case of SQM2. Moreover, c_s^{PCA} is at most a factor ~ 1.4 higher than c_s. In STT, Δc_B^{PCA} in the poloidal case is around a factor ~ 2 lower (higher) than Δc_B for the SQM1 (SQM2) EoS; in the toroidal case, it is a factor ~ 2 lower for both SQM1 and SQM2. The maximum error for approximating Δc_H using Eq. 17 increases to $\sim 30\% (\sim 50\%)$ for purely poloidal (toroidal) magnetic fields. Finally, Δc_s^{PCA} is around a factor ~ 1.7 lower than Δc_s.

A time-varying quadrupolar deformation leads to the emission of GWs. While in GR these are only of tensor nature, in the case of STTs a scalar channel is also present, which can contain any multipolar component. We only focus here on quadrupolar modes of GWs, both of tensor and scalar nature. As we have shown, NSs in GR and in STTs posses quite different quadrupolar deformations; for this reason, we compare the amount of GWs emitted by NSs in these two modes. To this end, we introduce the following quantity:

$$\mathcal{S} = \left|\frac{q_s}{q_g}\right|, \qquad (19)$$

where

$$q_s = 2\pi \int \alpha_s \mathcal{A}^4 \tilde{T} \left(3\sin^2\theta - 2\right) r^4 \sin\theta dr d\theta, \qquad (20)$$

$$q_g = \int \left[\pi \mathcal{A}^4(\tilde{\varepsilon} + \tilde{p}) - \frac{1}{8}\partial\chi\partial\chi\right] r^4 \sin\theta \left(3\sin^2\theta - 2\right) dr d\theta. \qquad (21)$$

The quantity q_s is related to the source of scalar waves. The mass quadrupole q_g is $\bar{I}_{zz} - \bar{I}_{xx} = \bar{e}\bar{I}_{zz}$ and is the source of tensor waves. Thus, the ratio $\mathcal{S}$ computed for a given NS model measures the relative amount of quadrupolar GWs emitted in the scalar and tensor channels. If $\mathcal{S} < 1$, the majority of GWs will be emitted in the tensor channel; if $\mathcal{S} > 1$, in the scalar channel. We found that the following quasi-universal relations hold for $\mathcal{S}$:

$$\mathcal{S}^{PCA} = \begin{cases} 1.98_{-0.05}^{+0.18} R_{10}^{-0.71} M_{1.6}^{-0.54} Q_1^{1.22} & \text{for poloidal,} \\ \\ 1.99_{-0.07}^{+0.18} R_{10}^{-0.74} M_{1.6}^{-0.60} Q_1^{1.23} & \text{for toroidal.} \end{cases} \qquad (22)$$

In Fig. 4 we plot the values of $\mathcal{S}$, computed through Eq. 19 for $\beta_0 \in \{-6, -5.75, -5.5, -5\}$, against their PCA approximation, computed through Eq. 22. The approximation is very accurate in both magnetic geometries, with an error that is mostly concentrated under $\sim 4\%$. Moreover, we see that the coefficients in Eq. 22 are almost identical in the poloidal and the toroidal cases, thus the two approximations are practically equivalent. It is possible that this similarity means that there exist a relation between the sources of scalar and tensor waves, q_s and q_g, that does not depend on either the magnetic field geometry or the EoS.

The quasi-universal relations we found are independent on the EoS of standard NSs. For this reason they may be useful in disentangling the effects of the EoS and

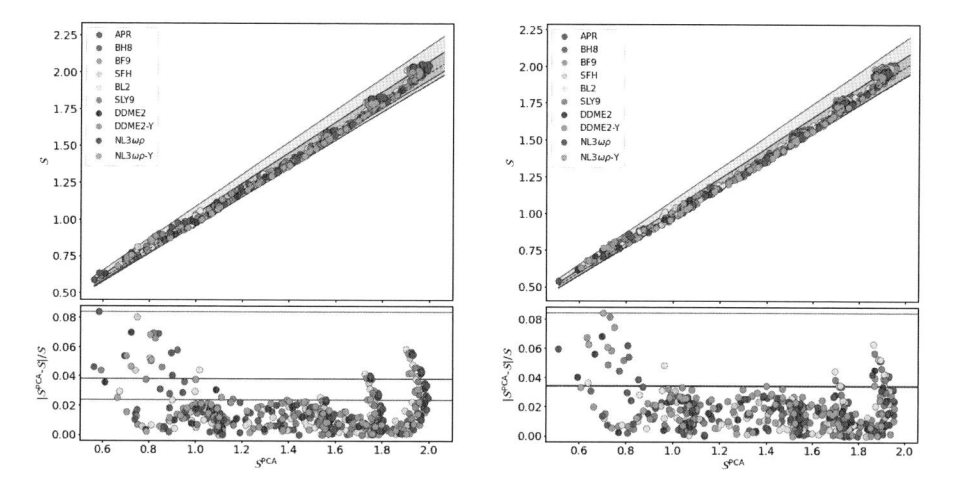

Fig. 4. Ratio $\mathcal{S}$ between scalar and tensor quadrupolar GW losses, calculated according to Eq. 19 in STT with $\beta_0 \in \{-6, -5.75, -5.5, -5\}$. This is plotted versus its approximation $\mathcal{S}^{\mathrm{PCA}}$, calculated with the quasi-universal relations in Eq. 22 (top plot in each panel). The corresponding relative devitations from the PCA are given in the bottom plot in each panel. The left panel refers to a purely poloidal magnetic field; the right panel refers to a purely toroidal magnetic field. The dashed line is $\mathcal{S} = \mathcal{S}^{\mathrm{PCA}}$. The magenta shaded area comprises all data points and the purple and magenta lines represent the upper and lower bounds of Eq. 22; the dark blue lines bounding the shaded blue area mark the 90th percentile error region. The EoS are color-coded, and ordered in the legend, according to the compactness $C = M_k/R_c$ calculated at $M_k = 1.4 M_\odot$ in GR: red for the highest compactness and blue for the lowest compactness. Adapted from Soldateschi et al., ArXiv e-prints (2021), arXiv:2106.00603v2 [astro-ph.HE].

the magnetic field structure of NSs, leaving their internal magnetic structure as the only major unknown in GR. In this sense, the most promising relation is that of c_s. On the one hand, c_s can be computed from its definition Eq. 12. In this case, one needs to measure both the magnetic field strength at the surface of the NS, B_s, and its quadrupolar deformation e, which, in turn, can be estimated from the strain of CGWs emitted by the NS: $h_0 \propto eI$, where I is the moment of inertia of the NS along its rotation axis, which can be computed through an EoS-independent relation by knowing the NS mass and its radius.[90] On the other hand, our quasi-universal relation Eq. 15 allows one to estimate c_s^{PCA} by knowing just the NS mass and radius. Comparing these values of c_s and c_s^{PCA} can give an insight into the internal magnetic geometry of the emitting NS: the quasi-universal relation Eq. 15 was found in the case of a purely poloidal field, that is an extreme configuration which exherts the maximum possible magnetic deformation on the NS. For example, a lower value of c_s inferred by observations may imply the existence of a toroidal component of the NS internal magnetic field, which counteracts the effect of the poloidal component and results in a lower magnetic deformation. In the opposite case, another source of deformation may be present other than the magnetic field.

The quasi-universal relations Eqs. 13-14 may be more useful to constrain B_{max} or $\mathcal{H}/W$ themselves, being these quantities generally not observable. In particular,

$B_\mathrm{max} \approx (e/c_\mathrm{B})^{1/2}$ and $\mathcal{H}/W \approx e/c_\mathrm{H}$. As in the case of c_s, we expect $c_\mathrm{B,H} < c_\mathrm{B,H}^\mathrm{PCA}$. If the NS mass and radius are known, one can esitimate a lower bound for both B_max and $\mathcal{H}/W$ by using the quasi-universal relations found in the purely poloidal and purely toroidal case. Moreover, the quasi-universal relations for c_B, c_H and c_s can be useful to easily compute the distortion coefficients from the mass and radius of a model, without having to fully simulate the NS model.

In the case of STTs, some of the effects of the EoS are degenerate with the presence of a scalar charge inside the NS. For this reason, quasi-universal relations Eqs. 16-17-18 may help to understand whether a distortion coefficient inferred through relations Eqs. 8-12, is compatible with the observed NS possessing a scalar charge, independently from its EoS. Relation Eq. 22 does not involve knowing the strength of the magnetic field, thus it is probably more promising. In particular, following our previous argument, it may be that $\mathcal{S} \approx \mathcal{S}^\mathrm{PCA}$ independently of the magnetic configuration. Then, the observation of CGWs coming from a given NS of known mass, radius, distance d and spin period P translates into a lower bound for a function of the scalar charge. On the other hand, the non-observation of CGWs from a given NS can be translated into an upper bound.

Finally, we can use the quasi-universal relations we found to assess the detectability of known NSs, in GR. Since the strain of CGWs emitted by a deformed NS, rotating with frequency f_rot and at a distance d, is $h_0 \propto eI f_\mathrm{rot}^2/d$, by using the quasi-universal relation for c_s Eq. 15 we can compute h_0 for the pulsars of the ATNF[91] catalogue. In this case, f_rot and d are taken from the data in ATNF catalogue, while $M_\mathrm{k}, B_\mathrm{s}$ are generated from the expected distributions.[92,93] The radius R_c is computed by assuming the two most diverse standard EoS among the ones we considered, APR and NL3$\omega\rho$, and using the corresponding mass-radius diagram. Our results are shown in Fig. 5, where they are compared to the sensitivity of the advanced LIGO (aLIGO) detector in the design configuration[a] and of the Einstein Telescope (ET) detector in the D configuration[b]: the blue (red) solid line represents the sensitivity of aLIGO (ET), while the blue (red) dot-dashed and dashed lines show the minimum strain detectable by aLIGO (ET) assuming a 1 month or 2 years observing time, respectively. The x-axis represents the frequency f of the emitted CGWs. In the general case, CGWs are emitted at two frequencies, $f = f_\mathrm{rot}$ and $f = 2f_\mathrm{rot}$. In this case, we consider only the $f = 2f_\mathrm{rot}$ wave. As we can see from Fig. 5, many millisecond pulsars contained in the ATNF catalogue have a chance to emit CGWs which could be potentially observed with the future ET detector, especially considering a 1 month or 2 year observing campaign. As for aLIGO, in the case of 1 month or 2 years observing time, a few tens of the ATNF millisecond pulsars could potentially be detected through CGWs. We note that the difference in radii given by the two different EoS does not significantly alter the strain of the

---

[a]The aLIGO design densitivity curves can be found at https://dcc.ligo.org/LIGO-T1800044/public.
[b]The ET sensitivity curves can be found at http://www.et-gw.eu/index.php/etsensitivities.

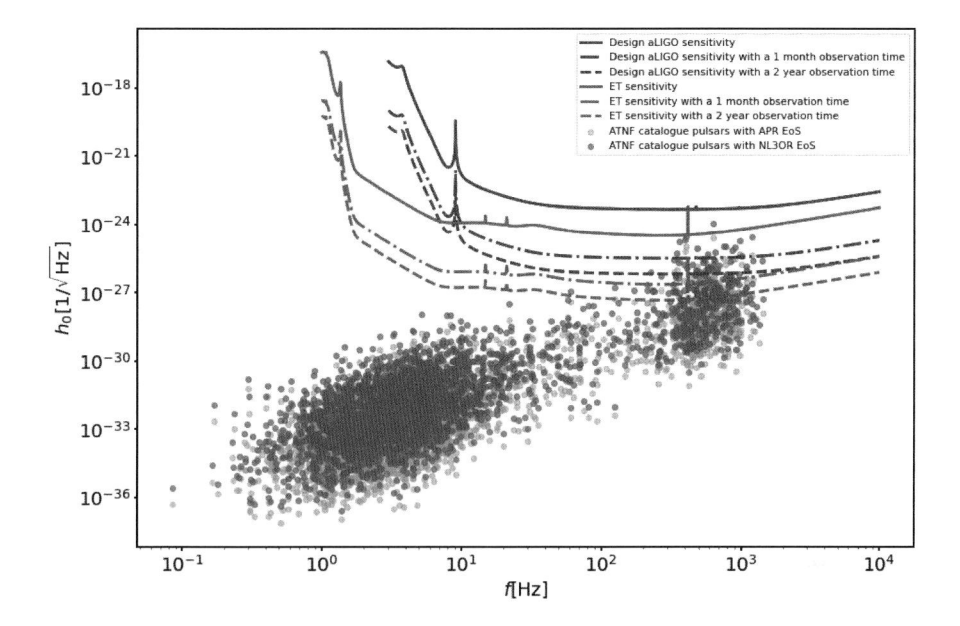

Fig. 5. CGWs strain h_0 computed for pulsars contained in the ATNF catalogue through the use of quasi-universal relation Eq. 15 and by assuming the APR EoS (orange points) or the NL3$\omega\rho$ EoS (green points). The x-axis represents the frequency f of the emitted CGWs. The blue (red) solid line represents the sensitivity of the aLIGO (ET) detector, while the blue (red) dot-dashed and dashed lines show the minimum strain detectable by aLIGO (ET) assuming a 1 month or 2 years observing time, respectively.

emitted CGWs. However, pulsars with smaller rotation period are much less likely to be observed, even with a 3rd generation detector like ET.

References

1. R. C. Duncan and C. Thompson, Formation of Very Strongly Magnetized Neutron Stars: Implications for Gamma-Ray Bursts, *ApJ* **392**, p. L9 (June 1992).
2. C. Thompson and R. C. Duncan, Neutron Star Dynamos and the Origins of Pulsar Magnetism, *ApJ* **408**, p. 194 (May 1993).
3. C. Thompson and R. C. Duncan, The soft gamma repeaters as very strongly magnetized neutron stars - I. Radiative mechanism for outbursts, *MNRAS* **275**, 255 (July 1995).
4. C. Thompson and R. C. Duncan, The Soft Gamma Repeaters as Very Strongly Magnetized Neutron Stars. II. Quiescent Neutrino, X-Ray, and Alfven Wave Emission, *ApJ* **473**, p. 322 (December 1996).
5. E. Asseo and D. Khechinashvili, The role of multipolar magnetic fields in pulsar magnetospheres, *MNRAS* **334**, 743 (08 2002).
6. H. C. Spruit, The source of magnetic fields in (neutron-) stars, in *Cosmic Magnetic Fields: From Planets, to Stars and Galaxies*, eds. K. G. Strassmeier, A. G. Kosovichev and J. E. Beckman, IAU Symposium, Vol. 259, April 2009.

7. L. Ferrario, A. Melatos and J. Zrake, Magnetic Field Generation in Stars, *Space Sci. Rev.* **191**, p. 77 (October 2015).
8. S. A. Olausen and V. M. Kaspi, The McGill Magnetar Catalog, *ApJS* **212**, p. 6 (May 2014).
9. S. B. Popov, Origins of magnetars in binary systems, *A&AT* **29**, 183 (January 2016).
10. N. Rea, P. Esposito, R. Turolla, G. L. Israel, S. Zane, L. Stella, S. Mereghetti, A. Tiengo, D. Götz, E. Göğüş and C. Kouveliotou, A Low-Magnetic-Field Soft Gamma Repeater, *Science* **330**, p. 944 (November 2010).
11. R. Staubert, J. Trümper, E. Kendziorra, D. Klochkov, K. Postnov, P. Kretschmar, K. Pottschmidt, F. Haberl, R. E. Rothschild, A. Santangelo, J. Wilms, I. Kreykenbohm and F. Fürst, Cyclotron lines in highly magnetized neutron stars, *A&A* **622**, p. A61 (February 2019).
12. L. Del Zanna and N. Bucciantini, Covariant and 3 + 1 equations for dynamo-chiral general relativistic magnetohydrodynamics, *MNRAS* **479**, 657 (06 2018).
13. R. Ciolfi, W. Kastaun, J. V. Kalinani and B. Giacomazzo, First 100 ms of a long-lived magnetized neutron star formed in a binary neutron star merger, *Phys. Rev. D* **100**, p. 023005 (July 2019).
14. K. Franceschetti and L. Del Zanna, General Relativistic Mean-Field Dynamo Model for Proto-Neutron Stars, *Universe* **6**, p. 83 (June 2020).
15. K. H. Prendergast, The Equilibrium of a Self-Gravitating Incompressible Fluid Sphere with a Magnetic Field. I, *ApJ* **123**, p. 498 (May 1956).
16. J. Frieben and L. Rezzolla, Equilibrium models of relativistic stars with a toroidal magnetic field, *MNRAS* **427**, p. 3406 (December 2012).
17. R. Ciolfi and L. Rezzolla, Twisted-torus configurations with large toroidal magnetic fields in relativistic stars, *MNRAS* **435**, L43 (August 2013).
18. K. Uryū, E. Gourgoulhon, C. M. Markakis, K. Fujisawa, A. Tsokaros and Y. Eriguchi, Equilibrium solutions of relativistic rotating stars with mixed poloidal and toroidal magnetic fields, *Phys. Rev. D* **90**, p. 101501 (November 2014).
19. A. G. Pili, N. Bucciantini and L. Del Zanna, Axisymmetric equilibrium models for magnetized neutron stars in general relativity under the conformally flat condition, *MNRAS* **439**, 3541 (2014).
20. L. Samuelsson and N. Andersson, Neutron star asteroseismology. Axial crust oscillations in the Cowling approximation, *MNRAS* **374**, 256 (January 2007).
21. H. Sotani, Torsional oscillations of neutron stars with highly tangled magnetic fields, *Phys. Rev. D* **92**, p. 104024 (November 2015).
22. D. Page, J. M. Lattimer, M. Prakash and A. W. Steiner, Minimal Cooling of Neutron Stars: A New Paradigm, *ApJS* **155**, 623 (December 2004).
23. D. N. Aguilera, J. A. Pons and J. A. Miralles, The Impact of Magnetic Field on the Thermal Evolution of Neutron Stars, *ApJ* **673**, p. L167 (February 2008).
24. B. Haskell, L. Samuelsson, K. Glampedakis and N. Andersson, Modelling magnetically deformed neutron stars, *MNRAS* **385**, 531 (March 2008).
25. R. O. Gomes, H. Pais, V. Dexheimer, C. Providência and S. Schramm, Limiting magnetic field for minimal deformation of a magnetized neutron star, *A&A* **627**, p. A61 (July 2019).
26. D. Kandel and R. W. Romani, Atmospheric circulation on black widow companions, *ApJ* **892**, p. 101 (April 2020).
27. T. L. S. Collaboration and the Virgo Collaboration, Gw170817: Measurements of neutron star radii and equation of state, *Phys. Rev. Lett.* **121**, p. 161101 (October 2018).
28. A. Bauswein, Equation of state constraints from multi-messenger observations of neutron star mergers, *Ann. Physics* **411**, p. 167958 (December 2019).

29. T. L. S. Collaboration and V. Collaboration, GW170817: Observation of Gravitational Waves from a Binary Neutron Star Inspiral, *Phys. Rev. Lett.* **119**, p. 161101 (October 2017).
30. P. T. H. Pang, I. Tews, M. W. Coughlin, M. Bulla, C. Van Den Broeck and T. Dietrich, Nuclear-Physics Multi-Messenger Astrophysics Constraints on the Neutron-Star Equation of State: Adding NICER's PSR J0740+6620 Measurement, *arXiv e-prints*, p. arXiv:2105.08688 (May 2021).
31. N.-B. Zhang and B.-A. Li, Impacts of NICER's Radius Measurement of PSR J0740+6620 on Nuclear Symmetry Energy at Suprasaturation Densities, *arXiv e-prints*, p. arXiv:2105.11031 (May 2021).
32. M. Ruderman, Spin-driven changes in neutron star magnetic fields, *J. Astrophys. Astron.* **16**, 207 (June 1995).
33. J. L. Zdunik and P. Haensel, Maximum mass of neutron stars and strange neutron-star cores, *A&A* **551**, p. A61 (March 2013).
34. P. Costa, M. Ferreira, H. Hansen, D. P. Menezes and C. Providência, Phase transition and critical end point driven by an external magnetic field in asymmetric quark matter, *Phys. Rev. D* **89**, p. 056013 (March 2014).
35. B.-J. Cai, F. J. Fattoyev, B.-A. Li and W. G. Newton, Critical density and impact of $\Delta(1232)$ resonance formation in neutron stars, *Phys. Rev. C* **92**, p. 015802 (July 2015).
36. A. Drago, A. Lavagno, G. Pagliara and D. Pigato, The scenario of two families of compact stars, *Eur. Phys. J. A* **52**, p. 40 (February 2016).
37. M. Bocquet, S. Bonazzola, E. Gourgoulhon and J. Novak, Rotating neutron star models with a magnetic field, *A&A* **301**, p. 757 (September 1995).
38. C. Cutler, Gravitational waves from neutron stars with large toroidal b fields, *Phys. Rev. D* **66**, p. 084025 (October 2002).
39. S. Dall'Osso and L. Stella, Millisecond Magnetars, *arXiv e-prints*, p. arXiv:2103.10878 (March 2021).
40. E. Papantonopoulos, *Modifications of Einstein's Theory of Gravity at Large Distances*, Lecture Notes in Physics (Springer International Publishing, 2015).
41. V. Trimble, Existence and Nature of Dark Matter in the Universe, *ARA&A* **25**, 425 (September 1987).
42. P. J. E. Peebles and B. Ratra, The cosmological constant and dark energy, *Rev. Mod. Phys.* **75**, 559 (April 2003).
43. S. Capozziello and M. de Laurentis, Extended Theories of Gravity, *Phys. Rep.* **509**, 167 (2011).
44. T. Damour, F. Piazza and G. Veneziano, Runaway Dilaton and Equivalence Principle Violations, *Phys. Rev. Lett.* **89**, p. 081601 (August 2002).
45. A. DeFelice, M. Hindmarsh and M. Trodden, Ghosts, instabilities, and superluminal propagation in modified gravity models, *J. Cosmology Astropart. Phys.* **2006**, p. 005 (August 2006).
46. A. De Felice and T. Tanaka, Inevitable Ghost and the Degrees of Freedom in f(R,G) Gravity, *Prog. Theor. Phys.* **124**, 503 (September 2010).
47. O. Bertolami and J. Páramos, Viability of nonminimally coupled f(R) gravity, *Gen. Relativ. Gravit.* **48**, p. 34 (March 2016).
48. T. Damour and G. Esposito-Farèse, Nonperturbative strong-field effects in tensor-scalar theories of gravitation, *Phys. Rev. Lett.* **70**, 2220 (April 1993).
49. D. M. Eardley, D. L. Lee and A. P. Lightman, Gravitational-wave observations as a tool for testing relativistic gravity, *Phys. Rev. D* **8**, 3308 (November 1973).

50. P. T. H. Pang, R. K. L. Lo, I. C. F. Wong, T. G. F. Li and C. Van Den Broeck, Generic searches for alternative gravitational wave polarizations with networks of interferometric detectors, *Phys. Rev. D* **101**, p. 104055 (May 2020).
51. M. Shibata, K. Taniguchi, H. Okawa and A. Buonanno, Coalescence of binary neutron stars in a scalar-tensor theory of gravity, *Phys. Rev. D* **89**, p. 084005 (April 2014).
52. H. Sotani and K. D. Kokkotas, Stellar oscillations in scalar-tensor theory of gravity, *Phys. Rev. D* **71**, p. 124038 (June 2005).
53. P. Pani and E. Berti, Slowly rotating neutron stars in scalar-tensor theories, *Phys. Rev. D* **90**, p. 024025 (Jul 2014).
54. D. D. Doneva, S. S. Yazadjiev, N. Stergioulas and K. D. Kokkotas, Rapidly rotating neutron stars in scalar-tensor theories of gravity, *Phys. Rev. D* **88**, p. 084060 (October 2013).
55. J. Soldateschi, N. Bucciantini and L. Del Zanna, Axisymmetric equilibrium models for magnetised neutron stars in scalar-tensor theories, *A&A* **640**, p. A44 (August 2020).
56. J. Soldateschi, N. Bucciantini and L. Del Zanna, Magnetic deformation of neutron stars in scalar-tensor theories, *A&A* **645**, p. A39 (2021).
57. J. Soldateschi, N. Bucciantini and L. Del Zanna, Quasi-universality of the magnetic deformation of neutron stars in general relativity and beyond, *arXiv e-prints*, p. arXiv:2106.00603 (June 2021).
58. N. Bucciantini and J. Soldateschi, Iron line from neutron star accretion discs in scalar tensor theories, *MNRAS* **495**, L56 (April 2020).
59. C. M. Will, The Confrontation between General Relativity and Experiment, *Living Rev. Relativ.* **17** (2014).
60. L. Shao, N. Sennett, A. Buonanno, M. Kramer and N. Wex, Constraining nonperturbative strong-field effects in scalar-tensor gravity by combining pulsar timing and laser-interferometer gravitational-wave detectors, *Phys. Rev. X* **7**, 041025 (October 2017).
61. G. Voisin, I. Cognard, P. C. C. Freire, N. Wex, L. Guillemot, G. Desvignes, M. Kramer and G. Theureau, An improved test of the strong equivalence principle with the pulsar in a triple star system, *A&A* **638**, p. A24 (June 2020).
62. F. M. Ramazanoğlu and F. Pretorius, Spontaneous Scalarization with Massive Fields, *Phys. Rev. D* **93**, p. 064005 (March 2016).
63. S. S. Yazadjiev, D. D. Doneva and D. Popchev, Slowly rotating neutron stars in scalar-tensor theories with a massive scalar field, *Phys. Rev. D* **93**, p. 084038 (April 2016).
64. R. Rosca-Mead, C. J. Moore, U. Sperhake, M. Agathos and D. Gerosa, Structure of neutron stars in massive scalar-tensor gravity, *Symmetry* **12**, p. 1384 (2020).
65. A. Oron, Relativistic magnetized star with poloidal and toroidal fields, *Phys. Rev. D* **66**, p. 023006 (July 2002).
66. A. G. Pili, N. Bucciantini and L. Del Zanna, General relativistic models for rotating magnetized neutron stars in conformally flat space-time, *MNRAS* **470**, 2469 (2017).
67. J. R. Wilson and G. J. Mathews, *Relativistic Numerical Hydrodynamics*, Cambridge Monographs on Mathematical Physics (Cambridge University Press, 2003).
68. J. A. Isenberg, Waveless approximation theories of gravity, *Int. J. Mod. Phys. D* **17**, 265 (February 2008).
69. N. Bucciantini and L. Del Zanna, A fully covariant mean-field dynamo closure for numerical 3 + 1 resistive GRMHD, *MNRAS* **428**, 71 (January 2013).
70. N. Tomei, L. Del Zanna, M. Bugli and N. Bucciantini, General relativistic magnetohydrodynamic dynamo in thick accretion discs: fully non-linear simulations, *MNRAS* **491**, 2346 (January 2020).

71. M. Alcubierre, *Introduction to 3+1 Numerical Relativity*, International Series of Monographs on Physics (OUP Oxford, 2008).
72. É. Gourgoulhon, *3+1 Formalism in General Relativity: Bases of Numerical Relativity*, Lecture Notes in Physics (Springer Berlin Heidelberg, 2012).
73. L. Del Zanna and C. Chiuderi, Exact solutions for symmetric magnetohydrodynamic equilibria with mass flow, *A&A* **310**, 341 (June 1996).
74. P. G. Bergmann, Comments on the scalar-tensor theory, *Int. J. Theor. Phys.* **1**, 25 (May 1968).
75. R. V. Wagoner, Scalar-Tensor Theory and Gravitational Waves, *Phys. Rev. D* **1**, 3209 (June 1970).
76. D. I. Santiago and A. S. Silbergleit, On the energy-momentum tensor of the scalar field in scalar-tensor theories of gravity, *Gen. Relativ. Gravit.* **32**, p. 565–582 (April 2000).
77. D. D. Doneva and S. S. Yazadjiev, Rapidly rotating neutron stars with a massive scalar field—structure and universal relations, *J. Cosmology Astropart. Phys.* **2016**, 019 (nov 2016).
78. X. Zhang, T. Liu and W. Zhao, Gravitational radiation from compact binary systems in screened modified gravity, *Phys. Rev. D* **95**, p. 104027 (May 2017), arXiv: 1702.08752.
79. X. Zhang, R. Niu and W. Zhao, Constraining the scalar-tensor gravity theories with and without screening mechanisms by combined observations, *Phys. Rev. D* **100**, p. 024038 (July 2019).
80. A. G. Pili, N. Bucciantini and L. Del Zanna, General relativistic neutron stars with twisted magnetosphere, *MNRAS* **447**, 2821 (March 2015).
81. N. Bucciantini, A. G. Pili and L. D. Zanna, The role of currents distribution in general relativistic equilibria of magnetized neutron stars, *MNRAS* **447**, 1 (2015).
82. N. Bucciantini and L. Del Zanna, General relativistic magnetohydrodynamics in axisymmetric dynamical spacetimes: the X-ECHO code, *A&A* **528**, A101 (2011).
83. D. G. Wentzel, Hydromagnetic Equilibria., *ApJS* **5**, p. 187 (December 1960).
84. J. P. Ostriker and J. E. Gunn, On the Nature of Pulsars. I. Theory, *ApJ* **157**, p. 1395 (September 1969).
85. E. Fonseca, H. T. Cromartie, T. T. Pennucci, P. S. Ray, A. Y. Kirichenko, S. M. Ransom, P. B. Demorest, I. H. Stairs, Z. Arzoumanian, L. Guillemot, A. Parthasarathy, M. Kerr, I. Cognard, P. T. Baker, H. Blumer, P. R. Brook, M. DeCesar, T. Dolch, F. A. Dong, E. C. Ferrara, W. Fiore, N. Garver-Daniels, D. C. Good, R. Jennings, M. L. Jones, V. M. Kaspi, M. T. Lam, D. R. Lorimer, J. Luo, A. McEwen, J. W. McKee, M. A. McLaughlin, N. McMann, B. W. Meyers, A. Naidu, C. Ng, D. J. Nice, N. Pol, H. A. Radovan, B. Shapiro-Albert, C. M. Tan, S. P. Tendulkar, J. K. Swiggum, H. M. Wahl and W. W. Zhu, Refined Mass and Geometric Measurements of the High-mass PSR J0740+6620, *ApJ* **915**, p. L12 (July 2021).
86. M. Fortin, C. Providencia, A. R. Raduta, F. Gulminelli, J. L. Zdunik, P. Haensel and M. Bejger, Neutron star radii and crusts: uncertainties and unified equations of state, *Phys. Rev. C* **94** (2016).
87. A. Guerra Chaves and T. Hinderer, Probing the equation of state of neutron star matter with gravitational waves from binary inspirals in light of GW170817: A brief review, *J. Phys. G: Nucl. Part. Phys.* **46**, p. 123002 (December 2019).
88. A. Bauswein, O. Just, H.-T. Janka and N. Stergioulas, Neutron-star radius constraints from gw170817 and future detections, *ApJ* **850**, p. L34 (Dec 2017).

89. T. E. Riley, A. L. Watts, P. S. Ray, S. Bogdanov, S. Guillot, S. M. Morsink, A. V. Bilous, Z. Arzoumanian, D. Choudhury, J. S. Deneva, K. C. Gendreau, A. K. Harding, W. C. G. Ho, J. M. Lattimer, M. Loewenstein, R. M. Ludlam, C. B. Markwardt, T. Okajima, C. Prescod-Weinstein, R. A. Remillard, M. T. Wolff, E. Fonseca, H. T. Cromartie, M. Kerr, T. T. Pennucci, A. Parthasarathy, S. Ransom, I. Stairs, L. Guillemot and I. Cognard, A NICER View of the Massive Pulsar PSR J0740+6620 Informed by Radio Timing and XMM-Newton Spectroscopy, *arXiv e-prints*, p. arXiv:2105.06980 (May 2021).
90. C. Breu and L. Rezzolla, Maximum mass, moment of inertia and compactness of relativistic stars, *MNRAS* **459**, 646 (June 2016).
91. R. N. Manchester, G. B. Hobbs, A. Teoh and M. Hobbs, The Australia Telescope National Facility Pulsar Catalogue, *AJ* **129**, 1993 (April 2005).
92. J. Antoniadis, T. M. Tauris, F. Ozel, E. Barr, D. J. Champion and P. C. C. Freire, The millisecond pulsar mass distribution: Evidence for bimodality and constraints on the maximum neutron star mass, *arXiv e-prints*, p. arXiv:1605.01665 (May 2016).
93. C.-A. Faucher-Giguère and V. M. Kaspi, Birth and Evolution of Isolated Radio Pulsars, *ApJ* **643**, 332 (May 2006).

Screening and elastic properties of the NS crust in the OCP approximation

D. Barba González*, C. Albertus Torres† and M.A. Pérez-García‡

Department of Fundamental Physics, University of Salamanca, Plaza de la Merced s/n E-37008, Salamanca, Spain
* david.barbag@usal.es, † albertus@usal.es, ‡ mperezga@usal.es

We study the stress tensor of the outer crust of Neutron Stars (NSs) under the approximation of the one component plasma (OCP) with screening. In our approach a system of identical ions is placed in an electron degenerate Fermi sea. By using Molecular Dynamics simulations at finite temperature we obtain the stress tensor components and associated pressure including Ewald sums for the electron screened ion potential. Our results show that a careful characterization of the crystallized phase at low temperature is necessary in order to obtain the true ground state. These ion phases are of interest for modelling the effects of large tidal forces and the gravitational wave signal linked to the violent events in binary NS mergers and possible crust crunching in NS continuous emission.

Keywords: Neutron star, dense matter, crust

1. Introduction

The extreme conditions of matter inside Neutron Stars (NSs) are hard to grasp based on our knowledge of regular low density condensed matter on Earth. Nevertheless it is crucial for our understanding of these objects to theoretically model their interior. High density matter present in their core is thought to be a homogeneous system of relativistic particles, mostly neutron rich. Typical NSs are believed to be formed out of nucleons and possibly heavier particles and a lepton sector providing electrical charge neutrality. Located in their outer shells, the crust is far from being a trivial phase.[1] It is composed of non-homogeneous matter, typically a set of irregular shapes, pasta phases,[2] that at lower densities end up forming a regular ion lattice. Besides, in order to maintain electrical charge neutrality there must be a degenerate electron Fermi gas surrounding these structures. Some of the neutrons leaking from these irregular shapes can pair into superfluid phases in the lower density part of the NS crust.[3]

Experimental constraints on the nature of NSs have been difficult to obtain, only in the last decades satellite missions or big water tank detectors have been able to deepen inside the electromagnetic or neutrino probes of dynamics of their interior in different stages of their birth and evolution. The dawn of Multi-Messenger Physics is thus a promising tool to help understand different aspects of NSs and has proven possible to observationally test some of the theoretical assumptions about the physical conditions of not only the crust, but also the core and the global Equation of State (EoS) of nuclear matter. In particular, another type of messengers, gravitational waves, show that the elastic properties of this material play a significant role in the strength and shape of measured signals involving these objects.

In this contribution we are interested in evaluating the impact of screening on forces, potential energies and stress tensor, as they are key to understand some mechanical properties of the very outer crust, which typically extend within hundreds of meters in the most external layers of the object.[4] Matter in this region is formed by a mixture of ions and electrons are stripped off them forming a degenerate Fermi sea. Typical ion mean densities[5] belong to the range between around 10^{-5} to 10^{-4} fm^{-3}.

As mentioned, in this region one expects to find a state of matter called Coulomb liquid, formed by different nuclear species, embedded in a degenerate electron gas. This gas makes sure that the system is kept charge neutral, and also screens the electromagnetic interactions between the ions so that this interaction is no longer pure Coulomb-wise but accounts for screening due to the electron gas. Thus the potential created by a positive charge Z_i (in units of electron charge e) at position $\vec{r}_i$, that describes this interaction at r is the so-called *Debye potential*, and has the form of a two-body Coulomb interaction with an exponential tail

$$\phi_i(\vec{r}) = \frac{Z_i}{|\vec{r}-\vec{r}_i|} e^{-\frac{|\vec{r}-\vec{r}_i|}{\lambda}}, \qquad (1)$$

where λ is the Thomas-Fermi screening length

$$\lambda = \frac{\pi^{\frac{1}{2}}}{(4\alpha k_F)^{\frac{1}{2}} (k_F^2 + m_e^2)^{\frac{1}{4}}} \sim \frac{1}{2k_F}\sqrt{\frac{\pi}{\alpha}}. \qquad (2)$$

k_F and m_e are the electron Fermi momentum and mass, respectively. α is the fine structure constant.

This potential ϕ_i is such that the interaction described tends to a pure Coulomb interaction when the screening length is much larger than the typical interparticle distance. In terms of the ion species that will be considered to describe the material in the outer NS crust, this will arise after the material in the hot protoNS cools down and its composition finally stabilizes and freezes to a ground state reached at $T \sim 10^5$ K. It is expected that the realistic composition in this layer is that of a multi-component plasma, comprised of different ion species. However, we would like to approach this complex problem by investigating only one, the most frequent nucleus, at a given density and temperature. This is known in the literature as the one-component plasma (OCP).[6]

Our approach is thus to assume that the material under inspection is comprised of a single ion species with fixed electrical charge and atomic mass number (Z, A)

embedded in the degenerate electron gas of number density equal to that of protons $n_e = n_p$, and whose interaction is described by the Debye potential. Note that in our calculation we will be using Molecular Dynamics and solving the equations of motion of ion degrees of freedom described in the quantum perspective as Gaussian charge density distributions. Similarly to the construction for the Coulomb interaction (which has an infinite range) we will consider the efficient Ewald summation technique[7] for the Debye potential.

2. Molecular Dynamics and the Ewald summation technique

Molecular Dynamics (MD) is a many-body technique to simulate the microscopic behaviour of matter in which the equations of motion of the individual degrees of freedom (ions in our case) are integrated while interacting via a prescribed potential. Typically for the integration of the equations of motion an algorithm is used. We use a Velocity Verlet one in our work. The final goal of this is obtaining the time evolution of the positions and velocities of the ions from which derived properties can be calculated once the system is thermalized. We use the NVT ensemble where ions (Fe or more general species with different Z and A) are the degrees of freedom for which we integrate the individual equations of motion, using the aforementioned Debye potential, as we are in the OCP approximation. The number of ions, size of the simulation box $L = V^{1/3}$, and the kinetic energy (or temperature T) remain fixed during the evolution starting from a random distribution. Also, the lepton fraction $Y_e = \frac{N_e}{N_p + N_n}$ obtained from number of protons (N_p), neutrons (N_n) and electrons ($N_e = N_p$) is fixed, as well as the OCP parameters (Z_i, A_i), for which we use fixed $Z_i = Z$, $A_i = A$. The crystallization parameter in the Coulomb case is defined as $\Gamma^{OCP} = \frac{Z^2}{k_B T}\left(\frac{4\pi}{3}n_I\right)^{1/3}$ and for $\Gamma^{OCP} > 175$ an ordered state is thought to arise.

The dynamics of the N_I ions are obtained by solving Newton's law $\vec{F}_i = m_i \vec{a}_i$, $i = 1, N_I$ assuming that the resulting potential is created by adding that of each ion. Note that the charge of each ion, ρ_i is spread into a Gaussian distribution, a more realistic case than the frequently assumed point-like charges, populating the layers in outer NS crusts. More in detail we have

$$\rho_{i,a}(r) = Z_i \left(\frac{a}{\pi}\right)^{\frac{3}{2}} e^{-ar^2}, \qquad (3)$$

where a is related to the Gaussian width, σ_a, as $a = \frac{1}{2\sigma_a^2}$ and r is the distance coordinate taken from the center of the Gaussian source.

The Debye interaction potential produced by such a Gaussian source with charge and inverse width Z_i, a at $\vec{r}_i$ is then obtained by solving the Poisson equation

$$-\frac{1}{r}\frac{d^2}{dr^2}(r\phi(r)) + \frac{\phi(r)}{\lambda^2} = 4\pi \left[Z\left(\frac{a}{\pi}\right)^{3/2} e^{-ar^2}\right], \qquad (4)$$

so that the solution is

$$\phi_{Z_i,a}(\vec{r}) = \frac{Z_i}{2|\vec{r}-\vec{r_i}|} e^{\frac{1}{4a\lambda^2}} \left[e^{-\frac{|\vec{r}-\vec{r_i}|}{\lambda}} \mathrm{erfc}\left(\frac{1}{2\sqrt{a}\lambda} - \sqrt{a}|\vec{r}-\vec{r_i}|\right) \right.$$
$$\left. - e^{\frac{|\vec{r}-\vec{r_i}|}{\lambda}} \mathrm{erfc}\left(\frac{1}{2\sqrt{a}\lambda} + \sqrt{a}|\vec{r}-\vec{r_i}|\right) \right], \qquad (5)$$

with erfc the complementary error function.

Even if the interaction between ions in our simulations is thought to be screened, it can reach longer than the size of the cubic simulation box $L = \left(\frac{N_I}{n_I}\right)^{1/3}$ where N_I and n_I are the number of ions and ion number density used. A proper treatment of the long-range part of the interaction is required. Usually, this is partly dealt with via periodic boundary conditions (PBC), thinking of the system as a infinite lattice of simulation boxes in which the ions interact with the closest neighbors of the different images of a selected box. By using the Ewald summation technique one takes advantage of including all the long-range interactions between ions irrespectively of the values of the screening length and the size of the simulation box. Some previous works have been developed for pure Coulomb potentials,[8] but to our knowledge this has not been done for electron screened versions. In this contribution we have developed the relevant expressions for the MD calculation of the microscopic state of matter.

In order to calculate the energies and accelerations in the Ewald summation scheme, we must first introduce *spurious* Gaussian charges into the system to screen the real ones. These are centered at the same positions as the real charges but have opposite sign, $-Z_i$, and display an inverse squared width α_{Ewald}

$$\rho_{-Z_i,\alpha_{Ewald}} = -Z_i \left(\frac{\alpha_{Ewald}}{\pi}\right)^{\frac{3}{2}} e^{-\alpha_{Ewald} r^2}. \qquad (6)$$

These are the so-called *screening charges*. Consequently as a way of maintaining the electrical charge neutrality of the system, we are forced to introduce compensating charges that are identical in shape to the screening ones except for the charge, which in this case is positive $\rho_{Z_i,\alpha_{Ewald}} = Z_i \left(\frac{\alpha_{Ewald}}{\pi}\right)^{\frac{3}{2}} e^{-\alpha_{Ewald} r^2}$.

It is key to note here that the parameter α_{Ewald} is an arbitrary square inverse length that we introduced for convenience to screen the original interaction. The physical observables that one can obtain from the simulation thus must not depend on this parameter.

The total interaction energy U_{tot} is then divided into three parts. Firstly, a short-range part, $U_{\text{short}-\text{range}}$, which is the interaction between the real charges and the sum of the real plus the screening charges. The total interaction potential, $\phi_{\text{tot},i}$ concerning this short-range part of the interaction is produced by this sum of real plus screening charges.

$$\phi_{\text{tot},i}\left(|\vec{r}-\vec{r_i}|\right) = \frac{Z_i}{2\,|\vec{r}-\vec{r_i}|}\left\{e^{-\frac{|\vec{r}-\vec{r_i}|}{\lambda}}\left[e^{\frac{1}{4a\lambda^2}}\operatorname{erfc}\left(\frac{1}{2\sqrt{a}\lambda} - \sqrt{a}\,|\vec{r}-\vec{r_i}|\right)\right.\right.$$
$$\left.-e^{\frac{1}{4\alpha_{\text{Ewald}}\lambda^2}}\operatorname{erfc}\left(\frac{1}{2\sqrt{\alpha_{\text{Ewald}}}\,\lambda} - \sqrt{\alpha_{\text{Ewald}}}\,|\vec{r}-\vec{r_i}|\right)\right]$$
$$-e^{\frac{|\vec{r}-\vec{r_i}|}{\lambda}}\left[e^{\frac{1}{4a\lambda^2}}\operatorname{erfc}\left(\frac{1}{2\sqrt{a}\lambda} + \sqrt{a}\,|\vec{r}-\vec{r_i}|\right)\right.$$
$$\left.\left.-e^{\frac{1}{4\alpha_{\text{Ewald}}\lambda^2}}\operatorname{erfc}\left(\frac{1}{2\sqrt{\alpha_{\text{Ewald}}}\,\lambda} + \sqrt{\alpha_{\text{Ewald}}}\,|\vec{r}-\vec{r_i}|\right)\right]\right\}. \quad (7)$$

When using the Coulomb interaction one can verify that expressions have a closed, analytical expression, but for the Debye case, instead, one has to perform numerical integrations each time step of the simulation in order to obtain the forces (as gradient of this potential). The final expression for this short-range part of the interaction energy is given by

$$U_{\text{short-range}} = \frac{1}{2}\sum_{i=1}^{N_I}\sum_{j\neq i=1}^{N_I} 2Z_j\left(\frac{a}{\pi}\right)^{\frac{1}{2}}\frac{e^{-ar_{ij}^2}}{r_{ij}}\int_0^\infty r'\phi_{\text{tot},i}(r')\,e^{-ar'^2}\sinh(2ar_{ij}r')\,dr'$$
$$-\frac{2\pi}{V}\sum_{i=1}^{N_I}\sum_{j=1}^{N_I} Z_j\int_0^\infty r'^2\phi_{\text{tot},i}(r')\,dr', \quad (8)$$

where $r_{ij} = |\vec{r_i} - \vec{r_j}|$ is the distance between the N_I ions labeled i and j.

The usefulness of the separation into short and long range contributions stands clear here as the long-range energy term has a dependence in the interparticle distance that tails off quickly, so that it converges very rapidly in real space. The upper limit of the numerical integration is set, practically, at the finite value $r' = \sqrt{2}L$.

The second energy term, U_1, of the scheme is produced by the interaction between real charges and the compensating charges in all the simulation boxes that exist in the infinite lattice that was created using PBCs. This is done by transforming Poisson's equation from the r-coordinate to the Fourier k-space. The derivation's endpoint is a summation over reciprocal lattice vectors, the interaction going to zero when the module of these vectors is high enough so that the sum converges in the Fourier space,

$$U_1 = \frac{1}{2}\sum_{i,j=1}^{N_I}\sum_{\vec{k}\neq 0}\frac{4\pi Z_iZ_j}{V\left(k^2 + \frac{1}{\lambda^2}\right)}e^{-\frac{k^2}{4}\left(\frac{1}{a}+\frac{1}{\alpha_{\text{Ewald}}}\right)}e^{i\vec{k}(\vec{r_i}-\vec{r_j})}, \quad (9)$$

where $\vec{k} = \frac{2\pi}{L}(n_{k,x}, n_{k,y}, n_{k,z})$ being $n_{k,x}, n_{k,y}, n_{k,z} \in \mathbb{Z}$ integers in the Cartesian XYZ directions. Finally, it remains to substract the interaction between the real particle and its own compensating charge in the same simulation box, as it is included spuriously in the long-range part. It also includes integrals that are to be numerically solved. This energy from self-interaction is given by

$$U_{self} = 2\pi \left(\frac{a}{\pi}\right)^{\frac{3}{2}} \sum_{i=1}^{N_I} Z_i \int_0^\infty r'^2 \phi_{Z_i,\alpha_{Ewald}}(r') e^{-ar'^2} dr', \qquad (10)$$

where $\phi_{Z_i,\alpha_{Ewald}}$ is the potential produced by the compensating charges alone, from equation 5. The global expression for the interaction energy is $U_{tot} = U_{short-range} + U_l - U_{self}$.

3. Stress tensor in the OCP approximation

In our study we focus on the OCP stress tensor. We can write the total stress tensor as follows[7]

$$\Pi_{\alpha\beta}^{tot} = \frac{1}{L^3} \sum_{i=1}^{N_I} m\dot{r}_{i\alpha}\dot{r}_{j\beta} + \Pi_{\alpha\beta} \qquad (11)$$

where m is the mass of ions. This second-order rank tensor can be put into the form $\Pi_{\alpha\beta} = \Pi_{\alpha\beta}^{real} + \Pi_{\alpha\beta}^{recip}$, arising from the interparticle forces. As the interactions in real space may be written in a pairwise fashion, the configurational part of the pressure tensor, $\Pi_{\alpha\beta}^{real}$, can be evaluated directly from the real forces by employing the virial expression

$$\Pi_{\alpha\beta}^{real} = \frac{1}{2V} \sum_{i,j \neq i=1}^{N_I} \left(F_{ij,\alpha}^{real} r_{ij,\beta} + F_{ij,\beta}^{real} r_{ij,\alpha}\right), \qquad (12)$$

where α, β are tensorial indexes running from 0 to 3 (time and XYZ spatial coordinates). We use Minkowski metric $g_{\alpha,\beta} = diag(1,-1,-1,-1)$.

The real space forces arise from the short-range part of the potential and take the form

$$\vec{F}_{ij,\,\text{short-range}} = 2 \left(\frac{a}{\pi}\right)^{\frac{1}{2}} \frac{Z_j e^{-ar_{ij}^2}}{r_{ij}^2} \left(\frac{\vec{r}_{ij}}{r_{ij}}\right)$$

$$\times \left\{ \int_0^\infty r' \phi_{tot,i}(r') e^{-ar'^2} \left[(1+2ar_{ij}^2)\sinh(2ar_{ij}r') - 2ar_{ij}r'\cosh(2ar_{ij}r')\right] dr' \right\}, \qquad (13)$$

while the reciprocal part is obtained as

$$\Pi_{\alpha\beta}^{recip} = \frac{1}{2} \sum_{\vec{k}\neq 0}^\infty \frac{4\pi}{V^2 \left(k^2 + \frac{1}{\lambda^2}\right)} e^{-\frac{k^2}{4}\left(\frac{1}{a} + \frac{1}{\alpha_{Ewald}}\right)} e^{i\vec{k}\cdot(\vec{r}_i - \vec{r}_j)}$$

$$\times \left\{ \delta_{\alpha\beta} - 2\left[\frac{1}{4}\left(\frac{1}{a} + \frac{1}{\alpha}\right) + \frac{1}{\left(k^2 + \frac{1}{\lambda^2}\right)}\right] k_\alpha k_\beta \right\}. \qquad (14)$$

Note that when solving the equations of motions for the ions the forces involved are not only those of real space but also the reciprocal space contribution from U_l. Their form reads

$$\vec{F}_{i,l} = \frac{1}{2} \sum_{\vec{k} \neq 0} \frac{8\pi Z_i}{V(k^2 + \frac{1}{\chi^2})} e^{-\frac{k^2}{4}\left(\frac{1}{\alpha} + \frac{1}{a_{Ewald}}\right)}$$

$$\times \left\{ \sin(\vec{k} \cdot \vec{r}_i) \left[\sum_j Z_j \cos(\vec{k} \cdot \vec{r}_j)\right] - \cos(\vec{k} \cdot \vec{r}_i) \left[\sum_j Z_j \sin(\vec{k} \cdot \vec{r}_j)\right] \right\} \vec{k}. \tag{15}$$

4. Results of the simulated OCP crystal

In this section we show the results obtained from our OCP MD simulations. In our NVT ensamble we use fixed N_I ions in a box of length $L = \left(\frac{N_I}{n_I}\right)^{1/3}$ for a given outer crust ion number density n_I at temperature T. Typically we set $T = 1$ MeV. In Fig. 1 we show two snapshots (planes XZ, XY) of particle positions for a run with $n_I = 0.017$fm^{-3}, and $N_I = 50$ particles. We set $a = 2\ fm^{-2}$ and $a_{Ewald} = 10\ fm^2$. Initial random positions are shown in red while those after thermalization ($t = 10^4$ fm/c) are depicted in blue. As shown an ordered crystal forms after this time evolution.

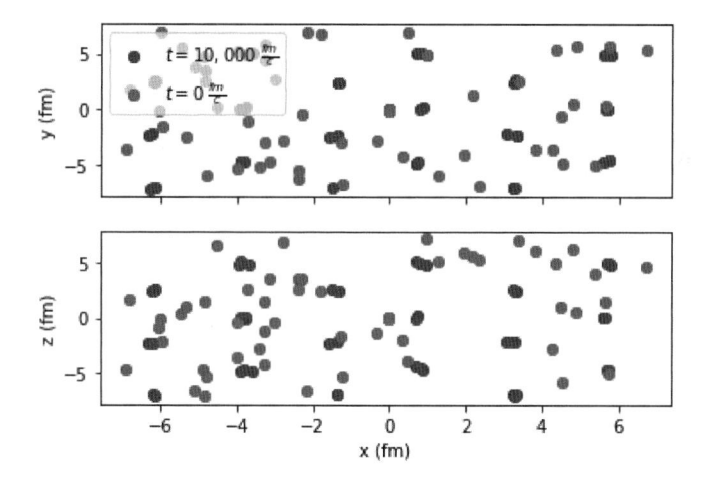

Fig. 1. Two dimensional snapshots of particle positions for a run with $n_I = 0.017\,\text{fm}^{-3}$, and $N_I = 50$ particles with $A = 56$, $Z = 26$. Initial positions are shown in red while those after thermalization ($t = 10^4$ fm/c) are depicted in blue. As shown an ordered crystal forms after this time evolution.

In Fig. 2 we show the pair correlation function $g(r)$ versus distance in units of simulation box length L with the same conditions as those depicted in system from Fig. 1. At small distances the repulsive interaction leads the distribution, however at larger distances the crystallized configurations arise as signaled by the different peaks. Normalization of $g(r)$ is such that $\int_0^\infty n_I g(r) 4\pi r^2 dr = N_I - 1$.

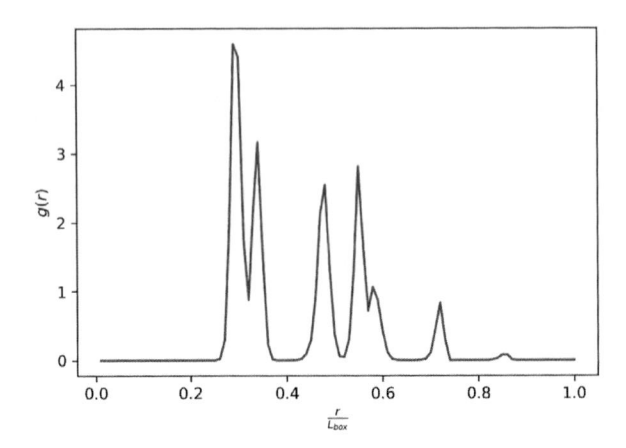

Fig. 2. Pair correlation function for $N_I = 50$ and same conditions as those in Fig. 1. Short range repulsion is shown along with the different peaks signaling the appearance of an ordered state with different neighbouring distances.

In Fig. 3 we show the energy per nucleon for a system of $N_I = 10$ ions with $A = 56$ at density $n_I = 0.0016$ fm^{-3}. Using the Ewald sum (we set $a = 2$ fm^{-2} and $a_{Ewald} = 10$ fm^{-2}) we explore the convergence and actual value of energy per nucleon as the electron screening length changes. We use $\lambda = 10, 50, 100$ fm and we also test the Coulomb case where $\lambda \to \infty$. We show that the screened interaction in the infinite range converges to existing calculations using the raw Coulomb case.[8] In the depicted case the change can be nearly 50%, making the system less bound.

In Fig. 4 we show the pressure as a function of the mass density along with the non-diagonal stress tensor components. We use $a = 2$ fm^{-2} and $a_{Ewald} = 10$ fm^{-2} for a system of $N_I = 25$ ions with $Z = 26$, $A = 56$ at different densities. Pressure is obtained for the crystallized sytem as $P = \frac{1}{3} Tr \Pi_{\alpha\beta}$, but an additional electron pressure is present from the Fermi gas such that $P_e = \frac{\pi^3 \hbar^2}{15m} \left(\frac{3n_e}{\pi}\right)^{\frac{5}{3}}$ and $n_e = n_p$ in the charge neutral system. It is important to note that the true ground state of the system must provide a zero pressure crystal (as it does not exert external force per unit area) and this is fitted by considering a variable box length in our simulation. The off-diagonal components are zero as the crystal is not distorted from equilibrium (no shear).

We conclude that a careful evaluation of screening effects in the evaluation of the energies as well as forces is key to obtain the true binding of ion matter in the outer crust of NSs. We find that when the Ewald sum is implemented screened matter is less bound than the regular Coulomb lattice and this has an impact on forces

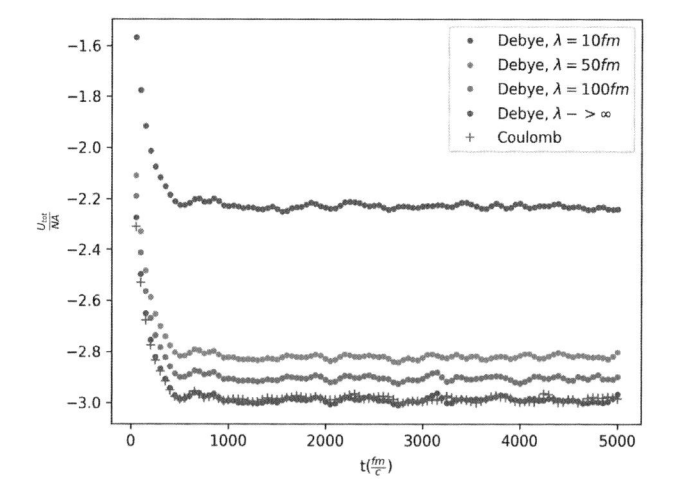

Fig. 3. Energy per nucleon as a function of simulation time for ions with $Z = 26$, $A = 56$, T=1 MeV and $n_I = 0.0016$ fm^{-3}. Colors represent simulations for different values of electron screening length λ, and for the Coulomb case. Ewald sums using Debye expressions in the limit $\lambda \to \infty$ provide results that converge to existing Coulomb calculations.[8]

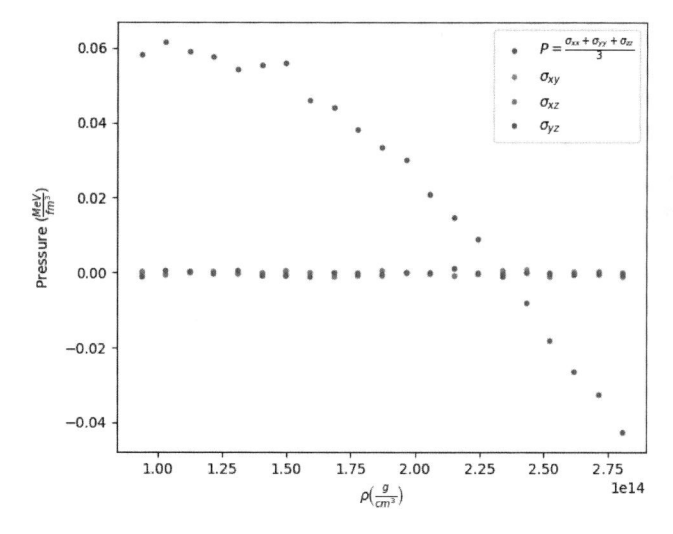

Fig. 4. Ion pressure and off-diagonal elements of the stress tensor as a function of mass density for ions with $Z = 26$, $A = 56$, T=1 MeV. It is seen that the total ion pressure is zero for a given value of the density. This is relevant to the definition of the true ground state of the system.

and thus on the mechanical properties derived from the stress tensor. In a future contribution we will detail how sizable this correction is with a complete analysis from density and temperature variation.

Acknowledgment

We acknowledge financial support from Junta de Castilla y León through the grant SA096P20, Agencia Estatal de Investigación through the grant PID2019-107778GB-100, Spanish Consolider MultiDark FPA2017-90566-REDC and PHAROS COST Actions MP1304 and CA16214. We thank A. Aguado for useful comments.

References

1. M. E. Caplan and C. J. Horowitz, Reviews of Modern Physics, 89, (2017).
2. Horowitz, C. J., M. A. Pérez-García, and J. Piekarewicz, *Phys. Rev. C* 69, 045804 (2004).
3. B. Haskell, A. Sedrakian, chapter in The Physics and Astrophysics of Neutron Stars, Astrophysics and Space Science Library, Springer, 457 (2018).
4. N. Chamel and P. Haensel, *Living Rev. Relativity*, **11**, (2008), 10.
5. J. M. Pearson, N. Chamel, A. Y. Potekhin, A. F. Fantina, C. Ducoin, A. K. Dutta and S. Goriely, *MNRAS* 481, 2994–3026 (2018).
6. A. F. Fantina et al., *Astronomy and Astrophysics* 633, A149 (2020).
7. A. Aguado, and P. A. Madden, *J. Chem. Phys.* 119, 7471 (2003).
8. G. Watanabe et al., *Phys. Rev. C* **68** 035806 (2003).

Tidal deformability as a probe of dark matter in neutron stars

D. Rafiei Karkevandi

ICRANet-Isfahan, Isfahan University of Technology,
Isfahan, 84156-83111, Iran
E-mail: davood.rafiei64@gmail.com

S. Shakeri

Department of Physics, Isfahan University of Technology,
ICRANet-Isfahan, Isfahan University of Technology,
Isfahan, 84156-83111, Iran
E-mail: s.shakeri@iut.ac.ir

V. Sagun

CFisUC, Department of Physics, University of Coimbra,
Coimbra, 3004-516, Portugal
E-mail: violetta.sagun@uc.pt

O. Ivanytskyi

Institute of Theoretical Physics, University of Wroclaw,
Wroclaw, 50-204, Poland
E-mail: oleksii.ivanytskyi@uwr.edu.pl

The concept of boson stars (BSs) was first introduced by Kaup and Ruffini and Bonazzola in the 1960s. Following this idea, we investigate an effect of self-interacting asymmetric bosonic dark matter (DM) according to Colpi et al. model for BSs (1986) on different observable properties of neutron stars (NSs). In this paper, the bosonic DM and baryonic matter (BM) are mixed together and interact only through gravitational force. The presence of DM as a core of a compact star or as an extended halo around it is examined by applying different boson masses and DM fractions for a fixed coupling constant. The impact of DM core/halo formations on a DM admixed NS properties is probed through the maximum mass and tidal deformability of NSs. Thanks to the recent detection of Gravitational-Waves (GWs) and the latest X-ray observations, the DM admixed NS's features are compared to LIGO/Virgo and NICER results.

Keywords: Bosonic Dark matter, Complex scalar field, Neutron Star, Gravitational-Wave

1. Introduction

The evidence for the existence of dark matter (DM) which constitutes up to 85% of the matter in the universe, is implied from various astrophysical and cosmological observations. However, despite the enormous experimental efforts in the past decades, the nature of these particles remains elusive. In addition to various terrestrial experiments, compact astrophysical objects such as neutron stars (NSs) can be served as valuable natural detectors to constrain the properties of DM. The presence of DM in NS interior depending on the various hypothesis of introducing them and their features, could have signficant effects on the properties of NSs.[1-8]

There are different scenarios assuming existence of DM in the NS interiors, which are mostly based on the DM accumulation during different stages of stellar evolution. The main of these stages are : a) progenitor, b) main sequence star, c) supernova explosion with formation of a proto-NS, and d) equilibrated NS.[4,9-13] As an alternative way, DM can be produced during the supernova explosion or NS merger leading to presence of DM in the NSs.[2,3] High level of DM fraction inside NS is reachable through other mechanisms such as (i) dark compact objects or DM clumps as the accretion center of baryonic matter (BM),[3,14,15] (ii) DM captured by NS in a binary system including Dark star and Dark star–NS merger,[7,15,16] (iii) NS can pass through a region in the Galaxy with extremely high DM density leading to accumulation of vast amount of DM.[16-19]

Two main and qualitatively different pictures leading to potentially observable impact of DM on the NS properties are a) Self-annihilating DM affecting luminosity, effective temperature and cooling process of NSs[20-25] and b) Asymmetric DM (ADM) with negligible annihilation rate caused by particle-antiparticle asymmetry in the dark sector.[26-29] We consider the second possibility allowing stable and massive DM particles to reside in a core of the NS. It was pointed out that the presence of DM particles in stellar cores can significantly decrease the mass of a compact object.[18,19,30,31] However, it was shown that light DM particles form an extended halo around the NS and can increase its gravitational mass.[2,4] It is worth mentioning that both of the aforementioned cases for combination of DM and BM within NS are known as DM admixed NS.

Regarding the ADM model, generally two methods have been utilized so far to extract the properties of the DM admixed NS from the Tolman-Oppenheimer-Volkof (TOV) equations.[32,33] 1) Single fluid formalism, for which an Equation of State (EoS) is considered for the whole star by inserting DM-BM interactions.[1,7,34-37] 2) Two-fluid formalism, for which DM and BM interact only through gravitational force, and two individual EoSs have to be considered for the DM and BM fluids.[15,16,38-41]

In this research, we apply a two-fluid formalism for the DM admixed NS. Bosonic DM is described by a complex scalar field with repulsive self-interaction. Historically, this model has been applied to describe hypothetical self-gravitating objects composed of bosons, so called boson stars. The idea of BS was first proposed by Kaup[42] and Ruffini-Bonazzola[43] for non-interacting bosons. The Heisenberg uncertainty principle was the only source of pressure of the BS matter resisting gravitational contraction. This leads to much lower maximum mass of BS compared to the Chandrasekhar mass. The pressure of the BS matter was significantly increased by introducing repulsive self-interaction proposed by Colpi et al.[44] Within this approach, stellar mass objects are supported by the DM particle mass about hundreds MeV and dimensionless coupling constant is of order of unity (see a comprehensive review on BSs in[45–47]). Another component, i.e. BM, is modeled by the induced surface tension (IST) EoS. It was successfully applied to describe the nuclear matter, heavy-ion collision data and dense matter existing inside NS.[48–50]

With this set up we study effects of self-repulsive bosonic ADM on the mass-radius (M-R) profile and tidal deformability parameter[2,3,13,36,37,51–54] inferred from the GW signals related to post-merger stages of NSs.[55–59] Such a combined analysis based on the recent LIGO/Virgo results[60,60,61,61] opens a new possibility to study the internal structure of compact objects which may contain DM.

To be specific, in this work we consider a model of Colpi et al.[44] with sub-GeV DM particles of mass $m_\chi \sim \mathcal{O}(100 \text{ MeV})$ and self-coupling constant $\lambda = \pi$. We analyze two key observational constraints of NSs, i.e. maximum mass and tidal deformability. The first of them is based on the NICER observation of the heaviest known pulsar PSR J0740+6620 with mass $2.072^{+0.067}_{-0.066} M_\odot$[62] and corresponds to requiring the maximal stellar mass to be at least $M_{max} = 2 M_\odot$. The merger event GW170817[63] leads to the second constraint on the dimensionless tidal deformability $\Lambda \leq 580$ for $M = 1.4 M_\odot$.[64] Using these constraints we probe DM admixed NSs at various masses and fractions of DM.

The rest of the paper is organized as follows. In Sec. 2 the DM and BM EoSs are described. In Sec. 3 we explain the two-fluid TOV formalism, DM halo and DM core formations and their impacts on mass-radius profile of DM admixed NSs. Sec. 4 is devoted to probing the effect of DM halo/core configurations on the tidal deformability. Our conclusions will be presented in Sec.5. We use units in which $\hbar = c = G = 1$.

2. Bosonic DM and BM models

2.1. *Dark Boson Star*

In the following we apply a model of complex scalar field as the bosonic DM with repulsive self-interaction potential, $V(\phi) = \frac{\lambda}{4}|\phi|^4$, minimally coupled to gravity and described by the action

$$S = \int d^4x \sqrt{-g} \left[\frac{M_{Pl}^2}{2} R - \frac{1}{2}\partial_\mu \phi \partial^\mu \phi^* - \frac{1}{2} m_\chi^2 |\phi|^2 - \frac{1}{4}\lambda |\phi|^4 \right], \quad (1)$$

where m_χ is the boson mass, λ stands for the dimensionless coupling constant and M_{Pl} corresponds to the Planck mass.[44,65] In this setup a coherent scalar field is governed by both Klein-Gordon and Einstein equations which can potentially form Bose-Einstein Condensate (BEC) if the temperature is sufficiently low.[66,67] It has been assumed a spherically symmetric configuration for the scalar field $\phi(r,t) = \Phi(r)e^{i\omega t}$ and a static metric to rewrite Klein-Gordon-Einstein (K.G.E) equations to a set of ordinary differential equations.[44] This leads to the following EoS describing a self-interacting and self-gravitating bosonic system so-called BS

$$P = \frac{m_\chi^4}{9\lambda}\left(\sqrt{1+\frac{3\lambda}{m_\chi^4}\rho}-1\right)^2. \qquad (2)$$

We recently presented an alternative derivation of this EoS in locally flat space-time by using the mean-field approximation (see appendix of[68]). This equation is valid in the parameter region for λ as

$$\lambda \gg 4\pi(m_\chi/M_{Pl})^2 = 8.43\times 10^{-36}\left(\frac{m_\chi}{100\,\text{MeV}}\right)^2 \qquad (3)$$

In this limit which is called strong coupling regime, the system can be approximated as a prefect fluid and the anisotropy of pressure will be ignored.[45,69,70] Stellar mass BSs can be formed for $\lambda \sim \mathcal{O}(1)$ and $m_\chi \sim \mathcal{O}(100\,\text{MeV})$,[45,71] in this section, we focus on this range of model parameters.

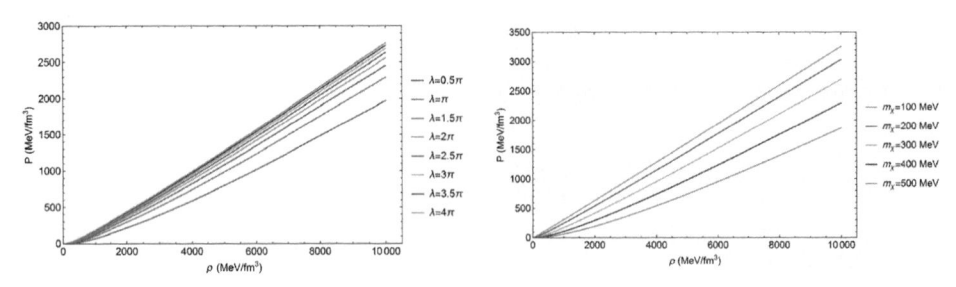

Fig. 1. Pressure as a function of density for bosonic matter obtained for $\lambda = \pi$ and various DM masses as labeled (right); for $m_\chi = 400$ MeV and different values of coupling constant (left).

Fig. 1 shows pressure of bosonic matter as a function of density for different masses and coupling constants as labeled. As it is shown in Fig. 1, (right panel) the pressure decreases with increasing of boson masses and (left panel) the pressure rises with the enhancement of the coupling constant or equivalently increasing the repulsive force between bosons.

In different density limits one can approximate Eq. (2) in a typical polytrope form $P = K\rho^\gamma$, where polytropic index at low density $\gamma \simeq 2$ and it smoothly reaches to $\gamma \simeq 1$ at high density. At low density regime, the bosonic DM EoS, Eq. (2), is reduced to

$$P \approx \frac{\lambda}{4m_\chi^4}\rho^2. \qquad (4)$$

However, for high density regime or correspondingly for very light bosons or high coupling constant, Eq. (2) reaches to radiation EoS with $P \approx \rho/3$. Similar equation to Eq. (4) has been obtained so far for a dilute self-interacting boson gas in a self-gravitating system (BS) known as Gross-Pitaevskii-Poisson (G.P.P) equation.[70,72,73] In fact, the G.P.P equation describes the BEC phase in a dilute gas where only two-body mean field interaction is considered near zero temperature.[74–76]

In Fig. 2, we present the M-R diagrams of BSs obtained by solving TOV equation for Eq. (2). As it is indicated in the right panel, by decreasing the boson mass, the maximum gravitational mass of BSs increases and even goes above $2M_\odot$[62,77,78] and the corresponding radius goes well above typical NS radius. In the left panel, it is shown that higher self-coupling constant at fixed mass $m_\chi = 400$ MeV leads to higher maximum masses of BSs. Both the decreasing of boson mass and increasing of the coupling constant cause an enhancement in pressure of the system and consequently the rise of the maximum mass.

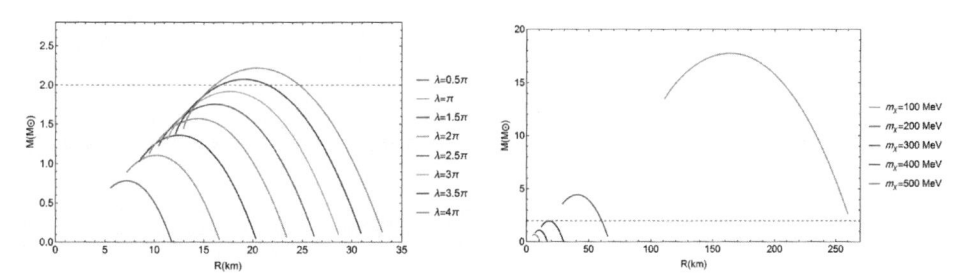

Fig. 2. M-R profile for BSs based on Eq. (2), (right panel) for the fixed value of coupling constant $\lambda = \pi$ and different boson masses. (Left panel) Calculations are made for fixed boson mass $m_\chi = 400$ MeV and different values of coupling constant as labeled at the figure. The gray dashed line shows the $2M_\odot$ limit.

Moreover, the variation of compactness $\mathcal{C} = M/R$ with respect to mass of BSs for different values of m_χ and λ is presented in Fig. 3. It shows the same dimensionless maximum compactness $\mathcal{C}_{(max)} \simeq 0.16$ for all cases. We see that the maximum compactness of a BS based on Eq. (2) is independent of free parameters of the model, namely m_χ and λ and for all the parameter space is well below the black hole formation limit $\mathcal{C} = 0.5$.[46,79]

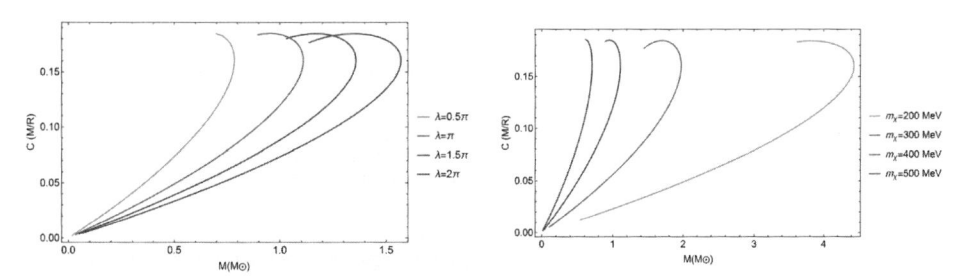

Fig. 3. Compactness of BSs as a function of their mass obtained for a fixed coupling constant $\lambda = \pi$ and different values of boson mass (right); fixed particle's mass $m_\chi = 400$ MeV and various λ values (left).

2.2. Neutron Star

For the baryon component (NS matter), we use the unified EoS with induced surface tension (IST) where both the short-range repulsion and long-range attraction between baryons have been taken into account.[49,50] The IST EoS reproduces the nuclear matter properties,[80] fulfills the proton flow constraint,[81] provides a high-quality description of hadron multiplicities created during the nuclear-nuclear collision experiments[82] as well as the matter inside compact stars.[48–50] The EoS is in a very good agreement with latest NS observations providing the maximum mass $M_{max} = 2.08 M_\odot$ and radius of the $1.4 M_\odot$ star equals to $R_{1.4} = 11.37$ km.[83] In our work the crust part of the NS's EoS is described via the polytropic EoS with $\gamma = 4/3$.[4] In Fig. 4, the change of pressure for a same density regime is plotted for BM and DM EoSs (left panel) and we show the M-R profiles of the NS and BS based on our considered EoSs (right panel).

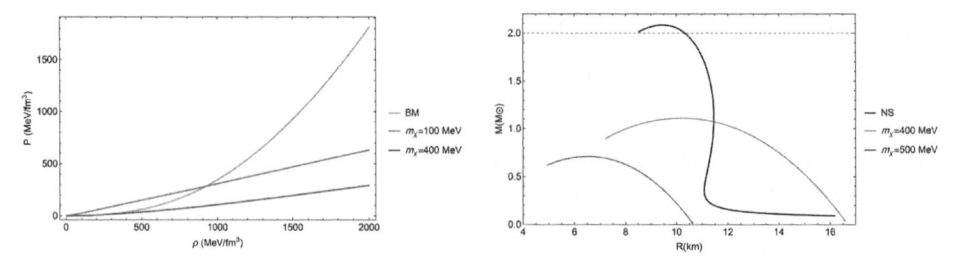

Fig. 4. Comparing BM and DM EoSs, left panel shows pressure vs. energy density for two different values of boson mass and $\lambda = \pi$. Right panel indicates M-R profiles for the NSs and BSs, considering $m_\chi = 400, 500$ MeV and the same coupling constant.

3. Two-fluid TOV equations and maximum mass

In order to study compact objects formed by the admixture of BM and DM that interact only through gravity, we use two-fluid TOV formalism[15,16] shown by Eqs. (5-6). Here $p = p_B + p_D$ and $M = M_T = \int_0^r 4\pi r^2 \epsilon_B(r) dr + \int_0^r 4\pi r^2 \epsilon_D(r) dr$. It can be seen that the total pressure and mass of the object have two contributions from BM and DM fluids shown by B and D indices. In order to solve two-fluid TOV equations

$$\frac{dp_B}{dr} = -(p_B + \epsilon_B) \frac{M + 4\pi r^3 p}{r(r - 2M)}, \quad (5)$$

$$\frac{dp_D}{dr} = -(p_D + \epsilon_D) \frac{M + 4\pi r^3 p}{r(r - 2M)}, \quad (6)$$

two central conditions related to both of the fluids have to be considered. By fixing two central pressures (p_B and p_D) together with the initial conditions at the center of the star ($M_B(r \simeq 0) = M_D(r \simeq 0) \simeq 0$) the Eqs. (5-6) are numerically integrated up to the radius at which the pressure of one of the components vanishes. In principle this radius can be realized as DM radius R_D or BM radius R_B. In the former case the DM distributed only inside the core while BM extends to larger radius ($R_B > R_D$), then we set $p_D(r > R_D) = 0$ and continue the numerical integration to reach the visible radius of the star where $p_B(R_B) = 0$. When we have a BM core, DM can exist as an extended halo around the core with $R_D > R_B$, where $p_B(r > R_B) = 0$. It should be mentioned that for both DM core and DM halo cases, the core of the object is a mixture of DM and BM. Based on our extensive analysis there is another possibility of DM admixed NSs' configurations for which $R_B \approx R_D$ and DM distributed within the entire NS (see Fig. 5).

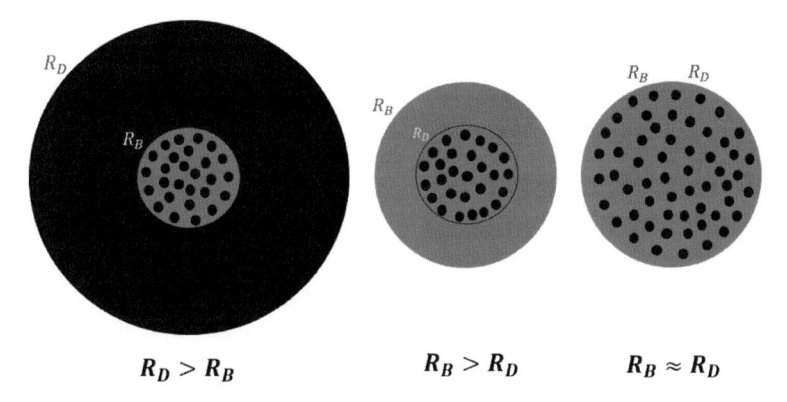

Fig. 5. Three possible configurations of a DM admixed NS, (left) DM halo, (middle) DM core and (right) DM is distributed in a whole NS. Note that for the DM core and halo cases the core of the object is a mixture of BM and DM. Green and black colors denote BM and DM, respectively.

For all of the possible DM admixed NSs' structures, the total gravitational mass of the mixed object is

$$M_T = M_B(R_B) + M_D(R_D). \qquad (7)$$

However, the observable radius of the star is still defined by R_B, this is due to the visibility of R_B compare to R_D and technical difficulties of indirect detection of dark radius R_D. Furthermore, the DM fraction that determines the amount of DM in a DM admixed NS is defined as

$$F_\chi = \frac{M_D(R_D)}{M_T}. \qquad (8)$$

Hereafter an effect of DM on NS properties is studied for m_χ of about hundreds MeV and and fixed coupling constant $\lambda = \pi$. Fig. 6 shows energy density profiles for a DM admixed NS where the BM (dashed red curves) and DM (solid red curves) components are plotted separately. The energy density profiles for pure BM and DM stars are presented by solid black and green curves, respectively. Here we consider $\lambda = \pi$ and $F_\chi = 20\%$, while the central values of pressure for BM and DM components are chosen in such a way that a desired DM fraction F_χ has been obtained.

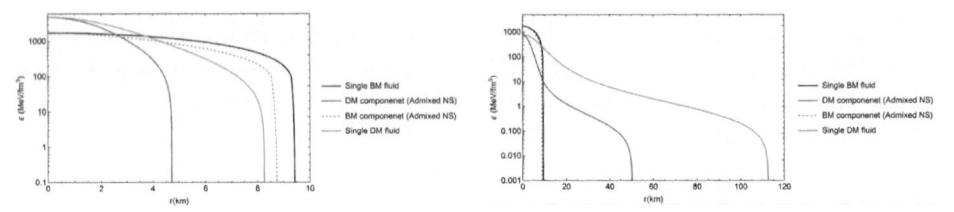

Fig. 6. Energy density profiles for pure BM and DM stars (black and green curves) shown together with the slitted DM and BM components of a DM admixed NS (solid and dashed red curves). Left panel corresponds to a DM core formation, while the right one to a DM halo, for $m_\chi = 400$ MeV and $m_\chi = 100$ MeV, respectively. For both of the cases, coupling constant is fixed at $\lambda = \pi$ and $F_\chi = 20\%$.

On the left panel which is obtained for $m_\chi = 400$ MeV, a DM core with $R_D \approx 5$ km is embedded in a BM structure with a larger radius. On the right panel, we fixed DM mass to $m_\chi = 100$ MeV which leads to the formation of a DM halo around the BM fluid with much larger radius. Interestingly, we see that for both DM core and DM halo formations, a reduction occurs in the energy density and the radius of DM and BM fluids in the mixed object compare to pure BM/DM star. This effect is much larger for the DM component and shows that the properties of the single DM fluid have significant effects in the admixed NS and in fact underly their features.

By comparing the left and right panels of Fig. 6, we see a transition from DM core to DM halo by changing m_χ from 400 MeV to 100 MeV. Therefore, by a thorough analysis of an effect of model parameters, as a general behaviour, we can conclude that light DM particles with $m_\chi < 200$ MeV, for low DM fractions, tend to form a halo around a NS, while heavier ones would mainly create a DM core inside a compact star (for more detailed analysis see[68]).

The M-R profiles for DM admixed NSs are shown in Fig. 7 in which $M = M_B + M_D$. Here R is the outermost radius of the star which is determined by R_B for the DM core and R_D for the DM halo. The solid black curve shows the M-R relation for the BM fluid (without DM), the gray dashed line indicates the $2M_\odot$ constraint on maximum mass of NSs and the shaded regions colored in magenta and cyan denote the causality and GR limits, respectively.

As it is shown in Fig. 7, two different boson masses, 100 MeV and 400 MeV lead to a DM halo and a DM core formations, respectively. In the left panel ($m_\chi = 400$ MeV), it is indicated that DM core formation causes a decrease of the maximum

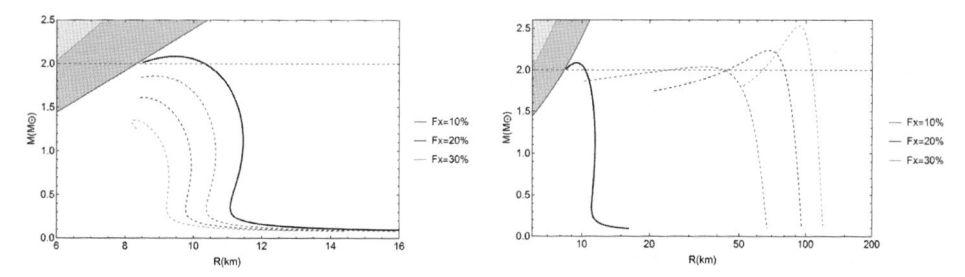

Fig. 7. Mass-Radius profiles for DM admixed NSs for $m_\chi = 400$ MeV (left) which corresponds to a DM core formation and $m_\chi = 100$ MeV (right) that represents an extended DM halo formation around a NS. Coupling constant is fixed to $\lambda = \pi$ and different F_χ are considered as labeled.

mass well below the $2M_\odot$ constraint,[62,77,78] and also a reduction of the corresponding radius. However, for $m_\chi = 100$ MeV (see the right panel in Fig. 7) for which a DM halo is formed around a NS, both maximum mass and radius are increased. Regarding the radius of the object for DM halo formation, it is increased significantly since is determined by R_D. It is seen that higher DM fractions enhance both of the above behaviours for DM core/halo structures. Note that for the cases in which a DM halo is formed ($R_D > R_B$), the visible radius of the star remains to be R_B.

To summarize, we see here that an effect of bosonic DM with repulsive self-interaction onto NSs is in agreement with previous studies which considered different DM models. Thus, an existence of a DM core decreases the maximum star's mass and the corresponding radius, while the formation of a DM halo increases these quantities.[2-4,30] In this regard, the most massive NS observed by NICER,[62] PSR J0740+6620 ($M_{max} \simeq 2M_\odot$) is compatible with the DM admixed NS scenario.

4. Tidal deformability of a DM admixed NS

GW signal from NS-NS mergers introduce tidal deformability as a new observable quantity to probe the internal structure of NSs and constrain their macroscopic features.[84-87] In this section, we analyse an impact of self-interacting bosonic DM on the tidal deformability of a DM admixed NS.

The idea of tidal deformability was first proposed by Tanja Hinderer in 2008[88,89] which comes from the fact that in a binary system of NSs both of the objects are deformed owing to the imposed tidal forces.[90-92] The tidal deformability expresses the ability of the gravitational field to change the quadrupole structure of a NS which alter the rotational phase of the binary system. Therefore, the GW signal is influenced during the inspiral phase due to the deformation effects of NSs when the binary orbital radius becomes comparable to the radius of NS. In fact, taking tidal deformability into account produces a phase shift in GW signal and accelerates the inspiral which leads to an earlier merging.[37,85,93]

The induced quadrupole moment Q_{ij} of a NS due to the external tidal field of its companion $\mathcal{E}_{ij}$ can be parameterized as follows[88,90]

$$Q_{ij} = \lambda_t \mathcal{E}_{ij}, \tag{9}$$

where λ_t is the tidal deformability parameter and can be defined based on k_2, the tidal love number, which is calculated from the system of equations including the TOV one. As is evident, k_2 and the tidal deformability strongly depend on the star's EoS.[88-90]

$$\lambda_t = \frac{2}{3} k_2 R^5 \tag{10}$$

Unlike λ_t which has dimension, dimensionless tidal deformability Λ can be defined as,

$$\Lambda = \frac{\lambda_t}{M^5} = \frac{2}{3} k_2 \left(\frac{R}{M}\right)^5. \tag{11}$$

where R and M are the radius and mass of the compact star. It should be mentioned that R in a DM admixed NS is the outermost radius of the object which for a DM halo $R = R_D$ and for a DM core $R = R_B$. As an observational constraint on the tidal deformability, we take $\Lambda_{1.4} = 190^{+390}_{-120}$ reported by[64] for $M = 1.4 M\odot$ in the case of GW170817.

In the following, we investigate the effect of self-interacting bosonic DM, as a DM core or a DM halo, on the tidal deformability Λ of a mixed object at various m_χ and F_χ. In Figs. 8 and 9 the variation of Λ is shown in terms of total mass and radius of DM admixed NSs. In these figures the gray horizontal dashed lines indicate the LIGO/Virgo upper bound $\Lambda_{1.4} = 580$,[64] the gray solid vertical lines show $M_T = 1.4 M_\odot$ and the colored dashed and solid vertical lines stand for $R_{1.4}$ radius for the corresponding model parameters. The tidal deformability calculated for the pure baryonic EoS is denoted by the solid black curve and its $\Lambda_{1.4}$ value is about 285 which is well below the LIGO/Virgo constraint.

As a general behaviour in these plots, it can be seen that tidal deformability is a decreasing function of total mass and rises by increasing the radius which is related to the definition of this parameter as a function of R/M through Eq. (11). It follows from the M-R profile of a combined system NS+DM, that approaching the maximum mass of the equilibrium sequence decreases the stellar radius and, consequently, R/M. In other words the lowest value of Λ corresponds to the maximum mass and minimum radius of the DM admixed NS.

The effect of variation of Λ caused by changing the DM mass at fixed coupling constant $\lambda = \pi$ and DM fraction $F_\chi = 10\%$ is shown on Fig. 8. It is seen that for low DM masses $m_\chi = 100, 120, 150$ MeV, leading to formation of the DM halo, $\Lambda_{1.4}$ is higher than in the cases of higher m_χ and purely baryonic NS. Indeed, the corresponding $R_{1.4}$ significantly exceeds the values obtained for purely baryonic NS. For $m_\chi = 300, 400, 500$ MeV, however, the situation is different. Formation of the

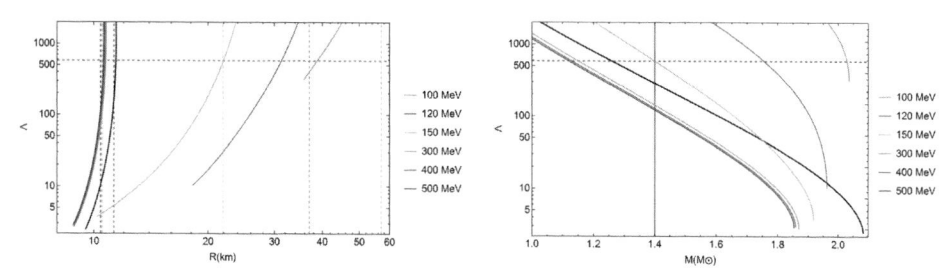

Fig. 8. Tidal deformability (Λ) in terms of total mass (right) and outermost radius (left) for stable sequences of DM admixed NSs. Various boson masses are considered, $m_\chi = 100, 120, 150$ MeV correspond to a DM halo formation while for $m_\chi = 300, 400, 500$ MeV a DM core is formed inside NS. Coupling constant and DM fraction are fixed at π and 10%, respectively.

DM core reduces the corresponding tidal polarizability, for which the $\Lambda - R$ curves are very similar to purely baryonic case. Regarding Fig. 8, we can conclude that DM halo yields large $\Lambda_{1.4}$, which even can exceed the observational constraint, while the DM core lowers Λ making it consistent with $\Lambda_{1.4} \leq 580$. This is related to the effect, which was mentioned in the previous section. Namely, DM halo increases the mass and radius of DM admixed NSs while DM core decreases these quantities. It is worth mentioning that GW observations during the inspiral phase of NS-NS coalescence correspond to lower frequencies detectable by Ad. LIGO. At this regime typical interstellar separation is $r < 150$ km. In order to prevent the technical difficulties caused by the overlap of DM halos we restrict their radii as $R_D \leq 75$ km.[2,3]

To give more insight, Fig. 9 shows modification of tidal polarizability due to variation of the DM fraction from 5% to 15% calculated at fixed $\lambda = \pi$ and $m_\chi = 100, 400$ MeV, corresponding to DM halo and DM core, respectively. As it is seen, higher F_χ increases $\Lambda_{1.4}$ and $R_{1.4}$ at $m_\chi = 100$ MeV and decreases theses parameters at $m_\chi = 400$ MeV. Remarkably, for $m_\chi = 100$ MeV (solid lines) tidal polarizability of the $M = 1.4 M\odot$ star exceeds 580 even at $F_\chi = 5\%$ since in this case Λ is more sensitive to DM fraction than at $m_\chi = 400$ MeV. Despite at this later case depicted by the dashed lines $\Lambda_{1.4}$ is in agreement with the upper observational constraint, the reduction of tidal deformability and $R_{1.4}$ should be consistent with the lower observational limits $\Lambda_{1.4} \gtrsim 70$ and $R_{1.4} \gtrsim 11$ km.[64, 94–97]

As the final remark of this section, in Fig. 10, we show the effect of increasing and decreasing tidal deformability in a NS with DM halo/core and purely baryonic one. It was explained in the beginning of this section that tidal deformability parameter shows how much the compact object is deformed due to the gravitational potential of its companion. Thus in this illustration, we see that DM admixed NS with a DM halo can be more deformed since it has higher values of Λ compared to purely baryonic NS and the DM admixed one with the DM core. In addition, considering tidal love number k_2 we note that mixed compact objects with stiffer EoS are more deformable due to the DM halo compared to the ones with softer EoS producing the DM core.

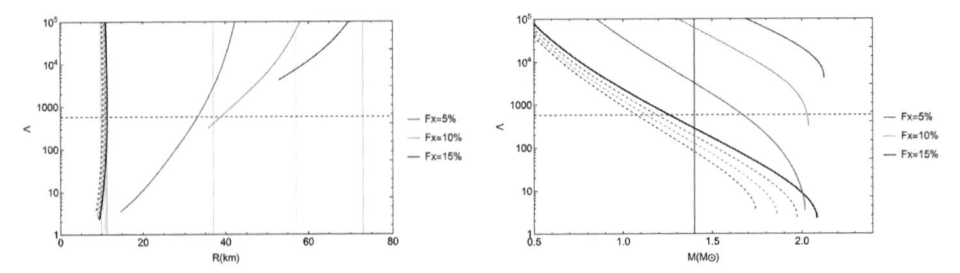

Fig. 9. Tidal deformability (Λ) in terms of total mass (right) and outermost radius (left) for stable sequences of DM admixed NSs. Two boson masses are considered, $m_\chi = 100$ MeV (solid lines) and $m_\chi = 400$ MeV (dashed lines) which correspond to DM halo and DM core formations, respectively. Various DM fractions are considered as labeled.

In summary, we note that in full agreement with the previous studies[2,3] DM halo increases tidal deformability, while DM core decreases it. Meanwhile, upper constraint on tidal deformability, $\Lambda_{1.4} = 580$, related to GW170817 event,[64] has been considered.

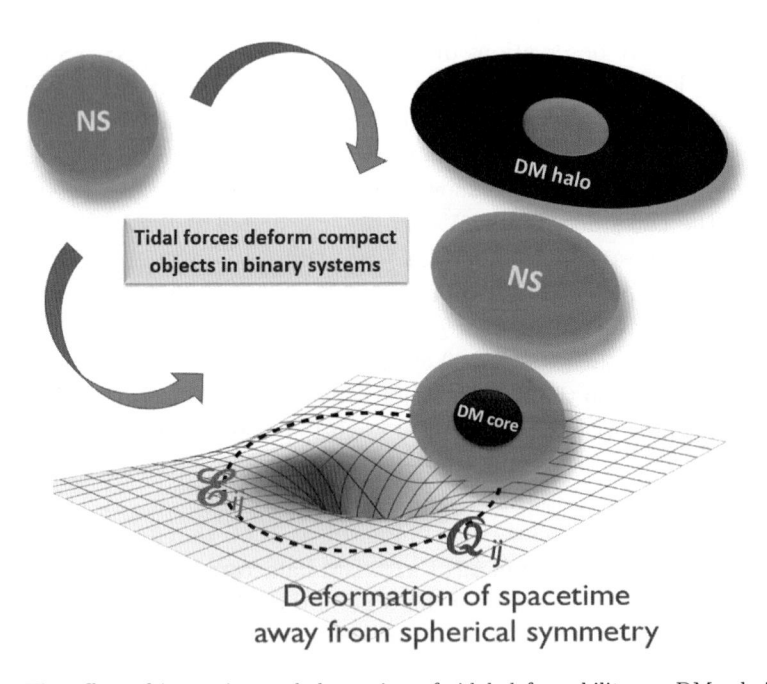

Fig. 10. The effect of increasing and decreasing of tidal deformability on DM admixed NS's deformation is compared with the pure BM object (NS). It is shown that higher value of Λ indicates more deformation in the compact object, therefore a DM halo deforms more in comparison with a pure NS and DM admixed NS with a DM core.

5. Conclusion and Outlook

Treating DM as a self-repulsing complex scalar field, various properties of single fluid BSs and two-fluid NSs has been studied within the TOV formalism. It is shown that for $\lambda = \pi$, light DM particles ($m_\chi \lesssim 200$ MeV) form BSs with much larger maximum mass and radius compared with typical NSs, while heavy DM particles lead to formation of BSs with much smaller radius and mass. Furthermore, we showed that for low DM fractions ($F_\chi < 20\%$), light bosons create a halo around the DM admixed NSs, while heavier DM particles form a DM core inside the BM component.

The effect of bosonic DM as a halo/core has been examined by considering the maximum mass, radius and tidal deformability of a DM admixed NS. We have indicated that DM halo formation causes an increase in the aforementioned observable quantities while a DM core reduces all of them. Considering various m_χ and F_χ, the maximum mass and tidal deformability of the mixed object has been compared to the latest upper observational bounds, $M_{max} = 2M\odot$ and $\Lambda_{1.4} \leq 580$ inferred from NICER (PSR J0740+6620) and LIGO/Virgo (GW170817) detections.

Regarding the impact of DM halo and DM core formations on NS's observable parameters and applying the observational limits for NSs' features, one could constrain the parameter space of DM model such as mass and coupling constant and also the amount of DM inside the compact object. In this regard, an extensive investigation has been done recently in[68] by the same authors of the present paper in which a constraint has been imposed on F_χ for sub-GeV DM particles by taking M_{max} and $\Lambda_{1.4}$ bounds. Moreover, as DM core decreases the visible radius of the DM admixed NS (R_B) and DM halo increases the invisible dark radius of the object (R_D), radius constraint for typical NSs ($M \approx 1.4 M\odot$) and most massive ones ($M \approx 2 M\odot$)[62,96,97] could be utilized to impose more stringent limits on DM parameter space and its fraction. In addition, any unusual observational results of NSs' properties could be explained by the DM admixed NS model. For instance, there are many effort among the community to explain the nature of the secondary compact object in the GW190814[98] event with the mass about $2.6 M\odot$ being higher than the maximum NS one. There are some works explaining the mass of this strange object by the DM core or halo formation within the DM admixed NS scenario.[52,99,100] Regarding our model, as an example, $m_\chi = 50$ MeV, $\lambda = \pi$ and $F_\chi \approx 20\%$ lead to formation of a DM admixed NS with $M_T = 2.6 M\odot$ and detectable radius about 10 km. As a final remark, upcoming modern facilities such as X-ray (NICER,[101] ATHENA,[102] eXTP[103] and STROBE-X[104]) and radio (MeerKAT,[105] ngVLA[106] and SKA[107]) telescopes, as well as GW (LIGO/Virgo/KAGRA[108] and Einstein[109,110]) detectors, shown in Fig. 11, would provide vast numbers of promising results for NSs' features bringing us to a golden age of NS investigations and consequently could help us to shed light on the nature of DM and its possible existence in compact objects.

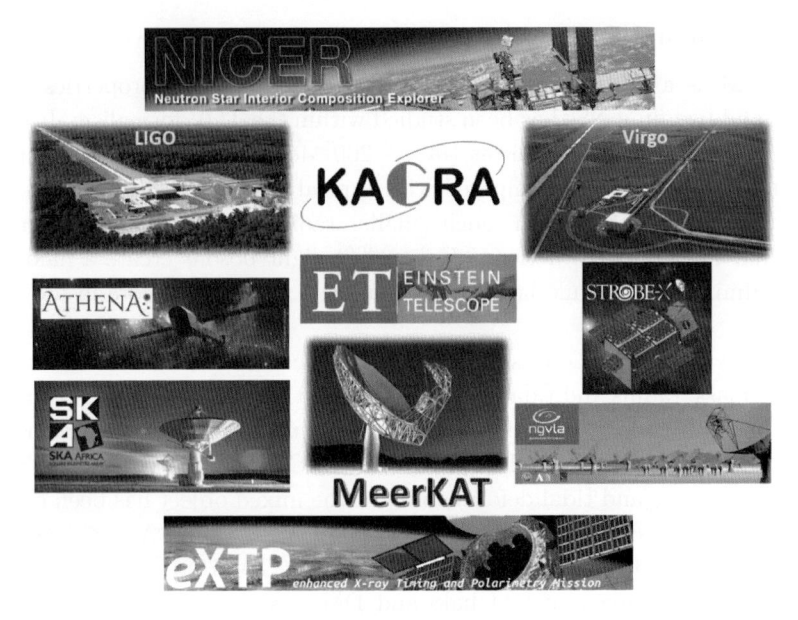

Fig. 11. Applying various innovative telescopes covering all kinds of observations from GW and X-ray to radio waves provide a unique opportunity for compact objects' research which may solve the puzzle of DM.

Acknowledgments

V.S. acknowledges the support from the Fundação para a Ciência e Tecnologia (FCT) within the projects UID/04564/2021. The work of O.I. was supported by the Polish National Science Center under the grant No. 2019/33/B/ST9/03059.

References

1. G. Panotopoulos and I. Lopes, Dark matter effect on realistic equation of state in neutron stars, *Physical Review D* **96** (Oct 2017).
2. A. E. Nelson, S. Reddy and D. Zhou, Dark halos around neutron stars and gravitational waves, *Journal of Cosmology and Astroparticle Physics* **2019**, p. 012–012 (Jul 2019).
3. J. Ellis, G. Hütsi, K. Kannike, L. Marzola, M. Raidal and V. Vaskonen, Dark Matter Effects On Neutron Star Properties, *Phys. Rev. D* **97**, p. 123007 (2018).
4. O. Ivanytskyi, V. Sagun and I. Lopes, Neutron stars: New constraints on asymmetric dark matter, *Phys. Rev. D* **102**, p. 063028 (Sep 2020).
5. Z. Rezaei, Study of Dark-Matter Admixed Neutron Stars using the Equation of State from the Rotational Curves of Galaxies, *Astrophys. J.* **835**, p. 33 (2017).
6. A. de Lavallaz and M. Fairbairn, Neutron Stars as Dark Matter Probes, *Phys. Rev. D* **81**, p. 123521 (2010).
7. M. I. Gresham and K. M. Zurek, Asymmetric Dark Stars and Neutron Star Stability, *Phys. Rev. D* **99**, p. 083008 (2019).

8. Y. Dengler, J. Schaffner-Bielich and L. Tolos, The Second Love Number of Dark Compact Planets and Neutron Stars with Dark Matter, *arXiv e-prints*, p. arXiv:2111.06197 (November 2021).
9. J. F. Navarro, C. S. Frenk and S. D. M. White, The Structure of cold dark matter halos, *Astrophys. J.* **462**, 563 (1996).
10. R. Ruffini, C. R. Argüelles and J. A. Rueda, On the core-halo distribution of dark matter in galaxies, *Monthly Notices of the Royal Astronomical Society* **451**, p. 622–628 (May 2015).
11. C. Argüelles, A. Krut, J. Rueda and R. Ruffini, Novel constraints on fermionic dark matter from galactic observables i: The milky way, *Physics of the Dark Universe* **21**, p. 82–89 (Sep 2018).
12. A. Del Popolo, M. Le Delliou and M. Deliyergiyev, Neutron Stars and Dark Matter, *Universe* **6**, p. 222 (November 2020).
13. R. Ciancarella, F. Pannarale, A. Addazi and A. Marciano, Constraining mirror dark matter inside neutron stars, *Phys. Dark Univ.* **32**, p. 100796 (2021).
14. I. Goldman, R. Mohapatra, S. Nussinov, D. Rosenbaum and V. Teplitz, Possible implications of asymmetric fermionic dark matter for neutron stars, *Physics Letters B* **725**, p. 200–207 (Oct 2013).
15. P. Ciarcelluti and F. Sandin, Have neutron stars a dark matter core?, *Physics Letters B* **695**, p. 19–21 (Jan 2011).
16. F. Sandin and P. Ciarcelluti, Effects of mirror dark matter on neutron stars, *Astroparticle Physics* **32**, p. 278–284 (Dec 2009).
17. A. Del Popolo, M. Deliyergiyev and M. Le Delliou, Solution to the hyperon puzzle using dark matter, *Phys. Dark Univ.* **30**, p. 100622 (2020).
18. M. Deliyergiyev, A. Del Popolo, L. Tolos, M. Le Delliou, X. Lee and F. Burgio, Dark compact objects: An extensive overview, *Physical Review D* **99** (Mar 2019).
19. A. Li, F. Huang and R.-X. Xu, Too massive neutron stars: The role of dark matter?, *Astropart. Phys.* **37**, 70 (2012).
20. C. Kouvaris, WIMP Annihilation and Cooling of Neutron Stars, *Phys. Rev. D* **77**, p. 023006 (2008).
21. S. A. Bhat and A. Paul, Cooling of Dark-Matter Admixed Neutron Stars with density-dependent Equation of State, *Eur. Phys. J. C* **80**, p. 544 (2020).
22. J. Fuller and C. Ott, Dark Matter-induced Collapse of Neutron Stars: A Possible Link Between Fast Radio Bursts and the Missing Pulsar Problem, *Mon. Not. Roy. Astron. Soc.* **450**, L71 (2015).
23. J. F. Acevedo, J. Bramante and A. Goodman, Nuclear fusion inside dark matter, *Phys. Rev. D* **103**, p. 123022 (2021).
24. A. Sedrakian, Axion cooling of neutron stars, *Phys. Rev. D* **93**, p. 065044 (2016).
25. A. Sedrakian, Axion cooling of neutron stars. II. Beyond hadronic axions, *Phys. Rev. D* **99**, p. 043011 (2019).
26. D. E. Kaplan, M. A. Luty and K. M. Zurek, Asymmetric Dark Matter, *Phys. Rev. D* **79**, p. 115016 (2009).
27. J. Shelton and K. M. Zurek, Darkogenesis: A baryon asymmetry from the dark matter sector, *Phys. Rev. D* **82**, p. 123512 (2010).
28. K. Petraki and R. R. Volkas, Review of asymmetric dark matter, *Int. J. Mod. Phys. A* **28**, p. 1330028 (2013).
29. C. Kouvaris and N. G. Nielsen, Asymmetric Dark Matter Stars, *Phys. Rev. D* **92**, p. 063526 (2015).
30. S. Leung, M. Chu and L. Lin, Dark-matter admixed neutron stars, *Phys. Rev. D* **84**, p. 107301 (2011).

31. Q.-F. Xiang, W.-Z. Jiang, D.-R. Zhang and R.-Y. Yang, Effects of fermionic dark matter on properties of neutron stars, *Phys. Rev. C* **89**, p. 025803 (Feb 2014).
32. R. C. Tolman, Static solutions of Einstein's field equations for spheres of fluid, *Phys. Rev.* **55**, 364 (1939).
33. J. R. Oppenheimer and G. M. Volkoff, On Massive neutron cores, *Phys. Rev.* **55**, 374 (1939).
34. A. Das, T. Malik and A. C. Nayak, Confronting nuclear equation of state in the presence of dark matter using GW170817 observation in relativistic mean field theory approach, *Phys. Rev. D* **99**, p. 043016 (2019).
35. H. C. Das, A. Kumar, B. Kumar, S. Kumar Biswal, T. Nakatsukasa, A. Li and S. K. Patra, Effects of dark matter on the nuclear and neutron star matter, *Mon. Not. Roy. Astron. Soc.* **495**, 4893 (2020).
36. D. Sen and A. Guha, Implications of Feebly Interacting Dark Sector on Neutron Star Properties and Constraints from GW170817, *Mon. Not. Roy. Astron. Soc.* **504**, p. 3 (2021).
37. H. C. Das, A. Kumar and S. K. Patra, Effects of dark matter on the inspiral properties of the binary neutron star (4 2021).
38. S. Mukhopadhyay, D. Atta, K. Imam, D. Basu and C. Samanta, Compact bifluid hybrid stars: Hadronic Matter mixed with self-interacting fermionic Asymmetric Dark Matter, *Eur. Phys. J. C* **77**, p. 440 (2017), [Erratum: Eur. Phys. J. C 77, 553 (2017)].
39. X. Li, F. Wang and K. Cheng, Gravitational effects of condensate dark matter on compact stellar objects, *Journal of Cosmology and Astroparticle Physics* **2012**, p. 031–031 (Oct 2012).
40. X. Li, T. Harko and K. Cheng, Condensate dark matter stars, *JCAP* **06**, p. 001 (2012).
41. L. Tolos and J. Schaffner-Bielich, Dark compact planets, *Physical Review D* **92** (Dec 2015).
42. D. J. Kaup, Klein-Gordon Geon, *Phys. Rev.* **172**, 1331 (1968).
43. R. Ruffini and S. Bonazzola, Systems of selfgravitating particles in general relativity and the concept of an equation of state, *Phys. Rev.* **187**, 1767 (1969).
44. M. Colpi, S. Shapiro and I. Wasserman, Boson Stars: Gravitational Equilibria of Selfinteracting Scalar Fields, *Phys. Rev. Lett.* **57**, 2485 (1986).
45. F. E. Schunck and E. W. Mielke, General relativistic boson stars, *Class. Quant. Grav.* **20**, R301 (2003).
46. S. L. Liebling and C. Palenzuela, Dynamical Boson Stars, *Living Rev. Rel.* **20**, p. 5 (2017).
47. L. Visinelli, Boson Stars and Oscillatons: A Review (9 2021).
48. K. A. Bugaev, V. V. Sagun, A. I. Ivanytskyi, I. P. Yakimenko, E. G. Nikonov, A. V. Taranenko and G. M. Zinovjev, Going beyond the second virial coefficient in the hadron resonance gas model, *Nucl. Phys. A* **970**, 133 (February 2018).
49. V. V. Sagun, I. Lopes and A. I. Ivanytskyi, The induced surface tension contribution for the equation of state of neutron stars, *Astrophys. J.* **871**, p. 157 (2019).
50. V. Sagun, I. Lopes and A. Ivanytskyi, Neutron stars meet constraints from high and low energy nuclear physics, *Nucl. Phys. A* **982**, 883 (2019).
51. A. Quddus, G. Panotopoulos, B. Kumar, S. Ahmad and S. K. Patra, GW170817 constraints on the properties of a neutron star in the presence of WIMP dark matter, *J. Phys. G* **47**, p. 095202 (2020).
52. K. Zhang and F.-L. Lin, Constraint on hybrid stars with gravitational wave events, *Universe* **6**, p. 231 (2020).

53. A. Le Tiec and M. Casals, Spinning Black Holes Fall in Love, *Phys. Rev. Lett.* **126**, p. 131102 (2021).
54. A. Das, T. Malik and A. C. Nayak, Confronting nuclear equation of state in the presence of dark matter using gw170817 observation in relativistic mean field theory approach, *Physical Review D* **99** (Feb 2019).
55. J. Ellis, A. Hektor, G. Hütsi, K. Kannike, L. Marzola, M. Raidal and V. Vaskonen, Search for Dark Matter Effects on Gravitational Signals from Neutron Star Mergers, *Phys. Lett. B* **781**, 607 (2018).
56. M. Bezares, D. Viganò and C. Palenzuela, Gravitational wave signatures of dark matter cores in binary neutron star mergers by using numerical simulations, *Phys. Rev. D* **100**, p. 044049 (2019).
57. M. Bezares and C. Palenzuela, Gravitational Waves from Dark Boson Star binary mergers, *Class. Quant. Grav.* **35**, p. 234002 (2018).
58. C. Horowitz and S. Reddy, Gravitational Waves from Compact Dark Objects in Neutron Stars, *Phys. Rev. Lett.* **122**, p. 071102 (2019).
59. A. Bauswein, G. Guo, J.-H. Lien, Y.-H. Lin and M.-R. Wu, Compact Dark Objects in Neutron Star Mergers (12 2020).
60. B. P. Abbott et al., GW170817: Observation of Gravitational Waves from a Binary Neutron Star Inspiral, *Phys. Rev. Lett.* **119**, p. 161101 (2017).
61. B. P. Abbott et al., GW190425: Observation of a Compact Binary Coalescence with Total Mass $\sim 3.4 M_\odot$, *Astrophys. J. Lett.* **892**, p. L3 (2020).
62. T. E. Riley et al., A NICER View of the Massive Pulsar PSR J0740+6620 Informed by Radio Timing and XMM-Newton Spectroscopy, *Astrophys. J. Lett.* **918**, p. L27 (2021).
63. B. Abbott, R. Abbott, T. Abbott, F. Acernese, K. Ackley, C. Adams, T. Adams, P. Addesso, R. Adhikari, V. Adya and et al., Gw170817: Observation of gravitational waves from a binary neutron star inspiral, *Physical Review Letters* **119** (Oct 2017).
64. B. P. Abbott et al., GW170817: Measurements of neutron star radii and equation of state, *Phys. Rev. Lett.* **121**, p. 161101 (2018).
65. A. Maselli, P. Pnigouras, N. G. Nielsen, C. Kouvaris and K. D. Kokkotas, Dark stars: Gravitational and electromagnetic observables, *Phys. Rev. D* **96**, p. 023005 (2017).
66. A. Arbey, J. Lesgourgues and P. Salati, Galactic halos of fluid dark matter, *Phys. Rev. D* **68**, p. 023511 (Jul 2003).
67. A. Suárez, V. H. Robles and T. Matos, A Review on the Scalar Field/Bose-Einstein Condensate Dark Matter Model, *Astrophys. Space Sci. Proc.* **38**, 107 (2014).
68. D. Rafiei Karkevandi, S. Shakeri, V. Sagun and O. Ivanytskyi, Bosonic Dark Matter in Neutron Stars and its Effect on Gravitational Wave Signal, *arXiv e-prints*, p. arXiv:2109.03801 (September 2021).
69. E. W. Mielke and F. E. Schunck, Boson stars: Alternatives to primordial black holes?, *Nucl. Phys. B* **564**, 185 (2000).
70. P.-H. Chavanis and T. Harko, Bose-Einstein Condensate general relativistic stars, *Phys. Rev. D* **86**, p. 064011 (2012).
71. C. Pacilio, M. Vaglio, A. Maselli and P. Pani, Gravitational-wave detectors as particle-physics laboratories: Constraining scalar interactions with a coherent inspiral model of boson-star binaries, *Phys. Rev. D* **102**, p. 083002 (2020).
72. X. Li, T. Harko and K. Cheng, Condensate dark matter stars, *JCAP* **06**, p. 001 (2012).
73. P.-H. Chavanis, Mass-radius relation of self-gravitating Bose-Einstein condensates with a central black hole, *Eur. Phys. J. Plus* **134**, p. 352 (2019).

74. F. Dalfovo, S. Giorgini, L. P. Pitaevskii and S. Stringari, Theory of bose-einstein condensation in trapped gases, *Reviews of Modern Physics* **71**, p. 463–512 (Apr 1999).
75. J. Rogel-Salazar, The gross–pitaevskii equation and bose–einstein condensates, *European Journal of Physics* **34**, p. 247–257 (Jan 2013).
76. C. J. Pethick and H. Smith, *Bose-Einstein Condensation in Dilute Gases*, 2 edn. (Cambridge University Press, 2008).
77. J. Antoniadis *et al.*, A Massive Pulsar in a Compact Relativistic Binary, *Science* **340**, p. 6131 (2013).
78. H. T. Cromartie *et al.*, Relativistic Shapiro delay measurements of an extremely massive millisecond pulsar, *Nature Astron.* **4**, 72 (2019).
79. P. Amaro-Seoane, J. Barranco, A. Bernal and L. Rezzolla, Constraining scalar fields with stellar kinematics and collisional dark matter, *JCAP* **11**, p. 002 (2010).
80. V. V. Sagun, A. I. Ivanytskyi, K. A. Bugaev and I. N. Mishustin, The statistical multifragmentation model for liquid-gas phase transition with a compressible nuclear liquid, *Nucl. Phys. A* **924**, 24 (2014).
81. A. I. Ivanytskyi, K. A. Bugaev, V. V. Sagun, L. V. Bravina and E. E. Zabrodin, Influence of flow constraints on the properties of the critical endpoint of symmetric nuclear matter, *Phys. Rev. C* **97**, p. 064905 (2018).
82. V. V. Sagun, K. A. Bugaev, A. I. Ivanytskyi, I. P. Yakimenko, E. G. Nikonov, A. V. Taranenko, C. Greiner, D. B. Blaschke and G. M. Zinovjev, Hadron resonance gas model with induced surface tension, *European Physical Journal A* **54**, p. 100 (June 2018).
83. V. Sagun, G. Panotopoulos and I. Lopes, Asteroseismology: radial oscillations of neutron stars with realistic equation of state, *Phys. Rev. D* **101**, p. 063025 (2020).
84. C. Raithel, F. Özel and D. Psaltis, Tidal deformability from GW170817 as a direct probe of the neutron star radius, *Astrophys. J. Lett.* **857**, p. L23 (2018).
85. K. Chatziioannou, Neutron star tidal deformability and equation of state constraints, *Gen. Rel. Grav.* **52**, p. 109 (2020).
86. E. R. Most, L. R. Weih, L. Rezzolla and J. Schaffner-Bielich, New constraints on radii and tidal deformabilities of neutron stars from GW170817, *Phys. Rev. Lett.* **120**, p. 261103 (2018).
87. S. De, D. Finstad, J. M. Lattimer, D. A. Brown, E. Berger and C. M. Biwer, Tidal Deformabilities and Radii of Neutron Stars from the Observation of GW170817, *Phys. Rev. Lett.* **121**, p. 091102 (2018), [Erratum: Phys. Rev. Lett. 121, 259902 (2018)].
88. T. Hinderer, Tidal Love numbers of neutron stars, *Astrophys. J.* **677**, 1216 (2008).
89. T. Hinderer, B. D. Lackey, R. N. Lang and J. S. Read, Tidal deformability of neutron stars with realistic equations of state and their gravitational wave signatures in binary inspiral, *Phys. Rev. D* **81**, p. 123016 (2010).
90. S. Postnikov, M. Prakash and J. M. Lattimer, Tidal Love Numbers of Neutron and Self-Bound Quark Stars, *Phys. Rev. D* **82**, p. 024016 (2010).
91. T. Zhao and J. M. Lattimer, Tidal Deformabilities and Neutron Star Mergers, *Phys. Rev. D* **98**, p. 063020 (2018).
92. S. Han and A. W. Steiner, Tidal deformability with sharp phase transitions in (binary) neutron stars, *Phys. Rev. D* **99**, p. 083014 (2019).
93. B. D. Lackey and L. Wade, Reconstructing the neutron-star equation of state with gravitational-wave detectors from a realistic population of inspiralling binary neutron stars, *Phys. Rev. D* **91**, p. 043002 (2015).
94. M. C. Miller *et al.*, PSR J0030+0451 Mass and Radius from *NICER* Data and Implications for the Properties of Neutron Star Matter, *Astrophys. J. Lett.* **887**, p. L24 (2019).

95. T. E. Riley *et al.*, A *NICER* View of PSR J0030+0451: Millisecond Pulsar Parameter Estimation, *Astrophys. J. Lett.* **887**, p. L21 (2019).
96. G. Raaijmakers, S. K. Greif, K. Hebeler, T. Hinderer, S. Nissanke, A. Schwenk, T. E. Riley, A. L. Watts, J. M. Lattimer and W. C. G. Ho, Constraints on the dense matter equation of state and neutron star properties from NICER's mass-radius estimate of PSR J0740+6620 and multimessenger observations (5 2021).
97. M. C. Miller *et al.*, The Radius of PSR J0740+6620 from NICER and XMM-Newton Data, *Astrophys. J. Lett.* **918**, p. L28 (2021).
98. R. Abbott *et al.*, GW190814: Gravitational Waves from the Coalescence of a 23 Solar Mass Black Hole with a 2.6 Solar Mass Compact Object, *Astrophys. J. Lett.* **896**, p. L44 (2020).
99. H. C. Das, A. Kumar and S. K. Patra, Dark matter admixed neutron star as a possible compact component in the GW190814 merger event, *Phys. Rev. D* **104**, p. 063028 (2021).
100. B. K. K. Lee, M.-c. Chu and L.-M. Lin, Can the GW190814 secondary component be a bosonic dark matter admixed compact star? (10 2021).
101. A. L. Watts, Constraining the neutron star equation of state using Pulse Profile Modeling, *AIP Conf. Proc.* **2127**, p. 020008 (2019).
102. R. Cassano *et al.*, SKA-Athena Synergy White Paper (7 2018).
103. J. J. M. in 't Zand *et al.*, Observatory science with eXTP, *Sci. China Phys. Mech. Astron.* **62**, p. 029506 (2019).
104. P. S. Ray *et al.*, STROBE-X: X-ray Timing and Spectroscopy on Dynamical Timescales from Microseconds to Years (3 2019).
105. M. Bailes *et al.*, MeerTime - the MeerKAT Key Science Program on Pulsar Timing, *PoS* **MeerKAT2016**, p. 011 (2018).
106. R. J. Selina, The next generation very large array: A technical overview https://arxiv.org/ftp/arxiv/papers/1806/1806.08405.pdf (2018).
107. A. Weltman *et al.*, Fundamental physics with the Square Kilometre Array, *Publ. Astron. Soc. Austral.* **37**, p. e002 (2020).
108. R. Abbott *et al.*, Observation of Gravitational Waves from Two Neutron Star–Black Hole Coalescences, *Astrophys. J. Lett.* **915**, p. L5 (2021).
109. M. Punturo *et al.*, The Einstein Telescope: A third-generation gravitational wave observatory, *Class. Quant. Grav.* **27**, p. 194002 (2010).
110. M. Maggiore *et al.*, Science Case for the Einstein Telescope, *JCAP* **03**, p. 050 (2020).

Binary neutron star mergers with quark matter equations of state

Atul Kedia[1,*], Hee Il Kim[2], Grant Mathews[1] and In-Saeng Suh[1,3]

[1] *Center for Astrophysics, Department of Physics, University of Notre Dame, Indiana, USA*
[2] *Center for Quantum Spacetime, Sogang University, Seoul 04107, Korea*
[3] *Center for Research Computing, University of Notre Dame, Indiana, USA*
* E-mail: akedia@nd.edu, atulkedia93@gmail.com

With recent observations of gravitational wave signals from binary neutron star mergers (BNSM) by LIGO-Virgo-KAGRA (LVK) Collaboration and NICER, the nuclear equation of state (EoS) is becoming increasingly testable by analysis with numerical simulations. Numerous simulations currently exist exploring the EoS at different density regimes for the constituent neutron stars. In this paper we summarize the GR three-dimensional hydrodynamics based simulations of BNSMs for EoSs with a specific emphasis on quark matter EoS at the highest densities.

Keywords: Neutron star binaries; Gravitational waves; Nuclear equation of state.

1. Introduction

Neutron stars are an ideal laboratory in which to probe the properties of matter at very high density. The microphysics of nuclear interactions in a neutron star reflects in its large structural features like its mass and radius. This results in modulation of the evolution of their binaries. This amplification of subatomic physics makes probing the physics at scales 10^{-14} m plausible at neutron star size 10^4 m scales. In particular, neutron star binary systems provide a means to analyze the pressure of nuclear matter at all domains of nuclear densities. Indeed, the first detection of gravitational waves from the binary neutron star merger GW170817 by the LIGO-Virgo Collaboration and the pulsar PSR J0740 by NICER has provided fundamental new insights into the nature of dense neutron-star matter.[1,2] The detected gravitational wave signal depends upon the tidal distortion of the neutron stars as they approach merger. For example, in the LIGO analysis[1,3] the tidal polarizability[4,5] was deduced from post-Newtonian dynamics implying that the radius of the stars of 1.4 $M_\odot$ is in the range 10.5 km $\leq R \leq$ 13.3 km. This has placed tight constrains on the equation of state (EoS) for nuclear matter as the stars approach merger.

Here we summarize the work done in the regime of quantum chromodynamics (QCD) formed during the merged neutron star binaries. The detection of the gravitational radiation during the postmerger could be used as a sensitive probe of both the order of the quark-hadron phase transition and the properties of matter in the non-perturbative regime of QCD.

The prospect of the postmerger evolution being used to explore EoS issues has been proposed for some time.[6] Indeed, there have been several investigations into the effects of the formation of quark matter in the BNSM.[7–10] For the most part these studies have considered effects of a first-order phase transition and the formation of a mixed quark-hadron phase. In this case the first-order transition can soften the EoS and hasten the formation of the black hole.

The neutron star-ringdown occurs in a frequency range 2-5 kHz and thus the strain strength for a binary at 50 Mpc is not easily accessible to aLIGO/aVirgo/KAGRA. However, the third generation GW observatories, the Einstein Telescope and the Cosmic Explorer, will have enhanced sensitivities in this frequency range and will be susceptible to observing postmerger evolution of a BNSM. Further, there is a suggestion in the literature (see Refs. 11, 12) of post merger energy output in gravitational radiation from the GW170817 event that appears to be an extended ringdown (see however Ref. [13].) In Ref. [12] it was hypothesized that such extended emission might result from spin down of a magnetar.

2. Equation of state

To describe the evolution of matter completely, the hydrodynamics equations require an additional constraint that relates the various state variables of the matter, i.e. pressure, density, electron fraction, chemical potentials, etc. in a neutron star.[14,15] Constraints on the equation of state (EoS) have been placed by aLIGO based upon the tidal polarizability deduced from the chirp associated with event GW170817.[1,3] Any realistic description of the equation of state (EoS) of matter formed in the merger of neutron stars must also include the consequences of a transition between hadronic matter and quark matter. As the merged system collapses to a black hole it unavoidably encounters all dense phases of matter, particularly the transition to quark matter.

It is worth noting that as the baryon density and chemical potential increase the QCD strong coupling constant α_s approaches unity and a nonperturbative approach to QCD is imperative. In particular, There is rich physics in this region of the quark-matter phase diagram including the generation of constituent quark masses, due to chiral symmetry breaking,[16] and quark pairing leading to color superconductivity.[17] The evolution of these effects until the asymptotic regime must be described during the collapse.

The transition from hadronic matter to quark matter is not yet fully understood.[18] However, people have proposed many interesting models to describe the transition from hadronic matter to quark matter at densities between 2-5 ρ_{nuc}.[19,20] Considering strongly interacting quark states for the crossover density region, people could have made the EoSs satisfying 2 times solar mass observational bound.[21] Also, many models having the first order phase transition features have been proposed to describe the transition.

3. Power spectral density of the gravitational waves

In addition to f_{max} which could be obtained from the instantaneous change of the phase of h, the power spectral density (PSD) of the strain, h, poses to reveal further features about the star's EoS. Refs. [22, 10] shows the presence of high frequency spectral features in the f_1, f_2 and f_3, as defined in Ref. [22] modes for binaries with different EoS description. The positioning and strength of the frequencies depends on the nature of the EoS. One of the important aspects about the power spectra of the mergers is that the strength of the PSD at 2 kHz to 5 kHz frequencies is weak enough that the current LVK detectors are unable to discern them from the noise. It is also pointed out that the third generation gravitational wave interferometers, the Einstein Telescope and the Cosmic Explorer, would have higher sensitivities at these frequencies making them more likely to resolve the f-modes. Further, Ref. [22] notes the occurrence of 'quasiuniversal' relations relating f-modes with compactness and the maximum frequency of chirp with tidal deformability of a single stable NS for the given EoS. These relations can be explained partially by the stiffness of the equation of state, softer EoSs leading to higher f-modes. Recent studies of the BNSM with the phase transtion have examined whether the features of the phase transition could be imprinted in the f-mode frequencies, for example, the shift of the peak frequencies.[8, 23] We are currently investigating the spectral features of the BNSM with a specific crossover EoS and have found some interesting postmerger behaviour showing elongated duration owning to the stiffened EoS.[18, 19, 24]

4. Conclusion

We have briefly summarized some recent studies on the BNSM with quark matter. An observation of the postmerger and the collapse in a BNSM could be used to determine the nature of the phase transition and the physics at the crossover densities. The next generation GW detectors will probe and unveil the physics of this dense matter physics with their highly improved power of detectabilities at higher GW frequencies.

Finally, noting a caveat that there have been no studies fully considering such as MHD and neutrino transport for the simulations, however, we expect that essential features of the non-perturbative characters of the QCD would be revealed and confirmed without taking these considerations into account.

References

1. B.P. Abbott et al. (LIGO Scientific Collaboration and Virgo Collaboration), Phys. Rev. Lett. 119, 161101 (2017).
2. M. C. Miller et al 2021, *The Astrophysical Journal Letters*, 918 L28
3. B. P. Abbott, et al. "Tests of general relativity with GW170817." Phys. Rev. Lett. 123.1 (2019): 011102.
4. T. Damour, M. Soffel, and C. Xu, Phys. Rev. D 45, 1017 (1992).
5. E. E. Flanagan and T. Hinderer, Phys. Rev. D 77, 021502 (2008).
6. A. Bauswein, H.-T. Janka, K. Hebeler, and A. Schwenk, Phys. Rev. D 86, 063001 (2012).

7. E. R. Most, L. Jens Papenfort, V. Dexheimer, M. Hanauske, H. Stoecker, and L. Rezzolla, On the de-confinement phase transition in neutron-star mergers, Eur. Phys. J. A 56, 59 (2020)
8. L. R. Weih, M. Hanauske, and L. Rezzolla, Postmerger Gravitational-Wave Signatures of Phase Transitions in Binary Mergers, Phys. Rev. Lett. 124, 171103 (2020).
9. S. L. Liebling, C. Palenzuela, and L. Lehner, Effects of High Density Phase Transitions on Neutron Star Dynamics, Class. Quant. Grav. 38, 115007 (2021)
10. A. Prakash, D. Radice, D. Logoteta, et al., arXiv:2106.07885 (2021)
11. H. M. P van Putten and D. V. Massimo, MNRAS, 482, L46 (2019).
12. H. M. P van Putten, D. V. Massimo, and A. Levinson, Astrophys. J. Lett. 876, L2 (2019).
13. M. Oliver, D. Keitel, A. Miller, et al. MNRAS, 485, 843 (2019).
14. D. Radice, A. Perego, F. Zappa, and S. Bernuzzi Ap. J. Lett. 852.2 (2018): L29.
15. J. Olson, *et al.*, arXiv:1612.08992 (2016).
16. Hatsuda, T., and Kunihiro, T. 1994, PhR, 247, 221
17. M. G. Alford, A. Schmitt, K. Rajagopal, and T. Schäfer, 2008, RvMP, 80, 1455.
18. Baym, G., Hatsuda, T., Kojo, T., et al. 2018, RPPh, 81, 056902
19. G. Baym, S. Furusawa, T. Hatsuda, T. Kojo, H. Togashi, ApJ, 885, 42 (2019)
20. E. Annala, E., T. Gorda, A. Kurkela, et al., Nature Physics, (2020), 16(9), 907-910.
21. P. B. Demorest, T. Pennucci, S. M. Ransom, et al. , Nature (London) 467, 1081 (2010).
22. K. Takami, L. Rezzolla, and L. Baiotti, Physical Review D 91.6 (2015): 064001
23. S. Blacker, NUF Bastian, A. Bauswein, et al., Physical Review D 102.12 (2020): 123023.
24. A. Kedia, H.I. Kim, I.S. Suh, G. Mathews, (2021) in preparation.

Probing dense matter physics with transiently-accreting neutron stars: The case of source MXB 1659-29

Melissa Mendes*, Andrew Cumming and Charles Gale

Department of Physics, McGill University,
3600 rue University, Montreal, QC, H3A 2T8, Canada
*E-mail: melissa.mendessilva@mail.mcgill.ca

Farrukh J. Fattoyev

Department of Physics, Manhattan College, Riverdale, NY 10471, USA

Recent observational data on transiently-accreting neutron stars has unequivocally shown fast-cooling sources, such as in the case of neutron star MXB 1659-29. Previous calculations have estimated its total neutrino luminosity and heat capacity, as well as suggested that direct Urca reactions take place in 1% of the volume of the core. In this paper, we reproduce the inferred luminosity of this source with detailed models of equations of state (EOS) and nuclear pairing gaps. We show that three superfluidity gap models are inconsistent with data for all EOS and another three are disfavoured because of fine tuning arguments. We also calculate the total heat capacity for all constructed stars and show that independent observations of mass and luminosity could set constraints on the core superfluidity of a source as well as the density slope of the symmetry energy, (L). This is an important step towards defining a universal equation of state for neutron stars and therefore, towards a better understanding of the phase diagram of asymmetric matter at high densities.

Keywords: Symmetry energy; neutron star composition; direct Urca; transiently-accreting neutron stars

1. Introduction

The composition of the core of neutron stars is still unknown. Their extreme densities make it impossible for similar conditions to be reproduced experimentally in laboratories, and their strongly-coupled hadronic nature represents a serious challenge for first-principles calculations. Therefore, there is a lot of uncertainty when it comes to the particle content and matter organization in neutron star cores. Even in the simplest model of neutron stars made only of neutrons, protons, electrons and muons, there is no agreement on the star's proton fraction – which determines electron and muon fractions, by the charge neutrality requirement – or how to describe proton superconductivity and neutron superfluidity, both expected to happen in matter at high densities.[1] The proton fraction is important because it determines whether neutrino cooling occurs via modified Urca or direct Urca reactions, which differ by orders of magnitude in emissivity.

Although BCS theory with polarization corrections[2,3] can describe superfluidity and superconductivity in a low density medium, at high densities, in-medium effects prevent an accurate description of neutron and proton pairing. This uncertainty forbids a precise determination of the critical temperatures as a function of density, that is, the gap amplitude and width of the pairing gap in neutron star cores. Nonetheless, a wide range of theoretical calculations of superfluidity at high densities exist, which have been summarized in the functional analytic form in Ref. 4. Its parameters mimic the effect of in-medium interactions, and thus define a range of possible models for nucleon pairing at high densities, each one with their specific amplitudes and widths.

These different gap models will predict different stellar cooling rates, as shown in Ref. 4, because both superfluidity and superconductivity suppress neutrino production through direct or modified Urca reactions.[5] Furthermore, Cooper pair formation produces pair-breaking-formation (PBF) cooling reactions, which enhance the star's cooling when its temperature is close to the superfluid critical temperature.[5] The suppression or enhancement of neutrino emission due to superfluidity depends on density, and therefore location within the neutron star core. By comparing these predictions with the star's observed luminosity, one can exclude or favor specific gap models.

Transiently-accreting neutron stars are ideal systems to perform these observations. These stars periodically accrete matter from a companion star, in cycles of accretion outbursts followed by periods of quiescence, in which accretion halts.[6,7] By observing X-ray emissions after the accretion period, the surface temperature of the star can be found. Combining that information with the mass accretion rate, one can obtain a consistent estimate of the star's neutrino luminosity and determine whether fast cooling reactions (such as direct Urca) or slow cooling reactions (such as modified Urca) are taking place in the neutron star's core.[7]

The source MXB 1659-29 is particularly interesting because it has shown more than one accretion-quiescence cycle, which allows for repeated measurements of accretion rates during outburst, luminosity and temperature during quiescence. Analysis of the energy balance between accretion-driven crustal heating in outburst and neutrino cooling during quiescence leads to the conclusion that this source is undergoing fast cooling processes in its core.[7,8] Furthermore, it has been suggested in Ref. 8 that measuring the decrease of external temperature of the neutron star MXB 1659-29 over an interval of ten years, combined with the observation of its neutrino luminosity, could set constraints on its total heat capacity, and therefore on its composition. This analysis would represent another avenue for finding, for example, the relative contribution of leptons to the total heat capacity of a specific source based on direct observations, which could set further constraints on its superfluidity.

Other transiently accreting sources such as KS 1731-260 have inferred neutrino cooling luminosities inconsistent with fast cooling, implying that they have slow cooling processes operating in their cores.[9] To explain this data, one should consider a combination of equation of state (EOS) describing a star's particle content, and a collection of nuclear pairing gap models that accommodate both fast and slow cooling processes. In this paper, we create detailed realistic scenarios for MXB 1659-29, to determine how the observed neutrino cooling rate of that source constrains the input physics. We use gap models described in Ref. 4, and a family of relativistic mean-field (RMF) EOS[10] based on FSUGold2, first described in Ref. 11. Their particularities are discussed in section 2. In section 3, we investigate the agreement of the calculated luminosities with data and we verify the suggestion made in Ref. 8 that direct Urca processes occur in approximately 1% of the volume of the star's core. Finally, in section 4, we discuss which gap models accurately describe this scenario and compute predictions for the neutron star heat capacity in each case.

2. Formalism

To determine the particle composition of the core of neutron stars, we use a family of equations of state (EOS) that are developed from the RMF model FSUGold2.[11] The original FSUGold2 model was created to reproduce the ground-state properties of finite nuclei such as binding energy and charge radii, their monopole response, and the maximum observed neutron star mass. In particular, the original model predicts both a stiff symmetry energy and a soft equation of state for symmetric nuclear matter, that is, matter with equal number of protons and neutrons. The symmetry energy is an essential ingredient of the EOS that strongly impacts the structure, dynamics, and composition of neutron stars and has received considerable attention over the last decade.[12,13] Customarily, one expands the total energy per nucleon $E(\rho, \alpha)$ at zero temperature—where $\rho = \rho_n + \rho_p$ is the total baryon density and $\alpha = (\rho_n - \rho_p)/\rho$ is the neutron-proton asymmetry parameter—around the energy of isospin symmetric matter with $\alpha = 0$,

$$E(\rho, \alpha) = E_{\text{SNM}}(\rho) + E_{\text{sym}}(\rho) \cdot \alpha^2 + \mathcal{O}\left(\alpha^4\right) \quad (1)$$

where $E_{\text{SNM}}(\rho) \equiv E(\rho, 0)$ is the energy per nucleon in symmetric nuclear matter (SNM) and $E_{\text{sym}}(\rho)$ the symmetry energy, which represents a correction of second order in parameter α, to the symmetric limit. No odd powers of α appear in the expansion above because the nuclear force is assumed to be isospin symmetric. To characterize the behavior of both $E_{\text{SNM}}(\rho)$ and $E_{\text{sym}}(\rho)$ near the nuclear saturation density $\rho_{\text{sat}} \approx 0.15$ fm^{-3}, one can further expand these quantities in a Taylor series,[14]

$$E_{\text{SNM}}(\rho) = B + \frac{1}{2}Kx^2 + \cdots \quad (2)$$

$$E_{\text{sym}}(\rho) = J + Lx + \frac{1}{2}K_{\text{sym}}x^2 + \cdots \quad (3)$$

where $x = (\rho - \rho_{\text{sat}})/3\rho_{\text{sat}}$ is a dimensionless parameter that quantifies the deviations of the density from its value at saturation, B is the energy per nucleon and K is the incompressibility coefficient of SNM. Similarly, J and K_{sym} represent the symmetry energy and the incompressibility coefficient of symmetry energy at saturation density and serve as corrections to the binding energy and incompressibility.

Unlike in SNM, whose pressure vanishes at saturation density, the slope of the symmetry energy L, and consequently, pressure of pure neutron matter, do not vanish at ρ_{sat}.

Since L is poorly constrained experimentally, we generated a family of the FSUGold2 models that are identical in their predictions for the EOS of SNM but vary in their predictions for the symmetry energy. It is well known that, at a sub-saturation density of $\rho \approx 0.1$ fm^{-3}, which represents an average value between the central and surface densities, the symmetry energy is well constrained by the binding energy of heavy nuclei with a significant neutron excess.[15–17] By fixing this value of the symmetry energy, we obtain a family of models with differing (J, L) values that are identical in their predictions for the ground state properties of finite nuclei but predict a range of the neutron skin thicknesses and neutron star radii consistent with the current experimental and observational data.[18–22]

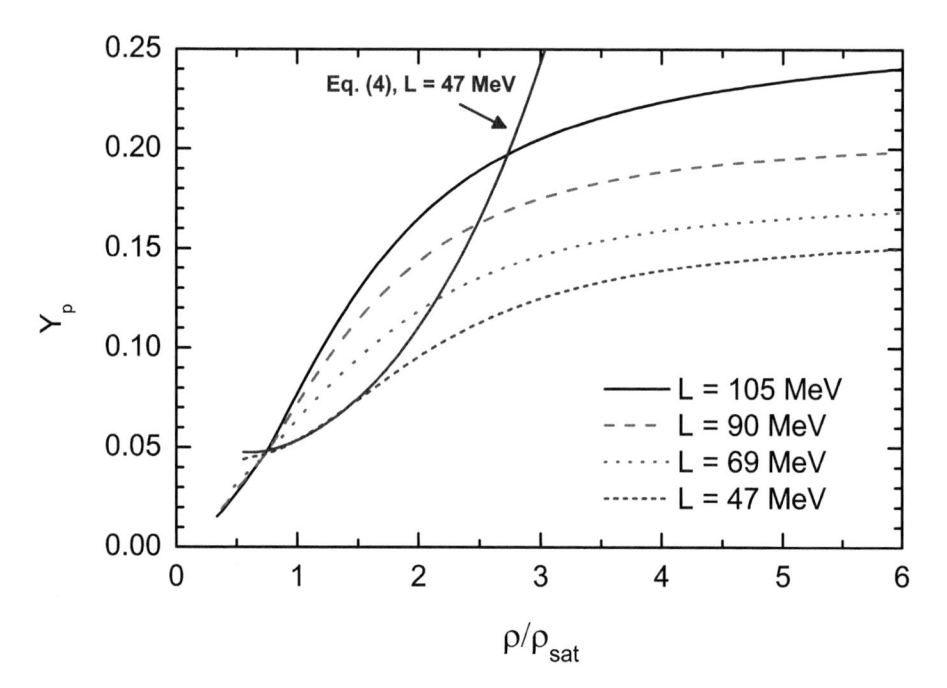

Fig. 1. Proton fraction Y_p versus baryon density ρ normalized by saturation density for EOS in the FSUGold2 family. Different curves correspond to EOS with different L values, in MeV. The blue solid curve shows the analytic approximation (Eq. 4).

Cold-catalyzed matter in neutron stars, ie. matter in the ground state with lowest energy per nucleon, is in a state of chemical equilibrium and is assumed to be electrically neutral. Therefore one must impose a charge neutrality and chemical equilibrium condition to obtain an EOS of neutron-star matter. We consider a minimal model in which neutrons, protons, electrons and muons are present inside neutron stars. Increasing the parameter L leads to a larger symmetry energy at supersaturation densities. This in turn makes it difficult for protons to convert into neutrons and thus increases the proton fraction $Y_\mathrm{p} = \rho_\mathrm{p}/\rho$ in the innermost region of the star, as shown in Fig. 1. For matter composed of neutrons, protons and electrons, Ref. 23 shows this proportionality explicitly by writing the beta equilibrium condition as a function of the proton fraction, such that for low proton fraction,

$$Y_\mathrm{p} \simeq \frac{64}{3\pi^2 \rho_\mathrm{sat}(3x+1)} \left(\frac{J + Lx + \frac{1}{2}K_\mathrm{sym}x^2}{\hbar c}\right)^3. \quad (4)$$

As displayed in Fig. 1, this approximation is only valid up to about $1.5\rho_\mathrm{sat}$, where proton fractions are small. Here we used the predicted bulk parameters of symmetry energy at saturation density $\rho_\mathrm{sat} = 0.15$ fm^{-3}, $J = 30.6$ MeV, $L = 47.0$ MeV and $K_\mathrm{sym} = 54.0$ MeV to generate the blue solid curve in Fig. 1.

The outer crust is described by the EOS from Ref. 24, whereas the EOS for the inner crust is described in Ref. 25. For the core we use the FSUGold2 family of EOS with different values of the slope of the symmetry energy L. We assume a non-rotating spherically-symmetric neutron star, and solve the Tolman-Oppenheimer-Volkoff (TOV) equations

$$\frac{dP}{dr} = -\frac{\mathcal{E}(r)}{c^2}\frac{Gm(r)}{r^2}\left[1 + \frac{P(r)}{\mathcal{E}(r)}\right]\left[1 + \frac{4\pi r^3 P(r)}{m(r)c^2}\right]\left[1 - \frac{2Gm(r)}{c^2 r}\right]^{-1}, \quad (5)$$

$$\frac{dm}{dr} = 4\pi r^2 \frac{\mathcal{E}(r)}{c^2}, \quad (6)$$

$$\frac{d\phi}{dr} = -\frac{1}{\mathcal{E}(r) + P(r)}\frac{dP}{dr} \quad (7)$$

where $m(r)$ is the mass within radius r, $P(r)$ is the pressure, $\mathcal{E}(r)$ is the energy density and $\phi(r)$ is the gravitational potential such that at the surface of the star, $r = R$ and $m = M$, the pressure vanishes, $P(R) = 0$ and $\phi(R) = \frac{1}{2}\ln(1-2GM/c^2 R)$.

Since our goal is to reproduce the inferred neutrino luminosity of MXB 1659-29, we consider the fast cooling process of direct Urca only. If there are no muons participating, direct Urca cooling takes place through the reactions

$$n \to p + e^- + \bar{\nu}_e, \quad p + e^- \to n + \nu_e. \quad (8)$$

This process conserves momentum only if

$$k_{Fn} \leq k_{Fp} + k_{Fe}, \quad (9)$$

which implies that for direct Urca reactions the proton fraction must exceed a threshold value

$$Y_p \geq Y_{p\,\mathrm{dUrca}} = \frac{\left[(3\pi^2 \hbar^3 \rho Y_n)^{1/3} - (3\pi^2 \hbar^3 \rho_e)^{1/3}\right]^3}{3\pi^2 \hbar^3 \rho}, \quad (10)$$

as explained in Ref. 5. Here, k_{Fx} are the Fermi momenta, a function of ρ_x, the number density for each species and the particle fraction Y_x. If there are no muons in the star at all, Eq. (10) can be simplified because of the star's charge neutrality condition $\rho_p = \rho_e$, hence $Y_{p\,\text{dUrca}} = 1/9 \approx 0.11$. However, for the EOS studied here, $Y_{p\,\text{dUrca}} \neq 1/9$ because even when muons are not participating in direct Urca reactions, they are present, such that the charge neutrality condition becomes $\rho_p = \rho_e + \rho_\mu$, thus, for our set of EOS, we have $0.131 \leq Y_{p\,\text{dUrca}} \leq 0.138$.

The direct Urca neutrino luminosity is given by

$$L_{\nu_{\text{dUrca}}} = \int_0^{R_{\text{core}}} \frac{4\pi r^2 \epsilon_0^{\text{dUrca total}}}{(1 - (2Gm(r)/c^2 r))^{1/2}} dr, \quad (11)$$

where the integral is over the neutron star core, and the local neutrino emissivity is[5]

$$\epsilon_0^{\text{dUrca total}} = \epsilon_0^{\text{dUrca }e^-} + \epsilon_0^{\text{dUrca }\mu^-} \quad (12)$$

$$\epsilon_0^{\text{dUrca }e^-} = \frac{457\pi}{10080} G_F^2 \cos^2\theta_C \left(1 + 3g_A^2\right) \frac{m_n^* m_p^* m_e^*}{\hbar^{10} c^3} (k_B T)^6 \Theta_{\text{npe}}, \quad (13)$$

where we used the weak coupling constant $G_F = 1.4361 0^{-62}\,\text{Jm}^3$, the Cabibbo angle $\theta_C = 0.227$, the axial vector coupling constant $g_A = -1.2601 \left(1 - \frac{\rho}{4.15(\rho_0 + \rho)}\right)$. M_x^* represents the effective mass of species x and Θ_{npe} is a step function specifying the densities where direct Urca reactions can happen, respecting momentum conservation. Note that, in general, muons can participate in these reactions at high densities, so that

$$n \to p + \mu^- + \bar{\nu}_{\mu^-}, \quad p + \mu^- \to n + \nu_{\mu^-} \quad (14)$$

Their emissivities are

$$\epsilon_0^{\text{dUrca }\mu^-} = \epsilon_0^{\text{dUrca }e^-}. \quad (15)$$

Including superfluidity and superconductivity in the neutron star core model changes the neutrino luminosity calculations. The formation of Cooper pairs reduces the number of neutrons and/or protons available for participating in direct Urca reactions, therefore the rate ϵ^{dUrca} is exponentially reduced, as described in Ref. 5, according to

$$\epsilon^{\text{dUrca}} = \epsilon_0^{\text{dUrca}} R \quad (16)$$

$$R = \exp\left(-v_{\text{triplet/singlet}}^*\right) \quad (17)$$

$$\text{for } v_{\text{triplet}}^* = 2.376\,(T_c/T), \text{ where } T_c = 0.1187\Delta(k_{\text{Fx}}) \quad (18)$$

$$\text{and } v_{\text{singlet}}^* = 1.764\,(T_c/T), \text{ where } T_c = 0.5669\Delta(k_{\text{Fx}}). \quad (19)$$

Here T_c is the critical temperature, calculated according to each gap model parametrization, and T is the local temperature of the core, $T = \tilde{T}\exp(-\phi(r))$, where $\tilde{T}$ is the temperature of the isothermal core as seen at infinity. The heat

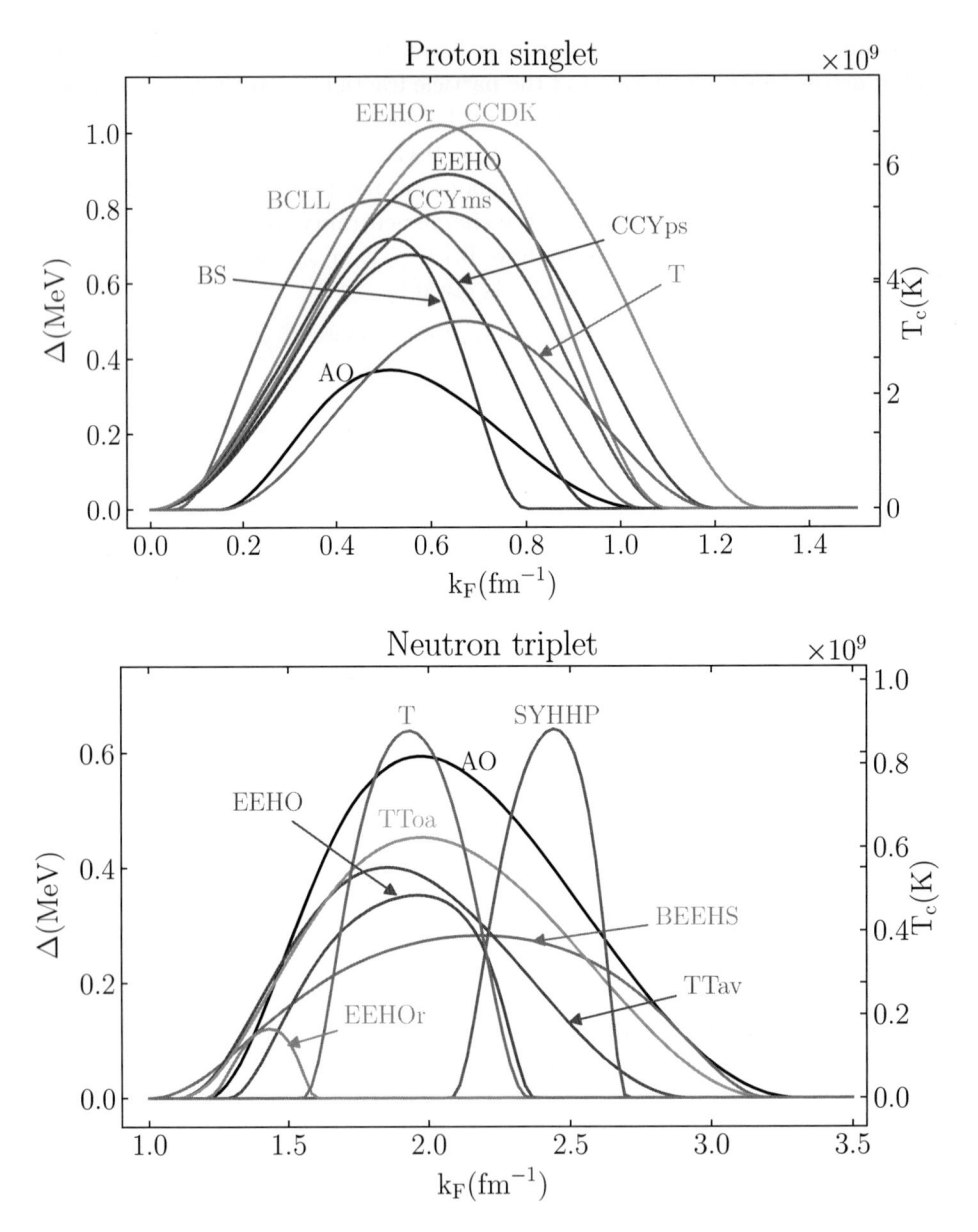

Fig. 2. Gap model parametrizations Δ (MeV) as a function of Fermi momenta k_F (fm^{-1}) for all models studied here (see Ref. 4 and references therein). (a) Proton singlet superconductivity (b) Neutron triplet superfluidity.

capacity of neutrons and protons is similarly reduced when they are superfluid or superconducting, $C_{p,n}^{\text{superfluid}} = C_{p,n} \, R$.

Equations (17)–(19) are simplifications of the results of full calculations, that find the proper quantum state rearrangements in the energy levels of the matter once neutron and proton pairing are taken into account.[5] We acknowledge the difference in the reduction rates between the full calculation and the approximations (Eq. (17)–(19)), especially at $T \ll T_c$ and when superconductivity and superfluidity are simultaneously present in the star's core. This difference becomes large only well-below the critical temperature T_c, where the neutrinos are already suppressed, thus our results are not expected to change qualitatively. Results of full calculations will be explored in a forthcoming paper.

To characterize the different gap models, we work with the polynomial parametrizations for the superfluid gap[4]

$$\Delta(k_{\text{Fx}}) = \Delta_0 \frac{(k_{\text{Fx}} - k_0)^2}{(k_{\text{Fx}} - k_0)^2 + k_1} \frac{(k_{\text{Fx}} - k_2)^2}{(k_{\text{Fx}} - k_2)^2 + k_3}, \qquad (20)$$

where Δ_0, k_0, k_1, k_2 and k_3 are free parameters fitted to adjust the amplitudes and widths of each gap model. The resulting superfluid gaps are shown in Fig. 2 and their parameters can be found in Ref. 4.

3. Results

3.1. *Direct Urca cooling and the dependence on gap model*

We first calculated neutron star models without the effects of pairing, to determine when direct Urca reactions are kinematically allowed, as a function of the neutron star mass M and slope of the symmetry energy L. The direct Urca threshold for all EOS is shown in Fig. 3. All stars with masses above the M_{dUrca} curve can have part or the entirety of their core emitting neutrinos through direct Urca reactions. For low L EOS, only stars with large masses ($M \geq 1.8 M_\odot$) have a proton fraction large enough to allow direct Urca. On the right hand side of the plot, high L EOS, which have a larger proton fraction, can accommodate direct Urca reactions even for very low mass neutron stars ($M \leq 1.0 M_\odot$). Note that we include neutron stars with $M < 1.0 M_\odot$ to show the full parameter space, although it is not expected that such low mass neutron stars are formed in reality.

The range of parameter space in which direct Urca cooling can occur may change once we include superfluidity, as a consequence of the exponential suppression of direct Urca rates in the presence of Cooper pairs. Depending on the range of density over which superfluidity occurs, there can be different effects on the direct Urca parameter space. For example, shown in Fig. 4, the gap model NT_T predicts that for $L \geq 60\,\text{MeV}$, part of the core of all neutron stars with masses $M \leq (1.7\text{–}1.8)\,M_\odot$ will be superfluid, thus reducing their total neutrino luminosity. Therefore, owing to the combination of the direct Urca threshold and the suppression by superfluidity, in this case only high mass stars $M \geq (1.7\text{–}1.8)\,M_\odot$ can significantly cool through direct Urca reactions, even for large values of L. In all figures where superfluidity gap models are taken into consideration, we also plot their closing curves, which are obtained by finding the densities for which the predicted gap model $T_c(\rho)$ matches

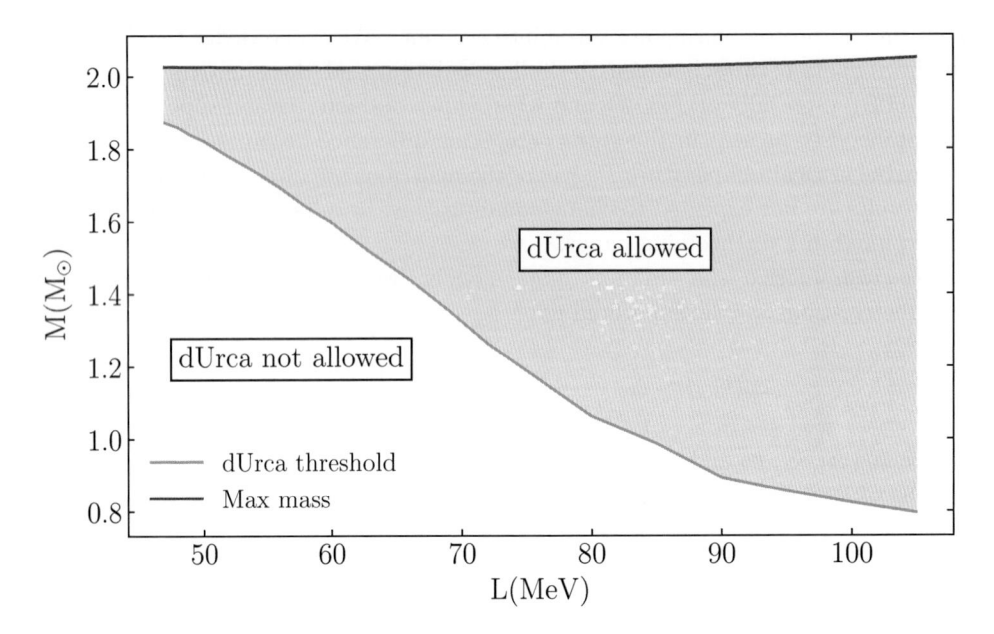

Fig. 3. Direct Urca threshold calculation (orange curve) for all EOS without nuclear pairing. The shaded area corresponds to the phase space where direct Urca reactions are allowed, the maximum mass reached for each EOS is also shown (blue curve).

the star's core temperature T, for $\tilde{T} = 2.5 \times 10^7$K, the inferred core temperature for MXB 1659-29.[8]

Another interesting situation is when there is a late opening of the superfluid gap, as in the case of NT_{SYHHP}, Fig. 5. In this situation, for large L ($L \geq 70$ MeV) and low mass stars ($M \leq 1.3 M_\odot - 1.4 M_\odot$), direct Urca reactions are allowed to happen because there is no superfluidity in the core yet. Cooper pair formation happens for larger mass stars or lower L, when direct Urca is suppressed, until there is no more superfluidity, that is, the gap closes, at higher masses. Therefore, direct Urca reactions are allowed again, close to maximum mass stars. In this situation, there are two regions of the phase diagram where direct Urca processes are significant: large L and low mass stars or very high mass stars ($M \approx 2.0 M_\odot$) for all L.

There are also cases in which the superfluid part of the core is in a region where direct Urca reactions do not happen. Then, superfluidity does not change the calculations of neutrino luminosity shown in Fig. 3. This is the case for gap models NT_{EEHOr}, PS_{BS} and PS_{CCYps}. The last possible situation is represented by gap models NT_{AO}, NT_{BEEHS} and NT_{TToa}, which predict that the whole core of the neutron star is superfluid, severely suppressing direct Urca for all EOS and all masses.

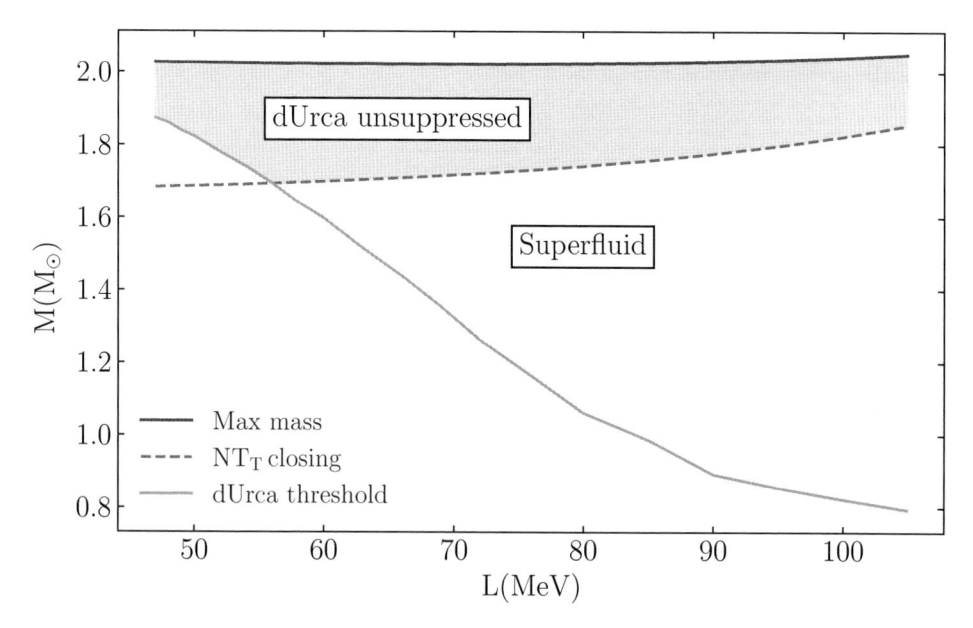

Fig. 4. Direct Urca threshold calculation (orange curve) and closing curve of superfluid gap model NT$_T$ (dashed olive). The area between the orange and dashed olive lines corresponds to exponential suppression of direct Urca reactions. Above the dashed line, there is no suppression.

3.2. *Application to MXB 1659-29*

We now discuss the predictions of our model for the accreting neutron star MXB 1659-29. As described in Ref. 8, knowing the total mass accreted onto the neutron star during an outburst, one can estimate the total energy deposited in the crust. Assuming this energy is almost completely conducted into the core, and, after the core reaches thermal equilibrium, radiated away by neutrinos, we get an estimate of the star's neutrino luminosity. For the source MXB 1659-29, this luminosity is estimated to be $L_\nu \approx 3 \times 10^{27}$ J/s $= 3 \times 10^{34}$ erg/s.

This estimate was shown[8] to be insensitive (less than a factor of two) to variations in accretion rate during outburst and the outburst recurrence time, neutron star mass or EOS, for a core temperature of $\tilde{T} = 2.5 \times 10^7$ K and a light element envelope composition. As detailed in Ref. 9, the envelope composition is a crucial parameter in modelling the relationship between the internal temperature of the star and its surface temperature. For this source, a heavy element envelope would correspond to a core temperature of $\tilde{T} = 5 \times 10^7$ K, which increases the star's predicted total neutrino luminosity by two orders of magnitude, however, this scenario is inconsistent with the measured accretion rates. Ref. 8 also found that the envelope's impurity parameter and distance uncertainties can change the inferred luminosity above by an additional factor of $\lesssim 2$. For this study, we will take the value $L_\nu = 3 \times 10^{34}$ erg/s as the correct value of neutrino luminosity.

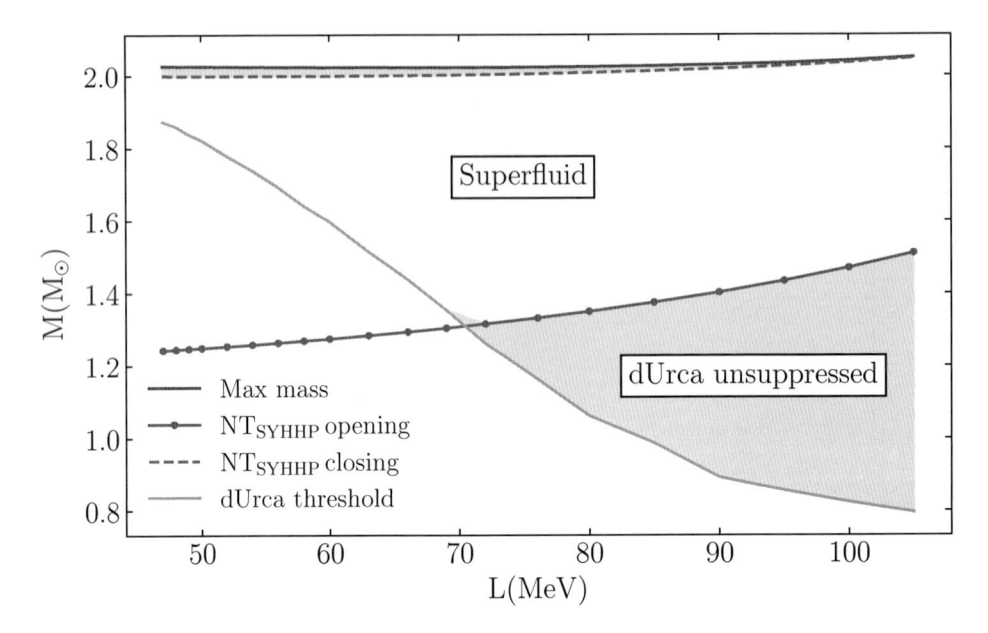

Fig. 5. The direct Urca threshold (orange curve), and the opening (dotted green) and closing (dashed green) curves of superfluid gap NT$_{\text{SYHHP}}$. The area bounded by the orange, the dotted green and the dashed green lines corresponds to exponential suppression of direct Urca reactions. In all highlighted areas, there is no suppression.

To attempt to match the inferred neutrino luminosity of the source MXB 1659-29, we calculate the masses of stars with that total luminosity, for all combinations of EOS and gap models. The results are shown in Fig. 6. Panel (a) displays only the no superfluidity case, whereas panel (b) contains the predictions for neutron triplet superfluidity and panel (c), for proton singlet superconductivity. In all cases, we observe that only a small fraction of the volume of the core, from 0.10% to 1.07% depending on the EOS, is involved in unsuppressed direct Urca cooling. These volume fractions are shown in the bottom panel of panel (a).

We also calculated the total neutron star heat capacity, for all combinations of EOS and gap models. The results are shown in Fig. 7. Note that larger mass stars have larger heat capacities, which is a trend one observes in the figure above and in Fig. 8. Specifically, for proton superconductivity, high L EOS have lower mass stars achieving the observed luminosity of $L_\nu = 3 \times 10^{34}$ erg/s, thus Fig. 7a shows a general trend of lower heat capacities for higher Ls. The opposite trend happens for neutron superfluidity, where most heat capacity curves increase with increasing L, reflecting that higher mass stars are produced in that region. The C-shaped curves on the right bottom of Fig. 8b are a consequence of this phenomenon. Note that different L EOS can generate stars with the same mass and luminosity, for a given gap model. The fact that we are not comparing same size stars on Fig. 7 explains

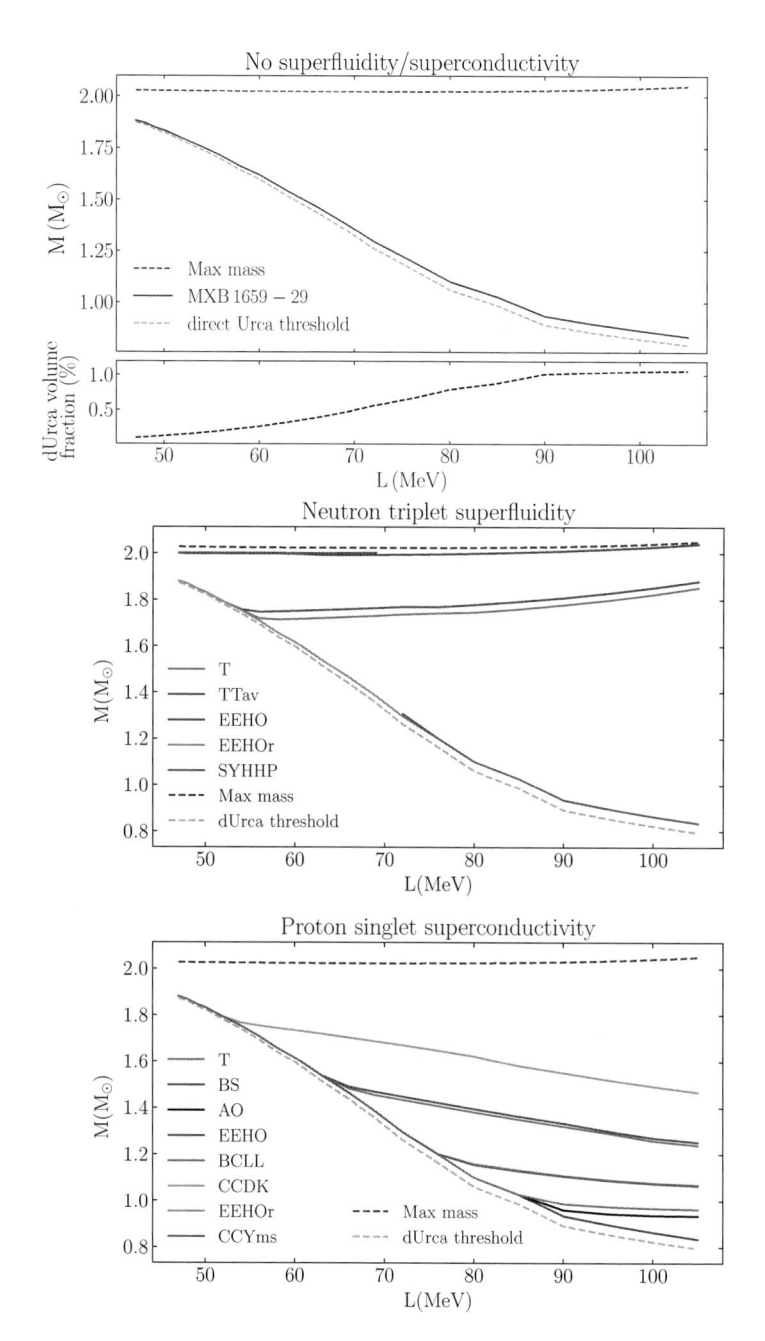

Fig. 6. Masses of stars with luminosity $L_\nu = 3 \cdot 10^{27}$ J/s, corresponding to MXB 1659-29 source, for all EOS. (a) No superfluidity/superconductivity (dark blue curve). The bottom panel displays the percentage of the core volume involved in unsupressed direct Urca reactions. (b) For all gap models of neutron triplet superfluidity. The curve displayed in panel a is under the gap model NT$_{EEHOOr}$ curve. (c) For all gap models of proton singlet superconductivity. Gap models PS$_{CCYps}$ and PS$_{BS}$ predict the same curve.

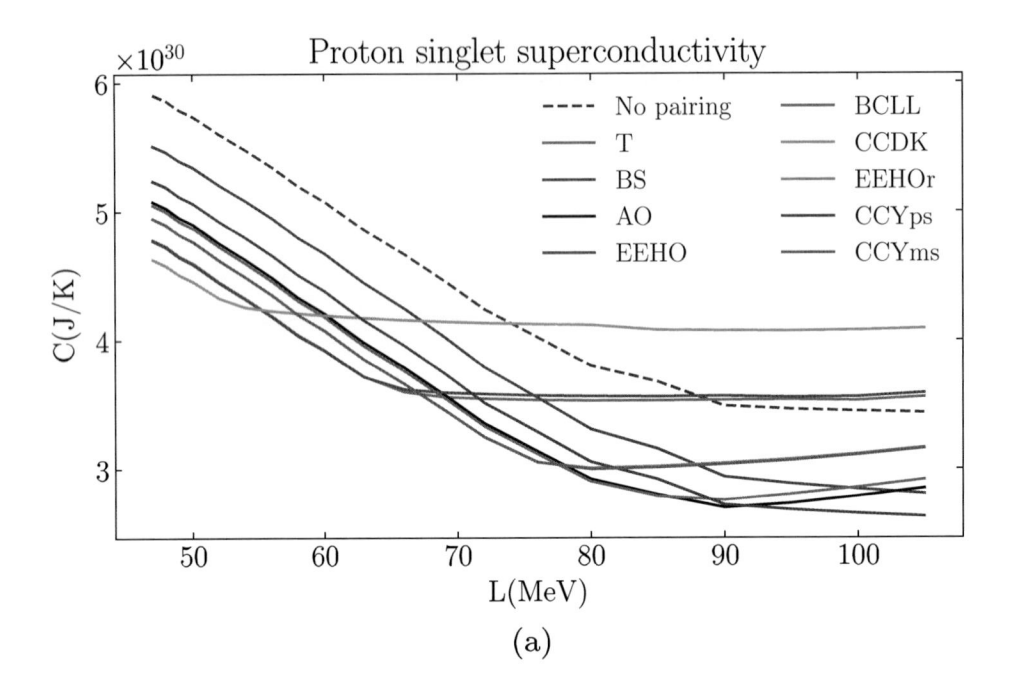

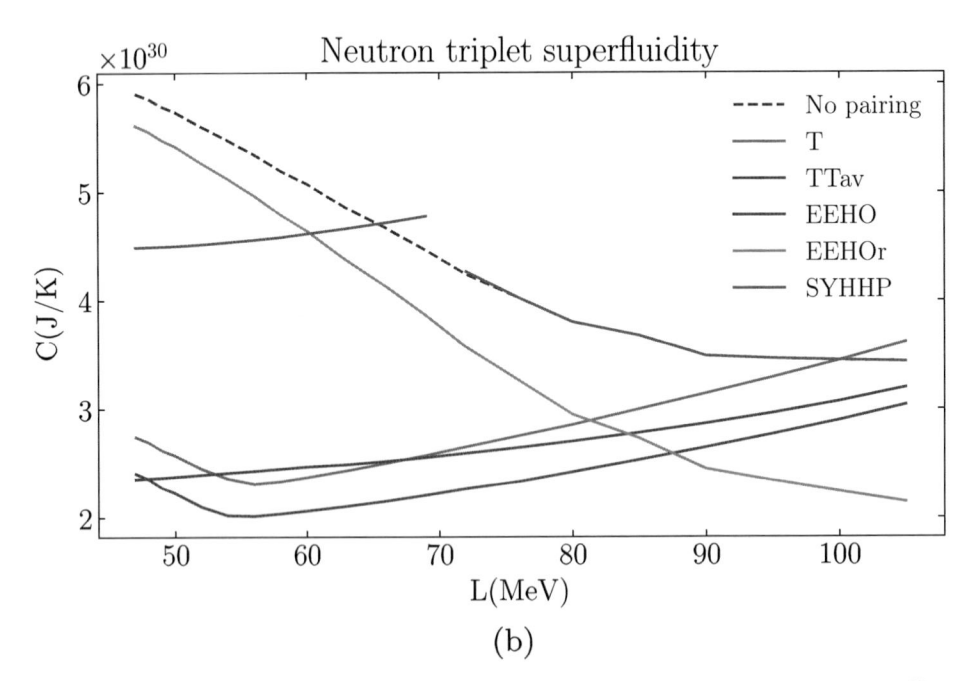

Fig. 7. Total heat capacity C (J/K) versus L (MeV) for stars with luminosity $L_\nu = 3 \cdot 10^{27}$ J/s for all EOS studied here. (a) Proton singlet superconductivity (b) Neutron triplet superfluidity.

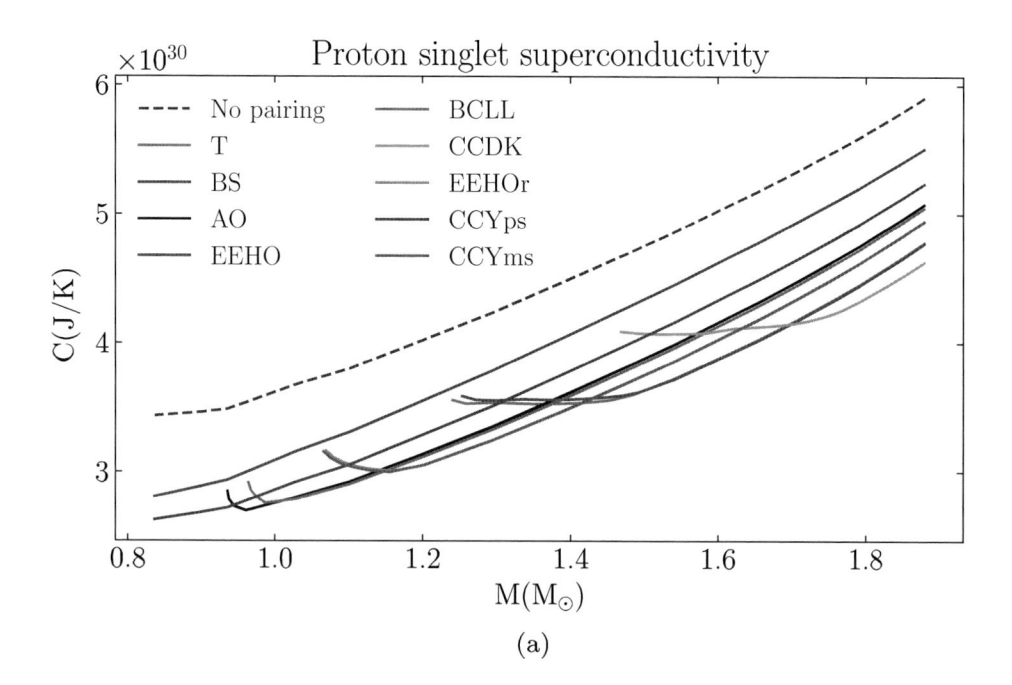

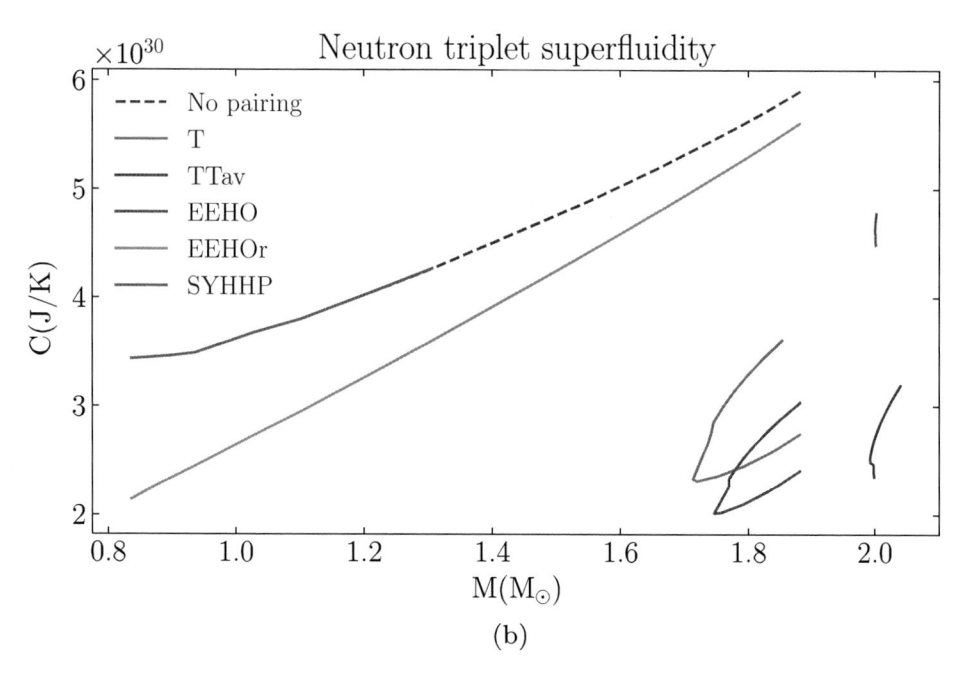

Fig. 8. Total heat capacity C (J/K) versus total mass M (M$_\odot$) for stars with luminosity $L_\nu = 3 \cdot 10^{27}$ J/s for all EOS studied here. (a) Proton singlet superconductivity (b) Neutron triplet superfluidity.

why some heat capacity curves of superfluid stars overcome the heat capacity curve of stars without nuclear pairing. This situation does not happen in Fig. 8.

4. Discussion

Comparing the predictions of each gap model and EOS combination with the inferred neutrino luminosity of the accreting neutron star MXB 1659-29 (Fig. 6), we find that three models are disfavoured and can be excluded. NT_{AO}, NT_{BEEHS} and NT_{TToa} predict that the whole core of the star will be superfluid at the core temperature of MXB 1659-29, hence direct Urca reactions are completely suppressed and we are not able to reproduce the inferred neutrino luminosity of MXB 1659-29. Other fast cooling processes would be equally suppressed by superfluidity, such that these models describe slow cooling stars for any EOS, thus, are inconsistent with the data. These gap models have similar opening and closing densities, but different amplitudes of the critical temperature T_c, suggesting that their location and width are the determinant factors in the luminosity prediction. This result is a consequence of the low temperature of MXB 1659-29's core in comparison with the models' T_c (Fig. 2). Therefore, we expect that any gap models with similar opening and closing densities will be unable to reproduce the data.

The other gap models can reproduce the observed neutrino luminosity. However, gap models NT_{EEHOr}, PS_{BS} and PS_{CCYps} are disfavoured, particularly for high L EOS. These models close before the onset of direct Urca for all EOS, hence their predictions for neutrino luminosity are the same as in the case without superfluidity. Their calculated star masses are very close to the direct Urca threshold masses, and for high L ($L \geq 85$ MeV), they predict that all neutron stars will be fast cooling, which is in disagreement with observations. For low L, their predictions agree with data if less than 0.5% of the core volume of the star is involved in unsuppressed direct Urca reactions, which suggests fine-tuning because it requires that the neutron star mass happens to lie within a narrow range of masses near the dURCA threshold.

Of the remaining gap models, we highlight NT_{SYHHP}, which predicts that only very high mass stars have unsuppressed direct Urca for low and intermediate L ($L \leq 70$ MeV), whereas for high L, both low mass stars and very high mass stars cool through this fast process. This superfluid model is the only one predicting direct Urca cooling in low mass stars ($M \leq 1.3\,M_\odot$), thus, a future observation consistent with this situation would favour this model and $L \geq 70$ MeV. At the same time, it is able to accommodate slow cooling for stars with masses $2.0\,M_\odot \geq M \geq 1.3\,M_\odot$, in agreement with luminosity data from other transiently-accreting and isolated sources, for example, the ones studied in Refs. 26, 27.

Proton superconductivity models PS_{AO}, PS_{BCLL}, PS_{EEHOr} and PS_{CCYms} also predict fast cooling for low mass stars with $L \geq 70$ MeV, but, differently from the superfluid model NT_{SYHHP}, by themselves they do not accomodate slow cooling for stars with masses $M \geq 1.3\,M_\odot$, thus are inconsistent with data from other sources. However, a more realistic description of a neutron star would include a combination of neutron superfluidity and proton superconductivity, which can significantly change the results shown here. Therefore, the proton superconductivity models above can not be excluded under this argument.

On Reference 9, it was discussed that the heat capacity and luminosity ratio can be written as

$$\frac{C_{38}}{L_{\nu,35}} = \left(\frac{\Delta \tilde{T}/\tilde{T}}{0.3\%}\right)^{-1} \left(\frac{t_q}{10\text{yr}}\right) \tilde{T}_8^{-1} \quad (21)$$

where $\Delta \tilde{T}$ corresponds to the difference in temperature measurements after a quiescence time interval t_q, $C_{38} = C/10^{38}$ and $L_{\nu,35} = L_\nu/10^{35}$. Therefore, knowing $\Delta \tilde{T}/\tilde{T}$ and the inferred luminosity of a source, one can find its total heat capacity, which is intrinsically dependent on the star's particle composition. In Figure 9, we show our calculations for the heat capacities and luminosities of stars with different masses and gap models. For better visualization, only neutron triplet results for two EOS are shown. We display $\Delta T_{\text{eff}}^\infty/T_{\text{eff}}^\infty$, which is related to $\Delta \tilde{T}/\tilde{T}$ through $\Delta \tilde{T}/\tilde{T} = 1.8\, \Delta T_{\text{eff}}/T_{\text{eff}}$.

The difference between heat capacities for each triplet gap model is a factor of 2 at most, thus, one needs a few percent precision in observations of temperature variation to discriminate between particle composition scenarios.[8] Note that the intersection between $\Delta \tilde{T}/\tilde{T}$ curves and the vertical line marking the luminosity of source MXB 1659-29 is only relevant for $\Delta \tilde{T}/\tilde{T} < 2\%$. Bigger temperature variations for that luminosity would imply that the star is completely superfluid, such that the heat capacity is dominated by leptonic contributions. That is an unrealistic scenario, as discussed before.

Knowing L with precision can eliminate or favour certain gap models. However, the current predictions from gravitational waves[21, 22] and nuclear experiments, such as PREX-II[10] are in tension, thus, unable to set reliable constraints on L. For this reason, we chose to investigate the whole phase space of L for the EOS family studied here. At the moment, our results are unable to set constraints for the EOS, however, with independent measurements of luminosity and mass of a neutron star source, this goal could be achieved. In this scenario, it will be particularly relevant to include more fast cooling processes in this framework, beyond direct Urca, as well as other equations of state, potentially with exotic components like hyperons, pions or free quarks.

We highlight that, for all cases studied here, the fraction of the core volume undergoing unsuppressed direct Urca is around 1%, which suggests that neutron stars with even higher neutrino luminosities and lower core temperatures should exist. Candidates for such cold stars are the sources SAX J1808.4-3658 and 1H 1905+000.[6] Further research is necessary to confirm whether the cooling of these sources is consistent with direct Urca reactions. Alternatively, one can speculate whether source MXB 1659-29 is actually a neutron star with a quark core or if it cools through exotic processes, such as neutrino emission from pion or kaon condensates. In some

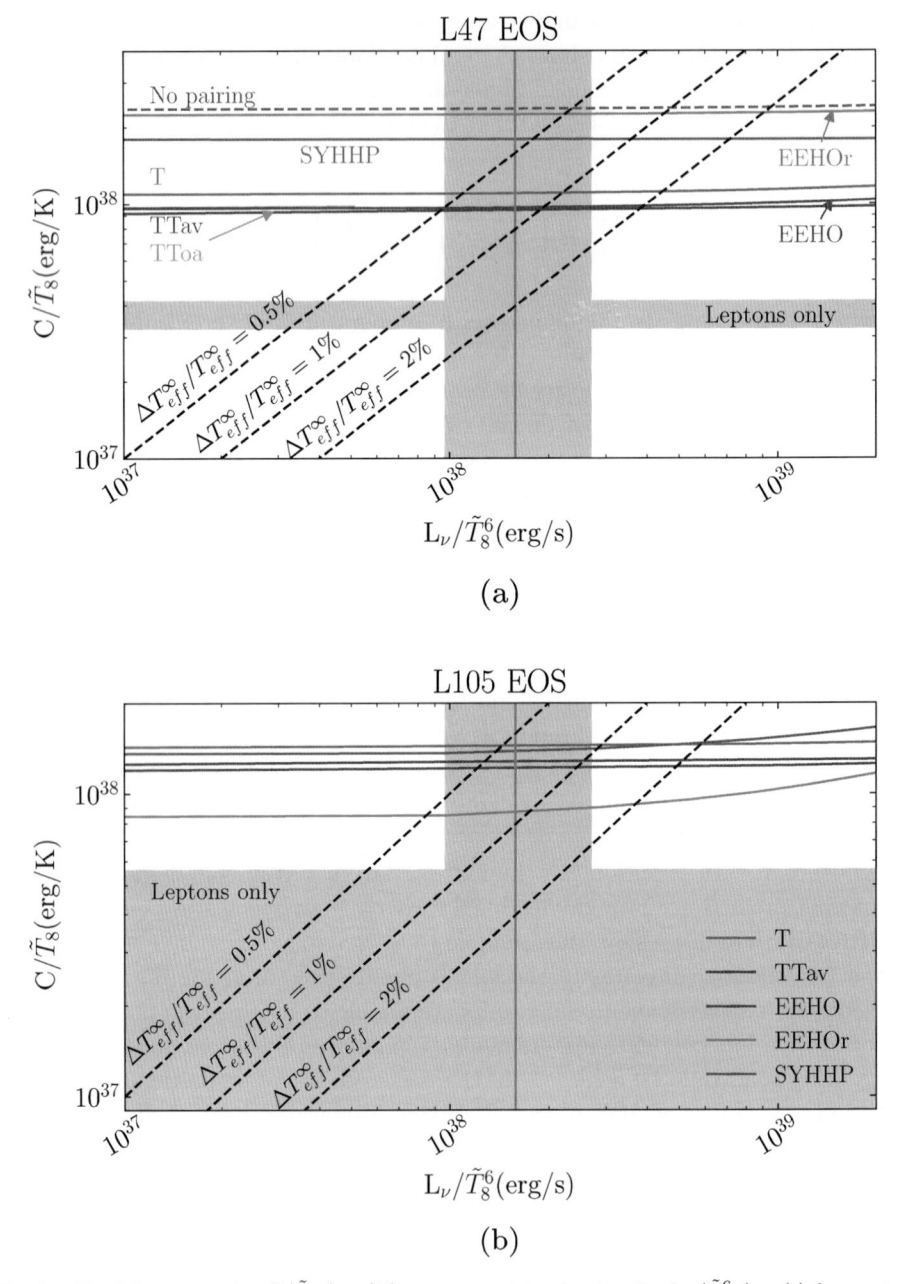

Fig. 9. Total heat capacity $C/\tilde{T}_8$ (erg/K) versus neutrino luminosity $L_\nu/\tilde{T}_8^6$ (erg/s) for neutron triplet gap models studied here. Only stars able to cool through direct URCA are displayed. C_{leptons} is the lower limit of only electrons and muons contributing, mimicking a completely superfluid star. The vertical line and grey region around it correspond to the inferred luminosity of $L_\nu = 3 \times 10^{34}$ erg/s and uncertainty for source MXB 1659-29, more details on Ref. 8. The diagonal lines $\Delta T_{\text{eff}}^\infty / T_{\text{eff}}^\infty$ indicate temperature variation of the star's effective temperature after a period of ten years in quiescence. (a) L47 EOS (b) L105 EOS. The "no pairing" curve is under the *SYHHP* curve.

of these cases, their emissivities could be lower by up to 3 orders of magnitude, as shown in Ref. 5, resulting in larger fractions of the core volume cooling through direct Urca emission.

5. Summary

In this paper, we studied a family of hadronic EOS with different values of the slope of the symmetry energy, L, combined with several models of proton superconductivity and neutron superfluidity in the neutron star core. Comparing the direct Urca neutrino luminosity calculations with data from transiently-accreting source MXB 1659-29, we can rule out gap models that predict superfluidity in the whole star's core, NT_{AO}, NT_{BEEHS} and NT_{TToa}. We predict that pairing models with similar opening and closing densities can also be excluded. Gap models NT_{EEHOr}, PS_{BS} and PS_{CCYps} are able to describe the observed luminosity but are disfavoured, because, for high L, they predict all neutron stars will be fast cooling and for low L, the masses need to be close to the direct Urca threshold. In a forthcoming paper, we will investigate neutron superfluidity and proton superconductivity simultaneous presence in the star's core.

We also calculated the total heat capacities for all stars which match the inferred neutrino luminosity of MXB 1659-29. Their values are within a factor of 2, hence one needs to distinguish between 1% and 2% of a variation of temperature over a decade[8] to differentiate between the particle composition scenarios. If independent observations of mass and luminosity can be made, they could be used to determine an accurate gap model description of the star's nuclear pairing, as well as the L parameter of its EOS. Furthermore, we were able to construct several detailed realistic scenarios where MXB 1659-29's estimated luminosity was obtained, consistent with direct Urca cooling at around 1% core volume, as previously estimated. This low percentage implies that stars with even larger neutrino luminosities and colder cores should exist. Alternatively, other fast cooling processes from exotic components with a lower emissivity could be operating over a larger fraction of the core.

Acknowledgments

We thank Sangyong Jeon for useful discussions and comments. This work was funded in part by the Natural Sciences and Engineering Research Council of Canada. M. M. acknowledges support by the Schlumberger Foundation Faculty for the Future Fellowship program. A. C. is a member of the Centre de Recherche en Astrophysique du Québec (CRAQ). M. M. and A. C. are members of the McGill Space Institute (MSI).

References

1. D. Page, J. M. Lattimer, M. Prakash and A. W. Steiner, *Stellar superfluids*, in *Novel Superfluids*, eds. K. H. Bennemann and J. B. Ketterson, International series of monographs on physics, Vol. 2 (Oxford, United Kingdom : Oxford University Press, 2013), ch. 21.
2. J. Bardeen, L. N. Cooper and J. R. Schrieffer, Theory of Superconductivity, *Phys. Rev.* **108**, 1175 (1957).
3. A. Gezerlis and J. Carlson, Strongly paired fermions: Cold atoms and neutron matter, *Phys. Rev. C* **77**, p. 032801 (2008).
4. W. C. G. Ho, K. G. Elshamouty, C. O. Heinke and A. Y. Potekhin, Tests of the nuclear equation of state and superfluid and superconducting gaps using the Cassiopeia A neutron star, *Phys. Rev. C: Nucl. Phys.* **91**, p. 015806 (2015).
5. D. G. Yakovlev, A. D. Kaminker, O. Y. Gnedin and P. Haensel, Neutrino emission from neutron stars, *Phys. Rep.* **354**, 1 (2001).
6. R. Wijnands, N. Degenaar and D. Page, Cooling of Accretion-Heated Neutron Stars, *J. Astrophys. Astron.* **38**, p. 49 (2017).
7. J. M. Lattimer, A Rapidly Cooling Neutron Star, *Physics Online Journal* **11**, p. 42 (2018).
8. E. F. Brown, A. Cumming, F. J. Fattoyev, C. J. Horowitz, D. Page and S. Reddy, Rapid Neutrino Cooling in the Neutron Star MXB 1659-29, *Phys. Rev. Lett.* **120**, p. 182701 (2018).
9. A. Cumming, E. F. Brown, F. J. Fattoyev, C. J. Horowitz, D. Page and S. Reddy, Lower limit on the heat capacity of the neutron star core, *Phys. Rev. C* **95**, p. 025806 (2017).
10. B. T. Reed, F. J. Fattoyev, C. J. Horowitz and J. Piekarewicz, Implications of PREX-II on the equation of state of neutron-rich matter, *Phys. Rev. Lett.* **126**, p. 172503 (2021).
11. W.-C. Chen and J. Piekarewicz, Building relativistic mean field models for finite nuclei and neutron stars, *Phys. Rev. C* **90**, p. 044305 (2014).
12. C. J. Horowitz, E. F. Brown, Y. Kim, W. G. Lynch, R. Michaels, A. Ono, J. Piekarewicz, M. B. Tsang and H. H. Wolter, A way forward in the study of the symmetry energy: experiment, theory, and observation, *J. Phys. G* **41**, p. 093001 (2014).
13. B.-A. Li, A. Ramos, G. Verde and I. Vidana, Topical issue on nuclear symmetry energy, *The European Physical Journal A* **50**, p. 1 (2014).
14. J. Piekarewicz and M. Centelles, Incompressibility of neutron-rich matter, *Phys. Rev. C* **79**, p. 054311 (2009).
15. C. J. Horowitz and J. Piekarewicz, Neutron star structure and the neutron radius of Pb-208, *Phys. Rev. Lett.* **86**, p. 5647 (2001).
16. R. J. Furnstahl, Neutron radii in mean field models, *Nucl. Phys. A* **706**, 85 (2002).
17. Z. Zhang and L.-W. Chen, Constraining the symmetry energy at subsaturation densities using isotope binding energy difference and neutron skin thickness, *Phys. Lett. B* **726**, 234 (2013).
18. D. Adhikari *et al.*, An Accurate Determination of the Neutron Skin Thickness of ^{208}Pb through Parity-Violation in Electron Scattering, *Phys. Rev. Lett.* **126**, p. 172502 (2021).
19. T. E. Riley *et al.*, A NICER View of PSR J0030+0451: Millisecond Pulsar Parameter Estimation, *Astrophys. J. Lett.* **887**, p. L21 (2019).

20. M. C. Miller *et al.*, PSR J0030+0451 Mass and Radius from NICER Data and Implications for the Properties of Neutron Star Matter, *Astrophys. J. Lett.* **887**, p. L24 (2019).
21. B. P. Abbott *et al.*, GW170817: Observation of Gravitational Waves from a Binary Neutron Star Inspiral, *Phys. Rev. Lett.* **119**, p. 161101 (2017).
22. B. P. Abbott *et al.*, GW170817: Measurements of neutron star radii and equation of state, *Phys. Rev. Lett.* **121**, p. 161101 (2018).
23. J. M. Lattimer and A. W. Steiner, Constraints on the symmetry energy using the mass-radius relation of neutron stars, *Eur. Phys. J. A* **50**, p. 40 (2014).
24. G. Baym, C. Pethick and P. Sutherland, The Ground State of Matter at High Densities: Equation of State and Stellar Models, *Astrophys. J.* **170**, 299 (1971).
25. J. Negele and D. Vautherin, Neutron star matter at sub-nuclear densities, *Nucl. Phys. A* **207**, 298 (1973).
26. S. Beloin, S. Han, A. W. Steiner and K. Odbadrakh, Simultaneous fitting of neutron star structure and cooling data, *Phys. Rev. C* **100**, p. 055801 (2019).
27. D. Page, J. M. Lattimer, M. Prakash and A. W. Steiner, Neutrino emission from cooper pairs and minimal cooling of neutron stars, *Astrophys. J.* **707**, 1131 (2009).

Vacuum properties and astrophysical implications

A. Pérez Martínez[1,*], M. Pérez-Garcia[1,†], E. Rodríguez Querts[2,‡] and A. Romero Jorge[2,§]

[1]*Departamento de Física Fundamental, Universidad de Salamanca,*
Plaza de la Merced s/n 37008, Spain
[2]*Departamento de Física Teórica, Instituto de Cibernética Matemática y Física (ICIMAF),*
Calle E esq 15 No. 309, Vedado, La Habana 10400, Cuba
[*] *aurorapm1961@usal.es,* [†] *maperezga@usal.es,* [‡] *elizabeth@icimaf.cu,* [§] *adrian@icimaf.cu*

QED's predictions that photons propagating in a magnetized vacuum should feel the vacuum birefringence are still standing. Magnetars have strong magnetic fields and may give us signals of this effect through the delay of photons travelling from this source to detectors and the polarization position or by the angle and degree of polarization of the radiation emitted. Starting from non linear electrodynamics, we analyze and discuss for weak and strong field approximations the theoretical predictions for both using a toy model of rotating neutron stars with dipolar magnetic field shape and photon trajectories that lie radial.

Keywords: Magnetic field, Neutron stars, Polarization, Magnetized vacuum.

1. Introduction

Quantum Electrodynamics is a very well-established and successful theory with great numbers of experimental test. The theory conceives that fluctuations from the virtual electron-positron pairs, the vacuum, give rise to very interesting phenomena, becoming a magnetized vacuum in non-linear interaction theory. One of these properties is birenfrigence, which means that electromagnetic waves propagating perpendicular to a constant electric or magnetic field suffer changes in their speed of propagation. This velocity is a function of the external field. As incredible as it seems, this phenomenon has not been detected experimentally yet. It is not clear the reason behind that. It could be due to the smallness of the effect of the magnetic fields generated in the lab, but it is not ruled out that it represents a manifestation of new physics.

One of the most relevant experiment designs for getting birefringence is the Polarization of Vacuum with Laser (PVLAS) experiment.[1] A magnetic field of 5.5×10^4 G was used in this experiment. The PVLAS-team blamed axions[a] as responsible for the discrepancy between the established theoretical QED birefrigence and the null experimental signal.[1]

---

[*]Departamento de Física Teórica, Instituto de Cibernética Matemática y Física (ICIMAF), Calle E esq 15 No. 309, Vedado, La Habana 10400, Cuba.
[a]hypothetical elementary particles with low mass, candidates for dark matter, and in this context, photons could decay in axions and a new physics may appear.

However Astrophysics could give information about birefringence and other exotic phenomena of the QED-vacuum. The Universe is our main lab, while experiments on Earth are being improved. Very exotic objects like neutron stars have huge magnetic fields that could give us signals of birefrigence of the vacuum but also the inestability of the vacuum and pair production. Neutron stars have magnetic fields of the order of Schwinger's critical field $B_c = 4.41 \times 10^{13}$G,[2] and beyond for magnetars.[3] The birefringence signal from these objects could be measured through the time delay that should undergo the emitted polarized radiation of NS to be detected.

Our work is focused on obtaining a theoretical estimate of the angle of polarization as a consequence of vacuum birefringence, considering that the pulsar magnetosphere is a magnetized vacuum. In that case, we analyze the propagation of photons in two limits, weak and strong magnetic fields, and consider the dipolar shape of the magnetic field.

We started using effective Euler Heisenberg Lagrangian[4] to obtain the modes of polarization of photons traveling perpendicular to the magnetic field ($k \perp B$). This calculation is equivalent to the previous one obtained by solving the photon dispersion equation, considering the radiative corrections given by the magnetized photon self-energy.[5]

2. Euler Heisenberg non-linear electrodynamics

The non linear Euler Heisenberg Lagrangian for the weak $B \ll Bc$, $E \ll Ec$ and strong limits $B \gg Bc$, $E \gg Ec$ is presented in this section. Despite the fact that this formulation does not cover all microscopic photon-photon interactions, it is very useful because it describes vacuum as a non-linear optical medium allowing us to investigate specific phenomena using traditional techniques and interpretation of non-linear optics in media.

For the approximation $B \ll B_c$ the EH lagrangian[4] has the form

$$\mathcal{L}_{EH}^W = \mathcal{L}_0 + \xi(\mathcal{L}_0^2 + \frac{7\epsilon_0^2 c^2}{4}(\mathbf{E}.\mathbf{B})^2), \quad \mathcal{L}_0 = \frac{\epsilon_0}{2}(E^2 - c^2 B^2), \tag{1}$$

$\mathcal{L}_0$ is the linear Lagrangian density and ϵ_0 and c are the dielectric constant and the speed of light in the vacuum respectively. QED vacuum corrections emerge through the constant $\xi = \frac{8\alpha^2 \hbar^3}{45 m_e^4 c^5}$ which encloses the interaction of virtual pairs with magnetic field and depends on charge and mass of electrons. The vacuum: electron-positron virtual pairs have an indirect photon interaction responsible of non linearity of lagrangian Eq. (1). In the limit $B \gg B_c$ we have for the EH Lagrangian the following expression[4,6]

$$\mathcal{L}_{EH}^S = -\frac{B^2}{2} + \frac{m^4}{24\pi^2}\frac{B}{B_c}\left(ln\left(\frac{B}{2B_c}\right) + \frac{6}{\pi^2}\xi^{i\prime}(2)\right). \tag{2}$$

where $\frac{6}{\pi^2}\xi^{i\prime}(2) = -0.5699610$ with $\zeta(x)$ the Riemann zeta-function. This limit is important in astrophysics because compact objects, such as neutron stars (magnetars), have a surface magnetic field of order $10^{13}-10^{15}$ G[7] which is higher than the critical magnetic field of B_c.

We start off from Lagrangian in two limits: weak and strong magnetic field to study the photon propagation perpendicular to a constant magnetic field B_e (in the direction x_3) in a vacuum. The photon can be described as electromagnetic wave with electric and magnetic field E_w and B_w which are orthogonal each other. Therefore, the total electric and magnetic fields are $E_t = E_w$, $B_t = B_w + B_e$.[8] The modified Maxwell equation solutions will be determined by whether the external magnetic field B_e is aligned with or orthogonal to the wave magnetic field B_w ($B_e \perp B_w$, $B_e \parallel B_w$), resulting in two physical polarization modes.[9,10] According to the case, we label along the paper $i = \perp, \parallel$ perpendicular and parallel respectively. Assuming E_w and B_w as plane wave $\sim exp(i(kz - \omega t))$ to solve modified Maxwell equations, doing some algebra and retaining only first term corrections, we may get the dispersion equations.[11] For the weak and strong field approximation reads as

$$\omega_\parallel^W = |\boldsymbol{k}| \sqrt{(1 - \frac{\xi}{4}(\boldsymbol{B_e} \times \hat{\boldsymbol{k}})^2)}, \quad \omega_\perp^W = |\boldsymbol{k}| \sqrt{(1 - \frac{7}{4}\xi(\boldsymbol{B_e} \times \hat{\boldsymbol{k}})^2)}, \quad (3)$$

$$\omega_\parallel^S = |\boldsymbol{k}| \sqrt{(1 - \frac{\alpha}{3\pi}(\hat{\boldsymbol{b}} \times \hat{\boldsymbol{k}}))}, \quad \omega_\perp^S = |\boldsymbol{k}| \sqrt{(1 - \frac{\alpha}{3\pi}\frac{B_e}{B_c}(\hat{\boldsymbol{b}} \times \hat{\boldsymbol{k}}))}. \quad (4)$$

For photon propagation perpendicular to the external magnetic field $\theta = \pi/2$. For weak field, both modes depend on the square of the external magnetic field. However, the strong magnetic field limit (SFL) has different behavior. In that case, we obtain where only the perpendicular mode depends on the magnetic field but linearly, while the mode parallel is independent of the magnetic field.

We define $\Delta n^{S,W} \equiv n_\perp - n_\parallel$ as the difference between the refraction indices of the two polarization modes,

$$\Delta n^S = \frac{\alpha}{4\pi}\frac{2}{15}\left(\frac{B_e}{B_c}\right)^2, \quad \Delta n^W = \frac{\alpha}{4\pi}\frac{2}{3}\left(\frac{B_e}{B_c} - 1\right). \quad (5)$$

Let us note that in a magnetized vacuum, not only do photons acquire different velocities according to their polarization, but also the polarization changes once a photon has travelled a certain distance. Initial photon linear polarization becomes elliptical and the angular rotation of the polarization plane of the electromagnetic wave travelling a path length L is $\phi = \Delta n^{S,W} \omega L$.

3. Polarization radiation of neutron stars

Our focus in this section is to revisit the polarization that would occur when photons propagate in the magnetosphere of a neutron star, considering only the effects of a magnetized vacuum. As we mentioned before, NS are very exotic astronomical objects, characterized by huge densities and magnetic fields. The surface magnetic field could be around 10^{12-15} G, but its geometry is complicated, and it is impossible to consider it constant and uniform throughout the star.

Therefore, to do our study we have to make three important approximations: photons propagate in a magnetosphere considered as a magnetized vacuum, the magnetic field shape is dipolar and photon trajectories are radial. These assumptions allow us to calculate the polarization degree (PD) of radiation using the evolution equation, $\frac{\partial \mathbf{s}}{\partial \hat{r}} = \hat{\mathbf{\Omega}} \times \mathbf{s}$, $|\hat{\mathbf{\Omega}}| = \frac{\omega}{c} \Delta n^{W,S}$, where $\hat{r}$ is the direction of propagation of the photons, $\mathbf{s} = \{S_1/S_0, S_2/S_0, S_3/S_0\}$ is the normalized Stokes vector and $\hat{\mathbf{\Omega}}$ is related to the refraction index (defined in Eq (5)). We estimate the polarization degree PD of photons consider the adiabatic approximation $\hat{\mathbf{\Omega}} \left(\frac{1}{|\hat{\mathbf{\Omega}}|} \frac{\partial |\hat{\mathbf{\Omega}}|}{\partial \hat{r}} \right)^{-1} \gtrsim 1/2$, obtained in.[13] This condition allows us to calculate the polarization-limiting radius r_L at which the degree of polarization begins to be constant and the polarization becomes elliptical. We consider a dipolar shape configuration for the magnetic field as $B_e(r) = B_0 \left(\frac{r_0}{r} \right)^3$, with B_0 and r_0 are the surface magnetic field and radius of the neutron star respectively. Because, regardless of the value of the surface magnetic field B_0, the important values of magnetic field strength are those where decoupling of polarization modes occurs, whether far or close to the neutron star, our calculations will be performed for the entire range of magnetic fields using the weak and strong field approximations. If the decoupling modes occur far enough from the star's surface, $r_L \gg r_0$, as the magnetic field goes as r^{-3}, the magnetic field will be significantly smaller. Then, $\Omega \sim \Delta n^W \sim B_e^2$. When decoupling arises for $r_0 \leq r_L < 2r_0$ the strong field approximation, $B_0/B_c \gtrsim 1$, is suitable, and $\Omega \sim \Delta n^S \sim B_e$. We assume rotating NS for both magnetic field regimes. Then, the angle ϕ is given by the relation $r_L - r_0 = \phi \frac{P}{2\pi}$ where P is the period of the pulsar.[12] The computed polarization angle is given by the equations

$$\phi(\omega, B, P) = \begin{cases} \frac{2\pi}{cP} \left(\left[\frac{\alpha}{90\pi} \frac{\omega}{c} \left(\frac{B_0}{B_c} \right)^2 r_0^6 \right]^{1/5} - r_0 \right), & B < B_c \text{ (weak)} \\ \frac{2\pi}{cP} \left(\left(\frac{\alpha}{9\pi} \frac{\omega}{c} \frac{B_0}{B_c} r_0^3 \right)^{1/2} - r_0 \right), & B > B_c \text{ (strong)} \end{cases} \quad (6)$$

and polarization degree is $\Pi(\omega, B, P) = 4\pi/cP \left((3/r_L)^2 + (4\pi/cP)^2 \right)^{-1/2}$. For higher frequencies, the radiation from neutron stars' magnetosphere is substantially polarized (fig. 1). Furthermore, neutron stars or magnetars with a higher magnetic field, release strongly polarized radiation. The polarization degree (PD) of radiation of a pulsar is inversely related to its period; millisecond pulsars have more polarization than second period pulsars. The behavior of angle and polarization degree with the magnetic field is depicted in fig. 1 for weak and strong field approximations. For magnetic fields greater than $2B_c$, strong field approximation contributes to an increase the polarization degree and polarization angle compared to weak field approximation.

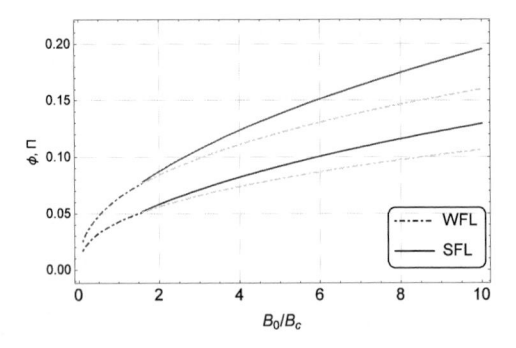

Fig. 1. Comparison of the polarization degree (Blue line) and polarization angle (Red line) for weak field limit (dotdashed line) and strong field limit (solid line) as function of the surface magnetic field of the pulsar. We take typical neutron star parameters, a radius $r_0 = 10$ km, a period of $P = 1$ s and radiation of $\omega = 2$ MeV of energy.

Our results are in agreement with previous obtained by Heyl et al[13] when weak field approximation is taken into account. Furthermore, studies on $RXJ1856.5 - 3764$ for polarization of visible and X radiation revealed that it is essential to include the influence of magnetized vacuum to explain the observational data of polarization of this source.[14]

For photon energy of $\omega = 1 MeV$ and typical values of the parameters $B_0 = 1.5 \times 10^{13}G$, $M = 1.4 M_\odot$, radius $r_0 = 12 km$, and $P = 7.06 s$, the angle and degree of polarization for $RXJ1856.5 - 3764$ owing to simply the effect of magnetized vacuum give $\phi = 6.4 \times 10^{-3}$ and $\Pi = 0.42\%$.[15,16] Obviously, when geometric factors are taken into account, this value rises.[14]

4. Conclusions

From non-linear electrodynamics we have obtained the refraction index and different phase velocity of photon propagating in strong magnetic field according to the polarization modes. We have also obtained the polarization angle that the radiation acquires as a consequence of crossing a magnetized vacuum. The calculations have been done in weak and strong field approximation for a constant magnetic field.

In addition, we investigated the influence of a magnetized vacuum on the polarization of radiation emitted by rotating NS. To do so, we considered the magnetosphere to be a magnetized vacuum with a dipolar magnetic field and photons traveling along radial trajectories.

Our findings are consistent with previous results based on weak field approximation.[13] More energetic photons have a greater polarization degree than the lower ones. Besides, the polarization degree is strongly dependent on the period of rotation of neutron stars since this can raise or decrease the polarization limiting radii, causing the couple or decouple of the propagation modes.

The authors of the work[14] claim that there is no way of explaining the polarization data from visible and X rays of the pulsar $RXJ1856.5 - 3764$ without considering the effect of magnetized vacuum. As a consequence, it might be a test of vacuum birefringence, albeit we expect it will be tested in terrestrial laboratories.

However, not all regarding vacuum birefringence has been said, and the door is opened for new physics. This work was undertaken as a starting point for developing more realistic models of polarization radiation emission of NS which will allow us to identify in robust way those linked to vacuum birefringence and may validate the QED prediction.

Acknowledgments

A.P.G and A.P.M acknowledge the support of the Agencia Estatal de Investigación through the grant PID2019-107778GB-100 from Junta de Castilla y Leon, Spanish Consolider MultiDark FPA2017-90566-REDC and PHAROS COST Actions MP1304 and CA16214. The work of E.R.Q. and A.W.R.J. were supported by the project of No. NA211LH500-002 from AENTA-CITMA, Cuba.

References

1. A. Ejlli, F. Della Valle, U. Gastaldi, G. Messineo, R. Pengo, G. Ruoso and G. Zavattini, *Phys. Rept.*, **871**, 1-74 (2020).
2. R. Ciolfi, *Astron. Nachr*, **335**, 624-629 (2014).
3. C. Kouveliotou, S. Dieters, T. Strohmayer et al., *Nature*, **393**, 235-237 (1998).
4. W. Heisenberg and H. Euler, *Z. Phys.*, **98**, nos. 11-12, 714-732 (1936).
5. A. W. Romero Jorge, E. Rodríguez Querts, A. Pérez Martínez et al. *Astron. Nachr.*, **340**, 852-586 (2020).
6. V. I. Ritus, *arXiv: High Energy Physics - Theory* (1998).
7. R. C. Duncan, *arXiv: Astrophysics*, **526**, 830-841 (2000).
8. H. Pérez Rojas, *J. Exp. Theor. Phys.*, **76**, 1 (1979).
9. H. Pérez Rojas and A. E. Shabad, *Ann. Phys.*, **121**, 432-455 (1979).
10. H. Pérez Rojas and E. Rodríguez Querts. *Phys. Rev. D*, **79**, 093002 (2009).
11. H. P. Rojas and E. R. Querts, *Jour. of Mod. Phys. D*, **19**, No. 810, 1599-1608 (2010).
12. J. S. Heyl and N. J. Shaviv, *Mon. Not. R. Astron. Soc.*, **311**, 555–564 (2000).
13. Jeremy S. Heyl, Nir J. Shaviv, Don Lloyd, *Monthly Notices of the Royal Astronomical Society*, Volume **342**, 1, 134–144 (2003).
14. R. P. Mignani, V. Testa, D. G. Caniulef, R. Taverna, R. Turolla, S. Zane and K. Wu, *Mon. Not. Roy. Astron. Soc.*, **465**, no. 1, 492-500 (2017).
15. A. M. Pires, F. Haberl, V. E. Zavlin, C. Motch, S. Zane, M. M. Hohle, *Astronomy and Astrophysics*, **563**, A50 (2014).
16. S. B. Popov, R. Taverna and R. Turolla, *Mon. Not. Roy. Astron. Soc.*, **464**, no. 4, 4390-4398 (2017).

Testing extended theories of gravity with GRBs

L. Mastrototaro

Dipartimento di Fisica "E.R Caianiello", Università degli Studi di Salerno,
Via Giovanni Paolo II, 132 - 84084 Fisciano (SA), Italy
Istituto Nazionale di Fisica Nucleare - Gruppo Collegato di Salerno,
Via Giovanni Paolo II, 132 - 84084 Fisciano (SA), Italy
E-mail: lmastrototaro@unisa.it

We present our studies on the neutrino pairs annihilation into electron-positron pairs ($\nu\bar{\nu} \to e^-e^+$) near the surface of a neutron star in the framework of extended theories of gravity. The latter modifies the maximum energy deposition rate near to the photonsphere and it might be several orders of magnitude greater than that computed in the framework of General Relativity. These results provide a rising in the Gamma-Ray Bursts energy emitted from a close binary neutron star system and might be a fingerprint of modified theories of gravity, changing our view of astrophysical phenomena.

Keywords: Extended theories of gravity, GRB, Neutrino energy deposition, Black Holes, Neutron Stars

1. Introduction

General Relativity (GR) is without any doubt the best theory of gravitational interaction. Its predictions have been tested with high accuracy on scales of the solar system (for example, the precession of the Mercury perihelion, the photons deviation and the gravitational leasing effect), on astrophysical scales (the gravitational waves), and cosmological scales (the cosmic microwave background radiation (CMBR) and the formation of primordial light elements (Big Bang Nucleosynthesis)). Despite these results, there are still open questions that make GR incomplete. The latter arise at short distances and small time scales (black hole and cosmological singularities, respectively), or at large distance scales, the rotational curve of the galaxies and the observed accelerated phase of the present Universe, for which any predictability is lost.

To solve these issues, deviations from the GR (hence from the Hilbert-Einstein action on which GR is based) are needed, and new ingredients, such as dark matter and dark energy, are required for fitting the present picture of our Universe.[1–6] Indeed, in the last years, several *alternative* or *modified* theories of gravity have been proposed, which try to answer all the opened questions of GR and the Cosmological Standard Model. To give an example, higher-order curvature invariants than the simple Ricci scalar R, allow getting inflationary behaviour, removing the primordial singularity, as well as explaining the flatness and horizon problems[7,8] (for further applications, see Refs.[9–37]). On the other hand, one can tend to preserve the GR and the Hilbert-Einstein action, adding only some two unidentified components: dark matter and dark energy. These two different approaches try to solve the same problems but at the moment there is not a final solution for that (modified gravity theories do not manage to solve all the problems while dark matters elements are still missing). One of the consequences of these approaches is that the metric tensor $g_{\mu\nu}$ describing the gravitational field generated by a massive source gets modified with respect to GR metric, in particular, the Schwarzschild or Kerr metric. The latter are recovered in the limit in which the parameters characterizing some specific theory of gravity beyond GR are set to zero.

In this proceeding, we highlight the differences between GR and extended theories of gravity arising from the mechanism of generation of Gamma-Ray Bursts (GRBs). We focus, in particular, on GRBs powered by neutrino annihilation processes $\nu\bar{\nu} \to e^+e^-$.[a]

The neutrinos annihilation process is relevant in many astrophysical frameworks: in the stellar envelope, as well as on the delay shock mechanism into the Type II Supernova (at late time, from the hot proto-neutron star, the energy is deposited into the supernova envelope via neutrino pair annihilation and neutrino-lepton scattering). These processes augment the neutrino heating of the envelope generating a successful supernova explosion.[44] Moreover, the neutrino annihilation process has been also proposed as the mechanism that power GRB in a binary neutron star system, which is the topic of this work. Simulations and analytical estimations performed within GR show that the mechanism is not sufficient to generate the required energy for explaining short GRB. Such a conclusion changes, as we will show, if the gravitational background is described by modified theories.

2. Neutrino energy deposition formulation

In this section we recall the main features to treat the energy deposition in curved spacetimes.[45,46] Previous calculations of the $\nu\bar{\nu} \to e^-e^+$ reaction in the vicinity of a neutron star have been first based on Newtonian gravity,[47,48] then the effect of gravity has been incorporated for static stars,[44,49] and then extended to rotating stars.[45,50] We consider the spacetime around a black hole described by the following diagonal metric

$$g_{\mu\nu} = \text{diag}\left(-f(r), h(r), r^2, r^2 \sin^2\theta\right),\quad (1)$$

The energy deposition per unit time and per volume is given by (considering $c = \hbar = 1$)[51]

$$\dot{q}(r) = \iint f_\nu(\mathbf{p}_\nu, r) f_{\bar{\nu}}(\mathbf{p}_{\bar{\nu}}, r) \\ \times \left[\sigma|\mathbf{v}_\nu - \mathbf{v}_{\bar{\nu}}|\varepsilon_\nu\varepsilon_{\bar{\nu}}\right]\frac{\varepsilon_\nu + \varepsilon_{\bar{\nu}}}{\varepsilon_\nu\varepsilon_{\bar{\nu}}} d^3\mathbf{p}_\nu d^3\mathbf{p}_{\bar{\nu}}, \quad (2)$$

---

[a]Indeed the state of the art of NS-NS merger simulations is special relativistic, axisymmetric hydrodynamic simulations for the final black hole-torus systems[38–43] from which emerge that neutrino-pair annihilation in ordinary GR models seems to be not efficient enough to power GRBs and the Blandford-Znajek process is currently considered a more promising mechanism for launching. In extended theories of gravity, the situation can be different as we will show in this proceeding.

where $f_{\nu,\bar{\nu}}$ are the neutrino number densities in phase space, $\mathbf{v}_\nu$ the neutrino velocity, and σ is the rest frame cross section. Since the term $\sigma |\mathbf{v}_\nu - \mathbf{v}_{\bar{\nu}}| \varepsilon_\nu \varepsilon_{\bar{\nu}}$ is Lorentz invariant, it can be calculated in the center-of-mass frame, and turns out to be

$$\sigma |\mathbf{v}_\nu - \mathbf{v}_{\bar{\nu}}| \varepsilon_\nu \varepsilon_{\bar{\nu}} = \frac{DG_F^2}{3\pi}(\varepsilon_\nu \varepsilon_{\bar{\nu}} - \mathbf{p}_\nu \cdot \mathbf{p}_{\bar{\nu}} c^2)^2, \qquad (3)$$

with $G_F = 5.29 \times 10^{-44}$ cm^2 MeV^{-2} the Fermi constant,

$$D = 1 \pm 4\sin^2\theta_W + 8\sin^4\theta_W, \qquad (4)$$

$\sin^2\theta_W = 0.23$ the Weinberg angle, and the plus sign for electron neutrinos and antineutrinos while the minus sign for muon and tau type. $T(r)$ is the temperature measured by the local observer and $\Theta(r)$ is the angular integration factor. At these energies, the mass of the electrons can be neglected and it is possible to obtain that the general expression of the rate per unit time and unit volume of the $\nu\bar{\nu} \to e^+e^-$ process[44]

$$\dot{q} = \frac{7DG_F^2\pi^3\xi(5)}{2}[kT(r)]^9\Theta(r). \qquad (5)$$

The evaluation of $T(r)$ and $\Theta(r)$ account for the gravitational redshift and path bending. To write the latter in terms of observed luminosity L_∞ one has to has to consider that temperature, like energy, varies linearly with red-shift and following the procedure of Ref.[44], one finds that:

$$\Theta(r) = \frac{2\pi^3}{3}(1-x)^4(x^2 + 4x + 5), \qquad (6)$$

$$T(r) = \frac{\sqrt{f(R)}}{\sqrt{f(r)}}T(R), \qquad (7)$$

$$L_\infty = f(R)L(R), \qquad (8)$$

$$L(R) = L_\nu + L_{\bar{\nu}} = \frac{7}{4}a\pi R^2 T^4(R). \qquad (9)$$

Here R is the neutrinosphere radius (the spherical surface where the stellar material is transparent to neutrinos and from which neutrinos are emitted freely), $L(R)$ is the neutrino luminosity, a the radiation constant, $x = \sin^2\theta_r$, θ_r is the angle between the trajectory and the tangent velocity in terms of local radial and longitudinal velocities[45] for which one can obtain that[46]

$$\cos\theta_r = \frac{R}{r}\sqrt{\frac{f(r)}{f(R)}}. \qquad (10)$$

This relation comes from the fact that the impact parameter b is constant on all the trajectory and is related to $\cos\theta_r$ by the relation

$$b = \left(\frac{f(r)}{r\cos\theta_r}\right)^{-1}. \qquad (11)$$

Moreover, photosphere radius R_{ph} exists below which a massless particle can not be emitted tangent to the stellar surface. The present discussion is therefore restricted to $R > R_{ph}$. The neutrino emission properties hence mainly depend on the geometry of spacetime. From the equation of the velocities

$$\dot{r}^2 = \left(E\dot{t} - L\dot{\phi}\right) f(r), \quad \dot{\phi} = \frac{L}{r^2}, \quad \dot{t} = -\frac{E}{f(r)},$$

where E and L are the energy and angular momentum at the infinity, one gets the effective potential V_{eff}, such that the photonsphere radius follows from the condition $\frac{\partial V_{eff}}{\partial r} = 0$. The circular orbit is derived by imposing $\dot{r}^2 = 0$. We note en passant that these results reduce to ones derived in the case of the Schwarzschild geometry, $R_{ph} = 3M$, as calculated in.[44]

The integration of $\dot{q}$ from R to infinity gives the total amount of local energy deposited by the neutrino annihilation process (for a single neutrino flavour) for time units

$$\dot{Q} = 4\pi \int_R^\infty dr \frac{r^2}{\sqrt{f(r)}} \dot{q}. \tag{12}$$

According to,[44] the total energy deposition from the neutrinosphere radius R_6 to infinity (for a symmetric spherical star that emits neutrinos from a spherical neutrinosphere) is given by

$$\dot{Q}_{51} = 1.09 \times 10^{-5} \mathcal{F}\left(\frac{M}{R}\right) DL_{51}^{9/4} R_6^{-3/2}. \tag{13}$$

Here $\dot{Q}_{51}$ is expressed in units of 10^{51} erg s^{-1}, L_{51} is neutrino luminosity in units of 10^{51} erg s^{-1}, $D = 1 \pm 4\sin^2\theta_W + 8\sin^4\theta_W$, $\sin^2\theta_W = 0.23$ and the plus sign is for electron neutrinos and antineutrinos while the minus sign is for muon and tau type, R_6 is the radius in units of 10 km and, for a generic diagonal metric of the form $g_{\mu\nu} = (g_{00}, -1/g_{00}, -r^2, -r^2 \sin^2\theta)$, the function $\mathcal{F}\left(\frac{M}{R}\right)$ is given by

$$\mathcal{F}\left(\frac{M}{R}\right) = 3g_{00}(R)^{9/4} \int_1^{R_{ch}} (x-1)^4 (x^2 + 4x + 5) \frac{y^2 g_{11}(yR)^{1/2} dy}{g_{00}(yR)^{9/2}}. \tag{14}$$

In the Newtonian limit one gets $\mathcal{F}(0) = 1$ so that it is convenient, for our analysis, to consider the ratio $\dot{Q}_{GR}/\dot{Q}_{Newt} = \mathcal{F}(M/R)$. Usually, almost all energy is carried out by electron neutrino thus we can approximate Eq. (13) considering $D = 1.23$.

Equations (13) and (14) allow obtaining the deposited energy of neutrinos and the energy that can be emitted to powering GRB. In the next Section, we will study the ratio (14) for astrophysical objects in various modified gravity theories.

3. Neutrino deposition in modified gravity

In what follows, we present three relevant cases that explain how relevant could be the modification to GR in this context. First of all, we take into consideration the

Einstein dilaton Gauss-Bonnet gravity. The action is[52]

$$S = \frac{1}{8\pi} \int d^4x \sqrt{-g} \left(\frac{R}{2} - \frac{1}{2} \partial_\mu \psi \partial^\mu \psi + \alpha \psi L_{GB} \right) ,\qquad(15)$$

where ψ is a scalar field and L_{GB} is the Gauss-Bonnet invariant: $L_{GB} = R^2 - 4R^{\alpha\beta}R_{\alpha\beta} + R^{\alpha\beta\gamma\delta}R_{\alpha\beta\gamma\delta}$. The solution considered is the Sotiriou-Zhau solution(solution in perturbation theory[53]), which lead to results in Fig. 1[46]:

$$ds^2 = -f(r)dt^2 + h(r)dr^2 + r^2 d\Omega^2 ,\qquad(16)$$

with

$$f(r) = \left(1 - \frac{2m}{r}\right)\left(1 + \sum_n A_n \bar{a}^n\right) ;$$

$$h(r) = \left(1 - \frac{2m}{r}\right)^{-1}\left(1 + \sum_n B_n \bar{a}^n\right) .$$

where, to the second order:

$$A_1 = B_1 = 0 ;$$

$$A_2 = -\frac{49}{40m^3 r} - \frac{49}{20m^2 r^2} - \frac{137}{30mr^3} + \frac{7}{15r^4} + \frac{52m}{15r^5} + \frac{40m^2}{3r^6} ;$$

$$B_2 = \frac{49}{40m^3 r} + \frac{29}{20m^2 r^2} + \frac{19}{10mr^3} - \frac{203}{15r^4} - \frac{436m}{15r^5} - \frac{184m^2}{3r^6} .$$

The maximum value taken for α, considering the perturbative regime of the solution, shown an increase of the 50% for the maximum amount of energy deposition respect to GR.

The second case that we want to analyze is the Brans Dicke theory. It represents a generalization of general relativity, where gravitational effects are in part due to geometry, in part due to a scalar field. The action is[54]

$$S = \int d^4x \sqrt{-g} \left[\psi R + \frac{16\pi}{c^4} L - \omega(\psi) \right] ,\qquad(17)$$

where L is the Lagrangian density of all the matter, including all non-gravitational field, ψ is a scalar field and ω is its Lagrangian density.

With this Lagrangian, expressing the line element in the isotropic form, we obtain the solution[54]

$$ds^2 = -e^{2\alpha}dt^2 + e^{2\beta}\left[dr^2 + r^2 d\Omega^2\right] ,\qquad(18)$$

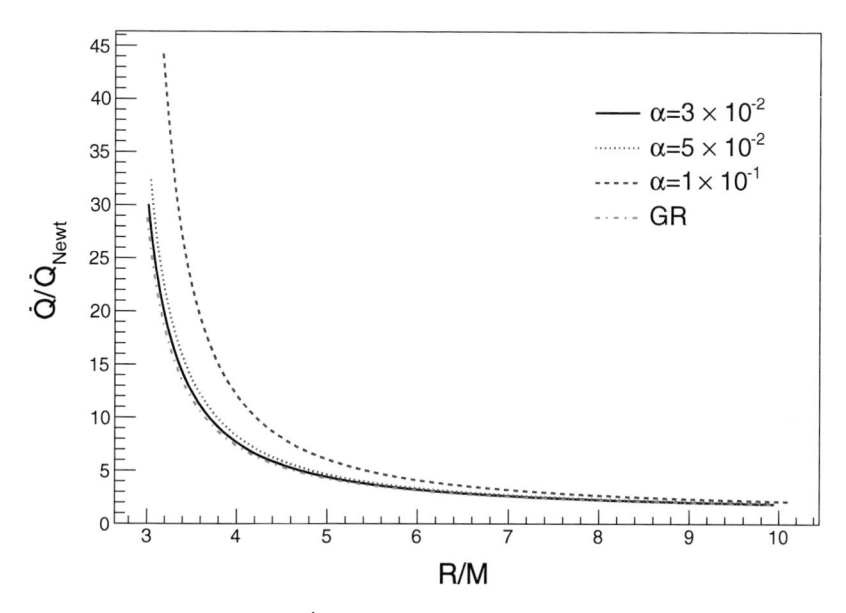

Fig. 1. Ratio of energy deposition $\dot{Q}$ for the the Sotiriou-Zhau metric to total Newtonian energy deposition $\dot{Q}_{\text{Newt}}$ for different values of α. The green curve shows the GR energy deposition for comparison.

where

$$\lambda = \sqrt{(C+1)^2 - C(1 - \frac{C\omega}{2})}$$

$$e^{2\alpha} = e^{2\alpha_0} \left[\frac{1 - \frac{B}{r}}{1 + \frac{B}{r}}\right]^{\frac{2}{\lambda}},$$

$$e^{2\beta} = e^{2\beta_0} \left(1 + \frac{B}{r}\right)^4 \left[\frac{1 - \frac{B}{r}}{1 + \frac{B}{r}}\right]^{\frac{2(\lambda - C + 1)}{\lambda}},$$

$$\psi = \psi_0 \left[\frac{1 - \frac{B}{r}}{1 + \frac{B}{r}}\right]^{-\frac{C}{\lambda}},$$

with ω positive constant and

$$\alpha_0 = \beta_0 = 0,$$
$$\psi_0 = \frac{4 + 2\omega}{3 + 2\omega},$$
$$C \sim -\frac{1}{2 + \omega},$$
$$B \sim \frac{M}{2\sqrt{\psi_0}}.$$

Using this metric, we obtain the shape for energy deposition in Fig. 2. Even with this model we have an enhancement of about 50% respect to the maximum value of $\dot{Q}/\dot{Q}_{\text{Newt}}$ 30 in GR.

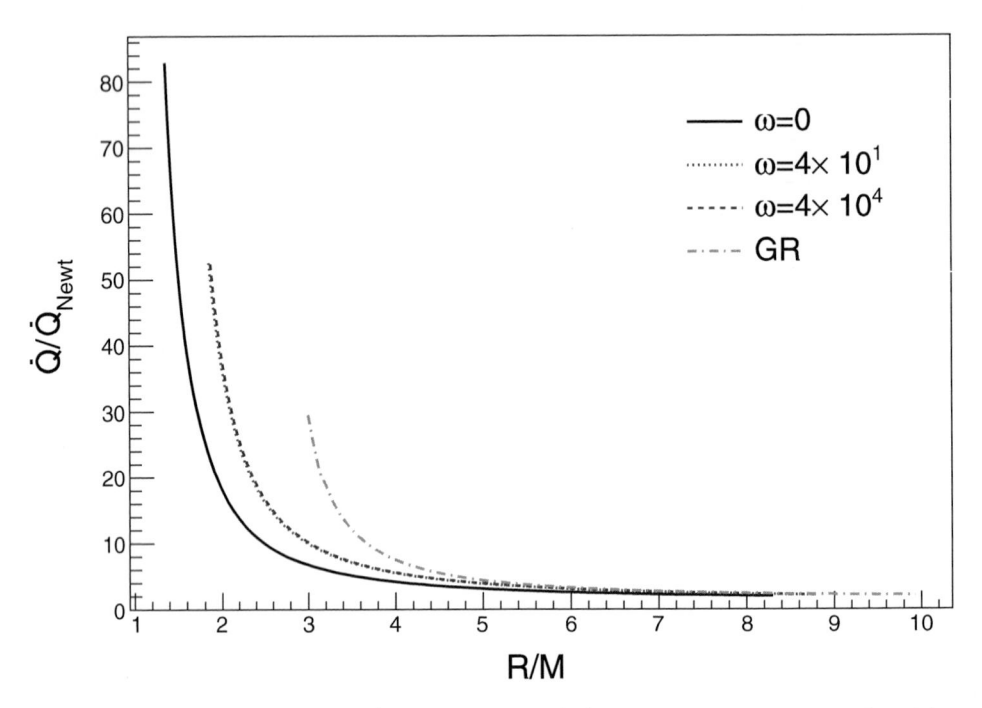

Fig. 2. Ratio of energy deposition $\dot{Q}$ for metric in Eq. (18) to total Newtonian energy deposition $\dot{Q}_{\text{Newt}}$ for different value of ω. The green curve shows the GR energy deposition for comparison.

Finally, we discuss the case of a BH surrounded by quintessence field. In this case

$$g_{00}(r) = 1 - \frac{2M}{r} - \frac{c}{r^{3\omega_q - 1}}, \qquad (19)$$

where c is a positive constant and $-1 < \omega_q < -1/3$. The quintessence parameter is constrained by the fact that increasing c, the model passes from describing a black hole with an event horizon to representing a naked singularity.

We chose to show only the case with $\omega = -0.4$, for which we obtain results in Fig. 3 and an enhancement of a factor 25 with respect to GR.

3.1. *GRB enhancement*

The above results show that modified gravity provides an enhancement of the neutrino annihilation process as compared to GR. Such an enhancement is relevant

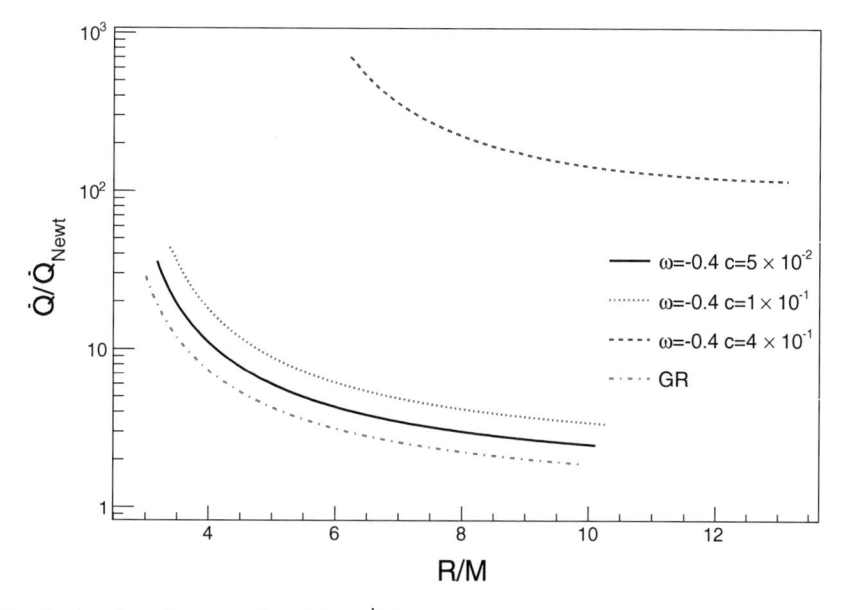

Fig. 3. Ratio of total energy deposition $\dot{Q}$ for $\omega = -0.4$ to total Newtonian energy deposition $\dot{Q}_{\text{Newt}}$ for three values of the parameter c. The green curve shows the GR energy deposition for comparison.

for powering GRBs for the model given by a closed neutron stars binary merging system. Neutrino emission happens in the last phase of the merging and the final configuration is a black hole (or neutron star) with an accretion disk. With the developed formalism, we can not describe the disk emission (we are considering a spherical system), so we restrict ourselves to the central BH. Taking into account total energy emitted into neutrinos from the central BH of $\mathcal{O}(10^{52})$ erg, a radius of $R = 20$ km, the maximum possible total energy released in GRB is

$$Q_{\text{GR}} \sim 2.5 \times 10^{49} \text{ erg}, \qquad (20)$$

which is too small to explain the short GRB from neutron star merging. Instead, considering the maximum enhancement that modified gravity induces shown in Figs. 1, 2 and 3, we have that the total possible energy released in GRB can exceed the maximum energy of $\mathcal{O}(10^{52})$ erg (we have to remind that we are considering only the neutrino emission from the central BH and therefore the true emitted energy is larger considering the whole BH+disk configuration). Moreover, considering that the deposited energy is converted very efficiently to the relativistic jet energy, we infer a constraint on the quintessence model. It is possible to obtain that the maximum allowed value of $\mathcal{F}(R_{ph})$ is $\mathcal{O}(10^4)$. The contour plots given in Figs. 4 and 5 show the value of $\mathcal{F}(R_{\text{ph}})$ for allowed value of ω_q and c. Therefore, one can infer, for $\mathcal{F}(R_{\text{ph}}) \sim \mathcal{O}(10^4\text{-}10^5)$, the values of the parameter c that are not allowed in the considered scenario.

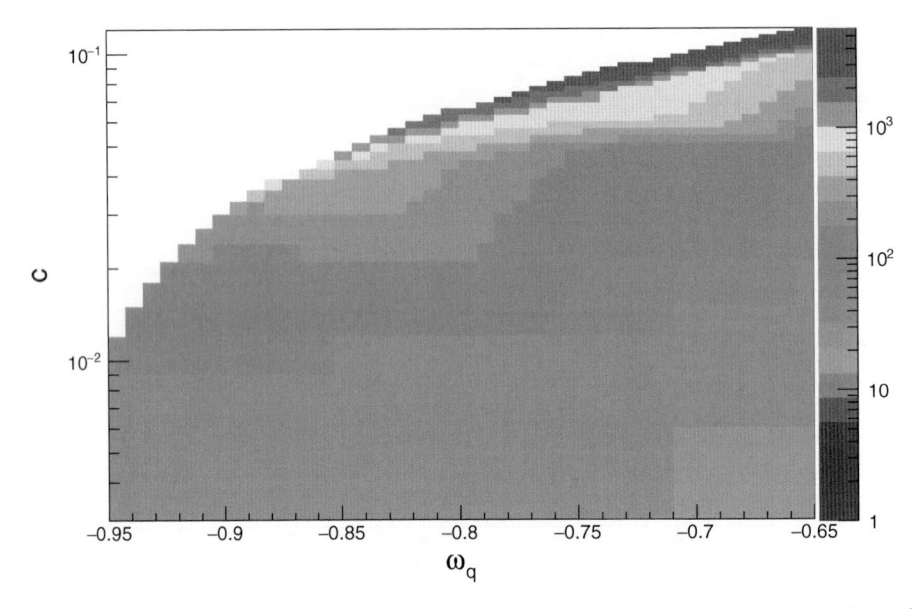

Fig. 4. Contour plot for $\omega_q \in\,]-1, -0.65[$. On the y axis are reported the excluded values of c due to the creation of a naked singularity (white part) and, on the right, the values of $\mathcal{F}(R_{\text{ph}})$. It can be also seen the values of the parameter c, for which $\mathcal{F}(R_{\text{ph}}) \sim \mathcal{O}(10^4\text{-}10^5)$, that are excluded by the energy deposition bounds.

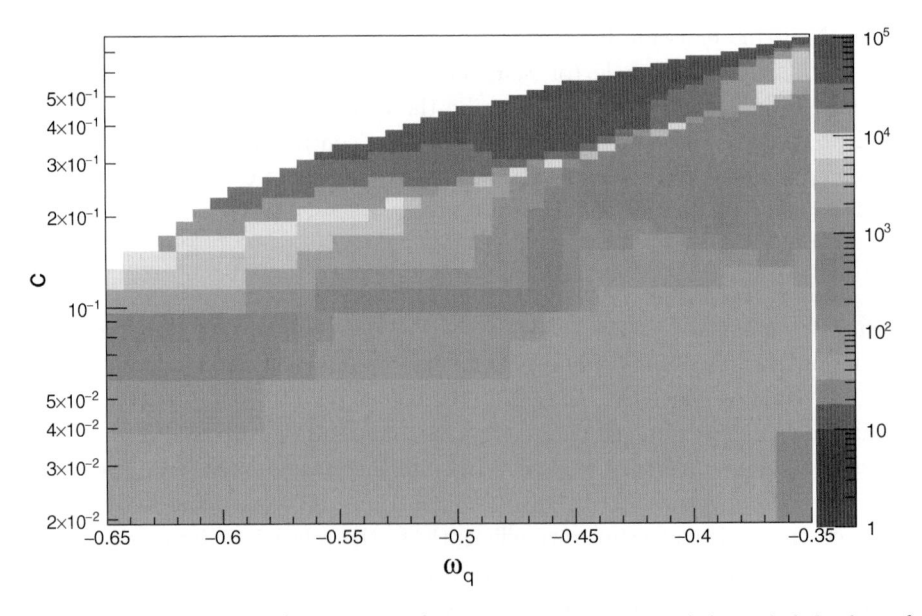

Fig. 5. Contour plot for $\omega_q \in\,]-0.65, -0.35[$. On the y axis are reported the excluded values of c due to the creation of a naked singularity (white part) and, on the right, the values of $\mathcal{F}(R_{\text{ph}})$. It can be also seen the values of the parameter c, for which $\mathcal{F}(R_{\text{ph}}) \sim \mathcal{O}(10^4\text{-}10^5)$, that are excluded by the energy deposition bounds.

4. Conclusion

In conclusion, we have analyzed the neutrino pair annihilation process $\nu\bar{\nu} \to e^+e^-$ near a BH in some modified gravitational theories. We have shown that, owing to a shift of the photosphere radius, there is an enhancement of the deposited energy rate ratio with respect to GR. Such an enhancement could be a relevant mechanism for the generation of GRBs in close neutron star binary merging, for which neutrino pairs annihilation has been proposed as a possible source. Moreover, the released energy may be larger than the Short GRB maximum energy observed of $\mathcal{O}(10^{52})$ erg as it happens in the quintessence model (cfr. Ref.[55]). In that case, one can constrain the value of ω and c such that the released energy is inferior to $\mathcal{O}(10^{52})$ erg. The $\nu\bar{\nu} \to e^+e^-$ processes are of great importance in astrophysics, as well as in modified gravity, since they lead to considerable differences with respect to GR and its phenomenology. Therefore, the results presented in this proceeding could provide a new astrophysical framework to search for a signature of gravitational theories beyond GR.

References

1. A. G. Riess *et al.*, Observational evidence from supernovae for an accelerating universe and a cosmological constant, *Astron. J.* **116**, 1009 (1998).
2. S. Perlmutter *et al.*, Measurements of Ω and Λ from 42 high redshift supernovae, *Astrophys. J.* **517**, 565 (1999).
3. S. Cole *et al.*, The 2dF Galaxy Redshift Survey: Power-spectrum analysis of the final dataset and cosmological implications, *Mon. Not. Roy. Astron. Soc.* **362**, 505 (2005).
4. G. Hinshaw *et al.*, Three-year Wilkinson Microwave Anisotropy Probe (WMAP) observations: temperature analysis, *Astrophys. J. Suppl.* **170**, p. 288 (2007).
5. S. M. Carroll, The Cosmological constant, *Living Rev. Rel.* **4**, p. 1 (2001).
6. V. Sahni and A. A. Starobinsky, The Case for a positive cosmological Lambda term, *Int. J. Mod. Phys. D* **9**, 373 (2000).
7. A. A. Starobinsky, A New Type of Isotropic Cosmological Models Without Singularity, *Adv. Ser. Astrophys. Cosmol.* **3**, 130 (1987).
8. A. A. Starobinsky, The Perturbation Spectrum Evolving from a Nonsingular Initially De-Sitter Cosmology and the Microwave Background Anisotropy, *Sov. Astron. Lett.* **9**, p. 302 (1983).
9. H. Oyaizu, M. Lima and W. Hu, Nonlinear evolution of $f(R)$ cosmologies. II. Power spectrum, *Phys. Rev. D* **78**, p. 123524 (Dec 2008).
10. L. Pogosian and A. Silvestri, The pattern of growth in viable f(R) cosmologies, *Phys. Rev. D* **77**, p. 023503 (2008), [Erratum: Phys. Rev. D 81, 049901 (2010)].
11. I. Sawicki and W. Hu, Stability of cosmological solutions in $f(R)$ models of gravity, *Phys. Rev. D* **75**, p. 127502 (Jun 2007).
12. B. Li and J. D. Barrow, Cosmology of $f(R)$ gravity in the metric variational approach, *Phys. Rev. D* **75**, p. 084010 (Apr 2007).
13. T. Clifton, Higher powers in gravitation, *Phys. Rev. D* **78**, p. 083501 (Oct 2008).
14. T. Clifton and J. D. Barrow, The power of general relativity, *Phys. Rev. D* **72**, p. 103005 (Nov 2005).
15. S. Capozziello and G. Lambiase, Higher order corrections to the effective gravitational action from Noether symmetry approach, *Gen. Rel. Grav.* **32**, 295 (2000).

16. S. Capozziello and G. Lambiase, Nonminimal derivative coupling and the recovering of cosmological constant, *Gen. Rel. Grav.* **31**, 1005 (1999).
17. S. Capozziello, G. Lambiase and H. Schmidt, Nonminimal derivative couplings and inflation in generalized theories of gravity, *Annalen Phys.* **9**, 39 (2000).
18. S. Nojiri and S. D. Odintsov, Inhomogeneous equation of state of the universe: Phantom era, future singularity, and crossing the phantom barrier, *Phys. Rev. D* **72**, p. 023003 (Jul 2005).
19. S. Capozziello, V. F. Cardone, E. Elizalde, S. Nojiri and S. D. Odintsov, Observational constraints on dark energy with generalized equations of state, *Phys. Rev. D* **73**, p. 043512 (Feb 2006).
20. I. Brevik, E. Elizalde, S. Nojiri and S. D. Odintsov, Viscous little rip cosmology, *Phys. Rev. D* **84**, p. 103508 (Nov 2011).
21. S. Nojiri and S. D. Odintsov, The New form of the equation of state for dark energy fluid and accelerating universe, *Phys. Lett. B* **639**, 144 (2006).
22. S. Nojiri and S. D. Odintsov, Non-singular modified gravity unifying inflation with late-time acceleration and universality of viscous ratio bound in F(R) theory, *Prog. Theor. Phys. Suppl.* **190**, 155 (2011).
23. G. Lambiase, Thermal leptogenesis in $f(R)$ cosmology, *Phys. Rev. D* **90**, p. 064050 (Sep 2014).
24. G. Lambiase, S. Mohanty and A. R. Prasanna, Neutrino coupling to cosmological background: A review on gravitational Baryo/Leptogenesis, *Int. J. Mod. Phys. D* **22**, p. 1330030 (2013).
25. G. Lambiase and G. Scarpetta, Baryogenesis in $f(R)$ theories of gravity, *Phys. Rev. D* **74**, p. 087504 (Oct 2006).
26. B. Jain, V. Vikram and J. Sakstein, Astrophysical Tests of Modified Gravity: Constraints from Distance Indicators in the Nearby Universe, *Astrophys. J.* **779**, p. 39 (2013).
27. L. Lombriser, A. Slosar, U. Seljak and W. Hu, Constraints on f(R) gravity from probing the large-scale structure, *Phys. Rev. D* **85**, p. 124038 (2012).
28. S. Ferraro, F. Schmidt and W. Hu, Cluster abundance in $f(R)$ gravity models, *Phys. Rev. D* **83**, p. 063503 (Mar 2011).
29. L. Lombriser, F. Schmidt, T. Baldauf, R. Mandelbaum, U. Seljak and R. E. Smith, Cluster density profiles as a test of modified gravity, *Phys. Rev. D* **85**, p. 102001 (May 2012).
30. F. Schmidt, A. Vikhlinin and W. Hu, Cluster constraints on $f(R)$ gravity, *Phys. Rev. D* **80**, p. 083505 (Oct 2009).
31. H. Motohashi, A. A. Starobinsky and J. Yokoyama, Cosmology Based on f(R) Gravity Admits 1 eV Sterile Neutrinos, *Phys. Rev. Lett.* **110**, p. 121302 (2013).
32. L. Buoninfante, G. Lambiase and L. Petruzziello, Quantum interference in external gravitational fields beyond General Relativity (4 2021).
33. A. Capolupo, G. Lambiase, A. Stabile and A. Stabile, Virial theorem in scalar tensor fourth order gravity, *Eur. Phys. J. C* **81**, p. 650 (2021).
34. V. A. S. V. Bittencourt, M. Blasone, F. Illuminati, G. Lambiase, G. G. Luciano and L. Petruzziello, Quantum nonlocality in extended theories of gravity, *Phys. Rev. D* **103**, p. 044051 (2021).
35. G. Lambiase, M. Sakellariadou and A. Stabile, Constraints on extended gravity models through gravitational wave emission, *JCAP* **03**, p. 014 (2021).
36. N. Bernal, A. Ghoshal, F. Hajkarim and G. Lambiase, Primordial Gravitational Wave Signals in Modified Cosmologies, *JCAP* **11**, p. 051 (2020).

37. G. Tino, L. Cacciapuoti, S. Capozziello, G. Lambiase and F. Sorrentino, Precision Gravity Tests and the Einstein Equivalence Principle, *Prog. Part. Nucl. Phys.* **112**, p. 103772 (2020).
38. M. Ruffert and H. T. Janka, Gamma-ray bursts from accreting black holes in neutron star mergers, *Astron. Astrophys.* **344**, 573 (April 1999).
39. R. Popham, S. E. Woosley and C. Fryer, Hyperaccreting black holes and gamma-ray bursts, *The Astrophysical Journal* **518**, 356 (Jun 1999).
40. T. D. Matteo, R. Perna and R. Narayan, Neutrino trapping and accretion models for gamma-ray bursts, *The Astrophysical Journal* **579**, 706 (Nov 2002).
41. S. Fujibayashi, Y. Sekiguchi, K. Kiuchi and M. Shibata, Properties of neutrino-driven ejecta from the remnant of a binary neutron star merger: Pure radiation hydrodynamics case, *The Astrophysical Journal* **846**, p. 114 (Sep 2017).
42. O. Just, M. Obergaulinger, H. T. Janka, A. Bauswein and N. Schwarz, Neutron-star merger ejecta as obstacles to neutrino-powered jets of gamma-ray bursts, *Astrophys. J. Lett.* **816**, p. L30 (2016).
43. F. Foucart, M. D. Duez, L. E. Kidder, R. Nguyen, H. P. Pfeiffer and M. A. Scheel, Evaluating radiation transport errors in merger simulations using a monte carlo algorithm, *Phys. Rev. D* **98**, p. 063007 (Sep 2018).
44. J. D. Salmonson and J. R. Wilson, General relativistic augmentation of neutrino pair annihilation energy deposition near neutron stars, *Astrophys. J.* **517**, 859 (1999).
45. A. Prasanna and S. Goswami, Energy deposition due to neutrino pair annihilation near rotating neutron stars, *Phys. Lett. B* **526**, 27 (2002).
46. G. Lambiase and L. Mastrototaro, Effects of modified theories of gravity on neutrino pair annihilation energy deposition near neutron stars, *ApJ.* **904**, 1 (2020).
47. J. Cooperstein, L. van den Horn and E. A. Baron, Neutrino flows in collapsing stars: a two-fluid model, *ApJ* **309**, p. 653 (1986).
48. J. Cooperstein, L. J. van den Horn and E. A. Baron, Neutrino Pair Energy Deposition in Supernovae, *ApJ* **321**, p. L129 (1987).
49. J. D. Salmonson and J. R. Wilson, Neutrino annihilation between binary neutron stars, *Astrophys. J.* **561**, 950 (2001).
50. R. Mallick, A. Bhattacharyya, S. K. Ghosh and S. Raha, General Relativistic effect on the energy deposition rate for neutrino pair annihilation above the equatorial plane along the symmetry axis near a rotating neutron star, *Int. J. Mod. Phys. E* **22**, p. 1350008 (2013).
51. J. Goodman, A. Dar and S. Nussinov, Neutrino Annihilation in type II Supernovae, *Astrophys. J. Lett.* **314**, L7 (1987).
52. S. Mukherjee and S. Chakraborty, Horndeski theories confront the Gravity Probe B experiment, *Phys. Rev. D* **97**, p. 124007 (2018).
53. T. P. Sotiriou and S.-Y. Zhou, Black hole hair in generalized scalar-tensor gravity: An explicit example, *Phys. Rev. D* **90**, p. 124063 (2014).
54. C. Brans and R. Dicke, Mach's principle and a relativistic theory of gravitation, *Phys. Rev.* **124**, 925 (1961).
55. G. Lambiase and L. Mastrototaro, Neutrino pair annihilation ($\nu\bar{\nu} \to e^-e^+$) in the presence of quintessence surrounding a black hole (12 2020).

News and views regarding PSR J1757–1854, a highly-relativistic binary pulsar

A. D. Cameron* and M. Bailes

ARC Centre of Excellence for Gravitational Wave Discovery (OzGrav)
Centre for Astrophysics and Supercomputing, Swinburne University of Technology,
PO Box 218, Hawthorn VIC 3122, Australia
*E-mail: andrewcameron@swin.edu.au

V. Balakrishnan, D. J. Champion, P. C. C. Freire, M. Kramer and N. Wex

Max-Planck-Institut für Radioastronomie (MPIfR)
Auf dem Hügel 69, D-53121 Bonn, Germany

S. Johnston

Australia Telescope National Facility, CSIRO Space and Astronomy
PO Box 76, Epping NSW 1710, Australia

A. G. Lyne and B. W. Stappers

Jodrell Bank Center for Astrophysics, University of Manchester
Alan Turing Building, Oxford Road, Manchester M13 9PL, UK

M. A. McLaughlin, N. Pol and H. Wahl

Department of Physics and Astronomy, West Virginia University
PO Box 6315, Morgantown, WV 26506, USA

C. Ng

Dunlap Institute for Astronomy & Astrophysics, University of Toronto
50 St. George Street, Toronto, ON M5S 3H4, Canada

A. Possenti

Istituto Nazionale di Astrofisica (INAF), Osservatorio Astronomico di Cagliari
Via della Scienza 5, 09047 Selargius (CA), Italy

A. Ridolfi

Istituto Nazionale di Astrofisica (INAF), Osservatorio Astronomico di Cagliari
Via della Scienza 5, 09047 Selargius (CA), Italy

Max-Planck-Institut für Radioastronomie (MPIfR)
Auf dem Hügel 69, D-53121 Bonn, Germany

We provide an update on the ongoing monitoring and study of the highly-relativistic double neutron star binary system PSR J1757–1854, a 21.5-ms pulsar in a highly eccentric, 4.4-hour orbit. The extreme nature of this pulsar's orbit allows it to probe a parameter space largely unexplored by other relativistic binary pulsars. For example, it displays one of the highest gravitational wave (GW) luminosities of any known binary pulsar, as well as the highest rate of orbital decay due to GW damping. PSR J1757–1854 is also notable in that it is an excellent candidate for exploring new tests of General Relativity and other gravitational theories, with possible measurements of both Lense-Thirring precession and relativistic orbital deformation (through the post-Keplerian parameter δ_θ) anticipated within the next 3–5 years.

Here we present a summary of the latest interim results from the ongoing monitoring of this pulsar as part of an international, multi-telescope campaign. This includes an update of the pulsar's long-term timing and post-Keplerian parameters, new constraints on the pulsar's proper motion and corresponding Shklovskii kinematic correction, and new limits on the pulsar's geodetic precession as determined by monitoring for secular changes in the pulse profile. We also highlight prospects for future work, including an updated timeline on new relativistic tests following the introduction of MeerKAT observations.

Keywords: Gravitation; binaries: close; pulsars: individual: PSR J1757–1854

1. Introduction

For many decades, relativistic binary pulsars have been one of the key tools for studying different theories of gravity in the strong field regime, the current paradigm being Einstein's theory of General Relativity (GR). Discovered in 2016 as part of the HTRU-S Galactic Plane pulsar survey,[1,2] the 21.5-ms pulsar PSR J1757–1854 ranks as one of the most extreme examples of this class. Its high eccentricity ($e \simeq 0.606$) and compact orbit (measured via the projected semi-major axis, $x \simeq 2.24$ lt-s) around a neutron star companion combine some of the best properties of other notable relativistic binary pulsars, including the high eccentricity of PSR B1913+16[3] (the 7.75-hr orbital period *'Hulse-Taylor pulsar'*, with $e \simeq 0.617$) and the compact orbit of PSR J0737–3039A/B[4,5] (the 2.45-hr orbital period *'Double Pulsar'*, with $x \simeq 1.42$ lt-s). The extreme nature of PSR J1757–1854 is further demonstrated by multiple records set by the pulsar, including the highest acceleration ($\sim 700\,\mathrm{m\,s^{-2}}$) and highest relative velocity ($\sim 1000\,\mathrm{km\,s^{-1}}$) seen in a binary pulsar, as well as the highest rate of orbital decay due to gravitational wave damping and one of the shortest predicted merger times of any Galactic double neutron star system (~ 76 Myr). Together, these properties make PSR J1757–1854 a highly promising candidate for providing new insights into theories of gravity.

Here, we describe some of the ongoing aspects of the work involving this pulsar, in advance of a more detailed peer-reviewed publication anticipated by mid-2022.

2. Current timing and post-Keplerian tests

Since its discovery in 2016, PSR J1757–1854 has been observed by multiple radio telescopes as part of an international collaboration, including the Parkes[a] (Australia), Effelsberg (Germany), Lovell (UK), Green Bank (GBT; USA) and MeerKAT (South Africa) telescopes. This data was analysed using a standard pulsar timing

---

[a] Also known by its indigenous Wiradjuri name *'Murriyang'*.

technique,[6] wherein summed, average pulse profiles are cross-correlated against high signal-to-noise (S/N) template profiles to produce a dataset of high-precision pulse 'times of arrival' (TOAs). Each TOA represents the mean arrival time of an integrated pulse profile from the pulsar. These are then iteratively fit using a *timing ephemeris* in order to develop a high-precision model of the pulsar's behaviour.

Currently, the GBT accounts for the overwhelming majority of PSR J1757–1854's TOAs, having produced over 22,000 TOAs since it began observing in mid-2016. Data from the GBT is recorded in a full-Stokes coherent search mode at both L and S-bands (800 MHz bandwidth centered at 1500 and 2000 MHz respectively). We currently record one 4.4-hr orbit at each frequency every two months.

Table 1. Latest timing parameters for PSR J1757–1854, based on data from the GBT and Parkes between MJD 57405–59363 and employing the DDH[7] binary model. Values in parentheses give the 1-σ uncertainties on the final digit.

Astrometric & spin parameters	
Right ascension, α (J2000)	17:57:03.78412(2)
Declination, δ (J2000)	-18:54:03.359(4)
Spin period, P (ms)	21.4972318900292(6)
Spin period derivative, $\dot{P}$	$2.627335(9) \times 10^{-18}$
Dispersion measure (pc cm^{-3})	378.203(2)
Proper motion in RA, μ_α (mas yr^{-1})	$-4.36(12)$
Proper motion in DEC, μ_δ (mas yr^{-1})	$-0.8(14)$
Period and position epoch (MJD)	57701
Orbital parameters	
Orbital period, P_b (d)	0.183537835854(7)
Eccentricity, e	0.6058171(3)
Projected semimajor axis, x (lt-s)	2.2378060(15)
Epoch of periastron, T_0 (MJD)	57700.92599421(3)
Longitude of periastron, ω (°)	279.34090(9)
Post-Keplerian parameters	
Rate of periastron advance, $\dot{\omega}$ (° yr^{-1})	10.36498(3)
Einstein delay, γ (ms)	3.5891(16)
Orbital period derivative, $\dot{P_b}$	$-5.294(6) \times 10^{-12}$
Orthometric amplitude, h_3 (μs)	5.08(18)
Orthometric ratio, ς	0.899(10)
Mass measurements (based on $\dot{\omega}$ and γ)	
Pulsar mass, m_p (M$_\odot$)	1.3406(5)
Companion mass, m_c (M$_\odot$)	1.3922(5)
Inclination angle, i (°)	85.0(2)

The most recent timing ephemeris for PSR J1757–1854 is given in Table 1. This includes five theory-independent post-Keplerian (PK) relativistic parameters, from which we can derive three independent tests of gravity. A mass-mass diagram showing the mass constraints imposed by each PK parameter under GR is shown in Figure 1. By fixing a solution for the masses of the pulsar and the companion neutron star using the intersection of $\dot{\omega}$ and γ (the most precisely measured PK parameters), the further intersection of each remaining PK parameter provides one additional test of consistency. Both the orthometric amplitude and ratio parameters of the Shapiro delay[7] (h_3 and ς) are consistent to within 3.7% and 1.9% of their GR-predicted values respectively, and are approximately consistent with the $\dot{\omega} - \gamma$ intersection. However, although the observed value of the orbital period derivative $\dot{P}_b$ is also consistent with GR to within at least 1%, its location on the mass-mass diagram is inconsistent with the constraints set by $\dot{\omega}$ and γ under the assumption of GR being correct. This is further discussed in Section 2.1.

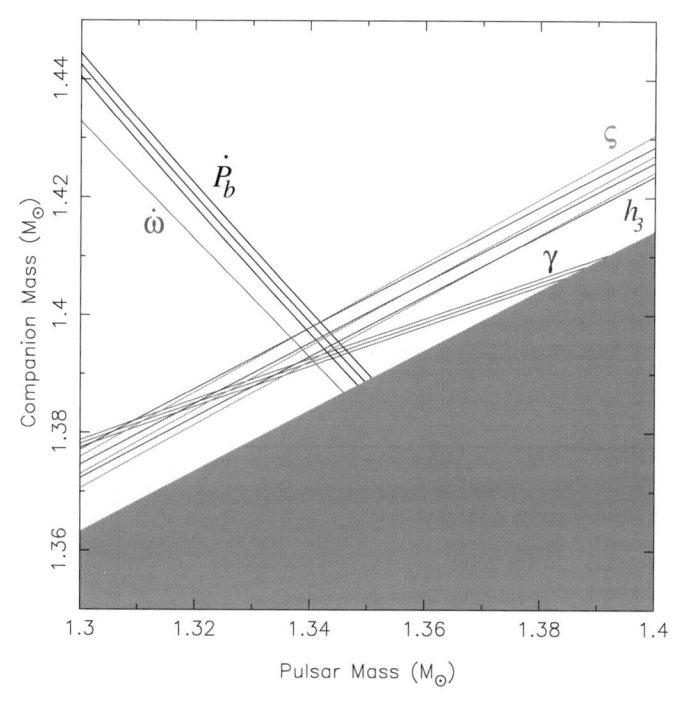

Fig. 1. Mass-mass diagram for PSR J1757–1854. Each coloured triplet of lines shows the constraints (with 1-σ uncertainty) placed by each of the measured PK parameters in Table 1 on the mass of the pulsar and the companion neutron star, in this case according to GR. The measured uncertainty of $\dot{\omega}$ is so small that it cannot be seen at this scale. The grey region in the bottom right is excluded due to orbital geometry.

2.1. *Proper motion and the radiative test of gravity*

A recent development in the timing of PSR J1757–1854 has been the first constrained measurement of the pulsar's proper motion, which is also listed in Table 1. The component in right ascension (μ_α) is detectable at approximately 36 σ, while the component in declination (μ_δ) remains poorly constrained, although its contribution to the total proper motion remains small given its value relative to μ_α. Together, these values indicate a total proper motion of

$$\mu_T = \sqrt{\mu_\alpha^2 + \mu_\delta^2} = 4.4\,(3)\ \mathrm{mas\,yr^{-1}}. \tag{1}$$

This allows us to attempt to quantify the contributions contaminating the observed value of the orbital period derivative, $\dot{P}_{b,\mathrm{obs}}$. We define the excess contribution as

$$\dot{P}_{b,\mathrm{exs}} = \dot{P}_{b,\mathrm{obs}} - \left(\dot{P}_{b,\mathrm{GR}} + \dot{P}_{b,\mathrm{Gal}} + \dot{P}_{b,\mathrm{Shk}}\right), \tag{2}$$

where $\dot{P}_{b,\mathrm{GR}}$ is the expected intrinsic contribution from GR (here calculated using the mass values derived from the observed $\dot{\omega}$ and γ as given in Table 1); $\dot{P}_{b,\mathrm{Gal}}$ is the contribution from the acceleration of the pulsar within the Galactic potential[8] (dependent on position, distance and the chosen model of the Galactic potential); and $\dot{P}_{b,\mathrm{Shk}}$ is the contribution from the Shklovskii effect[9] (dependent on distance and proper motion).

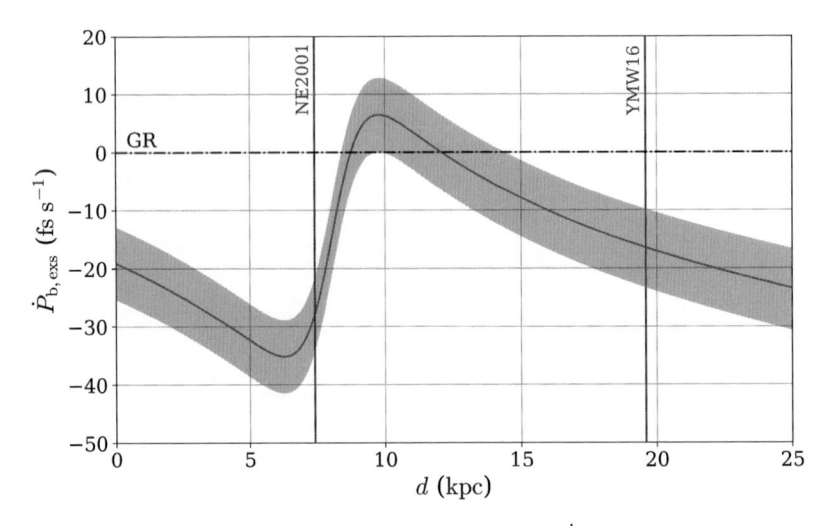

Fig. 2. The excess contribution to the orbital period derivative $\dot{P}_{b,\mathrm{exs}}$ as calculated by Equation 2, plotted (red) as a function of distance. The shaded region shows the 1-σ uncertainty. $\dot{P}_{b,\mathrm{Gal}}$ was calculated using the McMillan Galactic potential.[10] The vertical blue (left) and magenta (right) lines indicate the NE2001[11] and YWM16[12] DM-distance estimates respectively. The horizontal dashed black line shows the GR expectation of $\dot{P}_{b,\mathrm{exs}} = 0$.

For the radiative $\dot{P}_b$ test of GR to be considered 'passed', $\dot{P}_{b,\mathrm{exs}}$ must be consistent with zero, given that the other contributions have been accurately accounted for. However, although we have now quantified the pulsar's proper motion, we still lack an accurate estimate of the pulsar's distance. This is demonstrated in Figure 2, where we show how $\dot{P}_{b,\mathrm{exs}}$ depends on the distance to PSR J1757–1854.

Assuming GR, the distance to PSR J1757–1854 should fall between approximately 8.5–14.5 kpc. Therefore, available distance estimates based on the pulsar's dispersion measure (DM), including both the NE2001[11] (7.4 kpc) and the YMW16[12] (19.6 kpc) electron density models, are currently excluded. This is also shown in Figure 2. However, we note that these DM-distance estimates typically come with large uncertainties,[13] making a definitive determination difficult. Additionally, the McMillan Galactic potential model[10] we have used in our analysis has known shortcomings at distances of approximately 7–9 kpc in the central regions of the Galaxy near PSR J1757–1854's position, further complicating this assessment.

Without an accurate distance to PSR J1757–1854, the utility of the radiative test of gravity is unfortunately limited. As seen in Figure 2, the unknown distance introduces an approximate uncertainty to $\dot{P}_{\rm b,exs}$ of at least $\pm 20 \times 10^{-15}$, more than three times the current uncertainty of $\dot{P}_{\rm b,obs} = 6 \times 10^{-15}$, such that the precision of the radiative test of GR is limited to about 0.4 %. We are currently exploring ways of further refining the estimated distance to PSR J1757–1854 (e.g. through VLBI astrometry). However, by assuming GR, we will still be able to inform our understanding of the pulsar's evolution. For example, the currently allowed distance range indicates a transverse velocity based on $\mu_{\rm T}$ between 180–300 km s^{-1}, well in agreement with simulations of the neutron star kick associated with the second progenitor supernova.[2]

3. Attempts to detect the presence of geodetic precession

Our current understanding of the binary evolution of PSR J1757–1854 suggests the strong likelihood of a misalignment between the pulsar's spin vector and the orbital angular momentum vector.[2] As a result, we anticipate the presence of geodetic precession at a rate of $\Omega_{\rm geod} \simeq 3.07\,°\,{\rm deg\,yr}^{-1}$, which if detected may serve as another test of GR. We have therefore analysed the current GBT dataset for evidence of changes in the pulse profile, which would indicate a changing line-of-sight through the emission cone of the pulsar as expected from geodetic precession.[14]

Our method adapts an approach previously applied[15] to PSR J1022+1001. Each GBT observation (at both L and S-bands) spanning greater than 80% the orbital period is summed in time, frequency and polarisation before being fit by a template composed of three component Gaussian curves. We then normally re-sample each profile bin using the off-pulse root-mean-squared noise value to generate at least 1,000 randomly 're-noised' profiles, to which the template is re-fit. From each new fitted template, the positions and amplitudes of the major and minor peaks are then measured, as well as the intercept positions at 10% and 50% of the profile's maximum amplitude. The mean and standard deviation of each parameter's statistical distribution across all fitted templates are then taken as the nominal value and its uncertainty.

This approach has for the first time confirmed the presence of statistically significant profile change. An example of this is given in Figure 3, which shows that

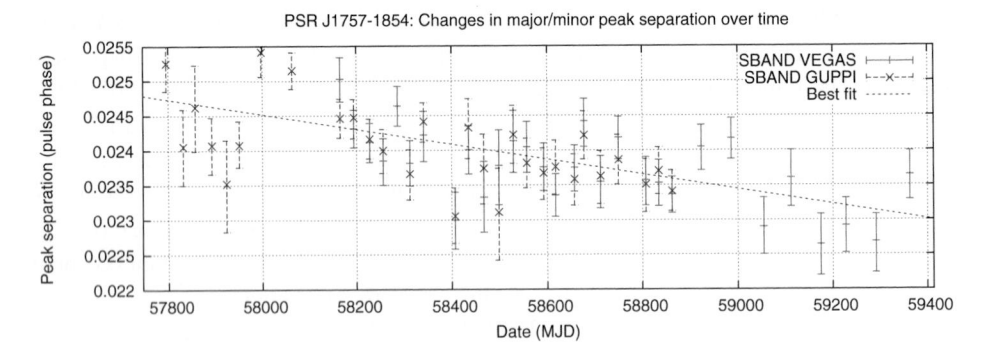

Fig. 3. Change in phase separation of the major and minor peaks of PSR J1757–1854's pulse profile, as measured by the GBT at S-band using the GUPPI and VEGAS backends. The line of best fit corresponds to a decreasing separation of $0.14\,(2)\,°\,\mathrm{yr}^{-1}$.

the separation between the two peaks of PSR J1757–1854's profile (termed the 'major' and 'minor' peaks) is decreasing (i.e. moving closer together) by an average rate of approximately $0.14\,(2)\,°\,\mathrm{yr}^{-1}$. The width of the profile at both 10% and 50% also appears to be shrinking at a commensurate rate, with all trends most pronounced at S-Band due to the decreased influence of scattering (with respect to lower-frequency L-band observations). The precise physical implications of these changes are to be explored in a future publication, but their detection provides fundamental evidence for the presence of geodetic precession, as well as evidence for the suspected spin/orbit misalignment present in the binary system.

4. Searches for the companion neutron star

If PSR J1757–1854's neutron star companion was confirmed to be an active radio pulsar, it would immensely enhance the scientific utility of this pulsar and its binary system. This is most obviously demonstrated by the prior example of the Double Pulsar, where the presence of the second pulsar PSR J0737–3039B allowed additional tests of gravity beyond those normally available, including the detection of geodetic precession[16] and an independent determination of the mass ratio.[17]

We have therefore conducted an ongoing search for evidence of pulsations from the neutron star companion to PSR J1757–1854. This search has focused on observations from the GBT, which are recorded in a coherently-dedispersed search mode so as to allow for optimal search sensitivity across all pulse periods. Given our precise knowledge of PSR J1757–1854's orbit as detailed in Table 1, each observation is re-sampled using the inferred orbit of the companion via the custom software package PYSOLATOR.[18] This allows the companion to appear stationary such that any pulsations would appear as a single narrow peak in a resulting Fourier spectrum. To account for the small degree of uncertainty in the companion orbit, different re-sampled trials are produced using values of the mass ratio $q = m_{\rm p}/m_{\rm c}$ between $0.9554 < q < 0.9661$ in increments of 0.00005. The resulting Fourier power spectra from each observation are then stacked and summed, boosting the total S/N of any pulsations.

To date, this search has unfortunately returned negative results, although the complete GBT dataset has yet to be analysed. In total, approximately 389.7 hr of GBT observations are currently on file, although there is significant overlap in this dataset between the VEGAS and GUPPI backends during intervals when both were recorded simultaneously. Ongoing searches for the companion neutron star will continue, as the companion may become detectable in the event that it precesses into view in the near future, given the expected precession rate of $\Omega_{\rm geod} \simeq 2.97\,^\circ\,{\rm deg\,yr^{-1}}$.

5. Future observations and anticipated tests of gravity

5.1. *Addition of MeerKAT*

Although observations with South Africa's MeerKAT telescope have been ongoing since 2019 as part of the MeerTIME program,[19] all these observations took place with MeerKAT's L-band receiver, which has a large 856 MHz bandwidth centered at 1283.5 MHz. This frequency band is located at lower frequencies than those of the GBT L-band receiver and therefore is much more susceptible to pulse broadening via scattering than the GBT L-band.[20] As a consequence, even though MeerKAT can achieve about twice the S/N of the GBT for this target, the available timing precision from both telescopes is roughly equivalent.

These effects are expected to be mitigated as part of the ongoing rollout of a fleet of MeerKAT S-band receivers (with a bandwidth of approximately 1750 MHz centred at 2625 MHz), designed by the MPIfR. The decreased influence of scattering at these higher frequencies combined with the wider bandwidth and the pulsar's relatively flat spectral index suggest an improvement in TOA precision to within $10\,\mu{\rm s}$ or better (compared with a typical TOA precision of 25–$30\,\mu{\rm s}$ currently achievable using similar TOA integration times with the current GBT and MeerKAT receivers). This will provide a significant advantage in the ongoing timing of the pulsar.

5.2. *Future tests of gravity*

PSR J1757−1854 is expected to provide new insight into two rarely-explored tests of gravity within the next few years. The first of these is the *relativistic orbital deformation*, characterised by the PK parameter δ_θ, which describes the deviation of the orbit from a pure Keplerian ellipse due to the effects of relativity. The measurability of δ_θ scales with both eccentricity and $\dot\omega$, positioning PSR J1757−1854 as an ideal system for providing constraint in the short-term. Meanwhile, the Hulse-Taylor pulsar[21] (lower $\dot\omega$) and the Double Pulsar (lower eccentricity) have to date only weakly constrained δ_θ despite having been studied for far longer.

The second anticipated test involves the detection of Lense-Thirring precession, which to date has not been detected in a double neutron star binary system. We intend to detect this effect via the measurement of a change in the semi-major axis,[22] $\dot{x}_{\rm LT}$. Although in general $\dot{x}_{\rm LT}$ becomes negligible for small misalignment angles between the pulsar spin and orbital angular momentum vectors, our recent detection of geodetic precession confirms that a significant misalignment is likely. The Lense-Thirring effect is also proportional to the neutron star moment of inertia; should the Lense-Thirring effect be detected here, it would lead to a rare measurement of this quantity and thereby provide insight into the neutron star equation of state.

The timescale over which each of these parameters is anticipated to be constrained was determined by a simulation of the anticipated timing campaigns. A simulation was produced by extrapolating the current GBT timing campaign until the end of 2024, and including an equivalent MeerKAT S-band campaign comprising one full orbit recorded every two months, starting in 2022. Timing ephemerides were fit to the data at set intervals, while averaging the results of 30 realisations of the dataset. Based on these simulations, we anticipate the achievement of a 3-σ constraint of δ_θ between approximately 2024–2025, and of $\dot{x}_{\rm LT}$ between 2025–2026.

Acknowledgments

The Parkes radio telescope is part of the Australia Telescope National Facility which is funded by the Australian Government for operation as a National Facility managed by CSIRO. We acknowledge the Wiradjuri people as the traditional owners of the Observatory site. The Green Bank Observatory is a facility of the National Science Foundation operated under cooperative agreement by Associated Universities, Inc. The MeerKAT telescope is operated by the South African Radio Astronomy Observatory, which is a facility of the National Research Foundation, an agency of the Department of Science and Innovation. Pulsar research at the Jodrell Bank Centre for Astrophysics and the observations using the Lovell Telescope are supported by a consolidated grant from the STFC in the UK. This work is also based on observations with the 100-m telescope of the Max-Planck-Institut für Radioastronomie at Effelsberg. AC and MB acknowledge OzGrav ARC grant CE170100004. AP and AR acknowledge that (part of) this work has been funded using resources from the research grant "iPeska" (P.I. Andrea Possenti) funded under the INAF national call Prin-SKA/CTA approved with the Presidential Decree 70/2016. AP and AR also acknowledge the support from the Ministero degli Affari Esteri e della Cooperazione Internazionale - Direzione Generale per la Promozione del Sistema Paese - Progetto di Grande Rilevanza ZA18GR02. AR acknowledges continuing valuable support from the Max-Planck Society. MAM and HW are members of the NANOGrav Physics Frontiers Center and supported by NSF awards 1430284 and 2020265.

References

1. M. J. Keith, A. Jameson, W. van Straten, M. Bailes, S. Johnston, M. Kramer, A. Possenti, S. D. Bates, N. D. R. Bhat, M. Burgay, S. Burke-Spolaor, N. D'Amico, L. Levin, P. L. McMahon, S. Milia and B. W. Stappers, The High Time Resolution Universe Pulsar Survey - I. System configuration and initial discoveries, *Monthly Notices of the Royal Astronomical Society* **409**, 619 (December 2010).
2. A. D. Cameron, D. J. Champion, M. Kramer, M. Bailes, E. D. Barr, C. G. Bassa, S. Bhandari, N. D. R. Bhat, M. Burgay, S. Burke-Spolaor, R. P. Eatough, C. M. L. Flynn, P. C. C. Freire, A. Jameson, S. Johnston, R. Karuppusamy, M. J. Keith, L. Levin, D. R. Lorimer, A. G. Lyne, M. A. McLaughlin, C. Ng, E. Petroff, A. Possenti, A. Ridolfi, B. W. Stappers, W. van Straten, T. M. Tauris, C. Tiburzi and N. Wex, The High Time Resolution Universe Pulsar Survey - XIII. PSR J1757-1854, the most accelerated binary pulsar, *Monthly Notices of the Royal Astronomical Society* **475**, L57 (March 2018).
3. R. A. Hulse and J. H. Taylor, Discovery of a pulsar in a binary system, *Astrophysical Journal* **195**, L51 (January 1975).
4. M. Burgay, N. D'Amico, A. Possenti, R. N. Manchester, A. G. Lyne, B. C. Joshi, M. A. McLaughlin, M. Kramer, J. M. Sarkissian, F. Camilo, V. Kalogera, C. Kim and D. R. Lorimer, An increased estimate of the merger rate of double neutron stars from observations of a highly relativistic system, *Nature* **426**, 531 (December 2003).
5. A. G. Lyne, M. Burgay, M. Kramer, A. Possenti, R. N. Manchester, F. Camilo, M. A. McLaughlin, D. R. Lorimer, N. D'Amico, B. C. Joshi, J. Reynolds and P. C. C. Freire, A Double-Pulsar System: A Rare Laboratory for Relativistic Gravity and Plasma Physics, *Science* **303**, 1153 (February 2004).
6. D. R. Lorimer and M. Kramer, *Handbook of Pulsar Astronomy* (Cambridge Univ. Press, Cambridge, 2005).
7. P. C. C. Freire and N. Wex, The orthometric parametrization of the Shapiro delay and an improved test of general relativity with binary pulsars, *Monthly Notices of the Royal Astronomical Society* **409**, 199 (November 2010).
8. T. Damour and J. H. Taylor, On the Orbital Period Change of the Binary Pulsar PSR 1913+16, *Astrophysical Journal* **366**, p. 501 (January 1991).
9. I. S. Shklovskii, Possible Causes of the Secular Increase in Pulsar Periods, *Soviet Astronomy* **13**, p. 562 (feb 1970).
10. P. J. McMillan, The mass distribution and gravitational potential of the Milky Way, *Monthly Notices of the Royal Astronomical Society* **465**, 76 (February 2017).
11. J. M. Cordes and T. J. W. Lazio, NE2001.I. A New Model for the Galactic Distribution of Free Electrons and its Fluctuations, *arXiv e-prints* (July 2002).
12. J. M. Yao, R. N. Manchester and N. Wang, A New Electron-density Model for Estimation of Pulsar and FRB Distances, *Astrophysical Journal* **835**, p. 29 (January 2017).
13. A. D. Cameron, D. J. Champion, M. Bailes, V. Balakrishnan, E. D. Barr, C. G. Bassa, S. Bates, S. Bhandari, N. D. R. Bhat, M. Burgay, S. Burke-Spolaor, C. M. L. Flynn, A. Jameson, S. Johnston, M. J. Keith, M. Kramer, L. Levin, A. G. Lyne, C. Ng, E. Petroff, A. Possenti, D. A. Smith, B. W. Stappers, W. van Straten, C. Tiburzi and J. Wu, The High Time Resolution Universe Pulsar Survey - XVI. Discovery and timing of 40 pulsars from the southern Galactic plane, *Monthly Notices of the Royal Astronomical Society* **493**, 1063 (March 2020).
14. M. Bailes, Geodetic precession in binary pulsars, *Astronomy and Astrophysics* **202**, 109 (August 1988).

15. P. V. Padmanabh, E. D. Barr, D. J. Champion, R. Karuppusamy, M. Kramer, A. Jessner and P. Lazarus, Revisiting profile instability of PSR J1022+1001, *Monthly Notices of the Royal Astronomical Society* **500**, 1178 (January 2021).
16. R. P. Breton, V. M. Kaspi, M. Kramer, M. A. McLaughlin, M. Lyutikov, S. M. Ransom, I. H. Stairs, R. D. Ferdman, F. Camilo and A. Possenti, Relativistic Spin Precession in the Double Pulsar, *Science* **321**, p. 104 (July 2008).
17. M. Kramer, I. H. Stairs, R. N. Manchester, M. A. McLaughlin, A. G. Lyne, R. D. Ferdman, M. Burgay, D. R. Lorimer, A. Possenti, N. D'Amico, J. M. Sarkissian, G. B. Hobbs, J. E. Reynolds, P. C. C. Freire and F. Camilo, Tests of General Relativity from Timing the Double Pulsar, *Science* **314**, 97 (October 2006).
18. A. Ridolfi, PYSOLATOR: Remove orbital modulation from a binary pulsar and/or its companion (March 2020).
19. M. Bailes, A. Jameson, F. Abbate, E. D. Barr, N. D. R. Bhat, L. Bondonneau, M. Burgay, S. J. Buchner, F. Camilo, D. J. Champion, I. Cognard, P. B. Demorest, P. C. C. Freire, T. Gautam, M. Geyer, J. M. Griessmeier, L. Guillemot, H. Hu, F. Jankowski, S. Johnston, A. Karastergiou, R. Karuppusamy, D. Kaur, M. J. Keith, M. Kramer, J. van Leeuwen, M. E. Lower, Y. Maan, M. A. McLaughlin, B. W. Meyers, S. Osłowski, L. S. Oswald, A. Parthasarathy, T. Pennucci, B. Posselt, A. Possenti, S. M. Ransom, D. J. Reardon, A. Ridolfi, C. T. G. Schollar, M. Serylak, G. Shaifullah, M. Shamohammadi, R. M. Shannon, C. Sobey, X. Song, R. Spiewak, I. H. Stairs, B. W. Stappers, W. van Straten, A. Szary, G. Theureau, V. Venkatraman Krishnan, P. Weltevrede, N. Wex, T. D. Abbott, G. B. Adams, J. P. Burger, R. R. G. Gamatham, M. Gouws, D. M. Horn, B. Hugo, A. F. Joubert, J. R. Manley, K. McAlpine, S. S. Passmoor, A. Peens-Hough, Z. R. Ramudzuli, A. Rust, S. Salie, L. C. Schwardt, R. Siebrits, G. Van Tonder, V. Van Tonder and M. G. Welz, The MeerKAT telescope as a pulsar facility: System verification and early science results from MeerTime, *Publications of the Astronomical Society of Australia* **37**, p. e028 (July 2020).
20. M. Kramer, I. H. Stairs, V. Venkatraman Krishnan, P. C. C. Freire, F. Abbate, M. Bailes, M. Burgay, S. Buchner, D. J. Champion, I. Cognard, T. Gautam, M. Geyer, L. Guillemot, H. Hu, G. Janssen, M. E. Lower, A. Parthasarathy, A. Possenti, S. Ransom, D. J. Reardon, A. Ridolfi, M. Serylak, R. M. Shannon, R. Spiewak, G. Theureau, W. van Straten, N. Wex, L. S. Oswald, B. Posselt, C. Sobey, E. D. Barr, F. Camilo, B. Hugo, A. Jameson, S. Johnston, A. Karastergiou, M. Keith and S. Osłowski, The relativistic binary programme on MeerKAT: science objectives and first results, *Monthly Notices of the Royal Astronomical Society* **504**, 2094 (June 2021).
21. J. M. Weisberg and Y. Huang, Relativistic Measurements from Timing the Binary Pulsar PSR B1913+16, *Astrophysical Journal* **829**, p. 55 (September 2016).
22. T. Damour and J. H. Taylor, Strong-field tests of relativistic gravity and binary pulsars, *Physical Review D (Particles, Fields, Gravitation, and Cosmology)* **45**, 1840 (March 1992).

On the origin of the unique isolated X-Ray pulsar 1E 161348-5055 with 6.7 hr. spin period

V. Yu. Kim

Fesenkov Astrophysical Institute
Almaty, 050020, Observatroriya 23, Kazakhstan
E-mail: kim@aphi.kz
www.aphi.kz

A scenario for the formation of an isolated X-ray pulsar 1E161348-5055 with an anomalously long period of 6.7 hours is proposed. It is shown that this pulsar can be a descendant of a massive X-ray binary system, which disintegrated about 2000 years ago after a supernova explosion caused by the core collapse of a massive component. X-ray radiation of this object in the present epoch is generated as a result of accretion of matter onto (about 10 million years old) neutron star from the residual non-Keplerian accretion disk. The pulsar's nebula RCW 103 is a supernova remnant formed by the explosion of its massive companion in the final evolutionary phase of a massive binary system.

Keywords: X-Ray pulsar, isolated neutron star, accretion, stellar evolution

Introduction

X-ray pulsar 1E 161348-5055 (hereinafter 1E 1613) was discovered in 1979 by means of the Einstein cosmic observatory, as a point X-ray source in the supernova remnant RCW 103.[1] The distance to RCW 103 was approximately estimated as $d \simeq 3.2 \pm 0.1$ kpc from the analysis of absorption of radio emission by neutral hydrogen in the 21 cm line.[2] The estimated age of RCW 103 from the expansion rate and size of the nebula is about $\tau \simeq 2000 \pm 1000$ yr.[2] The nebula is an atypical remnant of a SN II type. It has an almost rounded shape with a fibrous structure, a low expansion rate (~ 1100 km/s) and it has a relatively small spatial size 7.7 pc for its age.[3] Nebulae with such parameters account for less than 20 % of the currently known SN II supernova remnants, the explosion of which apparently occurred in a high-density gaseous medium.[4] After the discovery of this pulsar, it was suggested that this object is an isolated cooling neutron star in the peculiar supernova remnant RCW 103.[5] However, in the period 1997-1999, during the study of 1E 1613 by the ASCA space observatory, significant variations in the source brightness were detected and the thermal component emitted by a hot spot $kT \sim 0.6 - 0.8$ keV with a radius of $a_\mathrm{p} \sim 600$ m,[6,7] was found. It is not typical for a cooling neutron star, but typical for magnetized neutron stars accreting matter on their surface. This served as the basis for the hypothesis that 1E 1613 is a neutron star accreting matter in the area of the magnetic poles. The average X-ray luminosity of the source is $L_\mathrm{x} \sim 10^{34}$ erg/s.[6,7] The report about the possible X-Ray variability of 1E 1613 with a period of ~ 6 hours, discovered from the results of observations of this source by the "Chandra" observatory, stimulated the search for an optical companion of the neutron star. Observations made for this purpose with the ESO VLT telescope in the near infrared, however, allowed to establish only the upper limit of the luminosity of a hypothetical companion $L_{ir} \sim 10^{31}$ erg/s, which could be a star of a later spectral class than M4.[8] This result became a strong argument in favor of the fact that 1E 1613 is not part of a close binary system and it is an isolated neutron star, whose radiation is caused either by accretion of matter from the residual disk or by the rapid dissipation of a superstrong magnetic field.[9]

In 2006, by means of the XMM-Newton space telescope, it was possible to establish the spin period of 1E 1613 $P_s \simeq 6.67 \pm 0.003$ hr.[10] None of the known pulsars had such a long spin period. Almost immediately after the discovery of the period, several hypotheses were put forward about the nature of object 1E 1613. One of the first idea was the assumption that this object is a unique magnetar accreting matter from the surrounding residual (fall-back) disk, with a magnetic field $> 10^{15}$ G.[9,10] It was also hypothesized that 1E 1613 is a magnetar in a low-mass close binary system.[5] Subsequently, it was suggested that 1E 1613 is a millisecond pulsar in a close binary system, where the observed period (6.7 hours) was assumed as an orbital period (the so-called period mimicry).[11]

In 2011, from the analysis of the pulsation profiles obtained from space observatories: "Swift", "Chandra", "XMM-Newton", the upper limit of the rotation deceleration was calculated $\dot{P}_s \leq 1.6 \times 10^{-9}$ s/s or $\dot{\nu}_s \leq -2.8 \times 10^{18}$ Hz/s (here $\nu_s = 1/P_s$ - spin frequency).[12] Analyzing their result, the authors of this discovery noted that the moment of force applied to a neutron star in the present epoch is significantly less than the value expected in all previously proposed models of this source. The high stability of pulsations apparently indicates that the spin period of the star at the present epoch is close to the equilibrium period of its spin rotation, the value of which weakly depends on changes in the accretion rate in the residual disk. It was shown in the article[13] that such a situation is realized in the scenario of Magnetic Levitation accretion, in which a neutron star with a magnetic field 10^{12} G accrets onto its surface matter from the residual non-Keplerian magnetic disk.

1. Formation of an isolated pulsar during the decay of a binary system

We consider a situation in which 1E 1613 is a neutron star, born in a close massive binary system during the first supernova explosion. We assume that this did not lead to the disintegration of the system and the neutron star formed a close pair with its massive companion. The initial rotation period of the neutron star was fractions of a second and increased as the star successively passed the ejector and propeller states. Upon completion of this phase, the star passed into an accretor state, in which it remained until the second supernova explosion, caused by the collapse of the core of its massive companion. This event most likely led to the disintegration of the system,[14] and the old neutron star passed into the state of an isolated pulsar,

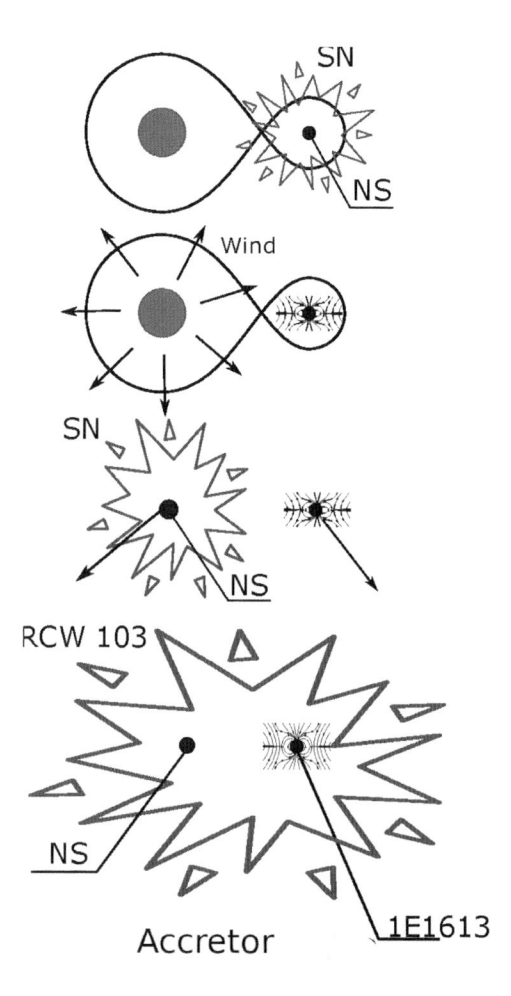

Fig. 1. Possible way of formation of isolated X-ray pulsar as a descendant of high-mass X-ray binary system

immersed in the remnant of its companion supernova, observed in the present epoch as the RCW 103 nebula.

2. Magnetorotational evolution

The scenario of the evolution of a high-mass X-ray binary system (HMXB) described above has been sufficiently studied by now and is perceived by most authors as canonical (see the article [Postnov et al., 2014][15] and the literature cited there). The lifetime of such a system is estimated by the evolution time of its optical component on the main sequence with mass M_{opt} corresponds to[16]:

$$t_{\text{ms}} \simeq 6 \times 10^6 \, yr \times \left(\frac{M_{\text{opt}}}{M_\odot}\right)^{-5/2} \tag{1}$$

Numerical modeling of the magnetorotational evolution of a neutron star in the framework of such a scenario with allowance for the dissipation of its magnetic field was carried out by Urpin et al.[17] According to the results of their calculations, the magnetic field of the star during t_{ms} decreases by an order of magnitude due to diffusion and accretion screening.[18] In particular, with an initial value of $\sim 10^{13}$ G, the magnetic field on the surface of a star that has evolved as part of HMXB system is $\sim 10^{12}$ G. Such a neutron star spends most of its evolution in the ejector state (see formula 17 in the paper[19]):

$$t_{ej} \simeq 3 \times 10^6 \, yr \times \mu_{30.5}^{-1} I_{45} \dot{M}_{14}^{1/2} v_7^{-1/2} \quad (2)$$

Here: $\mu_{30.5} = \mu_{ns}/3 \times 10^{30}$ G cm^3 - normalized magnetic dipole moment of a neutron star, $I_{45} = I_{ns}/10^{45}$ g cm^2 - its moment of inertia, $\dot{M}_{14} = \dot{M}/10^{14}$ g/s - normalized accretion rate, $v_7 = v_{rel}/10^7$ cm/s - related velocity of a neutron star into surrounded medium. During this stage, its magnetic field decreases by an average of 3 times (the rapid cooling of the star during this phase significantly reduces the rate of diffusion of the magnetic field in its crust[17]).

As the rotation period of the star reaches a critical value (see formula 16 in the paper[19]), it passes into the propeller state.

$$P_{ej} \sim 1.2\,s \times \mu_{30.5}^{1/2} \dot{M}_{14}^{-1/4} v_7^{-1/4} \quad (3)$$

At this stage, the spin-down torque applied to the star by the penetrating under its Bondi radius gas is determined by the expression $K_{sd}^{pr} \sim \mu_{ns}^2/r_m^3$. The duration of the propeller stage substantially depends on the geometry and physical parameters of the accretion flow.

$$\tau_{pr} = \frac{\pi I r_m^3}{\mu_{ns} P_{ej}} \quad (4)$$

This parameter reaches its minimum possible value in the case of the scenario of Magnetic Levitation accretion:[13]

$$\tau_{pr}^{(ml)} \simeq 6 \times 10^3 \, yr \times \alpha_{0.1}^{6/13} \mu_{30}^{-29/26} I_{45} m^{3/13} T_6^{-6/13} \dot{M}_{14}^{-35/52} v_7^{1/4} \quad (5)$$

In the paper[13] we showed that 1E 1613 could be in the accretor stage, the material for the accretion is supplied by the surrounding residual Magnetic Levitating disk or ML-disk formed from the supernova remnant RCW 103. The magnetic field strength 1E 1613 in this model (Magnetic Levitation accretion) corresponded to 10^{12} G, which corresponds to the canonical value of the magnetic field of neutron stars. For detailed explanation, see articles [Ikhsanov et al., 2013, 2015].[13,20]

3. Conclusions

The main conclusion of this study is to explain the origin of an isolated X-ray pulsar with a period of 6.7 hours within the canonical scenario of the evolution of a massive X-ray binary system without invoking the hypothesis of superstrong magnetic fields on the surface of a neutron star. Our proposed model is consistent with modern concepts of a relatively small value of the initial rotation period of neutron stars and does not require invoking the additional assumption of fall-back accretion onto a neutron star after its birth.

The age of a neutron star 1E 161348-5055, manifesting itself in the present epoch as an isolated X-ray pulsar, is comparable to the lifetime of a massive X-ray binary system, estimated by Eq. (1) and amounts to several million years. The lifetime of this star in the state of an isolated X-ray pulsar, however, is much shorter. It corresponds to the time elapsed since the collapse of the massive X-ray binary, which is comparable to the age of the RCW 103 nebula and is about 2000 years (see also the article[20]).

The residual accretion disk surrounding the magnetosphere of a neutron star in the present epoch could have been formed during its evolution as part of a massive X-ray binary system or after the disintegration of the system during the capture of matter by an old neutron star from an envelope ejected by its massive component during a supernova explosion.

Isolated X-ray pulsars with long periods, within the framework of our model, are descendants of the widest pairs in which a massive component at the last stage of its evolution does not fill its Roche lobe and the capture of matter from the stellar wind remains the dominant mechanism of mass exchange between the components of the system at all stages of its evolution. The lifetime of such a pulsar depends on the mass of the residual disk and the physical parameters of the gas, which determine the rate of diffusion of the magnetic field in it. The main candidates for descendants of close binary systems are isolated X-ray pulsars located in the supernova remnants formed during the explosion of massive companions.

Acknowledgments

This research has been funded by the Science Committee of the Ministry of Education and Science of the Republic of Kazakhstan (Grant No. AP09258811).

References

1. I. Tuohy and G. Garmire, Discovery of a compact X-ray source at the center of the SNR RCW 103, *Astrophys. J.* **239**, L107 (1980).
2. J. L. Caswell, J. D. Murray, R. S. Roger, D. J. Cole and D. J. Cooke, Neutral hydrogen absorption measurements yielding kinematic distances for 42 continuum sources in the galactic plane, *Astron. and Astrophys.* **45**, 239 (1975).
3. L. Carter, J. Dickel and D. Bomans, Expansion of the Supernova Remnant RCW 103, *Publ. Astron. Soc. Pacific* **109**, 990 (1997).
4. D. Marsden, R. E. Lingenfelter, R. E. Rothschild, and J. C. Higdon, Nature versus Nurture: The Origin of Soft Gamma-Ray Repeaters and Anomalous X-ray Pulsars, *Astrophys. J.* **550**, 397 (2001).
5. F. Pizzolato, M. Colpi, A. De Luca, S. Mereghetti, A. Tiengo, 1E 161348-5055 in the Supernova Remnant RCW 103: A Magnetar in a Young Low-Mass Binary System?, *Astrophys. J.* **681**, 530 (2008).

6. E. V. Gotthelf, R. Petre and U. Hwang, The Nature of the Radio-quiet Compact X-ray Source in Supernova Remnant RCW 103, *Astrophys. J.* **487**, L175 (1997).
7. E. V. Gotthelf, R. Petre and G. Vasisht, X-ray Variability from the Compact Source in the Supernova Remnant RCW 103, *Astrophys. J.* **514**, L107 (1999).
8. G. G. Pavlov, D. Sanwal and M.A. Teter, Young Neutron Stars and Their Environments, in *IAU Symp. 218*, p. 239, eds. F. Camilo and B. M. Gaensler (San Francisco: ASP, 2004).
9. X.-D. Li, The Nature of the Compact X-ray Source in Supernova Remnant RCW 103, *Astrophys. J.* **666**, L81 (2007).
10. A. de Luca, P. A. Caraveo, S. Mereghetti, A. Tiengo and G. F. Bignami, A Long-Period, Violently Variable X-ray Source in a Young Supernova Remnant, *Science* **313**, 814 (2006).
11. H. Bhadkamkar and P. Ghosh, Young pre-low-mass X-ray binaries in the propeller phase. Nature of the 6.7-h periodic X-ray source 1E 161348-5055 in RCW 103, *Astron. and Astrophys.* **1297**, 506 (2009).
12. P. Esposito, R. Turollia, A. De Luca, G. L. Israel, A. Possenti and D. N. Burrows, Swift monitoring of the central X-ray source in RCW 103, *Monthly. Not. Roy. Astron. Soc.* **418**, 170 (2011).
13. N. R. Ikhsanov, V. Yu. Kim, N. G. Beskrovnaya and L. A. Pustil'nik, A new look at the origin of the 6.67 hr period X-ray pulsar 1E 161348-5055, *Astrophys. and Space Sci.* **346**, 105 (2013).
14. S. B. Popov and M. E. Prokhorov, Progenitors with enhanced rotation and the origin of magnetars, *Monthly. Not. Roy. Astron. Soc.* **367**, 732 (2006).
15. K. A. Postnov and L. R. Yungelson, The Evolution of Compact Binary Star Systems, *Living Rev. in Relativity* **17**, 3 (2014).
16. D. Bhattacharya and E. P. J. van den Heuvel, Formation and evolution of binary and millisecond radio pulsars, *Phys. Rep.* **203**, 1 (1991).
17. V. Urpin, D. Konenkov and U. Geppert, Evolution of neutron stars in high-mass X-ray binaries, *Monthly. Not. Roy. Astron. Soc.* **299**, 73 (1998).
18. G. S. Bisnovatyi-Kogan and B. V. Komberg, Pulsars and close binary systems, *Soviet Astronomy* **51**, 373 (1974).
19. N. R. Ikhsanov, Signs of magnetic accretion in the young Be/X-ray pulsar SXP 1062, *Monthly. Not. Roy. Astron. Soc.* **434**, L39 (2012).
20. N. R. Ikhsanov, V. Yu. Kim and N. G. Beskrovnaya, A scenario of the formation of isolated X-ray pulsars with anomalously long period, *Astronomy Reports* **59**, 25 (2015).

Advantages of including globular cluster millisecond pulsars in Pulsar Timing Arrays

M. Maiorano*, F. De Paolis, A. A. Nucita and A. Franco

Department of Mathematics and Physics "Ennio De Giorgi",
University of Salento, Via Arnesano, I-73100 Lecce, Italy,
INFN, Sezione di Lecce, Via Arnesano, I-73100 Lecce, Italy
* E-mail: michele.maiorano@le.infn.com

Even though Pulsar Timing Arrays already have the potential to detect the gravitational wave background by finding a quadrupole correlation in the timing residuals, this goal has not yet been achieved. Motivated by some theoretical arguments, we analyzed some advantages of including the millisecond pulsars within globular clusters, especially those in their cores, in current and future Pulsar Timing Array projects for detecting the gravitational waves emitted by an ensemble of supermassive black holes.

Keywords: Black Holes; Gravitational Waves; Pulsars.

1. Introduction

Within the context of the Albert Einstein theory of General Relativity,[1] gravitational waves (GWs) are space perturbations propagating at the speed of light in the vacuum. Due to the smallness of their amplitude, which in most cases is less than 10^{-16}[a], their detection is a challenging problem and, in fact, it took a hundred years since they were predicted for the first time. Nowadays, ground-based gravitational interferometers, such as those of the LIGO (Laser Interferometer Gravitational-Wave Observatory), KAGRA (Kamioka Gravitational Wave Detector) and VIRGO collaboration, are currently the only instruments capable of efficiently detecting GWs. Their sensitivity allows to detect high-frequency (i.e. in the range 10–10^3 Hz) GWs emitted by compact object systems, such as black hole binaries,[2] neutron star binaries[3] and neutron star-black hole binaries,[4] in the final phase of the merger. The detection of low-frequency (i.e. in the frequency range $\simeq 10^{-5}$–1 Hz) GWs is more challenging because it requires space-based gravitational interferometers such as LISA (Laser Interferometer Space Antenna), which is planned to be launched for 2034 and consists of a constellation of three satellites, separated by about 1.5×10^6 km, in a triangular configuration, orbiting with Earth around the Sun.[5,6] However, ultra-low frequency (i.e. in the frequency range $\simeq 10^{-10}$–10^{-6} Hz) GWs, that may be generated by sources relevant for astrophysics and cosmology, such as supermassive black hole binaries (SMBHBs)[7] and cosmic strings,[8] and form the gravitational

---

[a]This is a dimensionless quantity describing how a spatial dimension is stretched or squeezed by the passage of a GW.

wave background (GWB), are out of the range of any kind of gravitational interferometers and can only be detected by Pulsar Timing Arrays (PTAs)[b].

PTAs constantly monitor the pulsed radio emission from the most stable isolated and binary millisecond pulsars across the sky to detect variation between the observed pulse time of arrival (ToA) and the one expected from the timing model. Such variation, referred to as timing residuals, may be GW-induced. Indeed, GWs can modify the distance between the Earth and the MSP, causing advances or delays in the pulse ToAs.[10, 11] As GWs, many other effects may induce timing residuals, so they must be distinguished from GWs. At present, the only way of doing this is by verifying that the cross-correlations between the timing residuals of each MSP pair follow the Hellings and Downs function, which is due to the quadrupole nature of GWs.[12]

The main PTA collaborations are the European Pulsar Timing Array (EPTA), the Indian Pulsar Timing Array (InPTA), the North American Nanohertz Observatory for Gravitational Waves (NANOGrav), and the Parkes Pulsar Timing Array (PPTA), and all of them are part of the International Pulsar Timing Array (IPTA). These PTAs have timed about forty MSPs for more than ten years with an accuracy that should be sufficient, in principle, to detect gravitational waves. Some clues of the presence of a common red process compatible with a GWB was found, but there is still not a strong enough evidence for or against it.[13–15] The reason behind that is yet unclear. Most likely, this could be due to the small number of MSPs available for PTAs, so continuing to add suitable MSPs should allow claiming detection, or to an insufficient observation time spawn, so it is essential to continue collecting data for many more years. Another option is that the standard GW search technique needs to be complemented by independent methods.

2. Back to the Theory

The GW-induced timing residuals are described, in a compact form, by[c]

$$r(t,\Omega^i) = \text{Re}\left\{\frac{h}{j\omega}\sum_{A=+,\times}\frac{1}{2}\frac{p^i p^j e^A_{ij}}{(1+\Omega_i p^i)}\left[e^{j(\omega\tilde{t}-\alpha^A)} - e^{j(\omega\tilde{t}-\omega\tau(1-\Omega_i p^i)-\alpha^A)}\right]_0^t\right\} \quad (1)$$

where h, ω, A, e^A_{ij}, and α^A indicate the GW amplitude, angular frequency, polarization state, polarization tensor, and the initial phase, respectively, $\tilde{t}$ is a mute variable, τ is the time distance between the Solar System Barycenter (SSB), Ω_i and p^i indicate the direction versors of the GW source and the MSP, respectively. The two terms in the square brackets are known as Earth[d] term and Pulsar term, and

---

[b]For a quick graphic overview of the different GW sources and GW detectors, see Ref. 9.
[c]For a complete theoretical description, see Ref. 16.
[d]The name "Earth" is a legacy of early work on PTAs.[17] In fact, since the Earth is not an inertial reference frame, the observer is assumed in SSB, whose position is known with great precision.

describe the metric in the proximity of the two objects[e]. Eq. (1) implies that, for an arbitrary MSP set, the Earth term is the same, while the Pulsar term changes. Since the latter term gives rise to an uncorrelated contribution in timing residuals, it is neglected in the standard GWB search[f]. This assumption is not entirely true if the MSP set is confined in a very small region, as in the case of globular clusters (GCs). Therefore, the GW-induced timing residuals of MSPs within GCs, especially those in their cores, should be strongly correlated, so considering these MSPs may offer a new instrument for GW detection.

3. Simulated Environment

The main target of the GW search with PTA is the GWBs produced by a hypothetical SMBHB population. Such a detection would give crucial information on the history of the Universe and, since that has not yet been achieved, it is worth considering improving PTAs by including MSPs within GCs.

We simulated the GW-induced timing residuals on GC core MSPs due to an SMBHB population. We arbitrarily assumed that the SMBHB chirp mass, distance, and GW emission frequency follow a log-normal distribution[g] and are in the ranges 10^8–10^9 $M_\odot$, 10^8–10^9 pc, and 10^{-9}–10^{-8} Hz, respectively, and that the SMBHB right ascension and declination follow a uniform distribution (see Fig. 1).

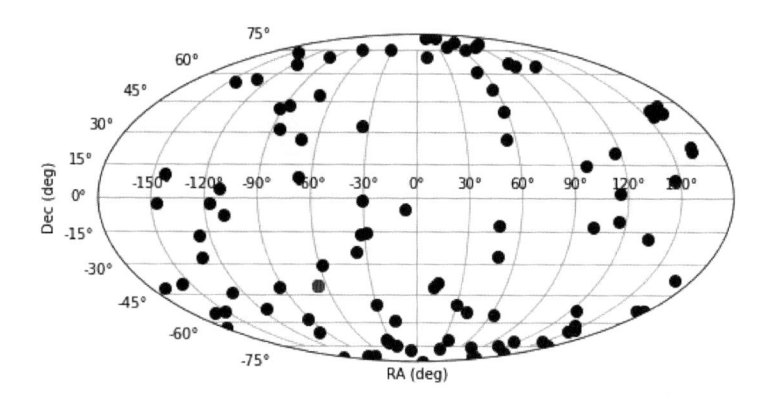

Fig. 1. Simulation of the SMBHB population. The position of 100 simulated SMBHBs, randomly scattered all over the sky is shown. The black dots indicate the SMBHB coordinates (RA and Dec), while the blue dot indicates the simulated GC coordinates.

---

[e]In this paper geometrical units c=G=1 have been adopted.
[f]However, it is important to remark that the pulsar term may play an important role in the detection of GW emitted by single sources.
[g]The properties of the SMBHB population are still a matter of debate. However, this paper aims to explain how PTAs can be improved by including MSPs within GCs, so we took the results in Refs. 18–20 just as a guide for building SMBHB distributions compatible with the GW-induced timing residuals observable by PTAs.

The SMBHB strain is, in good approximation, given by:

$$h = \sqrt{\frac{32}{5}} \frac{\mathcal{M}^{5/3}}{D} \left(\frac{2\pi f}{1+z}\right)^{2/3} \quad (2)$$

where $\mathcal{M}$, D, z, and f indicate the SMBHB chirp mass, distance, cosmological redshift, and GW emission frequency, respectively. Eq. (2) allows to determine the GW strain distribution for our SMBHB population (see Fig. 2).

(a) SMBHB chirp mass distribution.

(b) SMBHB distance distribution.

(c) GW frequency distribution.

(d) GW strain distribution.

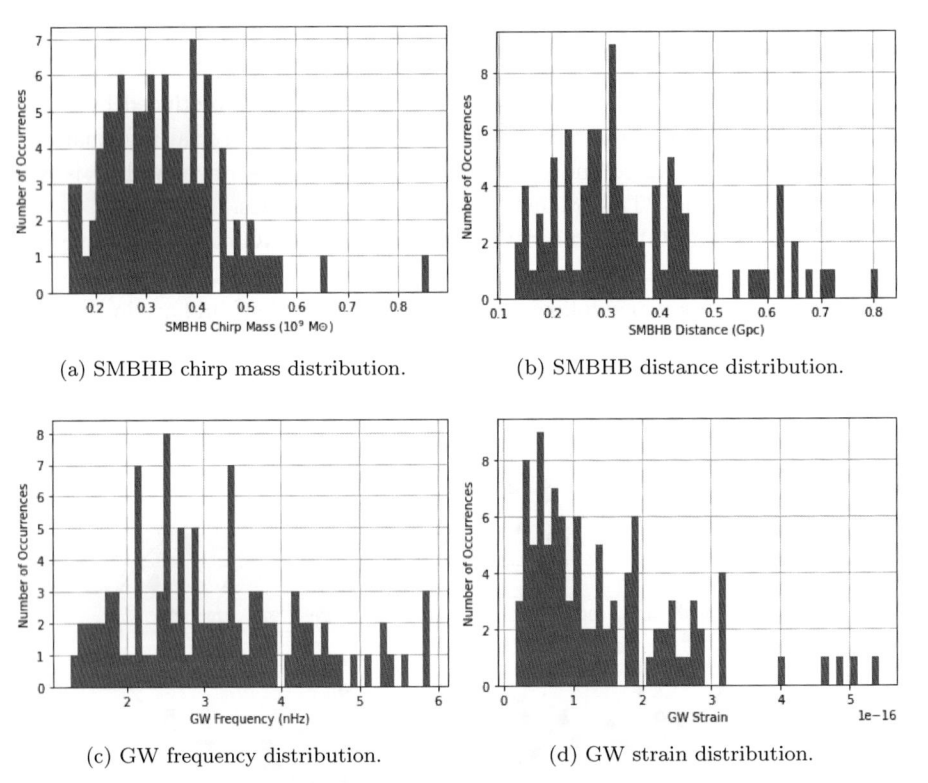

Fig. 2. SMBHB parameter simulation. Panel (a) shows the SMBHB chirp mass log-normal distribution, expressed in units of $10^9\ M_\odot$. Panel (b) shows the SMBHB distance log-normal distribution, expressed in Gpc. Panel (c) shows the GW frequency log-normal distribution, expressed in nHZ. Panel (d) shows the GW strain distribution, expressed in units of 10^{-16}. On the vertical axis of each panel is plotted the number of occurrences.

We also assumed that the GC core MSP distance[h], right ascension, and declination with respect to the GC center follow a uniform distribution[i]. To get a realistic

---

[h]In this paper, MSP distance refers to the distance with respect to the diametrical plane passing through the GC center and orthogonal to the line-of-sight.
[i]In accordance with what is described by the GC core mass-density distribution.[21]

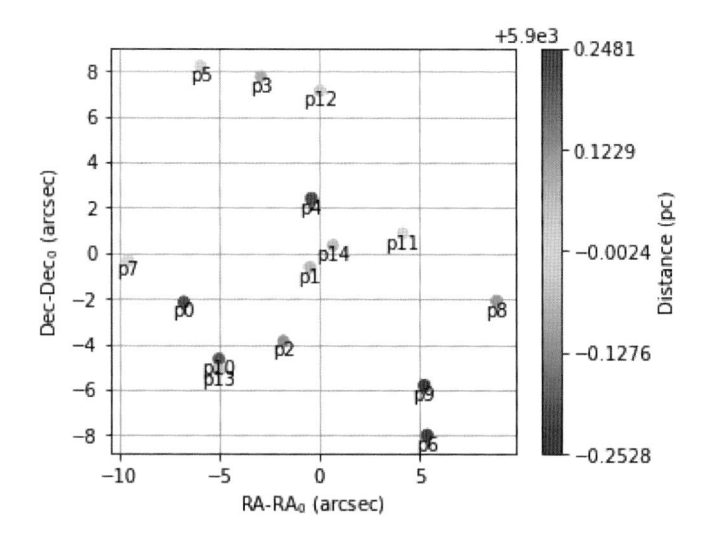

Fig. 3. Simulation of the MSP set. The position of 15 simulated GC core MSPs, randomly scattered within a GC core, whose distance and angular radius are 5.9 kpc and 0.16 arcmin, respectively, is shown. The dots indicate the MSP coordinates (RA and Dec), with respect to the GC center (RA_0 and Dec_0), expressed in arcsec, while the dot colors indicate, as described by the color bar, the MSP distance with respect to the GC core center, expressed in pc (the MSP distance with respect to the SSB can be obtained by summing the values expressed by the labels of the color bar with the quantity on its top).

result, we took the GC core distance, angular radius, and MSP number of the Terzan 5 GC since it is one of the most populated by MSPs[22–24] (see Fig. 3).

We finally calculated the simulated GW-induced timing residuals corresponding to each GC core MSP due to the overall contribution of the GW emission from each SMBHB (see Fig. 4).

4. Results

The simulation results (see Fig. 4) confirm what has been deduced in Sec. 2. In the PTA frequency band, the simulated GW-induced timing residual corresponding to each GC core MSP due to the overall contribution of the GW emission from each SMBHB appear to be strongly correlated. This property can be very useful in the GW search. Observing such correlation for the GC core MSPs would lead to a strong evidence for the GWB, especially if supported by stronger hints of a common red process compatible with a GWB. GC core MSPs can also be helpful for determining the quadrupolar nature of the cross-correlations between the timing residuals of each MSP pair. Indeed, the Hellings and Downs function has a global maximum when the angular distance between an MSP pair is null. Of course, it is unlikely to have an aligned MSP pair by chance, but this frequently happens in GCs due to physical reasons. Therefore, GCs offer the unique possibility of obtaining cross-correlation

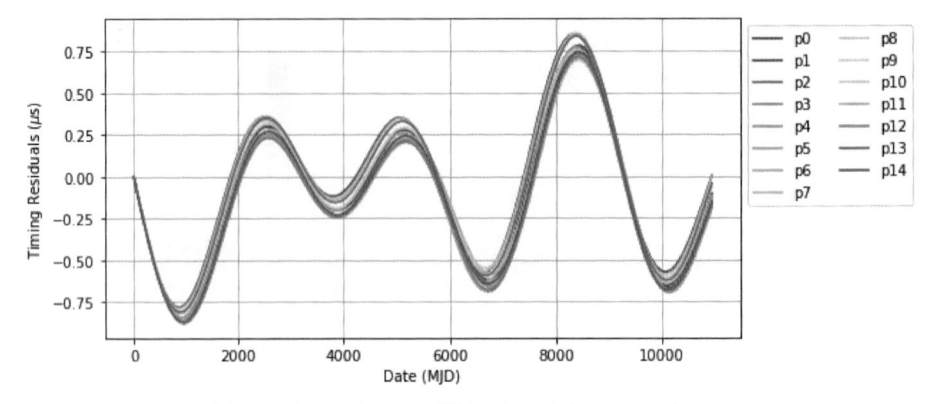

(a) Simulated 30 years GW-induced timing residuals.

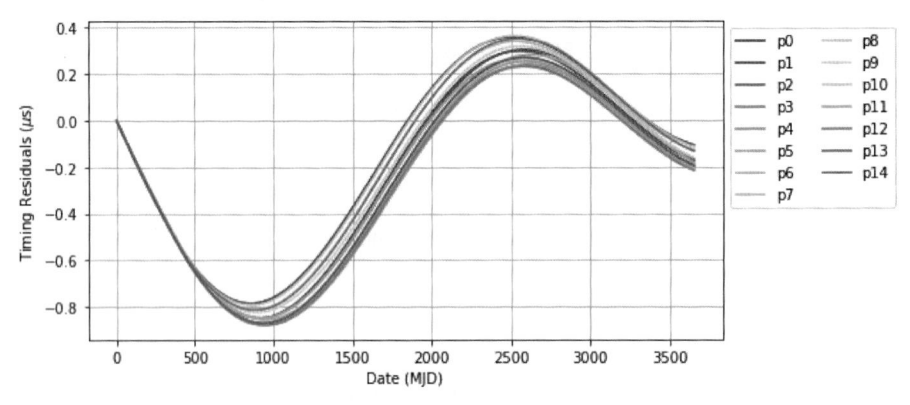

(b) Simulated 10 years GW-induced timing residuals.

Fig. 4. GW-induced timing residuals. Panel (a) shows the simulated GW-induced timing residuals corresponding to each GC core MSP due to the overall contribution of the GW emission from each SMBHB, plotted over a time interval of 30 years. Panel (b) shows the GW-induced timing residuals, plotted over a time interval of only 10 years. In both panels, the colored curves indicate the simulated GW-induced timing residuals, and have a different color for each GC core MSP, as described by the legend. On the horizontal axis of both panels the date measured from the arbitrary beginning of the simulated ToA observation, expressed in MJD, is plotted. On the vertical axis of both panels the timing residuals, expressed in μs, are plotted.

data for low angular separation MSPs, which can be very important because they might challenge or confirm the prediction of the Hellings & Downs function.

5. Conclusion

The proximity between the MSPs lying in a given GC, especially those in the GC core, can be exploited to get unique information about GWs and, for this reason, it is worth considering improving PTAs by including them.

It is important to note that, in the presented analysis, it has been considered an ideal situation to highlight some of the advantages of including MSPs within

GCs in PTAs. On the other hand, this class of MSPs is currently not timed with a precision adequate to detect GW-induced timing residual.[25,26]

Nevertheless, we expect that to change soon, thanks to new detectors, such as the Five hundred meter Aperture Spherical Telescope (FAST),[27] the MeerKAT radio telescope,[28] and the Square Kilometre Array (SKA).[29] SKA, in particular, will play a crucial role in ultra-low frequency GW detection. With its unprecedented sensitivity, it will be possible to time significantly better the GC MSPs, opening the possibility of adopting the strategy proposed in this paper, which is a summary of Ref. 30.

Acknowledgments

We warmly acknowledge Andrea Possenti, of the Istituto Nazionale di Astrofisica (INAF), for many useful discussions. We also acknowledge the support by the Theoretical Astroparticle Physics (TAsP) and Euclid projects of the Istituto Nazionale di Fisica Nucleare (INFN).

References

1. A. Einstein, Die grundlage der allgemeinen relativitätstheorie, *Ann. Phys.* **354**, 769 (1916).
2. B. P. Abbott *et al.*, Observation of gravitational waves from a binary black hole merger, *PRL* **116**, 061102 (2016).
3. B. P. Abbott *et al.*, Gravitational waves and gamma-rays from a binary neutron star merger: GW170817 and GRB170817A, *ApJ* **848**, L13 (2017).
4. R. Abbott *et al.*, Observation of gravitational waves from two neutron star-black hole coalescences, *ApJ* **915**, L5 (2018).
5. P. Amaro-Seoane *et al.*, Laser interferometer space antenna, *eprint arXiv:1702.00786* (2017).
6. Lisa https://https://sci.esa.int/web/lisa.
7. M. Rajagopal and R. W. Romani, Ultra-low-frequency gravitational radiation from massive black hole binaries, *ApJ* **446**, 543 (1995).
8. T. Damour and A. Vilenkin, Gravitational wave bursts from cusps and kinks on cosmic strings, *PRD* **64**, 064008 (2001).
9. Gravitational-wave sensitivity curves https://cplberry.com/2015/01/10/1408-0740/.
10. M. V. Sazhin, Opportunities for detecting ultralong gravitational waves, *Astronomicheskii Zhurnal* **55**, 65 (1978).
11. S. Detweiler, Pulsar timing measurements and the search for gravitational waves, *ApJ* **234**, 1100 (1979).
12. R. W. Hellings and G. S. Downs, Upper limits on the isotropic gravitational radiation background from pulsar timing analysis, *ApJ* **265**, L39 (1983).
13. Z. Arzoumanian *et al.*, The NANOgrav 12.5 yr data set: Search for an isotropic stochastic gravitational-wave background, *ApJ* **905**, L34 (2020).
14. S. Blasi, V. Brdar and K. Schmitz, Has NANOGrav found first evidence for cosmic strings?, *PhRvL* **126**, 041305 (2021).

15. B. Goncharov et al., On the evidence for a common-spectrum process in the search for the nanohertz gravitational-wave background with the parkes pulsar timing array, *ApJ* **917**, L19 (2021).
16. M. Maggiore, *Gravitational Waves. Vol. 2: Astrophysics and Cosmology* (Oxford University Press, 2008).
17. A. N. Lommen, Pulsar timing arrays: the promise of gravitational wave detection, *RPPh* **78**, 124901 (2015).
18. M. Tucci and M. Volonteri, Constraining supermassive black hole evolution through the continuity equation, *A&A* **600**, A64 (2017).
19. M. Celoria, R. Oliveri, A. Sesana and M. Mapelli, Lecture notes on black hole binary astrophysics, *eprint arXiv:1807.11489* (2018).
20. N. Sanchis-Gual, V. Quilis and J. A. Font, Estimate of the gravitational-wave background from the observed cosmological distribution of quasars, *PRD* **104**, 024027 (2021).
21. J. Binney and S. Tremaine, *Galactic dynamics* (Princeton University Press, 1987).
22. M. Cadelano et al., Discovery of three new millisecond pulsars in terzan 5, *ApJ* **855**, 125 (2018).
23. The ATNF pulsar database https://www.atnf.csiro.au/research/pulsar/psrcat/.
24. Pulsars in globular clusters https://www3.mpifr-bonn.mpg.de/staff/pfreire/GCpsr.html.
25. N. D'Amico et al., Timing and searching millisecond pulsars in globular clusters ATNF Proposal, (2009).
26. P. C. C. Freire, Long-term observations of the pulsars in 47 Tucanae - II. Proper motions, accelerations and jerks, *MNRAS* **471**, 857 (2017).
27. R. Nan, The five-hundred aperture spherical radio telescope (FAST) project, *IJMPD* **20**, 989 (2011).
28. M. Bailes et al., The MeerKAT telescope as a pulsar facility: System verification and early science results from MeerTime, *PASA* **37**, e028 (2020).
29. A. Weltman et al., Fundamental physics with the square kilometre array, *PASA* **37**, e002 (2020).
30. M. Maiorano, F. De Paolis and A. A. Nucita, Including millisecond pulsars inside the core of globular clusters in pulsar timing arrays, *in press on EPJP (https://doi.org/10.1140/epjp/s13360-021-02098-0), eprint arXiv:2110.11046* (2021).

Searching for pulsars in globular clusters with the MeerKAT Radio Telescope

F. Abbate on behalf of the MeerTIME/TRAPUM Collaboration

Max Planck Institut für Radioastronomie,
Auf dem Hügel 69, D-53121, Bonn, Germany
E-mail: abbate@mpifr-bonn.mpg.de

Globular clusters are known to host an unusually large population of millisecond pulsar when compared to the Galactic disk. This is thanks to the high rate of dynamical encounters occurring in the clusters that can create the conditions to efficiently recycle neutron stars into millisecond pulsars. The result is a rich population of pulsars with properties and companions difficult or impossible to replicate in the Galactic disk. For these reasons, globular clusters have been and still are a prime target of searches for new and exciting pulsars. Because of their large distances, the limiting factor inhibiting these discoveries is the telescope sensitivity. The MeerKAT radio telescope, a 64-dish interferometer in South Africa, guarantees unrivalled sensitivity for globular clusters in the southern sky. Observations of well-studied globular clusters with MeerKAT have already returned more than 35 new pulsars with many more expected. These exciting discoveries will help us to understand more about the neutron star equation of state, stellar evolution, accretion physics and to hunt for intermediate mass black holes. In this talk I will present the prospects and current discoveries of the globular cluster working group in the MeerTIME and TRAPUM programmes.

Keywords: Pulsars; globular dusters.

1. Pulsars in globular clusters

Globular clusters contain a very rich population of pulsars with 232 known in 36 cluster[a] and this population is quite peculiar when compared with the one in the Galactic disk. The abundance of pulsars per unit of stellar mass in globular clusters is ~ 100 times higher than that of the disk and the vast majority of the pulsars are millisecond pulsars (MSP) with rotation periods shorter than a few tens of ms.

The difference between the population of pulsars in globular clusters and in the Galactic disk is caused by the starkly different environments. Globular clusters have no sign of recent star formation and have very high stellar densities in their cores that can reach up to $\sim 10^{4-5}$ $M_\odot \, \mathrm{pc}^{-3}$ compared to $\sim 1 - 10$ $M_\odot \, \mathrm{pc}^{-3}$ in the Solar neighbourhood. This high stellar density favours dynamical encounters between stars that can lead to exchange encounters where neutron stars become part of new binary systems. The exchanges of companions increase the chance of the neutron star going through an accretion phase boosting the number of low mass

---

[a]An up-to-date count can be found in the webpage https://www3.mpifr-bonn.mpg.de/staff/pfreire/GCpsr.html

X-ray binaries (LMXB) that evole into MSPs. Once a neutron star has been recycled into an MSP, it is likely to remain active for a time even longer than the Hubble time due to the low magnetic field.

Due to the peculiar environment within globular clusters, the possibility of going through multiple stages of recycling and the lack of recent star formation, the majority of pulsars have very fast rotational periods usually smaller than 20 ms. The fastest pulsar known, PSR J1748−2446ad,[1] with a rotational period of 1.395 ms resides in the globular cluster Terzan 5. Not all of the pulsars in globular clusters are, however, very fast. There is a small population of pulsars where the accretion process was interrupted before completion,[2] possibly by external encounters, with period between 20-100 ms called 'mildly recycled'. Furthermore, there is, in some specific clusters, a small number of slow pulsars with periods over 100 ms with the record of 1004.04 ms being held by B1718−19A in NGC 6342.[3] The presence of these apparently 'young' pulsars is in contradiction with the known formation scenarios and the lack of new star formation. Apart from dynamic disruption of LMXB[2] other possible explanations have been put forward like accretion-induced collapse, direct collisions with a main sequence star,[4] or electron capture supernova of an OMgNe white dwarf.[5]

The MSPs populations of globular clusters is also quite different from the one in the Galactic disk. The percentage of isolated to binary MSPs can vary a lot between clusters with some like NGC 6624 and NGC 6517 having mostly isolated pulsars and others like M62 and M5 having mostly binary pulsars. This is linked to the dynamical parameters of the clusters.[2]

The multiple dynamical interactions create a population of binary MSPs that are in some cases very different from the Galactic disk population. Eclipsing systems with non-degenerate companions like 'black widows' and 'redbacks' are common.[3,6,7] Binary systems can acquire high eccentricities and massive companions through successive interactions or through exchange encounters like M15C,[8] NGC 1851A,[9] NGC 6544B,[10] and NGC6652A[11]. A very peculiar triple system with a white dwarf and a Jupiter-mass companion has also been observed in a globular cluster.[12,13]

1.1. Science with pulsars in globular clusters

The scientific achievements made possible by this unique population of pulsars together with the possibility of observing a large number of pulsars in the same telescope beam have made globular clusters a high priority target in the past decades.

The internal composition of neutron stars is determined by the equation-of-state that can be probed by measuring their masses. This can be achieved through pulsar timing by measuring the so-called post-Keplerian parameters, which quantify relativistic orbital effects.[14] One of these parameters is the relativistic precession of the periastron that is relatively easily accessible in highly eccentric systems, and can be used to place constraints on the total mass of the syseteem assuming general relativity. Thanks to this method, some neutron stars with the potential of breaking the current mass limit have been identified.[15,16] The importance of determining neutron star masses is not limited to the value of the maximum mass, also the minimum mass and the distribution of masses can be used to test various formation and recycling scenarios.[17]

Another avenue of research that can be pursued in globular clusters regards the maximum rotation speed. Currently the record of 1.395 ms is held by J1748-2446ad in Terzan 5[1] but even faster pulsars might be present in clusters and set more constraints on the equation of state.

Studies of eclipsing pulsars like 'black widows' and 'redbacks' are essential to study the possible evolution scenarios of MSPs and to constrain the properties of the companions.[18,19]

If we change focus from specific pulsars to the entire population of pulsars in a single cluster, the science perspective broadens to include the properties of the globular clusters themselves. The gravitational effects of the globular clusters on the pulsars are accessible through the derivatives of the rotational period.[20] With a significant number of pulsars, this can give us access to the structural parameters of the clusters and explore the possibility of the presence of an intermediate mass black hole in the center.[21–23]

Using the dispersion measures (DM) and estimating the 3-d position of the pulsars inside the cluster, it becomes possible to look for diffuse gas. This method has led to the first detection of ionized gas in a globular cluster.[23,24] If we add the information coming from the rotation measure, it becomes possible to probe also the magnetic fields. This led to the possible discovery of a magnetized outflow from the Galaxy in the direction of the globular cluster 47 Tucanae.[25]

The numerous scientific possibilities suggest that globular clusters pulsars should still be considered extremely profitable targets for fututre research. Simulations show that a significant population of potentially interesting pulsars is still undiscovered in the clusters.[26,27] These could include MSP-black hole systems, which would be invaluable for tests of gravitational theories.[28] However, despite the efforts, the number of new discoveries in the last ten years has been very low. The ones that were discovered were found in archival data using new search techniques.[29–31] This suggests that we had reached the sensitivity limit of the current observing facilities. To uncover the numerous and potentially interesting pulsars new and more sensitive facilities are needed. One such facility is FAST[32] in China that became operative in 2016 and has already discovered 32 pulsars in globular clusters.[33–35] Another new facility that recently came online and has the potential to revolutionize the field is MeerKAT[36] in South Africa.

2. Advantages of the MeerKAT radio telescope

The MeerKAT radio telescope is an interferometer composed of 64 antennas each with a diameter of 13.5 m. The maximum baseline within antennas is 8 km.

Thanks to its location in South Africa at a latitude of −30°, it can observe the entire Southern sky. When observing with all antennas it can reach telescope gains four times higher than Parkes, the only other radio telescope capable of observing pulsars in cm-wavelengths below a declination of −45°. The gain is also 1.4 times higher than the Green Bank Telescope giving MeerKAT a significant advantage when looking at the central regions of the Galaxy that are observable at high elevations for long hours.

MeerKAT is currently able to observe in UHF-band (544-1088 MHz), L-band (856-1712 MHz) showing remarkably RFI-clear bands. In near future also the S-band (1750-3500 MHz) receivers will be available for observations. A description of the capabilities and potentialities of MeerKAT as a pulsar observatory can be found in Bailes et al. 2020.[37]

Of the MeerKAT Large Science Projects (LSPs) that are currently using MeerKAT for observations, two include pulsars as the main target: MeerTIME[38] and TRAPUM.[39]

2.1. *MeerTIME*

MeerTIME[b] is an LSP based on timing already known pulsars with the high sensitivity of MeerKAT that started collecting data in early 2019. It has four main scientific goals: timing relativistic binary pulsars in order to measure the masses of the systems and test theories of gravity[40]; the Thousand Pulsars Array that monitors a wide variety of pulsars to study their geometries, magnetospheres and interstellar effects[41]; a pulsar timing array that monitors high precision pulsars to contribute to the search for nanohertz gravitational waves [Spiewak et al. submitted]; time pulsars in globular clusters.[42]

The project plans to observe globular cluster pulsars in order to study the eclipses, measure the masses of the pulsars, and study the properties of the globular clusters themselves.

MeerTIME can observe up to four tied array beams using the Pulsar Timing User Supplied Equipment (PTUSE) machines as the main data acquisition system. These beams can either be in "timing" mode where a pulsar is folded in real time using an ephemeris or in "search" mode where the data is saved in a "filterbank" style file and can be folded later or searched for new pulsars or single pulses from previously known ones. For both modes the observations are done with very high time resolution (9 μs), full polarimetric information, and real-time coherent de-dispersion.

Observing globular clusters has the advantage that a large number of pulsars fall within the same beam of the telescope and we are therefore capable of observing them simultaneously if the data is recorded in "search" mode. However, the beam of MeerKAT using the full array with a baseline of 8 km would be too small to

---

[b]http://www.meertime.org

observe all of the pulsars in some globular clusters so in most cases only the central 44 antennas with a maximum baseline of 1 km are used.

2.2. TRAPUM

The TRAnsients and PUlsars with MeerKAT (TRAPUM[c]) LSP focuses on searching for new pulsars. It searches for pulsars in unidentified Fermi sources, supernova remnants, pulsar wind nebulae, in the Galactic plane, in nearby galaxies and in globular clusters. The globular cluster working group is focused on searching both in clusters with known pulsars (which allows de-dispersion at the known DM of the cluster) and in clusters with no known pulsars. The project started taking data in April 2020.

TRAPUM uses Filterbanking Beam-former User Supplied Equipment (FB-FUSE) and the Accelerated Pulsar Search User Supplied Equipment (APSUSE), a 60 node computing cluster, to synthesize up to ~ 400 beams and record incoherently de-dispersed search-mode data for each one. This allows us to cover a large portion of the sky (up to $\sim 1 - 4$ arcmin in radius depending on the configuration) while keeping the full sensitivity of MeerKAT. In this way it is possible to cover the entire cluster with one pointing and search for pulsars in the center and in the outskirts of the cluster simultaneously. However, due to the very high data rate, it is not possible to retain full temporal and spectral resolution nor full polarimetric information.

Because of the complementarity of science goals, the globular cluster working groups of MeerTIME and TRAPUM have decided to collaborate sharing observing time and resources. This collaboration has already resulted in two publications.[42,43]

3. New discoveries

The joint collaboration has discovered 36 new pulsars in globular clusters[d]. The discoveries are summarized in Table 1 and 2 and can be split chronologically into two groups: the ones made with the PTUSE machine before TRAPUM became operative and the ones made possible by the APSUSE machine of TRAPUM.

3.1. MeerTIME discoveries

The first batch of discoveries made with observations taken by MeerTIME is already published.[42] This publication contains the description and the properties of 8 new millisecond pulsars found in six different globular clusters. Three of them are isolated pulsars while the rest are found in binary systems. The profiles of these pulsars are shown in Figure 1.

---

[c]http://www.trapum.org
[d]the full up-to-date list of discoveries can be found at http://www.trapum.org/discoveries.html

Table 1. Properties of the pulsars discovered by MeerTIME/TRAPUM using the PTUSE machine

Pulsar name	Period (ms)	DM (pc cm^{-3})	notes
Ter 5 an	4.8023	237.7	Binary
M62G	4.6081	113.6	Binary
NGC 6522D	5.5369	192.7	Isolated
NGC 6624G	6.0912	86.20	Binary
47 Tuc ac	2.7456	24.46	Ecl. Binary
47 Tuc ad	3.7460	24.41	Ecl. Binary
NGC 6752F	8.4854	33.20	Isolated
NGC 6624H	5.1301	86.85	Isolated
NGC 6440G	5.2157	219.7	Isolated
NGC 6440H	2.8486	222.6	Binary
M28M	9.5689	119.23	Binary

Table 2. Properties of the pulsars discovered by MeerTIME/TRAPUM using the APSUSE machine

Pulsar name	Period (ms)	DM (pc cm^{-3})	notes
NGC 6752G	4.7902	33.27	Isolated
M28N	3.3429	119.33	Binary
NGC 6342B	2.5683	71.44	Isolated
NGC 1851B	2.8162	52.07	Isolated
NGC 1851C	5.5648	52.05	Isolated
NGC 1851D	4.5543	52.17	Binary
NGC 1851E	5.5952	51.95	Binary
NGC 1851F	4.3294	51.63	Binary
NGC 1851G	3.8028	51.01	Binary
NGC 1851H	5.5061	52.26	Binary
NGC 6752H	2.0155	33.25	Isolated
NGC 6752I	2.6582	33.34	Isolated
NGC 6624I	4.3195	87.35	Isolated
NGC 6624J	20.8995	86.85	Isolated
NGC 6441E	251.1587	221.16	Isolated
NGC 6441F	6.0006	228.22	Binary
NGC 6441G	5.3522	229.20	Isolated
NGC 1851I	32.6538	52.42	Binary
NGC 1851J	6.6329	52.06	Isolated
NGC 1851K	4.6920	51.93	Isolated
NGC 1851L	2.9586	51.23	Binary
NGC 1851M	4.7977	51.66	Isolated
NGC 1851N	5.5679	51.11	Isolated
J1823-3022	2497.72	96.9	Isolated
NGC 6624K	2.7686	87.46	Isolated

These discoveries include two new eclipsing millisecond pulsars 47 Tuc ac and 47 Tuc ad. Fitting for the orbits of these pulsars suggest that 47 Tuc ac is a 'black widow' pulsar while 47 Tuc ad is a 'red-back'. Both of these discoveries were then

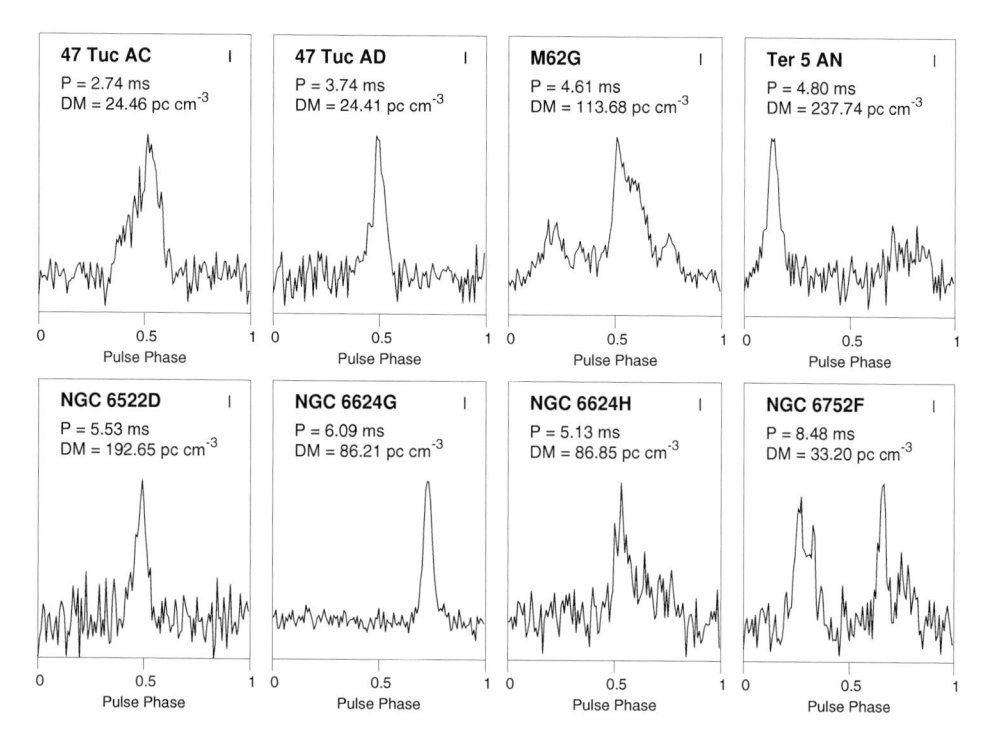

Fig. 1. Profiles of the eight new pulsar discoveries published in Ridolfi et al. 2021.[42]

re-detected in previous Parkes observations but due to scintillation effects and eclipses the detections were too few to allow for deriving phase-connected timing solutions.

Possibly the most interesting pulsar in this set of discoveries is NGC 6624G. This pulsar is found in a binary with orbital period of 1.54 days and eccentricity of 0.38. Because of the very high eccentricity it was possible to use only 11 months of data to measure the rate of advance of periastron $\dot{\omega} = 0.217 \pm 0.004$ deg yr^{-1}. Assuming that this advance is caused entirely by relativistic effects and using formulas derived in General Relativity (GR) it is possible to derive the total mass of the system, $M_{tot} = 2.65 \pm 0.07 M_\odot$. This parameter alone is not enough to measure precisely the mass of the pulsar itself, see Figure 2, but suggests that the neutron star is particularly heavy. Measurements of further post-keplerian parameters will be needed to accurately determine the mass. The companion mass is also particularly heavy suggesting that it was not the original companion that recycled the pulsar but a new companion gained in an exchange encounter. This is the type of secondary exchange products that we have been looking for.

Another newly discovered pulsar that has the potential of being particularly massive is Ter 5 an. This binary has an eccentricity of 0.0066, two orders of magnitude higher than the average millisecond pulsar binaries found in the Galactic field. It is likely caused by distant stellar encounters in the dense cluster environment. Also

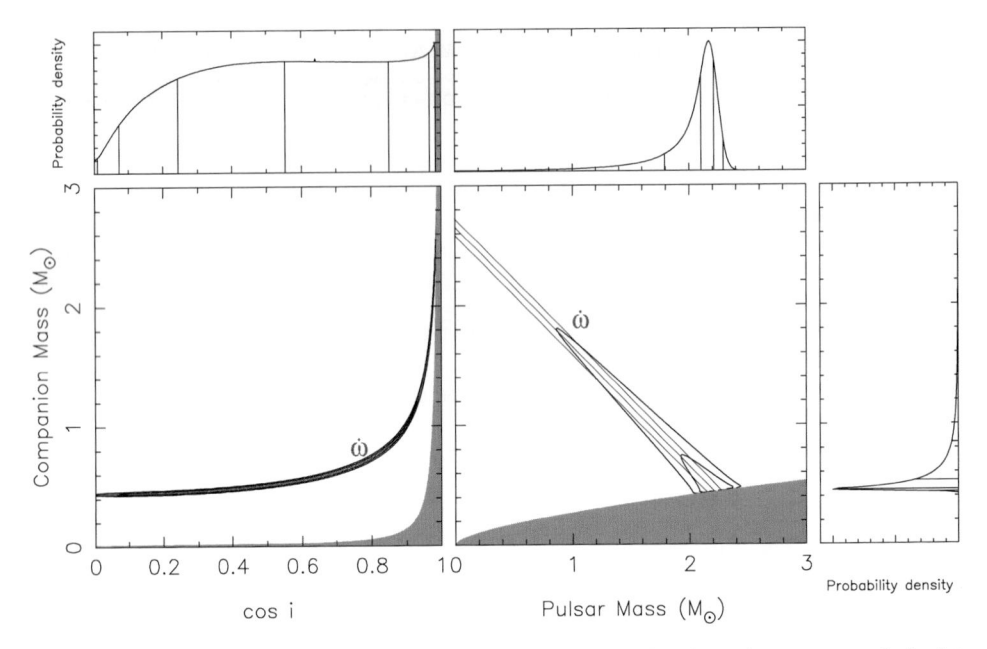

Fig. 2. Mass-inclination and mass-mass diagrams for NGC 6624G. The main square panels depict the $\cos i$-M_c and M_c-M_p planes. The grey areas in the former are excluded by the requirement that the mass of the pulsar is positive, the grey areas in the latter are excluded by the mass function and the requirement that $\sin i \leq 1$. The red lines depict the masses consistent with the measurement of $\dot{\omega}$ and its ± 1-σ uncertainties, under the assumption that this effect is dominated by the GR contribution and that GR is the correct theory of gravity. The contours include 68.3 and 95.4% of a 2-D probability distribution function (pdf) derived from the χ^2 of TEMPO fits that assumed all GR effects to be according to the masses and orbital inclination at each point. The side panels show the probability density functions for the $\cos i$ (top left), M_p (top right) and M_c (right) derived by marginalizing the aforementioned 2-D pdfs. we obtain a median for the pulsar mass of 2.1 $M_\odot$, but with a tail of probability that extends to lower masses: there is a 31% probability of $M_p < 2$ $M_\odot$ and a 3.8% probability of $M_p < 1.4$ $M_\odot$. Thus, either the pulsar is very massive, or it has a massive companion; the system was likely formed in an exchange encounter. Credits: Ridolfi et al. 2021.[42]

here, owing to the recovery of the system in data from the Green Banks Telescope and the resulting long baseline, it was possible to measure an advance of the periastron with a rate of $\dot{\omega} = 0.009 \pm 0.001$ deg yr^{-1}. With the assumption that it fully caused by GR effects, the total mass becomes $M_{tot} = 2.95 \pm 0.52 M_\odot$. The mass-inclination and mass-mass diagrams are shown in Figure 3. The uncertainties in this case are higher allowing for a greater range in pulsar mass.

The other pulsars discovered by MeerTIME are in the process of being published. Of these, one is particularly interesting: NGC 6440H. It is a binary pulsar with a very light companion. Assuming a pulsar mass of 1.4 $M_\odot$, the companion has a minimum mass of 0.0062 $M_\odot$. This very low mass of the companion suggests that it could be brown dwarf or a planet. If the planetary nature of the companion is confirmed, this would be only the second pulsar with such a companion.[12,13]

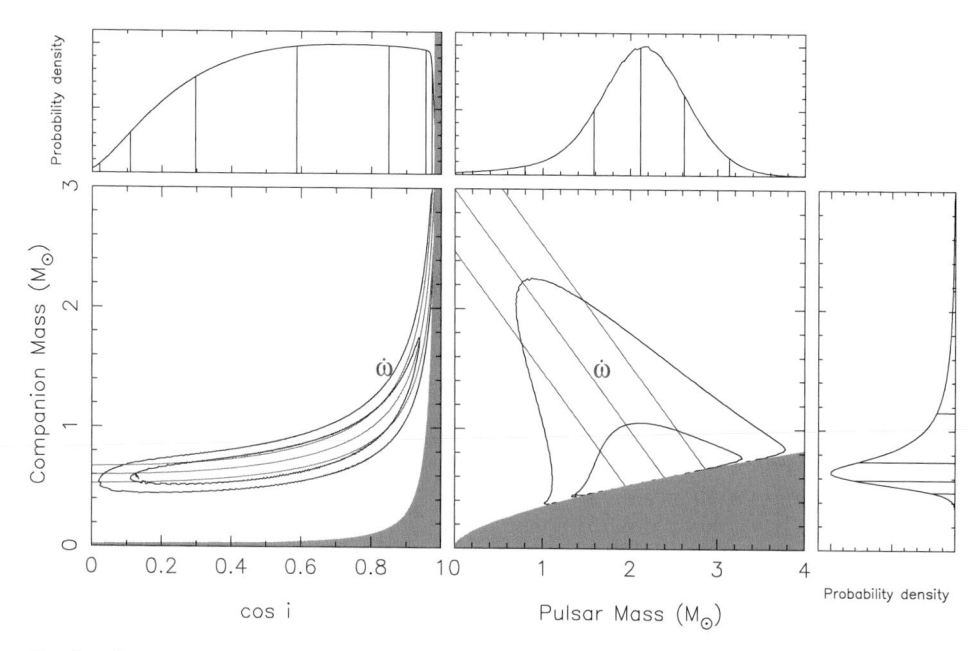

Fig. 3. Same mass-inclination and mass-mass diagrams as in Figure 2 but for Ter 5 an. The estimated median pulsar mass is 2.13 M$_\odot$ and median companion mass is 0.75 M$_\odot$. Credits: Ridolfi et al. 2021.[42]

3.2. TRAPUM discoveries

Only a small fraction of the observations of globular clusters with the APSUSE machine with TRAPUM have currently been processed. The large volumes of data produced in these observations require a large processing power to be properly analyzed. Despite this, the new pulsar discoveries are already more than double than those made using the PTUSE machines and only the central 44 antennas. The list is shown in Table 2.

More than half of these discoveries come from just one globular cluster NGC 1851. This is a core-collapsed cluster that was known to contain only one pulsar NGC 1851A. TRAPUM observations in just the central beam have confirmed the presence of 13 new pulsars. This large population makes NGC 1851 the third globular cluster for number of known pulsars together with M28. Once phase connected ephemerides are determined for all these pulsars it will be possible to probe the potential well and test the presence of gas and magnetic fields within the cluster.

Two of these new discoveries, NGC 1851D and NGC 1851E, are binary systems with very high eccentricities. NGC 1851E has an orbital period of around 7 days and an eccentricity of $e = 0.71$. This high value means that in the near future it will be possible to measure the rate of precession of the periastron to high accuracy and therefore the total mass of the system. Early fits to the orbit suggest that, assuming a pulsar mass of 1.4 M$_\odot$, the companion has a minimum mass of 1.5 M$_\odot$.

This suggests that there is a high probability of this being another double neutron star system.

The vast majority of the discoveries are fast spinning MSPs but there are some exceptions: NGC 6624J and NGC 1851I have periods respectively of 20.89 and 32.65 ms, that suggest that they are mildly recycled pulsars. Another exceptions is NGC 6441E, a slow pulsar with a period of 251.15 ms. Particularly interesting is also J1823-3022 with a period of 2497.72 ms. This potentially record breaking pulsar has been found in the outskirts of the globular cluster NGC 6624 and has a DM that is higher than the rest of the pulsars in the cluster. Because of these reasons it is not clear if it is really a member of the cluster or if it is a Galactic disk pulsar positioned along the same line of sight. All of these slow pulsars are in core-collapsed clusters validating the correlation between spin periods and dynamical state of the cluster suggested previously.[2]

These early results from a fraction of the observations suggest that many new discoveries are possible by analyzing the data that has already been captured.

4. Future plans

Early observations have showed that the future of the two projects MeerTIME and TRAPUM can prove revolutionary for the science of globular cluster pulsars.

MeerTIME will focus on timing the already discovered pulsars in order to measure the masses of the most interesting binaries and characterise the eclipses of the ecplising 'black-widows' and 'redbacks'. Furthermore, by improving the timing models of all pulsars it will be possible the study the properties of the clusters like the gas content, magnetic field and the presence of intermediate mass black holes.

TRAPUM, on the other hand, will continue to search for new pulsars broadening the scope in order to include clusters with no previously known pulsars. The searches will involve all of the available bands, going from the UHF band, where the pulsars are brighter but the interstellar medium is more noisy to the L band and the S band where the effects of scattering and the interstellar medium are minimized.

In closing, the last few years have shown an almost unprecedented growth in the number of pulsars in globular clusters going from 150 in 2018 to over 230 in 2021. The largest contributor is the MeerKAT telescope with 36 but a very close second is FAST with 32 new discoveries. These numbers are likely to increase in the following years and with them also the possibility of finding even more exotic systems like a double millisecond pulsar binary or a pulsar-black hole binary.

References

1. J. W. T. Hessels, S. M. Ransom, I. H. Stairs, P. C. C. Freire, V. M. Kaspi and F. Camilo, A Radio Pulsar Spinning at 716 Hz, *Science* **311**, 1901 (March 2006).
2. F. Verbunt and P. C. C. Freire, On the disruption of pulsar and X-ray binaries in globular clusters, *Astronomy and Astrophysics* **561**, p. A11 (January 2014).

3. A. G. Lyne, J. D. Biggs, P. A. Harrison and M. Bailes, A long-period globular-cluster pulsar in an eclipsing binary system, *Nature* **361**, 47 (January 1993).
4. A. G. Lyne, R. N. Manchester and N. D'Amico, PSR B1745-20 and Young Pulsars in Globular Clusters, *Astrophysical Journal Letters* **460**, p. L41 (March 1996).
5. J. Boyles, D. R. Lorimer, P. J. Turk, R. Mnatsakanov, R. S. Lynch, S. M. Ransom, P. C. Freire and K. Belczynski, Young Radio Pulsars in Galactic Globular Clusters, *The Astrophysical Journal* **742**, p. 51 (November 2011).
6. F. Camilo, D. R. Lorimer, P. Freire, A. G. Lyne and R. N. Manchester, Observations of 20 Millisecond Pulsars in 47 Tucanae at 20 Centimeters, *The Astrophysical Journal* **535**, 975 (June 2000).
7. S. M. Ransom, J. W. T. Hessels, I. H. Stairs, P. C. C. Freire, F. Camilo, V. M. Kaspi and D. L. Kaplan, Twenty-One Millisecond Pulsars in Terzan 5 Using the Green Bank Telescope, *Science* **307**, 892 (February 2005).
8. S. B. Anderson, P. W. Gorham, S. R. Kulkarni, T. A. Prince and A. Wolszczan, Discovery of two radio pulsars in the globular cluster M15, *Nature* **346**, 42 (July 1990).
9. P. C. Freire, Y. Gupta, S. M. Ransom and C. H. Ishwara-Chandra, Giant Metrewave Radio Telescope Discovery of a Millisecond Pulsar in a Very Eccentric Binary System, *Astrophysical Journal Letters* **606**, L53 (May 2004).
10. R. S. Lynch, P. C. C. Freire, S. M. Ransom and B. A. Jacoby, The Timing of Nine Globular Cluster Pulsars, *The Astrophysical Journal* **745**, p. 109 (February 2012).
11. M. E. DeCesar, S. M. Ransom, D. L. Kaplan, P. S. Ray and A. M. Geller, A Highly Eccentric 3.9 Millisecond Binary Pulsar in the Globular Cluster NGC 6652, *The Astrophysical Journal Letters* **807**, p. L23 (July 2015).
12. S. E. Thorsett, Z. Arzoumanian, F. Camilo and A. G. Lyne, The Triple Pulsar System PSR B1620-26 in M4, *The Astrophysical Journal* **523**, 763 (October 1999).
13. S. Sigurdsson, H. B. Richer, B. M. Hansen, I. H. Stairs and S. E. Thorsett, A Young White Dwarf Companion to Pulsar B1620-26: Evidence for Early Planet Formation, *Science* **301**, 193 (July 2003).
14. J. Antoniadis, P. C. C. Freire, N. Wex, T. M. Tauris, R. S. Lynch, M. H. van Kerkwijk, M. Kramer, C. Bassa, V. S. Dhillon, T. Driebe, J. W. T. Hessels, V. M. Kaspi, V. I. Kondratiev, N. Langer, T. R. Marsh, M. A. McLaughlin, T. T. Pennucci, S. M. Ransom, I. H. Stairs, J. van Leeuwen, J. P. W. Verbiest and D. G. Whelan, A Massive Pulsar in a Compact Relativistic Binary, *Science* **340**, p. 448 (April 2013).
15. P. C. C. Freire, S. M. Ransom, S. Bégin, I. H. Stairs, J. W. T. Hessels, L. H. Frey and F. Camilo, Eight New Millisecond Pulsars in NGC 6440 and NGC 6441, *The Astrophysical Journal* **675**, 670 (March 2008).
16. P. C. C. Freire, A. Wolszczan, M. van den Berg and J. W. T. Hessels, A Massive Neutron Star in the Globular Cluster M5, *The Astrophysical Journal* **679**, 1433 (June 2008).
17. A. Ridolfi, P. C. C. Freire, Y. Gupta and S. M. Ransom, Upgraded Giant Metrewave Radio Telescope timing of NGC 1851A: A possible millisecond pulsar - neutron star system, *Monthly Notices of the Royal Astronomical Society* **490**, 3860 (December 2019).
18. M. H. van Kerkwijk, V. M. Kaspi, A. R. Klemola, S. R. Kulkarni, A. G. Lyne and D. Van Buren, Optical Observations of the Binary Pulsar System PSR B1718-19: Implications for Tidal Circularization, *The Astrophysical Journal* **529**, 428 (January 2000).
19. S. Bogdanov, J. E. Grindlay and M. van den Berg, An X-Ray Variable Millisecond Pulsar in the Globular Cluster 47 Tucanae: Closing the Link to Low-Mass X-Ray Binaries, *The Astrophysical Journal* **630**, 1029 (September 2005).

20. E. S. Phinney, Pulsars as Probes of Globular Cluster Dynamics (January 1993).
21. B. J. Prager, S. M. Ransom, P. C. C. Freire, J. W. T. Hessels, I. H. Stairs, P. Arras and M. Cadelano, Using Long-term Millisecond Pulsar Timing to Obtain Physical Characteristics of the Bulge Globular Cluster Terzan 5, *The Astrophysical Journal* **845**, p. 148 (August 2017).
22. B. B. P. Perera, B. W. Stappers, A. G. Lyne, C. G. Bassa, I. Cognard, L. Guillemot, M. Kramer, G. Theureau and G. Desvignes, Evidence for an intermediate-mass black hole in the globular cluster NGC 6624, *Monthly Notices of the Royal Astronomical Society* **468**, 2114 (June 2017).
23. F. Abbate, A. Possenti, A. Ridolfi, P. C. C. Freire, F. Camilo, R. N. Manchester and N. D'Amico, Internal gas models and central black hole in 47 Tucanae using millisecond pulsars, *Monthly Notices of the Royal Astronomical Society* **481**, 627 (November 2018).
24. P. C. Freire, M. Kramer, A. G. Lyne, F. Camilo, R. N. Manchester and N. D'Amico, Detection of Ionized Gas in the Globular Cluster 47 Tucanae, *The Astrophysical Journal* **557**, L105 (August 2001).
25. F. Abbate, A. Possenti, C. Tiburzi, E. Barr, W. van Straten, A. Ridolfi and P. Freire, Constraints on the magnetic field in the Galactic halo from globular cluster pulsars, *Nature Astronomy* **4**, 704 (March 2020).
26. M. Bagchi, D. R. Lorimer and J. Chennamangalam, Luminosities of recycled radio pulsars in globular clusters, *Monthly Notices of the Royal Astronomical Society* **418**, 477 (November 2011).
27. P. J. Turk and D. R. Lorimer, An empirical Bayesian analysis applied to the globular cluster pulsar population, *Monthly Notices of the Royal Astronomical Society* **436**, 3720 (December 2013).
28. K. Liu, R. P. Eatough, N. Wex and M. Kramer, Pulsar-black hole binaries: Prospects for new gravity tests with future radio telescopes, *Monthly Notices of the Royal Astronomical Society* **445**, 3115 (December 2014).
29. Z. Pan, G. Hobbs, D. Li, A. Ridolfi, P. Wang and P. Freire, Discovery of two new pulsars in 47 Tucanae (NGC 104), *Monthly Notices of the Royal Astronomical Society* **459**, L26 (June 2016).
30. M. Cadelano, S. M. Ransom, P. C. C. Freire, F. R. Ferraro, J. W. T. Hessels, B. Lanzoni, C. Pallanca and I. H. Stairs, Discovery of Three New Millisecond Pulsars in Terzan 5, *The Astrophysical Journal* **855**, p. 125 (March 2018).
31. B. C. Andersen and S. M. Ransom, A Fourier Domain "Jerk" Search for Binary Pulsars, *The Astrophysical Journal Letters* **863**, p. L13 (August 2018).
32. R. Nan, D. Li, C. Jin, Q. Wang, L. Zhu, W. Zhu, H. Zhang, Y. Yue and L. Qian, The Five-Hundred Aperture Spherical Radio Telescope (fast) Project, *International Journal of Modern Physics D* **20**, 989 (January 2011).
33. Z. Pan, S. M. Ransom, D. R. Lorimer, W. C. Fiore, L. Qian, L. Wang, B. W. Stappers, G. Hobbs, W. Zhu, Y. Yue, P. Wang, J. Lu, K. Liu, B. Peng, L. Zhang and D. Li, The FAST Discovery of an Eclipsing Binary Millisecond Pulsar in the Globular Cluster M92 (NGC 6341), *The Astrophysical Journal Letters* **892**, p. L6 (March 2020).
34. L. Wang, B. Peng, B. W. Stappers, K. Liu, M. J. Keith, A. G. Lyne, J. Lu, Y.-Z. Yu, F. Kou, J. Yan, P. Jiang, C. Jin, D. Li, Q. Li, L. Qian, Q. Wang, Y. Yue, H. Zhang, S. Zhang, Y. Zhu and FAST Collaboration, Discovery and Timing of Pulsars in the Globular Cluster M13 with FAST, *The Astrophysical Journal* **892**, p. 43 (March 2020).
35. Z. Pan, L. Qian, X. Ma, K. Liu, L. Wang, J. Luo, Z. Yan, S. Ransom, D. Lorimer, D. Li and P. Jiang, FAST Globular Cluster Pulsar Survey: Twenty-four Pulsars Discovered in 15 Globular Clusters, *The Astrophysical Journal Letters* **915**, p. L28 (July 2021).

36. R. S. Booth and J. L. Jonas, An Overview of the MeerKAT Project, *African Skies* **16**, p. 101 (March 2012).
37. M. Bailes, A. Jameson, F. Abbate, E. D. Barr, N. D. R. Bhat, L. Bondonneau, M. Burgay, S. J. Buchner, F. Camilo, D. J. Champion, I. Cognard, P. B. Demorest, P. C. C. Freire, T. Gautam, M. Geyer, J. M. Griessmeier, L. Guillemot, H. Hu, F. Jankowski, S. Johnston, A. Karastergiou, R. Karuppusamy, D. Kaur, M. J. Keith, M. Kramer, J. van Leeuwen, M. E. Lower, Y. Maan, M. A. McLaughlin, B. W. Meyers, S. Osłowski, L. S. Oswald, A. Parthasarathy, T. Pennucci, B. Posselt, A. Possenti, S. M. Ransom, D. J. Reardon, A. Ridolfi, C. T. G. Schollar, M. Serylak, G. Shaifullah, M. Shamohammadi, R. M. Shannon, C. Sobey, X. Song, R. Spiewak, I. H. Stairs, B. W. Stappers, W. van Straten, A. Szary, G. Theureau, V. Venkatraman Krishnan, P. Weltevrede, N. Wex, T. D. Abbott, G. B. Adams, J. P. Burger, R. R. G. Gamatham, M. Gouws, D. M. Horn, B. Hugo, A. F. Joubert, J. R. Manley, K. McAlpine, S. S. Passmoor, A. Peens-Hough, Z. R. Ramudzuli, A. Rust, S. Salie, L. C. Schwardt, R. Siebrits, G. Van Tonder, V. Van Tonder and M. G. Welz, The MeerKAT telescope as a pulsar facility: System verification and early science results from MeerTime, *Publications of the Astronomical Society of Australia* **37**, p. e028 (July 2020).
38. M. Bailes, E. Barr, N. D. R. Bhat, J. Brink, S. Buchner, M. Burgay, F. Camilo, D. Champion, J. Hessels, A. Jameson, S. Johnston, A. Karastergiou, R. Karuppusamy, V. Kaspi, M. Keith, M. Kramer, M. McLaughlin, K. Moodley, S. Oslowski, A. Possenti, S. Ransom, F. Rasio, J. Sievers, M. Serylak, B. Stappers, I. Stairs, G. Theureau, W. van Straten, P. Weltevrede and N. Wex, MeerTime - the MeerKAT Key Science Program on Pulsar Timing (January 2016).
39. B. Stappers and M. Kramer, An Update on TRAPUM (January 2016).
40. M. Kramer, I. H. Stairs, V. Venkatraman Krishnan, P. C. C. Freire, F. Abbate, M. Bailes, M. Burgay, S. Buchner, D. J. Champion, I. Cognard, T. Gautam, M. Geyer, L. Guillemot, H. Hu, G. Janssen, M. E. Lower, A. Parthasarathy, A. Possenti, S. Ransom, D. J. Reardon, A. Ridolfi, M. Serylak, R. M. Shannon, R. Spiewak, G. Theureau, W. van Straten, N. Wex, L. S. Oswald, B. Posselt, C. Sobey, E. D. Barr, F. Camilo, B. Hugo, A. Jameson, S. Johnston, A. Karastergiou, M. Keith and S. Osłowski, The relativistic binary programme on MeerKAT: science objectives and first results, *Monthly Notices of the Royal Astronomical Society* **504**, 2094 (June 2021).
41. S. Johnston, A. Karastergiou, M. J. Keith, X. Song, P. Weltevrede, F. Abbate, M. Bailes, S. Buchner, F. Camilo, M. Geyer, B. Hugo, A. Jameson, M. Kramer, A. Parthasarathy, D. J. Reardon, A. Ridolfi, M. Serylak, R. M. Shannon, R. Spiewak, W. van Straten, V. Venkatraman Krishnan, F. Jankowski, B. W. Meyers, L. Oswald, B. Posselt, C. Sobey, A. Szary and J. van Leeuwen, The Thousand-Pulsar-Array programme on MeerKAT - I. Science objectives and first results, *Monthly Notices of the Royal Astronomical Society* **493**, 3608 (April 2020).
42. A. Ridolfi, T. Gautam, P. C. C. Freire, S. M. Ransom, S. J. Buchner, A. Possenti, V. Venkatraman Krishnan, M. Bailes, M. Kramer, B. W. Stappers, F. Abbate, E. D. Barr, M. Burgay, F. Camilo, A. Corongiu, A. Jameson, P. V. Padmanabh, L. Vleeschower, D. J. Champion, W. Chen, M. Geyer, A. Karastergiou, R. Karuppusamy, A. Parthasarathy, D. J. Reardon, M. Serylak, R. M. Shannon and R. Spiewak, Eight new millisecond pulsars from the first MeerKAT globular cluster census, *Monthly Notices of the Royal Astronomical Society* **504**, 1407 (June 2021).
43. F. Abbate, M. Bailes, S. J. Buchner, F. Camilo, P. C. C. Freire, M. Geyer, A. Jameson, M. Kramer, A. Possenti, A. Ridolfi, M. Serylak, R. Spiewak, B. W. Stappers and V. Venkatraman Krishnan, Giant pulses from J1823-3021A observed with the MeerKAT telescope, *Monthly Notices of the Royal Astronomical Society* **498**, 875 (October 2020).

Gravitational lensing by rotating Simpson–Visser black holes

Sushant G. Ghosh

Centre for Theoretical Physics, Jamia Millia Islamia, New Delhi 110025, India;
Astrophysics and Cosmology Research Unit, School of Mathematics, Statistics and Computer Science, University of KwaZulu-Natal, Private Bag 54001, Durban 4000, South Africa
E-mail: sgghosh@gmail.com, sghosh2@jmi.ac.in

Shafqat Ul Islam

Centre for Theoretical Physics, Jamia Millia Islamia, New Delhi 110025, India
E-mail: shafphy@gmail.com

We investigate gravitational lensing by rotating Simpson-Visser black hole in the strong field limit and find that deflection angle α_D, photon sphere radius x_m and ratio of the flux of the first image to all other images r_{mag} decreases. In contrast, angular position θ_1, angular separation s increases more rapidly with l and their behaviour is similar to that of the Kerr black hole. By considering the supermassive black holes NGC 4649, NGC 1332, Sgr A* and M87* as rotating Simpson-Visser black holes, we found that the latter can be quantitatively distinguished from the Kerr black hole when probed by gravitational lensing effects. The deviation of the lensing observables $\Delta\theta_1$ and Δs by considering the Sgr A* and M87* as rotating Simpson-Visser black holes from Kerr black hole for $0 < l/2M < 0.6$ ($a/2M = 0.45$) are in the range $0.0422 - 0.11658$ μas and $0.031709 - 0.08758$ μas, which are too small to be distinguished by the current Event Horizon Telescope observations, and one has to wait for future observations by new generation EHT that can pin down the exact constraint.

Keywords: Lensing, Simpson-Visser black hole

1. Introduction

The singularity theorems of Hawking and Penrose[1] (see also Ref.[2]) established that the end state of gravitational collapse of a sufficiently massive star ($\sim 3.5 M_\odot$) is a gravitational singularity i.e., spacetime ceases to exist and hence marking a breakdown of the laws of physics. Apart from the quantum gravity which is expected to resolve the singularity issue,[3] significant attention has also shifted to regular models which can allow one to understand the black hole interior. Sakharov[4] and Gliner[5] pioneered the idea of regular models that suggests a de Sitter core and the cosmological vacuum obeys the equation of state. Motivated by Sakharov[4] and Gliner,[5] Bardeen[6] proposed the first regular black hole with horizons.[7,8] The Bardeen black hole spacetime asymptotically reduces to Schwarzschild black hole[7] but acts like the de Sitter spacetime near the origin thus eventually settling with a regular center. Later, it was shown in Ref.[9] that Bardeen's model is an exact solution of general relativity coupled to nonlinear electrodynamics thereby an alteration of the

Reissner–Nordström black hole solution.[10] Bardeen's proposal with non-linear electrodynamics as the source has been extended to regular black holes,[11–13] and also on regular rotating black[8,14,15] holes.

Lately, Simpson-Visser propose an interesting spherically symmetric regular black hole spacetime[16–18] where a parameter l is introduced to cause a repulsive force to avoid singularity and is responsible for the regularisation of the metric at $r = 0$. The Simpson-Visser metric which interpolates between the Schwarzschild black hole and the Morris–Thorne traversable wormhole is regular everywhere as the scalar.[16] The Simpson-Visser spacetime received significant attention with a discussion on the energy conditions, causal structure, and innermost stable circular orbit (ISCO),[16] regularity, quasi-local mass, energy conditions and the causal structure of black bounce models,[18] gravitational lensing[19] and shadow formation.[22,23]

Graviatational lensing(GL), a vital and prior prediction of general relativity(GR) primarily in the strong field regime,[24] is considered an important test of GR. Since then, GL proved to be an essential tool for providing insights on the spacetime.[25] In the strong field regime, photon encircles the black hole more than once resulting in a bending angle greater than 2π radians and results in shadow,[26] photon rings[27] and relativistic images.[28–32] GL for various spacetimes has been discussed in detail.[29–39] Virbhadra and Ellis developed a numerical method[33] to study the large deflection of light rays in strong field. Later, Bozza analysed analytically the strong field gravitational lensing for general spherically symmetric and static spacetime.[29–32] Tsukamoto[37] worked on similar lines to study the lensing by spherically symmetric and static spacetime. GL began to be crucial in 1990's which triggered quantitative studies by Kerr black holes[29,40,41] and has since then recieved significant attention[42–49] due to the tremendous advancement of observational facilities.

This paper investigates the strong gravitational lensing by rotating Simpson-Visser black holes[20] and assess the phenomenological differences with the Kerr black holes; in particular, we discuss the effect of deformation parameter l on gravitational lensing observables and time delay between the relativistic images. Further, considering the supermassive black holes as the lens, we obtain the positions, separation, magnification, and time delay in the formation of relativistic images.

We adopt natural units $(8\pi G = c = 1)$

2. Rotating Simpson-Visser black holes

The rotating Simpson-Visser black hole metric apart from mass M and angular momentum a, has an additional parameter l, which in Boyer-Lindquist coordinates reads as[20]

$$ds^2 = -\left(1 - \frac{\sqrt{x^2+l^2}}{\Sigma}\right)dt^2 + \frac{\Sigma}{\Delta}dx^2 + \Sigma d\theta^2 - \frac{2a\sin^2\theta\sqrt{x^2+l^2}}{\Sigma}dtd\phi$$
$$+ \frac{\mathbb{A}\sin^2\theta}{\Sigma}d\phi^2, \tag{1}$$

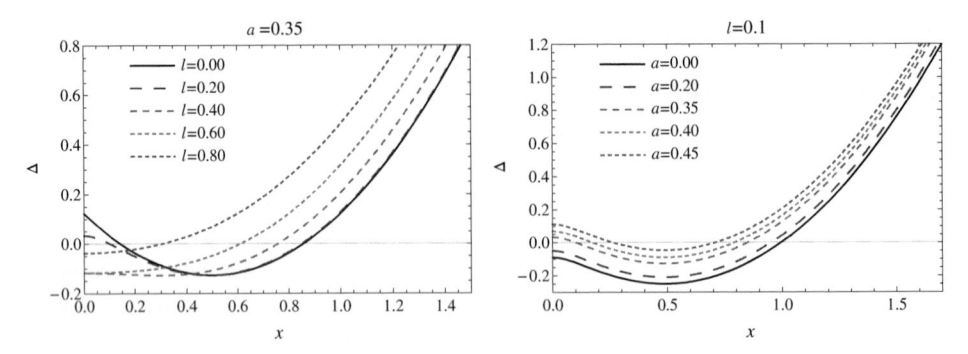

Fig. 1. The horizons (zeroes of Δ) of rotating Simpson-Visser black holes. The case $l = 0$ (Kerr black hole) is shown for comparison. For $l > l_c$ (e.g., for $a = 0.35$, $l_c \approx 0.1429$ and for $a = 0.45$, $l_c \approx 0.282$), the black holes admit only event horizon.

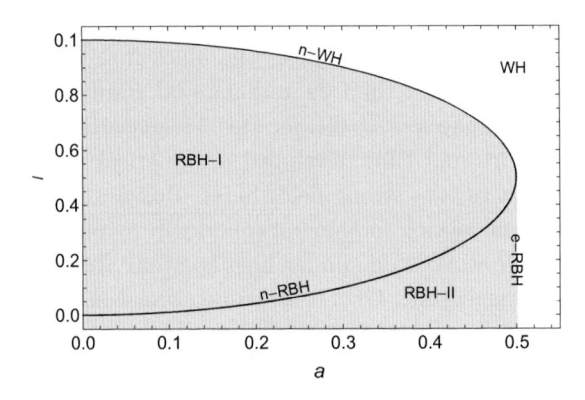

Fig. 2. Parameter space for the rotating Simpson-Visser black hole and the corresponding spacetime structure. For $a = 0.3$ the rotating Simpson-Visser black hole admits both Cauchy and event horizon for $0.0 < l_{cb} < 0.1$ and only event horizon for $0.1 < l_c < 0.9$. For $a = 0.45$, both Cauchy and event horizon exist for $0.0 < l_{cb} < 0.282055$ and only event horizon is present for $0.282055 < l_c < 0.717945$. We measure the quantities a and l in units of Schwarzschild radius $2M$.

where $\Sigma = x^2 + l^2 + a^2 \cos^2 \theta$, $\Delta = x^2 + l^2 + a^2 - 2\sqrt{x^2 + l^2}$ and $\mathbb{A} = (x^2 + l^2 + a^2)^2 - \Delta a^2 \sin^2 \theta$. We measure the quantities r, a, t, and l in units of Schwarzschild radius $2M$[31] and use x instead of radius r.

Moreover, the metric (1) is composed of identical portions around $x = 0$ which is a regular surface of finite size for $l \neq 0$, and the observer can easily cross.[20] Depending on the value of the parameter l, the metric (1) is either a regular black hole or a traversable wormhole.[20]

The points of coordinate singularities, which exist at $\Delta = 0$, are also the horizons of the black hole metric (1) and are located at $x_\pm$ (cf. Fig. 1). The horizons of the metric (1) exist when $|a| < 0.5$ and $l < 0.5 + \sqrt{(0.5)^2 - a^2}$ (cf. Fig. 1). Consequently, following cases are possible for the metric (1)

- For $l < 0.5 - \sqrt{(0.5)^2 - a^2}$, we have two horizons $x_\pm$, corresponding to the radii of outer (event) (x_+) and inner (Cauchy) (x_-) horizons (This corresponds to RBH-II, in Fig. 2).
- For $0.5 - \sqrt{(0.5)^2 - a^2} < l < 0.5 + \sqrt{(0.5)^2 - a^2}$, only event horizon exists. (This corresponds to RBH-I, in Fig. 2).
- For $|a| = 0.5$ and $l < 0.5$, Cauchy and event horizon correspond to extremal black hole (e-RBH) with degenerate horizons, while for $|a| = 0.5$ and $l > 0.5$, there are no horizons and so no black hole.
- The case $|a| > 0.5$ with no horizons, the metric (1) describes a traversable wormhole with a time-like throat, which becomes null for $|a| = 0.5$.[20]

We restrict the values of a and l in the range $|a| < 0.5$ and $0 < l < 0.5 + \sqrt{(0.5)^2 - a^2}$ for at least one horizon to exist and to qualify the spacetime as a black hole. We shall also consider the values $x > 0$ as the solution (1) is symmetric around $x = 0$.

3. Gravitational lensing

The rotating Simpson-Visser black hole in the equatorial plane takes the form

$$ds^2 = -A(x)dt^2 + B(x)dx^2 + C(x)d\phi^2 - D(x)dt\,d\phi, \tag{2}$$

where

$$A(x) = 1 - \frac{1}{\sqrt{\Sigma}}, \quad B(x) = \frac{\Sigma}{\Delta}, \quad C(x) = \frac{\mathbb{A}}{\Sigma}, \quad D(x) = \frac{2a}{\sqrt{\Sigma}},$$

$\Sigma = x^2 + l^2$ and $\mathbb{A} = (x^2 + l^2 + a^2)^2 - \Delta a^2$. Further, we also assume the source, which is located behind the lens, to be almost aligned along the optical axis such that the images are highly magnified and very prominent.

The projection of four-momentum p^μ along the two commuting Killing vectors $\xi^\mu_{(t)}$ and $\xi^\mu_{(\phi)}$ results in two linearly independent conserved quantities; energy E and axial angular momentum component L.

$$p_t = g_{tt}p^t + g_{t\phi}p^\phi = -E, \qquad p_\phi = g_{t\phi}p^t + g_{\phi\phi}p^\phi = L. \tag{3}$$

Solving the two coupled equations results in the following equations of motion for t and ϕ coordinates[56]

$$\Sigma\frac{dt}{d\tau} = a(L - aE\sin^2\theta) + \frac{x^2 + l^2 + a^2}{\Delta}[E(x^2 + l^2 + a^2) - La] \tag{4}$$

$$\Sigma\frac{d\phi}{d\tau} = \frac{L}{\sin^2\theta} - aE + \frac{a}{\Delta}[E(x^2 + l^2 + a^2) - La], \tag{5}$$

We follow the Hamilton-Jacobi equation and the integral approach pioneered by Carter[57] to obtain the equations of motion in the first-order differential form for

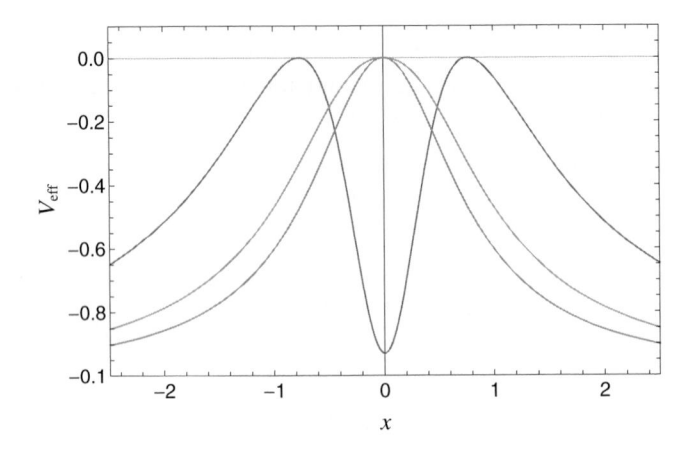

Fig. 3. The effective potential as a function of radial coordinate x. (a) The blue line represents the effective potential for rotating Simpson-Visser black hole black hole with $a = 0.334$ and $l = 0.698$ (b) the orange line represents the wormhole throat with $a = 0.5$ and $l = 0.7$ (c) the green line represents the traversable wormhole with $a = 0.884$ and $l = 0.746$.

the rotating Simpson-Visser black hole spacetime (1), where the equations descend from

$$\frac{\partial S}{\partial \tau} = -\frac{1}{2} g^{\mu\nu} \frac{\partial S}{\partial x^\mu} \frac{\partial S}{\partial x^\nu}, \qquad (6)$$

where S is the action and τ is the affine parameter along the geodesic. Using the conserved quantities p_t and p_ϕ, the Jacobi action S admits a separable solution in the first integral form as follows[57]

$$S = -Et + L\phi + S_x(x) + S_\theta(\theta). \qquad (7)$$

Here, $S_x(x)$ and $S_\theta(\theta)$, respectively, are functions only of the x and θ coordinates. On using the four-momentum relations

$$\frac{dS_x}{dx} = p_x = g_{xx}p^x = \frac{\Sigma}{\Delta}\frac{dx}{d\tau}, \qquad (8)$$

$$\frac{dS_\theta}{d\theta} = p_\theta = g_{\theta\theta}p^\theta = \Sigma\frac{d\theta}{d\tau}, \qquad (9)$$

in Eq. (6), the following system of first-order ordinary differential equations are obtained

$$\Sigma\frac{dx}{d\tau} = \pm\sqrt{\mathcal{R}(x)}, \qquad (10)$$

$$\Sigma\frac{d\theta}{d\tau} = \pm\sqrt{\Theta(\theta)}, \qquad (11)$$

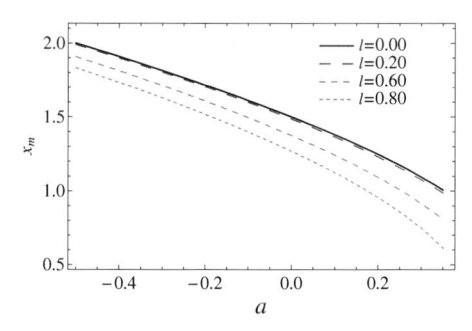

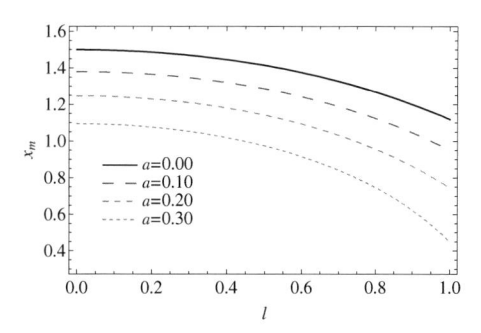

Fig. 4. Plot showing radii of unstable circular photon orbit for rotating Simpson-Visser black hole (dashed curve) in comparison to Kerr black hole (solid curve in the left plot).

where the effective potentials $\mathcal{R}(x)$ and $\Theta(\theta)$ for radial and polar motion are given by

$$\mathcal{R} = [E(x^2 + l^2 + a^2) - La]^2 - \Delta[(L - aE)^2 + \mathcal{K}], \tag{12}$$

$$\Theta = \mathcal{K} - \cos^2\theta \left[a^2 E^2 + \frac{L^2}{\sin^2\theta}\right]. \tag{13}$$

$\mathcal{K}$ is a separability constant related to the Carter constant that derives its existence from a Killing tensor. The motion of the photon is symmetric around the equatorial plane in the region $\mathcal{R} \geq 0$ and $\Theta(\theta) \geq 0$. The bound orbits can be identified by the solutions of[56,58]

$$\mathcal{R}|_{(x=x_m)} = \left.\frac{\partial \mathcal{R}}{\partial x}\right|_{(x=x_m)} = 0, \text{ and } \left.\frac{\partial^2 \mathcal{R}}{\partial x^2}\right|_{(x=x_m)} > 0, \tag{14}$$

where x_m is the unstable photon orbit radius. Eq.(10) can be rewritten as

$$\dot{x}^2 + V_{\text{eff}} = 0 \tag{15}$$

where V_{eff} is the effective potential. For simplicity we take $E = 1$ and plot the effective potential in Fig. 3.

The deflection angle of a photon moving on the equatorial plane using the geodesics Eqs. (5) and (10), for rotating Simpson-Visser black hole is given by[32]

$$\alpha_D(x_0) = 2\int_{x_0}^{\infty} \frac{\sqrt{A_0 B}\,(2AL + D)}{\sqrt{4AC + D^2}\sqrt{A_0 C - AC_0 + L\,(AD_0 - A_0 D)}} dx - \pi, \tag{16}$$

where x_0 is the distance of closest approach of the light to the lens, L is the projection of angular momentum and A_0 is defined by $A(x_0)$. Equation (14) gives the radii of photon sphere which can be rewritten as[32]

$$A(x)C'(x) - A'(x)C(x) + L(A'(x)D(x) - A(x)D'(x)) = 0. \tag{17}$$

The radii of unstable photon sphere is depicted in Fig. 4 and is smaller when compared with the Kerr black hole.[32] Further, the deflection angle when expanded in the SDL takes the form

$$\alpha_D(\theta) = -\bar{a}\log\left(\frac{\theta D_{OL}}{u_m} - 1\right) + \bar{b} + \mathcal{O}(u - u_m), \tag{18}$$

where u is the impact parameter and u_m is the value of impact parameter at $x_0 = x_m$ and is independent of the parameter l (cf. Table 1). The deflection angle in Eq.(18) is depicted in Fig. 6 wherein it is evident that deflection angle diverges at u_m.

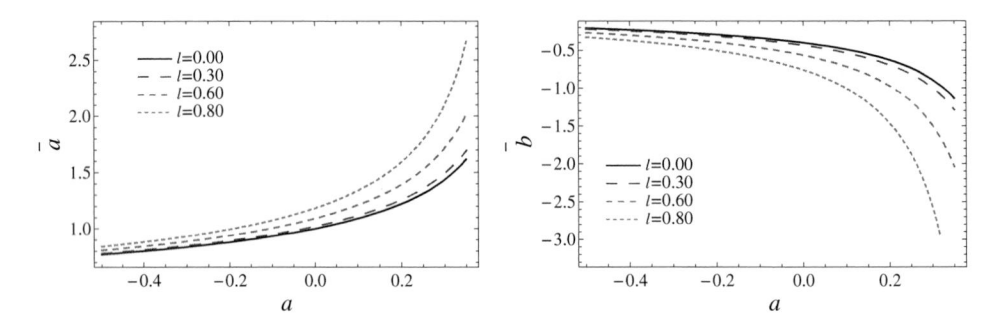

Fig. 5. Plot showing the behaviour of strong lensing coefficients $\bar{a}$ and $\bar{b}$. The solid black curve corresponds to Kerr black hole.

Table 1. Estimates for the strong lensing coefficients $\bar{a}$, $\bar{b}$ and the impact parameter u_m/R_s. We measure the quantities a and l in units of Schwarzschild radius $2M$.

a	l	$\bar{a}$	$\bar{b}$	u_m/R_s
		Lensing Coefficients		
	0.00	1.00000	-0.400230	2.59808
	0.25	1.01419	-0.423912	2.59808
	0.50	1.06066	-0.506783	2.59808
0.00	0.75	1.15470	-0.698106	2.59808
	0.95	1.29219	-1.03047	2.59808
	0.00	1.43692	-0.891314	1.91924
	0.25	1.47594	-0.965136	1.91924
	0.50	1.61535	-1.256170	1.91924
0.30	0.75	1.97301	-2.180740	1.91924
	0.90	2.52527	-4.037170	1.91924
	0.00	2.58352	-2.76735	1.42221
	0.30	2.79948	-3.26402	1.42221
	0.40	3.01084	-3.79273	1.42221
0.45	0.50	3.3693	-4.7799	1.42221
	0.60	4.05135	-6.94521	1.42221

The behaviour of coefficients $\bar{a}$ and $\bar{b}$ is similar to the Kerr black hole ($l = 0$) and spherical Simpson-Visser ($a = 0$) (cf. Fig. 5). The deflection angle for rotating

Simpson-Visser black hole in SDL (cf. Fig. 6) like Kerr black hole, is more than 2π radians and multiple images of the source are formed.

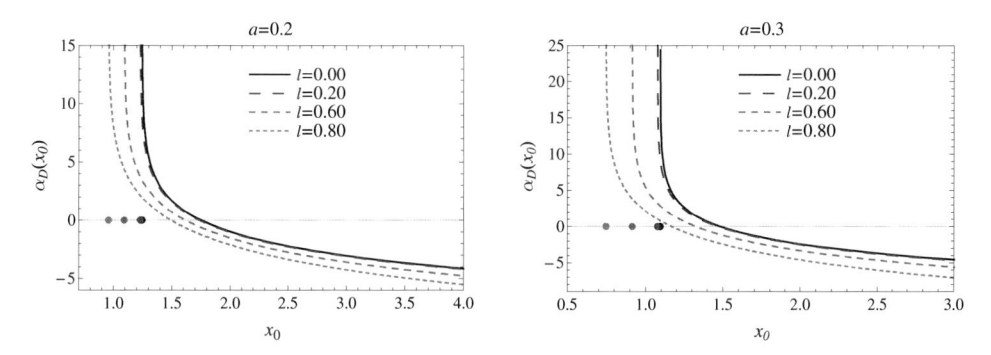

Fig. 6. Plot showing the variation of light deflection angle as a function of minimum distance x_0 for different values of a and l.

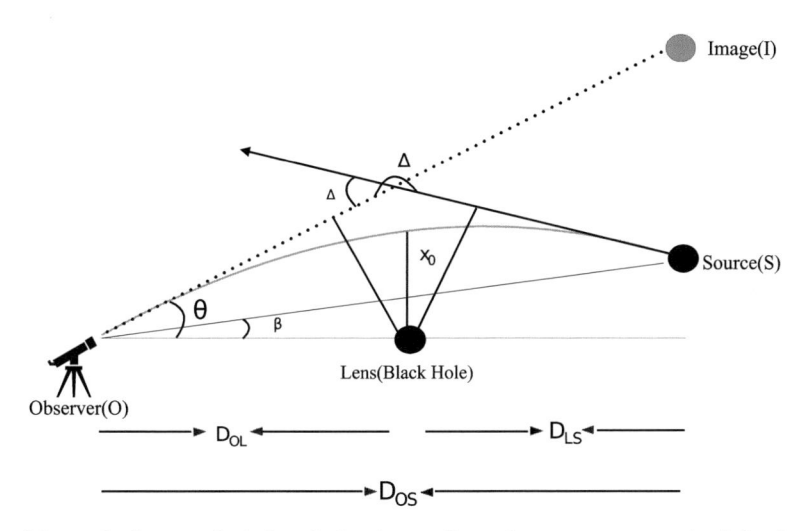

Fig. 7. Schematic diagram depicting the lensing configuration. α_D represent the deflection angle, where as θ and β are the angular positions of the image and source, respectively.

3.1. *Observables*

Next, we consider the lens equation to define a geometrical relationship between the observer, the source and the lens (cf. Fig. 7) as given in,[31,54]

$$\beta = \theta - \frac{D_{LS}}{D_{OL} + D_{LS}} \Delta\alpha_n, \qquad (19)$$

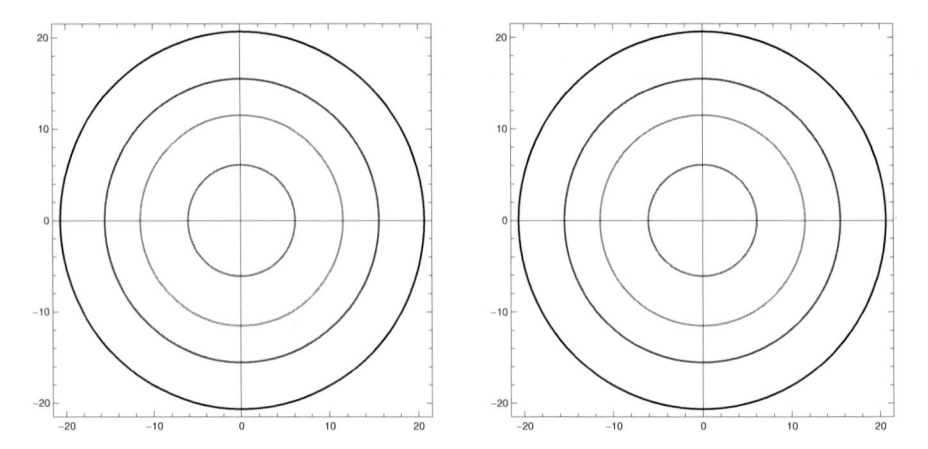

Fig. 8. The polar plot of θ_n^E (for $n = 1$): The angular radius of the outermost Einstein ring. Here, we consider Kerr black hole ($a = 0.25$ and $l = 0$) (left) and rotating Simpson-Visser balck hole ($a = 0.25$ and $l = 0.7$) (right) as supermassive black holes Sgr A* (black), M87* (blue), NGC 4649 (orange) and NGC 1332 (red).

where $\Delta\alpha_n$ is the extra deflection angle with $n \in N$ and $0 < \Delta\alpha_n \ll 1$. It has been acessed in[54] that lens equation discussed in[55] is bit more accurate than Eq.(19) but the latter has an advantage in analysing the observational effects more precisely. We shall estimate the observables for the strong gravitational lensing by rotating Simpson-Visser black hole as in.[31, 32, 42, 52] Using the lens Eq. (19) and Eq. (18), the angular separation between the lens and the n-th image is given by[32]

$$\theta_n = \frac{u_m}{D_{OL}}(1 + e_n) + \frac{D_{OL} + D_{LS}}{D_{LS}} \frac{u_m e_n}{\bar{a} D_{OL}}(\beta - \theta_n^0), \qquad (20)$$

where

$$e_n = \exp\left(\frac{\bar{b}}{\bar{a}} - \frac{2n\pi}{\bar{a}}\right). \qquad (21)$$

Here the first term corresponds to value of θ when photon travels $2n\pi$ radians around the black hole and second term is the correction part to $2n\pi$.[31] For $\beta = 0$, a ring-shaped image is produced, known as Einstein rings.[25] Solving Eq. (20) for $\beta = 0$ and $D_{OL} = D_{LS}$, the angular radius of the Einstein rings can be obtained as[31, 51]

$$\theta_n^E = \frac{u_m}{D_{OL}}(1 + e_n), \qquad (22)$$

where $n = 1$ is the angular radius of the outermost Einstein ring (cf. Fig. 8).[42, 52]

The brightness or magnification of the image is preserved in the deflection of the light but the appearance of the solid angle changes, thus magnifying the brightness of the images. The magnification of n-loop image is given by[31,32]

$$\mu_n = \left|\frac{\beta}{\theta}\frac{\partial \beta}{\partial \theta}\right|^{-1}_{\theta_n^0} = \frac{1}{\beta}\left[\frac{u_m}{D_{OL}}(1+e_n)\left(\frac{D_{OL}+D_{LS}}{D_{LS}}\frac{u_m e_n}{D_{OL}\bar{a}}\right)\right]. \quad (23)$$

Table 2. Estimates for the observable θ_∞ and time delay $\Delta T_{2,1}$ for supermassive black holes at the center of nearby galaxies. These observables are independent of l.

a	Sgr A*		M87*		NGC 4649		NGC 1332	
	$\theta_\infty(\mu as)$	$\Delta T_{2,1}(\min)$	$\theta_\infty(\mu as)$	$\Delta T_{2,1}(\text{hrs})$	$\theta_\infty(\mu as)$	$\Delta T_{2,1}(\text{hrs})$	$\theta_\infty(\mu as)$	$\Delta T_{2,1}(\text{hrs})$
0.00	26.3299	11.4968	19.782	289.647	14.6615	210.328	7.76719	113.185
0.30	19.4504	8.4928	14.6133	213.968	10.8307	155.374	5.73777	83.612
0.45	14.4132	6.29295	10.8289	158.543	8.02585	115.127	4.2518	61.9538

The Eq. (23) diverges at $\beta \to 0$, suggesting that the perfect alignment maximises the possibility of the detection of the images. If the first image can be distinguished from the rest packed ones, we can have three characteristic observables[31] as

$$\theta_\infty = \frac{u_m}{D_{OL}}, \quad (24)$$

$$s = \theta_1 - \theta_\infty \approx \theta_\infty \exp\left(\frac{\bar{b}}{\bar{a}} - \frac{2\pi}{\bar{a}}\right), \quad (25)$$

$$r_{\text{mag}} = \frac{\mu_1}{\sum_{n=2}^{\infty}\mu_n} \approx \frac{5\pi}{\bar{a}\log(10)}, \quad (26)$$

where, θ_∞ and θ_1 are the angular positions of the innermost image and outermost image, respectively and s is the angular separation between them. r_{mag} gives the ratio of the flux of the first image and the all other images. By observationally measuring these observables and inverting the Eqs. (24-26), the lensing coefficients $\bar{a}$, $\bar{b}$, the minimum impact parameter u_m can be obtained.[53]

The time delay, which is another important observable, is defined as the time difference between the formation of relativistic images considering the source with luminosity variations. If the time signal between the first and second image can be distinguished, the time delay $\Delta T_{2,1}$, when images are on the same side of the lens, can be approximated as[50]

$$\Delta T_{2,1} \approx \frac{2\pi}{\bar{a}\sqrt{c_{2m}}} \frac{2x^2\sqrt{B(x)A(x_0)}[C(x)-LD(x)]}{x_0\sqrt{C(x)(D(x)^2+4A(x)C(x))}}\left(1-\frac{1}{\sqrt{A(x_0)}f(z,x_0)}\right)$$
$$= 2\pi u_m, \quad (27)$$

To measure the time delay, it is necessary that the source should be pulsating and the pulses show up in the images with a temporal phase thus making it possible to measure the time difference.

Table 3. Estimates for the lensing observables for supermassive black holes at the center of nearby galaxies for different values of a and l.

		Sgr A*		M87*		NGC 4649		NGC 1332		
a	l	θ_1 (μas)	s (μas)	θ_1 (μas)	s (μas)	θ_1 (μas)	s (μas)	θ_1 (μas)	s (μas)	r_{mag}
	0.00	26.3628	0.0329517	19.8068	0.0247571	14.6799	0.0183488	7.77691	0.00972061	6.82188
	0.25	26.3652	0.0353455	19.8086	0.0265556	14.6812	0.0196818	7.77762	0.0104268	6.72647
	0.50	26.3735	0.0436767	19.8148	0.032815	14.6858	0.0243209	7.78008	0.0128844	6.43173
0.00	0.75	26.3922	0.0623325	19.8289	0.0468314	14.6962	0.0347092	7.78558	0.0183878	5.90792
	0.95	26.4216	0.091705	19.8509	0.0688993	14.7126	0.051065	7.79425	0.0270526	5.27931
	0.0	19.5823	0.131981	14.7125	0.0991593	10.9042	0.0734923	5.7767	0.0389338	4.74756
	0.25	19.5936	0.143258	14.721	0.107632	10.9105	0.0797717	5.78003	0.0422604	4.62205
	0.50	19.6331	0.18278	14.7507	0.137326	10.9325	0.101779	5.79169	0.0539194	4.22317
0.30	0.75	19.717	0.266607	14.8137	0.200306	10.9792	0.148458	5.81642	0.078648	3.45759
	0.90	19.777	0.326616	14.8587	0.245392	11.0126	0.181873	5.83412	0.0963504	2.70145
	0.0	14.8471	0.433859	11.1548	0.325965	8.26744	0.24159	4.37982	0.127986	2.64054
	0.30	14.8893	0.476064	11.1865	0.357674	8.29094	0.265092	4.39227	0.140437	2.43684
	0.40	14.9206	0.50742	11.21009	0.38123	8.3084	0.28255	4.40152	0.149689	2.26578
0.45	0.50	14.9537	0.540453	11.2349	0.40605	8.32679	0.30094	4.41126	0.15943	2.02472
	0.60	14.9636	0.550440	11.2424	0.41355	8.33235	0.306507	4.41421	0.162377	1.15820

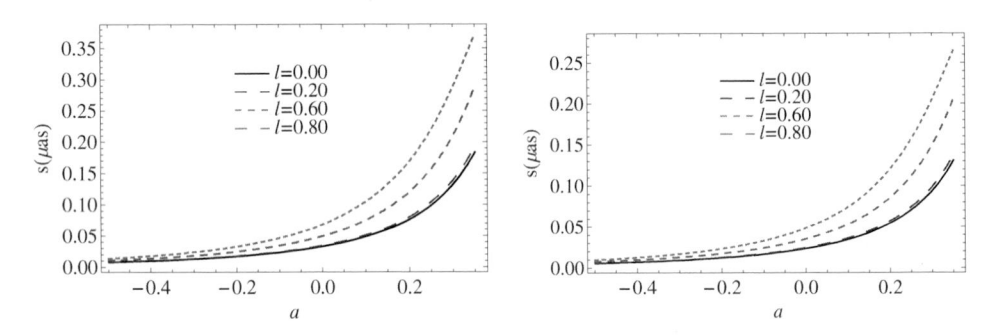

Fig. 9. Plot showing strong lensing observables s for the Sgr A*(left panel) and M87*(right panel) black holes.

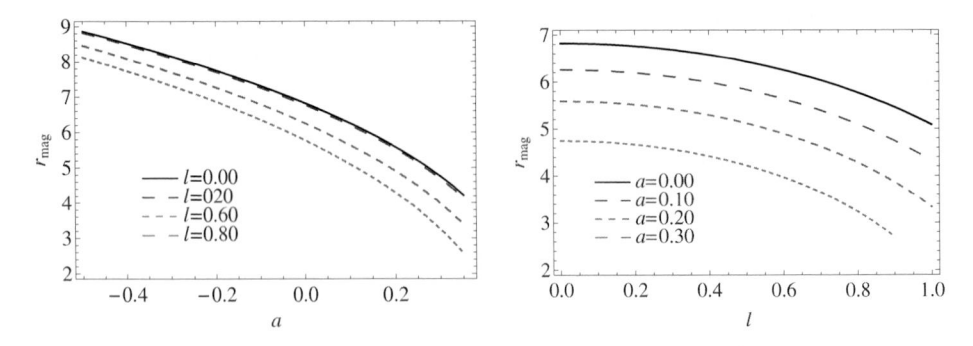

Fig. 10. Plot showing strong lensing observables r_{mag} for different parameters. r_{mag} is independent of the black hole mass or its distance from the observer.

4. Applications to supermassive black holes

Here, we model the supermassive black holes Sgr A*, M87*, NGC4649 and NGC1332 as the rotating Simpson-Visser black holes to estimate and compare the observables in SDL with the GR counterparts, and use mass and distance as in the Ref.[42]. The observables θ_∞ and time delay $\Delta T_{2,1}$ are independent of the parameter l and are shown in Table 2. We observe that θ_1 for Sgr A* and M87* is in the range of 14.84 μas $< \theta_1 <$ 26.36 μas and 11.15 μas $< \theta_1 <$ 19.80 μas, respectively. The observables s and r_{mag} for rotating Simpson-Visser black holes are depicted in Fig. 9 and 10, whereas their values, along with the position of the first image θ_1 are tabulated in Table 3. Further, the angular separation s between the first and inner most image due to the rotating Simpson-Visser black hole for Sgr A* and M87* are in the range of 32.95 $nas < s <$ 433.8 nas and 24.75 $nas < s <$ 413.55 nas, respectively (cf. Table 3). Although the rotating Simpson-Visser black holes deviate from the Kerr black hole but the deviation are beyond the threshold of the current EHT observation (cf. Table 4) and should wait for the next generation event horizon telescope (ngEHT). From the brightness difference, we find that Kerr black holes produces less intense images. The angular position and angular separation of the relativistic images are larger for the Sgr A* black hole than the M87*, NGC4649 and NGC1332 black holes. The time delay of the first image from that of the second image $\Delta T_{2,1}$, for Sgr A*, M87*, NGC4649 and NGC1332 respectively, can reach $\sim$ 11.49 min, $\sim$ 289.6 hrs, $\sim$ 210.3 hrs and $\sim$ 113.2 hrs (cf. Table 2).

Table 4. Deviation of the lensing observables of rotating Simpson Visser black holes from Kerr black hole for supermassive black holes at the center of nearby galaxies for $a = 0.3$ and $a = 0.45$. For $a = 0.3$ the rotating Simpson-Visser black hole admits both Cauchy and event horizon for $0.0 < l_{cb} < 0.1$ and only event horizon for $0.1 < l_c < 0.9$. For $a = 0.45$, both Cauchy and event horizon exist for $0.0 < l_{cb} < 0.282055$ and only event horizon is present for $0.282055 < l_c < 0.717945$. Here $\Delta(X) = X_{RSV} - X_{Kerr}$.

| | | Sgr A* | | M87* | | NGC 4649 | | NGC 1332 | | |
a	l	$\Delta\theta_1$(μas)	Δs (μas)	$\Delta\theta_1$(μas)	Δs (μas)	$\Delta\theta_1$(μas)	Δs (μas)	$\Delta\theta_1$(μas)	Δs (μas)	Δr_{mag}
	0.25	0.0112	0.0112769	0.0080	0.00803363	0.00627	0.00627941	0.0149	0.0149856	-0.125517
	0.50	0.0508	0.0507993	0.0362	0.0361893	0.02828	0.028287	0.0149	0.0149856	-0.524392
	0.75	0.1346	0.134626	0.0959	0.0959075	0.0749	0.0397141	0.0397	0.078648	-1.28997
0.30	0.90	0.1946	0.194635	0.1386	0.138658	0.108381	0.0574166	0.0574	0.0963504	-2.04612
	0.30	0.0422	0.042205	0.0317	0.0317098	0.0235	0.0235018	0.0124	0.0124505	-0.2037
	0.40	0.0735	0.073560	0.0552	0.0552727	0.0409	0.0409655	0.02170	0.0217022	-0.3747
	0.50	0.1065	0.10659	0.08008	0.0800856	0.05935	0.0593557	0.03144	0.0314447	-0.615823
0.45	0.60	0.1165	0.116582	0.08758	0.0875896	0.06491	0.0649173	0.03439	0.0343911	-0.956684

5. Conclusions

We have investigated the gravitational lensing of light in strong field limit due to rotating Simpson-Visser black holes which has an additional deviation parameter l besides mass M and spin a. We find that $\bar{a}$ increases whereas $\bar{b}$ and deflection angle α_D decrease with increasing l. On the other hand, u_m depends only on the spin of the black hole and is independent of the black hole parameter l. The observables θ_∞ and $\Delta T_{2,1}$ do not depend of l. Further, the relative magnification of the first and innermost images is independent of the black hole mass or its distance from the observer. Interestingly, it turns out that the separation between the two relativistic images for Simpson-Visser black holes is greater than that for the Kerr black holes.

Although, the gravitational lensing analysis (cf. Figs. 6, 9 and 10) and horizon structure (cf. Figs. 1 and 2), constrain the rotating Simpson-Visser black holes parameter l but the deviation produced in lensing observables by taking the rotating Simpson-Visser black holes as the supermassive black holes, namely, Sgr A*, M87*, NGC 4649 and NGC 1332, from those for Kerr black hole for $0 < l < 0.6$ ($a = 0.45$) are $\mathcal{O}(\mu as)$ (cf. Table 4). Our results are the generalization of previous discussions, on the Kerr black holes, in a more general setting in the limit $l \to 0$, reduced exactly to *vis-à-vis* the Kerr black hole results.

Acknowledgments

S.G.G. and S.U.I. would like to thank SERB-DST for the ASEAN project IMRC/AISTDF/CRD/2018/000042.

References

1. S.W. Hawking and R. Penrose, Proc. R. Soc. A **314**, 529 (1970).
2. S.W. Hawking and G.F.R. Ellis, The Large Scale Structure of Space and Time (Cambridge University Press, Cambridge, 1973).
3. J.A. Wheeler, Relativity, Groups, and Topology, edited by C. DeWitt and B. DeWitt (Gordon and Breach, New York, 1964).
4. A.D. Sakharov, Sov. Phys. JETP, **22**, 241 (1966).
5. E.B. Gliner, Sov. Phys. JETP, **22**, 378 (1966).
6. J. Bardeen, in *Proceedings of GR5* (Tiflis, U.S.S.R., 1968).
7. S. Ansoldi, [arXiv:0802.0330 [gr-qc]].
8. S.G. Ghosh, Eur. Phys. J. C **75**, 532 (2015).
9. E. A. Beato and A. Garcia, Phys. Lett. B **464**, 25 (1999); E.A. Beato and A. Garcia, Gen. Relativ. Gravit. **31**, 629 (1999).
10. H. Reissner, Ann. Phys. **355**, 9 (1916).
11. E. A. Beato and Alberto Garcia Phys. Rev. Lett. **80**, 5056 (1998); S.A. Hayward, Phys. Rev. Lett. **96**, 031103 (2006); I. Dymnikova, Gen Relativity Gravity **24**, 235 (1992); Z. Y. Fan and X. Wang, Phys. Rev. D **94**, 124027 (2016); O.B. Zaslavskii, Phys. Rev. D **80**, 064034 (2009).
12. J.P.S. Lemos and V.T. Zanchin, Phys. Rev. D **83**, 124005 (2011); J. C. S. Neves and A. Saa, Phys. Lett. B **734**, 44 (2014); L. Balart and E. C. Vagenas, Phys. Rev. D **90**, 124045 (2014); S. G. Ghosh and S. D. Maharaj, Phys. Dark Univ. **31**, 100793 (2021); M. S. Ali and S. G. Ghosh, Phys. Rev. D **98**, 084025 (2018); A. Kumar, D. Veer Singh and S. G. Ghosh, Eur. Phys. J. C **79**, 275 (2019); S. G. Ghosh, Class. Quant. Grav. **35**, 085008 (2018).
13. A. Cisterna, G. Giribet, J. Oliva and K. Pallikaris, Phys. Rev. D **101**, 124041 (2020).
14. A. Kumar, S. G. Ghosh and S. D. Maharaj, Phys. Dark Univ. **30**, 100634 (2020); R. Kumar, A. Kumar and S. G. Ghosh, Astrophys. J. **896**, 89 (2020); R. Kumar and

S. G. Ghosh, Class. Quant. Grav. **38**, 8 (2021); R. Kumar, S. G. Ghosh and A. Wang, Phys. Rev. D **100**, 124024 (2019); R. Kumar and S. G. Ghosh, Astrophys. J. **892**, 78 (2020); A. Abdujabbarov, M. Amir, B. Ahmedov and S. G. Ghosh, Phys. Rev. D **93**, 104004 (2016); M. Amir and S. G. Ghosh, Phys. Rev. D **94**, 024054 (2016); S. G. Ghosh and M. Amir, Eur. Phys. J. C **75**, 553 (2015); M. Amir and S. G. Ghosh, JHEP **07**, 015 (2015); S. G. Ghosh and S. D. Maharaj, Eur. Phys. J. C **75**, 7 (2015); C. Bambi and L. Modesto, Phys. Lett. B **721**, 329 (2013).
15. A. Eichhorn and A. Held, [arXiv:2103.07473 [gr-qc]]. A. Eichhorn and A. Held, [arXiv:2103.13163 [gr-qc]].
16. A. Simpson and M. Visser, JCAP **02**, 042 (2019).
17. A. Simpson, P. Martin-Moruno and M. Visser, Class. Quant. Grav. **36**, 145007 (2019).
18. F. S. N. Lobo, M. E. Rodrigues, M. V. d. S. Silva, A. Simpson and M. Visser, [arXiv:2009.12057 [gr-qc]].
19. N. Tsukamoto, Phys. Rev. D **103**, 024033 (2021).
20. J. Mazza, E. Franzin and S. Liberati, [arXiv:2102.01105 [gr-qc]].
21. K. A. Bronnikov, R. A. Konoplya and T. D. Pappas, [arXiv:2102.10679 [gr-qc]].
22. H. C. D. L. Junior, L. C. B. Crispino, P. V. P. Cunha and C. A. R. Herdeiro, [arXiv:2102.07034 [gr-qc]].
23. R. Shaikh, K. Pal, K. Pal and T. Sarkar, [arXiv:2102.04299 [gr-qc]].
24. L. C. B. Crispino and D. Kennefick, Nature Phys. **15**, 416 (2019); L. C. B. Crispino and S. Paolantonio, Nature Astron. **4**, 6 (2020).
25. A. Einstein, Science **84**, 506 (1936); S. Liebes, Phys. Rev. **133**, B835 (1964); Y. Mellier, Ann. Rev. Astron. Astrophys. **37**, 127 (1999); M. Bartelmann and P. Schneider, Phys. Rept. **340**, 291(2001); F. Schmidt, Phys. Rev. D **78**, 043002 (2008); Guzik, Jacek and Jain, Bhuvnesh and Takada, Masahiro, Phys. Rev. D. **81**, 023503 (2010).
26. J. L. Synge, Mon. Not. R. Astron. Soc. **131**, 463 (1966).
27. S. E. Gralla, D. E. Holz and R. M. Wald, Phys. Rev. D **100**, 024018 (2019); M. D. Johnson, A. Lupsasca, A. Strominger, G. N. Wong, S. Hadar, D. Kapec, R. Narayan, A. Chael, C. F. Gammie and P. Galison, *et al.* Sci. Adv. **6**, 1310 (2020); S. E. Gralla and A. Lupsasca, Phys. Rev. D **102**, 124003 (2020).
28. C. Darwin, Proc. R. Soc. A **249**, 180 (1959); P. V. P. Cunha and C. A. R. Herdeiro, Gen. Rel. Grav. **50**, 42 (2018).
29. V. Bozza, Gen. Rel. Grav. **42**, 2269 (2010).
30. V. Bozza, S. Capozziello, G. Iovane and G. Scarpetta, Gen. Rel. Grav. **33**, 1535 (2001).
31. V. Bozza, Phys. Rev. D **66**, 103001 (2002).
32. V. Bozza, Phys. Rev. D **67**, 103006 (2003).
33. K. S. Virbhadra and G. F. R. Ellis, Phys. Rev. D **62**, 084003 (2000).
34. S. Frittelli, T. P. Kling and E. T. Newman, Phys. Rev. D **61**, 064021 (2000).
35. E. F. Eiroa, G. E. Romero and D. F. Torres, Phys. Rev. D **66**, 024010 (2002)
36. S. V. Iyer and A. O. Petters, Gen. Rel. Grav. **39**, 1563 (2007).
37. N. Tsukamoto, Phys. Rev. D **95**, 064035 (2017); N. Tsukamoto and Y. Gong, Phys. Rev. D **95**, 064034 (2017).
38. K. S. Virbhadra and C. R. Keeton, Phys. Rev. D **77**, 124014 (2008).
39. R. Shaikh, P. Banerjee, S. Paul and T. Sarkar, JCAP **07**, 028 (2019).
40. Rauch K P and Blandford R D, Astrophys. J. **46** 421 (1994).
41. V. Bozza, Phys. Rev. D **78**, 063014 (2008).
42. S. G. Ghosh, R. Kumar and S. U. Islam, JCAP **03**, 056 (2021).
43. S. W. Wei, Y. X. Liu, C. E. Fu and K. Yang, JCAP **1210**, 053 (2012).
44. K. Beckwith and C. Done, Mon. Not. Roy. Astron. Soc. **359**, 1217 (2005).
45. Y. W. Hsiao, D. S. Lee and C. Y. Lin, Phys. Rev. D **101**, 064070 (2020).

46. D. Kapec and A. Lupsasca, Class. Quant. Grav. **37**, 015006 (2020).
47. S. E. Gralla and A. Lupsasca, Phys. Rev. D **101**, 044031 (2020).
48. O. James, E. von Tunzelmann, P. Franklin and K. S. Thorne, Class. Quant. Grav. **32**, 065001 (2015).
49. P. Cunha, V.P., C. A. R. Herdeiro and E. Radu, Universe **5**, 220 (2019).
50. V. Bozza and L. Mancini, Gen. Rel. Grav. **36**, 435 (2004).
51. Thomas Muller, Phys. Rev. D **77**, 124042 (2008).
52. S. U. Islam and S. G. Ghosh, [arXiv:2102.08289 [gr-qc]].
53. S. U. Islam, R. Kumar and S. G. Ghosh, JCAP **09**, 030 (2020); R. Kumar, S. U. Islam and S. G. Ghosh, Eur. Phys. J. C **80**, 1128 (2020).
54. V. Bozza, Phys. Rev. D **78**, 103005 (2008).
55. H. C. Ohanian, Am. J. Phys. 55 (May, 1987).
56. S. Chandrasekhar, *The Mathematical Theory of Black Holes* (Oxford University Press, New York, 1992).
57. B. Carter, Phys. Rev. D **174**, 1559 (1968).
58. V. P. Frolov and A. Zelnikov, *Introduction to Black Hole Physics* (Oxford University Press, New York, 2011).

Killing tensors in foliated spacetimes and photon surfaces

Igor Bogush[*], Kirill Kobialko[†] and Dmitri Gal'tsov[‡]

Faculty of Physics, Moscow State University, 119899, Moscow, Russia
[*] *E-mail: igbogush@gmail.com*
[†] *E-mail: kobyalkokv@yandex.ru*
[‡] *E-mail: galtsov@phys.msu.ru*

We discuss a recently proposed geometric method[1] for constructing a nontrivial Killing tensor of rank two in a foliated spacetime of codimension one that lifts trivial Killing tensors from slices to the entire manifold. The existence of nontrivial Killing tensor is closely related to generalized photon surfaces. The method is illustrated on some known cases and used to construct the hitherto unknown Killing tensor for the Nutty dyon in dilaton-axion gravity.

Keywords: Killing tensors, photon surfaces, gravitational lensing, black hole shadows.

1. Introduction

Killing tensors of the second rank express hidden symmetries of spacetime[2,3] providing integrals of motion for geodesics and wave operators in field theories. Some constructive procedures to find them were suggested for spaces with a warped/twisted product structure,[4] spaces admitting a hypersurface orthogonal Killing vector field,[5,6] or special conformal Killing vector fields.[7] Recently, some deformed Kerr metrics attracted attention when trying to find new physics in ultracompact astrophysical objects. Classes of such metrics were listed that admit Killing tensors,[8,9] but for others the separation of variables in geodesic equations is not guaranteed.

The new procedure[1] suggested for foliated spacetime of codimension one is based on lifting the trivial Killing tensors in slices with an arbitrary second fundamental form.[1] This remove some particular assumptions about slices, so, hopefully, we can move further in the study of separability. The method is closely related to formalism of fundamental photon surfaces introduced in.[10] This generalizes one previous observation[11] on the relationship between spacetime separability and spherical photon orbits. It is also worth noting that our method does not require sovling diffenerial equations at all.

As illustrations, we apply this new technique to some conventional metrics of Petrov type D demonstrating that this technique allows to obtain known Killing tensors[12,13] purely algebraically, without solving any differential equations. Then we successfully apply new technique to find Killing tensor for Gal'tsov-Kechkin solution[14,15] in dilaton-axion gravity which belongs to the general Petrov type I. The new method reveals the nature of Killing tensors as arising from isometries of low-dimensional slices of a smooth foliation.

In Sec. 2 we briefly describe the equations for the Killing vectors and Killing tensors of rank two. In Sec. 3 we consider spacetimes with foliation of codimension one and present the equations governing the interplay between symmetries in the bulk and in the slices. Eventually we describe the Killing generating technique. In Sec. 4 we reveal the connection between the Killing tensors and the fundamental photon surfaces. Sec. 5 provides examples with axial symmetry in different models.

2. Conventions

Let M be a Lorentzian manifold of dimension m with scalar product $\langle \cdot, \cdot \rangle$ and Levi-Civita connection ∇.[a]

Definition 2.1. A vector field $\mathcal{K}: M \to TM$ is called a Killing vector field if[16]

$$\underset{\mathcal{X} \leftrightarrow \mathcal{Y}}{\text{Sym}} \{\langle \nabla_{\mathcal{X}} \mathcal{K}, \mathcal{Y} \rangle\} = 0, \quad \forall \mathcal{X}, \mathcal{Y} \in TM. \tag{1}$$

Definition 2.2. A linear self-adjoint mapping $K(\,\cdot\,) : TM \to TM$ is called a Killing mapping if

$$\underset{\mathcal{X} \leftrightarrow \mathcal{Y} \leftrightarrow \mathcal{Z}}{\text{Sym}} \{\langle \nabla_{\mathcal{X}} K(\mathcal{Z}), \mathcal{Y} \rangle\} = 0, \quad \forall \mathcal{X}, \mathcal{Y}, \mathcal{Z} \in TM, \tag{2}$$

where the linear mapping $\nabla_{\mathcal{X}} K(\,\cdot\,) : TM \to TM$ is defined as follows

$$\nabla_{\mathcal{X}} K(\mathcal{Y}) \equiv \nabla_{\mathcal{X}}(K(\mathcal{Y})) - K(\nabla_{\mathcal{X}} \mathcal{Y}), \quad \forall \mathcal{X}, \mathcal{Y} \in TM. \tag{3}$$

One can introduce a Killing tensor as a symmetric form $K(\mathcal{X}, \mathcal{Y}) = \langle K(\mathcal{X}), \mathcal{Y} \rangle$, which is associated with the conservation law quadratic in momenta. Let $\mathcal{K}_\alpha$ be a set of n Killing vector fields. Then, one can define the following trivial Killing mapping

$$K(\mathcal{X}) = \alpha \mathcal{X} + \sum_{\alpha,\beta=1}^{n} \gamma^{\alpha\beta} \langle \mathcal{X}, \mathcal{K}_\alpha \rangle \mathcal{K}_\beta, \quad \gamma^{\alpha\beta} = \gamma^{\beta\alpha}, \tag{4}$$

where α and $\gamma^{\alpha\beta}$ is the set of $n(n+1)/2 + 1$ independent constants in M. Note that the trivial Killing mapping does not give new conservation laws. However, one can show the existence of manifolds with nontrivial Killing tensors, which are not associated with the manifold isometries directly.

3. Generation of a non-trivial Killing tensor

Consider a timelike/spacelike *foliation* of the manifold M by a smooth family of hypersurfaces S_Ω parameterized by $\Omega \in \mathbb{R}$ (slices) with the lapse function φ, and

---

[a]Here we also use the notation $\underset{\mathcal{X} \leftrightarrow \mathcal{Y}}{\text{Sym}} \{B(\mathcal{X}, \mathcal{Y})\} \equiv B(\mathcal{X}, \mathcal{Y}) + B(\mathcal{Y}, \mathcal{X})$.

vector field ξ normal to slices ($\langle\xi,\xi\rangle \equiv \epsilon = \pm 1$). Then, the second fundamental form $^\Omega\sigma(\,\cdot\,,\,\cdot\,): TS \times TS \to \mathbb{R}$ and the mean curvature of slices S_Ω are defined as follows

$$^\Omega\sigma(X,Y) \equiv \epsilon \langle \nabla_X Y, \xi\rangle, \quad \forall X, Y \in TS, \qquad H \equiv \mathrm{Tr}(^\Omega\sigma)/(m-1). \tag{5}$$

In particular, one can decompose the Killing vector field into the sum $\mathcal{K} = \mathcal{K}_\Omega + k_N \xi$, with the normal $k_N \xi$ and tangent $\mathcal{K}_\Omega \in TS_\Omega$ components. In the general case, the projection $\mathcal{K}_\Omega$ is not a Killing vector in the slices of foliation.[1,10] An exception is the case of totally umbilic or totally geodesic slice, where the projection of any Killing field is a conformal or ordinary Killing vector field respectively. Such slices arise if the field generating the foliation is a (conformal) Killing field and/or the spacetime has the structure of a warped/twisted product.[16] Therefore, the generation of the Killing vectors in M from Killing vectors $\mathcal{K}_\Omega$ with a nontrivial normal component k_N is possible in the case of the totally geodesic slices only. As we will see further, the case of Killing tensors is more intricate.

Similarly, the Killing mapping can be split to normal and tangent components $K(\,\cdot\,) = K_\Omega^{(\,\cdot\,)} + k_N^{(\,\cdot\,)}\xi$, where $k_N^{(\,\cdot\,)}\xi$ is a normal component and $K_\Omega^{(\,\cdot\,)} \in TS_\Omega$ is a tangent component. In the case of totally geodesic slices, one can lift the Killing tensor from the slice to the whole manifold and obtain a nontrivial normal component $k_N^{(\,\cdot\,)}$. This particular case of totally geodesic slices was considered, for example, in the Ref.[5]. Moreover, if we consider the conformal Killing tensors, a similar technique can be applied in the warped spacetimes,[4] where the foliation slices are totally umbilic.[16] In this paper, we consider the Killing tensor lift technique for arbitrary slices (not totally geodesic submanifolds). In this case, the second fundamental form $^\Omega\sigma$ is not trivial, and Killing equations imply $k_N^X = 0$, $K_\Omega^\xi = 0$. Then, the family of Killing mappings $K_\Omega : TS_\Omega \to TS_\Omega$ can be lifted from the slices to the Killing mapping $K(\,\cdot\,) = K_\Omega^{(\,\cdot\,)} + k_N^{(\,\cdot\,)}\xi$ in the manifold M with nontrivial normal components, if the following equations hold[1,10]

$$k_N^X = 0, \quad K_\Omega^\xi = 0, \quad \xi(k_N^\xi) = 0, \quad X(k_N^\xi) = 2k_N^\xi \nabla_X \ln \varphi - 2\nabla_{K_\Omega^X} \ln \varphi, \tag{6a}$$

$$\underset{X \leftrightarrow Y}{\mathrm{Sym}} \left\{ \frac{1}{2} \cdot \langle \nabla_\xi K_\Omega^X, Y\rangle + \epsilon \cdot {}^\Omega\sigma(X, K_\Omega^Y) - \epsilon k_N^\xi \cdot {}^\Omega\sigma(X,Y) \right\} = 0. \tag{6b}$$

Suppose that the manifold M has a collection $n \leq m-2$ of linearly independent Killing vector fields $\mathcal{K}_\alpha$ tangent to the slices S_Ω of the foliation $\mathcal{F}_\Omega$. Then, such vectors $\mathcal{K}_\alpha$ are also Killing vectors in the slices S_Ω, and a trivial Killing mapping of the form (4) is always defined. Substituting this mapping into equations (6a), (6b) we obtain

$$X(k_N^\xi) = 2(k_N^\xi - \alpha)\nabla_X \ln \varphi, \quad \xi(k_N^\xi) = 0, \quad X(\alpha) = 0, \quad X(\gamma^{\alpha\beta}) = 0, \tag{7a}$$

$$2\epsilon(k_N^\xi - \alpha) \cdot {}^\Omega\sigma(X,Y) = \xi(\alpha)\langle X,Y\rangle + \sum_{\alpha,\beta=1}^n \xi(\gamma^{\alpha\beta})\langle X, \mathcal{K}_\alpha\rangle\langle \mathcal{K}_\beta, Y\rangle, \tag{7b}$$

for any $X, Y \in TS_\Omega$. There is always a trivial solution for these equations

$$k_N^\xi = \alpha, \quad \xi(\alpha) = 0, \quad \xi(\gamma^{\alpha\beta}) = 0, \tag{8}$$

corresponding to the trivial Killing tensor in M. However, in some cases it can also have nontrivial solutions, which corresponds to the nontrivial Killing tensor and new conservation laws. Let us additionally assume that the Gramian matrix $\mathcal{G}_{\alpha\beta} = \langle \mathcal{K}_\alpha, \mathcal{K}_\beta \rangle$ is not degenerate ($\mathcal{G} \equiv \det(\mathcal{G}_{\alpha\beta}) \neq 0$). Then, we can introduce a basis $\{\mathcal{K}_\alpha, e_a\}$ in S_Ω in such a way that $e_a \in \{\mathcal{K}_\alpha\}^\perp$ with $a = 1, \ldots, m - n - 1$. A non-trivial Killing tensor can be generated using the technique from the following theorem[1]:

Theorem 3.1. *Let the manifold M contains a collection of $n \leq m-2$ Killing vector fields $\mathcal{K}_\alpha$ with a non-degenerate Gramian $\mathcal{G}_{\alpha\beta} = \langle \mathcal{K}_\alpha, \mathcal{K}_\beta \rangle$, tangent to the foliation slices S_Ω (partially umbilic if $n < m - 2$) with the second fundamental form[b]*

$$\Omega_\sigma = \begin{pmatrix} -\frac{1}{2}\epsilon \cdot \xi \mathcal{G}_{\alpha\beta} & 0 \\ 0 & h^\Omega \cdot \langle e_a, e_b \rangle \end{pmatrix} \tag{9}$$

Then, there is a nontrivial Killing tensor on manifold M, if the following steps can be successfully completed:

Step one: *Check compatibility and integrability conditions (10), (11)*

$$X(h^\Omega \cdot \varphi^3) = 0, \tag{10}$$

$$X\left(\mathcal{G}^{\alpha\beta} - \frac{\epsilon}{2h^\Omega} \cdot \xi \mathcal{G}^{\alpha\beta}\right) = 0. \tag{11}$$

Step two: *Obtain α from (12) and check the condition (13)*

$$\xi \ln \xi(\alpha) = \xi \ln h^\Omega - 2\epsilon h^\Omega, \tag{12}$$

$$X(\alpha) = 0. \tag{13}$$

Step three: *Define $\gamma^{\alpha\beta}$ from (14) using the conditions $\xi \nu^{\alpha\beta} = 0$, $X\gamma^{\alpha\beta} = 0$.*

$$\gamma^{\alpha\beta} = \epsilon \frac{\xi(\alpha)}{2h^\Omega} \cdot \mathcal{G}^{\alpha\beta} - \nu^{\alpha\beta}, \tag{14}$$

Step four: *Using the functions found in the previous steps, construct a Killing map and the corresponding Killing tensor:*

$$K(\mathcal{X}) = \alpha \mathcal{X} + \sum_{\alpha,\beta=1}^{n} \gamma^{\alpha\beta} \langle \mathcal{X}, \mathcal{K}_\alpha \rangle \mathcal{K}_\beta + \frac{\xi(\alpha)}{2h^\Omega} \langle \mathcal{X}, \xi \rangle \xi. \tag{15}$$

---

[b]The form of the left upper block is a consequence of the tangent Killing vectors, and this does not impose a new condition. The non-diagonal zero elements is a new condition, which is satisfied in many applications. The right lower block is a condition of partially umbilical surfaces, which imposes constraints if $\dim\{e_a\} > 1$.

4. Connection with photon submanifolds

Consider the case of a manifold with two Killing vectors spanning a timelike surface ($\mathcal{G} < 0$). Let us define a Killing vector field ρ^α with index $\alpha = 1, 2$ numbering Killing vectors of the basis $\{\mathcal{K}_\alpha\}$, which is supposed to have constant components $\rho^\alpha = (\rho, 1)$. The quantity ρ can be called the generalized impact parameter (see[10] for details). However, one can choose arbitrary parametrization of ρ^α up to the norm.

Proposition 4.1. *The fundamental photon surface is a partially umbilic surface with a second fundamental form of the form (9), with the following connection between h^Ω and $\mathcal{G}_{\alpha\beta}$*[10]

$$\rho^\alpha \mathcal{M}_{\alpha\beta} \rho^\beta = 0, \qquad \mathcal{M}_{\alpha\beta} \equiv \frac{1}{2h^\Omega} \cdot \xi \mathcal{G}_{\alpha\beta} - \mathcal{G}_{\alpha\beta} - \frac{1}{2h^\Omega} \cdot \xi \ln \mathcal{G} \cdot \mathcal{G}_{\alpha\beta}. \qquad (16)$$

If the surface under consideration is totally umbilic $\mathcal{M}_{\alpha\beta} = 0$, it is obviously a fundamental photon surfaces for any ρ. Since totally umbilic surfaces usually exist in spherically symmetric solutions (both static and non-static) or non-rotating solutions with NUT-charge,[17] and they have been considered in detail in a number of works,[18,19] we will focus on the case $\mathcal{M}_{\alpha\beta} \neq 0$.

Consider the foliation generating a nontrivial Killing tensor in accordance with Theorem 3.1, and ask the question whether its slice S_Ω is a fundamental photon surface. First of all, we need to solve the quadratic equation (16) for ρ and check the condition $\rho^\alpha \mathcal{G}_{\alpha\beta} \rho^\beta \geq 0$. It has nontrivial solution if the eigenvalues of the matrix $\mathcal{M}_{\alpha\beta}$ have different signs, that is $\mathcal{M} \equiv \det(\mathcal{M}_{\alpha\beta}) < 0$. Then the solution for ρ reads as

$$\rho = \frac{-\mathcal{M}_{12} \pm \sqrt{-\mathcal{M}}}{\mathcal{M}_{11}}. \qquad (17)$$

Condition $\rho^\alpha \mathcal{G}_{\alpha\beta} \rho^\beta \geq 0$ is satisfied if the following inequality holds

$$\pm 2(\mathcal{G}_{12}\mathcal{M}_{11} - \mathcal{G}_{11}\mathcal{M}_{12})\sqrt{-\mathcal{M}} - 2\mathcal{G}_{11} \cdot \mathcal{M} + \mathcal{M}_{11} \cdot \mathcal{G} \cdot \text{Tr}(\mathcal{M}) \geq 0, \qquad (18)$$

where $\text{Tr}(\mathcal{M}) = \mathcal{M}_{\alpha\beta} \mathcal{G}^{\alpha\beta} = -2 - (2h^\Omega)^{-1} \cdot \xi \ln \mathcal{G}$. Equation (18) defines the so-called photon region,[20,21] which arises as a flow of fundamental photon surfaces.[10] However, it has not been proven that the expression (17) for ρ is constant in every slice. But the integrability condition (11) guarantees that it is true in fact.[1] Therefore, we have the following theorem.

Theorem 4.1. *Let S_Ω be a non totally umbilic foliation slice with compact spatial section satisfying all conditions of the theorem 3.1 for $\dim\{\mathcal{K}_\alpha\} = 2$. Then maximal subdomain $U_{PS} \subseteq S_\Omega$ such that the inequality (18) holds for all $p \in U_{PS}$ is a fundamental photon surface*[c].

---

[c]In the case of not compact spatial section, the slice is not a fundamental photon surface by definition.[10] However, the theorem can be generalized for such not compact surfaces.

In particular, the region $U_{PR} \subseteq M$, such that the inequality (18) holds for any point $p \in U_{PR}$, is a photon region. This theorem generalizes the connection between the existence of Killing tensors of this type and photon surfaces or spherical null geodesics, which was noted in Refs.[11,19,22]. Unfortunately, in the opposite direction, the theorem is not fair, since the existence of fundamental photon surfaces does not guarantee the existence of the Killing tensor. As a counterexample, one can suggest Zipoy-Voorhees metric[23] where the fundamental photon surfaces exists[24] but there is no nontrivial Killing tensor.[25] Nevertheless, the existence of fundamental photon surfaces can serve as a sign that the Killing tensor can be presented in the corresponding metric, and it is advisable to check the conditions of consistency and integrability.

5. Axially symmetric spacetimes

Consider a Lorentzian manifold M with the metric tensor

$$ds^2 = -f(dt - \omega d\phi)^2 + \lambda dr^2 + \beta d\theta^2 + \gamma d\phi^2. \tag{19}$$

where all metric components depend on r and θ only and the foliation with timelike slices $r = \Omega$. Generally, this metric possesses two Killing vectors $\mathcal{K}_1 = \partial_t$, $\mathcal{K}_2 = \partial_\varphi$. One can find that the second fundamental form of these slices has the form (9) and other quantities are

$$\xi = \lambda^{-1/2}\partial_r, \quad h^\Omega = -\frac{1}{2}\lambda^{-1/2} \cdot \partial_r \ln \beta, \quad \varphi = \lambda^{1/2}, \quad \mathcal{G}^{\alpha\beta} = \frac{1}{\gamma}\begin{pmatrix} \omega^2 - \gamma f^{-1} & \omega \\ \omega & 1 \end{pmatrix}. \tag{20}$$

In this case, the number of Killing vector is one less than the slices dimension, so the boundary $n \geq m - 2$ saturates and the partially umbilic condition just imposes a relation on h^Ω. The compatibility and integrability conditions (10), (11) take the form

$$\partial_\theta(\lambda \cdot \partial_r \ln \beta) = 0, \quad \partial_\theta\left(\mathcal{G}^{\alpha\beta} + \frac{1}{\partial_r \ln \beta}\partial_r \mathcal{G}^{\alpha\beta}\right) = 0. \tag{21}$$

The Eq. (12) can be solved as follows

$$\alpha = A_\theta \cdot \beta + B_\theta, \tag{22}$$

where the arbitrary functions A_θ, B_θ depend on θ only, obeying the condition $\partial_\theta \alpha = 0$. As the result, we have one more necessary condition for the case in this section: the function β must be of the form

$$\beta(r, \theta) = \beta_1(\theta)\beta_2(r) + \beta_3(\theta), \tag{23}$$

where $\beta_{1,2,3}$ are some functions of the corresponding variables. In particular, the normal component is $k_N^\xi = B_\theta$. Next, we can define the matrix γ:

$$\gamma^{\alpha\beta} = -\beta A_\theta \cdot \mathcal{G}^{\alpha\beta} - \nu^{\alpha\beta}. \tag{24}$$

The integrability condition guarantees that $\gamma^{\alpha\beta}$ always satisfies the equations (7) for some $\nu^{\alpha\beta}$ depending only on θ. On the other hand, we have to find a $\nu^{\alpha\beta}$ that makes the equation $\partial_r \gamma^{\alpha\beta} = 0$ true. Therefore, we can omit the θ-dependent part in $\gamma^{\alpha\beta}$ to some constant matrix instead of looking for $\nu^{\alpha\beta}$. Combining everything together, we get the final Killing tensor in the holonomic basis

$$K^{\mu\nu} = \alpha g^{\mu\nu} + \sum_{\alpha,\beta=t,\phi} \gamma^{\alpha\beta} \mathcal{K}^{\mu}_{\alpha} \mathcal{K}^{\nu}_{\beta} - \beta A_{\theta} \lambda^{-1} \delta^{\mu}_r \delta^{\nu}_r. \tag{25}$$

The compatibility and integrability conditions, as well as the condition on the function β, are invariant under the multiplicative transformations of the form

$$\lambda \to \lambda' = u(r)\lambda, \quad \beta \to \beta' = v(\theta)\beta. \tag{26}$$

If β possesses the aforementioned form (23), one can simplify the integrability condition by the substitution $\mathcal{G}^{\alpha\beta} = \tilde{\mathcal{G}}^{\alpha\beta} \cdot \beta_1/\beta$. Then, the integrability condition is $\partial_\theta \partial_r \tilde{\mathcal{G}}^{\alpha\beta} = 0$, which is solved by $\tilde{\mathcal{G}}^{\alpha\beta} = \tilde{\mathcal{G}}^{\alpha\beta}_r(r) + \tilde{\mathcal{G}}^{\alpha\beta}_\theta(\theta)$. This generalizes the result of Ref.[26], where the similar condition was obtained from the separability of the Hamilton-Jacobi equation. In our case, we have also included the $\beta_1(\theta)$ term. Furthermore, the compatibility condition and the function form (23) leads to the form of $\lambda = \lambda_r(r)\beta/\beta_1$, where λ_r is an arbitrary function of r.

5.1. Kerr metric

As a simple illustration, consider Kerr solution in the Boyer-Lindquist coordinates:

$$ds^2 = -\frac{\Delta - a^2 \sin^2\theta}{\Sigma}(dt - \omega d\phi)^2 + \Sigma\left(\frac{dr^2}{\Delta} + d\theta^2 + \frac{\Delta \sin^2\theta}{\Delta - a^2 \sin^2\theta}d\phi^2\right), \tag{27}$$

$$\Sigma = r^2 + a^2 \cos^2\theta, \quad \omega = \frac{-2Mar\sin^2\theta}{\Delta - a^2\sin^2\theta}, \tag{28a}$$

$$\Delta = r(r - 2M) + a^2. \tag{28b}$$

In the Kerr metric, $\beta = r^2 + a^2 \cos^2\theta$, $\lambda = \beta/\Delta$, satisfy the compatibility condition. One can explicitly verify that $\mathcal{G}^{\alpha\beta}$ satisfies the integrability equation. In this case $\alpha = r^2$, $A_\theta = 1$ and $k^{\xi}_N = B_\theta = -a^2 \cos^2\theta$ (here we have fixed the multiplicative integration constant, which appears due to the linearity of Killing equations). The part of $\gamma^{\alpha\beta}$ independent on θ reads

$$\gamma^{\alpha\beta} = \Delta^{-1}\begin{pmatrix}(a^2+r^2)^2 & a(a^2+r^2)\\ a(a^2+r^2) & a^2\end{pmatrix}. \tag{29}$$

Finally, we get α and $\gamma^{\alpha\beta}$, which correspond to the well-known nontrivial Killing tensor for Kerr solution

$$K^{\mu\nu} = r^2 g^{\mu\nu} + \Delta^{-1} S^\mu S^\nu - \Delta \delta^\mu_r \delta^\nu_r, \tag{30}$$
$$S^\mu = s\delta^\mu_t + a\delta^\mu_\phi, \quad s = r^2 + a^2.$$

5.2. Plebanski-Demianski solution

This is a less trivial example of the type D solution of Einstein-Maxwell equations with the cosmological constant, which contains also an acceleration parameter. The metric line element ds^2 is more conveniently presented in the conformally related frame using the Boyer-Lindquist coordinates:

$$\Omega^2 ds^2 = \Sigma \left(\frac{dr^2}{\Delta_r} + \frac{d\theta^2}{\Delta_\theta} \right) + \frac{1}{\Sigma} \left((\Sigma + a\chi)^2 \Delta_\theta \sin^2\theta - \Delta_r \chi^2 \right) d\phi^2 \quad (31)$$

$$+ \frac{2}{\Sigma} \left(\Delta_r \chi - a(\Sigma + a\chi)\Delta_\theta \sin^2\theta \right) dt d\phi - \frac{1}{\Sigma} \left(\Delta_r - a^2 \Delta_\theta \sin^2\theta \right) dt^2, \quad (32)$$

where we have defined the functions

$$\Delta_\theta = 1 - a_1 \cos\theta - a_2 \cos^2\theta, \quad \Delta_r = b_0 + b_1 r + b_2 r^2 + b_3 r^3 + b_4 r^4, \quad (33)$$
$$\Omega = 1 - \lambda(N + a\cos\theta)r, \quad \Sigma = r^2 + (N + a\cos\theta)^2, \quad \chi = a\sin^2\theta - 2N(\cos\theta + C), \quad (34)$$

with the following constant coefficients in Δ_θ and Δ_r:

$$a_1 = 2aM\lambda - 4aN\left(\lambda^2(k+\beta) + \frac{\Lambda}{3}\right), \quad a_2 = -a^2\left(\lambda^2(k+\beta) + \frac{\Lambda}{3}\right), \quad b_0 = k + \beta, \quad (35)$$

$$b_1 = -2M, \quad b_2 = \frac{k}{a^2 - N^2} + 4MN\lambda - (a^2 + 3N^2)\left(\lambda^2(k+\beta) + \frac{\Lambda}{3}\right), \quad (36)$$

$$b_3 = -2\lambda\left(\frac{kN}{a^2 - N^2} - (a^2 - N^2)\left(M\lambda - N\left(\lambda^2(k+\beta) + \frac{\Lambda}{3}\right)\right)\right), \quad (37)$$

$$b_4 = -\left(\lambda^2 k + \frac{\Lambda}{3}\right), \quad (38)$$

$$k = \frac{1 + 2MN\lambda - 3N^2\left(\lambda^2\beta + \frac{\Lambda}{3}\right)}{1 + 3\lambda^2 N^2(a^2 - N^2)}(a^2 - N^2), \quad \lambda = \frac{\alpha}{\omega}, \quad \omega = \sqrt{a^2 + N^2}. \quad (39)$$

Generally, the coordinates t and r range over the whole $\mathbb{R}$, while θ and ϕ are the standard coordinates on the unit two-sphere. Seven independent parameters $M, N, a, \alpha, \beta, \Lambda, C$ can be physically interpreted as mass, NUT parameter (magnetic mass), rotation parameter, acceleration parameter, $\beta = e^2 + g^2$ comprises the electric e and magnetic g charges, Λ is the cosmological constant, and the constant C defines the location of the Misner string.

The first step is to check the compatibility and integrability conditions (10), (11). The first one holds if $\alpha \cdot a = 0$, i.e. either the acceleration α or the rotation a are zero. Indeed, as shown in Ref.[12], the general PD solution with acceleration possesses a conformal Killing tensor, but not the usual one. In the case $a = 0$, the second condition does not hold. So, further we will consider the solution with zero acceleration $\alpha = 0$, which corresponds to the dyonic Kerr-Newman-NUT-AdS solution.

In the **second step** we pick up the r-dependent part from $\beta = \Sigma/\Delta_\theta$ for α

$$\beta = \frac{\Sigma}{\Delta_\theta} \Rightarrow \alpha = r^2, \quad A_\theta = \Delta_\theta. \tag{40}$$

Similarly, as the **third step**, the r-dependent part for $\gamma^{\alpha\beta}$ is defined as

$$\gamma^{\alpha\beta} = \Delta_r^{-1} \begin{pmatrix} s^2 & as \\ as & a^2 \end{pmatrix}, \quad s = \Sigma + a\chi = r^2 + a^2 - 2aCN + N^2. \tag{41}$$

In the last **fourth step**, we obtain the nontrivial Killing tensor for the Kerr-Newman-NUT-AdS metric:

$$K^{\mu\nu} = r^2 g^{\mu\nu} + \Delta_r^{-1} S^\mu S^\nu - \Delta_r \delta_r^\mu \delta_r^\nu, \quad S^\mu = s\delta_t^\mu + a\delta_\varphi^\mu. \tag{42}$$

6. Gal'tsov-Kechkin (GK) solution

In 1994 one of the present authors in collaboration with O. Kechkin derived the general stationary charged black hole solution within the Einstein-Maxwell- dilaton-axion (EMDA) gravity, which is the $\mathcal{N} = 4, D = 4$ supergravity consistently truncated to the theory with one vector field.[14] This solution was seven-parametric, containing mass M, electric and magnetic charges Q, P, rotation parameter a, NUT N and asymptotic values of the dilaton and axion (irrelevant for the metric) as independent parameters. Less general (without NUT) solution was derived by A. Sen[27] in the context of the dimensionally reduced effective action of the heterotic string, and now it is commonly referred as Kerr-Sen metric. Non-rotating solutions with NUT were independently obtained by Kallosh et al.[28] and Johnson and Myers.[29] Now the Kerr-Sen metric is often considered as a deformed Kerr solution in modeling deviations from the standard picture of black holes.

The GK solution[14] was shown[15] to belong to type Petrov I, contrary to Kerr-Newman-NUT solution in the Einstein-Maxwell gravity. The same was shown for Kerr-Sen solution without NUT.[30] Though the Kerr-Sen metric is not type D, the Hamilton-Jacoby equation was shown to be separable for it,[31,32] though the Killing tensor was not found explicitly (for further discussion see[9]). But for the solution with NUT, it was claimed that no second rank Killing tensor exists.[33] So here we use the new technique to resolve this controversy.

The line element of the GK solution can be written in the form (27) where the functions Δ, ω, Σ are redefined as follows

$$\Delta = (r - r_-)(r - 2M) + a^2 - (N - N_-)^2,$$
$$\Sigma = r(r - r_-) + (a\cos\theta + N)^2 - N_-^2,$$
$$\omega = \frac{-2w}{\Delta - a^2 \sin^2\theta}, \quad w = N\Delta \cos\theta + a\sin^2\theta \left(M(r - r_-) + N(N - N_-)\right).$$

The full solution also contains Maxwell, dilaton ϕ and axion κ fields (whose form can be found in[14]), and represents a family with seven parameters: mass M,

NUT charge N, rotation parameter a, electric and magnetic charges Q and P, and asymptotic complex axidilaton charge $z_\infty = \kappa_\infty + ie^{-2\phi_\infty}$, irrelevant for the metric. The following abbreviations are used:

$$r_- = \frac{M|\mathcal{Q}|^2}{|\mathcal{M}|^2}, \quad N_- = \frac{N|\mathcal{Q}|^2}{2|\mathcal{M}|^2}, \quad \mathcal{M} = M + iN, \quad \mathcal{Q} = Q - iP, \quad \mathcal{D} = -\frac{\mathcal{Q}^{*2}}{2\mathcal{M}}. \tag{43}$$

The metric is presented in the Kerr-like form, but the metric functions are essentially different. The solution reduces to Kerr-NUT for $Q = P = 0$.

Now we apply our procedure to construct the Killing tensor. It can be easily verified that the consistency (10) and the integrability (11) conditions are satisfied. The uplift turns out to be as simple as in the vacuum Kerr example, leading to the result

$$K^{\mu\nu} = r(r - r_-)g^{\mu\nu} + \Delta^{-1}S^\mu S^\nu - \Delta \delta_r^\mu \delta_r^\nu, \tag{44}$$
$$S^\mu = s\delta_t^\mu + a\delta_\varphi^\mu, \quad s = r(r - r_-) + a^2 + N^2 - N_-^2.$$

This expression is new and is applicable both to the Kerr-Sen solution $N = N_- = 0$, and for the full GK solution.

7. Conclusions

In this article, we reviewed new geometric method of generating Killing tensor in spacetimes with codimension one foliation.[1] Using our general lift equations one can try to rise a trivial Killing tensor defined in the slices into a nontrivial Killing tensor in the bulk. For this, the foliation must satisfy some consistency and integrability conditions, which we have presented explicitly. Furthermore, we have completely solved the lifting equations in terms of the functions α, $\gamma^{\alpha\beta}$ and formulated the theorem (3.1) for generation of the non-trivial Killing tensor.

Finding a foliation compatible with integrability and consistency conditions can be a challenging task. The existence of such a foliation means that the slices represent fundamental photon surfaces provided the corresponding inequalities hold. This generalizes the result of Ref.[19] to the case of general stationary spaces. Conversely, the existence of fundamental photon surfaces, though does not guarantee the existence of the Killing tensor, but may serve as an indication that such tensor may exist. Therefore, it is recommended to check the consistency and integrability conditions for fundamental photon surfaces, if these are known. This property makes the search for fundamental photon surfaces important also for studying the integrability of geodesic motion. It is tempting to conjecture that the existence of fundamental photon surfaces implies the existence of Killing tensor if the slice is equipotential or spherical.[34]

Using this technique, we were able to derive Killing tensor for EMDA dyon with NUT (GK solution[14]), which is also valid for Kerr-Sen solution as a particular case.

Acknowledgements

The work was supported by the Russian Foundation for Basic Research on the project 20-52-18012Bulg-a, and the Scientific and Educational School of Moscow State University "Fundamental and Applied Space Research". I.B. is also grateful to the Foundation for the Advancement of Theoretical Physics and Mathematics "BASIS" for support.

References

1. K. Kobialko, I. Bogush and D. Gal'tsov, Killing tensors and photon surfaces in foliated spacetimes, *Phys. Rev. D* **104**, p. 044009 (2021).
2. B. Carter, Killing Tensor Quantum Numbers and Conserved Currents in Curved Space, *Phys. Rev. D* **16**, p. 3395 (1977).
3. V. Frolov, P. Krtous and D. Kubiznak, Black holes, hidden symmetries, and complete integrability, *Living Rev. Rel.* **20**, p. 6 (2017).
4. P. Krtous, D. Kubiznak and I. Kolar, Killing-Yano forms and Killing tensors on a warped space, *Phys. Rev. D* **93**, p. 024057 (2016).
5. D. Garfinkle and E. N. Glass, Killing Tensors and Symmetries, *Class. Quant. Grav.* **27**, p. 095004 (2010).
6. D. Garfinkle and E. N. Glass, Killing-Yano tensors in spaces admitting a hypersurface orthogonal Killing vector, *J. Math. Phys.* **54**, p. 032501 (2013).
7. R. Rani, S. B. Edgar and A. Barnes, Killing tensors and conformal Killing tensors from conformal Killing vectors, *Class. Quant. Grav.* **20**, p. 1929 (2003).
8. Z. Carson and K. Yagi, Asymptotically flat, parameterized black hole metric preserving Kerr symmetries, *Phys. Rev. D* **101**, p. 084030 (2020).
9. G. O. Papadopoulos and K. D. Kokkotas, On Kerr black hole deformations admitting a Carter constant and an invariant criterion for the separability of the wave equation, *Gen. Rel. Grav.* **53**, p. 21 (2021).
10. K. V. Kobialko and D. V. Gal'tsov, Photon regions and umbilic conditions in stationary axisymmetric spacetimes: Photon Regions, *Eur. Phys. J. C* **80**, p. 527 (2020).
11. G. Pappas and K. Glampedakis, On the connection of spacetime separability and spherical photon orbits, *arXiv*, p. 1806.04091 (2018).
12. D. Kubiznak and P. Krtous, On conformal Killing-Yano tensors for Plebanski-Demianski family of solutions, *Phys. Rev. D* **76**, p. 084036 (2007).
13. M. Vasudevan, Integrability of some charged rotating supergravity black hole solutions in four and five dimensions, *Phys. Lett. B* **624**, p. 287 (2005).
14. D. V. Galtsov and O. V. Kechkin, Ehlers-Harrison type transformations in dilaton - axion gravity, *Phys. Rev. D* **50**, p. 7394 (1994).
15. A. Garcia, D. Galtsov and O. Kechkin, Class of stationary axisymmetric solutions of the Einstein-Maxwell dilaton - axion field equations, *Phys. Rev. Lett.* **74**, p. 1276 (1995). doi:10.1103/PhysRevLett.74.1276
16. B. Y. Chen, Pseudo-Riemannian Geometry, δ-Invariants and Applications, *WorldScientific, Hackensack*, (2011).
17. D. V. Gal'tsov and K. V. Kobialko, Completing characterization of photon orbits in Kerr and Kerr-Newman metrics, *Phys. Rev. D* **99**, p. 084043 (2019)
18. C. M. Claudel, K. S. Virbhadra and G. F. R. Ellis, The Geometry of photon surfaces, *J. Math. Phys.* **42**, p. 818-838 (2001).
19. Y. Koga, T. Igata and K. Nakashi, Photon surfaces in less symmetric spacetimes, *Phys. Rev. D* **103**, p. 044003 (2021).

20. A. Grenzebach, V. Perlick and C. Lämmerzahl, Photon Regions and Shadows of Kerr-Newman-NUT Black Holes with a Cosmological Constant, *Phys. Rev. D* **89**, p. 124004 (2014).
21. A. Grenzebach, V. Perlick and C. Lämmerzahl, Photon Regions and Shadows of Accelerated Black Holes, *Int. J. Mod. Phys. D* **24**, p. 1542024 (2015).
22. K. Glampedakis and G. Pappas, Modification of photon trapping orbits as a diagnostic of non-Kerr spacetimes, *Phys. Rev. D* **99**, p. 124041 (2019).
23. H. Kodama and W. Hikida, Global structure of the Zipoy-Voorhees-Weyl spacetime and the delta=2 Tomimatsu-Sato spacetime, *Class. Quant. Grav.* **20**, p. 5121 (2003).
24. D. V. Gal'tsov and K. V. Kobialko, Photon trapping in static axially symmetric spacetime, *Phys. Rev. D* **100**, p. 104005 (2019)
25. G. Lukes-Gerakopoulos, The non-integrability of the Zipoy-Voorhees metric, *Phys. Rev. D* **86**, p. 044013 (2012).
26. T. Johannsen, Regular Black Hole Metric with Three Constants of Motion, *Phys. Rev. D* **88**, p. 044002 (2013).
27. A. Sen, Rotating charged black hole solution in heterotic string theory, *Phys. Rev. Lett.* **69**, p. 1006 (1992).
28. R. Kallosh, D. Kastor, T. Ortin and T. Torma, Supersymmetry and stationary solutions in dilaton axion gravity, *Phys. Rev. D* **50**, p. 6374 (1994).
29. C. V. Johnson and R. C. Myers, Stringy twists of the Taub - NUT metric, *arXiv*, p. 9409177 (1994).
30. A. Burinskii, Some properties of the Kerr solution to low-energy string theory, *Phys. Rev. D* **52**, p. 5826 (1995).
31. R. A. Konoplya, Z. Stuchlík and A. Zhidenko, Axisymmetric black holes allowing for separation of variables in the Klein-Gordon and Hamilton-Jacobi equations, *Phys. Rev. D* **97**, p. 084044 (2018).
32. X. G. Lan and J. Pu, Observing the contour profile of a Kerr–Sen black hole, *Mod. Phys. Lett. A* **33**, p. 1850099 (2018).
33. H. M. Siahaan, Kerr-Sen-Taub-NUT spacetime and circular geodesics, *Eur. Phys. J. C* **80**, p. 1000 (2020).
34. C. Cederbaum and G. J. Galloway, Photon surfaces with equipotential time-slices, *J. Math. Phys.* **62**, p. 032504 (2021).

Decoding black hole metrics from the interferometric pattern of relativistic images

V. Bozza

Dipartimento di Fisica "E.R. Caianiello", Università di Salerno,
Fisciano, 84084, Italy
E-mail: valboz@sa.infn.it
www.unisa.it

The image of a source around a black hole is replicated an infinite number of times by photons performing an arbitrary number of turns around the black hole. Such relativistic images generate a characteristic staircase structure in the complex visibility measured in interferometric observations. For a quasi-static source, we present analytical formulae describing the visibility function in the strong deflection limit of gravitational lensing. These formulae are then used to extract the properties of the metric from features in the visibility.

Keywords: Black hole, gravitational lensing, interferometry

1. Introduction

The sensational observation of the image of the supermassive black hole at the center of M87* by the EHT collaboration has opened the era of the investigation of black holes at high resolution.[1] Black holes typically appear as a dark spot surrounded by a light ring created by the radiation emitted by the accreting matter revolving around the black holes thanks to the strong gravitational fields.[2,3] This is possible because an unstable circular orbit for photons exists at a specific radius, depending on the black hole parameters and the inclination of the photon trajectory with respect to the equatorial plane. For this reason, any compact sources around the black hole generate two infinite sequences of images asymptotically approaching the light ring.[4–7]

Higher order images of the accretion disk should generate concentric light rings asymptotically approaching the shadow border.[8] Such structure would be detectable in very long baseline interferometry, since the complex visibility should have a staircase structure, with each step generated by an image at specific order.[9]

We propose to describe the complex visibility generated by a compact source using the tools of gravitational lensing in the strong deflection limit. With an analytical description at hand, it is then possible to track the dependence of the observables on the black hole metric and disentangle the metric parameters from the source characteristics.[10]

2. Relativistic images of a compact source

Consider a source at distance r_S from a black hole at angle ϕ_S from the optical axis (i.e. the line joining the observer to the black hole). The direct image will be formed by weakly deflected light rays and will be the largest one, thus dominating the lower angular frequencies in the visibility. Relativistic images are formed by light rays performing n turns around the black hole before reaching the observer.[4] The angular separation of these images from the black hole in the observer sky can be described in the strong deflection limit by a simple exponential formula[11]

$$\theta_{n,\pm} = \theta_m(1 + \epsilon_{n,\pm}), \tag{1}$$

where θ_m is the angular radius of the shadow,

$$\epsilon_{n,\pm} = \eta_O \eta_S e^{\frac{b \pm \phi_S - 2n\pi}{a}}, \tag{2}$$

$$\eta_O = 1 - \frac{r_m}{r_O} \qquad \eta_S = 1 - \frac{r_m}{r_S}, \tag{3}$$

r_O is the observer's distance and r_m is the radius of the unstable circular orbit for photons.

The quantities r_m, u_m, a and b are all functions of the specific black hole metric and can be calculated by standard algorithms.[11] Therefore, in principle, the observation of higher order images can be used to constrain the metric of the black hole. The tangential extension of higher order images $\Delta\vartheta_I$ is the same as the tangential extension of the source $\Delta\vartheta_S$ in the hypothesis of spherical symmetry. The radial extension is obtained by differentiation of Eq. (1)

$$\Delta\theta_{n,\pm} = \Delta\theta_0 \, \epsilon_{n,\pm} \tag{4}$$

$$\Delta\theta_0 = \frac{\theta_m}{a}\Delta\phi_S + \theta_m \frac{r_m}{r_S^2}\left(\frac{1}{\eta_S} + \frac{g_1(\eta_S)}{a}\right)\Delta r_S. \tag{5}$$

Higher order n are exponentially thinner with n. The coefficient $\Delta\theta_0$ does not depend on n, instead.

3. Complex visibility of a compact source

Interferometric observations measure the amplitude of the complex visibility, which is calculated by a Fourier transform of the image pattern.[9] If we assume a static source with a Gaussian profile, the images will be aligned along one axis in the observer sky (say the x-axis). The complex visibility expressed in the angular frequencies (u, v) conjugate to the angular coordinates (x, y) will be

$$V(u,v) = N(v) \sum_{p=\pm 1} \sum_{n=1}^{+\infty} \epsilon_{n,p} \, e^{-2\pi^2 \Delta\theta_{n,p}^2 u^2} e^{-2\pi i p \theta_{n,p} u}, \tag{6}$$

$$N(v) = 2\pi I_0 \theta_m \Delta\theta_0 \Delta\vartheta_S e^{-2\pi^2 \theta_m^2 \Delta\vartheta_S^2 v^2}. \tag{7}$$

The shape of the visibility in the v direction $N(v)$ does not depend on n and is the same for all contributions. In the u direction, each image contributes with a Gaussian function whose size scales with $1/\Delta\theta_n$ and thus increases exponentially with n. As the contribution of order n decays, the order $n+1$ dominates, generating the staircase structure already suggested in Ref. 9. Fig. 1 shows this structure for various source positions ϕ_S.

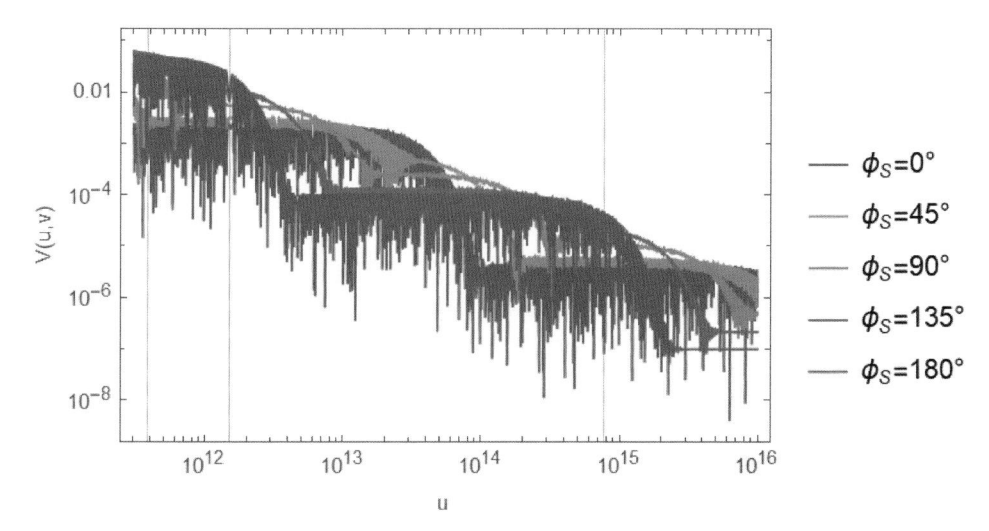

Fig. 1. Visibility function in Schwarzschild space-time for various source azimutal angles. The three vertical lines correspond to Moon baseline, Lagrangian point L2 baseline and Jupiter semi-major axis respectively at the wavelength $\lambda = 1$mm.

The direct image only contributes to low angular frequencies and rapidly decays, leaving space to higher order images at high angular frequencies. Such contributions are analytically expressed by Eq. (6), which can be used to relate the main characteristics such as amplitude, size and periodicity of each contribution to the characteristics of the black hole metric.[10]

Simple algebra allows to invert such expressions so as to write down the gravitational lensing parameters as functions of the observables.[10] The coefficient a is given by the ratio of the amplitude $h_{n,+}$ of contributions by images of consecutive orders

$$a = \frac{2\pi}{\ln(h_{n,+}/h_{n+1,+})}. \tag{8}$$

The source angular position is obtained by comparing the amplitude of contributions by positive and negative parity images

$$\phi_S = \frac{a}{2}\ln(h_{n,+}/h_{n,-}). \tag{9}$$

The angular radius of the shadow and the coefficient b are derived from the frequencies $\nu_{n,\pm}$ of the periodicities in the visibility at scales when two contributions interfere

$$\theta_m = \frac{1}{4}\left\{e^{\frac{2\pi}{a}}\left[\nu_{n,-} + e^{-\frac{2\phi_S}{a}}(\nu_{n,-} - \nu_{n,+})\right] - \nu_{n,+}\right\}\left(\coth\frac{\pi}{a} - 1\right), \quad (10)$$

$$\eta_0\eta_S e^{\frac{b-2n\pi}{a}} = \frac{2(\nu_{n,+} - \nu_{n,-})}{\nu_{n,-}\left(e^{\frac{\phi_S}{a}} + e^{-\frac{\phi_S}{a}}\right) - \nu_{n,+}\left(e^{\frac{\phi_S-2\pi}{a}} + e^{-\frac{\phi_S}{a}}\right)}. \quad (11)$$

These analytical formulae allow to constrain the coefficients of gravitational lensing in the strong deflection limit, which are functions of the black hole metric. It could be possible, therefore, to distinguish between different metrics through the observation of the visibility of a compact source.[10]

4. Discussion and conclusions

As pointed before, the baselines needed for the resolution of higher order images are of the order of millions km.[9] The great scientific expectations on such observations are pushing forward projects for very long baseline interferometry in space, which could be available in the next decades.[12,13]

The physical setup analyzed in this study is very basic: a single static compact source at some distance from a spherically symmetric black hole. In this framework, the complex visibility generated by the infinite sequence of higher order images is simple enough to be described in a fully analytical form. The properties of the metric can be extracted in a clean and source-independent way, something that is quite difficult for non-compact sources or with the whole accretion flow.[14]

However, in order to apply this idealized case to real astrophysical situations, we need a powerful source dominating over the accretion flow with its higher order images. In the mm band this may happen with a very powerful flare in the accretion flow due to some local change in the magnetic fields.[15] In the Near Infrared, we may consider bright stars orbiting the black hole as compact sources.[16] Secondly, in order to have all images aligned on the same axis, we need perfect spherical symmetry and a quasi-static source. In fact, higher order images are formed by photons taking longer paths as they revolve around the black hole. Therefore, such images would follow an orbiting source with some delay.[17] This limits the applicability of this framework to sources far enough to neglect their orbital motion.

In spite of these limitations, this fully analytical calculation stands as a reference limiting case for more complicated calculations and opens the investigation to more complete physical setups.

References

1. Event Horizon Telescope Collaboration, K. Akiyama, A. Alberdi, W. Alef et al., First M87 Event Horizon Telescope Results. i. The Shadow of the Supermassive Black Hole, *ApJ* **875**, p. L1 (April 2019).

2. J. M. Bardeen, Timelike and null geodesics in the Kerr metric., in *Black Holes (Les Astres Occlus)*, January 1973.
3. V. Perlick and O. Y. Tsupko, Calculating black hole shadows: review of analytical studies, *arXiv e-prints*, p. arXiv:2105.07101 (May 2021).
4. C. G. Darwin, The gravity field of a particle, *Proceedings of the Royal Society of London. Series A. Mathematical and Physical Sciences* **249**, 180 (1959).
5. H. C. Ohanian, The black hole as a gravitational "lens", *American Journal of Physics* **55**, 428 (May 1987).
6. K. S. Virbhadra and G. F. R. Ellis, Schwarzschild black hole lensing, *Phys. Rev. D* **62**, p. 084003 (October 2000).
7. V. Bozza, Gravitational lensing in the strong field limit, *Phys. Rev. D* **66**, p. 103001 (November 2002).
8. J. P. Luminet, Image of a spherical black hole with thin accretion disk., *A&A* **75**, 228 (May 1979).
9. M. D. Johnson, A. Lupsasca, A. Strominger, G. N. Wong *et al.*, Universal interferometric signatures of a black hole's photon ring, *Science Advances* **6**, p. eaaz1310 (March 2020).
10. F. Aratore and V. Bozza, Decoding a black hole metric from the interferometric pattern of relativistic images, *arXiv e-prints*, p. arXiv:2107.05723 (July 2021).
11. V. Bozza and G. Scarpetta, Strong deflection limit of black hole gravitational lensing with arbitrary source distances, *Physical Review D* **76**, p. 083008 (2007).
12. D. Pesce, K. Haworth, G. J. Melnick *et al.*, Extremely long baseline interferometry with Origins Space Telescope, in *Bulletin of the American Astronomical Society*, September 2019.
13. A. S. Andrianov, A. M. Baryshev, H. Falcke *et al.*, Simulations of M87 and Sgr A* imaging with the Millimetron Space Observatory on near-Earth orbits, *MNRAS* **500**, 4866 (January 2021).
14. A. Chael, M. D. Johnson and A. Lupsasca, Observing the Inner Shadow of a Black Hole: A Direct View of the Event Horizon, *arXiv e-prints*, p. arXiv:2106.00683 (June 2021).
15. Event Horizon Telescope Collaboration, K. Akiyama, J. C. Algaba, A. Alberdi *et al.*, First M87 Event Horizon Telescope Results. VIII. Magnetic Field Structure near The Event Horizon, *ApJ* **910**, p. L13 (March 2021).
16. Gravity Collaboration, R. Abuter, A. Amorim, M. Bauböck, J. P. Berger *et al.*, Detection of faint stars near Sagittarius A* with GRAVITY, *A&A* **645**, p. A127 (January 2021).
17. V. Bozza and L. Mancini, Time Delay in Black Hole Gravitational Lensing as a Distance Estimator, *General Relativity and Gravitation* **36**, 435 (February 2004).

Symplectic evolution of an observed light bundle

N. Uzun

*Univ Lyon, Ens de Lyon, Univ Lyon1, CNRS, Centre de Recherche Astrophysique de Lyon
Lyon, UMR5574, F69007, France
E-mail: nezihe.uzun@ens-lyon.fr
http://www.univ-lyon1.fr*

Each and every observational information we obtain from the sky regarding the brightnesses, distances or image distortions resides on the deviation of a null geodesic bundle. In this talk, we present the symplectic evolution of this bundle on a reduced phase space. The resulting formalism is analogous to the one in paraxial Newtonian optics. It allows one to identify any spacetime as an optical device and distinguish its thin lens, pure magnifier and rotator components. We will discuss the fact that the distance reciprocity in relativity results from the symplectic evolution of this null bundle. Other potential applications like wavization and its importance for both electromagnetic and gravitational waves will also be summarized.

Keywords: General relativity, geodesic deviation, optics, symplectic

1. Introduction

When we make an observation on the sky, we deduce the brightness, distance and image distortion information about astrophysical objects via a bundle of null rays. This geodesic bundle connects the emitter and the observer that are located at two distant regions of a spacetime. Nevertheless, they receive reciprocal information about each other.

For example, an observer located at point O on Earth, obtains the distance to a galaxy cluster located at point G, by making use of the observed solid angle at point O, and the estimated cross–sectional area on the sky at point G. This gives the angular diameter distance, D_A. Such a distance estimation is mostly relevant for standard rulers in cosmology as, for example, baryon acoustic oscillations. Likewise, an observer at point G can estimate the distance to a point O in a similar fashion. According to an observer on Earth, on the other hand, this information is contained in the luminosity distance, D_L. Namely, by using the observed flux

$$F_{\text{observed}} = \frac{\text{Source luminosity}}{\text{Surface area}} = \frac{L_{\text{source}}}{4\pi D_U^2}, \tag{1}$$

one can deduce an *uncorrected* luminosity distance, D_U. When the relativistic corrections are included, one obtains a corrected luminosity distance, D_L, via

$$D_L = (1+z)^{-1} D_U, \tag{2}$$

where z is the redshift factor. The relationship between the luminosity distance and the angular diameter distance is given by Etherington's distance reciprocity theorem[1]

$$D_L = (1+z)D_A. \qquad (3)$$

The distance reciprocity, eq (3), was originally derived for light propagation within a single spacetime. This means that the initial point of the propagation is an observation point at which the geodesic deviation vector becomes zero. Eventually, it can be shown that the distance reciprocity follows from the symmetries of the Riemann curvature tensor.[1,2]

Previously, we showed that[3] one can extend the proof for more generic scenarios. Namely, for a ray bundle propagating in multiple geometries, one needs to propagate a bundle with arbitrary initial conditions. Such a scenario was used, for example, in Fleury et al.[4,5] In those investigations, there exists a 4×4 Wronskian matrix which takes the initial ray bundle variables to the final ones. A similar construction can be found[6-9] where the Wronskian in question is 8–dimensional and it includes more information regarding the light bundle evolution. We demonstrated[3] that the Wronskian matrix of Fleury et al. is indeed symplectic and the most general form of the distance reciprocity follows from the symplectic symmetries of this transformation matrix. This was achieved by following a Hamiltonian formalism defined on a 4–dimensional phase space. Note that our approach is analogous to the reduced phase space optics formalism developed for classical paraxial rays.[10,11]

In classical optics, one starts with Fermat's action in order to obtain a Hamiltonian formalism in which rays are the geodesic solutions of the corresponding optical metric of Fermat. Likewise, we implemented the usage of geodesic actions applied to a null bundle. The outcome is an effective geodesic deviation action which was originally derived up to higher orders in Vines' work.[12]

The aim of this talk is to give a brief summary of our previous formalism,[3] along with discussing the importance of implementing such new techniques to gravitational optics. We summarize the aforementioned symplectic phase space approach in Section (2). Some perspectives on the symplectic ray bundle evolution is given in Section (3) and we conclude with Section (4).

2. Symplectic evolution of light bundles on phase space

2.1. Vines' bi–local geodesic deviation action

It is known that connecting two geodesics is, in general, non–local. Therefore, if one wants to obtain a geodesic deviation action, one needs to consider a bi–local formalism. Vines[12] achieves this for generic curves by following the definition of Synge's world function[13] $\sigma(x,y)$. This is a bi–local object which depends on two spacetime points x and y. Those two points are connected by a unique geodesic, Σ, such that

$$\sigma(x,y) = \frac{1}{2} \begin{cases} (\text{proper distance})^2, & \Sigma : \text{spacelike} \\ 0, & \Sigma : \text{null} \\ -(\text{proper time})^2, & \Sigma : \text{timelike}. \end{cases}$$

Now consider a bundle whose outer most null geodesic, $\Upsilon(v)$, has a tangent vector $\vec{k}'$ (See Fig. 1.). The central null geodesic, $\chi(v)$, with a tangent vector $\vec{k}$, can also be parameterized with the same affine parameter v. This is called isosynchronous parameterization. Then those tangent vectors satisfy $\nabla_{\vec{k}'}\vec{k}' = 0$ and $\nabla_{\vec{k}}\vec{k} = 0$ where ∇ denotes the covariant derivative operator defined at a specified point. Moreover, physical sizes of the objects on the sky are estimated by the proper sizes. Therefore, a spacelike world function, being the measure of proper distance between two spacetime points, is the most relevant tool for our construction.

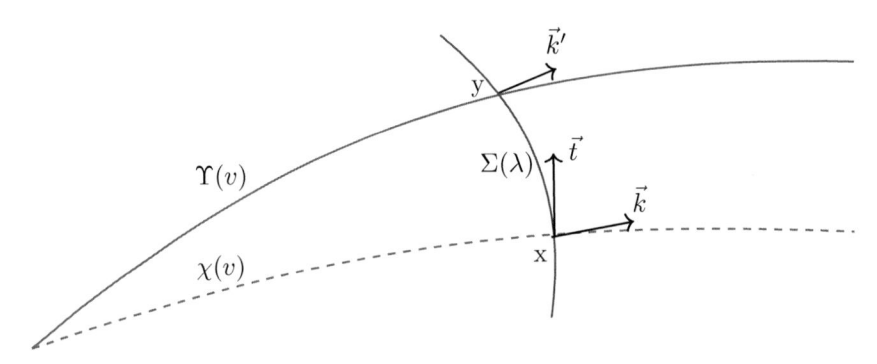

Fig. 1. The central null geodesic $\chi(v)$ is plotted with dashed lines. The red curve represents $\Sigma(\lambda)$ given by Synge's world function that is spacelike. The outermost null geodesic $\Upsilon(v)$ can be uniquely obtained through $\chi(v)$ and $\Sigma(\lambda)$.

Now consider a spacelike geodesic, $\Sigma(\lambda)$, that connects $\Upsilon(v)$ to $\chi(v)$. One can define an exponential map on $\Sigma(\lambda)$ via the derivatives of the world function $\sigma(x,y)$. This results in a bi–local object $\vec{\eta}$, whose variation with respect to the affine parameter that parameterizes the null bundle, is given by[3,12]

$$\dot{\eta}^\alpha = \frac{\mathbb{D}\eta^\alpha}{dv} = \left(k^\beta \nabla_\beta + k'^\mu \nabla_\mu\right)\eta^\alpha. \qquad (4)$$

Note that for an arbitrarily large separation one needs to consider the covariant derivatives of $\vec{\eta}$ at two distinct points along the null bundle as in eq. (4). In that case, one can write the action functional of $\Upsilon(v)$, i.e., $S_\Upsilon = \int \frac{1}{2} k'^2 dv$, by making use of the action functional, $S_\chi = \int \frac{1}{2} k^2 dv$, of the central null geodesic, $\chi(v)$, and some additional terms,[3,12] i.e.,

$$S_\Upsilon = S_\chi + \int \frac{1}{2}\left[2\vec{k}\cdot\dot{\vec{\eta}} + \dot{\vec{\eta}}\cdot\dot{\vec{\eta}} - R_{\vec{\eta}\vec{k}\vec{\eta}\vec{k}} + O(\vec{\eta},\dot{\vec{\eta}})^3\right] dv. \qquad (5)$$

Here, $R^\alpha{}_{\gamma\beta\delta}$ is the Riemann curvature tensor. In order to obtain the second integral, that appears on the r.h.s of eq. (5), one solves eq. (4) for $\vec{k}'$ and substitutes it in $S_\Upsilon = \int \frac{1}{2} k'^2 dv$. However, this is not a straightforward calculation as it requires the bi–local object $\dot{\eta}^\alpha$ to be Taylor expanded in the coincidence limit. We advice the reader to see the original derivation of Vines[12] for generic scenarios or our previous paper[3] for further details in this context.

On the other hand, for the observations on the sky, what is relevant is a thin bundle of null geodesics, rather than the ones with large separations. Thus, once the local limit of eq. (5) is taken for an infinitesimally thin bundle, one can consider $\vec{\eta}$ as a local geodesic deviation vector. Then, one obtains an effective action

$$S = \int \left(\frac{1}{2} \dot{\vec{\eta}} \cdot \dot{\vec{\eta}} + \frac{1}{2} R_{\vec{\eta}\vec{k}\vec{k}\vec{\eta}} \right) dv, \tag{6}$$

whose extremization results in a first order geodesic deviation equation

$$\ddot{\eta}^\alpha = R^\alpha{}_{\vec{k}\vec{k}\vec{\eta}}. \tag{7}$$

Note that as from eq. (6), and onwards, the overdot represents a local covariant derivative with respect to the central ray $\vec{k}$.

In the next section, we will introduce a local tetrad and an associated screen basis around an observation point. This will allow us to rewrite the action functional (6) in terms of the observable variables in the following sections.

2.2. Screen basis, cross–sections and solid angles

Consider an observer with 4–velocity $\vec{u}$. Assume that (s)he observes a thin null bundle with a central geodesic whose tangent vector is given by $k^\alpha = \omega(u^\alpha + r^\alpha)$. Here, the observed frequency of light is given by $\omega = -\vec{k} \cdot \vec{u}$ and $\vec{r}$ is a spacelike vector and thus $\vec{u} \cdot \vec{r} = 0$. We will also consider a 2–dimensional spacelike screen represented by the Sachs basis,[14,15] s_a^α, with $\{a, b\} = \{1, 2\}$. Then,

$$\vec{s}_a \cdot \vec{s}_b = \delta_{ab}, \qquad \vec{u} \cdot \vec{s}_a = 0, \qquad \vec{r} \cdot \vec{s}_a = 0, \qquad \nabla_{\vec{k}} \vec{s}_a = 0, \tag{8}$$

are satisfied. This orthogonal screen is the one on which the observables are projected.

For an observational bundle, $\vec{k} \cdot \vec{\eta} = 0$ holds initially as the null bundle converges into a vertex point where the observer is located. Note that this condition is preserved throughout the evolution of the bundle as (i) $\nabla_{\vec{k}} \vec{\eta} = \nabla_{\vec{\eta}} \vec{k}$ holds due to the propagation vector, $\vec{k}$, and its Jacobi field, $\vec{\eta}$, being Lie dragged along each other,[16] (ii) the propagation vector satisfies the null condition, (iii) the first order geodesic deviation equation, (7), is satisfied. Therefore, one can decompose the deviation vector as[3,15]

$$\vec{\eta} = \eta^k \vec{k} + \eta^1 \vec{s}_1 + \eta^2 \vec{s}_2. \tag{9}$$

Note that we will denote components of $\vec{\eta}$ residing on the orthogonal screen as $\eta := \eta^1 \vec{s}_1 + \eta^2 \vec{s}_2$.

Those screen–projected components are useful in identifying observationally relevant objects. For example, the cross–sectional area, $d\mathcal{A}$, of an extended object and an observed solid angle, $d\Theta$, are respectively given by[2]

$$d\mathcal{A} := \left|\eta^1 \wedge \eta^2\right|, \qquad d\Theta := \left|\frac{d\eta^1}{d\ell} \wedge \frac{d\eta^2}{d\ell}\right|. \tag{10}$$

where $|d\ell| = \omega dv$ is the infinitesimal proper length written in terms of the affine parameter, v, of the null bundle and the observed frequency of light, ω. The symbol $\wedge$ represents the exterior product.

In the next section, we will introduce a Hamiltonian formalism associated with the action functional, (6). This Hamiltonian will be defined on a phase space whose coordinates are constructed via the screen–projected deviation vector, η, and its derivatives, $\dot{\eta}$.

2.3. *A reduced phase space and its Hamiltonian*

In general relativity, the standard way of constructing an optical phase space resides on a $3 + 1$ decomposition of a spacetime. Specifically, one chooses the phase space coordinates as the ones induced on a 3–dimensional spacelike hypersurface and the phase space momenta are chosen as the induced 3–momenta of a photon. Alternatively, we show that[3] a 4–dimensional phase space can be effectively constructed for a null bundle via treating the screen–projected deviation vector, as phase space Darboux coordinates, q^a, and its derivatives along the bundle as phase space momenta, p_b. Then a phase space vector can be defined as

$$\boldsymbol{\varkappa} = \begin{bmatrix} q^a \\ p_b \end{bmatrix} = \begin{bmatrix} \eta^1 \\ \eta^2 \\ \dot{\eta}_1 \\ \dot{\eta}_2 \end{bmatrix}. \tag{11}$$

Note that, the overdot in eq. (11) now denotes a standard total derivative with respect to the evolution parameter v as we are considering only the dyad components of $\vec{\eta}$.

Let us reconsider the effective geodesic deviation action functional given in eq. (6). By (i) treating the integrant of the action functional as a Lagrangian, (ii) using the symmetries of the Riemann tensor and (iii) rewriting the Lagrangian in terms of the phase space coordinates, one can obtain a reduced Lagrangian. A passage to the Hamiltonian formalism gives us a reduced Hamiltonian

$$H = \frac{1}{2}\delta^{ab}\dot{\eta}_a\dot{\eta}_b - \frac{1}{2}\mathcal{R}_{ab}\,\eta^a\eta^b, \tag{12}$$

where $\mathcal{R}_{ab} := R_{a\vec{k}\vec{k}b}$ is known as the *optical tidal matrix* in cosmology.[15,17]

Then, the corresponding Hamiltonian equations can be written as a matrix equation

$$\dot{\boldsymbol{\varkappa}} = \mathbf{L_H}\,\boldsymbol{\varkappa}, \qquad \text{with} \qquad \mathbf{L_H} = \begin{bmatrix} 0_2 & \delta^{ab} \\ \hline \mathcal{R}_{ab} & 0_2 \end{bmatrix}, \tag{13}$$

where $\mathbf{L_H}$ is the Hamiltonian matrix representation of the Lie operator defined through the reduced Hamiltonian, H, given in eq (12) and $\mathbf{0_2}$ is a 2×2 zero matrix.

Let us now investigate the solutions of the Hamiltonian equations, (13), in the next section.

2.4. *Symplectic evolution and its symmetries*

The Hamiltonian equations, (13), presented in the previous section are linear equations as $\mathbf{L_H} = \mathbf{L_H}(v)$. Then, its solutions are given by a linear transformation of an input phase vector, $\varkappa_0$, defined at v_0, which gives an output phase space vector, $\varkappa$, at some value of v, i.e.,

$$\varkappa = \mathbf{T}(v, v_0) \varkappa_0. \tag{14}$$

Substituting eq. (14) back into eq. (13) shows that the ray bundle transfer matrix, $\mathbf{T}$, satisfies a similar equation as the phase space vector $\varkappa$, i.e., $\dot{\mathbf{T}} = \mathbf{L_H} \mathbf{T}$. Then, its solution is given by taking an ordered exponential (OE) map,

$$\mathbf{T}(v, v_0) = \mathrm{OE}\left[\int_{v_0}^{v} \mathbf{L_H} dv\right] \mathbf{T}(v_0, v_0), \quad \text{with} \quad \mathbf{T}(v_0, v_0) = \mathbf{I_4}, \tag{15}$$

and $\mathbf{I_4}$ is a 4×4 identity matrix. In that case, $\mathbf{T}$, is a symplectic matrix which satisfies

$$\mathbf{T}^\mathsf{T} \mathbf{\Omega} \mathbf{T} = \mathbf{\Omega}, \quad \det \mathbf{T} = 1, \tag{16}$$

as exponential map of Hamiltonian matrices are symplectic matrices. Here, $^\mathsf{T}$ denotes the transpose operator and $\mathbf{\Omega}$ is the well–known *fundamental symplectic matrix* whose components are given by

$$\Omega^{ij} = \left[\begin{array}{c|c} \mathbf{0_2} & \mathbf{I_2} \\ \hline -\mathbf{I_2} & \mathbf{0_2} \end{array}\right]. \tag{17}$$

This allows one to treat the ray bundle evolution in general relativity analogous to a dynamical problem in classical mechanics. A similar approach has indeed been developed in paraxial Newtonian optics much earlier (Cf. references in[10, 11]). In that case, this approach is also known as the *ABCD–matrix method* as it is very common to represent a symplectic matrix, $\mathbf{T}$, in a block form

$$\mathbf{T} = \left[\begin{array}{c|c} \mathbf{A} & \mathbf{B} \\ \hline \mathbf{C} & \mathbf{D} \end{array}\right]. \tag{18}$$

In our case, the submatrices in eq. (18) are all 2×2 matrices which satisfy certain symmetry conditions

$$\mathbf{AB}^\mathsf{T}, \mathbf{A}^\mathsf{T}\mathbf{C}, \mathbf{B}^\mathsf{T}\mathbf{D} \text{ and } \mathbf{CD}^\mathsf{T} \text{ are symmetric,}$$
$$\mathbf{AD}^\mathsf{T} - \mathbf{BC}^\mathsf{T} = \mathbf{I_2}, \tag{19}$$

due to **T** being a symplectic matrix, i.e., eq. (16) is satisfied. Then, the Hamiltonian equations, (13), become equivalent to,

$$\dot{\mathbf{A}} = \mathbf{C}, \qquad \mathbf{A}(v_0, v_0) = \mathbf{I}_2,$$
$$\dot{\mathbf{B}} = \mathbf{D}, \qquad \mathbf{B}(v_0, v_0) = \mathbf{0}_2,$$
$$\dot{\mathbf{C}} = \mathcal{R}\mathbf{A}, \qquad \mathbf{C}(v_0, v_0) = \mathbf{0}_2,$$
$$\dot{\mathbf{D}} = \mathcal{R}\mathbf{B}, \qquad \mathbf{D}(v_0, v_0) = \mathbf{I}_2. \qquad (20)$$

Therefore, once the solutions of the equation set above is found, one can find the explicit form of the transfer matrix, **T**, and the geodesic deviation variables of the null bundle in question. This allows one to estimate certain observables as we discuss in the next section.

3. Some perspectives on the symplectic ray bundle evolution

3.1. *Distance reciprocity*

The relationship of the ray bundle transfer matrix, **T**, to the observables is not immediately obvious. In order to estimate the distance to an object located at G, for example, one starts with propagating the bundle with the initial phase space vector $\varkappa_o = (\mathbf{0}, \dot{\eta}_o)^{\mathsf{T}}$ at the observation point O (See Fig. 2.). Then, one can calculate the cross–sectional area, $d\mathcal{A}$, at G by (i) making use of the definitions of $d\mathcal{A}$ and the solid angle, $d\Theta$, given in eq. (10), (ii) inputting the information of the measured $d\Theta$ at point O in the initial phase space vector, $\varkappa_o = (\mathbf{0}, \dot{\eta}_o)^{\mathsf{T}}$, and (iii) considering the ray bundle transformation matrix **T** that transfers the initial phase space vector to a final one as in eq. (14). In that case, the estimated distance in question is the angular diameter distance given by $D_A = (d\mathcal{A}_G/d\Theta_O)^{1/2}$. Likewise, a similar distance estimation can be done by an observer located at point G. Then, the estimated distance is the luminosity distance given by $D_L = (d\mathcal{A}_O/d\Theta_G)^{1/2}$.

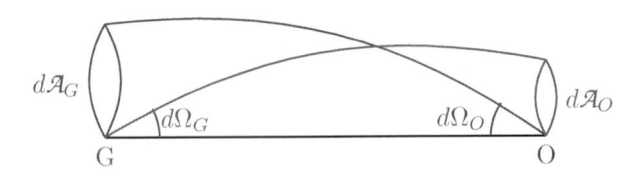

Fig. 2. Observer at O measures a solid angle $d\Omega_O$ and estimates the cross-sectional area of an astrophysical object at G as $d\mathcal{A}_G$. Same thing is applicable for an observer at G as well. Reciprocity of the estimated distances is written as $d\mathcal{A}_O/d\Omega_G = (1+z)^2 \, d\mathcal{A}_G/d\Omega_O$.

As the solution of a phase space vector is given by eq. (14) in which **T** is represented in a block form (18), one obtains the angular diameter and luminosity distances respectively by making use of only the submatrix **B**, i.e.,

$$D_A = \omega_O \det\left[\mathbf{B}\left(v_G, v_O\right)\right]^{1/2}, \qquad D_L = \omega_G \det\left[\mathbf{B}\left(v_O, v_G\right)\right]^{1/2}. \qquad (21)$$

Here, ω_O and ω_G are the frequencies measured at respective points through which a redshift parameter is defined as $1 + z = \omega_G/\omega_O$. Note that the frequency terms appear in the process of transforming the proper length, as it appears in the definition of solid angle in eq.(10), to the affine parameter, v, as we discussed in Section (2.2). The abbreviation "det" refers to the determinant of a given matrix.

In order for Etherington's distance reciprocity, eq. (3), to hold one needs to show that $\det [\mathbf{B}(v_G, v_O)] = \det [\mathbf{B}(v_O, v_G)]$ holds. Indeed, this was previously proven by making use of the symmetries of the Riemann tensor.[15] Note that such a case is applicable for light propagation within a single geometry. For scenarios that include light propagation in multiple spacetimes, one needs to propagate the bundle not only from the initial vertex point but also from arbitrary initial phase space points to other arbitrary ones. In that case, the information about the light bundle transformation is not only contained in the submatrix $\mathbf{B}$ but in all of the submatrices of $\mathbf{T}$. For example, this is applicable for light propagation in Swiss–cheese type models.[4,5]

Previously, we showed that distance reciprocity follows from the symplectic conditions, eq. (19), of the ray bundle transfer matrix for generic scenarios.[3] To be more specific, consider a ray bundle matrix, $\mathbf{T}(v_f, v_i)$, which takes an initial phase space vector, $\varkappa(v_i)$, to a final one, $\varkappa(v_f)$. Such a linear transformation should be equal to its inverse, once the initial and final points are traversed, i.e., $\mathbf{T}(v_i, v_f) = \mathbf{T}^{-1}(v_f, v_i)$. Moreoever, symplectic matrices form a group, thus inverse of a symplectic matrix is also symplectic. This requires $\mathbf{T}^{-1}(v_f, v_i) = \mathbf{\Omega}^{-1}\mathbf{T}^{\intercal}(v_f, v_i)\mathbf{\Omega}$. Then, it is easy to show that the distance reciprocity indeed follows from $\mathbf{T}(v_i, v_f) = \mathbf{\Omega}^{-1}\mathbf{T}^{\intercal}(v_f, v_i)\mathbf{\Omega}$. See our previous work[3] for further details in which we show this result more explicitly.

3.2. Decomposition of an optical propagation

One of the earliest predictions of Einstein's general relativity was on the light propagation within our Solar System. Back then, the idea of a spacetime structure was so hard to grasp that the astronomers conceptualized the effect of a massive object on the trajectory of light as "bending". Similarly, the name "gravitational lensing" remained within the community after Eddington performed his famous Solar eclipse experiment. Even more than 100 years after this observation, the researchers in the field use the term gravitational lensing in a loose sense.

On the other hand, in Newtonian optics a lens is defined more rigorously. For the paraxial case, for example, it is identified as a linear transformation that creates a shearing affect on the phase space defining the ray propagation. Though, lenses are not the only type of optical devices and there is a common practice in Newtonian optics in order to identify the components of light propagation. This is achieved by an Iwasawa decomposition[18] where a symplectic ray transformation matrix is decomposed into its submatrices belonging to a nilpotent subgroup, an abelian subgroup and a maximally compact subgroup for 1–dimensional systems.

This allows one to identify the thin lens, the pure magnifier and the fractional Fourier transformer components of an optical propagation problem uniquely. In higher dimensions, such an identification is known as Iwasawa factorization whose components can be obtained via the submatrices of the transformation matrix **T** (Cf.[10] for further details).

Previously, we proposed that any spacetime can be treated as an optical device within our formalism[3] which allows one to identify the lenses, the magnifiers and the rotators of an optical propagation in general relativity in a rigorous manner. In that case, spacetimes can be compared and contrasted in terms of their significance in different types of optical transformations, by making use of the Iwasawa factorization of their symplectic ray bundle transfer matrices.

3.3. *From rays back to waves*

Finding the exact solutions of the Maxwell's equation on a curved background is not an easy task in general relativity. There exists a similar problem in Newtonian optics for light propagation in media with an arbitrary refractive index. Within the paraxial regime of Newtonian optics, there exist certain "wavization" techniques that are adopted from quantum mechanics in order to find approximate solutions of the Maxwell equations.

The analogy between classical optics and quantum mechanics follows from the similarities between the Schrödinger equation of a particle wavefunction and the Maxwell equation of a complex amplitude of a classical wave in the scalar theory.[19,20] The $\hbar \to 0$ limit of quantum mechanics is said to give classical mechanics, and $\lambda \to 0$ limit of wave optics gives ray optics. Moreover, both the classical mechanics and the paraxial ray optics are constructed on symplectic phase spaces. Thus, in the first order limit, a wave picture can be attained back by making use of some phase space techniques that were initially introduced within quantum mechanics. In that case, phase space distribution functions, like Wigner function (or other analogous definitions), and metaplectic operators that are responsible for the spreading of a wave, play the central role in the wavization process.[11]

We proposed[3] that such methods can be adopted from Newtonian optics as we also reduced the problem of light bundle propagation into a symplectic evolution problem in phase space. Note that this is immediately relevant for gravitational lensing studies because when the wavelength of light is not much smaller than the gravitational lensing object, the wave effects on lensing become important. It is known that the wave effects amplify the estimated intensity of a wave in general.[21,22] Also, an earlier result showed that the wave and ray optics do not agree in terms of the position of the image formation for a specific geometry.[23] However, there is not much known in terms of the image formation in wave optics of light.[24] There are limited number of studies that investigate the wave optics and those usually only focus on the lensing problem on static background.[25–27] We propose that symplectic methods can be quite useful in this respect.

Moreover, it is known that gravitational waves also have null propagation vectors similar to light rays. Therefore, geometric optics is relevant for the investigation of gravitational waves at the linear order.[28, 29] Also, the interaction of gravitational waves with matter fields is known to be weak. Thus, their coherence is expected to be preserved even over cosmological distances.[30] Then, the interplay between the ray and wave behaviours can be used to study gravitational waves within our formalism. Also note that wave effects on the lensing of the gravitational waves have been investigated in some studies only lately.[24, 31–37] However, all of those studies focus on wave effects on specific geometries.

In addition, recently, new ideas are introduced to the literature regarding the wave effects. For example, the spin Hall effect which is normally studied in condensed matter field, is known to bring corrections to the geometrical optics limit in the case of light rays. Oancea *et al.*[38] found an analogous effect for the case of gravitational waves. Similarly, the Aharonov-Bohm effect is known from quantum electromagnetism. Baraldo *et al.*[30] found that there exists an analogous effect for the gravitational waves. Namely, a shift is predicted on the interference pattern of the gravitational waves due to the angular momentum of a lensing object.

Therefore, we propose that once a wavization procedure is applied to our symplectic null bundle propagation, evolution of gravitational waves and their lensing can be studied within more generic scenarios as well.

4. Conclusion

In this talk, we summarized our work[3] which reduces an observational light bundle evolution in general relativity analogous to a classical optical problem in phase space. This requires simultaneous implementation of a null geodesic action to the outermost null curve and the central null curve of an observational light bundle. One then obtains an effective geodesic deviation action which can be written in terms of the screen–projected variables of the null geodesic deviation. This reduces the problem by one order and a 4–dimensional reduced phase space can be obtained by treating the screen–projections of the geodesic deviation vectors as canonical coordinates and their derivatives along the central null ray as canonical momenta. The Hamiltonian equations of this first order problem can be written as a matrix equation whose solutions are obtained via linear symplectic transformations. We shortly discussed (i) a generic proof of the distance reciprocity in general relativity by making use of the symmetries of the symplectic ray bundle transfer matrix, (ii) decomposition of the light bundle propagation into thin lens, pure magnifier and fractional Fourier transformation portions such that any spacetime can be rigorously identified as an optical device, (iii) the relevance of our method to the wave optics for electromagnetic and gravitational waves which have been drawing increasing interest in the literature lately.

Acknowledgements

The author thanks Thomas Buchert for his comments. This work is a part of a project that has received funding from the European Research Council (ERC) under the European Union's Horizon 2020 research and innovation programme (grant agreement ERC advanced Grant 740021ARTHUS, PI: Thomas Buchert).

References

1. I. M. H. Etherington, On the definition of distance in general relativity, *Philos. Mag.* **15**, p. 761 (1933).
2. G. F. R. Ellis, Relativistic cosmology, *Gen. Rel. Grav.* **41**, p. 581 (2009).
3. N. Uzun, Reduced phase space optics for general relativity: Symplectic ray bundle transfer, *Class. Quant. Grav.* **37**, p. 045002 (2020).
4. P. Fleury, H. Dupuy and J. P. Uzan, Interpretation of the Hubble diagram in a nonhomogeneous universe, *Phys. Rev. D* **87**, p. 123526 (2013).
5. P. Fleury, Swiss-cheese models and the Dyer-Roeder approximation, *J. Cosmol. Astropart. Phys.* **06**, p. 054 (2014).
6. M. Grasso, M. Korzyński and J. Serbenta, Geometric optics in general relativity using bilocal operators, *Phys. Rev. D* **99**, p. 064038 (Mar 2019).
7. M. Korzyński and E. Villa, Geometric optics in relativistic cosmology: New formulation and a new observable, *Phys. Rev. D* **101**, p. 063506 (Mar 2020).
8. M. Korzyński, J. Miśkiewicz and J. Serbenta, Weighing the spacetime along the line of sight using times of arrival of electromagnetic signals, *Phys. Rev. D* **104**, p. 024026 (Jul 2021).
9. M. Grasso, E. Villa, M. Korzyński and S. Matarrese, Isolating nonlinearities of light propagation in inhomogeneous cosmologies, *Phys. Rev. D* **104**, p. 043508 (Aug 2021).
10. K. B. Wolf, *Geometric Optics on Phase Space*, Theoretical and Mathematical Physics, Theoretical and Mathematical Physics (Springer, Berlin Heidelberg, 2004).
11. A. Torre, *Linear Ray and Wave Optics in Phase Space: Bridging Ray and Wave Optics via the Wigner Phase-Space Picture* (Elsevier Science, 2005).
12. J. Vines, Geodesic deviation at higher orders via covariant bitensors, *Gen. Rel. Grav.* **47**, p. 59 (2015).
13. J. L. Synge, *Relativity: the general theory*, Series in Physics, Series in Physics (North Holland, 1960).
14. R. Sachs, Gravitational waves in general relativity. VI. The outgoing radiation condition, *Proc. R. Soc. London* **264**, p. 309 (1961).
15. V. Perlick, Gravitational Lensing from a Spacetime Perspective, *Living Rev. Rel.* **7**, p. 9 (2004).
16. R. M. Wald, *General Relativity* (Chicago Univ. Pr., Chicago, USA, 1984).
17. S. Seitz, P. Schneider and J. Ehlers, Light propagation in arbitrary spacetimes and the gravitational lens approximation, *Class. Quantum Grav.* **11**, p. 2345 (1994).
18. K. Iwasawa, On Some Types of Topological Groups, *Ann. Math.* **50**, p. 507 (1949).
19. D. Dragoman, *Phase space correspondence between classical optics and quantum mechanics*, Progress in Optics Vol. 43 (Elsevier, 2002), p. 433.
20. D. Dragoman, Applications of the Wigner Distribution Function in Signal Processing, *EURASIP J. Appl. Signal Process.* **2005**, p. 1520 (2005).
21. T. T. Nakamura and S. Deguchi, Wave Optics in Gravitational Lensing, *Prog. Theor. Phys. Supplement* **133**, 137 (01 1999).

22. N. Matsunaga and K. Yamamoto, The finite source size effect and the wave optics in gravitational lensing, *J. Cosmol. Astropart. Phys.* **01**, p. 023 (2006).
23. E. Herlt and H. Stephani, Wave Optics of the Spherical Gravitational Lens. II. Diffraction of a Plane Electromagnetic Wave by a Black Hole, *Int. J. Theor. Phys.* **17**, 189 (March 1978).
24. Y. Nambu, Wave optics and image formation in gravitational lensing, *J. Phys.: Conference Series* **410**, p. 012036 (Feb 2013).
25. Y. Nambu and S. Noda, Wave optics in black hole spacetimes: The Schwarzschild case, *Class. Quant. Grav.* **33**, p. 075011 (Apr 2016).
26. S. G. Turyshev and V. T. Toth, Diffraction of electromagnetic waves in the gravitational field of the sun, *Phys. Rev. D* **96**, p. 024008 (Jul 2017).
27. S. G. Turyshev and V. T. Toth, Wave-optical treatment of the shadow cast by a large sphere, *Phys. Rev. A* **97**, p. 033810 (Mar 2018).
28. K. S. Thorne, The theory of gravitational radiation — An introductory review, in *Gravitational Radiation*, January 1983.
29. S. R. Dolan, Geometric optics for scalar, electromagnetic and gravitational waves on curved spacetime, *Int. J. Mod. Phys. D* **27**, p. 1843010 (2018).
30. C. Baraldo, A. Hosoya and T. T. Nakamura, Gravitationally induced interference of gravitational waves by a rotating massive object, *Phys. Rev. D* **59**, p. 083001 (Mar 1999).
31. R. Takahashi and T. Nakamura, Wave effects in gravitational lensing of gravitational waves from chirping binaries, *Astrophys. J.* **595**, 1039 (2003).
32. A. J. Moylan, D. E. McClelland, S. M. Scott, A. C. Searle and G. V. Bicknell, Numerical wave optics and the lensing of gravitational waves by globular clusters, in *11th Marcel Grossmann Meeting on General Relativity*, 10 2007.
33. C.-M. Yoo, T. Harada and N. Tsukamoto, Wave Effect in Gravitational Lensing by the Ellis Wormhole, *Phys. Rev. D* **87**, p. 084045 (2013).
34. R. Takahashi, Arrival time differences between gravitational waves and electromagnetic signals due to gravitational lensing, *Astrophys. J.* **835**, p. 103 (2017).
35. L. Dai and T. Venumadhav, On the waveforms of gravitationally lensed gravitational waves, *arXiv: 1702.04724* (2 2017).
36. L. Dai, S.-S. Li, B. Zackay, S. Mao and Y. Lu, Detecting lensing-induced diffraction in astrophysical gravitational waves, *Phys. Rev. D* **98**, p. 104029 (Nov 2018).
37. A. K. Meena and J. S. Bagla, Gravitational lensing of gravitational waves: wave nature and prospects for detection, *Mon. Not. Roy. Astro. Soc.* **492**, 1127 (2020).
38. M. A. Oancea, J. Joudioux, I. Y. Dodin, D. E. Ruiz, C. F. Paganini and L. Andersson, Gravitational spin hall effect of light, *Phys. Rev. D* **102**, p. 024075 (Jul 2020).

Shadow of black holes with a plasma environment in 4D Einstein-Gauss-Bonnet gravity

Javier Badía[1,2,*] and Ernesto F. Eiroa[1,†]

[1] *Instituto de Astronomía y Física del Espacio (IAFE, CONICET-UBA),*
Casilla de Correo 67, Sucursal 28, 1428, Buenos Aires, Argentina
[2] *Departamento de Física, Facultad de Ciencias Exactas y Naturales,*
Universidad de Buenos Aires, Ciudad Universitaria Pab. I, 1428, Buenos Aires, Argentina
* E-mail: jbadia@iafe.uba.ar
† E-mail: eiroa@iafe.uba.ar

We study the shadow cast by rotating black holes surrounded by plasma in the context of the 4D Einstein-Gauss-Bonnet theory of gravity. The metric for these black holes results from applying the Newman-Janis algorithm to a spherically symmetric solution. We obtain the contour of the shadow for a plasma frequency model that allows a separable Hamilton-Jacobi equation. We introduce three observables in order to characterize the position, size, and shape of the shadow.

Keywords: Black hole shadow; Modified gravity; Plasma.

1. Introduction

It is well known that Einstein-Gauss-Bonnet theory in four spacetime dimensions is purely topological and thus equivalent to general relativity. A novel gravity theory was recently proposed[1] by rescaling the coupling constant and taking the limit $D \to 4$ in the D-dimensional Einstein-Gauss-Bonnet theory, with the intention of overcoming this standard result. But this approach, based on some particular solutions, lacks of a complete set of field equations and does not have an intrinsically four-dimensional description in terms of a covariantly conserved rank-2 tensor in four dimensions.[2] A theory with a Gauss-Bonnet term in four dimensions that provide a solution to these problems was then presented,[3,4] which propagates a scalar field in addition to the metric tensor and the full action belongs to the Horndeski class of scalar-tensor theories of gravity. The action, obtained by a regularization procedure in a way that is free from divergences, produces well behaved second-order field equations. This theory, usually dubbed regularized or scalar-tensor 4D Einstein-Gauss-Bonnet gravity (4DEGB), includes a nonvanishing contribution coming from the Gauss-Bonnet term.[3,4]

The number of theoretical studies on black hole shadows[5,6] has sharply increased since the Event Horizon Telescope (EHT)[7,8] collaboration obtained the first reconstructed image of the supermassive black hole M87*, located at the center of the giant elliptical galaxy M87. Many articles have been published on this topic in recent years, here we can mention only a few of them,[9–12] in which more references can be found. The presence of plasma surrounding a black hole affects the characteristics of the shadow,[13–15] because photons with different frequencies follow distinct trajectories, resulting in chromatic effects. In this work, we consider the shadow due to rotating black holes[16,17] in the scalar-tensor 4DEGB gravity, within a plasma environment. We define three observables to describe how the presence of plasma affects the size, the deformation and the position of the shadow. We analyze in detail the case of a Shapiro plasma, with the shadow seen by an equatorial observer. We use units such that $G = c = \hbar = 1$.

2. Black holes in 4D Einstein-Gauss-Bonnet gravity

The scalar-tensor 4DEGB action reads[3,4]

$$S = \int_\mathcal{M} d^4x \sqrt{-g} \Big[R + \gamma \Big(4G^{\mu\nu}\nabla_\mu\phi\nabla_\nu\phi - \phi\mathcal{G} + 4\Box\phi(\nabla\phi)^2 + 2(\nabla\phi)^4 \Big) \Big] + S_m. \quad (1)$$

The theory is free of divergences and belongs to the Horndeski class, with functions $G_2 = 8\gamma X^2$, $G_3 = 8\gamma X$, $G_4 = 1 + 4\gamma X$, and $G_5 = 4\gamma \ln X$, where $X = -(1/2)\nabla_\mu\phi\nabla^\mu\phi$. The field equations are obtained[3,4] by varying this action with respect to the metric

$$G_{\mu\nu} = \gamma \mathcal{H}_{\mu\nu} + T_{\mu\nu}, \quad (2)$$

where $\mathcal{H}$ is a complicated second order function in the derivatives of the scalar field ϕ; there is another equation that is found[3,4] by varying with respect to the scalar field ϕ. The expressions of these equations are not relevant for our purposes.

The 4DEGB field equations in vacuum admit the spherically symmetric and asymptotically flat solution[1,4] with the metric given by

$$ds^2 = -\left(1 - \frac{2m(r)}{r}\right) dt^2 + \left(1 - \frac{2m(r)}{r}\right)^{-1} dr^2 + r^2(d\theta^2 + \sin^2\theta\, d\varphi^2), \quad (3)$$

where

$$m(r) = \frac{r^3}{64\pi\gamma} \left(\sqrt{1 + \frac{128\pi\gamma M}{r^3}} - 1 \right). \quad (4)$$

The parameter γ of the theory has units of mass squared. We only consider $\gamma > 0$, since the square root becomes imaginary for a finite value of r if $\gamma < 0$. The limit $\gamma \to 0$ corresponds to the Schwarzschild geometry. The black hole mass is M, since we have $m(r) \to M$ as $r \to \infty$.

A rotating solution was subsequently found by applying a modified version of the Newman-Janis algorithm,[16,17] having in the Boyer-Lindquist coordinates the form

$$ds^2 = -\frac{\rho^2 \Delta}{\Sigma} dt^2 + \frac{\Sigma \sin^2\theta}{\rho^2} \left[d\varphi - \frac{2am(r)r}{\Sigma} dt \right]^2 + \frac{\rho^2}{\Delta} dr^2 + \rho^2 d\theta^2, \quad (5)$$

where $a = J/M$ is the rotation parameter and

$$\rho^2 = r^2 + a^2 \cos^2\theta,$$
$$\Delta = r^2 - 2m(r)r + a^2,$$
$$\Sigma = (r^2 + a^2)^2 - a^2 \Delta \sin^2\theta. \quad (6)$$

The limit $\gamma \to 0$ recovers the Kerr black hole. The radius r_h of the event horizon corresponds to the largest real and positive solution of the equation $\Delta = 0$. It can be seen numerically that the condition $\gamma/M^2 < 0.00129$ is necessary for the existence of the event horizon, otherwise there is a naked singularity.

3. Photon geodesics in a plasma environment

The motion of photons in a pressureless, nonmagnetized plasma is governed by the Hamiltonian[18]

$$\mathcal{H} = \frac{1}{2}\left(g^{\mu\nu}(x)p_\mu p_\nu + \omega_p(x)^2\right), \qquad (7)$$

with $g^{\mu\nu}$ the inverse of the metric tensor, x^μ the spacetime coordinates, p^μ the conjugate momenta, and ω_p the plasma electron frequency

$$\omega_p^2 = \frac{4\pi e^2}{m_e}N, \qquad (8)$$

where e and m_e are the electron charge and mass respectively, and N the electron number density. We assume that the plasma frequency is stationary and axisymmetric, so it does not depend on the Boyer-Lindquist coordinates t and φ. As it happens for the Kerr geometry,[13] the inequality $\omega_0^2 \geq -g_{tt}\omega_p^2$ is a necessary and sufficient condition for a light ray with frequency ω_0 (measured by an observer at infinity) to exist at a given point of the spacetime.

3.1. Hamilton-Jacobi equation

We can write down the Hamilton-Jacobi (HJ) equation for photons, which reads

$$\mathcal{H}\left(x, \frac{\partial S}{\partial x}\right) = 0 \qquad (9)$$

and we introduce the ansatz

$$S = -\omega_0 t + p_\varphi \varphi + S_r(r) + S_\theta(\theta). \qquad (10)$$

By substituting it in the HJ equation, we arrive at

$$\Delta(S_r')^2 - \frac{1}{\Delta}\left[(r^2+a^2)^2\omega_0^2 + 4am(r)r\omega_0 p_\varphi + a^2 p_\varphi^2\right]$$
$$+ (S_\theta')^2 + a^2\omega_0^2\sin^2\theta + \frac{p_\varphi^2}{\sin^2\theta} + \rho^2\omega_p^2 = 0, \qquad (11)$$

where the prime denotes the derivative with respect to the corresponding coordinate. The HJ equation is separable if and only if the plasma frequency takes the form[13]

$$\omega_p^2 = \frac{f_r(r) + f_\theta(\theta)}{\rho^2}, \qquad (12)$$

with $f_r(r)$ and $f_\theta(\theta)$ arbitrary functions of the coordinates r and θ, respectively. The spacetime is axisymmetric, stationary, and asymptotically flat, therefore the quantities $p_t = -\omega_0$ and p_φ are conserved along the geodesics of photons; $E = \omega_0$ is the photon energy and p_φ is the z component of the angular momentum. Since ω_p only depends on the coordinates r and θ, the quantities E and p_φ are still conserved in the presence of plasma. A third constant of motion for photons is $\mathcal{H} = 0$. By substituting ω_p into the Hamilton-Jacobi equation, we can separate it as

$$(S'_\theta)^2 + \left(a\omega_0 \sin\theta - \frac{p_\varphi}{\sin\theta}\right)^2 + f_\theta = -\Delta(S'_r)^2 + \frac{1}{\Delta}\left[\omega_0(r^2 + a^2) - ap_\varphi\right]^2 - f_r. \quad (13)$$

Since the left hand side is a function only of θ and the right hand side a function only of r, they should both be equal to a constant $\mathcal{K}$. For convenience, we use instead the Carter constant,[19] defined by $\mathcal{Q} = \mathcal{K} - (p_\varphi - a\omega_0)^2$, as the fourth constant of motion. From the Hamilton equations, using that $\dot{x}^\mu = p^\mu = g^{\mu\nu} p_\nu$ (the dot denotes the derivative with respect to the curve parameter λ) and $p_\nu = \partial S/\partial x^\nu$, the equations of motion read

$$\rho^2 \dot{t} = \frac{r^2 + a^2}{\Delta} P(r) - a(a\omega_0 \sin^2\theta - p_\varphi), \quad (14)$$

$$\rho^2 \dot{\varphi} = \frac{a}{\Delta} P(r) - a\omega_0 + \frac{p_\varphi}{\sin^2\theta}, \quad (15)$$

$$\rho^2 \dot{r} = \pm\sqrt{R(r)}, \quad (16)$$

$$\rho^2 \dot{\theta} = \pm\sqrt{\Theta(\theta)}, \quad (17)$$

where

$$R(r) = P(r)^2 - \Delta[\mathcal{Q} + (p_\varphi - a\omega_0)^2 + f_r], \quad (18)$$

$$\Theta(\theta) = \mathcal{Q} + \cos^2\theta \left(a^2\omega_0^2 - \frac{p_\varphi^2}{\sin^2\theta}\right) - f_\theta, \quad (19)$$

$$P(r) = \omega_0(r^2 + a^2) - ap_\varphi. \quad (20)$$

These first-order equations determine the movement of the photons in the presence of plasma.

3.2. Spherical photon orbits

The orbits of photons with constant r should fulfill the two conditions given by $R(r) = R'(r) = 0$; such solutions are unstable, satisfying $R''(r) > 0$. From the equation $R(r) = 0$ we find that

$$\mathcal{Q} + (p_\varphi - a\omega_0)^2 + f_r = \frac{(\omega_0(r^2 + a^2) - ap_\varphi)^2}{\Delta}. \quad (21)$$

Then, substituting into $R'(r) = 0$, we obtain

$$R' = 4\omega_0 r(\omega_0(r^2 + a^2) - ap_\varphi) - \frac{\Delta'}{\Delta}(\omega_0(r^2 + a^2) - ap_\varphi)^2 - \Delta f'_r = 0, \quad (22)$$

which is a quadratic equation for p_φ, with the solution

$$p_\varphi = \frac{\omega_0}{a}\left[r^2 + a^2 - \frac{2r\Delta}{\Delta'}\left(1 \pm \sqrt{1 - \frac{\Delta' f'_r}{4\omega_0^2 r^2}}\right)\right]. \quad (23)$$

Then, after some algebra, we can obtain $\mathcal{Q}$ in terms of r, which reads

$$\mathcal{Q} = -\frac{\omega_0^2 r^4}{a^2} + \frac{4\omega_0^2 r^2 \Delta}{a^2 \Delta'}\left[r - \frac{2}{\Delta'}(\Delta - a^2)\right]\left(1 \pm \sqrt{1 - \frac{\Delta' f_r'}{4\omega_0^2 r^2}}\right) + \frac{\Delta f_r'}{\Delta' a^2}(\Delta - a^2) - f_r. \tag{24}$$

We have found the critical values of p_φ and $\mathcal{Q}$ associated with the spherical orbits of photons. Any trajectory should have $\Theta \geq 0$, then

$$\mathcal{Q} + \cos^2\theta\left(a^2\omega_0^2 - \frac{p_\varphi^2}{\sin^2\theta}\right) - f_\theta(\theta) \geq 0. \tag{25}$$

This equation defines the photon region: spherical orbits exist at values of r and θ for which this inequality is satisfied.

3.3. Shadow

For a distant observer, the shadow is determined by the set of photon directions that never reach infinity and instead cross the event horizon. The boundary consists of those rays that asymptotically approach the spherical photon orbits of the spacetime, so they have the same conserved quantities. In order to relate the directions in the sky with the constants of motion, we take an observer at rest in the asymptotically flat region (large r_o) with an inclinaton angle θ_o from the spin axis of the black hole, and we construct the orthonormal tetrad as usual[9]:

$$e_{\hat{t}} = \partial_t, \qquad e_{\hat{r}} = \partial_r, \qquad e_{\hat{\theta}} = \frac{1}{r_o}\partial_\theta, \qquad e_{\hat{\varphi}} = \frac{1}{r_o \sin\theta_o}\partial_\varphi, \tag{26}$$

so that the components of the four-momentum in this frame read

$$p^{\hat{t}} = \omega_0, \qquad p^{\hat{r}} = p^r, \qquad p^{\hat{\theta}} = r_o p^\theta, \qquad p^{\hat{\varphi}} = r_o \sin\theta_o p^\varphi = \frac{p_\varphi}{r_o \sin\theta_o}. \tag{27}$$

For the plasma model, we assume that

$$\lim_{r \to \infty} \omega_p(r, \theta) = 0, \tag{28}$$

which is equivalent to

$$\lim_{r \to \infty} \frac{f_r(r)}{r^2} = 0, \tag{29}$$

so photons propagate in vacuum far away from the black hole. We adopt the celestial coordinates for an observer at infinity[5]

$$\alpha = -r_o \frac{p^{\hat{\varphi}}}{p^{\hat{t}}}\bigg|_{r_o \to \infty}, \tag{30}$$

$$\beta = -r_o \frac{p^{\hat{\theta}}}{p^{\hat{t}}}\bigg|_{r_o \to \infty}; \tag{31}$$

replacing p^θ in terms of the conserved quantities, they read

$$\alpha = -\frac{p_\varphi}{\omega_0 \sin\theta_o}, \tag{32}$$

$$\beta = \pm\frac{1}{\omega_0}\sqrt{\mathcal{Q} + \cos^2\theta_o\left(a^2\omega_0^2 - \frac{p_\varphi^2}{\sin^2\theta_o}\right) - f_\theta(\theta_o)}. \tag{33}$$

The contour of the black hole shadow is described by the parametric curve $(\alpha(r), \beta(r))$.

3.4. Observables

We define three observables[10]: the area of the shadow, its oblateness, and the horizontal displacement of its centroid, as follows:

- The area is calculated from

$$A = 2\int \beta\, d\alpha = 2\int_{r_+}^{r_-}\beta(r)|\alpha'(r)|\, dr, \tag{34}$$

with the factor 2 arising from the up-down symmetry of the shadow and taking the plus sign in Eq. (33).

- The oblateness is related to the deformation of the shadow as compared to a circle

$$D = \frac{\Delta\alpha}{\Delta\beta}, \tag{35}$$

where $\Delta\alpha$ and $\Delta\beta$ are the horizontal and vertical extent of the shadow.

- The horizontal coordinate of the centroid is given by

$$\alpha_c = \frac{2}{A}\int \alpha\beta\, d\alpha = \frac{2}{A}\int_{r_+}^{r_-}\alpha(r)\beta(r)|\alpha'(r)|\, dr, \tag{36}$$

with the same factor 2 as in the definition of the area.

These observables allow a characterization of the shadow by only three numbers.

4. Example: Shapiro plasma

We consider, in order to provide an example, the well known model of plasma consisting of dust that is at rest at infinity, introduced by Shapiro.[20] In the Kerr spacetime, the mass density and the squared plasma frequency go as $r^{-3/2}$, and they are independent of θ to a very good approximation. However, for this plasma distribution the equations cannot be brought into a separable form; therefore, we take the frequency to have an additional θ dependency[13] by adopting $f_r(r) = \omega_c^2\sqrt{M^3 r}$ and $f_\theta(\theta) = 0$, resulting in a plasma electron frequency

$$\omega_p^2 = \omega_c^2\frac{\sqrt{M^3 r}}{r^2 + a^2\cos^2\theta}, \tag{37}$$

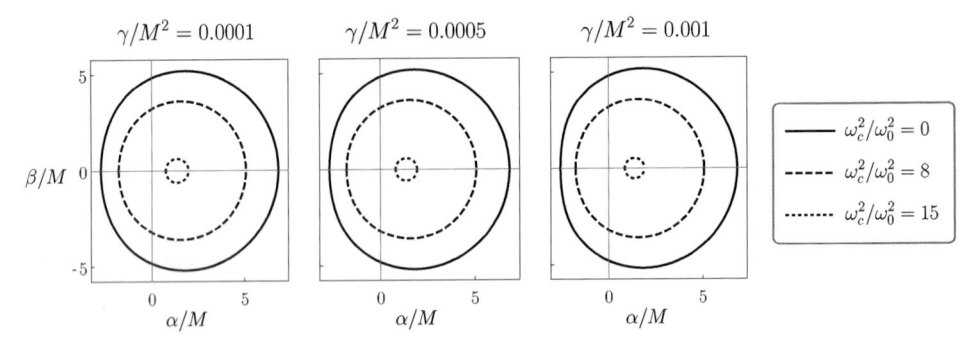

Fig. 1. Shadow of a 4D Einstein-Gauss-Bonnet black hole with spin $a/M = 0.9$ surrounded by a Shapiro-type plasma distribution with $f_r(r) = \omega_c^2 \sqrt{M^3 r}$, for an equatorial observer.

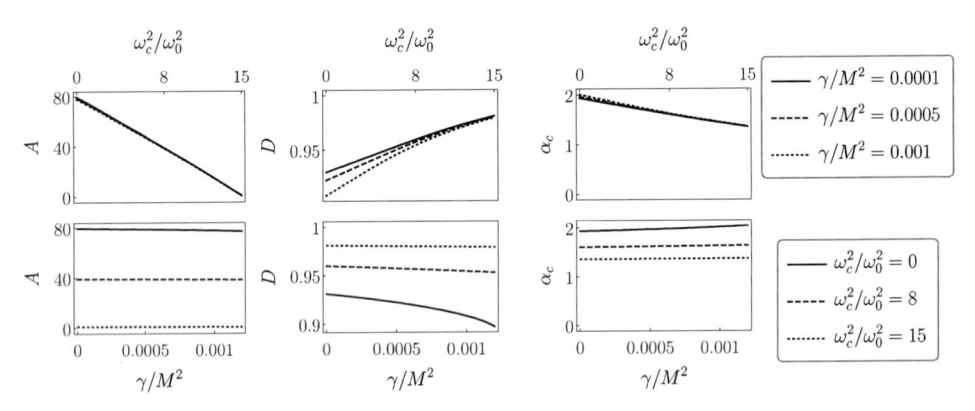

Fig. 2. The area (A), the oblateness (D), and the centroid (α_c) of the shadow. Top: the observables as functions of the frequency ratio ω_c/ω_0, for three values of the EGB parameter γM^2. Bottom: the observables as functions of γM^2, for three values of the frequency ratio ω_c/ω_0.

where ω_c is a constant that characterizes the fluid. At large distances from the black hole, the metric approaches the Kerr one, i.e. $m(r) \to M$, so we expect that the Shapiro model is still valid; but at small distances the metric may be quite different, so we assume that the plasma density is not significantly affected. The trajectories of photons with frequency ω_0 depend only on the ratio ω_c/ω_0. We present in Figs. 1 and 2 some plots of black hole shadows and the corresponding observables, for an equatorial observer, $a/M = 0.9$, and suitably chosen values of the other parameters. For a given value of the plasma frequency ω_c, we can see that:

- For fixed parameter γ/M^2, the shadow reduces in size, is less deformed, and has a smaller centroid displacement, as the photon frequency ω_0 decreases. In particular, the shadow disappears entirely below a certain photon frequency, due to the appearance of the forbidden region. This forbidden region starts as two caps around the poles and grows towards the equatorial plane as the frequency decreases, leading to a reduction of the shadow size.

- For a fixed photon frequency ω_0, the shadow slightly reduces in size, is less deformed, and the centroid displacement slightly grows, as γ/M^2 increases. The effect of increasing the parameter γ/M^2 is more prominent for high frequency photons, particularly in the case of the oblateness.

The existence of plasma surrounding the black hole results in a smaller and less deformed shadow than in vacuum, which corresponds to $\omega_c = 0$.

5. Final remarks

We have studied how the presence of plasma modifies the shadow corresponding to rotating black holes in the scalar-tensor 4-dimensional Einstein-Gauss-Bonnet theory with respect to the vacuum case. These black holes were obtained in previous works from spherically symmetric solutions by applying the Newman-Janis algorithm. We have neglected the gravitational influence of the plasma itself and any processes of scattering, emission or absorption. We have shown that the Hamilton-Jacobi equation for photons is separable if the plasma frequency obeys the usual separability condition introduced for the Kerr spacetime. Light follows timelike curves in the presence of plasma, resulting in a modification of the photon regions and frequency-dependent forbidden regions, where photons cannot travel. We have obtained the expressions for the celestial coordinates of the shadow contour as viewed by a far away observer, which reduce to the already known for vacuum when the plasma frequency goes to zero or the photon frequency to infinity. In order to characterize the size, the shape, and the position, we have presented three observables: the area, the oblateness, and the centroid of the shadow. With the intention to provide a concrete example, we have taken a variation of the Shapiro plasma distribution, which models dust at rest at infinity surrounding a black hole. We have considered an equatorial observer, for simplicity and also because the effects on the shadow in this case are more prominent. For a fixed the plasma frequency $\omega_c \neq 0$ and given values of the mass M and the parameter γ, the shadow becomes smaller and less deformed as the photon frequency ω_0 decreases, with the appearance of a forbidden region around the black hole as a distinctive feature. This forbidden region begins as two caps around the poles and grows towards the equatorial plane for decreasing ω_0, resulting in a sharp reduction of the shadow size and in its eventual disappearance. The presence of plasma always leads to a smaller and less deformed shadow than in the case of vacuum ($\omega_c = 0$). The work presented here is a particular case of the shadow cast by a class of rotating black holes surrounded by plasma, which results from applying the Newman-Janis algorithm to spherically symmetric spacetimes[15] determined by a mass function $m(r)$ satisfying that $m(r) \to M$ when $r \to \infty$.

Acknowledgments

This work has been supported by CONICET and Universidad de Buenos Aires.

References

1. D. Glavan and C. Lin, Einstein-Gauss-Bonnet Gravity in Four-Dimensional Spacetime, *Phys. Rev. Lett.* **124**, 081301 (2020).
2. M. Gurses, T. C. Sisman, and B. Tekin, Is there a novel Einstein–Gauss–Bonnet theory in four dimensions?, *Eur. Phys. J. C* **80**, 647 (2020).
3. P. G. S. Fernandes, P. Carrilho, T. Clifton, and D. J. Mulryne, Derivation of regularized field equations for the Einstein-Gauss-Bonnet theory in four dimensions, *Phys. Rev. D* **102**, 024025 (2020).
4. R. A. Hennigar, D. Kubizňák, R. B. Mann, and C. Pollack, On taking the $D \to 4$ limit of Gauss-Bonnet gravity: Theory and solutions, *JHEP* **07** (2020) 027.
5. J. M. Bardeen, in *Black Holes*, Eds. C. De Witt, B. S. De Witt, p. 215-239 (1973).
6. H. Falcke, F. Melia, and E. Agol, Viewing the Shadow of the Black Hole at the Galactic Center, *Astrophys. J.* **528**, L13 (2000).
7. K. Akiyama *et al.* (Event Horizon Telescope), First M87 Event Horizon Telescope Results. I. The Shadow of the Supermassive Black Hole, *Astrophys. J. Lett.* **875**, L1 (2019).
8. K. Akiyama *et al.* (Event Horizon Telescope), First M87 Event Horizon Telescope Results. V. Physical Origin of the Asymmetric Ring, *Astrophys. J. Lett.* **875**, L5 (2019).
9. N. Tsukamoto, Black hole shadow in an asymptotically flat, stationary, and axisymmetric spacetime: The Kerr-Newman and rotating regular black holes, *Phys. Rev. D* **97**, 064021 (2018).
10. J. Badía and E. F. Eiroa, Influence of an anisotropic matter field on the shadow of a rotating black hole, *Phys. Rev. D* **102**, 024066 (2020).
11. H. C. D. Lima Junior, L. C. B. Crispino, P. V. P. Cunha, and C. A. R. Herdeiro, Spinning black holes with a separable Hamilton–Jacobi equation from a modified Newman–Janis algorithm, *Eur. Phys. J. C* **80**, 1036 (2020).
12. V. Perlick and O. Y. Tsupko, Calculating black hole shadows: review of analytical studies, arXiv:2105.07101 [gr-qc].
13. V. Perlick and O. Y. Tsupko, Light propagation in a plasma on Kerr spacetime: Separation of the Hamilton-Jacobi equation and calculation of the shadow, *Phys. Rev. D* **95**, 104003 (2017).
14. H. Yan, Influence of a plasma on the observational signature of a high-spin Kerr black hole, *Phys. Rev. D* **99**, 084050 (2019).
15. J. Badía and E. F. Eiroa, Shadow of axisymmetric, stationary and asymptotically flat black holes in the presence of plasma, *Phys. Rev. D* **104**, 084055 (2021).
16. R. Kumar and S. G. Ghosh, Rotating black holes in 4D Einstein-Gauss-Bonnet gravity and its shadow, *JCAP* **07** (2020) 053.
17. S. Wei and Y. Liu, Testing the nature of Gauss–Bonnet gravity by four-dimensional rotating black hole shadow, *Eur. Phys. J. Plus* **136**, 436 (2021).
18. J. L. Synge, *Relativity: The General Theory* (North-Holland, Amsterdam, 1960).
19. B. Carter, Global Structure of the Kerr Family of Gravitational Fields, *Phys. Rev.* **174**, 1559 (1968).
20. S. Shapiro, Accretion onto black holes: The emergent radiation spectrum. III. Rotating (Kerr) black holes, *Astrophys. J.* **189**, 343 (1974).

Aspects of neutrino mass hierarchy in gravitational lensing

Himanshu Swami

Department of Physical Sciences,
Indian Institute of Science Education & Research (IISER) Mohali,
SAS Nagar, Manauli-140306, Punjab, India
E-mail: himanshuswami@iisermohali.ac.in

We study neutrino flavour oscillations in curved spacetime especially emphasising neutrino lensing in Schwarzschild spacetime, and highlight the role that neutrinos lensing induced by a gravitational source can play in inferring neutrino absolute mass and mass hierarchy. Further, the wave packet approach in neutrino lensing and its modifications compared with the plane wave approach is analysed. Finally, we discuss the decoherence effect in the wave packet approach and its possible use in inferring absolute neutrino mass and neutrino mixing parameters.

Keywords: Neutrino mass hierarchy; gravitational lensing.

1. Neutrino oscillations in flat and curved spacetime

It is now clear from experiments that neutrinos have masses, and that they mix and neutrino flavour eigenstates $|\nu_\alpha\rangle$ are now related to their mass eigenstates $|\nu_i\rangle$ by 3×3 unitary matrix[1–3] U

$$|\nu_\alpha\rangle = \sum_i U^*_{\alpha i}|\nu_i\rangle, \tag{1}$$

where $\alpha = e, \mu, \tau$ and $i = 1, 2, 3$. A neutrino flavour state propagation from source S to detector D, located at $\mathbf{x}_S$ and $\mathbf{x}_D$ respectively, is described by

$$|\nu_\alpha(t_D, \mathbf{x}_D)\rangle = N \sum_i U^*_{\alpha i} \psi_i(x_D, x_S) |\nu_i(t_S, \mathbf{x}_S)\rangle, \tag{2}$$

where N is a normalisation factor. $\psi_i(x_D, x_S)$ is the wavefunction, evolved between the time of production (t_S) and detection (t_D), for i^{th} massive neutrino. Assuming neutrino wave-function as a plane wave, the flavour transition probability from $\nu_\alpha \to \nu_\beta$ at the detection point is given by

$$\mathcal{P}_{\alpha\beta} \equiv |\langle\nu_\beta|\nu_\alpha(t_D, \mathbf{x}_D)\rangle|^2 = \sum_{i,j} U_{\beta i} U^*_{\beta j} U_{\alpha j} U^*_{\alpha i} \exp(-i(\Phi_i - \Phi_j)). \tag{3}$$

Now, neutrino mass eigenstates develop different phases Φ_i, which gives rise to neutrino oscillation phenomena.[4] Massive neutrino phase in flat spacetime is given by

$$\Phi_i = E_i(t_D - t_S) - \mathbf{p}_i \cdot (\mathbf{x}_D - \mathbf{x}_S). \tag{4}$$

Assuming that all the mass eigenstates in a flavour eigenstate initially produced have equal momentum or energy.[4,5] This assumption together with $(t_D - t_S) \simeq |\mathbf{x}_D - \mathbf{x}_S|$

for relativistic neutrinos ($E_i \gg m_i$) gives

$$\Delta\Phi_{ij} \equiv \Phi_i - \Phi_j \simeq \frac{\Delta m_{ij}^2}{2E_0} |\mathbf{x}_D - \mathbf{x}_S|, \tag{5}$$

where $\Delta m_{ij}^2 \equiv m_i^2 - m_j^2$. E_0 is the average energy of the relativistic neutrinos produced at S. Substitution of Eq. (5) in Eq. (3) for two flavours of neutrinos lead to the following oscillation formula:

$$\mathcal{P}_{e\mu} = \sin^2 2\alpha \, \sin^2\left(\frac{\Delta m_{12}^2 L}{4E_0}\right) \tag{6}$$

where $L = |\mathbf{x}_D - \mathbf{x}_S|$ and the angle α parameterize elements of matrix U. We see a constant universal shift in the squared masses, i.e. $m_i^2 \to m_i^2 + C$, leaves the expression of $\mathcal{P}_{\alpha\beta}$ unchanged, therefore, $\mathcal{P}_{\alpha\beta}$ depends on the difference of squared masses and not on the absolute masses. In a curved spacetime, the phase in Eq. (4) can be replaced by its covariant form[6]

$$\Phi_i = \int_S^D p_\mu^{(i)} \, dx^\mu, \tag{7}$$

where $p_\mu^{(i)}$ is the canonical conjugate momentum to the coordinate x^μ for the ith neutrino mass eigenstate. As in a general curved spacetime, more than one different geodesics starting from the same spacetime point can intersect later, therefore, accounting for all neutrino paths (m) a neutrino flavour state is now given by

$$|\nu_\alpha(t_D, \mathbf{x}_D)\rangle = \sum_i U_{\alpha i}^* \sum_m N\psi_i^m(x_D, x_S) |\nu_i(t_S, \mathbf{x}_S)\rangle. \tag{8}$$

Now, normalisation (N), in general, can depend on the path m.

2. Neutrino lensing in Schwarzschild spacetime

We now examine neutrino oscillations in Schwarzschild spacetime specifically emphasizing on the neutrino lensing. The line element in Schwarzschild metric is given by

$$ds^2 = B(r) \, dt^2 - \frac{1}{B(r)} dr^2 - r^2 \left(d\theta^2 + \sin^2\theta d\phi^2\right), \tag{9}$$

where $B(r) = 1 - \frac{R_s}{r}$, and R_s is Schwarzschild radius. With no lose of generality, we will take $\theta = \pi/2$. Further, it is assumed that the neutrinos are produced as a plane wave.

In the weak gravity limit, there are two paths denoted by impact parameters b_1 and b_2 that neutrino may take to reach at the detector location O. Neutrino flavor transtion probability from α flavour (produced at the source) to β flavour (detected at the detector location) is, then, given by[7]

$$\mathcal{P}_{\alpha\beta}^{\text{lens}} = |N|^2 \bigg(2\sum_i |U_{\beta i}|^2 |U_{\alpha i}|^2 (1 + \cos(\Delta b^2 B_{ii})) + \sum_{i,j \neq i} U_{\beta i} U_{\beta j}^* U_{\alpha j} U_{\alpha i}^*$$
$$\times \left(\exp(-i\Delta m_{ij}^2 A_{11}) + \exp(-i\Delta m_{ij}^2 A_{22}) + 2\cos\left(\Delta b^2 B_{ij}\right) \right.$$
$$\left. \times \exp\left(-i\Delta m_{ij}^2 A_{12}\right) \right) \bigg), \tag{10}$$

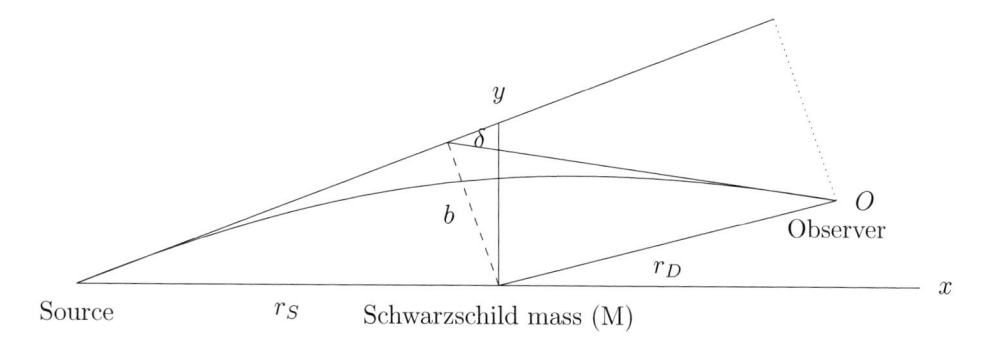

Fig. 1. Diagrammatic representation of weak lensing of neutrinos. Neutrinos are created at the source (S) and get lensed by a Schwarzschild mass (M) and detected at location (O).

with

$$|N|^2 = \left(2 + 2\sum_i |U_{\alpha i}|^2 \cos(\Delta b^2 B_{ii})\right)^{-1} \qquad (11)$$

where $\Delta b_{12}^2 \equiv \Delta b^2$. It is noted that many similar versions of Eq. (10) are available in literature,[9–11] however, with some subtle differences. Though, the role of normalisation (Eq. (11)) has been neglected in literature[9, 11] which is crucial in understanding the neutrino oscillation interference effects.

The change in oscillation phase calculated along neutrino massive trajectory for path (m) is given by

$$\Phi_j^{massive} \simeq \frac{m_j^2}{E_0}(r_S + r_D)\left(1 - \frac{b_m^2}{2r_S r_D} + \frac{2GM}{r_S + r_D}\right), \qquad (12)$$

where b_m is the impact parameter and related with deflection angle (δ) as $\delta = -2R_s/b + O\left(R_s m_j^2/bE_0^2\right)$.[8] However, the phase change if calculated along null trajectory for path (m) gives[9]

$$\Phi_j^{null} \simeq \frac{m_j^2}{2E_0}(r_S + r_D)\left(1 - \frac{b_m^2}{2r_S r_D} + \frac{2GM}{r_S + r_D}\right), \qquad (13)$$

which is half of $\Phi_j^{massive}$. Despite of this difference in oscillation phase, the bulk of literature employs null ray approximations to calculate the change in the neutrino phase. So, to keep in tune with the bulk of the existing literature on neutrino oscillation, we will employ null ray approximation to study weak lensing. Nevertheless, the results of lensing remain qualitatively consistent if one uses massive trajectories instead of null trajectories. The other quantities in Eq. (10) are related to the phase difference $\Delta \Phi_{ij}^{mn}$ as[7]

$$\Delta \Phi_{ij}^{mn} = \Phi_i^m - \Phi_j^n = \Delta m_{ij}^2 A_{mn} + \Delta b_{mn}^2 B_{ij}, \qquad (14)$$

where

$$A_{mn} = \frac{(r_S + r_D)}{2E_0}\left(1 + \frac{2GM}{r_S + r_D} - \frac{\sum b_{mn}^2}{4r_S r_D}\right),$$

$$B_{ij} = -\frac{\sum m_{ij}^2}{8E_0}\left(\frac{1}{r_S} + \frac{1}{r_D}\right). \tag{15}$$

Here, $\sum b_{mn}^2 = b_m^2 + b_n^2$ and $\sum m_{ij}^2 = m_i^2 + m_j^2$. We note that unless mixing angle $\alpha = \pi/4$ (in the two flavour case) (1) normalization Eq. (11) is not invariant under $m_i \leftrightarrow m_j$ due to $|U_{\alpha i}|^2$ and (2) the neutrino phase Eq. (13) is not invariant under a universal shift $m_i^2 + C$ due to B_{ij} term, unless $\Delta b_{mn}^2 \equiv b_m^2 - b_n^2$ vanishes. Hence, transition probability will be sensitive to both aforementioned points. Fig. 2 shows flavour transition probability for the lensed neutrino, which are lensed by the Sun and detected on the Earth. The Earth trajectory is taken to be circular in the plots. From Fig. 2 one can see the difference in transition probability as the value of mass m_1 changes. Also, the change in mass ordering gives quite a significant difference in transition probabilities and oscillation frequency. We observe that neutrino oscillation frequency increases as we increase the value of m_1. Therefore, one can utilise neutrino lensing to infer neutrino mass. One such way to extract information about absolute mass is to find the flipping point (ϕ_D^e), i.e., where all flavour changing probabilities become the same. The flipping angle in the two flavour case is given by[7]

$$\sum m^2 = \frac{16n\pi E_0 r_S r_D}{Z\Delta b^2} + \frac{16E_0 r_S r_D}{Z\Delta b^2}\cot^{-1}\left(\tan\left(\frac{\Delta m^2 Z \Delta b^2}{16 E_0 r_S r_D}\right)\right.$$
$$\left. \times G\left(r_S, r_D, \phi_D^e, \alpha, \Delta m^2, R_s\right)\right), \tag{16}$$

$$G_{\pm}\left(r_S, r_D, \phi_D^e, \alpha, \Delta m^2, R_s\right)$$
$$\equiv \frac{2\cos 2\alpha \cos^2\alpha - \sin^2 2\alpha \cos\zeta \pm \sqrt{\sin^4 2\alpha \cos^2\zeta + \sin^2 2\alpha \cos^2 2\alpha}}{2\cos 2\alpha \cos^2\alpha + \sin^2 2\alpha \cos\zeta \mp \sqrt{\sin^4 2\alpha \cos^2\zeta + \sin^2 2\alpha \cos^2 2\alpha}}, \tag{17}$$

where $\zeta \equiv \Delta m^2 \left(r_S + r_D + R_s - (r_S + r_D)\sum b^2/4r_S r_D\right)/2E_0$, $Z = r_S + r_D$. In the flipping equation (16), all the measurable quantities are on the right-hand side of the equation, and the term related to absolute mass is on the left-hand side.

3. Neutrino decoherence in gravitational lensing

In a realistic setup neutrinos are produced and detected as a wave packet. So writing detector and neutrino source states in momentum space by using non coordinate tetrad basis,[12] we arrive at the amplitude of flavour transition probability in the

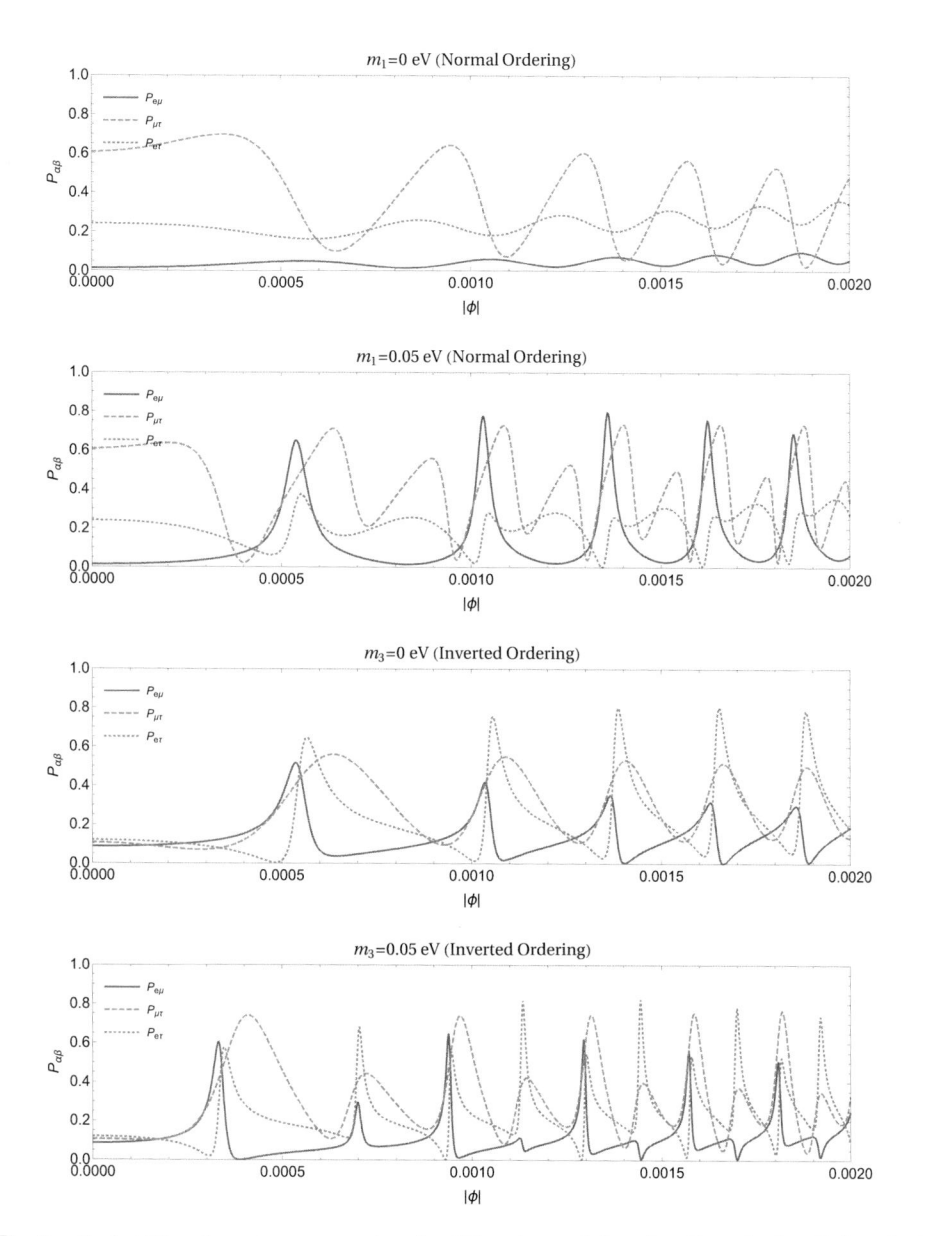

Fig. 2. Probability of $\nu_\alpha \to \nu_\beta$ conversion, for different α and β, as function of azimuthal angle ϕ in three flavour case. We take $R_s = 3$ km, $r_D = 10^8$ km, $r_S = 10^5 r_D$ and $E_0 = 10$ MeV. Neutrino mass squared differences (Δm_{ij}^2), mixing angle and the Dirac CP phase values are taken from (NuFIT 4.1 (2019)) global fit.[3]

wave packet picture and is given by[4,13,14]

$$\mathcal{A}_{\alpha\beta}^m \equiv \langle \nu_\beta(\vec{x}_D)|\nu_\alpha(t,\vec{x})\rangle = \sum_i U_{\beta i} U_{\alpha i}^* \int \frac{d^3 p}{(2\pi)^3} f_{i,\vec{x}}^{D*}\left(\vec{p},\vec{p}_i^D\right) f_{i,\vec{x}}^{S}\left(\vec{p},\vec{p}_i^S\right) e^{-i\Phi_i^m}. \tag{18}$$

The probability of transition $\nu_\alpha \to \nu_\beta$, then, can be computed from the amplitude using[7,14]

$$P_{\alpha\beta} = \frac{\left|\sum_m \mathcal{A}_{\alpha\beta}^m\right|^2}{\sum_\beta \left|\sum_m \mathcal{A}_{\alpha\beta}^m\right|^2}. \tag{19}$$

Here, we assume the detection process is time-independent[4] to arrive at the Eq. (18). Further, taking $f_{i,\vec{x}}^{S,D}\left(\vec{p}, \vec{p}_i^{S,D}\right)$ as Guassian which has a sharp peak around $\vec{p}_i^S$. We, then, substitute Φ_i^m with its series expansion at $\vec{p} = \vec{p}_i^S$ in Eq. (18)

$$\Phi_i^m(\vec{p}) = \Phi_i^m(\vec{p}_i^S) + \vec{X}_i^m \cdot (\vec{p} - \vec{p}_i^S) + \mathcal{O}(p^2), \tag{20}$$

where $\vec{X}_i^m = \partial_{\vec{p}} \Phi_i^m(\vec{p} = \vec{p}_i^S)$. Furthermore, for simplification, we take $\vec{p}_i^{D,S} = \vec{p}^{D,S}$ and $\sigma_{i\,D,S} = \sigma_{D,S}$, to arrive at following transition amplitude[14] $\mathcal{A}_{\alpha\beta}^m$ and transition probability[14] $P_{\alpha\beta}$

$$\mathcal{A}_{\alpha\beta}^m = 2\sqrt{2}\left(\frac{\sigma_D \sigma_S}{\sigma_D^2 + \sigma_S^2}\right)^{3/2} \sum_i U_{\beta i} U_{\alpha i}^* e^{-i\left(\Phi_i^m - \frac{\sigma_S^2}{\sigma_D^2 + \sigma_S^2}\vec{X}_i^m \cdot (\vec{p}^D - \vec{p}^S)\right)}$$

$$\times e^{-\frac{\sigma_D^2 \sigma_S^2 |\vec{X}_i^m|^2 + (\vec{p}^D - \vec{p}^S)^2}{2(\sigma_D^2 + \sigma_S^2)}}, \tag{21}$$

$$P_{\alpha\beta} = \frac{\sum_{i,j} U_{\beta i}^* U_{\alpha i} U_{\beta j} U_{\alpha j}^* \sum_{m,n} e^{-i\Phi_{ij}^{mn}} e^{-D_{ij}^{mn}}}{\sum_i U_{\alpha i} U_{\alpha i}^* \sum_{m,n} e^{-i\Phi_{ii}^{mn}} e^{-D_{ii}^{mn}}}, \tag{22}$$

where

$$\Phi_{ij}^{mn} \equiv (\Phi_i^m - \Phi_j^n) - \frac{\bar{\sigma}^2}{\sigma_D^2}(\vec{p}^D - \vec{p}^S) \cdot (\vec{X}_i^m - \vec{X}_j^n), \tag{23}$$

$$D_{ij}^{mn} = \mathbf{X}_{ij}^{mn} - \mathbf{X}_{ii}^{\hat{m}\hat{n}}, \tag{24}$$

$$\mathbf{X}_{ij}^{mn} \equiv \frac{1}{2}\bar{\sigma}^2\left(|\vec{X}_i^m|^2 + |\vec{X}_j^n|^2\right), \tag{25}$$

where $\bar{\sigma}^2 = \sigma_D^2 \sigma_S^2/(\sigma_D^2 + \sigma_S^2)$. From Eq. (22), we define D_{ij}^{mn} to be decoherence factor. In D_{ij}^{mn} (Eq. (24)), the term $\mathbf{X}_{ii}^{\hat{m}\hat{n}}$ is choosen be the the smallest among $\mathbf{X}_{ij}^{mn}$, such that D_{ij}^{mn} are, by construction, greater than or equal to zero. We note that as D_{ij}^{mn} get large, probabilities approach to values which only depend on neutrino mixing matrix elements, i.e., $P_{\alpha\beta} \to U_{\beta 1}^* U_{\beta 1} = |U_{\beta 1}|^2$. We, also, note that the oscillation phase obtained in Eq. (23) is modified from the one obtained assuming neutrinos as plane waves. Now, oscillation phase also depends on the source and the detector wave profile. The difference between plane wave phase and modified phase become negligible if the neutrino wave packets at production and detection follow $\vec{p}^D \simeq \vec{p}^S$ condition. Now considering the Schwarzschild neutrino lensing, taking $b_2 < b_1$ and $m_1 < m_2 < m_3$, one finds the term D_{ij}^{mn}, which approaches last to zero, is given by D^{11}_{12}. Hence, the coordinate distance at which the transition probability gets suppressed by at least a factor of e^{-1} is given by following condition[14]

$$(r_D + r_S)\left(1 - \frac{b_1^2}{2r_S r_D} + \frac{R_S}{r_D + r_S}\right) \geq 2\sqrt{\frac{2}{B(r_S)}} \frac{E_0^2}{\bar{\sigma}\sqrt{m_2^4 - m_1^4}}. \tag{26}$$

Eq. (26) can readily be used to estimate decoherence length, i.e., the distance to which the coherent oscillations last. For the radial outward propagation in the flat and Schwarzschild spacetime, respectively, with the same dilution in probability e^{-1} and written in physical length, is given by

$$L_p^F = r_D - r_S \geq 2\sqrt{2}\frac{E_0^2}{\bar{\sigma}\sqrt{m_2^4 - m_1^4}}, \tag{27}$$

and

$$L_p^S - R_s \ln\frac{r_D}{r_S} \geq 2\sqrt{\frac{2}{B(r_S)}} \frac{E_0^2}{\bar{\sigma}\sqrt{m_2^4 - m_1^4}}. \tag{28}$$

From Eq. (27) and Eq. (28) we observe for the same physical distance $L_p^F = L_p^S$ between the source and the detector, neutrino decoher more in the flat spacetime, whereas due to R_s term neutrino decoher less in the Schwarzschild spacetime. This is true even for the non radial and the lensing case. Also, from Eq. (26), Eq. (27) and Eq. (28), we see that rate of dilution depend not only on Δm^2, but also on $\sum m^2$ term. Hence, length at which oscillations cease to exist due to suppression of all terms in transition probability can be used to infer absolute neutrino masses. To make above point clear we take two neutrino flavour case and plot change in transition probability taking $y_D = 0$ and varying only x_D, also now we have $x_D = r_D$. Fig. 4 shows maximum and minimum probability as a function of r_D near dechorence region, we see for $m_1 = 0$ eV decoherence occurs, i.e. $P_{e\mu} \to \sin^2\alpha = 1/2$, later compares to the $m_1 = 0.1$ eV case. We also note from Fig. 3, that decoherence is consistent with $D^{11}_{12} \geq 2$. Right panel of Fig. 3 compute correlations between $\bar{\sigma}$ and r_D for $D^{11}_{12} = 1$. The estimation is done for two different values of the lightest neutrino mass m_1 keeping $m_2^2 - m_1^2 = 10^{-3} eV^2$ fixed.

4. Summary

By studying neutrino lensing in Schwarzschild background, we explicated that neutrino lensing is sensitive to neutrino mass ordering and absolute neutrino masses, contrary to the vacuum neutrino flavour oscillations in flat spacetime. In curved spacetime, neutrinos can take more than one path to arrive at the detector; this gives rise to path difference in the neutrino phase, giving a novel contribution in oscillation probabilities that depends on absolute neutrinos mass. We presented a method for inferring individual neutrino mass from flipping angles/points, i.e. locations in the space where all the neutrino flavours have equal probabilities of being detected by the detector. Using the Sun-Earth model, we explicitly demonstrate

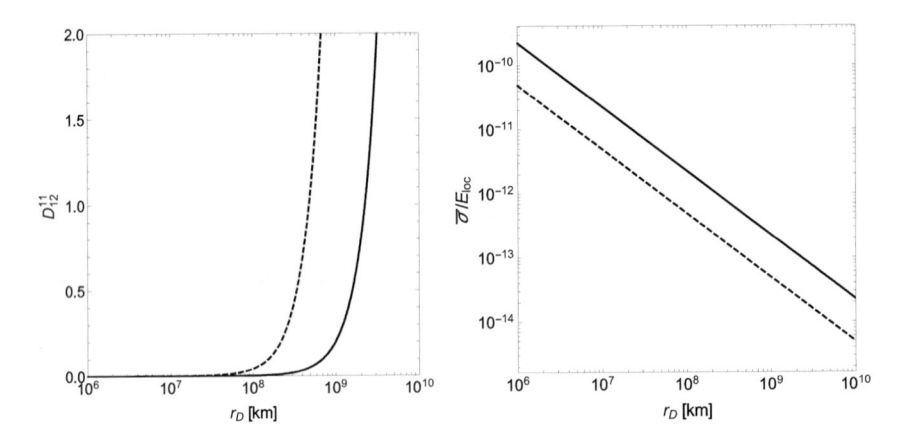

Fig. 3. Left panel: the damping factor D_{12}^{11} as function of r_D for $\bar{\sigma}/E_{\text{loc}} = 10^{-13}$. Right panel: contours corresponding to $D_{12}^{11} = 1$. In both the panels, the solid (dashed) line corresponds to $m_1 = 0$ ($m_1 = 0.1$) eV. The other parameters are $r_S = 10^5 r_D$, $R_S = 3$ km, $m_2^2 - m_1^2 = 10^{-3}$ eV^2 and $E_{\text{loc}} = 10$ MeV.

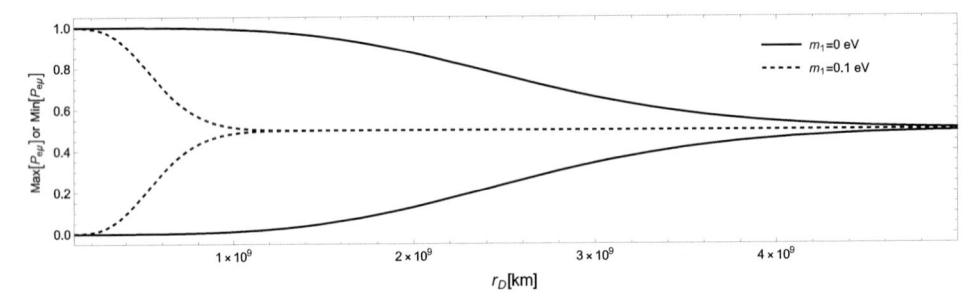

Fig. 4. Maximum and minimum transition probability envelop as a function of r_D for two flavour case. The solid (dashed) line corresponds to $m_1 = 0$ ($m_1 = 0.1$) eV. The mixing angle is $\alpha = \pi/4$ and all the other parameters are as given in the caption of Fig. 3.

oscillation sensitivity on individual neutrino masses in neutrino lensing. Neutrino oscillation frequency increases as we increase the value of m_1. Further, using the Gaussian wavepacket profile for the neutrino and the detector, we find wave packet profile modifies the neutrino phase. Now, the oscillation phase depends on the source and detector wave packet profile $\sigma_{D,S}$ and $\bar{p}^{D,S}$, and reduces to the plane wave neutrino phase when mean momentum $\bar{p}^{D,S}$ of the source and detector are same. The wave packet approach also introduces a new length scale, i.e. decoherence length, after which neutrino oscillations cease to exist. The decoherence length depends not only on Δm^2 but also on $\sum m^2$. Also, in a weak gravity limit, neutrino travels more in the Schwarzschild spacetime as compare to the flat spacetime before decoupling due to decoherence. Further, we highlight that neutrino flavour transition probability settles to the fundamental values of neutrino mixing matrix elements after decoherence. Therefore, the sensitivity of flavour oscillations probabilities and neutrino decoherence on $\sum m^2$ can reveal absolute neutrino mass and their ordering. Hence, neutrino lensing can be one of the viable methods for inferring individual neutrino mass. Conversely, one can also use decoherence length and neutrino mass to infer values of neutrino mixing parameters.

References

1. F. Capozzi, G. L. Fogli, E. Lisi, A. Marrone, D. Montanino, and A. Palazzo, "Status of three- neutrino oscillation parameters, circa 2013," *Phys. Rev.* **D89**, 093018 (2014), https://arxiv.org/abs/1312.2878.
2. P. F. de Salas, D. V. Forero, C. A. Ternes, M. Tortola, and J. W. F. Valle, "Status of neutrino oscillations 2018: 3σ hint for normal mass ordering and improved CP sensitivity," *Phys. Lett.* **B782**, 633-640 (2018), https://arxiv.org/abs/1708.01186.
3. Ivan Esteban, M. C. Gonzalez-Garcia, Alvaro Hernandez-Cabezudo, Michele Maltoni, and Thomas Schwetz, "Global analysis of three-flavour neutrino oscillations: synergies and tensions in the determination of θ_{23}, δ_{CP}, and the mass ordering," *JHEP* **01**, 106 (2019), https://arxiv.org/abs/1811.05487.
4. Evgeny Kh. Akhmedov and Alexei Yu. Smirnov, "Paradoxes of neutrino oscillations," *Phys. Atom. Nucl.* **72**, 1363-1381 (2009), https://arxiv.org/abs/0905.1903.
5. E. Kh. Akhmedov and A. Yu. Smirnov, "Neutrino oscillations: Entanglement, energy-momentum conservation and QFT," *Found. Phys.* **49**, 1279-1306 (2011), https://arxiv.org/abs/1008.2077.
6. Christian Y. Cardall and George M. Fuller, "Neutrino oscillations in curved spacetime: An Heuristic treatment," *Phys. Rev.* **D55**, 7960-7966 (1997), https://arxiv.org/abs/hep-ph/9610494.
7. Himanshu Swami, Kinjalk Lochan, and Ketan M. Patel, "Signature of neutrino mass hierarchy in gravitational lensing," *Phys. Rev.* **D102**, 024043 (2020), https://arxiv.org/abs/2002.00977.
8. Thanu Padmanabhan, "Gravitation: Foundations and Frontiers," *Cambridge University Press*, ISBN:978-0-521-88223-1 (2010).
9. N. Fornengo, C. Giunti, C. W. Kim, and J. Song, "Gravitational effects on the neutrino oscillation," *Phys. Rev.* **D56**, 1895-1902 (1997), https://arxiv.org/abs/hep-ph/9611231.
10. Roland M. Crocker, Carlo Giunti, and Daniel J. Mortlock, "Neutrino interferometry in curved spacetime," *Phys. Rev.* **D69**, 063008 (2004), https://arxiv.org/abs/hep-ph/0308168.
11. Jean Alexandre and Katy Clough, "Black hole interference patterns in flavor oscillations," *Phys. Rev.* **D98**, 043004 (2018), https://arxiv.org/abs/1805.01874.
12. E. Mitsou and J. Yoo, "Tetrad Formalism for Exact Cosmological Observables," SpringerBriefs in Physics (Springer, 2020), https://arxiv.org/abs/1908.10757.
13. E. K. Akhmedov and J. Kopp, "Neutrino oscillations: Quantum mechanics vs. quantum field theory," *JHEP* **04**, 008 (2010), [Erratum: JHEP 10, 052 (2013)], https://arxiv.org/abs/1001.4815.
14. Himanshu Swami, Kinjalk Lochan, and Ketan M. Patel, "Aspects of gravitational decoherence in neutrino lensing," https://arxiv.org/abs/2106.07671.

Photon regions in stationary axisymmetric spacetimes and umbilic conditions

K. V. Kobialko* and D. V. Gal'tsov[†]

Faculty of Physics, Moscow State University, 119899, Moscow, Russia
* E-mail: kobyalkokv@yandex.ru
† E-mail: galtsov@phys.msu.ru

We present the fundamentals of the recently proposed geometric description[1] of *photon regions* in terms of foliation into *fundamental photon hypersurfaces*, which satisfies the umbilic condition for the subbundle of the tangent bundle defined by the generalized impact parameter.

Keywords: Photon regions, photon surfaces, gravitational lensing, black hole shadows.

1. Introduction

Formation of shadows and relativistic images of stationary black holes is closely related to *photon regions*,[2,3] which are defined as compact domains where photons can travel endlessly without escaping to infinity or disappearing at the event horizon. Indeed, the boundary of the gravitational shadow corresponds to the set of light rays that inspiral asymptotically onto the part of the spherical surfaces in photon regions on which closed spherical photon orbits are located.[4–6]

Spherical surfaces in the photon region are just as important for determining the shadow of a stationary black hole as the *photon surfaces*[7,8] in the static case[a]. Recall that an important property of the photon surfaces is established by the theorem asserting that these are timelike *totally umbilic* hypersurfaces S in spacetime. This means that their second fundamental form II[11] is proportional to the induced metric:

$$\mathrm{II}(X,Y) = \mathrm{H}\langle X,Y\rangle, \quad \forall X,Y \in TS. \tag{1}$$

This property can serve as a constructive definition for analyzing photon surfaces instead of solving geodesic equations. It is especially useful in the cases when the geodesic equations are non-separable, and their analytic solution can not be found.[12–17]

However, in rotating spacetime such as Kerr, spherical surfaces in the photon region do not fully satisfy the umbilic condition and have a boundary. Such surfaces usually form a family, parameterized by the value of the azimuthal impact parameter $\rho = L/E$, where L, E are the integrals of motion corresponding to the timelike and azimuthal Killing vector fields.[18,19] To describe these surfaces and the photon

---

[a]For recent review of strong *gravitational lensing* and shadows see.[6,9,10]

region geometrically, we introduce the concept of *partially umbilic* submanifolds that weaken the condition (1). Namely, it is possible to impose the condition (1) not on *all* vectors from the tangent space TS, but only on some subset of TS specified by the azimuthal impact parameter. In addition, we must specify the boundary conditions for the submanifolds so that the photon does not escape through them. Together, this leads to the definition of *fundamental photon submanifolds*[1,20] - as generalization of *fundamental photon orbits*.[17] The slices consisting of the fundamental photon surfaces form generalized photon regions.

In this article, we give a concise presentation of the main concepts of the geometric approach to fundamental photon submanifolds and regions. Section 2 describes the partition of the tangent space of the manifold into sectors specified by the azimuthal impact parameter of the geodesics $\rho = L/E$. Then, in the section 3, we introduce the notion of partially umbilic submanifolds on the ρ-constrained sector of the tangent space and define the *fundamental photon submanifolds*. The Section 4 contains the geometric definition of the photon region.

2. Geodesic classes

Let M be a m dimensional Lorentzian manifold[11] with scalar product $\langle \cdot, \cdot \rangle$, Levi-Civita connection ∇, a tangent bundle TM and supposed to possess two commuting Killing vector fields $\mathcal{K}_\alpha$ ($\alpha = t, \varphi$) defining a stationary axisymmetric spacetime such that $\mathcal{G} = \det(\mathcal{G}_{\alpha\beta}) < 0$, where $\mathcal{G}_{\alpha\beta} = \langle \mathcal{K}_\alpha, \mathcal{K}_\beta \rangle$.

Let us define a Killing vector field $\hat{\rho} \in \{\mathcal{K}_\alpha\}$[20] with index numbering Killing vectors fields of the frame $\{\mathcal{K}_\alpha\}$

$$\hat{\rho} = \rho^\alpha \mathcal{K}_\alpha, \quad \rho^\alpha = (\rho, 1), \tag{2}$$

which is determined by arbitrary constant parameter ρ. In addition, we will introduce a vector field $\hat{\tau}$ in $\{\mathcal{K}_\alpha\}$ orthogonal to $\hat{\rho}$:

$$\tau^\alpha = \mathcal{G}^{\alpha\lambda} \epsilon_{\lambda\beta} \rho^\beta, \quad \langle \hat{\tau}, \hat{\tau} \rangle = -\langle \hat{\rho}, \hat{\rho} \rangle, \quad \langle \hat{\tau}, \hat{\rho} \rangle = 0, \tag{3}$$

where $\epsilon_{\lambda\beta}$ is the two-dimensional Levi-Civita tensor.

Then there is frame $\{\hat{\tau}, e_a\} \cong \hat{\rho}^\perp$, such that $\{e_a\}$ ($a = 1, m-2$) is a frame in euclidean orthogonal complement $\{\mathcal{K}_\alpha\}^{\perp b}$.

Let γ be some geodesic on M, and $\dot{\gamma}$ denotes the tangent vector field to γ. Then there is the following general relationship between geodesics γ and orthogonal complement $\hat{\rho}^\perp$.

Proposition 2.1. *At every point $p \in M$ there is a one-to-one correspondence*[c] *between geodesics γ (with nonzero energy $E \equiv -\langle \mathcal{K}_t, \dot{\gamma} \rangle \neq 0$) with impact parameter $\rho = -\langle \mathcal{K}_\varphi, \dot{\gamma} \rangle / \langle \mathcal{K}_t, \dot{\gamma} \rangle$ and tangent vector fields $\mathcal{X} \in \hat{\rho}^\perp$ with $\langle \mathcal{K}_t, \mathcal{X} \rangle \neq 0$.*

---

[b]Orthogonal complement $\perp$ defined in.[11] If $\langle \hat{\rho}, \hat{\rho} \rangle = 0$, then $\hat{\tau}$ and $\hat{\rho}$ are simply proportional and the orthogonal complement $\hat{\rho}^\perp$ will contain only one null vector $\hat{\rho}$ and spacelike e_a.
[c]Accurate to the geodesics reparametrization.

Proof. If geodesic γ has ρ as an impact parameter, then $\rho = -\langle \mathcal{K}_\varphi, \dot\gamma \rangle / \langle \mathcal{K}_t, \dot\gamma \rangle$ and multiplying by $\langle \mathcal{K}_t, \dot\gamma \rangle \neq 0$ we get $0 = \langle \rho\mathcal{K}_t + \mathcal{K}_\varphi, \dot\gamma \rangle = \langle \hat\rho, \dot\gamma \rangle$ and therefore $\dot\gamma \in \hat\rho^\perp$. If $\langle \hat\rho, \mathcal{X} \rangle = 0$ and $\langle \mathcal{K}_t, \mathcal{X} \rangle \neq 0$, then at any point $p \in M$ the any vector $\mathcal{X}|_p$ is a tangent vector to some geodesic γ, which always exists and unique at least in some vicinity of $p \in M$ as solution of ODE with initial conditions $\gamma(0) = p$ and $\dot\gamma(0) = \mathcal{X}|_p$. The geodesic γ has ρ as an impact parameter insofar as $0 = \langle \hat\rho, \dot\gamma(0) \rangle = \langle \rho\mathcal{K}_t + \mathcal{K}_\varphi, \dot\gamma(0) \rangle$ and we get $\rho = -\langle \mathcal{K}_\varphi, \dot\gamma(0) \rangle / \langle \mathcal{K}_t, \dot\gamma(0) \rangle$. $\square$

It is clear that in the general case the Killing vector field $\hat\rho$ can be timelike on the some part of the manifold M. In this case, its orthogonal complement $\hat\rho^\perp$ will not have the Lorentzian signature everywhere, and therefore not all manifolds will be available for null geodesics with a given impact parameter ρ. So, our goal is to find the suitable region $\mathcal{C} \subset M$ in the original manifold M such that $\langle \hat\rho, \hat\rho \rangle |_\mathcal{C} \geq 0$.

Proposition 2.2. *If $\nabla_{\hat\rho}\hat\rho \neq 0$ for all null $\hat\rho$, the smooth function $\langle \hat\rho, \hat\rho \rangle$ defines m dimensional manifold with boundary*

$$\mathcal{C} \subset M : \langle \hat\rho, \hat\rho \rangle |_\mathcal{C} \geq 0, \tag{4}$$

with interior $\mathcal{O} : \langle \hat\rho, \hat\rho \rangle |_\mathcal{O} > 0$ and $m-1$ dimensional boundary $\partial\mathcal{C} : \langle \hat\rho, \hat\rho \rangle |_{\partial\mathcal{C}} = 0$ with outward normal

$$\mathcal{N} = \nabla_{\hat\rho}\hat\rho, \quad \langle \mathcal{N}, \hat\rho \rangle = 0. \tag{5}$$

Proof. Let $\mathcal{X} \in TM$ be an arbitrary vector field in M, then using Killing equation we get

$$\langle \nabla \langle \hat\rho, \hat\rho \rangle, \mathcal{X} \rangle \equiv \nabla_\mathcal{X} \langle \hat\rho, \hat\rho \rangle = 2 \langle \nabla_\mathcal{X} \hat\rho, \hat\rho \rangle = -2 \langle \nabla_{\hat\rho}\hat\rho, \mathcal{X} \rangle, \tag{6}$$

$$\Updownarrow$$

$$\nabla \langle \hat\rho, \hat\rho \rangle = -2\nabla_{\hat\rho}\hat\rho. \tag{7}$$

Thus $\nabla \langle \hat\rho, \hat\rho \rangle |_{\partial\mathcal{C}} \neq 0$ and the boundary $\partial\mathcal{C}$ is a hypersurface in M with the normal field $\mathcal{N}$ proportional to $\nabla_{\hat\rho}\hat\rho$. Choosing an outward normal, i.e. directed so that the function $\langle \hat\rho, \hat\rho \rangle$ decreases along the $\mathcal{N}$ we get first condition in (5). Applying Killing equation again we get second condition in (5) since

$$\langle \mathcal{N}, \hat\rho \rangle = \langle \nabla_{\hat\rho}\hat\rho, \hat\rho \rangle = -\langle \nabla_{\hat\rho}\hat\rho, \hat\rho \rangle = 0. \tag{8}$$
$\square$

Definition 2.1. A connected manifold $\mathcal{C}$ will be called causal region. The manifold $\mathcal{O}$ will be called accessible region.[1]

From the point of view of geodesics, and, in particular, the fundamental photon orbits, the region $\mathcal{C}$ represents an accessible region for the null geodesics motion in some effective potential.[17,21] Physical meaning of the causal region $\mathcal{C}$ is that any point can be theoretically observable for any observer in the same region. This causal region may contain spatial infinity (if any) and then will be observable for an asymptotic observer. In some cases, several causal regions may exist, while null geodesics with a given ρ cannot connect one to another. The boundary $\partial \mathcal{C}$ of the causal region is defined as the branch of the solution of the equation $\langle \hat{\rho}, \hat{\rho} \rangle = 0$ and is the set of turning points of null geodesics.

3. Photon submanifold

Let M and S be Lorentzian manifolds, of dimension m and n respectively, and $S \to M$ an isometric embedding[11] defining S as a submanifold[d] in M. We adopt here the following convention for the second fundamental form II of the submanifold[11]:

$$\nabla_Y X = \mathcal{D}_Y X + \mathrm{II}(X, Y), \quad X, Y \in TS, \tag{9}$$

where $\mathcal{D}_X Y \in TS$, $\mathrm{II}(X,Y) \in TS^\perp$ and ∇ and $\mathcal{D}$ are the Levi-Civita connections on M and S respectively.

Definition 3.1. We will call a submanifold S invariant, if the Killing vector fields $\mathcal{K}_\alpha$ and $[\mathcal{K}_\alpha, \mathcal{K}_\beta]$ in M are tangent vector fields to S.

For invariant submanifolds the Killing vectors of M will be also the Killing vectors on the submanifold S[20] and well defined restrictions $\hat{\rho}^\perp$ and $\mathcal{C}$ on TS and S respectively. We now define a weakened version of the standard umbilic condition (1) requiring it to be satisfied only for some subbundle $V \subset TS$ in the tangent bundle TS.

Definition 3.2. A submanifold S will be called totally V umbilic if[1]

$$\mathrm{II}(X, Y) = \mathrm{H}|_V \langle X, Y \rangle, \quad \forall X, Y \in V. \tag{10}$$

In particular, every totally umbilic submanifold is trivially totally V umbilic for any V. We also note that in the general case $\mathrm{H}|_V$ appearing in this formula is only part of the mean curvature[11] i.e the trace of II on the subbundle V. For invariant totally V umbilic submanifolds, an important theorem on the behavior of null geodesics holds, generalizing the classical result.[7,11]

Proposition 3.1. *Any null geodesic γ with impact parameter ρ in an invariant Lorentzian submanifold $S \subset \mathcal{O}$ is a null geodesic in M if and only if S is totally $\hat{\rho}^\perp$ umbilic submanifold.*

Proof. Let S be a totally $\hat{\rho}^\perp$ umbilic invariant Lorentzian submanifold and γ be an arbitrary affinely parameterized null geodesic with impact parameter ρ in S i.e. $\mathcal{D}_{\dot\gamma} \dot\gamma = 0$ and $\dot\gamma \in \hat{\rho}^\perp \subset TS$. Then by the Gauss decomposition (9)

$$\nabla_{\dot\gamma} \dot\gamma = \mathcal{D}_{\dot\gamma} \dot\gamma + \mathrm{II}(\dot\gamma, \dot\gamma) = \mathrm{H}|_{\hat\rho^\perp} \langle \dot\gamma, \dot\gamma \rangle = 0, \tag{11}$$

consequently γ is a null geodesic in M.

---

[d] A hypersurface if $n = m - 1$

Conversely, let every null geodesic γ with impact parameter ρ in S be a null geodesic in M, then from the Gauss decomposition (9)

$$\mathrm{II}(\dot\gamma,\dot\gamma) = 0, \tag{12}$$

for any null $\dot\gamma \in \hat\rho^\perp \subset TS$. Since we limited ourselves to the accessible region $\mathcal{O}$ we can choose an orthonormal Lorentzian frame $\{\hat\tau/||\hat\tau||, e_a\} \cong \hat\rho^\perp \subset TS$ ($a = 1, n-2$). Then the equality (12) for null vectors $\dot\gamma = \hat\tau/||\hat\tau|| \pm e_a$ in the new frame takes the form

$$\mathrm{II}(\hat\tau/||\hat\tau||, \hat\tau/||\hat\tau||) + \mathrm{II}(e_a, e_a) = 0, \quad \mathrm{II}(\hat\tau/||\hat\tau||, e_a) = 0. \tag{13}$$

And for null vectors $\dot\gamma = \hat\tau/||\hat\tau|| \pm (e_a \pm e_b)/\sqrt{2}$

$$\mathrm{II}(e_a, e_b) = 0. \tag{14}$$

□

Physical meaning of the Proposition 3.1 is that the null geodesics with a given impact parameter ρ initially touching the spatial section of the invariant totally $\hat\rho^\perp$ umbilic submanifold remain on it for an arbitrarily long time, unless of course they leave it across the boundary. This is a well-known property of a photon sphere and its generalization - a photon surface.[7] Thus, we obtain a generalization of the classical definition of the photon surfaces to the case of a class of geodesics with a fixed impact parameter.

It is useful to obtain an equation for the second fundamental form of the totally $\hat\rho^\perp$ umbilic submanifold in the original basis $\{\mathcal{K}_\alpha, e_a\}$.

Proposition 3.2. *For the invariant $\hat\rho^\perp$ umbilic submanifold, the second fundamental form* II *in the basis* $\{\mathcal{K}_\alpha, e_a\}$ *has the form*

$$\mathrm{II} = \begin{pmatrix} -\frac{1}{2}\nabla^\perp \mathcal{G}_{\alpha\beta} & -\sum_{A=1}^{m-n} \epsilon_A \langle \nabla_{\xi_A}\mathcal{K}_\alpha, e_b\rangle \xi_A \\ -\sum_{A=1}^{m-n} \epsilon_A \langle \nabla_{\xi_A}\mathcal{K}_\beta, e_a\rangle \xi_A & \mathrm{H}|_{\hat\rho^\perp} \langle e_a, e_b\rangle \end{pmatrix}, \tag{15}$$

where $\mathrm{H}|_{\hat\rho^\perp}$ *and* $\mathcal{G}_{\alpha\beta}$ *satisfy the master equation*[20]

$$\rho^\alpha \mathcal{M}_{\alpha\beta}\rho^\beta = 0, \quad \mathcal{M}_{\alpha\beta} = \frac{1}{2}\nabla^\perp\left(\mathcal{G}^{-1}\mathcal{G}_{\alpha\beta}\right) - \mathrm{H}|_{\hat\rho^\perp}\left(\mathcal{G}^{-1}\mathcal{G}_{\alpha\beta}\right), \tag{16}$$

$$\mathcal{G}^{\alpha\lambda}\epsilon_{\lambda\beta}\rho^\beta \mathrm{II}(\mathcal{K}_\alpha, e_a) = 0, \tag{17}$$

and the derivative along the unit normals $\xi_A \in TS^\perp$ ($A = 1, m-n$) *of the submanifold* S *is defined as*

$$\nabla^\perp(\,\cdot\,) = \sum_{A=1}^{m-n} \epsilon_A \nabla_{\xi_A}(\,\cdot\,)\xi_A, \quad \epsilon_A \equiv \langle \xi_A, \xi_A\rangle. \tag{18}$$

Proof. From the Killing equation for $X \in \{e_a\}$ we find

$$\mathrm{II}(X, \mathcal{K}_\alpha) = \pi^\perp(\nabla_X \mathcal{K}_\alpha) = \sum_{A=1}^{m-n} \epsilon_A \langle \nabla_X \mathcal{K}_\alpha, \xi_A\rangle \xi_A = -\sum_{A=1}^{m-n} \epsilon_A \langle \nabla_{\xi_A}\mathcal{K}_\alpha, X\rangle \xi_A. \tag{19}$$

Using the Killing equation again we get

$$\langle \nabla_{\mathcal{K}_\alpha} \mathcal{K}_\beta, \xi_A \rangle = - \langle \nabla_{\xi_A} \mathcal{K}_\beta, \mathcal{K}_\alpha \rangle = -\nabla_{\xi_A} \langle \mathcal{K}_\alpha, \mathcal{K}_\beta \rangle - \langle \xi_A, \nabla_{\mathcal{K}_\beta} \mathcal{K}_\alpha \rangle. \tag{20}$$

Then, using the involutivity condition $[\mathcal{K}_\alpha, \mathcal{K}_\beta] \in TS$ we finally find

$$\mathrm{II}(\mathcal{K}_\alpha, \mathcal{K}_\beta) = \sum_{A=1}^{m-n} \epsilon_A \langle \nabla_{\mathcal{K}_\alpha} \mathcal{K}_\beta, \xi_A \rangle \xi_A = -\frac{1}{2} \sum_{A=1}^{m-n} \epsilon_A \nabla_{\xi_A} \langle \mathcal{K}_\alpha, \mathcal{K}_\beta \rangle \xi_A. \tag{21}$$

and

$$\mathrm{II}(\hat{\tau}, \hat{\tau}) = -\frac{1}{2} \tau^\alpha \tau^\beta \nabla^\perp \mathcal{G}_{\alpha\beta} = -\rho^\alpha \rho^\beta \left(\frac{1}{2} \nabla^\perp \mathcal{G}_{\alpha\beta} + \mathcal{G}^{\lambda\gamma} \epsilon_{\lambda\alpha} \nabla^\perp \epsilon_{\gamma\beta} \right) \tag{22}$$

$$= \frac{1}{2} \rho^\alpha \rho^\beta \left(-\nabla^\perp \mathcal{G}_{\alpha\beta} + \mathcal{G}_{\alpha\beta} \nabla^\perp \ln \mathcal{G} \right). \tag{23}$$

Substituting this expression into the equation (10), we get (16). □

Alternatively, the master equation can be rewritten as expression for the mean curvature

$$\mathrm{H}|_{\hat{\rho}^\perp} = \frac{1}{2} \nabla^\perp \ln \left(\mathcal{G}^{-1} \langle \hat{\rho}, \hat{\rho} \rangle \right). \tag{24}$$

If the submanifold under consideration is totally umbilic we'll get $\mathcal{M}_{\alpha\beta} = 0$.

The notion of an invariant $\hat{\rho}^\perp$ umbilic submanifold is however too general (as is the notion of an umbilic surface by itself[22]) and is not yet defined at the boundary of the causal region $\partial \mathcal{C}$. Generally speaking, these submanifolds are geodesically not complete (in the sense that null geodesics can leave them across the boundary) or have a non-compact spatial section (geodesics can go into the asymptotic region). Moreover, for each ρ there can be an infinite number of them, just as there are an infinite number of umbilic surfaces, but only one photon sphere in the static Schwarzschild[23] solution. Therefore, it is necessary to introduce a more specific definition of fundamental photon submanifolds.[1, 20]

Definition 3.3. A fundamental photon submanifold $S \subset \mathcal{C}$ is an invariant Lorentzian submanifold with compact spatial section such that:
  (a) The boundary ∂S (if any) lie in $\partial \mathcal{C}$.
  (b) The second fundamental form II has the form (15) and satisfies the master equation/inequality

$$\mathcal{M}(\hat{\rho}, \hat{\rho}) = 0, \quad \langle \hat{\rho}, \hat{\rho} \rangle \geq 0. \tag{25}$$

In the case $n = m - 1$, the fundamental photon submanifold is a timelike fundamental photon hypersurface (FPH).

Proposition 3.3. *Every null geodesic γ with an impact parameter ρ at least once touching an arbitrary fundamental photon submanifold S lies in it completely i.e. $\gamma \subset S$.*

Proof. Obviously condition (b) in Definition 3.3, by virtue of Proposition 3.1, prevents null geodesics from leaving the fundamental photon submanifold at all interior points $(S/\partial S) \cap \mathcal{O}$.

Conditions (a-b) for boundary points ∂S and interior points $S \cap \partial \mathcal{C}$ prevents the possibility of null geodesics to leave fundamental photon submanifolds through them. Indeed, $\partial \mathcal{C}$ is the set of turning points for null geodesics in M that cannot move in the direction of the normal $\mathcal{N}|_{\partial S}$, while condition $\mathrm{II}(\hat{\rho},\hat{\rho})|_{\partial S} = 0$ following from (25) not only prevents geodesics from moving in the normal directions ξ_A but also ensures that the normal $\mathcal{N}_{\partial S}$ to ∂S in S coincides with the normal $\mathcal{N}|_{\partial S}$ to the $\partial \mathcal{C}$ in M.

$$\mathcal{N}|_{\partial S} = \nabla_{\hat{\rho}}\hat{\rho}|_{\partial S} = \{\mathcal{D}_{\hat{\rho}}\hat{\rho} + \mathrm{II}(\hat{\rho},\hat{\rho})\}|_{\partial S} = \mathcal{D}_{\hat{\rho}}\hat{\rho}|_{\partial S} = \mathcal{N}_{\partial S}. \tag{26}$$

□

From this statement, it is clear that the so-defined fundamental photon submanifolds have trapping properties even at the boundary and contain

(a) non-periodic trapped photon orbits,
(b) periodic fundamental photon orbits.[17]

In stationary and axisymmetric geometry, there exists a vector field

$$\hat{\omega} = \omega^\alpha \mathcal{K}_\alpha, \quad \omega^\alpha = (1,\omega), \tag{27}$$

orthogonal to the all spatial slices Σ of manifold M^e. In such slices, one can define fundamental photon submanifolds in terms of *principal curvatures*.

Proposition 3.4. *The principal curvatures λ of the spatial section S' of the invariant totally $\hat{\rho}^\perp$ umbilic submanifold S satisfy the master equation*

$$\lambda_a - \lambda_\varphi = \nabla^\perp \ln(||\hat{\rho}||/||\hat{\omega}||), \tag{28}$$

with

$$\lambda_\varphi = -\frac{1}{2}\nabla^\perp \ln \mathcal{G}_{\varphi\varphi}, \quad \lambda_a = \mathrm{H}|_{\hat{\rho}^\perp}. \tag{29}$$

Proof. From the general theory for the second fundamental form II' of the spatial section $S' \subset \Sigma$ of the invariant totally $\hat{\rho}^\perp$ umbilic submanifold S we find that

$$\mathrm{II}'(X,Y) = \mathrm{II}(X,Y) = \mathrm{H}|_{\hat{\rho}^\perp} \langle X,Y \rangle, \quad \mathrm{II}'(\mathcal{K}_\varphi,\mathcal{K}_\varphi) = \mathrm{II}(\mathcal{K}_\varphi,\mathcal{K}_\varphi) = -\frac{1}{2}\nabla^\perp \mathcal{G}_{\varphi\varphi},$$

$$\mathrm{II}'(\mathcal{K}_\varphi, X) = \mathrm{II}(\mathcal{K}_\varphi, X) = -\sum_{A=1}^{m-n} \epsilon_A \langle \nabla_{\xi_A}\mathcal{K}_\varphi, X \rangle \xi_A, \quad X \in \{e_a\}.$$

In what follows, we will assume that $\mathrm{II}(\mathcal{K}_\varphi, X) = 0$.[1] Due to the shape of the second fundamental form of the spatial slices Σ and the expression for mixed components, we find $\mathrm{II}(\hat{\omega}, X) = 0$, and therefore from $\mathrm{II}(\mathcal{K}_\varphi, X) = 0$ follows $\mathrm{II}(\mathcal{K}_t, X) = 0$ and

---

[e]The norm $||\hat{\omega}||$ of vector field $\hat{\omega}$ is called the lapse function.

the second umbilic condition (17) is fulfilled identically. Further, from the master equation (24) and expressions for the determinant $\mathcal{G}$

$$\begin{aligned}\mathcal{G} &= \langle \mathcal{K}_t, \mathcal{K}_t \rangle \langle \mathcal{K}_\varphi, \mathcal{K}_\varphi \rangle - \langle \mathcal{K}_t, \mathcal{K}_\varphi \rangle^2 \\ &= (\langle \hat{\omega}, \hat{\omega} \rangle - 2\omega \langle \mathcal{K}_t, \mathcal{K}_\varphi \rangle - \omega^2 \langle \mathcal{K}_\varphi, \mathcal{K}_\varphi \rangle) \langle \mathcal{K}_\varphi, \mathcal{K}_\varphi \rangle - \omega^2 \langle \mathcal{K}_\varphi, \mathcal{K}_\varphi \rangle^2 \\ &= \langle \hat{\omega}, \hat{\omega} \rangle \langle \mathcal{K}_\varphi, \mathcal{K}_\varphi \rangle. \end{aligned} \qquad (30)$$

we get (28). $\square$

4. Photon region

We now define the concept of a fundamental photon region and a fundamental photon function – a generalization of the classical three-dimensional photon region in the Kerr metric.[2,3,24]

Definition 4.1. The fundamental photon function PF will be called the mapping[1]

$$PF : \rho \to \bigcup S \qquad (31)$$

which associates with each ρ one or the union of several fundamental photon submanifolds with the same ρ.

The function PF can be continuous, defining some connected smooth submanifold in the extended manifold $\{M, \rho\}$. At the same time, several continuous functions PF can exist in which different FPHs correspond to one ρ. In particular, for a given ρ, photon and antiphoton FPHs ((un)stable photon surface[25]) can occur simultaneously, indicating the instability of the solution.[8]

Definition 4.2. The fundamental photon region is the complete image of the function PF

$$PR = \bigcup_\rho PF. \qquad (32)$$

A fundamental photon region is a standard region in the space M in which there are fundamental photon orbits and, in particular, the classical photon region in the Kerr metric. However, the mapping PF can several times cover the image of PR or part of it when the parameter ρ is continuously changed. For example, in the case of a static space, PR is covered at least two times, i.e. PF is a two-sheeted function.

The photon region can also be described using an algebraic equation.[20] To do this, rewrite the equations and the inequality (25) as

$$\mathcal{M}_{tt} \rho^2 + 2\mathcal{M}_{t\varphi} \rho + \mathcal{M}_{\varphi\varphi} = 0, \qquad (33)$$

$$\mathcal{G}_{tt} \rho^2 + 2\mathcal{G}_{t\varphi} \rho + \mathcal{G}_{\varphi\varphi} \geq 0. \qquad (34)$$

Then, excluding ρ, we find

$$2(-\mathcal{M}_{t\varphi} \pm \sqrt{\mathcal{M}_{t\varphi}^2 - \mathcal{M}_{tt}\mathcal{M}_{\varphi\varphi}})(\mathcal{G}_{t\varphi} - \mathcal{G}_{tt}\mathcal{M}_{t\varphi}/\mathcal{M}_{tt})/\mathcal{M}_{tt}$$
$$+(\mathcal{G}_{\varphi\varphi} - \mathcal{G}_{tt}\mathcal{M}_{\varphi\varphi}/\mathcal{M}_{tt}) \geq 0, \qquad (35)$$

or

$$\pm 2(\mathcal{G}_{t\varphi}\mathcal{M}_{tt} - \mathcal{G}_{tt}\mathcal{M}_{t\varphi})\sqrt{-\mathcal{M}} - 2\mathcal{G}_{tt} \cdot \mathcal{M} + \mathcal{M}_{tt} \cdot \mathcal{G} \cdot \mathrm{Tr}(\mathcal{M}) > 0. \qquad (36)$$

These inequality describe a generalized photon region.

5. Conclusion

In this article, we briefly presented a purely geometric approach to defining characteristic surfaces and regions filled with closed photon orbits, based on some generalization of umbilic hypersurfaces. The main new concept is a *partially* umbilic surface, which has umbilic properties with respect to a correctly defined subbundle of the tangent bundle. This approach does not address the integration of geodesic equations, and thus is applicable to spacetimes with a non-integrable geodesic structure.

We tried to give a more clear and concise idea of the main geometric notions presented in,[1] supplementing them with a number of new useful expressions and relations, which, in particular, turned out to be useful for analyzing their connection with Killing tensor fields.[20] We hope that this formalism will pave the way for obtaining new topological constraints, Penrose-type inequalities (and other estimates),[26-28] uniqueness theorems,[23,29-33] similar to ones known for photon spheres and transversally trapping surfaces.[34,35]

The work is supported by the Russian Foundation for Basic Research on the project 20-52-18012Bulg-a, and the Scientific and Educational School of Moscow State University "Fundamental and Applied Space Research".

References

1. K. V. Kobialko and D. V. Gal'tsov, Photon regions and umbilic conditions in stationary axisymmetric spacetimes: Photon Regions, *Eur. Phys. J. C* **80**, p. 527 (2020).
2. A. Grenzebach, V. Perlick and C. Lämmerzahl, Photon Regions and Shadows of Kerr-Newman-NUT Black Holes with a Cosmological Constant, *Phys. Rev. D* **89**, p. 124004 (2014).
3. A. Grenzebach, V. Perlick and C. Lämmerzahl, Photon Regions and Shadows of Accelerated Black Holes, *Int. J. Mod. Phys. D* **24**, p. 1542024 (2015).
4. D. C. Wilkins, Bound Geodesics in the Kerr Metric, *Phys. Rev. D* **5**, p. 814 (1972).
5. E. Teo, Spherical orbits around a Kerr black hole, *Gen. Rel. Grav.* **53**, p. 10 (1972).
6. V. I. Dokuchaev and N. O. Nazarova, Silhouettes of invisible black holes, *Usp. Fiz. Nauk* **190**, p. 627-647 (2020).
7. C. M. Claudel, K. S. Virbhadra and G. F. R. Ellis, The Geometry of photon surfaces, *J. Math. Phys.* **42**, p. 818-838 (2001).

8. G. W. Gibbons and C. M. Warnick, Aspherical Photon and Anti-Photon Surfaces, *Phys. Lett. B* **763**, p. 169-173 (2016).
9. V. Perlick and O. Y. Tsupko, Calculating black hole shadows: Review of analytical studies, *arXiv*, p. 2105.07101 (2021).
10. P. V. P. Cunha and C. A. R. Herdeiro, Shadows and strong gravitational lensing: A brief review, *Gen. Rel. Grav.* **50**, p. 42 (2018).
11. B. Y. Chen, Pseudo-Riemannian Geometry, δ-Invariants and Applications, *World Scientific, Hackensack* (2011).
12. N. J. Cornish and G. W. Gibbons, The Tale of two centers, *Class. Quant. Grav.* **14**, p. 1865 (1997).
13. P. V. P. Cunha, J. Grover, C. Herdeiro, E. Radu, H. Runarsson and A. Wittig, Chaotic lensing around boson stars and Kerr black holes with scalar hair, *Phys. Rev. D* **94**, p. 104023 (2016).
14. O. Semerak and P. Sukova, Free motion around black holes with discs or rings: Between integrability and chaos - I, *Mon. Not. Roy. Astron. Soc.* **404**, p. 545 (2010).
15. J. Shipley and S. R. Dolan, Binary black hole shadows, chaotic scattering and the Cantor set, *Class. Quant. Grav.* **33**, p. 175001 (2016).
16. P. V. P. Cunha, C. A. R. Herdeiro and M. J. Rodriguez, Does the black hole shadow probe the event horizon geometry?, *Phys. Rev. D* **97**, p. 084020 (2018).
17. P. V. P. Cunha, C. A. R. Herdeiro and E. Radu, Fundamental photon orbits: Black hole shadows and spacetime instabilities, *Phys. Rev. D* **96**, p. 024039 (2017).
18. D. V. Gal'tsov and K. V. Kobialko, Completing characterization of photon orbits in Kerr and Kerr-Newman metrics, *Phys. Rev. D* **99**, p. 084043 (2019).
19. D. V. Gal'tsov and K. V. Kobialko, Photon trapping in static axially symmetric spacetime, *Phys. Rev. D* **100**, p. 104005 (2019).
20. K. Kobialko, I. Bogush and D. Gal'tsov, Killing tensors and photon surfaces in foliated spacetimes, *Phys. Rev. D* **104**, p. 044009 (2021).
21. G. Lukes-Gerakopoulos, The non-integrability of the Zipoy-Voorhees metric, *Phys. Rev. D* **86**, p. 044013 (2012).
22. L. M. Cao and Y. Song, Quasi-local photon surfaces in general spherically symmetric spacetimes, *arXiv*, p. 1910.13758 (2019).
23. C. Cederbaum and G. J. Galloway, Photon surfaces with equipotential time-slices, *J.Math. Phys.* **62**, p. 032504 (2021).
24. J. Grover and A. Wittig, Black Hole Shadows and Invariant Phase Space Structures, *Phys. Rev. D* **96**, p. 024045 (2017).
25. Y. Koga and T. Harada, Stability of null orbits on photon spheres and photon surfaces, *Phys. Rev. D* **100**, p. 064040 (2019).
26. T. Shiromizu, Y. Tomikawa, K. Izumi and H. Yoshino, Area bound for a surface in a strong gravity region, *PTEP* **2017**, p. 033E01 (2017).
27. X. H. Feng and H. Lu, On the size of rotating black holes, *Eur. Phys. J. C* **80**, p. 551 (2020).
28. R. Q. Yang and H. Lu, Universal bounds on the size of a black hole, *Eur. Phys. J. C* **80**, p. 949 (2020).
29. C. Cederbaum and G. J. Galloway, Uniqueness of photon spheres in electro-vacuum spacetimes, *Class. Quant. Grav.* **33**, p. 075006 (2016).
30. S. S. Yazadjiev, Uniqueness of the static spacetimes with a photon sphere in Einstein-scalar field theory, *Phys. Rev. D* **91**, p. 123013 (2015).
31. S. Yazadjiev and B. Lazov, Uniqueness of the static Einstein–Maxwell spacetimes with a photon sphere, *Class. Quant. Grav.* **32**, p. 165021 (2015).

32. S. Yazadjiev and B. Lazov, "Classification of the static and asymptotically flat Einstein-Maxwell-dilaton spacetimes with a photon sphere," *Phys. Rev. D* **93**, p. 083002 (2016).
33. M. Rogatko, Uniqueness of photon sphere for Einstein-Maxwell-dilaton black holes with arbitrary coupling constant, *Phys. Rev. D* **93**, p. 064003 (2016).
34. H. Yoshino, K. Izumi, T. Shiromizu and Y. Tomikawa, Transversely trapping surfaces: Dynamical version, *PTEP* **2020**, p. 023E02 (2020).
35. H. Yoshino, K. Izumi, T. Shiromizu and Y. Tomikawa, Formation of dynamically transversely trapping surfaces and the stretched hoop conjecture, *PTEP* **2020**, p. 053E01 (2020).

Gravitational lensing by charged accelerating black holes

Torben C. Frost

ZARM, University of Bremen, 28359 Bremen, Germany and Institute for Theoretical Physics,
Leibniz University Hannover, 30167 Hannover, Germany
E-mail: torben.frost@zarm.uni-bremen.de

Current astrophysical observations show that on large scale the Universe is electrically neutral. However, locally this may be quite different. Black holes enveloped by a plasma in the presence of a strong magnetic field may have acquired a significant electric charge. We can also expect that some of these charged black holes are moving. Consequently to describe them we need spacetime metrics describing moving black holes. In general relativity such a solution is given by the charged C-de Sitter-metric. In this article we will assume that it can be used to describe moving charged black holes. We will investigate how to observe the electric charge using gravitational lensing. First we will use elliptic integrals and functions to solve the geodesic equations. Then we will derive lens equation, travel time and redshift. We will discuss the impact of the electric charge on these observables and potential limitations for its observation.

Keywords: Black Holes; Gravitational Lensing

1. Introduction

X-ray and gravitational wave observations indicate that stellar mass black holes are widely distributed in our galaxy.[1,2] In addition, the motion of gas and stars[3,4] around galactic centres as well as the recent observation of the shadow of the compact object in the centre of the galaxy M87[5] indicate that in the centre of most galaxies we can find at least one supermassive black hole (SMBH). While the resolution of these observations are not yet precise enough to exclude all alternative theories of gravity or different types of compact objects all observational features indicate that these compact objects can be described either by the Schwarzschild metric or the Kerr metric.

Concurrent astrophysical observations show that our Universe is electrically neutral. This indicates that all astrophysical objects, among them black holes, do not carry a significant electric charge. However, if a black hole is surrounded by a plasma with sufficiently large magnetic fields, the black hole may acquire a significant electric charge.[6] In general relativity charged black holes that are at rest and do not carry a spin are described by the Reissner-Nordström metric, or, if we want to take the cosmological expansion into account, by the Reissner-Nordström-de Sitter metric. In the case that we consider real astrophysical environments it is very unlikely that black holes are at rest. Instead it is more realistic to assume that they constantly undergo accelerated motion. Consequently we need spacetimes describing accelerating black holes to describe them accurately. In the framework of general relativity a family of such solutions is described by the charged C-de Sitter metric.[7]

The metric is an exact solution to Einstein's electrovacuum field equations with cosmological constant. It generalises the Reissner-Nordström-de Sitter metric by introducing the acceleration parameter α in addition to the mass parameter m, the electric charge e and the cosmological constant Λ. The charged C-de Sitter metric is axisymmetric and static and describes a charged accelerating black hole with cosmological constant. The acceleration of the black hole results from conical singularities on the axes, which are commonly interpreted as a string pulling the black hole and a strut pushing the black hole. These conical singularities make the spacetime on a first view appear unphysical. However, it may still serve as an approximation for black holes undergoing accelerated motion. Gravitational lensing in the C-metric only attracted attention relatively recently. Grenzebach, Perlick and Lämmerzahl[8,9] investigated the shadow of accelerating black holes in the whole Plebański-Demiański family with acceleration.[10] Sharif and Iftikhar[11] calculated the deflection angle for light rays in the equatorial plane for accelerating Kerr-NUT black holes. The method they used explicitly assumes that the light rays are located in the equatorial plane of the spacetime. However, Alrais Alawadi, Batic and Nowakowski[12] and subsequently Frost and Perlick[13] demonstrated that the C-metric possesses a photon cone $\vartheta_{ph} \neq \pi/2$ and therefore the method of Sharif and Iftikhar cannot be directly applied. Alrais Alawadi, Batic and Nowakowski[12] calculated the deflection angle on the photon cone. Only a short time later Frost and Perlick[13] investigated gravitational lensing in the C-metric. In their work Frost and Perlick[13] used the canonical form of the elliptic integrals and Jacobi's elliptic functions to solve the geodesic equations. Then, following the apporach of Grenzebach, Perlick and Lämmerzahl,[8] they fixed an observer in the region of outer communication and introduced an orthonormal tetrad to relate latitude and longitude on the observer's celestial sphere to the constants of motion of the light rays. Using the conventions in Bohn et al.[14] they formulated a lens equation, they derived the redshift and the travel time of individual light rays on the celestial sphere of the observer. In this article we will extend their approach to the charged C-de Sitter metric. For this purpose the remainder of this article is structured as follows. As not all readers may be familiar with the charged C-de Sitter metric we will provide a short overview of its physical properties in Section 2. In Section 3 we will demonstrate how to solve the equations of motion. In Section 4 we will first introduce the orthonormal tetrad and show how to parameterise the light rays using the angles on the observer's celestial sphere. Then we will introduce the lens map, formulate the lens equation, and calculate the redshift and the travel time of light rays. In Section 5 we will shortly summarise our results and conclusions. Throughout the whole article we will use geometric units with $c = G = 1$. The metric signature is chosen as $(-, +, +, +)$.

2. The Charged C-de Sitter-Metric

The charged C-de Sitter metric is a solution to Einstein's electrovacuum field equations with cosmological constant. It belongs to the Plebański-Demiański family of

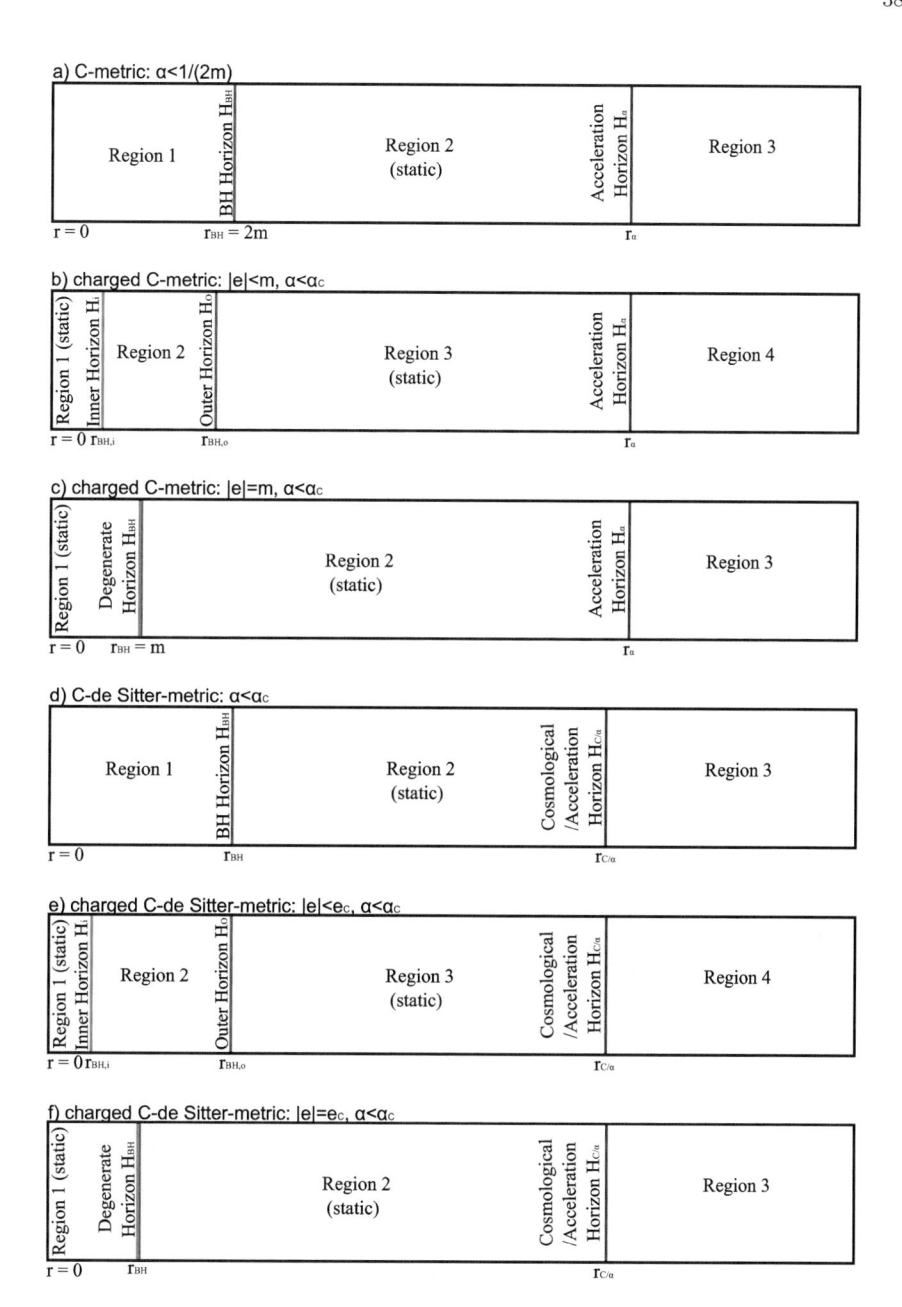

Fig. 1. Position of the curvature singularity at $r = 0$ and the coordinate singularities in a) the C-metric, the charged C-metric with b) $|e| < m$ and c) $|e| = m$, d) the C-de Sitter metric and the charged C-de Sitter metric with e) $|e| < e_C$ and f) $|e| = e_C$. Note that the angular coordinates are suppressed and other singularities are not shown.

spacetimes of Petrov type D[10] and is axisymmetric and static. The spacetime is characterised by four parameters: the mass parameter m, the electric charge e, the cosmological constant Λ, and the acceleration parameter α. Its line element reads[7]

$$g_{\mu\nu}\mathrm{d}x^\mu \mathrm{d}x^\nu = \frac{1}{\Omega(r,\vartheta)^2}\left(-Q(r)\mathrm{d}t^2 + \frac{\mathrm{d}r^2}{Q(r)} + \frac{r^2\mathrm{d}\vartheta^2}{P(\vartheta)} + r^2\sin^2\vartheta P(\vartheta)\mathrm{d}\varphi^2\right), \quad (1)$$

where

$$Q(r) = (1-\alpha^2 r^2)\left(1 - \frac{2m}{r} + \frac{e^2}{r^2}\right) - \frac{\Lambda}{3}r^2, \quad (2)$$

$$P(\vartheta) = 1 - 2\alpha m \cos\vartheta + \alpha^2 e^2 \cos^2\vartheta, \quad (3)$$

$$\Omega(r,\vartheta) = 1 - \alpha r \cos\vartheta. \quad (4)$$

When we set $\alpha = 0$ the metric reduces to the Reissner-Nordström-de Sitter family of spacetimes including the Schwarzschild metric ($e = 0$, $\Lambda = 0$), the Reissner-Nordström metric ($\Lambda = 0$), and the Schwarzschild-de Sitter metric ($e = 0$). For $e = 0$ and $\Lambda = 0$ the metric reduces to the regular C-metric. For $e = 0$ it reduces to the C-de Sitter metric and for $\Lambda = 0$ it reduces to the charged C-metric. In accordance with observations we choose $0 < m$. Theoretically the electric charge e can take any real value but because the line element (1) only contains its square we restrict it such that we have $0 \le e \le e_C$. Because we live in an expanding Universe we will assume that $0 \le \Lambda < \Lambda_C$. α can be restricted from the symmetry of the spacetime. When we replace α by $-\alpha$ and substitute $\vartheta \to \pi - \vartheta$ we see that (1) is invariant and consequently we can restrict the acceleration parameter to $0 < \alpha < \alpha_C$. Here, e_C, Λ_C and α_C are critical parameters that have to be chosen according to the desired interpretation of the spacetime. In the charged C-de Sitter metric the time coordinate t can assume any real value. In addition we choose the angular coordinates ϑ and φ such that they represent the angular coordinates on the two sphere S^2. The range of the r coordinate is determined by the singularity structure of the spacetime, in particular the singularities arising from $Q(r)$ and $\Omega(r,\vartheta)$. We will discuss these singularities and their implications for the r coordinate in the following. The spacetime admits several singularities. We start by discussing the singularities arising from $Q(r)$. In total $Q(r)$ can lead to up to five singularities in the metric. The equation $Q(r) = 0$ can lead to up to four singularities. In addition the metric has another singularity at $r = 0$. The singularity at $r = 0$ is a curvature singularity. For $e \ne 0$ the curvature singularity is timelike. Because lightlike and timelike geodesics cannot cross the curvature singularity particle motion is limited to $0 < r$. In addition the conformal factor becomes singular when $\Omega(r,\vartheta) = 0$. This singularity corresponds to conformal infinity and limits the radius coordinate r. The singularity starts at $r = 1/\alpha$ on the axis $\vartheta = 0$ and extends to $r = \infty$ for $\pi/2 \le \vartheta$. The other singularities are only coordinate singularities r_H that can be removed using appropriate coordinate transformations (for the C-metric the procedure is demonstrated in Ref. 15). In this article we restrict to black hole spacetimes and consequently all coordinate singularities with $0 < r_H$ are horizons. In general the horizon struture of each metric depends on the parameters of the spacetime. For each spacetime the critical parameters e_C, Λ_C and α_C have to be chosen such that all horizons are real and that they lead to physically meaningful black hole spacetimes. The horizon structure of the whole family of charged C-de Sitter metrics is shown in Fig. 1. Panel a) shows the horizon struture of the C-metric. The C-metric has two horizons, a black hole horizon at $r_{BH} = 2m$ and an acceleration horizon at $r_{BH} < r_\alpha = 1/\alpha$. Between the horizons the spacetime is static. In the other two regions the spacetime is non-static. Panels b) and c) show the horizon structure for the charged C-metric. The main difference to the C-metric is that the spacetime now contains an inner and an outer black hole horizon $r_{BH,i} \leq r_{BH,o} < r_\alpha$. When $e = m$ both horizons coincide and form a degenerate horizon at $r_{BH} = m$. The regions $0 < r < r_{BH,i}$ and $r_{BH,o} < r < r_\alpha$ are static. The other two regions are non-static. When we include the cosmological constant Λ (panels d) to f)) the radius coordinates of the horizons change, however, the horizon structure remains unchanged. For a more detailed discussion of the horizon structure in the C-metric we refer the interested reader to Ref. 13. In our case we always choose e_C such that $P(\vartheta)$ does not lead to singularities in the metric. Finally, the spacetime has two singularities on the axes at $\sin \vartheta = 0$. As demonstrated in Refs. 7 and 15 these singularities are conical singularites. They are associated with a deficit angle ($\vartheta = 0$) and a surplus angle ($\vartheta = \pi$). The charged C-de Sitter metric is usually interpreted such that it describes a charged accelerating black hole with cosmological constant. In its full analytic extension the spacetime describes two causally separated charged black holes accalerating away from each other. The conical singularity at $\vartheta = 0$ is commonly interpreted as a string pulling the black hole, while the conical singularity at $\vartheta = \pi$ is interpreted as a strut pushing the black hole. As demonstrated in Refs. 7 and 15 one of the conical singularities can always be removed, however, as in our previous work[13] here we will retain both singularities to show the effects of both, the string and the strut on geodesic motion.

3. Equations of Motion

In the charged C-de Sitter metric the equations of motion for light rays are fully separable. In Mino parameterisation[16] they read[8,13]

$$\frac{dt}{d\lambda} = \frac{r^2 E}{Q(r)}, \tag{5}$$

$$\left(\frac{dr}{d\lambda}\right)^2 = E^2 r^4 - r^2 Q(r) K, \tag{6}$$

$$\left(\frac{d\vartheta}{d\lambda}\right)^2 = P(\vartheta) K - \frac{L_z^2}{\sin^2 \vartheta}, \tag{7}$$

$$\frac{d\varphi}{d\lambda} = \frac{L_z}{\sin^2\vartheta P(\vartheta)}, \tag{8}$$

where the Mino parameter λ is related to the affine parameter s by

$$\frac{d\lambda}{ds} = \frac{\Omega(r,\vartheta)^2}{r^2}. \tag{9}$$

Here, the three constants of motion E, L_z and K are the energy, the angular momentum about the z axis and the Carter constant of the light ray, respectively. In this article we choose the energy E such that $dt/d\lambda > 0$. In the following we will briefly discuss the equations of motion, the turning points of the r and the ϑ motion and identify the locations of the photon sphere and the photon cone. Then we will turn to solving the equations of motion. We will derive the solutions to the equations of motion for arbitrary initial conditions $(x_i^\mu) = (x^\mu(\lambda_i)) = (t_i, r_i, \vartheta_i, \varphi_i)$ closely following the procedures described in Refs. 13 and 17. Because the main focus of this article will be to apply our results to gravitational lensing we will limit our discussion to lightlike geodesics in the region of outer communication between photon sphere and the cosmological/acceleration horizon.

3.1. *The r Motion*

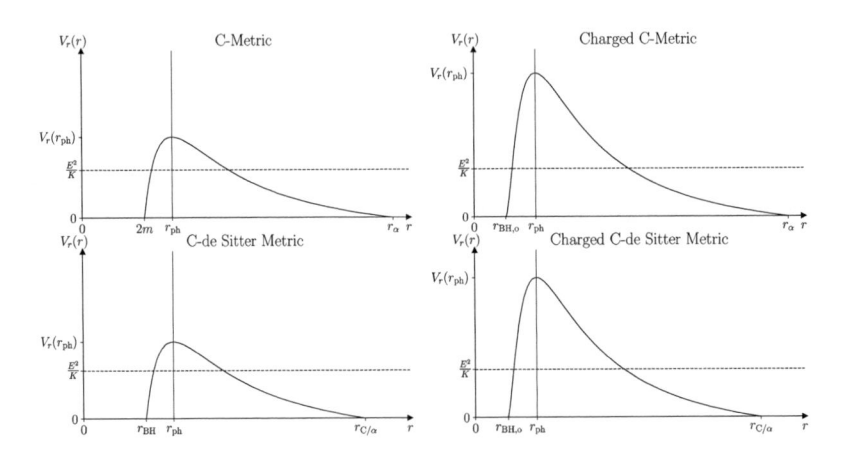

Fig. 2. Potential $V_r(r)$ of the r motion in the C-metric (top left), the charged C-metric (top right), the C-de Sitter metric (bottom left) and the charged C-de Sitter metric (bottom right) for $\Lambda = 1/(200m^2)$, $e = m$, and $\alpha = 1/(10m)$. The axes have the same scale in all four plots.

We begin with discussing the r motion. Following Ref. 13 we first rewrite (6) in terms of the potential $V_r(r)$

$$\frac{1}{r^4 K}\left(\frac{dr}{d\lambda}\right)^2 + V_r(r) = \frac{E^2}{K}, \tag{10}$$

where

$$V_r(r) = \left(\frac{1}{r^2} - \alpha^2\right)\left(1 - \frac{2m}{r} + \frac{e^2}{r^2}\right) - \frac{\Lambda}{3}. \tag{11}$$

Fig. 2 shows the potentials for the C-metric (top left), the charged C-metric (top right), the C-de Sitter metric (bottom left) and the charged C-de Sitter metric (bottom right). For all four metrics the potential has a similar structure. The most striking difference occurs close to the (outer) black hole horizon. For $e \neq 0$ the maximum of $V_r(r)$ is much higher than in the uncharged case. In addition for $\Lambda > 0$ $V_r(r)$ approaches zero at a smaller radius coordinate $r_{C/\alpha} < r_\alpha$. The maximum of the potential at $E^2/K = V_r(r_{\rm ph})$ marks the radius coordinate of an unstable photon sphere. We can calculate the radius coordinate of the photon sphere by calculating $dr/d\lambda = d^2r/d\lambda^2 = 0$. Combining both conditions leads to the determining equation

$$r^3 + \frac{1 - \alpha^2 e^2}{m\alpha^2}r^2 - \frac{3}{\alpha^2}r + \frac{2e^2}{m\alpha^2} = 0 \tag{12}$$

for the radius of the photon sphere $r_{\rm ph}$. It is remarkable that although the spherical symmetry is broken by the acceleration parameter the cosmological constant does not have any effect on the radius coordinate of the photon sphere. The roots of this equation can be analytically obtained using Cardano's method. As long as $e^2 < 1/\alpha^2$ we get three real solutions. Only the largest root lies in the region of outer communication $r_{\rm BH,o} < r < r_{C/\alpha}$ and thus marks the position of the photon sphere. When $e = 0$ the polynomial reduces to second order and $r_{\rm ph}$ is given by[12,13]

$$r_{\rm ph} = \frac{6m}{1 + \sqrt{1 + 12\alpha^2 m^2}}. \tag{13}$$

We can read from Fig. 2 that at $r_{\rm ph}$ $V_r(r_{\rm ph})$ has always a maximum and thus orbits of geodesics on the photon sphere are unstable. Here, unstable means that if the orbit of a lightlike geodesic on the photon sphere was radially infinitesimally perturbed the light ray would either fall into the black hole or escape to (conformal) infinity. Using the potential we can distinguish three different types of lightlike motion. For $E^2/K > V_r(r_{\rm ph})$ lightlike geodesics have no turning points. Here we have to distinguish between the cases $K = 0$ (we will see in Section 3.3 that these geodesics are principal null geodesics) and $K > 0$. For $E^2/K > V_r(r_{\rm ph})$ and $K = 0$ (6) was already solved in Ref. 13. In this case the solution reads:

$$r(\lambda) = \frac{r_i}{1 - i_{r_i} r_i E(\lambda - \lambda_i)}, \tag{14}$$

where $i_{r_i} = \text{sgn}\left(dr/d\lambda|_{r=r_i}\right)$. In the case $E^2/K > V_r(r_{\rm ph})$ and $K > 0$ (6) has two real and two complex conjugated roots. We label them such that $r_1 > r_2$ and $r_3 = \bar{r}_4 = R_3 + iR_4$. To solve (6) we now substitute[17,18]

$$r = \frac{r_1 \bar{R} - r_2 R + (r_1 \bar{R} + r_2 R)\cos\chi_r}{\bar{R} - R + (\bar{R} + R)\cos\chi_r}, \tag{15}$$

where
$$R = \sqrt{(R_3 - r_1)^2 + R_4^2} \quad \text{and} \quad \bar{R} = \sqrt{(R_3 - r_2)^2 + R_4^2}. \tag{16}$$

Then we follow the steps described in Appendix B of Ref. 13 and obtain the solution in terms of Jacobi's elliptic cn function. It reads

$$r(\lambda) = \frac{r_1 \bar{R} - r_2 R + (r_1 \bar{R} + r_2 R)\operatorname{cn}(a_r(\lambda - \lambda_i) + \lambda_{r_i, k_1}, k_1)}{\bar{R} - R + (\bar{R} + R)\operatorname{cn}(a_r(\lambda - \lambda_i) + \lambda_{r_i, k_1}, k_1)}, \tag{17}$$

where

$$a_r = i_{r_i}\sqrt{\left(E^2 + \left(\alpha^2 + \frac{\Lambda}{3}\right)K\right)R\bar{R}}, \quad \lambda_{r_i, k_1} = F_L(\chi_{r_i}, k_1), \tag{18}$$

$$\chi_{r_i} = \arccos\left(\frac{(r_i - r_2)R - (r_i - r_1)\bar{R}}{(r_i - r_2)R + (r_i - r_1)\bar{R}}\right), \quad k_1 = \frac{(R + \bar{R})^2 - (r_1 - r_2)^2}{4R\bar{R}}.$$

The condition $E^2/K = V_r(r_{\text{ph}})$ characterises lightlike geodesics asymptotically coming from or going to the photon sphere. In this case (6) has four real roots, two of which are equal. We label them such that $r_1 = r_2 = r_{\text{ph}} > r_3 > r_4$. In this case we substitute

$$r = r_3 + \frac{3a_{3,r}}{12y - a_{2,r}}, \tag{19}$$

where

$$a_{2,r} = 6\left(E^2 + \left(\alpha^2 + \frac{\Lambda}{3}\right)K\right)r_3^2 - 6m\alpha^2 K r_3 - (1 - \alpha^2 e^2)K, \tag{20}$$

$$a_{3,r} = 4\left(E^2 + \left(\alpha^2 + \frac{\Lambda}{3}\right)K\right)r_3^3 - 6m\alpha^2 K r_3^2 - 2(1 - \alpha^2 e^2)K r_3 + 2mK. \tag{21}$$

Then we follow the steps described in Section 3.2.3 in Ref. 13 and obtain as solution for $r(\lambda)$:

$$r(\lambda) = r_3 - \frac{(r_{\text{ph}} - r_3)(r_3 - r_4)}{r_{\text{ph}} - r_3 - (r_{\text{ph}} - r_4)\tanh^2\left(b_r + i_{r_i}\sqrt{\frac{a_{3,r}(r_{\text{ph}} - r_4)}{4(r_{\text{ph}} - r_3)(r_3 - r_4)}}(\lambda_i - \lambda)\right)}, \tag{22}$$

where

$$b_r = \operatorname{artanh}\left(\sqrt{\frac{(r_i - r_4)(r_{\text{ph}} - r_3)}{(r_i - r_3)(r_{\text{ph}} - r_4)}}\right). \tag{23}$$

All remaining lightlike geodesics have $E^2/K < V_r(r_{\text{ph}})$. These geodesics have four real roots and can pass through a turning point. Outside the photon sphere this turning point is always a minimum. For solving (6) we now label the roots such that $r_1 = r_{\min} > r_2 > r_3 > r_4$. Then we substitute[17,18]

$$r = r_2 + \frac{(r_1 - r_2)(r_2 - r_4)}{r_2 - r_4 - (r_1 - r_4)\sin^2 \chi_r}. \tag{24}$$

Again we apply the steps described in Appendix B of Ref. 13. This time we obtain the solution to (6) in terms of Jacobi's elliptic sn function

$$r(\lambda) = r_2 + \frac{(r_1 - r_2)(r_2 - r_4)}{r_2 - r_4 - (r_1 - r_4)\mathrm{sn}^2\left(c_r\left(\lambda - \lambda_i\right) + \lambda_{r_i,k_2}, k_2\right)}, \tag{25}$$

where

$$c_r = \frac{i_{r_i}}{2}\sqrt{\left(E^2 + \left(\alpha^2 + \frac{\Lambda}{3}\right)K\right)(r_1 - r_3)(r_2 - r_4)}, \quad \lambda_{r_i,k_2} = F_L(\chi_{r_i}, k_2), \tag{26}$$

$$\chi_{r_i} = \arcsin\left(\sqrt{\frac{(r_i - r_1)(r_2 - r_4)}{(r_i - r_2)(r_1 - r_4)}}\right), \quad k_2 = \frac{(r_2 - r_3)(r_1 - r_4)}{(r_1 - r_3)(r_2 - r_4)}.$$

3.2. The t Coordinate

Now we calculate the time coordinate t. The right-hand side of (5) depends only on $r(\lambda)$. Therefore, we first rewrite (5) as a differential of r. For this purpose we divide (5) by the root of (6). Then we integrate over r starting at $t(\lambda_i) = t(r_i) = t_i$. The resulting integral reads

$$t(\lambda) = t_i + \int_{r_i...}^{...r(\lambda)} \frac{Er'^2 dr'}{Q(r')\sqrt{E^2 r'^4 - r'^2 Q(r') K}}. \tag{27}$$

Here, we have to choose the sign of the root in accordance with the r motion and the dots in the limits of the integration indicate that we have to split the integral at the turning points. The procedure to integrate (27) is straight forward. We have to distinguish the same types of motion as for $r(\lambda)$ in Section 3.1. First we perform a partial fraction decomposition of $r'^2/Q(r')$. Then we follow the procedure described in Refs. 13 and 17 to express (27) in terms of elementary functions and elliptic integrals. Note that some of the elliptic integrals cannot immediately be expressed in form of elementary functions and elliptic integrals of first, second and third kind. However, we can easily rewrite them using the procedures described in Appendix B in Ref. 17 and Appendix A in Ref. 13.

3.3. The ϑ Motion

Again we start by rewriting (7) in terms of the potential $V_\vartheta(\vartheta)$

$$\frac{\sin^2 \vartheta}{K}\left(\frac{d\vartheta}{d\lambda}\right)^2 + V_\vartheta(\vartheta) = -\frac{L_z^2}{K}, \tag{28}$$

where

$$V_\vartheta(\vartheta) = -\sin^2\vartheta(1 - 2\alpha m\cos\vartheta + \alpha^2 e^2 \cos^2\vartheta). \tag{29}$$

Fig. 3 shows the potentials $V_\vartheta(\vartheta)$ of the ϑ motion for the C-(de Sitter) metric (left) and the charged C-(de Sitter) metric (right). Although in the right plot we set $e = m$ the differences are invisibly small. The potential has always a minimum at a

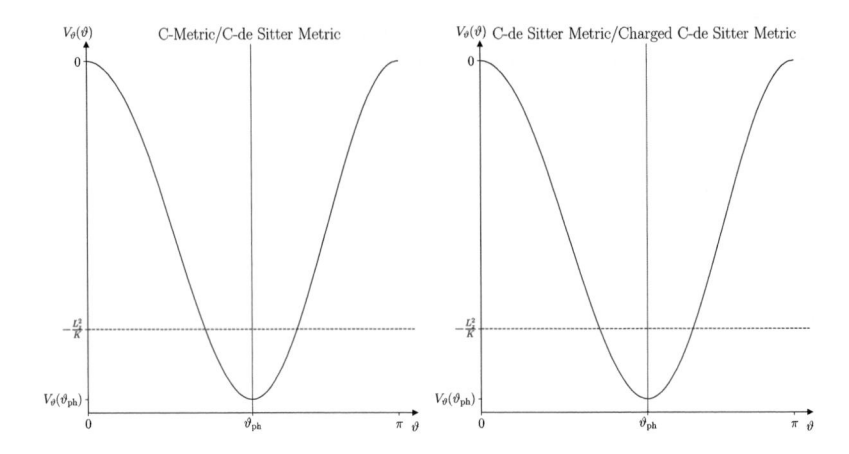

Fig. 3. Potential $V_\vartheta(\vartheta)$ of the ϑ motion in the C-metric/C-de Sitter metric (left) and the charged C-metric/C-de Sitter metric (right) for $e = m$ and $\alpha = 1/(10m)$. The axes have the same scale in both plots.

single value ϑ. At this minimum we have $d\vartheta/d\lambda = d^2\vartheta/d\lambda^2 = 0$. Combining both conditions leads to the determining equation

$$\cos^3 \vartheta - \frac{3m}{2\alpha e^2} \cos^2 \vartheta + \frac{1 - \alpha^2 e^2}{2\alpha^2 e^2} \cos \vartheta + \frac{m}{2\alpha e^2} = 0. \tag{30}$$

We determine the roots of this equation using Cardano's method. Within the permissible range $0 \leq \vartheta \leq \pi$ the equation has exactly one real root $\vartheta_{\rm ph}$. This is the photon cone of the charged C-(de Sitter) metric. Note that we cannot determine the limits $e \to 0$ or $\alpha \to 0$ from the calculated $\vartheta_{\rm ph}$ directly. When we approach these limits we see that for $e \to 0$ $\vartheta_{\rm ph}$ reduces to[12,13]

$$\vartheta_{\rm ph} = \arccos\left(\frac{-2\alpha m}{1 + \sqrt{1 + 12\alpha^2 m^2}}\right) \tag{31}$$

and for $\alpha \to 0$ it reduces to $\vartheta_{\rm ph} = \pi/2$. The photon cone is unstable. Here unstable means that when light rays on the photon cone are infinitesimally perturbed in ϑ direction they will begin to oscillate between a minimum $\vartheta_{\min}$ and a maximum $\vartheta_{\max}$. Based on the potential $V_\vartheta(\vartheta)$ we can distinguish two different types of motion. From (7) we can immediately read that we have $L_z = 0$ when $K = 0$ and the right-hand side of (7) vanishes. Because $L_z = 0$ implies $d\varphi/d\lambda = 0$ these are the already in Section 3.1 mentioned principal null geodesics. Also for lightlike geodesics on the photon cone ($-L_z^2/K = V_\vartheta(\vartheta_{\rm ph})$) the right-hand side of (7) vanishes because we have two coinciding roots at $x = \cos\vartheta_{\rm ph}$. Thus for principal null geodesics and lightlike geodesics on the photon cone the solution to (7) reads $\vartheta(\lambda) = \vartheta_i$. For all other lightlike geodesics we have $-L_z^2/K \neq V_\vartheta(\vartheta_{\rm ph})$. These geodesics oscillate between a minimum $\vartheta_{\min}$ and a maximum $\vartheta_{\max}$ and each geodesic can potentially have arbitrary many turning points. In this case we first rewrite (7) in terms of

$x = \cos\vartheta$. It is easy to see that in the new parameterisation (7) reduces to a polynomial of third order in x when $e = 0$. This case was already treated in Ref. 13 and thus we do not reproduce it here. For $e \neq 0$ we always have two turning points, however, depending on the choice of L_z and K the right-hand side of (7) has two different root structures. In the first case two of the roots are real. We label them such that $x_2 = \cos\vartheta_{\max} < x_1 = \cos\vartheta_{\min}$. The other two roots are complex conjugated and we label them as $x_3 = \bar{x}_4 = X_3 + iX_4$. As first step to solve (7) we now substitute[18]

$$x = \frac{x_1\bar{X} + x_2 X + (x_1\bar{X} - x_2 X)\cos\chi_\vartheta}{\bar{X} + X + (\bar{X} - X)\cos\chi_\vartheta}, \qquad (32)$$

where X and $\bar{X}$ are given by (16). In the second step we again follow the steps described in Appendix B of Ref. 13. We obtain $\vartheta(\lambda)$ in terms of Jacobi's elliptic cn function. It reads

$$\vartheta(\lambda) = \arccos\left(\frac{x_1\bar{X} + x_2 X + (x_1\bar{X} - x_2 X)\mathrm{cn}\left(a_\vartheta(\lambda - \lambda_i) + \lambda_{\vartheta_i,k_3}, k_3\right)}{\bar{X} + X + (\bar{X} - X)\mathrm{cn}\left(a_\vartheta(\lambda - \lambda_i) + \lambda_{\vartheta_i,k_3}, k_3\right)}\right), \qquad (33)$$

where $i_{\vartheta_i} = \mathrm{sgn}\left(\mathrm{d}\vartheta/\mathrm{d}\lambda|_{\vartheta=\vartheta_i}\right)$ and

$$a_\vartheta = i_{\vartheta_i}\sqrt{\alpha^2 e^2 K X\bar{X}}, \qquad \lambda_{\vartheta_i,k_3} = F_L(\chi_{\vartheta_i}, k_3), \qquad (34)$$

$$\chi_{\vartheta_i} = \arccos\left(\frac{(\cos\vartheta_i - x_1)\bar{X} + (\cos\vartheta_i - x_2)X}{(x_1 - \cos\vartheta_i)\bar{X} + (\cos\vartheta_i - x_2)X}\right), \quad k_3 = \frac{(x_1 - x_2)^2 - (X - \bar{X})^2}{4X\bar{X}}.$$

In the second case all four roots are real and we label them such that $x_4 = \cos\vartheta_{\max} < x_3 = \cos\vartheta_{\min} < x_2 < x_1$. In this case we substitute[18]

$$x = x_1 - \frac{(x_1 - x_3)(x_1 - x_4)}{x_1 - x_3 + (x_3 - x_4)\sin^2\chi_\vartheta}. \qquad (35)$$

We again follow the steps described in Appendix B of Ref. 13. This time we obtain $\vartheta(\lambda)$ in terms of Jacobi's elliptic sn function

$$\vartheta(\lambda) = \arccos\left(x_1 - \frac{(x_1 - x_3)(x_1 - x_4)}{x_1 - x_3 + (x_3 - x_4)\mathrm{sn}^2\left(b_\vartheta(\lambda_i - \lambda) + \lambda_{\vartheta_i,k_4}, k_4\right)}\right), \qquad (36)$$

where

$$b_\vartheta = \frac{i_{\vartheta_i}}{2}\sqrt{\alpha^2 e^2 K(x_1 - x_3)(x_2 - x_4)}, \qquad \lambda_{\vartheta_i,k_4} = F_L(\chi_{\vartheta_i}, k_4) \qquad (37)$$

$$\chi_{\vartheta_i} = \arcsin\left(\sqrt{\frac{(\cos\vartheta_i - x_4)(x_1 - x_3)}{(x_1 - \cos\vartheta_i)(x_3 - x_4)}}\right), \quad k_4 = \frac{(x_1 - x_2)(x_3 - x_4)}{(x_1 - x_3)(x_2 - x_4)}.$$

3.4. The φ Motion

The φ motion is governed by (8). We immediately read that for $L_z = 0$ the right-hand side vanishes. For $K = 0$ these are the principal null geodesics. In this case we obtain the solution to (8) as $\varphi(\lambda) = \varphi_i$. If $K \neq 0$ these are geodesics crossing the axes. What happens to these geodesics now depends on whether we assume that the string and the strut are opaque or transparent. In the former case the lightlike geodesics terminate at the string and we observe it as a black line blocking out all light emitted by sources located behind it. In the latter case the lightlike geodesics pass through the string. To see what happens when a lightlike geodesic passes through the axes we consider a series of lightlike geodesics continually approaching the axes for $L_z > 0$ and $L_z < 0$.[13] We observe that for $L_z > 0$ and $L_z < 0$ the φ coordinate has different limits. Hence geodesics crossing the axes have two different continuations and the φ coordinate is not continuous.

Next we turn to lightlike geodesics with a double root at $x = \cos\vartheta_{\text{ph}}$ ($-L_z^2/K = V_\vartheta(\vartheta_{\text{ph}})$). These are lightlike geodesics on the photon cone with $\vartheta(\lambda) = \vartheta_{\text{ph}}$. In this case the right-hand side of (8) is constant and the solution $\varphi(\lambda)$ reads

$$\varphi(\lambda) = \varphi_i + \frac{L_z(\lambda - \lambda_i)}{\sin^2\vartheta_{\text{ph}} P(\vartheta_{\text{ph}})}. \tag{38}$$

Last we turn to lightlike geodesics with $-L_z^2/K \neq V_\vartheta(\vartheta_{\text{ph}})$. In this case we want to express $\varphi(\lambda)$ in terms of elementary functions and elliptic integrals. For this purpose we first substitute $x = \cos\vartheta$ in (7) and (8). Then we divide (8) by the root of (7) and integrate. Now $\varphi(\lambda)$ reads

$$\varphi(\lambda) = \varphi_i + \int_{\cos\vartheta_i\ldots}^{\ldots \cos\vartheta(\lambda)} \frac{L_z dx'}{(1-x'^2)P(x')\sqrt{(1-x'^2)P(x')K - L_z^2}}. \tag{39}$$

Here, we have to choose the sign of the root such that it corresponds to the sign of the $\cos\vartheta$ motion and the dots in the limits indicate that we have to split the integral at the turning points. Again we rewrite the elliptic integral using elementary functions and the canonical forms of the elliptic integrals. For this purpose we now perform a partial fracion decomposition of $(1-x^2)^{-1}P(x)^{-1}$. Then we use (41) in Ref. 13 and (32) and (35) to rewrite (39) in terms of elementary functions and elliptic integrals of first, second and third kind. Note that we again encounter elliptic integrals which do not immediately have a canonical form. Again we rewrite them using the procedures described in Appendix B in Ref. 17 and Appendix A in Ref. 13 (although here we have $n^2/(n^2-1) < 1$ and not $1 < n^2/(n^2-1)$ the basic integration procedure is the same).

4. Gravitational Lensing

4.1. Celestial Sphere

In astronomy the position of a light source on the sky is identified using latitude and longitude coordinates. For this purpose astronomers fix the main target of their observation at the centre of their image and measure the position of all other objects relative to the centre. In our discussion of gravitational lensing in the charged C-de Sitter metric we follow this approach. For this purpose we first fix an observer at coordinates $(x_O^\mu) = (t_O, r_O, \vartheta_O, \varphi_O)$ in the region of outer communication between photon sphere and cosmological/acceleration horizon. Then we choose the black hole as main target of our observation and introduce an orthonormal tetrad following Refs. 8 and 13:

$$e_0 = \left.\frac{\Omega(r,\vartheta)}{\sqrt{Q(r)}}\partial_t\right|_{(x_O^\mu)}, \quad e_1 = \left.\frac{\Omega(r,\vartheta)\sqrt{P(\vartheta)}}{r}\partial_\vartheta\right|_{(x_O^\mu)}, \quad (40)$$

$$e_2 = -\left.\frac{\Omega(r,\vartheta)}{r\sin\vartheta\sqrt{P(\vartheta)}}\partial_\varphi\right|_{(x_O^\mu)}, \quad e_3 = -\left.\Omega(r,\vartheta)\sqrt{Q(r)}\partial_r\right|_{(x_O^\mu)}.$$

We will call the angles on the celestial sphere surrounding the observer Σ (latitude) and Ψ (longitude). The angle Σ is measured from the axis along e_3 connecting lens and observer and the angle Ψ is measured in the direction of e_2 from the axis along the direction of e_1.

Before we can investigate gravitational lensing in the charged C-de Sitter metric we first have to derive the relations between the constants of motion E, L_z and K and the angles on the observer's celestial sphere Σ and Ψ. For this purpose we consider a lightlike geodesic ending at the position of the observer. Now we first write down the tangent vector to this geodesic. It reads

$$\frac{d\eta}{d\lambda} = \frac{dt}{d\lambda}\partial_t + \frac{dr}{d\lambda}\partial_r + \frac{d\vartheta}{d\lambda}\partial_\vartheta + \frac{d\varphi}{d\lambda}\partial_\varphi. \quad (41)$$

At the position of the observer we can also express the tangent vector of the geodesic by the angles on the observer's celestial sphere and the tetrad vectors e_0, e_1, e_2 and e_3

$$\frac{d\eta}{d\lambda} = \sigma\left(-e_0 + \sin\Sigma\cos\Psi e_1 + \sin\Sigma\sin\Psi e_2 + \cos\Sigma e_3\right), \quad (42)$$

where σ is a normalisation constant

$$\sigma = g\left(\frac{d\eta}{d\lambda}, e_0\right). \quad (43)$$

In our convention we have $E > 0$ and thus σ has to be negative. Because the Mino parameter λ is defined up to an affine transformation without loss of generality we can choose $\sigma = -r_O^2/\Omega(r_O,\vartheta_O)^2$.[13] Now we insert σ in (42) and (43). Then a comparison of the coefficients of (41) and (42) leads to[13]

$$E = \frac{\sqrt{Q(r_O)}}{\Omega(r_O,\vartheta_O)}, \quad L_z = \frac{r_O\sqrt{P(\vartheta_O)}\sin\vartheta_O\sin\Sigma\sin\Psi}{\Omega(r_O,\vartheta_O)}, \quad K = \frac{r_O^2\sin^2\Sigma}{\Omega(r_O,\vartheta_O)^2}. \quad (44)$$

4.2. Angular Radius of the Photon Sphere

The shadow of a black hole is a higly idealised concept. It is constructed as follows. First we place an observer in the region of outer communication between photon sphere and cosmological/acceleration horizon. Then we distribute light sources everywhere except between observer and the black hole. Therefore the former region is associated with brightness on the observer's sky while the latter is associated with darkness. Now we shoot back light rays exactly on the boundary between these areas of brightness and darkness. These are geodesics asymptotically going to the photon sphere. They have the same constants of motion as light rays on the photon sphere and thus a double root at $r_{\rm ph}$. We now use this fact to calculate the angular radius of the shadow. For this purpose we first insert (44) in (6). Then we employ that $dr/d\lambda|_{r=r_{\rm ph}} = 0$. Now we solve for Σ and get as angular radius of the shadow[13]

$$\Sigma_{\rm ph} = \arcsin\left(\frac{r_{\rm ph}}{r_O}\sqrt{\frac{Q(r_O)}{Q(r_{\rm ph})}}\right). \qquad (45)$$

4.3. Lens Map

The lens map or lens equation maps images on the observer's sky back to the source surface. This article is an extension of the work presented in Ref. 13 and therefore we will closely follow their definition of the lens map. To set up the lens map we first distribute light sources on a sphere with radius $r_O < r_L$ in the region of outer communication. Then we shoot light rays backwards in time from the position of the observer (x_O^μ). Some of the light rays, but not all, will intersect with the sphere of light sources. These geodesics form a map from the celestial sphere of the observer to the sphere of light sources

$$(\Sigma, \Psi) \to (\vartheta_L(\Sigma, \Psi), \varphi_L(\Sigma, \Psi)). \qquad (46)$$

This is our lens equation. Now we have to calculate $\vartheta_L(\Sigma, \Psi)$ and $\varphi_L(\Sigma, \Psi)$ to obtain the lens map for the charged C-de Sitter metric. For this purpose we set $(x_i^\mu) = (x_O^\mu)$ and insert (44) into the solutions of the equations of motion derived in Section 3. Due to the symmetry of the charged C-de Sitter metric we can choose t_O and φ_O arbitrarily. Similarly λ is only defined up to an affine transformation. Therefore, to ease all following calculations we choose them such that $\lambda_O = 0$, $t_O = 0$ and $\varphi_O = 0$.

As first step towards calculating $\vartheta_L(\Sigma, \Psi)$ and $\varphi_L(\Sigma, \Psi)$ we calculate the Mino parameter $\lambda_L < \lambda_O$

$$\lambda_L = \int_{r_O\ldots}^{\ldots r_L} \frac{\Omega(r_O, \vartheta_O) dr'}{\sqrt{Q(r_O) r'^4 - r_O^2 \sin^2 \Sigma r'^2 Q(r')}}. \qquad (47)$$

Again for lightlike geodesics passing through a turning point we have to split the integral and choose the sign of the root in the denominator in agreement with the r motion. Now we insert λ_L in the appropriate solution for $\vartheta(\lambda)$ in Section 3.3 and obtain $\vartheta_L(\Sigma, \Psi)$. Next we count the number of turning points n of the ϑ motion. For this purpose we calculate the Mino parameter up to the first turning point of the ϑ motion λ_0. In the next step we calculate the difference of the Mino parameter between two subsequent turning points of the ϑ motion $\Delta\lambda$. Now we count how many turning points occur while $\lambda_L < \lambda_n = \lambda_0 + n\Delta\lambda$. Finally we calculate $\varphi_L(\Sigma, \Psi)$ from (39) as described in Section 3.4.

C-Metric	Charged C-Metric
C-de Sitter Metric	Charged C-de Sitter Metric

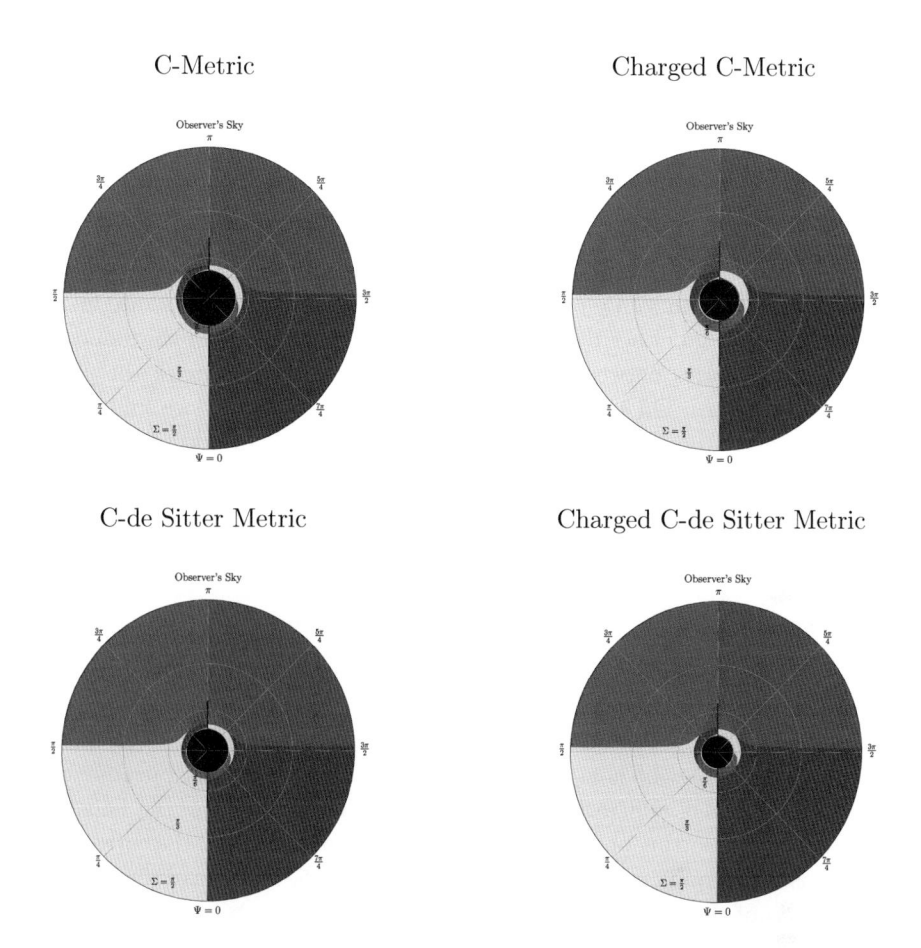

Fig. 4. Lens equation for the C-metric[13] (top left), the charged C-metric (top right), the C-de Sitter metric (bottom left) and the charged C-de Sitter metric (bottom right) for $\Lambda = 1/(200m^2)$, $e = m$ and $\alpha = 1/(10m)$. The observer is located at $r_O = 8m$, $\vartheta_O = \pi/2$ and the sphere of light sources is located at $r_L = 9m$. The colour convention follows Refs. 13 and 14 and is as follows: $0 \leq \vartheta_L \leq \frac{\pi}{2}$: red/green; $\frac{\pi}{2} < \vartheta_L \leq \pi$: yellow/blue $0 \leq \varphi_L < \pi$: green/blue; $\pi \leq \varphi_L < 2\pi$: red/yellow. The black lines at $\Psi = 0$ and $\Psi = \pi$ mark light rays that cross the axes at least once.

Fig. 4 shows plots of the lens equation in stereographic projection for the C-metric (top left), the charged C-metric (top right), the C-de Sitter metric (bottom left) and the charged C-de Sitter metric (bottom right) for $\Lambda = 1/(200m^2)$, $e = m$ and $\alpha = 1/(10m)$. The observer is located at $r_O = 8m$ and $\vartheta_O = \pi/2$. The sphere of light sources is located at $r_L = 9m$. The black lines at $\Psi = 0$ and $\Psi = \pi$ mark lightlike geodesics that cross the string or the strut at least once. The black circle in the centre of each image is the shadow of the black hole. The images clearly show that the angular radius Σ_{ph} of the shadow decreases when $0 < \Lambda$ and $0 < e$. All four images basically show the same features up to a scaling. The symmetry with respect to $\Psi = \pi/2$ and $\Psi = 3\pi/2$ is clearly broken. Thus in all four cases light rays ending parallel to the surface $\vartheta = \pi/2$ generally come from light sources not located at $\vartheta = \pi/2$. However, the shape of the features shown in the images is clearly symmetric with respect to the line marked by $\Psi = 0$ and $\Psi = \pi$. On the right side of the line of symmetry at the outer boundary of each image we first have a region coloured in blue and green. In this region we find images where the covered angle $0 < \Delta\varphi < \pi$. These are images of first order. Adjacent to these images, closer to the shadow we find a region coloured in yellow and red. In this region we find images for which the light ray covered the angle $\pi < \Delta\varphi < 2\pi$. These are images of second order. If we go closer to the shadow we also find images of third and fourth order. The boundaries between the images of different orders mark the positions of the critical curves. On the left side of the line of symmetry we find the same features, however, the ordering of the colours is reversed. In addition we observe that at $\Psi = \pi$ images of second order already occur further away from the shadow than for $\Psi = 0$. This implies that light rays passing close to the string cover the same angle $\Delta\varphi$ faster than light rays passing close to the strut.

4.4. Redshift

The redshift z of a light ray relates its energy at the time of emission by a light source to its energy at the position at which it is detected by an observer. It is directly accessible to observation via the frequency shift of atomic or molecular absorption lines. We will now construct redshift maps. For this purpose we will use the same settings and results we obtained from constructing the lens map in Section 4.3. In this setting observer and light source are static and the corresponding general redshift formula can be found in Ref. 19, pp. 45. After inserting the metric coefficients g_{tt} of the charged C-de Sitter metric it reads[13]

$$z = \sqrt{\frac{g_{tt}|_{x_O}}{g_{tt}|_{x_L}}} - 1 = \sqrt{\frac{Q(r_O)}{Q(r_L)} \frac{\Omega(r_L, \vartheta_L(\Sigma, \Psi))}{\Omega(r_O, \vartheta_O)}} - 1. \qquad (48)$$

Fig. 5 shows plots of the redshift maps for the same observer-source geometry as for the lens maps in Fig. 4 In all four plots the outer region is dominated by redshifts. The redshift has two maxima around $\Psi = \pi$ and at $\Psi = 0$ (close to the shadow). In addition in all images we observe a region of blueshifts centered around $\Psi = 0$. Another crescent shaped region of blueshifts can be found at $\Psi = \pi$ close to the shadow. What are now the effects of the cosmological constant Λ and the electric charge e? Comparing the images with $\Lambda = 0$ in the upper row with the images with $\Lambda = 1/(200m^2)$ in the lower row shows that when we turn on the cosmological constant the redshift range shifts from $-1 < z < 2$ to $-0.8 < z < 6$, respectively. The two blueshift areas move to lower latitudes closer to the centre of the shadow. In addition the fraction of the images covered by blueshifts decreases. The effects of the electric charge e are less strongly pronounced. When we compare the images on the left ($e = 0$) to the images on the right ($e = m$) we observe that in the top row the areas with blueshift move to slightly lower latitudes while they still seem

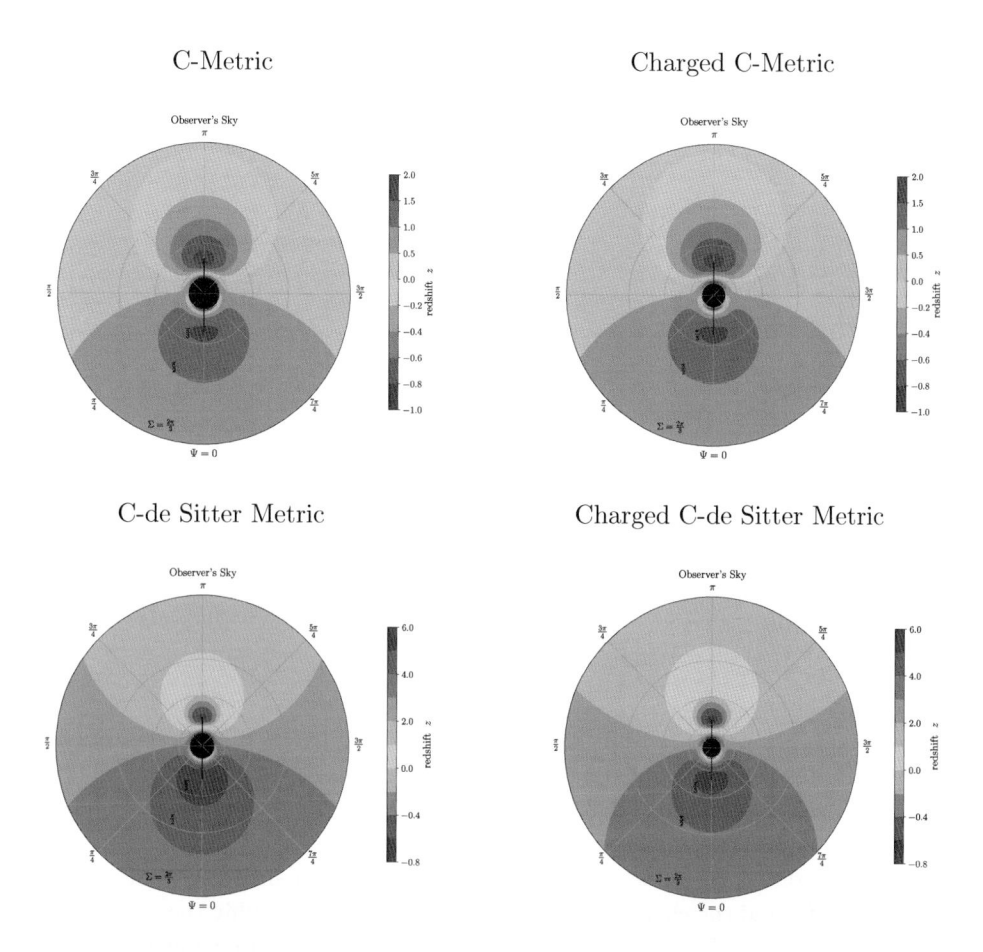

Fig. 5. Redshift maps for the C-metric[13] (top left), the charged C-metric (top right), the C-de Sitter metric (bottom left) and the charged C-de Sitter metric (bottom right) for $\Lambda = 1/(200m^2)$, $e = m$ and $\alpha = 1/(10m)$. The observer is located at $r_O = 8m$, $\vartheta_O = \pi/2$ and the sphere of light sources is located at $r_L = 9m$. The black lines at $\Psi = 0$ and $\Psi = \pi$ mark light rays that cross the axes at least once.

to cover roughly the same fraction of the image. However, comparing both images in the lower row indicates that in the presence of a cosmological constant turning on the electric charge leads to an increase of the fraction of the image covered by blueshifts. In addition the areas of blueshifts shift to lower latitudes but appear to be located at angular distances further away from the shadow.

4.5. *Travel Time*

The travel time $T = t_O - t_L$ measures in terms of the time coordinate t the elapsed time between the emission of a light ray by a source at a time t_L and the detecion of the same light ray by an observer at the time t_O. We obtain the travel time integral

| C-Metric/Charged C-Metric | C-de Sitter Metric/Charged C-de Sitter Metric |

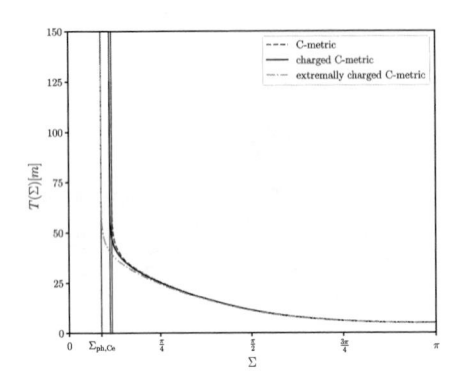

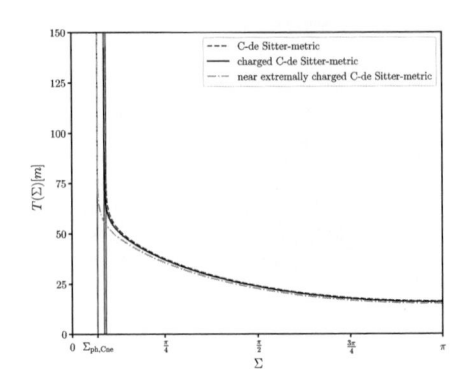

Fig. 6. Travel time $T(\Sigma)$ for the C-metric and the charged C-metric (left), and the C-de Sitter metric and the charged C-de Sitter metric (right) for $\Lambda = 1/(200m^2)$, $e = m$ in the extremal and near extremal case, otherwise $e = m/2$ and $\alpha = 1/(10m)$. The observer is located at $r_O = 8m$ and the sphere of light sources is located at $r_L = 9m$. $\Sigma_{\text{ph,Ce}}$ and $\Sigma_{\text{ph,Cne}}$ mark the position of the angular radius of the shadow on the observer's celestial sphere for the extremally charged C-metric and the near extremally charged C-de Sitter metric, respectively.

by inserting (44) and $t_O = 0$ in (27). We evaluate the travel time as described in Section 3.2. Fig. 6 shows the travel time for the (charged) C-metric (left) and the (charged) C-de Sitter metric (right) for $\Lambda = 1/(200m^2)$, $e = m/2$ in the regular case, $e = m$ in the (near) extremal case and $\alpha = 1/(10m)$. The observer is located at $r_O = 8m$ and the light source is located at $r_L = 9m$. The left plot shows that for $\Sigma > \pi/2$ in the C-metric and the charged C-metric the travel time is roughly the same. When we turn on the cosmological constant this drastically changes. In comparison to the (charged) C-metric the travel time gets significantly longer. However, turning on the electric charge in presence of a positive cosmological constant leads to a decrease of the travel time. In addition both plots indicate that for $e = m/2$ the travel time close to Σ_{ph} is slightly shorter than for $e = 0$ while it is significantly longer for $e = m$.

5. Summary and Implications for Observations

In this article we extended the work presented for the C-metric in Ref. 13 to the charged C-de Sitter metrics. In the first part we discussed and solved the equations of motion using elementary as well as elliptic functions and ellitpic integrals. In the second part we used the derived analytical solutions to investigate gravitational lensing in the charged C-de Sitter metrics.

How can we now use these results in combination with observational data to distinguish between the different black hole spacetimes and in particular to measure the electric charge of a black hole?

In the charged C-de Sitter metrics the shape of the shadow is always circular. Its angular radius decreases with increasing Λ, e and α. However, because the distance between the observer on Earth and the black hole lens is not a priori known it alone cannot be used to determine the nature of the black hole. The length of the travel time in particular close to the shadow is more characteristic for each spacetime. Unfortunately in real astrophysical settings (multiple imaging systems) we can only measure travel time differences leading to similar ambiguities as for the shadow. However, the charged C-de Sitter spacetimes also admit two very characteristic lensing features that distinguish them from their non-accelerating counterparts ($\alpha = 0$). The first characteristic is the breaking of symmetry with respect to the equatorial plane on the celestial sphere of the observer in the lens maps. Here, the most salient feature was the observation that images of second order occur at larger (lower) angular distance from the shadow close to the string (strut). The second characteristic is that the redshift z is a function of the coordinates on the observer's celestial sphere. The breaking of symmetry can be tested by observing multiple images from the same light source gravitationally lensed by a black hole. In such a system we can measure the position of the images on the celestial sphere of the observer relative to the lens and then compare it with theoretical predictions. Similarly although our construction of the redshift map is highly idealised we may be able to find astrophysical systems similar to this configuration. In such a system, we can measure the redshift of known emission lines and construct a partial redshift map to determine if it is a function of the coordinates on the observer's celestial sphere. Observing the symmetry breaking and showing that the measured redshift is a function on the observer's celestial sphere tells us with high certainty that the observed black hole is accelerating and can be described by one of the charged C-de Sitter metrics. However, due to the ambiguity introduced by the a-priori unknown distance between observer and black hole lens we cannot use these measurements alone to determine Λ, e and α. Therefore, to correctly identify the nature of the spacetime describing the black hole we observe, and having the chance to accurately measure the mass parameter m, the cosmological constant Λ, the electric charge e and the acceleration parameter α we need to combine high accuracy measurements of the angular diameter of the shadow, the redshift function on the observer's celestial sphere and of the position of and the travel time differences between two or more multiple images from the same source. Unfortunately even with very high accuracy observations for most black holes the electric charge e is likely to be far to low to be measured and one may only be able to estimate an upper limit.

Acknowledgments

I would like to thank Volker Perlick for the helpful discussions. I acknowledge financial support from QuantumFrontiers. I also acknowledge support from Deutsche Forschungsgemeinschaft within the Research Training Group 1620 Models of Gravity.

References

1. J. M. Corral-Santana, J. Casares, T. Muñoz-Darias, F. E. Bauer, I. G. Martínez-Pais and D. M. Russell, BlackCAT: A catalogue of stellar-mass black holes in X-ray transients, *Astron. Astrophys.* **587**, p. A61 (2016).
2. R. Abbott et al., Population Properties of Compact Objects from the Second LIGO–Virgo Gravitational-Wave Transient Catalog, *Astrophys. J. Lett.* **913**, p. L7 (2021).
3. K. Gültekin, E. M. Cackett, J. M. Miller, T. Di Matteo, S. Markoff and D. O. Richstone, A CHANDRA Survey of Supermassive Black Holes with Dynamical Mass Measurements, *Astrophys. J.* **749**, p. 129 (2012).
4. GRAVITY Collaboration, Detection of the gravitational redshift in the orbit of the star S2 near the Galactic centre massive black hole, *Astron. Astrophys.* **615**, p. L15 (2018).
5. The Event Horizon Telescope Collaboration, First M87 Event Horizon Telescope Results. I. The Shadow of the Supermassive Black Hole, *Astrophys. J. Lett.* **875**, p. L1 (2019).
6. E. Castellanos, J. C. Degollado, C. Lämmerzahl, A. Macías and V. Perlick, Bose-Einstein condensates in charged black–hole spacetimes, *JCAP* **2018**, p. 043 (2018).
7. J. B. Griffiths and J. Podolský, *Exact Space-Times in Einstein's General Relativity* (Cambridge University Press, Cambridge, 2009).
8. A. Grenzebach, V. Perlick and C. Lämmerzahl, Photon regions and shadows of accelerated black holes, *Int. J. of Mod. Phys. D* **24**, p. 1542024 (2015).
9. A. Grenzebach, *The Shadow of Black Holes*, Springer Briefs in Physics, Springer Briefs in Physics (Springer, Heidelberg, 2016).
10. J. F. Plebanski and M. Demianski, Rotating, Charged, and Uniformly Accelerating Mass in General Relativity, *Ann. Phys. (N. Y.)* **98**, 98 (1976).
11. M. Sharif and S. Iftikhar, Equatorial gravitational lensing by accelerating and rotating black hole with NUT parameter, *Astrophys. Space Sci.* **361**, p. 36 (2016).
12. M. Alrais Alawadi, D. Batic and M. Nowakowski, Light bending in a two black hole metric, *Class. Quantum Grav.* **38**, p. 045003 (2021).
13. T. C. Frost and V. Perlick, Lightlike geodesics and gravitational lensing in the spacetime of an accelerating black hole, *Class. Quantum Grav.* **38**, p. 085016 (2021).
14. A. Bohn, W. Throwe, F. Hébert, K. Henriksson, D. Bunandar, M. A. Scheel and N. W. Taylor, What does a binary black hole merger look like?, *Class. Quantum Grav.* **32**, p. 065002 (2015).
15. J. B. Griffiths, P. Krtouš and J. Podolský, Interpreting the C-metric, *Class. Quantum Grav.* **23**, 6745 (2006).
16. Y. Mino, Perturbative approach to an orbital evolution around a supermassive black hole, *Phys. Rev. D* **67**, p. 084027 (2003).
17. S. E. Gralla and A. Lupsasca, Null geodesics of the Kerr exterior, *Phys. Rev. D* **101**, p. 044032 (2020).
18. H. Hancock, *Elliptic Integrals*, Mathematical Monographs, 1st edn. (New York John Wiley & Sons, 1917).
19. N. Straumann, *General Relativity*, Graduate Texts in Physics, Graduate Texts in Physics, 2 edn. (Springer, Heidelberg, 2013).

A manmade experiment aimed to clarify the gravity law in the Solar system

Alexander P. Yefremov* and Alexandra A. Vorobyeva†

Institute of Gravitation and Cosmology, RUDN University,
Miklukho-Maklay str. 6, Moscow, Russia, 117198
*E-mail: efremov-ap@rudn.ru
†E-mail: vorobyeva-aa@rudn.ru
www.rudn.ru

Ultra-sensitivity of a planet's gravity assist to changes of the test-body impact parameter prompts a space experiment testing the nature of the gravitational field in the Solar system. The Sun, Earth and Venus serve as the space lab with a primitive space probe (space ball) as a test body moving on a ballistic trajectory from the Earth to Venus (rendering GA) and backwards to the Earth's orbit. We explain why in Newton and Einstein gravity, the probe's final positions (reached at the same time) may differ greatly; an Earth's observer can measure the gap.

Keywords: Gravitation; General Relativity; Gravity assist.

Introduction

Recent experiments supporting validity of GR, in our opinion, have at least two weak features. First, we are, in fact, dealing with isolated observations of very rare natural phenomena, mostly it is motion and merging of some massive objects. Second, these objects are very far from the observer. If binary pulsars are observed at distances of "only" 10 thousand light-years, then the sources of the gravitational radiation is determined at about 1.3 billion light-years. So, in fact we examine the past.

This seems to violate the basic principles of an experiment: possibility to repeated it and to deal with physical laws "valid here and now". But it is not the case yet, therefore, the claims about the absolute acceptability of Einstein's theory of gravity are hardly convincing enough.

Well, we understand that a repeatable experiment testing very small GR effects in the near space (in the Solar system) is a very challenging task.

In this presentation we will try to demonstrate that such an experiment (and a series of experiments) aimed to specify the law of the Sun's gravity with good accuracy is quite possible.

The Gravity Assist Maneuver

The main idea of the experiment is to use the so-called gravity assist maneuver of a space probe near a close planet.[1–3]

Reading papers on the space missions (where the gravity assist has become a habitual instrument) we paid attention at a great precision of the impact parameter value (or value of the close parameter — pericenter, the shortest distance between the planet rendering the assistance and a spacecraft). On the Solar system scale of hundred million kilometers, the impact parameter is normally precalculated with the accuracy of one kilometer.

This precision should reflect a great sensibility of results of the gravity assist maneuver to the pericenter value; small deflection must entail great trouble for the mission. However, we could find no sensible information about the gravity-assist sensitivity function. So, we had to determine it ourselves.

The Standard Flight

At first, we designed a scheme of a "standard flight" in Newton's gravity of the Sun. It represents a space probe flight in a planetary system comprising a central star and planets imitating the Sun, Earth, and Venus. For simplicity, it is assumed that the planets move in circular orbits, however, the other physical parameters of the system are very close to the observation data.

The pattern flight looks as follows. A space probe is launched from the Earth (or from the Earth's orbit — since we ignore here non-essential Earth's gravity). From the launch point at initial zero-time moment and azimuth (polar angle) also zero,

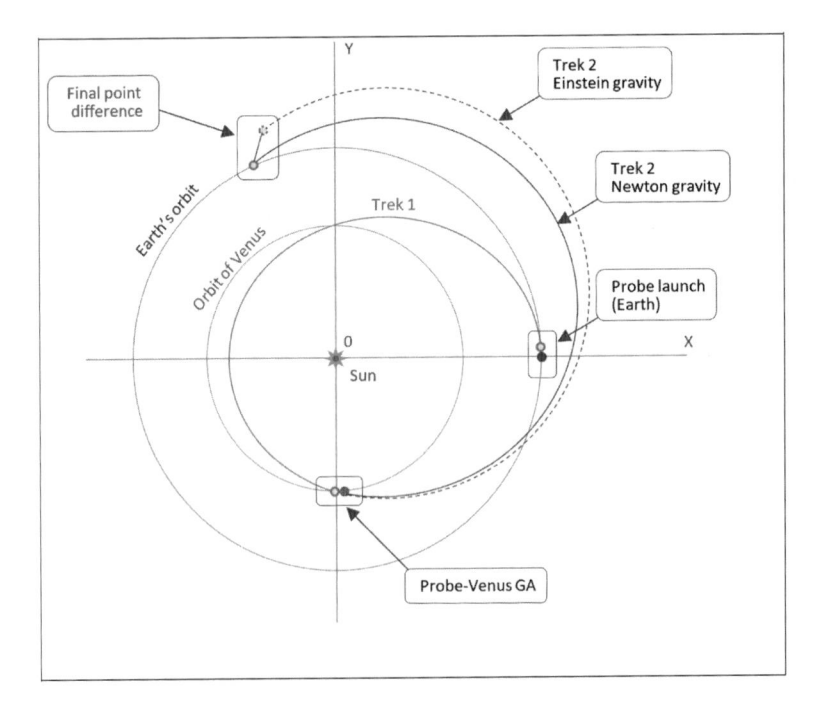

Fig. 1. The standard flight and the Gravity assist effects for different gravity laws.

the probe falls freely towards Venus by a Kepler elliptic leg (trek 1 in Fig. 1), and after a sufficiently prolonged flight it arrives at the Venus gravity-assist point. The initial conditions are chosen so, that the probes' perihelion has azimuth 180 deg, while the gravity assist point has azimuth of 270 deg, and strictly precomputed pericenter value. The Venus gravity assist accelerates the probe so that after flight by another elliptic leg (trek 2 in Fig. 1) it returns to the Earth's orbit, and at the assigned time sends a signal received by the Earth's observer who thus determines the probe's final position.

The Gravity-Assist Sensitivity as a Function of Pericenter Value

Slightly changing the initial conditions, we manage to make the chosen pericenter shorter by 1 km and let it move freely to the final position the same time. Then the calculated distance between the probe's final positions (with the pericenter difference of 1 km) gives us the gravity- assist sensitivity function for the chosen pericenter value.

Subsequently changing the initial conditions, we found the sensitivity values analytically for 20 pericenter lengths (from 18 000 km to 8 000 km — that is from 12 000 km to 2 000 km altitude) and obtained the following result. The sensitivity turns out quite a non-linear function.

At a greater pericenter value (18 000 km) the sensitivity is about 20 000 (this means that one-kilometer difference (i.e. 17 999 km) throws the probe aside its assigned final point at 20 000 km. In other words, the sensitivity is about 104. At smaller pericenter value, about 10 000 km (it is 4 000 km altitude) the sensitivity grows ten times as 105. That is at the final point the probe is thrown aside at 100 000 km.

Thus, the gravity assist maneuver may work as a powerful amplifier of small pericenter changes caused by some physical agents on its first elliptic leg (Trek 1).

We should say that we cross-checked the analytical evaluation of the sensitivity function values by a pure numerical construction of respective probe trajectories with the help of iterative program (realized within Python 3 system), choosing the time interval of 1 second, so that the probe's trajectories are built on 35–50 million points.

The results of analytical calculation and numerical construction of the trajectories turned out quite close.

The plots of GA sensitivity function are represented in Figs. 2–3.

The first physical factor to distort Kepler's Trek 1 is Einstein's general relativistic gravity; so we made preliminary computations, and again by two methods: analytically and numerically (and again the results are very close).

The GR gravity brings three reasons making he pericenter shorter. First, the GR-ellipse slightly shrinks, second, it is subject to a slow precession, and third, on a shorter trajectory the probe arrives at the gravity-assist point a earlier so that Venus is met a bit closer.

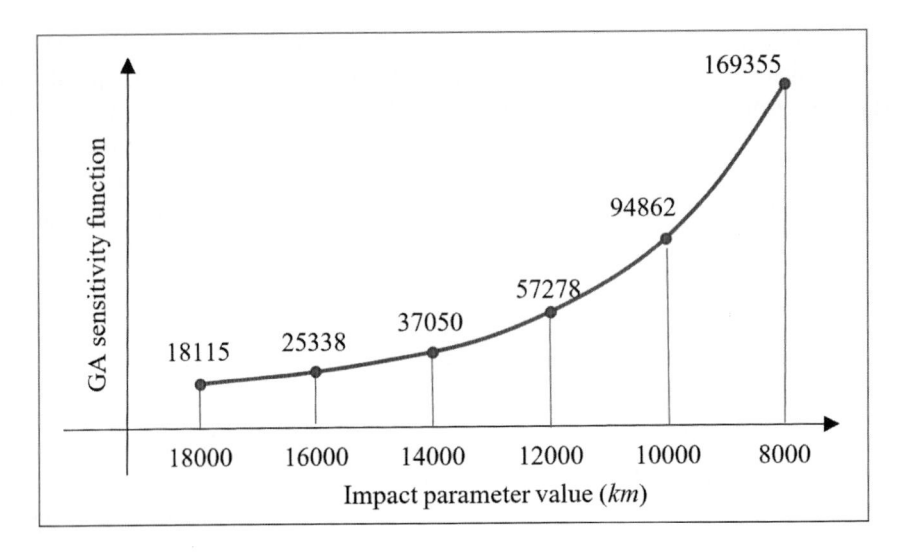

Fig. 2. Math calculation of GA sensitivity as function of IP value.

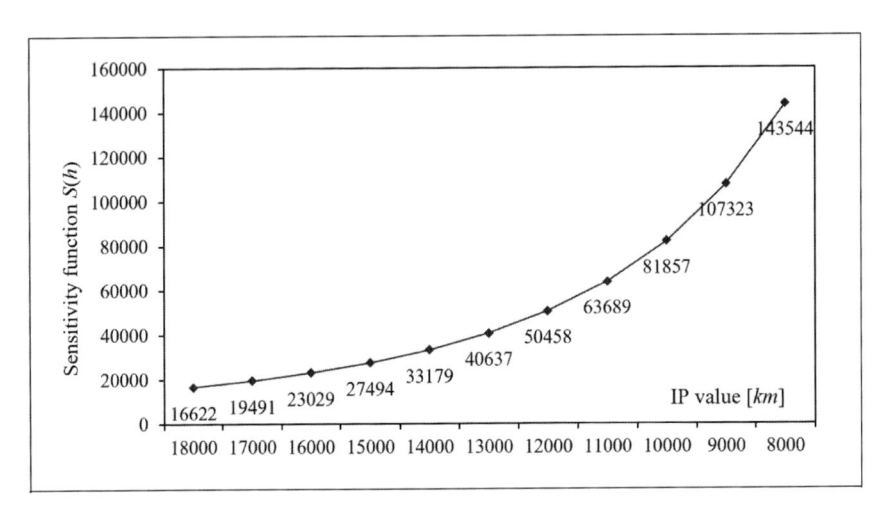

Fig. 3. GA sensitivity function $S(h) = dl/dh$ where dl is FP difference [km] for $dh = 1$ km.

Then under identical initial conditions the probe's pericenter becomes about 40 km shorter. Therefore, if the pericenter is 18 000 km, then at the final point the observer must detect about 800 000 km distance from assigned position. This difference will be much more (millions of km) for shorter pericenter values. These distances are big enough; their experimental detection by the observer should indicate in favor of Einstein's gravity.

Conclusion

The experiment seems not too hard to perform and it does not require excessive costs. Existing computational means allow distinguishing pure gravity effects among other physical agents, influence of other planets, Sun's oblateness, solar wind, etc. The space probe need not be a sophisticated station packed with expensive tools; a primitive space-ball able to send receivable signals is sufficient. We think that many cosmic agencies of different states and private companies can afford this job. We hope, someone will be the first.

References

1. A. P. Yefremov, Sensitivity of the Gravity Assist to Variations of the Impact Parameter, *Grav. Cosmol.* **26**, 118 (2020).
2. A. P. Yefremov and A. A. Vorobyeva, A planet's gravity assist as a powerful amplifier of small physical effects in the Solar system, *Acta Astronautica* **180**, 205, 2021.
3. A. P. Yefremov and A. A. Vorobyeva, A "space-ball" experiment to specify the nature of gravity in the solar system. [Submitted to: *Acta Astronautica* (2021)]

Gravitomagnetic field generation using high permittivity materials in superconducting magnetic energy storage devices

G. V. Stephenson

Seculine Consulting
Cupertino, CA 95014, USA
E-mail: seculine@gmail.com

A method is described for creating a measurable unbalanced gravitational acceleration using a gravitomagnetic field surrounding a superconducting toroid as described by Forward.[1] An experimental superconducting magnetic energy storage toroid configuration of wound superconducting nanowire is proposed to create a measurable acceleration field along the axis of symmetry, providing experimental confirmation of the additive nature of a Lense–Thirring derived gravitomagnetic field. In the present paper gravitational coupling enhancement of this effect is explored using high-permittivity material, as predicted by Sarfatti[2] and his modification to Einstein's general relativity field equations for gravitational coupling in matter.

Keywords: Gravitational; Gravitomagnetic; Lense–Thirring; Superconducting magnetic energy storage; SMES; Nanorods; Nanowires; Super dielectric materials; SDM; Super capacitors; High permittivity; Gravitomagnetic permeability; Gravitational coupling.

1. Introduction

When Forward[1] proposed a gravitomagnetic toroid to produce unbalanced gravitational force in 1962, a prototype was quite impractical. Recent advances in high-temperature superconducting (HTSC) nanorod wires (nanowires)[3,4] has enabled a new class of superconducting magnetic energy storage (SMES) devices operating at current densities sufficient to develop measurable gravitomagnetic fields.

In the present paper, an experimental SMES toroid configuration is proposed that uses a super dielectric material (SDM; e.g., high-permittivity super capacitor) to substantially improve gravitational coupling of mass flow to the curvature of spacetime as predicted by Sarfatti.[2] Depending on the nature of gravitational coupling, it is predicted that a set of standard accelerometers could measure acceleration fields along the axis of symmetry of the toroidal coil, thus providing experimental confirmation of the additive nature of the gravitomagnetic fields, as well as the production of a linear component of the overall acceleration field (Fig. 1).

In the instantiation of Forward's gravitational generation coil described in this paper, superconducting electron flow provides the change in mass current in the toroid. A high-permittivity material such as a SDM[5] is added to the space in the center of the toroid to improve gravitational coupling. Alternatively or additionally high-permittivity insulators may be used as an exterior jacket to the conducting portion of the nanowire to further boost gravitational coupling; gravitomagnetic effects are largest adjacent to the mass flow.

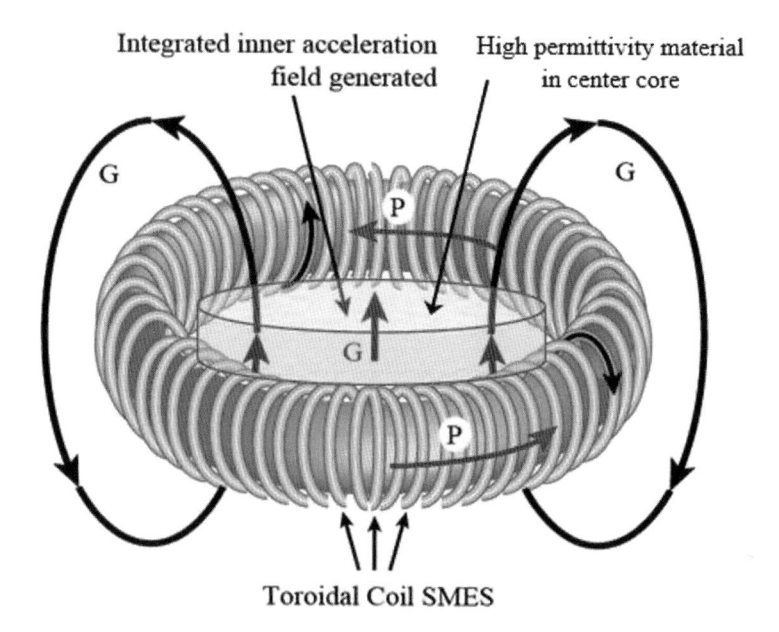

Figure 1. Gravitational force generation coil from Forward[1] with an inspiraling mass current, with a vector potential P, creating gravitomagnetic field G, with high-index material in the center to improve coupling.

2. Gravitomagnetic Force Equation for Toroid Mass Flow

As first developed in Forward,[1] the linear force G_f developed by gravitomagnetic force in the mass flow toroid of Fig. 1 is given by Eq. (1)

$$G_f = \left(\frac{\eta}{4\pi}\right)\left(\frac{N\dot{T}r^2}{R^2}\right), \tag{1}$$

where η is gravitomagnetic permeability, $\eta = \eta_o \eta_r$,[3] N is the number of turns in the toroid coil winding, $\dot{T}$ represents the mass flow, r is the cross-sectional radius of the toroid, and R is the overall radius of the toroid.

Mass flow can be generated by an electrical current by virtue of the electrons' mass in motion. Single-electron mass flow (Fig. 2) is given by mass momentum:

$$T_e = p_e = (\Omega \times r)m_e, \tag{2}$$

where Ω is the angular rate, angular velocity is $v = \Omega \times r$ in the classical case.[6]

Change in mass flow for the single-electron flow shown in Fig. 2 is

$$\dot{T}_e = \dot{p}_e = a \cdot m_e = (\Omega \times v)m_e. \tag{3}$$

This is equivalent to centripetal force,

$$\dot{T}_e = F_e = \frac{m_e v^2}{r} = m_e a_e = m_e\left(\omega^2 r\right), \tag{4}$$

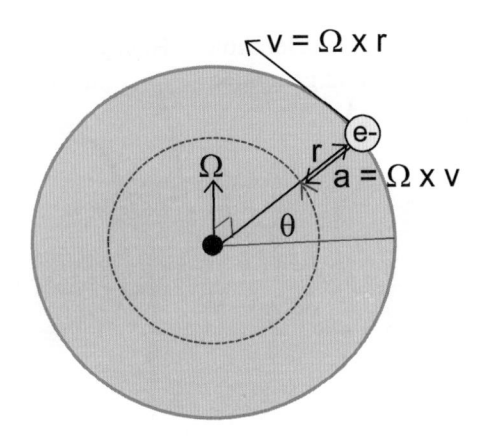

Figure 2. Electron orbit around one loop of SMES toroid.

where ω is the angular rate:

$$\omega = \frac{2\pi}{t_p} = \frac{d\theta}{dt}. \tag{5}$$

3. Current in Idealized SMES

We now estimate the possible inspiraling current flux enabled by the emerging SMES technology as it relates to the core geometry constraints described in Fig. 3, a toroid with torus geometry. We start with the assumptions needed to calculate the number of turns, N.

From Eq. (1), the torus assumptions made in Fig. 3 can be factored into Eq. (6):

$$G_f = \left(\frac{\eta_o \eta_r}{4\pi}\right) S \left(\frac{N\dot{T}r^2}{R^2}\right), \tag{6}$$

where

G_f = gravitomagnetic force
η_o = absolute gravitomagnetic permeability
η_r = relative gravitomagnetic permeability
N = number of turns in the torus coil
S = Sarfatti scaling factor
$\dot{T}$ = change in mass or mass flow
r = cross-section radius of torus
R = centerline radius of torus

Note that Eq. (6) differs from Forward's original formulation in that it includes the scaling factor S which accounts for the scaling of gravitational coupling due to high-index matter or metamaterials, which was first expressed by Sarfatti as

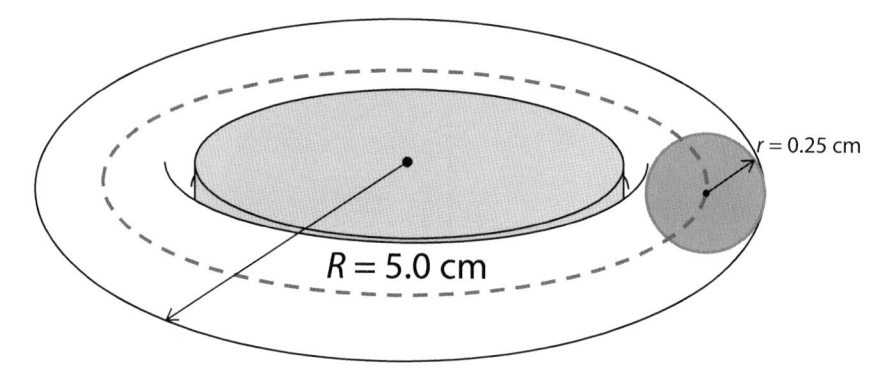

Figure 3. Toroid with a torus-shaped core geometry, including high-permittivity scaling matter in center.

an additional zero-rank tensor in Einstein's field equations[2,7] based on combining Lentz's[8] work with that of Medina and Stephany:[9]

$$R_{\mu\nu} - \frac{1}{2}Rg_{\mu\nu} = \left(\frac{8\pi G}{c^4}\right) ST_{\mu\nu}, \quad (7)$$

where

$$R_{\mu\nu} = \text{Ricci curvature tensor},$$
$$Rg_{\mu\nu} = \text{Ricci scalar curvature},$$
$$G = \text{gravitational constant}$$
$$c = \text{speed of light}$$
$$S = \text{Sarfatti scaling tensor}$$
$$T_{\mu\nu} = \text{Stress Energy Tensor}$$

For the purposes of describing an idealized case with a realistic geometry, we describe a device bounded by a 10 cm toroid (outer mold line diameter), shown in Fig. 3 and Fig. 4, with a 0.5 cm cross-sectional diameter. Furthermore, 16 sectors are defined as shown in Fig. 4.

We further add additional assumptions regarding conductor wrapping around the toroid to determine constraints on the number of conductive loops that can be accommodated using the described technology.[3] As shown in Fig. 5 via cross section, we assume here a conductor winding depth of 0.1 cm.

The inner edge of a single segment of the cross section, C_s, is 1/16 of the toroid's centerline circumference:

$$C_s = \frac{2\pi r_i}{16} = 1.77 \text{ cm} \quad (8)$$

With a depth D, the minimum inner loop cross-sectional area can be described as

$$A_{\text{sec}} = D \cdot C_s = (0.1 \text{ cm})(1.77 \text{ cm}) = 0.177 \text{ cm}^2. \quad (9)$$

This area is shown packed with conductors in Fig. 6 in depth and along the sector circumference.

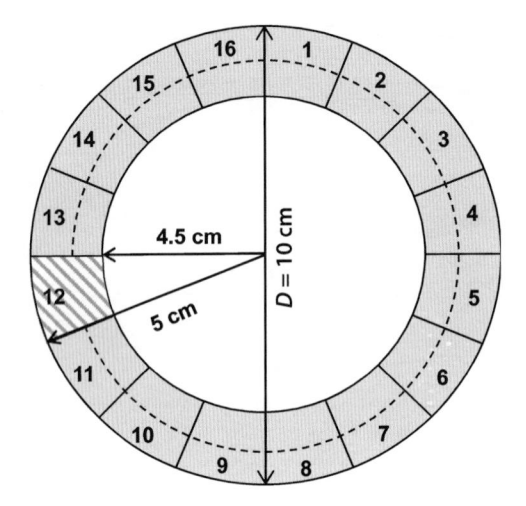

Figure 4. Torus section definition.

Assuming each nanowire conductor has a diameter d_c of 100 µm, the cross-sectional area of each conductor will be given by

$$A_c = \pi r_c^2 = 7.854 \times 10^{-9} \, \text{m}^2. \tag{10}$$

For packing nanowire conductors in a cross-sectional area described in Fig. 6, assume as a worst case a rectangular area described by the shortest edges such that

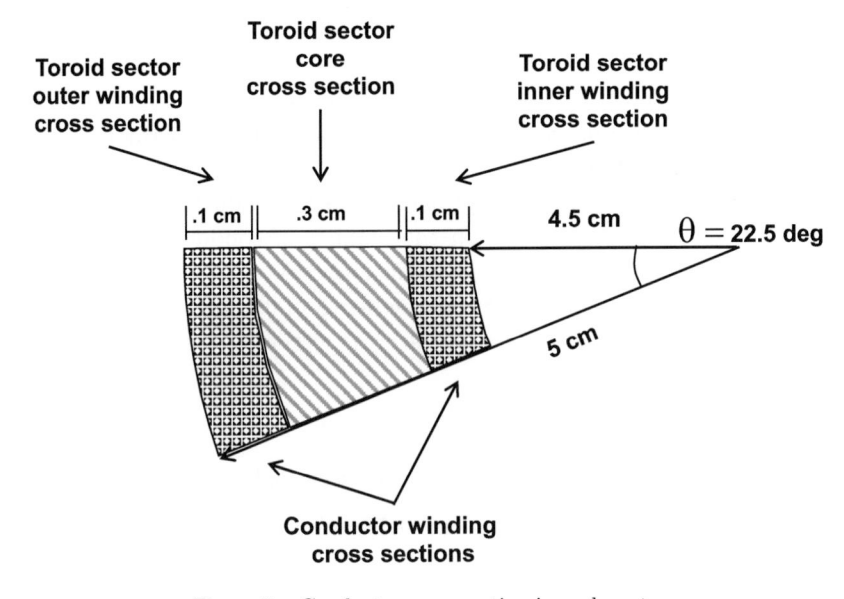

Figure 5. Conductor cross section in each sector.

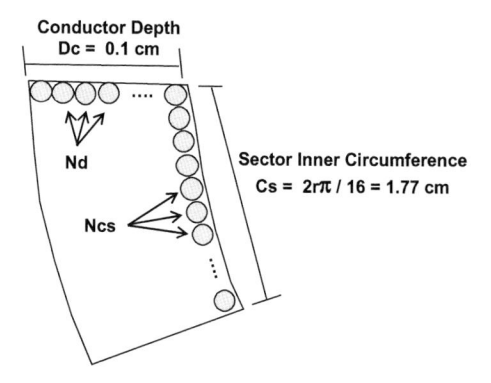

Figure 6. Conductor packing in each sector.

a number of conductors in depth, N_d, may be packed in one dimension, with the number of conductors, N_cs, packed in the other dimension. These packing counts may be calculated in Eq. (11) and Eq. (12) as follows:

$$N_\mathrm{d} = D_\mathrm{c}/d_\mathrm{c} = \frac{0.1\,\mathrm{cm}}{100\,\mathrm{\mu m}} = 10 \tag{11}$$

$$N_\mathrm{cs} = C_\mathrm{s}/d_\mathrm{c} = \frac{1.77\,\mathrm{cm}}{100\,\mathrm{\mu m}} = 177 \tag{12}$$

The total number of windings by sector will therefore be the product $N_\mathrm{d} \times N_\mathrm{cs}$:

$$N_\mathrm{sec} = N_\mathrm{d} \cdot N_\mathrm{cs} = (10)(177) = 1770. \tag{13}$$

With 16 sectors, the total number of windings for the entire toroid will be

$$N = 16 N_\mathrm{sec} = 28{,}320. \tag{14}$$

What is $\dot{T}$ with the forgoing assumptions? In this idealized case electrons circulate about a coil of circumference c_r, or slightly larger:

$$c_\mathrm{r} = 2\pi r = 1.57\,\mathrm{cm}. \tag{15}$$

3.1. Electron motion

Assume further a supply voltage of 16 kV, resulting in 16 KeV of kinetic energy for each electron, which corresponds with the upper limit of a nonrelativistic case, where $v = 0.25c$, so that $\gamma = 1.06 \approx 1.0$.

Then from Eq. (4) for nonrelativistic circular motion, the vector change in DC current flow is

$$\dot{T}_\mathrm{e} = \frac{m_\mathrm{e} v^2}{r}, \tag{16}$$

which, for a single electron, has the following values

$$m_e = \text{mass of the electron} = 9.11 \times 10^{-31} \text{ kg}$$
$$v = \text{velocity of the electron} = 0.25c = 0.75 \times 10^8 \frac{\text{m}}{\text{s}}$$
$$r = 0.25 \text{ cm}$$

for the assumed geometry

The angular acceleration of the electron is

$$a_e = \frac{v^2}{r} = 2.25 \times 10^{18} \frac{\text{m}}{\text{s}^2} \tag{17}$$

The change in mass flow represents centripetal acceleration in the case of circular motion:

$$\dot{T}_e = m_e \cdot a_e = 20.48 \times 10^{-13} \text{ N}. \tag{18}$$

Eq. (18) corresponds to the change in mass flow for one electron in one loop of coil. Total mass flow change is therefore the mass flow change per electron times the number of electrons:

$$\dot{T} = \dot{T}_e \cdot N_e. \tag{19}$$

3.2. Electron current

What is the number of electrons, N_e, in motion in one loop (part of the mass flow) at a given time for an assumed velocity of $v = .25c$? N_e in one loop can be described by the current I times the period of a single loop circulation Δt:

$$N_e = I \cdot \Delta t, \tag{20}$$

where the period of an orbit can be described by

$$\Delta t = \frac{c_r}{v} = \frac{2\pi r}{v} = 0.2094 \text{ ns}. \tag{21}$$

What is the possible current inside the idealized device for the case where the entire winding is in series? We assume the max current stays below the critical current density of $250 \frac{\text{MA}}{\text{m}^2}$.[3,4]

Current is limited by the maximum permissible current density and the cross section of the conductor:

$$I = J \cdot A_c, \tag{22}$$

where J is material dependent. For the nanowire assumed in Ref. 3, $J = 250 \frac{\text{MA}}{\text{m}^2}$ and the cross-sectional area, $A_c = 7.854 \times 10^{-9} \text{ m}^2$, as given in Eq. (10). Therefore, the maximum current for this conductor diameter is $I = 1.96$ A.

Expanding on Eq. (22), the number of electrons N_e in circulation in one loop may be calculated by noting that there are 6.2415×10^{18} electrons per Coulomb:

$$N_e = \left(\frac{\text{electron}}{\text{Coulomb}}\right) I \left(\frac{\text{Coulomb}}{\text{second}}\right) \cdot \Delta t = 5.12 \times 10^9 \text{ electron} \tag{23}$$

4. Forces in Idealized SMES

Expressing Eq. (19) as force per electron times the number of electrons in motion in one loop:

$$\dot{T} = \dot{T}_e \left(\frac{\text{Newton}}{\text{electron}} \right) \cdot N_e = 5.25 \, \text{mN} \tag{24}$$

Thus, each loop experiences about $5.25\,\text{mN}$ of integrated centripetal force ($\dot{T}$) due to the electrons in circulation within. We now describe the scale factor to couple this force to the gravitomagnetic effect. Revisiting Eq. (6), which describes the overall linear force developed at the center of the toroidal coil, total gravitomagnetically developed force will be

$$G_f = (\eta_o \eta_r)(S) \left(\frac{N \dot{T} r^2}{4\pi R^2} \right) = (\eta_o \eta_r)(S)(0.0295\,\text{N}), \tag{25}$$

where known variables have been grouped on the right and unknown variables have been collected on the left. What are the correct values for η_o and η_r?

4.1. *Predicted force using gravitational potential scaling*

If η_o goes as $G/2c$ as does gravitomagnetic potential (Ref. 10, Eq. (1.5)), then

$$\eta_o = -\frac{G}{2c} = 1.11 \times 10^{-19}. \tag{26}$$

This leads to $G_f = (\eta_r) 3.275 \times 10^{-21}$. Values of η_r are experimentally unknown at this time. However, if values of η_r track values of ϵr^2, then values as high as $\eta_r = 10^{16}$ may be possible, yielding $G_f = 0.03275\,\text{mN}$. For a test mass of 1 kg this is equivalent to an easily measurable $3.35\,\upmu\text{G}$. This is for a scaling factor of $G/2c$. If the scaling factor is G/c^2, then the effect drops to an unmeasurably low $1.12 \times 10^{-14}\,G$, even for $\eta_r = 10^{16}$.

4.2. *Predicted force using gravitational field scaling*

If the scaling factor is G/c^3 or G/c^4, then the effect is negligible for $\eta_r = 10^{16}$, so a much higher-index material will need to be found to improve coupling, or other means must be found to improve either the S tensor or the gravitomagnetic permeability η_r.

Consider the case where η_o goes as $8\pi G/c^4$ as does the coupling constant in Einstein's Field Equations:

$$\eta_o = \frac{8\pi G}{c^4} = 2.07 \times 10^{-43}, \tag{27}$$

which gives the total gravitational force developed as

$$G_f = (\eta_o \eta_r)(S)(0.0295\,\text{N}) = (\eta_r)(S) 0.61 \times 10^{-44}\,\text{N}. \tag{28}$$

A value of $\eta_r = 10^{16}$ gives $G_f = (S)4.43 \times 10^{-23}$ N, which requires a scalar value of S of at least an additional 10^{16} to obtain a measurable value for G_f. For an isotropic material, S can be written as[7]

$$S = \frac{1}{2}\left(\epsilon^2 + \frac{1}{\mu^2}\right) = \frac{1}{2}\frac{n^4+1}{\mu^2}. \tag{29}$$

Therefore, either a permittivity of $\epsilon = 10^8$ or an index of $n = 10^4$ with $\mu = 1$ would be sufficient to provide the necessary 16 orders of magnitude in coupling improvement. However, care should be taken that effects captured by the S factor are not duplicative of those accounted for in the value of η_r.

Super dielectrics can provide up to $\epsilon = 10^9$,[5] which, if we simultaneously had $\eta_r = 10^{16}$ via some unrelated phenomena, would improve the overall generated gravitational force to a marginally measurable level:

$$G_f = (\eta_r)(S) \times 0.61 \times 10^{-44} = 0.061 \, \text{nN}. \tag{30}$$

Alternatively metamaterials could also be investigated to establish whether non-isotropic materials may create a more advantageous gravitational coupling.

4.3. Lenz's law implications

Is there an equivalent of Lenz's Law for gravitomagnetics? Consider a hypothetical case where a Forward toroid capable of supporting sufficient current and coupling to develop 1 G of acceleration. As a thought experiment, imagine disconnecting the power supply and shorting the toroidal coil to itself, such that it is one continuous closed loop of nanowire, and equip a flying craft with such a coil.

At the surface of the Earth such a properly oriented toroidal coil would be immersed in a 1 G gravitational field. Should not such a field generate a counter-current in a toroidal coil capable of supporting a current of that level, essentially providing a self-powered counter field? If so, a craft so equipped would be able to hover using a counter-field equal but opposite to the Earth's gravitational field without need of additional power sources.

Similarly, additional closed-loop toroidal coils, properly oriented, could also be used to "current charge," collecting energy from a static gravitational field, potentially providing power that could be directed to other propulsive or nonpropulsive functions of such a hypothetical craft.

5. Conclusions

An argument is made for using high-permittivity materials in the core or donut hole or nanowire insulators of an SMES toroid to improve gravitomagnetic coupling for the creation of an acceleration field, possibly of measurable amplitude. Improved coupling will be beneficial for shrinking device scale and complexity and overcoming the very weak coupling between mass flow and gravitomagnetic spacetime curvature.

Acronyms

HTSC – high temperature superconductor
SDM – super dielectric material
SMES – superconducting magnetic energy storage

Acknowledgments

The author wishes to acknowledge Jack Sarfatti for helpful correspondence on his insights into altering Einstein's field equations in the presence of matter and metamaterials. The financial support of Seculine Consulting is gratefully acknowledged.

References

1. R. Forward, Guidelines to antigravity, *Proc. Gravit. Res. Found.* (New Boston, 1962).
2. J. Sarfatti, Explaining US Navy close encounters with tic tac UAV metric engineering, *Proc. Estes Park Adv. Prop. Workshop* (Space Studies Institute, North Hollywood, 2020).
3. G. Stephenson, W. Rieken, and A. Bhargava, Extended cases of laboratory generated gravitomagnetic field measurement devices, *J. High Energy Phys. Gravit. Cosmol.* **5**, 375–394 (2019), https://doi.org/10.4236/jhepgc.2019.52021.
4. W. Rieken, A. Bhargava, R. Horie, J. Akimitsu, and H. Daimon, $YBa_2Cu_3O_x$ superconducting nanorods, *Jpn. J. Appl. Phys.* **57**, Aritcle 023101 (2018).
5. S. Fromille and J. Phillips, Super dielectric materials, *Materials*, **7** (12), 8197–8212 (2014), https://doi.org/10.3390/ma7128197.
6. J. M. Knudsen and P. G. Hjorth, *Elements of Newtonian Mechanics: Including Nonlinear Dynamics* 3rd edn. (Springer, New York, 2000).
7. G. Stephenson, 2000–2020 summary of gravitational work, *APEC Proc.*, https://doi.org/10.13140/RG.2.2.23735.34720.
8. E. W. Lentz, *Breaking the Warp Barrier: Hyper-Fast Solitons in Einstein–Maxwell–Plasma Theory* (2020), https://arxiv.org/abs/2006.07125.
9. R. Medina and J. Stephany, The Energy–Momentum Tensor of Electromagnetic Fields in Matter (2017), https://arxiv.org/abs/1703.02109v1.
10. B. Mashhoon, *Gravitoelectromagnetism: A Brief Review* (2008), https://arxiv.org/abs/gr-qc/0311030.

Large ring laser gyroscopes: Geometry stabilization and laser control

U. Giacomelli

GSSI
L'Aquila, Italy
E-mail: umberto.giacomelli@gssi.it
www.gssi.it

N. Beverini, G. Carelli, D. Ciampin, A. Di Virgilio, F. Fuso, E. Maccioni and P. Marsili

Dipartimento di Fisica
Università di Pisa
Pisa, Italy

A. Di Virgilio and A. Simonelli

INFN-Sez Pisa
Pisa, Italy

Ring laser Gyroscopes (RLG) are very versatile devices that find application in many fields as navigation, seismology and geophysics. Moreover, thanks to their sensitivity and accuracy, in the last years they have been used in fundamental physics research field.

GINGER (Gyroscopes IN GEneral Relativity) research group aims to exploit a large RLG to test general relativity theory. Our research team has two working RLG, both with a square shape, one installed in Pisa and named GP2. (1.6 m side), and the other installed in the INFN underground laboratory of Gran Sasso near L'Aquila named GINGERINO (3.6 m side). The final goal of GINGER is to measure the Earth rotation rate with enough precision to take into consideration general relativity predicted corrections.

To reach this target, one of the requirements is the stability of the laser and the optical cavity of the RLG. We will show the last developed techniques aimed to satisfy this stability requirement. Working on GP2 we have tested two different techniques to control the ring shape. One is based on the stabilization of the two Fabry-Pèrot resonators formed along the square diagonals by the opposite mirrors of the RLG. The other, consist in controlling the ring perimeter by monitoring its free spectral range through a beet-note between one of the counterpropagating beams and a frequency stabilized laser source. We will show the characteristics, the potentialities and the tests of these two methods.

Keywords: Large Frame Ring Laser, Sagnac Effect, frequency control, Laser stabilization

1. Introduction

Large frame ring laser gyroscopes (RLG), which exploit Sagnac effect, are the most sensitive devices for detecting absolute angular motions in a huge range of frequency, extending from kHz down to DC.[1] Thanks to their sensitivity and accuracy, in the last years they have been used in the fundamental physics research field.

In this framework, the project GINGER (Gyroscopes IN GEneral Relativity) of the Istituto Italiano di Fisica Nucleare (INFN) was developed in 2010.[2,3] The goal of the project is to measure the Lense-Thirring and De Sitter effects using an on

Earth device via a very precise and accurate measurement of the Earth rotation rate. Binding rigidly a RLG to the ground it is possible to exploit the Sagnac effect to measure the Earth rotation rate. Due to this effect, two counter-propagating beams that circulate in a rotating close path have an optical frequency difference proportional to the rotation rate. This frequency difference, known as the Sagnac frequency (f_S), is linked to the reference frame rotation rate via the geometrical characteristics of the ring as descibed in Eq. (1)

$$f_S = \frac{4A}{\lambda P} \vec{\Omega} \cdot \hat{n} \qquad (1)$$

where A and P are respectively the area and the perimeter of the optical path, λ is laser wavelength without the path rotation, $\vec{\Omega}$ is the rotation rate of the reference frame and $\hat{n}$ is the normal area versor of the optical path.

It is possible to demonstrate that Eq. (1) is still valid in General Relativity (GR) with only one difference: $\vec{\Omega}$.[4] In fact, in the relativistic formulation, $\vec{\Omega}$ includes all the gravitational field effects, which is exactly what we want to measure.

$$\vec{\Omega} = \vec{\Omega}_\oplus + \vec{\Omega}_G + \vec{\Omega}_{LT} \qquad (2)$$

$\vec{\Omega}_\oplus = 7.29 \times 10^{-5}$ rad/s is the Earth instantaneous angular rotation velocity, $\vec{\Omega}_G$ is the geodetic (or De Sitter effect), $\vec{\Omega}_{LT}$ is the Lense-Thirring effect.

These terms are estimated to be, respectively, $6.98 \cdot 10^{-10}\Omega_\oplus$ the geodetic part and $2.31 \cdot 10^{-10}\Omega_\oplus$ the Lense-Thirring one.[5,6] This estimation gives the sensitivity level required to be able to measure the general relativity correction upon the Earth rotation rate.

GINGER research group aims to reach this level of sensitivity with an array of large frame RLGs. In order to reconstruct the Earth rotation rate vector with enough precision to evaluate the De Sitter and Lense-Thirring contribution. To obtain this goal the also the ratio $4A/\lambda P$ of Eq. (1) must be known and stable at a level of 10^{-10}. This ratio is known as *scale factor* (for simplicity in the following we will refer to this quantity as scale factor or k). In the following, we will describe two different techniques to stabilize this value.

2. GP2 and the geometry control

Our research group has two RLGs, the first one, named GP2[7–9] installed in the INFN (Istituto Nazionale di Fisica Nucleare) laboratory in Pisa, and the second one, GINGERINO[10–14] installed in the underground laboratory of LNGS (Laboratori Nazionale del Gran Sasso) near L'Aquila.

This second one is our prototype of high precision large frame RLG. It is a square ring of 3.6m side located inside a quiet environment like those of the underground laboratories of LNGS inside the Gran Sasso mount. It has been built to test the quality of this kind of site for the installation of a device for GR measurements.

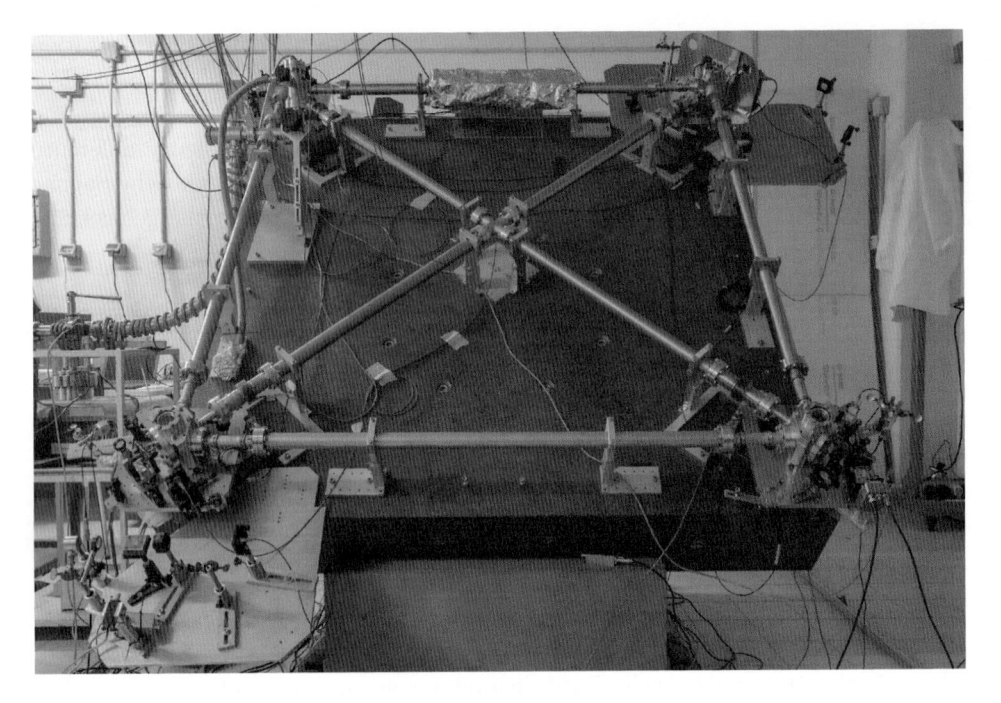

Fig. 1. Pictures of GP2.

Moreover, it has also shown that can be a suitable instrument also for geophysics ad geodesy.[15–17]

In this work we will focus on the first one GP2, that is our *test* ring laser (see Fig. 1). It is a square ring of 1.6m side, tilted of $\sim 45°$ in order to maximize the scalar product in Eq. (1). In addition to the square cavity, it has other two resonance cavities: the diagonals, and 4PZT actuators (one for each corner) able to move the whole corner along the diagonal direction. The structure of both our RLGs is etherolithic. This means that active geometry stabilization is essential to fix the scale factor value during the measurement period.

We have developed two different methods to control the ring geometry, the first is based on controlling the length of square diagonals and the second is based on stabilizing its perimeter length.

2.1. *Diagonal Control*

First of all, we have designed a mathematical model to parameterize all possible deformation that can affect the ring shape.[8] Basing this model on the diagonals deformation we have identified six fundamental deformations. Tn the hypothesis of small perturbation of a perfect square we can reconstruct any kind of shape perturbation using these six fundamental deformations. Using this parametrization

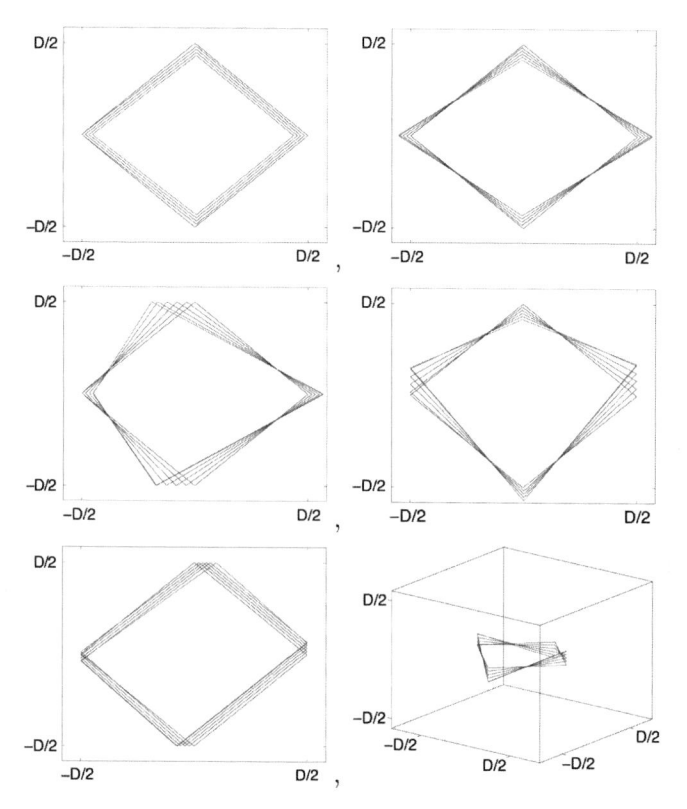

Fig. 2. Graphical representation of the optical paths six fundamental deformation of ring shape. First row: diagonal common mode stretching E_1 (left); differential mode stretching E_2 (right). Second row: shear planar deformations E_3 (left), E_4 (right). Third row: diagonal tilt E_5 (left); out of plane tilt E_6 (right). From Fig. 2 of [8]

we have recalculate the scale factor obtaining:

$$k = \frac{L}{\lambda}\left[1 - \frac{\tau_1}{\sqrt{2}L} + \frac{\tau_1^2}{2L^2} - \frac{\tau_2^2}{4L^2} - \frac{2L+\sqrt{2}r}{4L\left(r-\sqrt{2}L\right)^2}\left(\tau_3^2 + \tau_4^2\right) - \frac{L+2\sqrt{2}r}{L\left(4r-\sqrt{2}L\right)^2}\tau_6^2\right] \quad (3)$$

were each τ_α represent the coefficients that quantify the magnitude of each deformation, L the is the unperturbed ring side length and r is the curvature radius of each mirror. The assumption of of small perturbation means that $10^{-2} < \tau_\alpha/L < 10^{-1}$. In view of this, from Eq. (3) it is clear that an accuracy of 1 part in 10^{10} on k can be reached only if the relative amplitude of E_1 deformation is 10^{-10} or less. This means that stabilizing only the diagonals length is enough to reach our purpose.

We have realized an opto-electronic system able to transfer the frequency stability of an He-Ne iodine stabilized laser to the length stability of a Fabry-Pérot cavity (the diagonals). Firstly we have tested this system on two probe cavities on optical bench[7] and then we have implemented it on GP2.[9]

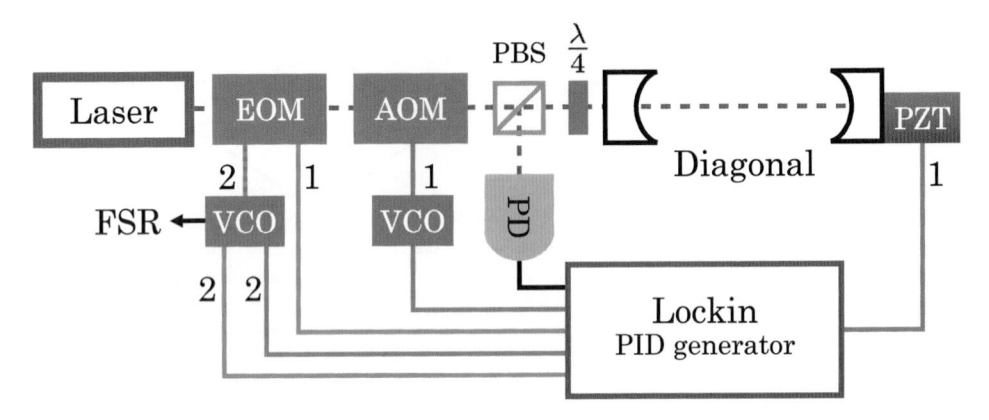

Fig. 3. Control loop scheme. Orange lines are the modulation signals, green lines are the corrections generated by the feedback system and black line is the modulated signal. Lines labeled with 1 are the first control loop and those ones with 2 are the second.

Fig. 3 shows a schematization of a control loop for a single diagonal. The control system is divided into two loops (see lines labeled with 1 and 2 in Fig. 3). The first is the one that fixes the length of the diagonal via two different actuators the piezoelectric (PZT) and the Acousto-Optic Modulator (AOM). The second one is used to measure the cavity Free Spectral Range (FSR) in order to test the control system efficiency.

The results of the measurement with this control technique are summarized in Fig. 4. The plots show the comparison between the measured Earth rotation rate estimated by the reconstructed Sagnac frequency and the Earth rotation rate

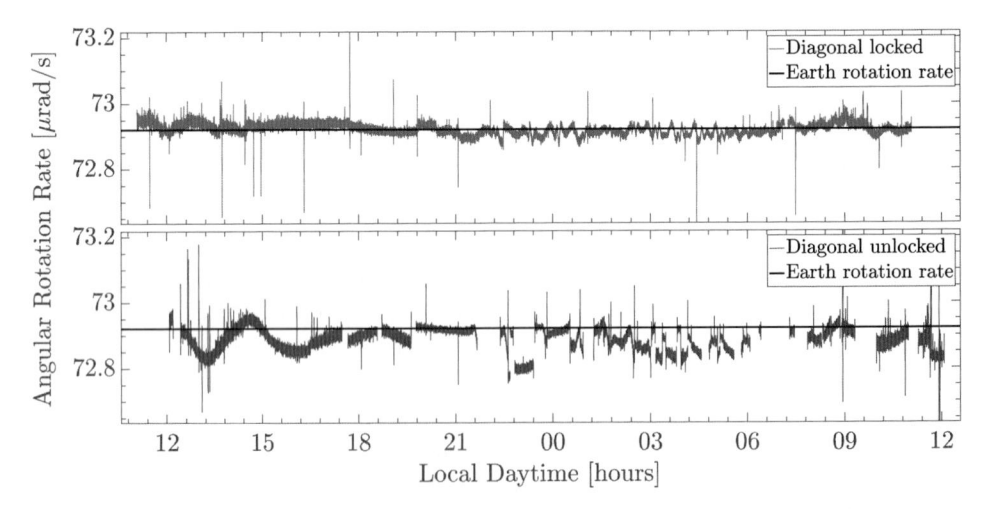

Fig. 4. Reconstructed value of Earth rotation rate from Sagnac frequency in μrad/s compared with the known value while the diagonals are locked (TOP) and free-running (BOTTOM).

nominal value. Both quantities are expressed in μrad/s. On top, the comparison when the diagonals are locked is shown, while on the bottom when the diagonals are unlocked.

A clear improvement due to the presence of the cavity stabilization system is the increase of the duty-cycle of the measurements. In our case, the duty-cycle is defined as the ratio between the period during which it is possible to reconstruct the Sagnac frequency, divided by the entire acquisition time. It is straightforward to see the effect of the stabilization on the so-defined duty-cycle. The "holes" present in the bottom plot are generated by the period of split mode of the RLG. In this condition, we have a duty-cycle of about 78%. This value increases up to 99% when we active the lock as the top plot shows. In addition, the presence of the control loop increases the effectiveness of the frequency reconstruction algorithm reducing the spread of the data with respect to the Earth rotation rate known value.

A more detailed discussion of this technique can be found in [9, 18].

2.2. Perimeter Control

Our studies demonstrate that the diagonal control technique is the main way to obtain the necessary stability for GR measurement. Nevertheless, we explored other geometry control methods. One of them consists of keeping fixed the ring perimeter.

There are two possible ways to measure the ring perimeter, the first consists of generating a beat-note between one of the two counter-propagating beams and a frequency stabilized laser. The second is the self-beat-note technique. If the laser inside the ring has enough power to excite the fundamental and the first longitudinal mode, using a fast photodiode we can acquire the beat-note of these two modes that

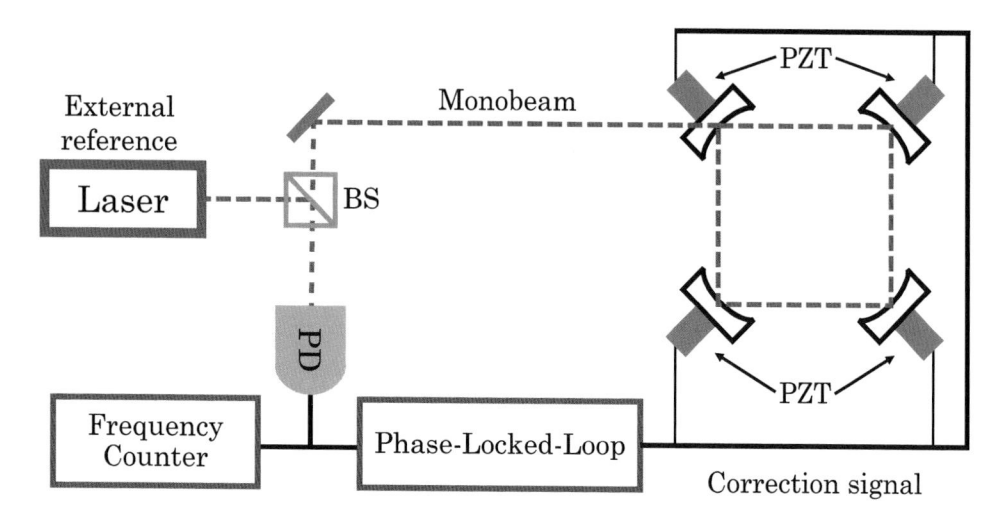

Fig. 5. Scheme of perimeter lock loop via comparison with an external laser source. The one that exploit the self-beat-note is analogous but without the Beam Splitter (BS) and the external laser.

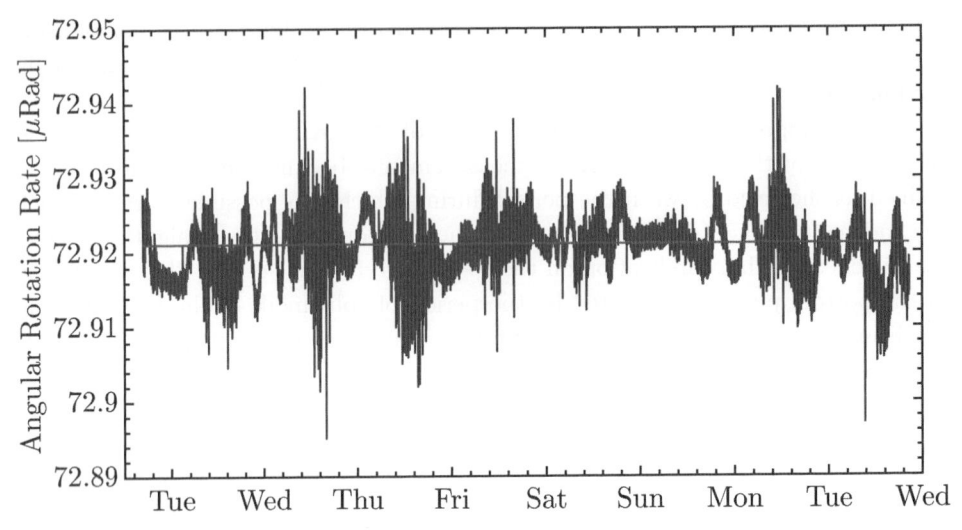

Fig. 6. Reconstructed value of Earth rotation rate from Sagnac frequency in μrad/s compared with the known value while the perimeter is locked.

is exactly the Free Spectral Range (FSR) of the cavity. This method has an intrinsic lower level of stability than the first one. So we chose the external reference laser method.

Fig. 5 shows a schematization of the perimeter control loop. The beat-note between monobeam and reference laser is acquired from a fast photodiode and sent to a frequency counter, used as a monitor, and to a Phased-Locked-Loop (PLL), used to generate the correction signal.

As in the case of diagonal control, we tested the perimeter lock loop acquiring the Sagnac frequency. Fig. 6 shows the result of this test. Also in this case we have both the benefits present in the diagonals control method. The spread of the data around the nominal value of Earth rotation rate is about 0.3‰ and the duty-cycle close to 99%.

3. Conclusions

In this work, we have shown two different methods to stabilize the geometry of a large frame RLG. The diagonal control method is the one suitable for GR application. Our mathematical model demonstrates that we can fix the scale factor value simply by controlling the diagonal length. Also, preliminary tests on GP2 showed important enhanced in the quality of the Sagnac frequency data in view of an application on a new generation device dedicated to measuring De Sitter and Lense-Thirring contribution to the Earth rotation rate.

Despite it is not the chosen one for GR measurement, also the perimeter control method has some interesting features. It is easier to realize, especially if we use the self-beat-note technique. Moreover, as in the case of diagonal control, it increases the duty-cycle of an RLG at a level neat to 100% and it improves the Sagnac frequency data quality. Thanks to these it can be useful for the geological and geophysical application of an RLG. In this field, the requested stability is lower than the one of GR.

References

1. K. U. Schreiber and J.-P. R. Wells, Invited Review Article: Large ring lasers for rotation sensing, *Review of Scientific Instruments* **84**, p. 041101 (4 2013).
2. A. Di Virgilio, K. U. Schreiber, A. Gebauer, J.-P. R. We, A. Tartaglia, J. Belfi, N. Beverini and A. Ortolan, A laser gyroscope system to detect the gravito-magnetic effect on Earth, *International Journal of Modern Physics D* **19**, 2331 (12 2010).
3. A. Di Virgilio, J. Belfi, W.-T. Ni, N. Beverini, G. Carelli, E. Maccioni and A. Porzio, GINGER: A feasibility study, *The European Physical Journal Plus* **132**, p. 157 (4 2017).
4. F. Bosi, G. Cella, A. Di Virgilio, A. Ortolan, A. Porzio, S. Solimeno, M. Cerdonio, J. P. Zendri, M. Allegrini, J. Belfi, N. Beverini, B. Bouhadef, G. Carelli, I. Ferrante, E. Maccioni, R. Passaquieti, F. Stefani, M. L. Ruggiero, A. Tartaglia, K. U. Schreiber, A. Gebauer and J.-P. R. J.-P. R. Wells, Measuring gravitomagnetic effects by a multi-ring-laser gyroscope, *Physical Review D* **84**, p. 122002 (12 2011).
5. A. Tartaglia, A. Di Virgilio, J. Belfi, N. Beverini and M. L. Ruggiero, Testing general relativity by means of ring lasers: Ring lasers and relativity, *European Physical Journal Plus* **132**, 1 (2 2017).
6. A. Di Virgilio, J. Belfi, F. Bosi, F. Morsani, G. Terreni, N. Beverini, G. Carelli, U. Giacomelli, E. Maccioni, A. Ortolan, A. Porzio, C. Altucci, R. Velotta, A. Donazzan, G. Naletto, D. Cuccato, A. Beghi, M. Pelizzo, M. Ruggiero, A. Tartaglia, G. De Luca and G. Saccorotti, The GINGER Project, in *Nuclear and Particle Physics Proceedings*, 10 2017.
7. J. Belfi, N. Beverini, D. Cuccato, A. Di Virgilio, E. Maccioni, A. Ortolan, R. Santagata, A. D. Virgilio, E. Maccioni, A. Ortolan and R. Santagata, Interferometric length metrology for the dimensional control of ultra-stable ring laser gyroscopes, *Classical and Quantum Gravity* **31**, p. 225003 (11 2014).
8. R. Santagata, A. Beghi, J. Belfi, N. Beverini, D. Cuccato, A. Di Virgilio, A. Ortolan, A. Porzio and S. Solimeno, Optimization of the geometrical stability in square ring laser gyroscopes, *Classical and Quantum Gravity* **32**, p. 055013 (3 2015).
9. N. Beverini, G. Carelli, A. Di Virgilio, U. Giacomelli, E. Maccioni, F. Stefani and J. Belfi, Length measurement and stabilization of the diagonals of a square area laser gyroscope, *Classical and Quantum Gravity* **37**, p. 065025 (3 2020).
10. J. Belfi, N. Beverini, F. Bosi, G. Carelli, D. Cuccato, G. De Luca, A. Di Virgilio, A. Gebauer, E. Maccioni, A. Ortolan, A. Porzio, R. Santagata, A. Simonelli and G. Terreni, First Results of GINGERino, a deep underground ringlaser, *Review of Scientific Instruments* **88**, p. 034502 (1 2016).
11. J. Belfi, N. Beverini, F. Bosi, G. Carelli, D. Cuccato, G. De Luca, A. Di Virgilio, A. Gebauer, E. Maccioni, A. Ortolan, A. Porzio, G. Saccorotti, A. Simonelli and G. Terreni, Deep underground rotation measurements: GINGERino ring laser gyroscope in Gran Sasso, *Review of Scientific Instruments* **88**, p. 034502 (3 2017).
12. J. Belfi, N. Beverini, G. Carelli, A. D. Virgilio, U. Giacomelli, E. Maccioni, A. Simonelli, F. Stefani, G. Terreni, A. Di Virgilio, U. Giacomelli, E. Maccioni,

12. A. Simonelli, F. Stefani and G. Terreni, Analysis of 90 day operation of the GINGERINO gyroscope, *Appl. Opt.* **57**, 5844 (10 2018).
13. A. D. V. Di Virgilio, A. Basti, N. Beverini, F. Bosi, G. Carelli, D. Ciampini, F. Fuso, U. Giacomelli, E. Maccioni, P. Marsili, A. Ortolan, A. Porzio, A. Simonelli and G. Terreni, Underground Sagnac gyroscope with sub-prad/s rotation rate sensitivity: Toward general relativity tests on Earth, *Physical Review Research* **2**, p. 032069 (9 2020).
14. S. Capozziello, C. Altucci, F. Bajardi, A. Basti, N. Beverini, G. Carelli, D. Ciampini, A. D. V. Di Virgilio, F. Fuso, U. Giacomelli, E. Maccioni, P. Marsili, A. Ortolan, A. Porzio, A. Simonelli, G. Terreni and R. Velotta, Constraining theories of gravity by GINGER experiment, *Eur. Phys. J. Plus* **136**, p. 394 (2021).
15. A. Simonelli, J. Belfi, N. Beverini, A. D. V. Di Virgilio, U. Giacomelli, G. De Luca and H. Igel, Love waves trains observed after the MW 8.1 Tehuantepec earthquake by an underground ring laser gyroscope, in *AGU Fall Meeting, S33G-2954* (New Orleans, 2017).
16. A. Simonelli, H. Igel, J. Wassermann, J. Belfi, A. Di Virgilio, N. Beverini, G. De Luca and G. Saccorotti, Rotational motions from the 2016, Central Italy seismic sequence, as observed by an underground ring laser gyroscope, *Geophysical Journal International* **214**, 705 (7 2018).
17. A. Simonelli, G. De Luca, U. Giacomelli, G. Terreni and A. Di Virgilio, Observation by Means of An Underground Ring Laser Gyroscope of Love Waves Generated in the Mediterranean Sea: Source Direction and Comparison with Models, *Seismological Research Letters* (3 2020).
18. U. Giacomelli, Geometry control and stabilization of a large ring laser gyroscope, PhD thesis, Università di Pisa.

Dark gravitomagnetism with LISA and gravitational waves space detectors

A. Tartaglia

OATo, INAF and DISAT, Politecnico
Corso Duca degli Abruzzi 24, 10129 Torino, Italy
E-mail: angelo.tartaglia@inaf.it
www.polito.it

M. Bassan and G. Pucacco

Dip. Fisica, Tor Vergata University and INFN/Roma2, Via della Ricerca Scientifica 1
00133 Rome, Italy
E-mail: bassan@roma2.infn.it

V. Ferroni and D. Vetrugno

Dip. Fisica, Trento University and TIFPA, Via Sommarive 14
38123 Povo TN, Italy
E-mail: valerio.ferroni@unitn.it

We present here the proposal to use the LISA interferometer for detecting the gravitomagnetic field due to the rotation of the Milky Way, including the contribution given by the dark matter halo. The galactic signal would be superposed to the gravitomagnetic field of the Sun. The technique to be used is based on the asymmetric propagation of light along the closed contour of the space interferometer (Sagnac-like approach). Both principle and practical aspects of the proposed experiment are discussed. The strategy for disentangling the sought for signal from the kinematic terms due to proper rotation and orbital motion is based on the time modulation of the time of flight asymmetry. Such modulation will be originated by the annual oscillation of the plane of the interferometer with respect to the galactic plane. Also the effect of the gravitomagnetic field on the polarization of the electromagnetic signals is presented as an in principle detectable phenomenon.

Keywords: Gravito-magnetism; Galactic halo; Sagnac effect; Space interferometers.

1. Introduction

Among the possible space-times consistent with the Einstein equations and with various matter distributions, a special interest deserve those endowed with a chiral symmetry about the time axis of a given observer. The chiral symmetry may sometime appear as a simple local coordinates artifact, in which case the symmetry disappears with an appropriate choice of the reference frame. Clearly, the most interesting situations are when the symmetry is indeed in the curvature of space-time, which happens when the source of gravity is a spinning mass distribution. In terms of the metric tensor, the presence of the symmetry we are interested in is manifested by non-null time-space off-diagonal terms. It is of course always possible to choose a local reference frame where all off-diagonal terms are brought to zero, but this is in general not possible *globally*, when the source of gravity is spinning. In weak field conditions (the most common situation in the universe) the symmetry we are considering appears in the form of a *gravito-magnetic* field. The name derives from the fact that in weak field approximation the Einstein equations assume a form quite similar to Maxwell's equations of electromagnetism (e.m.), so that the interaction between moving masses (just as moving charges in e.m.) may be described in terms of forces due to two vector fields: the *gravito-electric* (analogous to the electric field, but always attractive), and the *gravito-magnetic* field (analogous to the magnetic field of classical e.m.). This formalism is well known and we refer to the vast literature and to basic texts of general relativity (GR): see for example Ref. [1].

It is, however, worth remarking that the gravito-magnetic force is usually much weaker than the gravito-electric one, making thus hard to identify measurable effects. So far, physically relevant phenomena associated with the aforementioned symmetry are expected, upstream of any approximation, in strong field conditions such as near Kerr black holes or, when the gravito-electromagnetic approximation is applied, in the behaviour of peculiar systems where gravity is still strong enough to allow the gravito-magnetic component to emerge in an observable way. The latter is the case of the double pulsar, whose internal dynamics, readable from the signals received by our radiotelescopes, indirectly hints to the gravito-magnetic (GM) interactions between the spins and the orbital motions of the two stars in the pair.[2]

In the Solar System, the effects due to the angular momenta of the Sun and of the planets are extremely weak. Until now the only measured effects are those of the terrestrial gravito-magnetic field. They have been observed monitoring the motion of the moon along its orbit by Laser ranging[3] and doing the same with the LAGEOS and LAGEOS2 satellites:[4] what was found was the Lense-Thirring drag[5] on their motion. Direct evidence has been obtained by the dedicated Gravity Probe B experiment which measured the induced precession on gyroscopes carried on a circumterrestrial satellite in polar orbit.[6] Laser ranging is also the main tool used to analyze the orbit of the dedicated LARES mission, which is producing the best accuracy so far for the GM field of the Earth.[7] On the surface of our planet it is expected to measure the GM field using ring lasers.[8–10]

A way to compensate for the weakness of the sought effects is to use very large sensors and measuring devices, that could not be hosted on a single spacecraft or in a laboratory on Earth. This is one of the reasons pushing toward peculiar configurations of a plurality of measuring devices in space, either around the Earth[11] or at the scale of the inner solar system.[12]

An extremely interesting opportunity is the LISA interferometer,[13] designed and under development for detecting gravitational waves. What we propose here is to use LISA, which, as we shall see, is already fit for the purpose, also to reveal the GM field in which the device is immersed. The interesting sources that could be studied are both the solar angular momentum and the angular momentum of the Milky Way (or, to say better, the part of it which is relevant for the solar system). A further reason of interest for the galactic angular momentum is that it reasonably depends both on the visible and on the dark component of our galaxy. So far, dark matter (DM), which is an important ingredient of the cosmic cocktail, is postulated only on the basis of its direct gravitational (gravito-electric) effect. However, if DM exists and we trust GR, we may expect also phenomena related to the proper rotation of DM distributions. It is currently accepted that most galaxies (including ours) are immersed in huge DM halos; if so, it is also reasonable to expect such halos to rotate together with the visible part of the galaxy: in fact, if dark and visible interact gravitationally, any little localized inhomogeneity on one side or the other acts as a hook that drags or brakes the other component so that, after some remote transitory, both end up revolving together. The consequence is that DM should represent a relevant contribution to the angular momentum of the whole, then to the GM component of the gravitational interaction.

In what follows we outline how LISA could be used to measure both the angular momentum of the Sun and of the Milky Way. Reliable estimates of the angular momentum of the visible Milky Way exist: by difference, we could thus measure the galactic Dark content.

2. Internal space-time of the Milky Way

Globally and in the first instance we can attribute an axial symmetry to the distribution of matter of the Milky Way and imagine also that it is in uniform rotation condition (stationary space-time). If so the typical line element may be written as follows:

$$ds^2 = U(r,z)c^2 dt^2 - 2N(r,z)r d\phi c dt - W(r,z)r^2 d\phi^2 - Q(r,z)(dr^2 + dz^2) \quad (1)$$

Cylindrical space coordinates have been used. An additional symmetry we assume is reflection symmetry about the galactic plane. U, N, W, Q are dimensionless functions of r and z only. They are everywhere regular (except possibly in the origin). The only constraint expressing the reflection symmetry is

$$\frac{\partial U}{\partial z}\bigg|_{z=0} = \frac{\partial N}{\partial z}\bigg|_{z=0} = \frac{\partial W}{\partial z}\bigg|_{z=0} = \frac{\partial Q}{\partial z}\bigg|_{z=0} = 0 \quad (2)$$

Our interest is on the view point of an observer at rest with the Sun, so for the moment it is convenient to assume that the r axis is corotating with the Milky Way. This assumption does not spoil the symmetry we have assumed, but implies that the U, N, W, Q functions implicitly include also the effects of the choice of the observer (which in general treatments is assumed to be at rest with the center of the mass distribution and located at infinity, whereas here it is co-moving with the Sun).

We cannot a priori say more about the shape of the functions because we are considering an observer inside the mass distribution (visible or dark it may be) and we do not know exact solutions of Einstein's equations within a rotating distribution of matter. Nonetheless, if we succeed in detecting specific effects of the rotation of the Milky Way, we may also deduce relevant information on the way DM is distributed. This is because the non trivial parts of the elements of the metric tensor contain the mass density of the Milky Way and the rotation curve of the stars in it: since we know how the visible mass is distributed and the rotation curve of the galaxy (which we have assumed to be the same for DM also), from the evaluation of the total GM field we may deduce relevant information on the DM density distribution, which contributes to the effect.

2.1. *Galactic gravito-magnetism*

Line element (1) is quite general, but we may equally well adopt the language and the images of the weak field, since that is indeed the case. We may also focus our attention on the situation on and near the galactic plane considering that the Sun is not far from it. This said, we read the ratio N/U as the only non-zero component of a three-vector, which is the analog of the vector potential $\bar{A}$ of classical electromagnetism.[14]

Under the above conditions, whenever the metric tensor is independent of time the equation of geodesic motion can be written in a form analogous to Lorentz's equation of e.m.

$$\frac{d^2\bar{x}}{dt^2} = -c^2\left(\bar{\nabla}U - 2\frac{\bar{v}}{c}\times\bar{\nabla}\times\bar{A}_g\right) \qquad (3)$$

$\bar{v}$ and $\bar{x}$ are the three-dimensional velocity and position of the test mass with respect to the observer. The functions U and $\bar{A}_g$ are given in terms of the elements of the metric tensor $g_{\mu\nu}$ by:

$$U = g_{00}; \quad A_{(g)i} = \frac{g_{0i}}{g_{00}} \qquad (4)$$

In our case it is

$$\bar{A}_g = \left(0, \frac{N}{U}, 0\right) \quad \text{or} \quad \bar{A}_g = \frac{N}{U}\hat{\phi} \qquad (5)$$

Here $\hat{\phi}$ is the unit transverse vector in the direction of rotations about the symmetry axis. Our space basis for covariant vectors is $(dr, rd\phi, dz)$ so that all components of $\bar{A}_g$ are dimensionless and the field lines of the vector are circles centered on the space symmetry axis, contained in planes perpendicular to that axis. The next step, formally recognizing the weak field approximation, is to calculate a *gravito-magnetic field* $\bar{B}_g$ from $\bar{A}_g$ just in the same way we would do in classical electromagnetism:

$$\bar{B}_g = \bar{\nabla}\times\bar{A}_g = \frac{N}{U}\left(\frac{\partial_z U}{U} - \frac{\partial_z N}{N}\right)\hat{r} + \frac{N}{U}\left(\frac{\partial_r N}{N} - \frac{\partial_r U}{U}\right)\hat{z} \qquad (6)$$

∂_r and ∂_z are a shorthand notation for $\partial/\partial r$ and $\partial/\partial z$; each component of $\bar{B}_g$ has the dimension of the inverse of a length.

If we limit ourselves to the symmetry plane (the galactic plane) the r component of the field vanishes and the vector turns out to be perpendicular to the plane, then parallel to the axis of the Milky Way.

3. The propagation of light

In the peculiar space-time we are considering, the propagation of light displays an interesting behaviour. Whenever some physical device (mirrors, waveguides or else) constrains light to move along a closed path, the time of flight (ToF) it takes to make a full turn is different depending on whether the travel is right- or respectively left-handed. The sense of the circulation is with respect to the field lines of $\bar{B}_g$.

Actually this asymmetry is not peculiar of light only. It holds true for any signal or voyager, provided its velocity is locally the same in both directions at any position along the path.[15] The effect we are recalling is sometimes improperly called 'Sagnac effect', though the latter is an effect of special instead of general relativity and concerns the non inertial rotational motion of the observer rather than the curvature of space-time.

When considering the situation from a four-dimensional viewpoint, light leaves the source at a given event of the worldline of the observer, then comes back to the observer at a different point along its worldline: the path is of course open. When starting in the opposite direction, the light ray will meet again the observer at a different event of its worldline. Locally measuring the proper time (τ) difference between the arrivals (the length of the intercepted interval of the observer's worldline) we deduce an information concerning the proper angular momentum of the source of gravity (possibly combined with rotational motion of the observer, if it is present).

The difference in proper time can be expressed in terms of the components of the metric tensor. Using the standard notation of GR we have:[16]

$$\Delta\tau = -\frac{2}{c}\sqrt{g_{00}} \oint \frac{g_{0i}}{g_{00}} dx^i \qquad i = 1, 2, 3 \qquad (7)$$

The square root of g_{00} is evaluated at the position of the observer and accounts for the gravitational field there; it does not coincide with the g_{00} under the integral sign, since the latter expresses the gravitational field along the integration path. Here x^i is a generic space coordinate and the integration is performed along the space closed contour traveled by the light beam.

Restricting the description to the space-time with the symmetries described above, and using the typical notation of gravito-electromagnetism, the time delay becomes:

$$|\Delta\tau| = \frac{2}{c}\sqrt{U} \oint A_{gi} dx^i = \frac{2}{c}\sqrt{U} \int \bar{B}_g \cdot \hat{u}_n dS \qquad (8)$$

The last term on the right is obtained applying the Stokes theorem of usual three-dimensional geometry and converts the line integral into a flux; dS is the surface element of the area contoured by the closed path in space and $\hat{u}_n$ is the unit three-vector perpendicular to the given surface element.

3.1. *Galactic gravito-magnetism in the Solar System*

Our purpose is to consider an experiment carried out at the scale of the inner solar system and indeed at the Earth's orbit. The galactic GM field $\bar{B}_g$ does in fact depend on the distance from the center of the Milky Way. The Sun is approximately $R_S \cong 2.35 \times 10^{20}$m (28,000 light years) away from the center of the Milky Way. If we think of an instrument revolving around the Sun in correspondence of the orbit of our planet, its distance from the center of the Milky Way changes at most by plus or minus 1 astronomical unit (AU), i.e. $\Delta R_S \sim 3 \times 10^{11}$ m. The relative fluctuation of the distance, under these conditions, would then be $\Delta R_S/R_S \sim 10^{-9}$. Even though we have no explicit expression for the functions appearing in line element (1), just looking at what happens in electromagnetic analogies, we may reasonably expect $\Delta B_g/B_g$ to be of the same order of magnitude as $\Delta R_S/R_S$. If so, if we additionally assume such a relative change to be negligible for our purposes, it follows that in practice $\bar{B}_g$ of the Milky Way is a constant for our experiment. Under this assumption eq. (8) simplifies to:

$$|\Delta \tau| \cong \frac{2}{c}\sqrt{U} B_g S \cos\gamma \qquad (9)$$

S is now the total area enclosed in the path of light, assuming that the contour is contained in a plane; γ is the angle between the perpendicular to that plane and the direction of the gravito-magnetic field of the Milky Way at the Sun. As far as the Sun may be considered to lay in the galactic plane, the direction of $\bar{B}_g$ coincides with that of the axis of the Milky Way.

If we are able to measure $|\Delta \tau|$, we may then deduce from eq. (9) information on U and in particular on N, since U, being related to the local ordinary gravitational potential, can also be obtained by other means.

4. Space interferometers and LISA

It follows from previous considerations and from eq. (9) that a good strategy to detect the presence of a gravito-magnetic field is to resort to the measurement of time asymmetries in the propagation of light; eqs. (8) and (9) show that we need a vast area S in order to enhance the sensitivity of the experiment. This is why appropriate configurations of receivers and transponders in space are particularly interesting. For instance, it has been proposed[11] to use constellations of satellites around the Earth (such as the Galileos), but even more appropriate and promising may be the opportunity to use LISA, an orbiting interferometer designed to detect gravitational waves around the mHz frequency band.

LISA will monitor the distance between pairs of free falling test masses (TM) at a distance $L = 2.5$ million km with a continuous interferometric laser ranging scheme to detect strain distance variation due to gravitational waves. The TM pairs will be lodged in three spacecraft arranged to form a big equilateral triangular constellation. So far we considered the observer as being co-moving with the Sun, but actually the plane of the LISA constellation will form an angle $\beta = 30°$ with the ecliptic plane and that plane is at an angle $\alpha \simeq 60°$ with respect to the galactic plane; the whole constellation will rotate around the Sun at a distance of 1 AU, lagging by $20°$ the orbit of the Earth; it will also rotate on its plane, around the center of mass, with the same 1 year period. The geometry of such configuration is shown in Fig. 1.

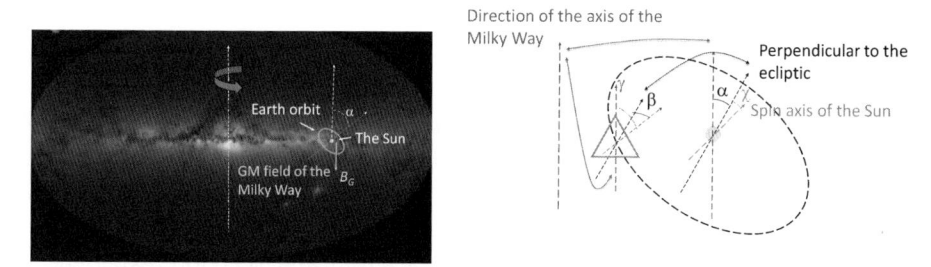

Fig. 1. The LISA interferometer in the Milky Way. a) (left) Freely falling constellation in the terrestrial orbit. b) (right) Orientation of the triangular constellation with respect to the galaxy and to the ecliptic.

Keplerian dynamics causes, in the yearly rotation period, changes of up to 10^4 km in armlength and 10 m/s in spacecraft velocity: this phenomenon, called *flexing* of the arms, forbids equal path interferometry. However, the use of post-processing techniques (Time Delay Interferometry: TDI)[17,18] allows to synthesise equal arm interferometry to better than 1 ns. Among TDI combinations there are several that mimic the output of a Sagnac interferometer,[19,20] thus suppressing the GW signals. By interfering electromagnetic signals traveling in opposite directions along the LISA triangle, we could measure the ToF difference at one of the corners: Eq. (8) will then allow us to deduce the intensity of the gravito-magnetic flux through the interferometer.

In the reference frame comoving with the spacecraft, $\bar{B}_g$ will contain various contributions including those due to the proper and orbital motion of the device (Sagnac effect). The components of interest would be the galactic contribution (both from visible and dark matter) and the gravito-magnetic field originating from the angular momentum of the Sun. In principle also the Earth and other planets would contribute, but it is easily verified that those components would indeed be much weaker than the galactic and solar ones.

4.1. *Gravito-magnetism from the Sun*

The GM field of the Sun, $\bar{B}_{g\odot}$, has a simple form, as long as our star is treated as a compact spherical spinning source. The configuration of the field is dipolar and in the solar equatorial plane, where $\bar{B}_{g\odot}$ is perpendicular to the plane, it is (net of kinematic contributions, i.e. for a non-rotating observer in a Sun-centered reference frame)[8]

$$\bar{B}_{g\odot} = \frac{2G}{c^3 r^3} \bar{J}_\odot = 2.8 \cdot 10^{-28} \mathrm{m}^{-1} \qquad (10)$$

G is Newton's constant and $\bar{J}_\odot$ is the angular momentum of the Sun; r is the observer's distance from the center of the star.

In our approximation, we can take $U = 1 - 2\frac{GM_\odot}{c^2 r} \simeq 1$, and the ToF asymmetry, for the solar effect alone, would then be:

$$|\Delta\tau|_\odot \simeq \frac{2}{c} \int |\bar{B}_{g\odot}| \cos\eta\, dS \simeq \frac{4G}{c^4} \int \frac{|\bar{J}_\odot|}{r^3} \cos\eta\, dS \qquad (11)$$

The flux is calculated over the LISA triangle: actually, the area of the constellation is tilted with respect to the ecliptic, and this has two consequences: 1) part of the area is slightly above and part slightly below the ecliptic plane so that there $\bar{B}_{g\odot}$ has also a small radial component; and 2) the three spacecrafts have different instantaneous distances from the Sun ($\delta r/r \lesssim 0.6\%$) and therefore experience a different strength of the dipolar field. In the following, we shall neglect, for sake of simplicity, both corrections. η is the angle between the normal to the plane of the triangle and the axis of the Sun. Since the latter is in turn inclined with respect to the north of the ecliptic[21] by the angle $\chi \simeq 7°$, η changes periodically during the year oscillating between $\eta_{min} = \beta - \chi$ and $\eta_{max} = \beta + \chi$; β and χ are shown in Fig. 1b.

5. Proposed measurements

The experiment we would like to consider uses LISA as the triangular closed path along which e.m. signals are sent in opposite directions, in order to measure the ToF difference. Letting, for the moment, all practical problems aside, we note a multiplicity of contributions simultaneously acting upon the interferometer. GR is a non-linear theory so that, in principle, it is not an easy task to disentangle the various terms. In particular, beside the solar and galactic contribution, we have the kinematic terms related to the rotational movements of the configuration, i.e. the proper rotation of the triangle, its orbital motion around the Sun and the rotation of the Sun about the axis of the Milky Way. These kinematic terms may legitimately be considered as manifestations of the Sagnac effect; in a treatment that wanted to be "exact" all terms (both kinematic signals and "physical" i.e. GM terms) combine non-linearly with each other, so that it is extremely difficult to distinguish them. Fortunately, the fact that all effects are small or very small (the GM terms are expected to be much weaker than the kinematic ones) helps us, in the sense that in an approximate treatment we are allowed to truncate the expansion at the lowest order. Indeed the lowest approximation is the linear one where a simple superposition principle is applied.

Even accepting the linear approximation, the problem remains of separating the different addends of the sum. This separation would be possible if we knew at least the kinematic terms with an accuracy better than the size of the unknown "physical" contributions. This is a difficult task, because the gravitomagnetic effect is expected to be many orders of magnitude smaller than the Sagnac effect; we need some sort of signature that highlights the terms of interest and the "marking" we may exploit is the time dependence of the signals. Looking at Fig. 1b we see that our triangle oscillates yearly with respect to the galactic plane between an angle $\gamma_{max} \simeq \alpha + \beta$ and an angle $\gamma_{min} \simeq \alpha - \beta$, where $\alpha \simeq 60°$ is the angle between the ecliptic and galactic planes. The oscillation is not simply sinusoidal and we use $\simeq$ instead of just $=$ because the axes of the Milky Way, of the ecliptic and of the LISA triangle never turn out to be exactly co-planar. Furthermore, when looking at the solar contribution, we find the already mentioned oscillation with respect to the solar spin axis.

Thus, both GM contributions exhibit yearly periodicity but with a different phase, whereas the Sagnac effect is nearly constant with small harmonic components (including the yearly one) due to flexing, which can be, in principle, calculated and subtracted.

As for the detectable signal, we may estimate its minimal amplitude for the Sun GM from eq. (11), with a LISA constellation area, neglecting the above mentioned oscillations, $S = (\sqrt{3}/4)L^2 \simeq 2.7 \times 10^{18} m^2$. The target displacement sensitivity for LISA, is $c|\Delta \tau_{min}| \sim 10^{-11}$ m. With this sensitivity both the solar GM and the galactic one should be detectable by LISA (see Fig. 2), although with marginal signal to noise ratio.

Eq. 9 shows that the minimum detectable GM field would then be

$$B_{(min)} \sim 1.8 \times 10^{-30} m^{-1} \qquad (12)$$

In order to see what this number means, consider that the terrestrial GM field on the surface of the Earth (at the equator) is $\sim 10^{-22} m^{-1}$. Proper Sagnac terms (which depend on the angular velocities around the Sun, around the constellation center and around the galactic center) are many orders of magnitude larger than the value in eq.(12), whereas the solar contribution is only a factor 100 above the minimum detectable signal. On the basis of estimates of the angular momentum of the visible mass, the galactic GM field is expected to be just above the edge of detectability.

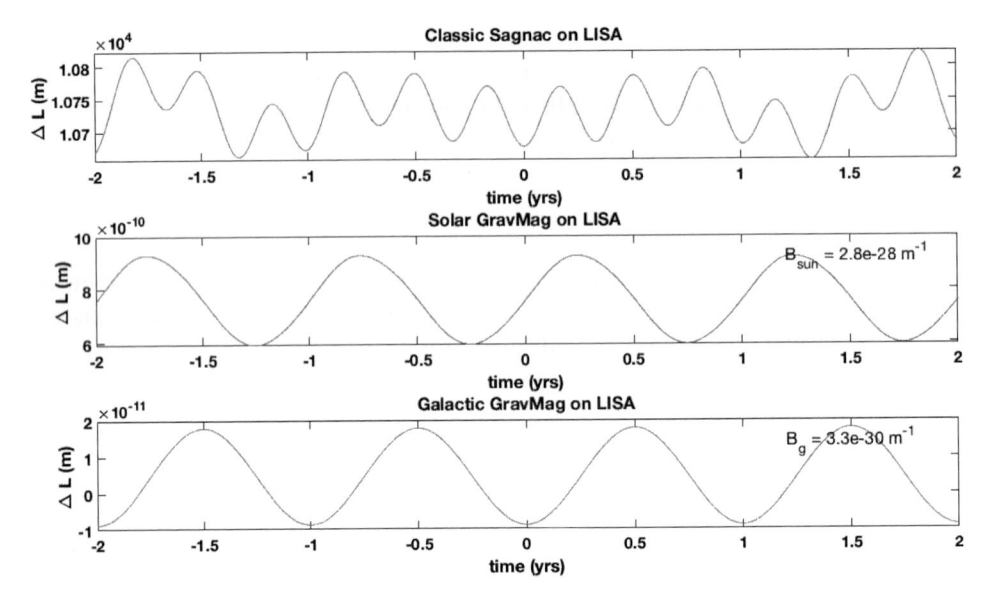

Fig. 2. Time dependence of the expected signals (expressed as lengths) on a noiseless LISA constellation:

TOP: Sagnac effect, due to the triangle rotations both around the Sun and around its center. The signal has an almost constant value, with small ($\sim 1\%$) oscillations due to the flexing of the arms and ensuing change of the area.

MIDDLE: GM effect from the Sun; the yearly modulation is due to the inclination of $J_\odot$ with respect to the ecliptic.

BOTTOM: signal from the galactic Gravito Magnetism; this measurement would be performed *within* the source mass current, and no certainties can be offered about its strength. We hypothesized, for this plot, a field $B_{MW} = 3 \cdot 10^{-30} m^{-1}$, neglecting the contribution of the external part of the Milky Way (that would actually act to reduce this strength).

6. GM effect on light polarization

The only GM effect we have considered so far is the asymmetry in the ToF of light, but there are other consequences to be considered. The analogy with classical e.m. suggests that we may also expect the analog of the Faraday effect. In other words, if a linearly polarized light beam propagates along the field lines of a GM field the direction of the polarization vector should rotate around the direction of the propagation.[23]

Using the formalism of GR, the electromagnetic field is described (in four dimensions) by the so called Faraday anti-symmetric tensor $F_{\mu\nu}$ and, regardless of any approximation, when there is propagation producing a four-dimensional area $\delta S^{0i} = (\delta\tau \delta x^i) = (\delta x^i)^2/c$ (movement along the direction of x^i at the speed of light) the corresponding change in $F_{\mu\nu}$ is

$$\delta F^{\mu\nu} = (R^\mu_{\epsilon 0 i} F^{\epsilon\nu} + R^\nu_{\epsilon 0 i} F^{\mu\epsilon})\delta S^{0i} \qquad (13)$$

$R^\mu_{\nu\lambda\rho}$ are the components of the Riemann tensor which account for the curvature of space-time.

Whenever the propagation takes place over a distance l in a direction non-perpendicular to the GM field, the change in the Faraday tensor corresponds to a rotation of the polarization vector of the wave around the propagation line by an angle ψ:[23]

$$\psi \simeq -\frac{\sqrt{g_{00}}}{2} \bar{B}_g \cdot \bar{l} = \pm \frac{l}{2} \frac{N}{\sqrt{U}} \left(\frac{\partial_r N}{N} - \frac{\partial_r U}{U} \right) \qquad (14)$$

The last expression in Eq. (14) refers to the case of the Milky Way and uses the notation introduced in Eq. (6) applied on the galactic plane and for light travelling in a direction perpendicular to that plane.

The solar GM will produce, in any LISA arm, a rotation of the polarization plane of $\sim 3 \cdot 10^{-19}$ prad. The two laser beams propagating in each arm in opposite directions would undergo opposite rotations. In principle the effect would cumulate with the laser beam going around the constellation if the transmission of the light from satellite to satellite preserves the polarization. LISA will use linearly polarized light for the strain measurements. The unwanted polarisation component present in the received beam will be removed, when entering the measurement chain, by a PBS (polarising beam splitter); this fraction, containing the GM signal, could be in principle detected by an additional, dedicated photo diode. In fact, in the LISA-Pathfinder (LPF) mission it has been observed that, because of non perfect performance of the PBS, part of this light can still contaminate the strain measurement, yielding additional noise in the form of read-out noise and spurious laser pressure. Thus the GM rotation effect in LISA would possibly result in a decreased sensitivity of the observatory. That signal could be reconstructed in post-processing, as it was done in LPF, using a well shaped model of the measurement chain.[22]

7. Conclusion

We have discussed the relevant sources that could contribute to the gravito-magnetic field in the solar system far from the planets and within 1 AU from the Sun. In particular we have considered the relevance of the field in producing an asymmetry in the propagation of electromagnetic signals along closed space paths. We have then discussed the possibility to use the big triangle formed by the LISA satellite constellation applying an approach similar to that of the Sagnac effect.

A quantitative evaluation of the effects shows that the sensitivity of such an arrangement would be sufficient to measure the solar GM field. Such measurement would give an important information on the internal structure of the Sun, from which the angular momentum of our star depends. But LISA, used à la Sagnac, would probably be able to reveal the weak GM field of the Milky Way as well. This is increasingly interesting and important since the galactic gravitomagnetism depends of course on the distribution of visible matter in the Milky Way, but also, in a non marginal way, on the presence of dark matter, that, on the whole, is expected to have a mass much greater than that visible.

The GM field also causes a rotation of the polarization of the e.m. signals that will travel along the arms of the interferometer. The effect is tiny, and its detection is extremely challenging, but should in principle be considered, in view of future technological advances. This would yield additional and complementary information on the intensity of the field.

LISA will send its "raw" data to Earth, to be off-line processed and syntethized in interferometric signals: in view of this strategy, pursuing the search for GM signatures on the data, a challenging, though not impossible task, should require no further hardware development, and no additional task for the mission.

For these reasons and for the importance of the objectives pursued it would be worthwhile to carry out the experiment.

References

1. Misner C. W., Thorne K. S. and Wheeler J. A., *Gravitation* (Freeman, New York, 1973).
2. Breton R. P. et al., *Relativistic Spin Precession in the Double Pulsar* - Science **321**, 104 (2008).
3. Nordtvedt K., *Lunar Laser Ranging - a comprehensive probe of post-Newtonian gravity* in Proceedings of Villa Mondragone International School of Gravitation and Cosmology, 2002; arXiv, gr-qc/0301024 (2003).
4. Ciufolini I. and Pavlis E. C., *A confirmation of the general relativistic prediction of the Lense-Thirring effect* - Nature, **431** (7011) 958 (2004).
5. Lense J. and Thirring H., Phys. Z. **19**, 156 (1918); the English translation is available in B. Mashhoon, F.W. Hehl, and D. S. Theiss, Gen. Relativ. Gravit. **16**, 711 (1984).
6. Everitt, C. W. F., et al., *Gravity probe B: Final results of a space experiment to test general relativity*, Phys. Rev. Lett. **10**, 221101 (2011).
7. Lucchesi, D. M. et al., *A 1% Measurement of the Gravitomagnetic Field of the Earth with Laser-Tracked Satellites* Universe **6**, 139 (2020).
8. Bosi F. et al., *Measuring gravitomagnetic effects by a multi-ring-laser gyroscope*, Phys. Rev. D **84**, 122002-1–122002-23 (2011).
9. Di Virgilio, A. et al., *A ring lasers array for fundamental physics*, C. R. Phys. **15**, 866–874 (2014).
10. Tartaglia, A., et al., *Testing general relativity by means of ring lasers*, Eur. Phys. J. Plus **132**, 73 (2017).
11. Ruggiero M. L. and Tartaglia A., *Test of gravitomagnetism with satellites around the Earth*, European Physical Journal Plus, **134**, 205 (2019).
12. Tartaglia A. et al., *Detecting the gravito-magnetic field of the dark halo of the Milky Way - the LaDaHaD mission concept*, Experimental Astronomy, https://doi.org/10.1007/s10686-021-09700-4 (2021).
13. Wanner G. et al., *Space-based gravitational wave detection and how LISA Pathfinder successfully paved the way*, Nature Physics 15 200-202, 2019.
14. Tartaglia A., *Rotation Effects and The Gravito-Magnetic Approach*, in *General Relativity and Gravitational Physics: 16th Sigrav Conference on General Relativity and Gravitational Physics*; G. Esposito, G. Lambiase, G. Marmo, G. Scarpetta and G. Vilasi Eds., (AIP Conference Proceedings **751**, 136-145, 2005); https://doi.org/10.1063/1.1891538.

15. Ruggiero M. L. and Tartaglia A., *A note on the Sagnac effect for matter beams*, Eur. Phys. J. Plus **130**, 90 (2015).
16. Kajari E., Buser M., Feiler C. and Schleich W. P., *Rotation in relativity and the propagation of light*, Riv. Nuovo Cimento Soc. Ital. Fis. **32**, 339 (2009).
17. Tinto M. and J. W. Armstrong, *Cancellation of laser noise in an unequal-arm interferometer detector of gravitational radiation* Phys. Rev. D 59, 102003 (1999).
18. Cornish N. Neil J. Cornish and Hellings R. W. *The effects of orbital motion on LISA time delay interferometry*, Class. Quantum Grav. 20 4851 (2003).
19. Shaddock D., *Operating LISA as a Sagnac interferometer*, Phys. Rev. D 69, 022001 (2004).
20. Muratore M., Vetrugno D. and Vitale S., *Revisitation of time delay interferometry combinations that suppress laser noise in LISA*, Class. Quantum Grav. 37, 185019 (2020).
21. Pijpers, F. P., *Helioseismic determination of the solar gravitational quadrupole moment* Monthly Notices of the Royal Astronomical Society **297**, L76-L80 (1998).
22. Kaune B., *In-orbit Stability Analysis of the LISA Pathfinder Optical Metrology: Photoreceivers and Polarisation*, Doctoral Thesis, Der Fakultät für Mathematik und Physik der Gottfried Wilhelm Leibniz Universität Hannover, 2021.
23. Ruggiero M. L. and Tartaglia A., *Gravitational Faraday rotation in binary pulsar systems*, Monthly Notices of the Royal Astronomical Society, **374**, 847-851 (2007).

Light rays in the Solar system experiments: Phases and displacements

Pravin Kumar Dahal* and Daniel R. Terno

Department of Physics and Astronomy, Macquarie University,
Sydney, NSW 2109, Australia
* E-mail: pravin-kumar.dahal@hdr.mq.edu.au

Geometric optics approximation is sufficient to describe the effects in the near-Earth environment. In this framework Faraday rotation is purely a reference frame (gauge) effect. However, it cannot be simply dismissed. Establishing local reference frame with respect to some distant stars leads to the Faraday phase error between the ground station and the spacecraft of the order of 10^{-10} in the leading post-Newtonian expansion of the Earth's gravitational field. While the Wigner phase of special relativity is of the order 10^{-4}–10^{-5}. Both types of errors can be simultaneously mitigated by simple encoding procedures. We also present briefly the covariant formulation of geometric optic correction up to the subleading order approximation, which is necessary for the propagation of electromagnetic/gravitational waves of large but finite frequencies. We use this formalism to obtain a closed form of the polarization dependent correction of the light ray trajectory in the leading order in a weak spherically symmetric gravitational field.

Keywords: Geometric optics; Wigner phase; Gravitational Faraday rotation; Post-Newtonian expansion; Gravitational spin Hall effect.

1. Introduction

Space deployment of quantum technology[1–3] brings it into a weakly relativistic regime. As an unintended but fortunate side effect, low-Earth orbit (LEO) quantum communication satellites provide new opportunities to test fundamental physics. Once the tiny putative physical effects fall within the sensitivity range of these devices, they may impose constraints on practical quantum communications, timekeeping, or remote sensing tasks.[4–6] A more futuristic technology, such as the proposed solar gravity telescope[7–9] actually needs the general-relativistic effects for its operation.

For flying qubits that are implemented as polarization states of photons[10] the dominant source of relativistic errors in this setting is the Wigner rotation (or phase), an effect special relativity (SR).[4,6] Gravitational polarization rotation, also known as the gravitational Faraday effect[11,12] occurs in a variety of astrophysical systems, such as accretion disks around astrophysical black hole candidates[13] or gravitational lensing.[14] This effect was the subject of a large number of theoretical investigations, primarily within the geometric optics approximation,[11,12,14–17] and also from the perspective of quantum communications.[18] Interpretation of these results was until recently sometimes contradictory, as it is important to carefully analyze the relation between the reference frames of the emitter and the detector. Moreover, even if at the leading order the gravitationally induced polarization rotation in the near-Earth environment is pure gauge effect, it cannot be simply dismissed. We provide a simple estimation of this emitter- and observer-dependent phase and give its explicit form in several settings.

Already in the leading post-eikonal order trajectories of light beams are affected by polarization.[19–21] The optical gravitational spin Hall effect has recently received a comprehensive treatment in Refs. 22, 23. Using this formalism we obtain a closed form of the leading correction in case of a weak spherically symmetric gravitational field. As expected, on the scale of the Solar system — be it the near-Earth environment or a focal plane of the solar gravity telescope at 600a.u.— the effect is negligible. However, it is interesting conceptually and its scaling indicates that it may play a much more important role in the strong gravity regions.[23]

The rest of this article is organized as follows. In Sec. 2 we review the SR effects. Polarization rotation in general stationary spacetimes is described in Sec. 3, where we also evaluate the effects in communication with Earth-orbiting satellites. In Sec. 4 we briefly summarize the main techniques of Refs. 22, 23 and then obtain the polarization-dependent changes in the light ray trajectories in the solar system experiments.

We work with $c = \hbar = G = 1$. The constants G and c are restored in a small number of expressions where their presence is helpful. The spacetime metric $g_{\mu\nu}$ has a signature $-+++$. The four-vectors are distinguished by the sans font, k, $k^\mu = (\mathsf{k})^\mu$. The three-dimensional spatial metric is denoted as γ_{mn}, and three-dimensional vectors are set in boldface, **k**, or are referred to by their explicit coordinate form, k^m. The inner product in the metric γ is denoted as $\mathbf{k}\cdot\mathbf{f}$, and the unit vectors in this metric are distinguished by the caret, $\hat{\mathbf{k}}$, $\hat{\mathbf{k}}\cdot\hat{\mathbf{k}} \equiv 1$. Post-Newtonian calculations employ a fiducial Euclidean space. Euclidean vectors are distinguished by arrows, $\vec{k}$. Components of the two types of vectors may coincide, $(\mathbf{v})^m = (\vec{b})^m$, but $\vec{b}\cdot\vec{k} = \sum_{k=1}^3 v^m k^m$. Accordingly, the coordinate distance is the Euclidean length of the radius vector, $r \equiv \sqrt{\vec{x}\cdot\vec{x}}$.

2. Wigner rotation and special relativistic effects

Consider one round of communications between the ground station (GS) and a low energy orbit spacecraft (SC). The problem is most conveniently analyzed in the geocentric system, the origin of which coincides with the centre of the Earth at the moment of emission. If we direct the z-axis of the system along the Earth's angular momentum, then the velocity **v** of the GS lies in the xy-plane. Whereas, the velocity **u** of the SC and the initial propagation direction $\hat{\mathbf{k}}$ are arbitrary when expressed in the global frame. This setting is depicted in Fig. 1.

Quantum states of a photon with a definite four-momentum $\mathsf{k} = (|\mathbf{k}|, \mathbf{k})$ can be represented either as Hilbert space vectors or as complex polarization vectors in the usual three-dimensional space,

$$|\Psi_\mathsf{k}\rangle = f_+|\mathsf{k},+\rangle + f_-|\mathsf{k},-\rangle \quad \Leftrightarrow \quad \hat{\mathbf{f}}_\mathbf{k} = f_+\hat{\mathbf{b}}_{\hat{\mathbf{k}}}^+ + f_-\hat{\mathbf{b}}_{\hat{\mathbf{k}}}^-, \qquad (1)$$

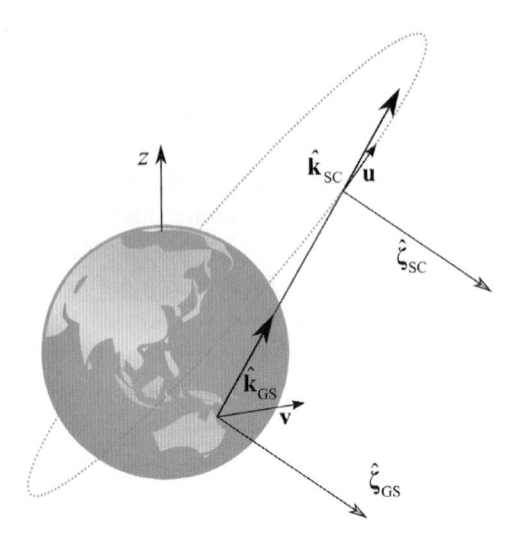

Fig. 1. Scheme of the communication round between the ground station (GS) and the spacecraft (SC). The light ray is highlighted in blue. All the vectors are indicated in the Earth-centered inertial frame. In the flat spacetime approximation the unit tangent vectors to the ray $\hat{\mathbf{k}}_{GS}$ and $\hat{\mathbf{k}}_{SC}$ at the GS and the SC, as well as the direction to an infinitely distant guide star, $\hat{\zeta}_{GS}$ and $\hat{\zeta}_{SC}$, respectively coincide. Velocity of the GS at the emission of the signal is $\mathbf{v}$ and velocity of the SC at the moment of detection is $\mathbf{u}$.

with the transversal vectors $\hat{\mathbf{b}}_{\mathbf{k}}^{\pm}$, $\mathbf{k} \cdot \hat{\mathbf{b}}_{\mathbf{k}}^{\pm} = 0$. The correspondence is rooted in the relationship between finite-dimensional and unitary representations of the Poincaré group.[24, 25]

Unitary operators U that describe the state transformation between the Lorentz frames are obtained via the induced representation of the Poincaré group. Basis states that correspond to an arbitrary momentum $(k)^\mu \equiv k^\mu$ are defined with the help of standard Lorentz transformation $L(k^\mu)$, that takes the four momentum from the standard value k_S^μ to k^μ. For massless particles, $k_S^\mu = (1, 0, 0, 1)$ and

$$L(k^\mu) = R(\hat{\mathbf{k}}) B_z(\xi_{|\mathbf{k}|}), \qquad (2)$$

where $R(\hat{\mathbf{k}}) = R_z(\phi) R_y(\theta)$ rotates the z-axis into the direction $\hat{\mathbf{k}}$ by performing rotations around the y- and z-axis by angles θ and ϕ, respectively. These rotations follow the boost $B_z(\xi_{|\mathbf{k}|})$ along the z-axis, that brings the magnitude of momentum to $|\mathbf{k}|$.

The states of an arbitrary momentum are defined via

$$|\mathbf{k}, \pm\rangle := U\big(L(\mathbf{k})\big) |\mathbf{k}_S, \pm\rangle, \qquad (3)$$

while the standard right- and left-circular polarization vectors are defined as

$$\hat{\mathbf{b}}_{\mathbf{k}}^{\pm} := R(\hat{\mathbf{k}})(\hat{\mathbf{x}} \pm i\hat{\mathbf{y}})/\sqrt{2}, \qquad (4)$$

where the linear polarization vectors are $\hat{\mathbf{b}}_1 := R(\hat{\mathbf{k}})\hat{\mathbf{x}}$ and $\hat{\mathbf{b}}_2 := R(\hat{\mathbf{k}})\hat{\mathbf{y}}$, respectively.

Alternatively, these vectors can be obtained as

$$\hat{b}_2 = \frac{\hat{z} \times \hat{k}}{|\hat{z} \times \hat{k}|}, \qquad \hat{b}_1 = \hat{b}_2 \times \hat{k}. \tag{5}$$

The explicit form of the polarization four-vector f_k, $f_k \cdot k = 0$ depends on the gauge.[4,18,26]

Under arbitrary Lorentz transformation, states transform (apart from the normalization factor) via

$$U(\Lambda)|k, \pm\rangle = U(\Lambda L(k))|k_S, \pm\rangle = U(L(\Lambda k))U(W)|k_s, \pm\rangle, \tag{6}$$

where the transformation $W = L^{-1}(\Lambda k)\Lambda L(k)$ to the subgroup (Wigner's little group) group that leaves k_s invariant,

$$U(W)|k_S, \sigma\rangle = \sum_{\pm'} D(W)_{\sigma\sigma'}|k_S, \sigma'\rangle. \tag{7}$$

The matrices $D(W)_{\sigma\sigma'}$ form the representation of the little group. For massless particles an element of the little group W can be decomposed as

$$W = SR_z(\varpi), \tag{8}$$

where S is a translation in the (xy)-plane and $R_z(\varpi)$ a rotation. As translations do not contribute to the physical degrees of freedom of photons, the state $|k, \pm\rangle$ transforms as

$$U(\Lambda)|k, \pm\rangle = e^{\pm i\varpi}|\Lambda k, \pm\rangle. \tag{9}$$

There are no generic explicit expressions for ϖ. Their evaluation is not considerably simpler if $\Lambda = \mathcal{R}$, where $\mathcal{R}$ is a rotation (as there is no risk of confusion we use the same designation for the four-dimensional matrices of spatial dimensions and for their 3×3 blocks). However, as the transformation law of $\hat{f}$ can be obtained from the three-dimensional form of the Lorentz transformations of the transversal electromagnetic wave, in this case[4,27]

$$U(\mathcal{R})|\Psi_k\rangle \Leftrightarrow \mathcal{R}\hat{f}_k. \tag{10}$$

Moreover, an arbitrary rotation around the direction $\hat{b}_2$, $R_{\hat{b}_2}(\alpha)$, does not introduce a phase ϖ.[16] This provides the motivation for introduction of the so-called Newton gauge that we review below.

In communications with the Earth-orbiting satellites settings of Fig. 1 the Wigner phase is the dominant relativistic effect.[28] While the Wigner phase is of the order 10^{-4}–10^{-5}, we will see below that establishing the local reference frame with respect to some distant stars leads to the Faraday phase error of the order of 10^{-10}.

3. Faraday rotation and general relativistic effects

Here we describe the effects of gravity on polarization in the geometric optics approximation, wave it can be considered a vector that is simply affected by the geodesic motion of null particles to which it is attached. We present the gravitational Faraday effect in a way that clearly separates the gauge-independent part from the effects of the reference frame choices[16] and is convenient for the near-Earth calculations that use the post-Newtonian approximation. Then we demonstrate that at the leading order the polarization rotation is a purely gauge effect and evaluate it for a practically useful choice of the reference frames.

The equation of geometric optics are obtained by performing the short wave expansion of the wave equation in the Lorentz gauge,[29,30]

$$A^\mu = a^\mu e^{i\psi}, \tag{11}$$

where a^μ is the slowly varying complex amplitude and ψ is the rapidly varying real phase. In later calculations, we use the wave vector $k_\mu := \psi_{,\mu}$, the squared amplitude $a = (a^{\mu *} a_\mu)^{1/2}$ and the polarization vector $f^\mu = a^\mu/a$ is transverse to the trajectory, $f^\mu k_\mu = 0$.

The eikonal equation

$$g^{\mu\nu} \frac{\partial \psi}{\partial x^\mu} \frac{\partial \psi}{\partial x^\nu} = 0, \tag{12}$$

is the leading term in the expansion of the wave equation[29,30] is the Hamilton-Jacobi equation for a free massless particle on a given background spacetime. It allows description of light propagation in terms of fictitious massless particles.

The wave vector k_μ, which is normal to the hypersurface of constant phase is null $k^\mu k_\mu = 0$, and is geodesic

$$k^\mu \nabla_\mu k^\nu = 0, \tag{13}$$

as it is the gradient of a scalar function. Similarly, the polarization vector f^μ is parallel propagated along it

$$k^\mu \nabla_\mu f^\nu = 0. \tag{14}$$

A convenient three dimensional representation of the evolution of polarization vectors is possible in stationary spacetimes. Static observers follow the congruence of timelike Killing geodesics that define projection from spacetime manifold $\mathcal{M}$ onto the three dimensional space Σ_3, $\Pi : \mathcal{M} \to \Sigma_3$. The metric $g_{\mu\nu}$ on $\mathcal{M}$ can be written in terms of three dimensional scalar h, a vector $\mathbf{g}$ with component g_m and a metric γ_{mn} on Σ_3 as

$$ds^2 = -h \left(dx^0 - g_m dx^m \right)^2 + dl^2, \tag{15}$$

where $h = -g_{00}$, $g_m = -g_{0m}/g_{00}$, and the three dimensional distance $dl^2 = \gamma_{mn} dx^m dx^n$, where

$$\gamma_{mn} = g_{mn} - \frac{g_{0m} g_{0n}}{g_{00}}. \tag{16}$$

Using the relationships between the three and four dimensional covariant derivatives, the propagation equations in a stationary spacetimes result in the following three dimensional equations

$$\frac{D\hat{\mathbf{k}}}{Ds} = \mathbf{\Omega} \times \hat{\mathbf{k}}, \qquad \frac{D\hat{\mathbf{f}}}{Ds} = \mathbf{\Omega} \times \hat{\mathbf{f}}, \qquad (17)$$

where D/Ds is the covariant derivative in three dimensional space with metric γ_{mn}. Thus, both the polarization and propagation vectors are rigidly rotated with an angular velocity

$$\mathbf{\Omega} = 2\boldsymbol{\omega} - (\boldsymbol{\omega}\cdot\hat{\mathbf{k}})\hat{\mathbf{k}} - \mathbf{E}_g \times \hat{\mathbf{k}}, \qquad (18)$$

where $\boldsymbol{\omega}$ and $\mathbf{E}_g$ could be interpreted as the gravitoelectric and gravitomagnetic field respectively

$$\boldsymbol{\omega} = -\frac{1}{2}k_0 \nabla \times \mathbf{g}, \qquad \mathbf{E}_g = -\frac{\nabla h}{2h}. \qquad (19)$$

In flat spacetimes, polarization basis is uniquely fixed by the Wigner little group construction. However, in general curved background, Wigner construction must be performed at every point. This is because, in the absence of a global reference direction, the standard polarization triad $(\hat{\mathbf{b}}_1, \hat{\mathbf{b}}_2, \hat{\mathbf{k}})$ is different at every locations. Given such choice, the net polarization can be found by starting with the initial polarization $f_{\text{fin}}(x_{\text{in}})$, parallel propagating it according to the rule Eq. (17) and then using the decomposition

$$f_{\text{fin}}(x_{\text{fin}}) = \cos\chi \hat{\mathbf{b}}_1 + \sin\chi \hat{\mathbf{b}}_2, \qquad (20)$$

to read off an angle. For Schwarzschild spacetime, $\boldsymbol{\omega} = 0$, and thus differentiation of this equation gives

$$\frac{d\chi}{ds} = \frac{1}{\hat{\mathbf{f}}\cdot\hat{\mathbf{b}}_1}\hat{\mathbf{f}} \cdot \frac{D\hat{\mathbf{b}}_2}{Ds}. \qquad (21)$$

This equation implies that polarization rotation is a pure gauge effect. The phase remains zero if the standard directions are set with the help of the local free fall acceleration $\mathbf{w}$ of a stationary observer. At each point in the spacetime we choose the direction of the standard reference momentum, or equivalently the z-axis of our standard polarization triad, to be $\hat{\boldsymbol{\zeta}} := \mathbf{w}$. For a photon with momentum $\mathbf{k}$ we choose the linear polarization vector $\hat{\mathbf{b}}_2$ to point in the direction $\hat{\boldsymbol{\zeta}} \times \hat{\mathbf{k}}$, and finally we choose $\hat{\mathbf{b}}_1 := \hat{\mathbf{b}}_2 \times \hat{\mathbf{k}}$ such that it completes the orthonormal triad $(\hat{\mathbf{b}}_1, \hat{\mathbf{b}}_2, \hat{\mathbf{k}})$. This construction is known as the Newton gauge.[16] With this convention $\mathbf{\Omega} = -\mathbf{E}_g \times \mathbf{k} \equiv \Omega \hat{\mathbf{b}}_2$ and thus $\chi \equiv 0$ along the trajectory. However, such choice of standard polarization direction is practically unfeasible. We will see below the consequences of setting the z-axis with the help of a guide star.

Electromagnetic radiation and massless particles are not affected by Newtonian gravity. The post-Newtonian expansion[31] is conveniently organized in powers of $\epsilon^2 \sim GM/c^2\ell \sim v^2/c^2$, where $-GM/\ell$ is the (maximal) typical potential and v is a typical velocity of massive particles. The parameter ϵ helps to keep track of the orders and is set to unity at the end of the calculations. The leading post-Newtonian contributions are of order ϵ^2; to take gravitomagnetic effects into account, we need contributions up to ϵ^3.

The post-Newtonian expansion of the metric near a single slowly rotating quasi-rigid gravitating body, up to ϵ^3, assuming that the underlying theory of gravity is general relativity is

$$ds^2 = -V^2(r)c^2 dt^2 + \vec{R}\cdot d\vec{x}cdt + W^2(r)d\vec{x}\cdot d\vec{x}, \qquad (22)$$

where

$$V(r) = 1 - \epsilon^2 \frac{U}{c^2}, \qquad W(r) = 1 + \epsilon^2 \frac{U}{c^2}. \qquad (23)$$

The Newtonian gravitational potential $-U = -GMQ(r,\theta)/r \simeq -GM/r$ depends on the mass M and the higher order multipoles. The frame-dragging term is

$$\vec{R} = -\epsilon^3 \frac{4G}{c^3} \frac{\vec{J}\times\vec{x}}{r^3}, \qquad (24)$$

where $\vec{J}$ is the angular momentum of the rotating body. Hence, we see that the gauge invariant polarization rotation is absent in the leading order post-Newtonian expansion and the Faraday phase at order ϵ^2 is a reference frame effect. We again revert to the units $G = c = 1$. To obtain leading order contributions to the phase and polarization, photon trajectories only need to be expanded up to ϵ^2

$$\vec{k} = \vec{n} - \epsilon^2 \frac{2M}{r(t)}\vec{n} - \epsilon^2 \frac{2M\vec{d}}{d^2}\left(\frac{\vec{x}(t)\cdot\vec{n}}{r(t)} - \frac{\vec{x}_0\cdot\vec{n}}{r_0}\right), \qquad (25)$$

where $\vec{x}(t) = \vec{x}_0 + (t-t_0)\vec{n} + \mathcal{O}(\epsilon^2)$ and $\vec{d} = \vec{x}_0 - (\vec{x}_0\cdot\vec{n})\vec{n}$ is the vector joining the centre of the earth and the point of closest approach of the unperturbed ray. Here, $\vec{n}$ is the initial propagation direction, $\vec{n}\cdot\vec{n} = 1$.

The leading order post-Newtonian metric is spherically symmetric. Note that the initial polarization that is perpendicular to the propagation plane remains perpendicular to it. So, we select the reference frame differently from that we have done in special relativistic calculations. Here we focus only on gravitational effects and treat them separately from the effects of rotation and relative motion. We take $z = 0$, the plane where the ray from GS to SC lies, set their velocities zero and consider the polarization vector

$$\vec{f} = (0,0,1) = \text{const}. \qquad (26)$$

The gauge dependent Faraday phase results from the change in the definitions of standard polarization directions along the trajectory. The reference directions $\hat{\zeta}_i$ (unit vector pointing to the distant star), $i = $ GS, SC are obtained from the tangents to the rays from the fixed guide star that arrive to the GS and SC respectively.

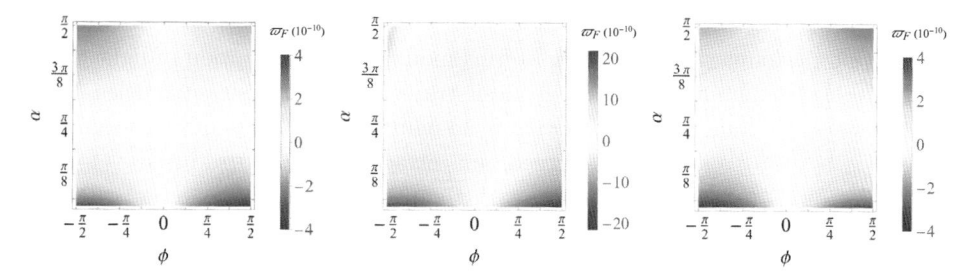

Fig. 2. Faraday phase ϖ_F depends on the choice of the reference direction $\vec{\zeta}(\alpha,\beta)$ and the initial propagation direction $\vec{n}(\phi)$. The angles are defined in Eqs. (31) and (32). *(left)* $\beta = 0$. *(center)* $\beta = 7\pi/16$. *(right)* $\beta = \pi$.

We assume the reference star to be infinitely far. Approximating the differences in reference directions as arising solely form the gravitational field of the earth,

$$\vec{\zeta}_i = \vec{l}\left(1 - \epsilon^2 \frac{2M}{r_i}\right) - \epsilon^2 \frac{2M\vec{d}_i}{d_i^2}\left(\frac{\vec{x}_i \cdot \vec{l}}{r_i} - 1\right), \tag{27}$$

where $\vec{l}\cdot\vec{l} = 1$; $-\vec{l}$ is the flat spacetime direction from the infinitely distant star to the observers. Standard polarization vectors at GS and SC could be defined as

$$\hat{\mathbf{b}}_{2i} = \frac{\vec{\zeta}_i \times \vec{k}}{|\vec{\zeta}_i \times \vec{k}|}, \qquad \hat{\mathbf{b}}_{1i} = \hat{\mathbf{b}}_{2i} \times \hat{\mathbf{k}}. \tag{28}$$

So, from Eq. (21), we get

$$\Delta\chi \cos\chi = \hat{\mathbf{f}}_{SC}\cdot\hat{\mathbf{b}}_{2SC} - \hat{\mathbf{f}}_{GS}\cdot\hat{\mathbf{b}}_{2GS} \tag{29}$$

or,

$$\Delta\chi = \frac{1}{\hat{\mathbf{f}}_{GS}\cdot\hat{\mathbf{b}}_{1GS}}(\hat{\mathbf{f}}_{SC}\cdot\hat{\mathbf{b}}_{2SC} - \hat{\mathbf{f}}_{GS}\cdot\hat{\mathbf{b}}_{2GS}). \tag{30}$$

If we choose the x-axis to pass through GS, then

$$\vec{n} = (\cos\phi, \sin\phi, 0), \qquad -\frac{1}{2}\pi < \phi < \frac{1}{2}\pi, \tag{31}$$

$$\vec{l} = (\cos\alpha, \sin\alpha\sin\beta, \sin\alpha\cos\beta), \qquad 0 \le \alpha \le \frac{1}{2}\pi, \tag{32}$$

where the altitude of the guided star is $\pi/2 - \alpha$. When the reference direction $\vec{\zeta}$ and the propagation direction $\vec{k}$ are collinear, then the standard polarization directions are undefined. If $\vec{\zeta}$ lies in the plane determined by GS, SC and centre of earth, then the Faraday phase is zero. Moreover, the post-Newtonian phase fails in the limit of $\alpha = 0$ or $\beta = \pi/2, 3\pi/2$. The plot of the Faraday phase for different reference and propagation direction is shown in Fig. 2.

4. Polarization-dependent trajectory

Taking into account the post-eikonal terms modifies the description of light propagation along the null rays that are geodesic trajectories of massless particles. These particles are still null, but their motion is no more geodesic. It is most conveniently described by using a specially designed null tetrad.[17,32] It is introduced as follows.

Trajectory $X(s)$ of a null particle with the tangent vector K can be written as

$$\frac{dX^\mu}{ds} = K^\mu, \qquad K^\mu K_\mu = 0. \tag{33}$$

This trajectory is typically is not a geodesic,[22,23] and the acceleration vector w is defined by

$$w^\mu := K^\nu K^\mu_{;\nu}, \qquad K^\mu w_\mu = 0. \tag{34}$$

The second tetrad vector n, $n^2 = 0$ is chosen to satisfy

$$\mathsf{K} \cdot \mathsf{n} = -1. \tag{35}$$

A pair of complex conjugated null vectors, m and $\bar{\mathsf{m}} = \mathsf{m}^*$, are built from two spacelike vectors and satisfy

$$\mathsf{m} \cdot \bar{\mathsf{m}} = 1. \tag{36}$$

All other inner products vanish and the metric can be expressed as

$$g_{\mu\nu} = -K_{(\mu} n_{\nu)} + m_{(\mu} \bar{m}_{\nu)}. \tag{37}$$

It is possible to reparameterize the null curves and rescale the vectors of the null tetrad while preserving orthonormality relations,[17,32]

$$\mathsf{K} \to A\mathsf{K}, \qquad \mathsf{n} \to A^{-1}\mathsf{n}, \tag{38}$$

$$\mathsf{K} \to \mathsf{K}, \quad \mathsf{m} \to \mathsf{m} + a\mathsf{K}, \quad \bar{\mathsf{m}} \to \bar{\mathsf{m}} + a^*\mathsf{K}, \quad \mathsf{n} \to \mathsf{n} + a^*\mathsf{m} + a\bar{\mathsf{m}} + aa^*\mathsf{K}, \tag{39}$$

$$\mathsf{m} \to e^{i\phi}\mathsf{m}, \quad \mathsf{m} \to e^{-i\phi}\bar{\mathsf{m}}. \tag{40}$$

Using this freedom it is possible to choose the tetrad in such a way[23] that the vector n is parallel propagated along the ray,

$$\nabla_\mathsf{K} \mathsf{n} = 0, \tag{41}$$

while

$$\nabla_\mathsf{K} \mathsf{m} = -\kappa \mathsf{n}, \qquad \nabla_\mathsf{K} \bar{\mathsf{m}} = -\kappa^* \mathsf{n}, \tag{42}$$

where

$$\kappa = -\mathsf{w} \cdot \mathsf{m} = -m^\mu K^\nu K_{\mu;\nu}. \tag{43}$$

With this choice of the null tetrad the polarization-dependent correction to the trajectory that takes into account the frequency ω is finite, and given by[23]

$$\frac{D^2 X^\mu}{Ds^2} = K^\nu K^\mu_{;\nu} = -\frac{i\sigma}{\omega} R^\mu{}_{\nu\alpha\beta} K^\nu m^\alpha \bar{m}^\beta =: F^\mu, \tag{44}$$

where $R^\mu{}_{\nu\alpha\beta}$ is the Riemann tensor. At this stage no assumptions about the space-time were made. Effects of this term in the solar system are adequately described by the weak field expansion of the Schwarzschild metric. We will shortly see that in the leading order the polarization-dependent acceleration is of the order of ϵ^2. We also treat Eq. (44) as a correction to the null geodesic. Thus the uperturbed motion can be confined to the equatorial plane.

The trajectory is decomposed as

$$X^\mu(s) = x^\mu(s) + \alpha x^\mu_\sigma(s), \tag{45}$$

where $x^\mu(s)$ is a null geodesic (that we assume can be affinely parameterized by s), $x^\mu_\sigma(s)$ is the polarization-dependent correction, and the formal arbitrary infinitesimal parameter α is introduced to ease the perturbative manipulations. The tangent vector

$$K^\mu = k^\mu + \alpha \Lambda^\mu, \tag{46}$$

is null so,

$$k^\mu \Lambda_\mu = 0. \tag{47}$$

For the weak gravity regime it is convenient use the usual post-Newtonian expansion (the standard choice of the coordinates (t, x, y, z), but without switching to the coordinate time t as an evolution parameter). On the dimensional grounds we expect as the famous light deflection[29,31] is the ϵ^2 effect ($\Delta\phi = 2r_g/\ell$, where ℓ is the impact parameter and $r_g = 2M$ is the gravitational radius), the leading polarization-dependent effect is of the order $\alpha = \epsilon^2 \lambda/\ell$, where λ is the characteristic wave length. Taking this into account and writing M explicitly, we note that at the leading order

$$k^\mu = k^\mu_{(0)} + M k^\mu_{(1)}, \tag{48}$$

$$\Lambda^\mu = M q^\mu, \tag{49}$$

where the components $k^\mu_{(0)}$ are constant. Taking into account that $q^\mu_{;\nu} = q^\mu_{,\nu} + \mathcal{O}(M)$, we have

$$K^\nu K^\mu_{;\nu} = M k^\nu_{(0)} q^\mu_{,\nu} + \mathcal{O}(M^2). \tag{50}$$

It is convenient to describe the unperturbed null geodesic using the full Schwarzschild solution. The symmetry allows to restrict the motion to the equatorial plane. The tangent can be taken as

$$k^\mu = \left(\frac{1}{f(\bar{r})}, \pm\sqrt{1 - \frac{\ell^2}{\bar{r}^2} f(\bar{r})}, 0, \frac{\ell}{\bar{r}^2} \right), \tag{51}$$

where $f(\bar{r}) = 1 - 2M/r$. Here $\bar{r}$ is the Schwarzschild radial coordinate (i.e. the circumferential radius). In the weak field regime it is related to the isotropic radial coordinate $r = \sqrt{\vec{x}\cdot\vec{x}}$ as $\bar{r} \approx r + M$.

We used the freedom of rescaling the null vectors to set the energy of a fictitious photon to $E = 1$, so the reduced angular momentum $\ell := L/E$ equals to the impact parameter.[17] The sign of k^r depends on whether the photon approaches the origin (i.e. the Sun), or moves away from it. In the equatorial plane we have $\mathsf{k}\nabla_\mathsf{k}\mathsf{k} = 0$.

The second vector of the null tetrad

$$n^\mu = \left(\frac{\bar{r}^2}{2(\bar{r}^2 - \ell^2 f(\bar{r}))}, \mp \frac{\bar{r} f(\bar{r})}{2\sqrt{\bar{r}^2 - \ell^2 f(\bar{r})}}, 0, \frac{\ell f(\bar{r})}{2(\bar{r}^2 - \ell^2 f(\bar{r}))} \right), \quad (52)$$

is chosen so that $\mathsf{k} \cdot \mathsf{n} = -1$, and the complex-conjugate pair of null vectors is given by

$$m^\mu = \frac{1}{\sqrt{2}} \left(\frac{i\ell}{\sqrt{\bar{r}^2 - \ell^2 f(\bar{r})}}, 0, \frac{1}{r}, \frac{i}{\sqrt{\bar{r}^2 - \ell^2 f(\bar{r})}} \right), \quad \bar{m}^\mu = m^{\mu*}. \quad (53)$$

These three vectors are to be adjusted to satisfy the conditions required for the validity of Eq. (44). This adjustment is quite straightforward, as in our setting

$$\nabla_\mathsf{k}\mathsf{n} = i\alpha(\mathsf{m} - \bar{\mathsf{m}}), \quad (54)$$

and

$$\nabla_\mathsf{k}\mathsf{m} = i\alpha\mathsf{k}, \qquad \nabla_\mathsf{k}\bar{\mathsf{m}} = -i\alpha\mathsf{k}, \quad (55)$$

where

$$\alpha = \pm \frac{\ell(r - 3M)}{\sqrt{2} r (\bar{r}^2 - \ell^2 f(\bar{r}))}, \quad (56)$$

where the sign of α coincides with that of k^r.

In the leading order approximation the trajectories are geodesic, and the parallel transport of k results in $\kappa = 0$. In turn it enables the parallel transport of the tetrad if the function a satisfies

$$a_{,r} = -i\alpha/k^r = \frac{i\ell(\bar{r} - 3M)}{\sqrt{2}(\bar{r}^2 - \ell^2 f(\bar{r}))^{3/2}}, \quad (57)$$

where the sign does not change on transition from decreasing to increasing distance.

Null geodesics in the Schwarzschild spacetime are classified[17] according to the behaviour of the three roots of the equation $C(\bar{r}) = r^3 - \ell^2(\bar{r} - 2M) = 0$. Only one root is relevant for the trajectories we study,

$$\bar{r}_0 = \ell - M + \mathcal{O}(M^2). \quad (58)$$

Up to the terms of the third order in M the roots are $2M$ and $r \pm \bar{r}_0$. Using this we find

$$\int a_{,r} dr = \frac{i\ell(3rM - \bar{r}_0^2)}{\sqrt{2(\bar{r}^2 - \bar{r}_0^2)\bar{r}_0^2}} + \mathcal{O}(M^3), \quad (59)$$

that is sufficient to obtain the desired $a(\bar{r})$ at any point of the trajectory apart from $r = \bar{r}_0$.

The same expression is valid for both increasing and decreasing r. For $r > \ell \sim \bar{r}_0 \gg M$ we can approximate it as

$$a = -\frac{i\ell}{\sqrt{2}\sqrt{\bar{r}^2 - \ell^2}} - \frac{3iM}{\sqrt{2}\ell}\left(1 - \frac{\bar{r}^3}{(\bar{r}^2 - \ell^2)^{3/2}}\right) + \mathcal{O}(M^2). \tag{60}$$

It is convenient to express the acceleration F^μ in terms of the original tetrad vectors as

$$F^\mu = -\frac{i\sigma}{\omega} R^\mu{}_{\alpha\beta\gamma}(k^\alpha m^\beta \bar{m}^\gamma + ak^\alpha k^\beta \bar{m}^\gamma + a^* k^\alpha m^\beta k^\gamma). \tag{61}$$

Only one component is non-zero at the leading order:

$$F^\theta = -\frac{\sigma}{\omega} \frac{3\ell M}{\bar{r}^4}\left(\frac{1}{\sqrt{\bar{r}^2 - \ell^2 f(\bar{r})}} + \frac{\sqrt{2}a(\bar{r})\ell}{\bar{r}^2}\right). \tag{62}$$

Using again the decomposition of $C(\bar{r})$ it becomes

$$F^\theta \approx \frac{\sigma}{\omega} \frac{3\ell M}{\bar{r}^4 \sqrt{\bar{r}^2 - \bar{r}_0^2}}\left(-1 + \frac{\ell^2}{\bar{r}^2}\right) = -\frac{\sigma}{\omega} \frac{3\ell M}{\bar{r}^6} \frac{\bar{r}^2 - \ell^2}{\sqrt{\bar{r}^2 - \bar{r}_0^2}}, \tag{63}$$

We evaluate the correction $x_\sigma(s)$ using the post-Newtonian formalism that was outlined above. It is important to note that to use only the leading order ϵ^2 while using the order of α polarization correction to describe a particular trajectory is unjustified, as the next post-Newtonian correction for the geometric optics term is still higher. Using the setting that is described below $\epsilon^2 = r_g/\ell = 4.2 \times 10^{-6}$, while $\lambda/\ell = 1.4 \times 10^{-9}$ for $\lambda = 1$m. However, as the exact general relativistic calculation within the geometric optics approximation leads to polarization-independent results, calculation of the polarization-dependent shift can be done using only the ϵ^2 expansion.

To obtain an estimate of the effect we neglect the difference between $\bar{r}_0$ and ℓ, essentially regularizing the expressions near the closest approach radius. The difference between the isotropic radial coordinate that is used in the post-Newtonian analysis and the Schwarzschild radial coordinate is of the order of $2M \ll \ell$ and affects only the higher-order terms. The unperturbed motion is confined to the z-plane. We can assume that $\vec{k} = (-1, 0, 0)$, that corresponds to $\ell > 0$. In this approximation

$$F^z = +\frac{3\sigma\ell M}{\omega r^5}\sqrt{r^2 - \ell^2} + \mathcal{O}(M^2), \tag{64}$$

while all other components are zero at the leading order. Then the explicit equation for the leading polarization-dependent correction is

$$q^z_{,x} = -\frac{3\sigma\ell}{\omega r^5}\sqrt{r^2 - \ell^2}. \tag{65}$$

We are interested in a light ray that comes from afar ("minus infinity"), grazes the sun and is detected at some finite (but large) distance $r_2 \gg \ell$, the initial off-plane displacement and velocity are zero. Similarly to the calculations of corrections for the classical tests of general relativity[29,31] we use the unperturbed (i.e. flat spacetime trajectory with $r_0 = \ell$

$$y = \ell, \qquad x = -t. \qquad (66)$$

Then the correction $\delta z = Mq^z$ is obtained by an elementary integration. For the far field ($r \gg \ell$) the trajectory approaches a straight line with

$$\theta_\infty = \frac{2\sigma}{\omega} \frac{M}{\ell^2}, \qquad (67)$$

giving at the distance r from the sun the transversal shift

$$\Delta z = \frac{4M}{\omega \ell^2} r. \qquad (68)$$

This shift coincides with the result obtained using the polarization-dependent part of the angle of deflection $\Delta\phi$ between in-and outgoing polarized rays that was reported in Ref. 20. On the other hand, this approximation is too crude to identify a convergence of the initially divergent trajectories that was reported in Ref. 22), and a more delicate approximations will be investigated in the follow-up work.

5. Summary

Describing propagation of electromagnetic waves in vacuum in terms of rays that follow null geodesics is a very good approximation in the high-frequency regime. Within this approximation the polarization rotation in the Schwarzschild metric, and as a result in the leading post-Newtonian approximation, is a purely gauge effect. This phase will be present as a consequence of practical methods of setting up reference frames in the Earth-to-spacecraft communications. However, for the near-Earth experiments these effects are typically about 10^{-5} weaker than the SR effects. Observable gravity-induced deviations from the geometric optics approximation are expected only in ultra-strong gravitational fields.

References

1. S.-K. Liao, et al., *Nature* **549**, 43 (2017).
2. P. Kómár et al., *Nature Phys.* **10**, 582 (2014); H. Dai et al., *Nature. Phys.* **16**, 848 (2020).
3. D. K. L. Oi, et al., *EPJ Quantum Tech.* **4**, 6 (2017); L. Mazzarella, et al., *Cryptography* **4**, 7 (2020).
4. A. Peres and D. R. Terno, *Rev. Mod. Phys.* **76**, 93 (2004).
5. R. B. Mann and T. C. Ralph, *Relativisitc Quantum Information, Class. Quant. Grav.* **29** (22) (2012).
6. D. Rideout et al., *Class. Quant. Grav.* **29**, 224011 (2012).
7. Landis, G. A., arXiv:1604.06351 (2016).
8. S. G. Turyshev, and V. T. Toth, *Phys. Rev. D* **96**, 024008 (2017).
9. V. T. Toth and S. G. Turyshev, *Phys. Rev. D* **103**, 124038 (2021).
10. F. Flamini, N. Spagnolo, and F. Sciarrino, *Rep. Prog. Phys.* **82**, 016001 (2019).

11. G. V. Skrotskiĭ, *Sov. Phys. Dokl.* **2**, 226 (1957); J. Plebanski, *Phys. Rev.* **118**, 1396 (1960)
12. M. Nouri-Zonoz, *Phys. Rev. D* **60**, 024013 (1999); M. Sereno, *Phys. Rev. D* **69**, 087501 (2004); S. M. Kopeikin and B. Mashhoon, *Phys. Rev. D* **65**, 064025 (2002).
13. R. F. Stark and P. A. Connors, *Nature* **266**, 429 (1977)
14. P. P. Kronberg, C. C. Dyer, E.M. Burbidge, and V. T. *Astrophys. J.* **613**, 672 (2004).
15. F. Fayos and J. Llosa, *Gen. Rel. Grav.* **14**, 865 (1982).
16. A. Brodutch, T. F. Demarie, and D. R. Terno, *Phys. Rev. D* **84**, 104043 (2011); A. Brodutch and D. R. Terno, *Phy. Rev. D* **84**, 121501((R) (2011).
17. S. Chandrasekhar, *The Mathematical Theory of Black Holes* (Oxford University Press, Oxford, England, 1992).
18. P. M. Alsing and G. J. Stephenson, Jr, arXiv:0902.1399; M. Rivera-Tapia, A. Delgao, G. Rubilar, *Class. Quant. Grav.* **37**, 195001 (2020).
19. B. Mashhoon, *Phy. Rev. D* **11**, 2679 (1974).
20. P. Gosselin, A. Bérard, and H. Mohrbach, *Phy. Rev. D* **75**, 084035 (2007).
21. V. P. Frolov and A. A. Shoom, *Phy. Rev. D* **84**, 044026 (2011).
22. M. A. Oancea, J. Joudioux, I. Y. Dodin, D. E. Ruiz, C. F. Paganini, and L. Andersson, *Phys. Rev. D* **102**, 024075 (2020).
23. V. Frolov, *Phys. Rev. D* **102**, 084013 (2020).
24. E. Wigner, *Ann. Math.* **40**, 149 (1939). https://doi.org/10.2307/1968551.
25. W.-K. Tung, *Group Theory in Physics* (World Scientific, Singapore, 1985).
26. D. Han, Y. S. Kim, and D. Son, *Phys. Rev. D* **31**, 328 (1985). https://doi.org/10.1103/PhysRevD.31.328.
27. N. H. Lindner, A. Peres, and D. R. Terno, *J. Phys. A* **36**, L449 (2003).
28. P. K. Dahal and D. R. Terno, *Phys. Rev. A (in press)*, arXiv:2106.13426 (2021).
29. C.W. Misner, K. S. Thorn, and J. A. Wheeler, *Gravitation* (Freeman, San Francisco, 1973).
30. A. I. Harte, *Gen. Relativ. Gravit.* **51**, 14 (2019).
31. C. M. Will, *Theory and Experiment in Gravitational Physics*, 2nd edition (Cambridge University Press, 2018).
32. H. Stephani, D. Kramer, M. A. H. MacCallum, C. Hoenselaers, and E. Herlt, *Exact Solutions of Einstein's Field Equations*, 2nd ed. (Cambridge University Press, Cambridge, 2003).

The Ginger project – preliminary results

C. Altucci[1,2], F. Bajardi[1,2], A. Basti[3,4], N. Beverini[3,4], S. Capozziello[1,2], G. Carelli[3,4,*],
D. Ciampini[3,4], G. De Luca[5], R. Devoti[5], G. Di Stefano[5], A.D.V. Di Virgilio[4], F. Fuso[3,4],
U. Giacomelli[3,4], A. Govoni[5], E. Maccioni[3,4], P. Marsili[3,4], A. Ortolan[6], A. Porzio[2,7],
A. Simonelli[4], G. Terreni[4] and R. Velotta[1,2]

[1] *Università di Napoli Dipartimento di Fisica*
[2] *Instituto Nazionale di Fisica Nucleare – Sezione di Napoli*
[3] *Università di Pisa Dipartimento di Fisica "E. Fermi"*,
[4] *Instituto Nazionale di Fisica Nucleare – Sezione di Pisa*
[5] *Instituto Nazionale di Geofisica e Vulcanolgia*
[6] *Instituto Nazionale di Fisica Nucleare – Laboratori Nazionali di Legnaro*
[7] *Consiglio Nazionale delle Ricerche – SPIN*
E-mail: giorgio.carelli@unipi.it
https://web.infn.it/GINGER/index.php/it/home

GINGER (Gyroscopes IN General Relativity) project aims to directly measure the Lense–Thirring (LT) and de Sitter (dS) effects on the Earth and it is based on an array of underground Ring Laser Giroscopes (RLG), the most sensitive inertial sensors to measure the rotation rate of the Earth. Since LT and dS act on a ring laser as angular rotation vectors summed to the earth rotation rate, by using at least two gyroscopes it is possible to retrieve the General Relativity (GR) contribution to the rotation rate. The kinematic component is independently measured by the International Earth Rotation and Reference Systems Service (IERS) with very high accuracy. Ginger could also make it possible to discriminate among different theories, minimizing modeling. The measurement of the Earth angular rotation rate, in order to be fruitful for a fundamental physics test, has to have sensitivity of 1 part in 10^9 or better. The most recent analysis of our prototype GINGERINO data indicate a sensitivity better than 1 part 10^{12}, i.e. 0.1% of the LT term.

Keywords: Ring laser gyroscope, Lense–Thirring, gravito-magnetic effect, length of the day

1. Introduction

The debate on gravitational theories, to extend or modify General Relativity is very active for the issues related to ultra-violet and infra-red behavior of Einstein's theory. The first is connected to the Quantum Gravity problem, the other to Dark Matter and Dark Energy governing large scale structure and cosmology. Up to now, no final theory, capable of explaining gravitational interaction at any scale, has been formulated, and it is important to say that for the discrimination between different theories sensitivity breakthrough is certainly required. Earth based experiments can be in principle advantageous allowing a thorough analysis of the systematic, little modelling of external perturbation and the feasibility of upgrades. The GINGER project, an array of Sagnac gyroscopes, can be used for Earth based gravity measurements, in particular to constrain parameters of gravity theories, like scalar-tensor or

Horava-Lifshitz gravity, by considering their post-Newtonian limits matched with experimental. This effect has been measured by the Gravity Probe B space experiments (10% level)[1] and by Lageos and Lares, reaching the 4% level.[2,3] Gravity Probe B has finished its operational life, while Lares is still providing data, and Lares II will be launched soon. This test is based on reconstructing the trajectories of geodetic satellites, i.e. mechanical simple objects to minimise the effect of the different drags affecting the trajectories, and combining laser ranging data coming from different stations. The Lense-Thirring test using the reconstruction of the nodes of the trajectories, requires the independent map of the Earth gravity fields, independently measured, and the final result at the end is limited by the accuracy of the accuracy of the map. It is necessary to accurately model the zonal tides, since their influence on the nodes of the geodetic satellites is larger than the Lense Thirring itself. The test provided by GINGER, which being Earth based provides the measurement at fixed latitude, is very different. The Lense-Thirring, relying on the Sagnac effect, does not require to combine data coming from different places or to use the accurate map of the Earth gravitational field. Recently, it has been pointed out by Jay Tasson of Carlton that RLG can effectively contribute to the Lorentz Violation quest. In this respect Jay has shown that a level of sensitivity of 1 part in 10^9 for the Earth rotation rate would provide interesting measurements of two Lorentz-violating terms in the framework of the Standard-Model Extension. In one case, sensitivities that are competitive with recent laboratory and perhaps solar system tests would result.[4]

The Earth rotation is a tool to investigate fundamental physics, since it is related to GR terms, as de Sitter and Lense–Thirring, and can provide unique data to investigate Lorentz violation. Its usefulness for fundamental physic is connected to sensitivity, which is quite often express in relative to the average Earth rotation rate; the boundary to be meaningful to fundamental physics is to reach 1 part in 10^9 and long term continuous operation. Present high sensitivity ring laser gyroscope have already fulfilled those requirements.

The Sagnac effect states that two light beams counter propagating inside a closed path complete the path at different times, t_c and t_{cc} for clockwise and anti-clockwise beam respectively, if the closed path rotates; in general the Sagnac effect, $\Delta t = t_c - t_{cc}$ is proportional to the non reciprocity between the two paths. Based on the Sagnac effect, several devices have been developed mainly for inertial navigation. The closed path of the devices with higher sensitivity is defined by an optical ring cavity, and two different technology are feasible: passive and active. The Sagnac gyroscope is identified by its area vector, and measures the scalar product between the local angular rotation and its area vector, in return the gravitomagnetic, and geodetic components act as angular rotations summed to the cinematic ones. The passive gyroscopes requires an external laser source. The active device, called Ring Laser Gyro (RLG), has an active medium inside the cavity, to feed the two counter propagating beams. It is a rather convenient solution, since external laser source with high spectral purity is not required. At present the RLGs, with perimeter from 10 up to 36 m, have the sensitivity record for angular rotation rate measurement.

RLGs are a very promising tool for GR measurements given their features:

- since the effect of the Earth is a function of the latitude, they works at a fixed latitude, can be oriented at will and an independent gravity map of the Earth is not needed;
- they are not averaged, the synchronization of different clocks is not necessary.

Moreover the working prototypes demonstrated unattended continuous operation for months, typically sub-prad/s sensitivity in 1 second of measurement, very large bandwidth, fast response, in principle as fast as milli-seconds and very large dynamic range. High sensitivity RLG are attached to the Earth crust, so are able to measure the Earth rotation rate Ω_{geo}; at present several RLGs are operative: in Germany, G[5] of the geodetic observatory of Wettzell and ROMY in the geophysical observatory of Bavaria,[6] GINGERINO in the underground Gran Sasso laboratory, in Italy,[7] ER1 of the University of Canterbury,[8] in New Zealand, and HUST-1[9] passive gyroscope at HUST, part of the TianQin project, at Wuhan in China.

2. Our text bench: The Earth rotation

The GINGER project is devoted to fundamental physics and it is based on an array of RLG, a first prototype, GINGERINO was built inside the underground Gran Sasso laboratory to validate the site for GINGER. The Earth angular rotation is the natural "test bench" of our prototype. The device is taking data with high duty cycle since several years. Being an inertial sensor, it is sensitive to Ω_{geo} and its variations as polar motion, annual and Chandler wobbles, tides and crust deformations; quantities constantly measured with very high accuracy by the international system IERS. All this signal can be used to investigate the characteristics and the sensitivity of GINGERINO. Its sensitivity has been carefully investigated with standard statistical means, using 103 days of continuous operation and the available geodesic measurements of the Earth angular rotation rate. Sensitivity of 0.1 frad/s appears, with 600 s bandwidth at frequency of 40 days, indicating the feasibility of 1 part 10^{13} of the Earth rotation rate, and accordingly for GINGER the gravitomagnetism test on Earth at the 0.1% level or even better. Fig. 2 shows a view of the experimental apparatus. The general relativity test will require high accuracy, not only sensitivity. It is certainly challenging, but it is an apparatus which will be able to provide unique information for fundamental physics, and to other research fields, as geodesy and geophysics in general.

RLGs have the drawback to deal with the non linear dynamic of the laser, a problem that has highly limited their diffusion. Our analysis of the data from

GINGERINO shows that the large disturbances induced by the dinamic of the laser can be subtracted by a suitable tecnique. We are confident that the technique is finally mature to propose GINGER, a project based in 10 years experience and which contains many experimental details aiming at improving the long term stability, reducing instrumental disturbances.

The true Sagnac signal ω_s is recovered taking into account the laser dynamic, and assuming that it is $\omega_s = \omega_{geo} + \omega_{local}$, where ω_{geo} indicates the scalar product of the total variations of the Earth with the RLG area vector, ω_{local} the signals of local origin, related to temperature fluctuations and local tilts. Comparing the recorded data with the IERS measurements, the different terms are recovered using linear regression and standard statistical means based on minimum square, providing clear indication about the sensitivity of the apparatus, for example see Fig. 1.[10]

GINGERINO operates far from external disturbances and protected from large thermal excursions in the deep underground environment of Gran Sasso. Its data are compared with the evaluated global signal provided by IERS. he analysis takes into account and eliminates the nonlinear laser disturbances and recovers the global IERS signal with all tiny features.[11,12] At the same time disturbances of an instrumental and local origin are estimated using the environmental signals as temperature and local tilts. The obtained residuals, i.e. the unmodeled part of the Sagnac signal indicate a rotational sensitivity below the frad/s level. Disturbances are mainly of an instrumental origin, suggesting the need for improvements in the mechanical design of the RLG structure. By injecting probe signals in the GINGERINO data, we conclude that the sensitivity is 0.1 frad/s with 600 s integration time, more than a factor one hundred below the expected noise for this class of instruments.[13,14] In the near future it will be necessary to investigate this aspect from a theoretical side, and to develop a detailed Monte Carlo study in order to carefully investigate the analysis procedure.

3. Next step

We are ready to build a large-frame 3-dimensional array of ring laser gyroscopes to be mounted inside the under- ground Gran Sasso Laboratory (LNGS). The Ginger final aim is to measure the Earth angular velocity in the laboratory co-rotating frame and to compare it with the Earth angular velocity as observed in the Cosmic inertial frame. GR foresees that, in low field approximation, the De Sitter or geo-electric effect and Lense–Thirring or geo-magnetic effect have to be taken into account. For this purpose it is necessary an instrumental accuracy of the order of 10^{-14} rad s^{-1}. Such an accuracy offers also the possibility of measuring fundamental geodetic parameters related to the fluctuations of the Earth rotational velocity and of the Earth axis orientation, the so-called 'length of the day' and 'polar motion'. In parallel to the experimental studies onto our running prototypes, we have investigated different array configurations. The goal was finding the most simple and

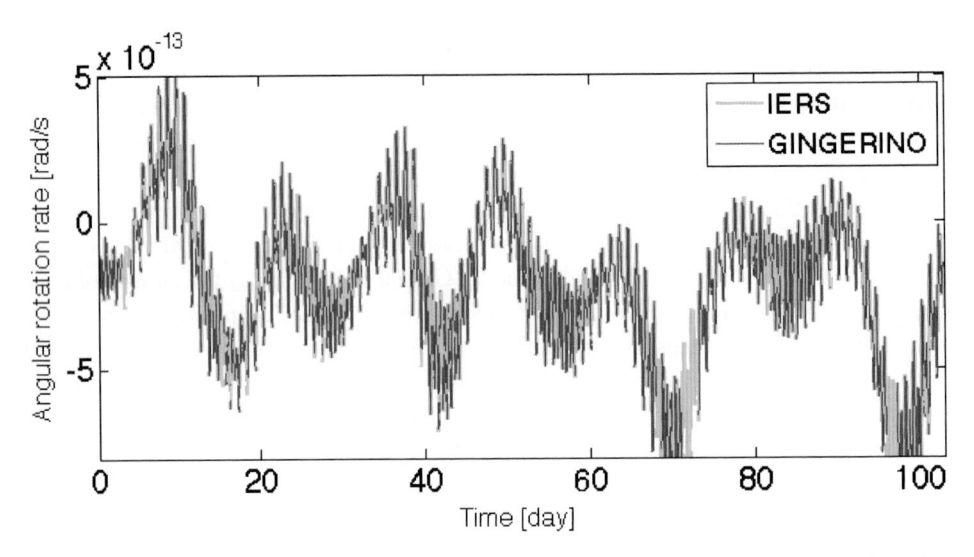

Fig. 1. Agreement of the variations of the LoD Earth rotation rate variations with higher frequency effects due to deformations, evaluated with the linear regression and the data provided by the international system IERS.

cost-effective setup, a sort of minimal instrument that enables the measurement of GR effects with the required reliability. We are fully aware that for this kind of very high sensitivity measurements, redundancy, i.e., the possibility of correlating measurements coming from different instruments and possibly different locations, is a key feature for reducing the influence of systematic as well as stochastic noise sources. In a "future scenario" a second apparatus, not necessarily co-located with the first one, is an option for further reducing the measurement uncertainty and, possibly, accessing further very tiny gravitational effects. As already stated, the final aim of GINGER is to reconstruct, with the required precision, the Earth rotation vector. In principle, measuring a 3D vector by scalar quantities, like the Sagnac frequencies, would require three independent measurements that fixes a local 3D frame. From this basic concept, we arrived, in 2011, at the octahedral configuration mentioned above. To reduce the number of required rings one should have an "external" information or measurement on the vector, or should be able to set two rings so that the plane defined by their oriented area vectors contains the Earth rotation one.[15] So doing this, the pair of rings define a plane where the rotation vector locally lies, and the problem dimensionality reduces from 3 to 2. We note that this plane, in the case of the Earth rotation, is nothing but the meridian one. Thus, in principle, a pair of rings would play the game and, if the conditions on their positioning are fulfilled with a given precision, the full vector can be reconstructed. Then, the problem movesto a different perspective, how to properly align the two rings so that the plane defined by their area vectors contains the Earth angular velocity vector.

Fig. 2. Pictorial view of GINGER (Gyroscopes IN GEneral Relativity), based on an array of RLG, underground located in order to reduce the environmental disturbances and provide suitable very low frequency measurements

We have proven that the best configuration for the two rings is to orient one along the Earth rotation axis. With this choice, the Sagnac frequency of the ring is at its maximum value (a saddle point). As a consequence, orientation errors will affect only quadratically the measured signal and, very important fact, the RLG at maximum provides the modulus of the angular rotation rate. The relative orientation of the second ring is not so critical, although a horizontal ring can be preferable, owing to the possibility of locally defining its orientation by the local vertical. This is, however, a critical issue because its orientation with respect to the angular rotation axis must be known with a very high precision. The comparison with the RLG at the maximum value of the Sagnac frequency provides with adequate sensitivity the absolute orientation with respect to the rotational axis. The addition of a third RLG completes the measurement in all three degrees of freedom and provides redundancy, which is certainly welcome taking into account the very small signals we are looking for.

References

1. C. W. F. Everitt, D. B. DeBra, B. W. Parkinson, J. P. Turneaure, J. W. Conklin, M. I. Heifetz, G. M. Keiser, A. S. Silbergleit, T. Holmes, J. Kolodziejczak, M. Al-Meshari, J. C. Mester, B. Muhlfelder, V. G. Solomonik, K. Stahl, P. W. Worden, W. Bencze, S. Buchman, B. Clarke, A. Al-Jadaan, H. Al-Jibreen, J. Li, J. A. Lipa, J. M. Lockhart, B. Al-Suwaidan, M. Taber and S. Wang, Gravity probe b: Final results of a space experiment to test general relativity, *Phys. Rev. Lett.* **106**, p. 221101 (May 2011).

2. I. Ciufolini and E. C. Pavlis, A confirmation of the general relativistic prediction of the Lense–Thirring effect, *Nature* **431**, p. 958 (Oct 2004).
3. I. Ciufolini, A. Paolozzi, E. C. Pavlis, G. Sindoni, J. Ries, R. Matzner, R. Koenig, C. Paris, V. Gurzadyan and R. Penrose, An improved test of the general relativistic effect of frame-dragging using the lares and lageos satellites, *The European Physical Journal C* **79**, p. 872 (2019).
4. S. Moseley, N. Scaramuzza, J. D. Tasson and M. L. Trostel, Lorentz violation and sagnac gyroscopes, *Phys. Rev. D* **100**, p. 064031 (Sep 2019).
5. K. U. Schreiber and J.-P. R. Wells, Invited review article: Large ring lasers for rotation sensing, *Review of Scientific Instruments* **84**, p. 041101 (2013).
6. H. Igel, K. U. Schreiber, A. Gebauer, F. Bernauer, S. Egdorf, A. Simonelli, C.-J. Liny, J. Wassermann, S. Donner, C. Hadziioannou, S. Yuan, A. Brotzer, J. Kodet, T. Tanimoto, U. Hugentobler and J.-P. R. Wells7, ROMY: A Multi-Component Ring Laser for Geodesy and Geophysics, *Geophysical Journal International* **225** (2021), ggaa614.
7. A. Di Virgilio, J. Belfi, W.-T. Ni, N. Beverini, G. Carelli, E. Maccioni and A. Porzio, GINGER: A feasibility study, *The European Physical Journal Plus* **132**, p. 157 (Apr 2017).
8. D. Zou, R. J. Thirkettle, A. Gebauer, G. K. MacDonald, K. U. Schreiber and J.-P. R. Wells, Gyroscopic performance and some seismic measurements made with a 10 meter perimeter ring laser gyro housed in the ernest rutherford building, *Appl. Opt.* **60**, 1737 (Feb 2021).
9. K. Liu, F. Zhang, Z. Li, X. Feng, K. Li, Y. Du, K. Schreiber, Z. Lu and J. Zhang, Noise analysis of a passive resonant laser gyroscope., *Sensors* **20** (2020).
10. A. D. V. Di Virgilio, A. Basti, N. Beverini, F. Bosi, G. Carelli, D. Ciampini, F. Fuso, U. Giacomelli, E. Maccioni, P. Marsili, A. Ortolan, A. Porzio, A. Simonelli and G. Terreni, Underground sagnac gyroscope with sub-prad/s rotation rate sensitivity: Toward general relativity tests on earth, *Phys. Rev. Research* **2**, p. 032069 (Sep 2020).
11. A. D. V. Di Virgilio, N. Beverini, G. Carelli, D. Ciampini, F. Fuso and E. Maccioni, Analysis of ring laser gyroscopes including laser dynamics, *The European Physical Journal C* **79**, p. 573 (Jul 2019).
12. A. D. V. Di Virgilio, N. Beverini, G. Carelli, D. Ciampini, F. Fuso, U. Giacomelli and E. Maccioni, Identification and correction of sagnac frequency variations, *The European Physical Journal C* **80**, p. 163 (2020).
13. A. D. Di Virgilio, C. Altucci, F. Bajardi, A. Basti, N. Beverini, S. Capozziello, G. Carelli, D. Ciampini, F. Fuso, U. Giacomelli, E. Maccioni, P. Marsili, A. Ortolan, A. Porzio, A. Simonelli, G. Terreni and R. Velotta, Sensitivity limit investigation of a sagnac gyroscope through linear regression analysis, *The European Physical Journal C* **81**, p. 400 (2021).
14. A. Basti, N. Beverini, F. Bosi, G. Carelli, D. Ciampini, A. D. V. Di Virgilio, F. Fuso, U. Giacomelli, E. Maccioni, P. Marsili, G. Passeggio, A. Porzio, A. Simonelli and G. Terreni, Effects of temperature variations in high-sensitivity sagnac gyroscope, *The European Physical Journal Plus* **136**, p. 537 (2021).
15. A. Tartaglia, A. Di Virgilio, J. Belfi, N. Beverini and M. L. Ruggiero, Testing general relativity by means of ring lasers, *The European Physical Journal Plus* **132**, p. 73 (Feb 2017).

Varying fundamental constants and dark energy in the ESPRESSO era

C. J. A. P. Martins

Centro de Astrofísica da Universidade do Porto, and
Instituto de Astrofísica e Ciências do Espaço, Universidade do Porto,
Rua das Estrelas, 4150-762 Porto, Portugal
E-mail: Carlos.Martins@astro.up.pt

The observational evidence for the recent acceleration of the universe shows that canonical theories of cosmology and particle physics are incomplete and that new physics is out there, waiting to be discovered. A compelling task for astrophysical facilities is to search for, identify and ultimately characterize this new physics. I present very recent developments in tests of the stability of nature's fundamental constants, as well as their impact on physics paradigms beyond the standard model. Specifically I discuss new observational constraints at low redshifts and at the BBN epoch, and highlight their different implications for canonical quintessence-type models and for non-canonical string-theory inspired models. Finally I also present new forecasts, based on realistic simulated data, of the gains in sensitivity for these constraints expected from ELT-HIRES, on its own and in combination with Euclid.

Keywords: Cosmology; Fundamental constants; Dark energy.

1. Introduction

The observational evidence for the acceleration of the universe shows that our canonical theories of cosmology and particle physics are at least incomplete, and possibly incorrect. Is dark energy a cosmological constant (i.e. vacuum energy)? If the answer is yes, it is ten to some large power times smaller than our Quantum Field Theory based expectations. If the answer is no, then the Einstein Equivalence Principle must be violated. Either way, new physics is out there, waiting to be discovered; we must search for, identify and characterize this new physics.

The CosmoESPRESSO team uses the universe as a laboratory to address, with precision spectroscopy and other observational, computational and theoretical tools, 6 grand-challenge questions:

(1) Are the laws of physics universal?
(2) Is gravity just geometry (i.e., a fictitious force)?
(3) What makes the universe accelerate?
(4) Can we find fossil relics of the early universe?
(5) How do we optimize next-generation facilities?
(6) How do we prepare next-generation (astro) physicists?

In what follows I will highlight recent contributions of the CosmoESPRESSO team to this fundamental quest, pertaining to fundamental constants.

2. Scalars, because they are there

We know since 2012 (thanks to the LHC) that fundamental scalar fields are among Nature's building blocks. Even before this discovery they were already widely used in cosmology, e.g., to describe inflation, cosmic defects, dynamical dark energy, and dynamical fundamental couplings. We also expect that cosmological scalar fields will naturally couple to the rest of the model, leading to long-range forces and "varying constants".[1-3] Of particular interest in what follows are electromagnetic sector couplings, which yield spacetime variations of the fine-structure constant, with multiple testable fingerprints. A recent theoretical and observational overview of the field can be found in Ref. 4.

One of the most actively pursued test of the stability of fundamental couplings consists of high resolution astrophysical spectroscopy measurements of the fine-structure constant α, the proton to electron mass ratio μ, the proton gyromagnetic ratio g_p, or combinations thereof. A recent joint likelihood analysis of all currently available data[5] leads to a very mild (one to two standard deviations of statistical significance) preference for astrophysical variations (as compared to the local laboratory values), at the parts per million level of relative variation, All this data spans the redshift range $0.2 < z < 4.2$. However, it is also known that, at least in the case of α measurements which make up most of the full dataset, there are systematics at the level of at least parts per million. A new generation of more robust measurements is therefore necessary.

3. Aiming higher

In the most natural and physically realistic models for time (redshift) variations of fundamental couplings, such variations are monotonic. Moreover, one expects that the putative scalar field driving this variation will be significantly damped at the onset of the dark energy domination phase of the universe (i.e., the recent acceleration phase). Both of these are theoretical motivations for testing the stability of fundamental constants such as α, though direct measurements, at higher redshifts—in other words, deep into the matter era, where any relative variations are expected to be larger.

An example of work towards this goal relies on using observations of the redshift $z = 7.085$ quasar J1120+0641[6] to constrain variations of α over the redshift range $z = 5.51$ to $z = 7.06$. These led to the four highest redshift direct measurements of α (the previous highest redshift direct measurement was at $z = 4.18$), with the latter corresponding to a look-back time 12.96 Gyr (for the current best-fit cosmological parameters in the standard ΛCDM model). A total of about 30 hours of data from the X-SHOOTER spectrograph on the European Southern Observatory's Very Large Telescope (VLT) was used, which also makes this the first direct measurement of α in the infrared. Finally, the analysis relied on a new AI-based method, aiming to remove some possible dependency of the final result on human-made choices.

The weighted mean strength of the electromagnetic force over this redshift range in this location in the universe, reported in Ref. 7, is measured to be

$$\frac{\Delta \alpha}{\alpha} = \frac{\alpha(z) - \alpha_0}{\alpha_0} = (-2.18 \pm 7.27) \times 10^{-5}, \quad (1)$$

where α_0 denotes the local laboratory value, i.e. we find no evidence for a time variation. The sensitivity of the combined measurement is only at the tens of parts per million level, as compared to the parts per million (nominal) sensitivity of optical measurements at lower redshifts, but this first result should primarily be seen as a proof of concept analysis, demonstrating that such high redshift measurements can indeed be done.

As for measurements in the optical, the arrival of the ESPRESSO spectrograph,[8] operating at the combined Coudé focus of the VLT, enables new and more stringent tests. Preliminary analyses already demonstrate that the dominant sources of systematics limiting previous high resolution spectrographs are not present,[9] and the first results of its measurements of the fine-structure constant should be reported soon.

Broadly speaking, the direct impact of ESPRESSO on cosmology and fundamental physics will come from at least five different types of observations:

(1) Direct measurements of the fine-structure constant α, at redshifts between $z \sim 1$ and $z \sim 4$, using various ions
(2) Direct measurements of the proton to electron mass ratio μ, at redshifts between $z \sim 2$ and $z \sim 4$, using molecular Hydrogen and Carbon Monoxide
(3) Direct measurements of the cosmic microwave background temperature at redshifts, at redshifts between $z \sim 2$ and $z \sim 4$, using Carbon Monoxide and neutral Carbon
(4) New measurements of the primordial Deuterium abundance (of relevance for BBN, as discussed in what follows)
(5) Additional probes, including deep spectra, lensed QSOs and precursor redshift drift measurements.

In addition to their direct fundamental relevance, these will also impact the quest to characterize dark energy properties.[10]

4. BBN with GUTs

Big Bang Nucleosynthesis is one of the cornerstones of the Hot Big Bang model, but its success has been limited by the long-standing Lithium problem;[11] more recently, a possible Deuterium discrepancy has also been suggested.[12]

If a fiducial theoretical model is chosen and the relevant sensitivity coefficients are known, BBN can be studied perturbatively. This approach is Well-known for relevant cosmological parameters, such as the neutron lifetime, number of neutrinos and baryon-to-photon ratio.[12] More recently, this has been self-consistently extended for a broad class of Grand Unified Theories,[13–15] where all couplings are allowed to vary.

The Lithium problem can be expressed as a statistical preference for a 70% depletion of its theoretically predicted primordial (cosmological) abundance, with respect to the astrophysically measured one,[15] with otherwise standard physics. When the analysis is repeated for a broader class of GUT models, one finds[15] a mild (ca. two to three standard deviations) statistical preference for larger values of the fine-structure constant at the BBN epoch, at the parts per million level of relative variation, while the preferred Lithium depletion drops to about 65%. These results are qualitatively consistent across various models, although quantitatively the best-fit values of the relevant parameters do have a mild model dependence, further discussed in Ref. 15.

This means that the preference for a $\Delta\alpha/\alpha > 0$ is not due to the Lithium problem, but to the aforementioned Deuterium discrepancy. A few ppm variation of α solves D discrepancy, given their positive correlation. Such a variation is consistent with all other currently available cosmological, astrophysical and local constraints. This helps with the Lithium problem, reducing the astrophysical depletion required, but only by a moderate amount. Thus the most likely explanation for the Lithium problem is an astrophysical one, and Ref. 15 further shows that the amount of depletion needed to solve the Lithium problem can be accounted for by transport processes of chemical elements in stars—specifically, the combination of atomic diffusion, rotation and penetrative convection. On the other hand, the Helium4 abundance has relatively little statistical weight in the above analysis, given the very tight observational constraints on the primordial Deuterium abundance.

These results show that BBN is a very sensitive probe of new physics: it is quite remarkable that one can constrain the strength of the electromagnetic interaction, to parts per million level, when the universe was seconds to minutes old. Going forward, improving observed abundances of Deuterium and Helium4 by a factor of 2 to 3 will lead to stringent tests of this GUT class of models, and in particular will confirm or rule out the current preference for a $\Delta\alpha/\alpha > 0$. A cosmological measurement of the Helium3 abundance (which is currently not possible) would also provide a key consistency test of the underlying physics. These will be crucial tasks for the next generation of high-resolutions ultra-stable astrophysical spectrographs.

5. Dynamical dark energy

Realistic models for a varying fine-structure constant usually rely on a fundamental or effective scalar field, and can be phenomenologically divided into two broad classes, dubbed Class I and Class II, for which astrophysical tests of the stability of α will play different roles as probes of the underlying cosmological model.[4]

Class I contains the models where the same degree of freedom yields dynamical dark energy and the varying α. In this case the cosmological evolution of α is parametrically determined, meaning that its redshift dependence can be expressed as a function of cosmological parameters (including the matter density and those describing the dark energy equation of state) together with one or more parameter describing the coupling of the scalar field to the electromagnetic sector. In these models, constraints on α constrain the dark energy equation of state,[16–18] and in particular may enable an observational discriminating test between freezing and thawing dark energy models.[19] The simplest example of this class are quintessence models, provided one does not forget the coupling to the electromagnetic sector.

A recent example are the Euclid forecast constraints on dark energy coupled to electromagnetism, with astrophysical and laboratory data.[20] These show that α measurements improve the Euclid dark energy Figure of merit by between 8 and 26 percent, depending on the correct fiducial model (with larger improvements occurring in the null case, where the fiducial model is ΛCDM). Inter alia, these forecasts confirm the expectation[21] that increasing redshift lever arm of the measurements, which the α data enables, is crucial.

Class II contains the models where the dynamical degree of freedom responsible for the varying α has a negligible effect on cosmological dynamics, and therefore has little or no contribution to the acceleration of the universe. Such models are identifiable through consistency tests comparing cosmological and astrophysical (or local) data, and in this case α measurements still constrain model parameters. Typically they do not directly constrain cosmological parameters, but they may still indirectly help constrain them by breaking degeneracies in the overall parameter space (which will include cosmological and particle physics parameters). The simplest example of this class are the Bekenstein type models.[22,23] In some cases, such as the Dirac-Born-Infeld type models, astrophysical measurements of α may be the only possible observational probe that, given already available constraints, can distinguish these models from ΛCDM.[24]

Importantly, in all these models the scalar field inevitably couples to nucleons, leading to Weak Equivalence Principle violations.[2,3] Therefore measurements of α constrain the Eotvos parameter η. The current bound, including the available α measurements together with the MICROSCOPE bound,[25] has been reported in Ref. 26, and is

$$\eta < 4 \times 10^{-15}. \qquad (2)$$

This is three times stronger than the bound from MICROSCOPE alone, and 30 time tighter than the best ground-based direct bounds, with the caveat that the constraint includes a mild model dependence (ca. factor of 2). This will be further improved by ESPRESSO, and later on by ELT-HIRES. ESPRESSO observations can probably reach a sensitivity of 2×10^{-16} (about 5 times better than the final MICROSCOPE results, due to appear imminently) while the ELT-HIRES expected sensitivity is at the few times 10^{-18} level, similar to that of proposed STEP.

6. So what's your point?

The acceleration of the universe shows that canonical theories of cosmology and particle physics are incomplete, if not incorrect. Precision astrophysical spectroscopy provides a direct and competitive probe of the (still unknown) new physics that must be out there. This already provides highly competitive constraints, and will take an increasingly stronger role in the coming years.

So far one can say that nothing is varying at the few parts per million level of relative variation. This is already a very tight bound. It is orders of magnitude stronger than the few percent level of the constraints on the deviation of the dark energy equation of state from a cosmological constant, and also one order of magnitude stronger than the Cassini bound on the Eddington parameter. Tests of the stability of α also lead to the best available Weak Equivalence Principle constraint, a situation that is expected to remain even after MICROSCOPE's final results.

The ESPRESSO spectrograph is here, and new and more robust measurements are coming soon. Together with the final MICROSCOPE results, stringent new tests will become possible. In the longer term, the ELT will be the flagship tool in a new generation of precision consistency tests of fundamental physics, leading to competitive 'guaranteed science' implications for dark energy as well as unique synergies with other facilities, including Euclid and the SKA.

Acknowledgments

This work was financed by FEDER—Fundo Europeu de Desenvolvimento Regional funds through the COMPETE 2020—Operational Programme for Competitiveness and Internationalisation (POCI), and by Portuguese funds through FCT - Fundação para a Ciência e a Tecnologia in the framework of the project POCI-01-0145-FEDER-028987 and PTDC/FIS-AST/28987/2017.

References

1. R. H. Dicke, Experimental relativity, in *Relativité, Groupes et Topologie: Proceedings, École d'été de Physique Théorique, Session XIII, Les Houches, France, Jul 1 - Aug 24, 1963*, 1964.
2. S. M. Carroll, Quintessence and the rest of the world, *PRL* **81**, 3067 (1998).
3. T. Damour and J. F. Donoghue, Phenomenology of the Equivalence Principle with Light Scalars, *Class. Quant. Grav.* **27**, p. 202001 (2010).
4. C. J. A. P. Martins, The status of varying constants: A review of the physics, searches and implications, *Rep. Prog. Phys.* **80**, p. 126902 (2017).
5. C. J. A. P. Martins and M. Vila Miñana, Consistency of local and astrophysical tests of the stability of fundamental constants, *Phys. Dark Univ.* **25**, p. 100301 (2019).
6. D. J. Mortlock et al., A luminous quasar at a redshift of $z = 7.085$, *Nature* **474**, p. 616 (2011).
7. M. R. Wilczynska et al., Four direct measurements of the fine-structure constant 13 billion years ago, *Sci. Adv.* **6**, p. eaay9672 (2020).

8. F. Pepe et al., ESPRESSO at VLT - On-sky performance and first results, *Astron. Astrophys.* **645**, p. A96 (2021).
9. T. M. Schmidt et al., Fundamental physics with ESPRESSO: Towards an accurate wavelength calibration for a precision test of the fine-structure constant, *Astron. Astrophys.* **646**, p. A144 (2021).
10. A. Leite, C. Martins, P. Molaro, D. Corre and S. Cristiani, Dark energy constraints from ESPRESSO tests of the stability of fundamental couplings, *PRD* **94**, p. 123512 (2016).
11. B. D. Fields, The primordial lithium problem, *Ann. Rev. Nucl. Part. Sci.* **61**, 47 (2011).
12. C. Pitrou, A. Coc, J.-P. Uzan and E. Vangioni, A new tension in the cosmological model from primordial deuterium?, *Mon. Not. Roy. Astron. Soc.* **502**, p. 2474 (2021).
13. M. T. Clara and C. J. A. P. Martins, Primordial nucleosynthesis with varying fundamental constants: Improved constraints and a possible solution to the Lithium problem, *Astron. Astrophys.* **633**, p. L11 (2020).
14. C. J. A. P. Martins, Primordial nucleosynthesis with varying fundamental constants: Degeneracies with cosmological parameters, *Astron. Astrophys.* **646**, p. A47 (2021).
15. M. Deal and C. J. A. P. Martins, Primordial nucleosynthesis with varying fundamental constants: Solutions to the Lithium problem and the Deuterium discrepancy, *Astron. Astrophys.* **653**, p. A48 (2021).
16. C. J. A. P. Martins and A. M. M. Pinho, Fine-structure constant constraints on dark energy, *Phys. Rev. D* **91**, p. 103501 (2015).
17. C. J. A. P. Martins, A. M. M. Pinho, R. F. C. Alves, M. Pino, C. I. S. A. Rocha and M. von Wietersheim, Dark energy and Equivalence Principle constraints from astrophysical tests of the stability of the fine-structure constant, *JCAP* **08**, p. 047 (2015).
18. C. J. A. P. Martins, A. M. M. Pinho, P. Carreira, A. Gusart, J. López and C. I. S. A. Rocha, Fine-structure constant constraints on dark energy: II. Extending the parameter space, *Phys. Rev. D* **93**, p. 023506 (2016).
19. J. M. A. V. Boas, D. M. N. Magano, C. J. A. P. Martins, A. Barbecho and C. Serrano, Distinguishing freezing and thawing dark energy models through measurements of the fine-structure constant, *Astron. Astrophys.* **635**, p. A80 (2020).
20. M. Martinelli et al., Euclid: constraining dark energy coupled to electromagnetism using astrophysical and laboratory data (5 2021).
21. E. Calabrese, M. Martinelli, S. Pandolfi, V. F. Cardone, C. J. A. P. Martins, S. Spiro and P. E. Vielzeuf, Dark Energy coupling with electromagnetism as seen from future low-medium redshift probes, *Phys. Rev. D* **89**, p. 083509 (2014).
22. A. C. O. Leite and C. J. A. P. Martins, Current and future constraints on Bekenstein-type models for varying couplings, *Phys. Rev. D* **94**, p. 023503 (2016).
23. C. S. Alves, A. C. O. Leite, C. J. A. P. Martins, T. A. Silva, S. A. Berge and B. S. A. Silva, Current and future constraints on extended Bekenstein-type models for a varying fine-structure constant, *Phys. Rev. D* **97**, p. 023522 (2018).
24. V. C. Tavares and C. J. A. P. Martins, Varying alpha generalized Dirac-Born-Infeld models, *Phys. Rev. D* **103**, p. 023525 (2021).
25. P. Touboul et al., Space test of the Equivalence Principle: first results of the MICROSCOPE mission, *Class. Quant. Grav.* **36**, p. 225006 (2019).
26. C. J. A. P. Martins and M. Prat Colomer, Fine-structure constant constraints on late-time dark energy transitions, *Phys. Lett. B* **791**, 230 (2019).

Testing the general relativistic nature of the Milky Way rotation curve with Gaia DR2

Mariateresa Crosta

Italian National Institute for Astrophysics, OATo,
Turin, Italy
E-mail: mariateresa.crosta@inaf.it

The ESA mission Gaia directly measures the kinematics of the stellar component of the Galaxy with the goal to create the largest, most precise three-dimensional map of the Milky Way. The very core of the Gaia data analysis and processing involves General Relativity to guarantee accurate scientific products. In parallel, any Galactic model should be developed consistently with the relativistic-compliant kinematics delivered by Gaia. In this respect, this contribution presents the first test for a relativistic Galactic rotation curve with the Gaia second release products. Both a general relativistic model and a classical analogue were fit to the best-ever kinematics, derived exclusively from Gaia data, of a carefully selected homogenous sample of disk stars tracing the axisymmetric part of the Galactic potential. The relativistic rotation curve results statistically indistinguishable from its state-of-the-art dark-matter-based analogue. This supports the ansatz that the background geometry could drive the stellar velocities in the plane of our Galaxy far away from its center and mimic dark matter. Furthermore, one of Einstein's equations provides the necessary baryonic matter density to close the observed gap with respect to the expected Newtonian velocities without the need of extra mass.

Keywords: Gravitation; Galaxy: kinematics and dynamics; General Relativity; Relativistic Astrometry; Gravitational Astrometry; Local Cosmology; Dark Matter

1. General Relativity in the Gaia context

Gaia is the ESA cornerstone astrometric mission[1] - a wide European effort involving almost 450 scientists - launched in December 2013. Gaia implements Relativistic Astrometry for the data analysis and processing that, as part of fundamental physics, can be named Gravitational Astrometry.

Astrometry is the oldest branch of astronomy, it provides positions and motions of stars since Babilonian times. Astrometrists have compared tiny movements in the sky with increasing accuracy through the ages. In practice they measured smaller and smaller angles. The same measurement principle applies for the Gaia mission, but in order to achieve high precision, nowadays we need to operate from space. Gaia provides positions (direction and distance) along with velocities of over 1 billion stars in our Galaxy with an accuracy of up to 10 millionths-of arcsecond, i.e. 1-microarsecond (μas), that corresponds to the angular size of the star on the top of Mole as seen from Jupiter. At the end-of-mission the astrometric accuracies will be better than 5-10 μas for brighter stars and 130-600μas for faint targets. Nevertheless, smaller angles mean larger distances. In astrometry the location of an object is considered reliable if the relative parallax error is less 10%. This implies that with 1 microsecond of accuracy we obtain reliable distances up to the Galactic scale.[2] Then, the final goal is unraveling the structure, the formation, and the evolution of the Milky Way (MW). As matter a fact, since Gaia is continuously scanning the sky, the main goal is to produce a map of about 1-2 billion celestial objects in 3 dimensions. Each celestial object will be observed on average 70 times (a true Galilean method applied to the sky!). Thanks to the combinations on the focal plane of astrometry (positions, proper motions parallaxes), photometry (spectral classification, photometric distances, brightness, temperature, mass, age, chemical composition) and spectroscopy (radial velocity, chemical abundances), the Gaia survey is detailed star by star along with the knowledge of their intrinsic properties.

According to different parallaxes accuracies, the Gaia scientific outputs span from the Solar System scale to the MW one and comprise, among many others, tests on General Relativity (GR), ten thousands exoplanet detections within 200 pc, accurate calibration of the HR diagram, accurate distance scale, cosmological tests such as local Λ-CDM predictions.[2] However, to guarantee all its scientific outputs Gaia requires an appropriate relativistic modelling of the observable and the observer. Gaia is operating at L2 point of the Earth-Sun system and the few-microarcsecond level of its measurements requires to consider the overlapping non-stationary weak gravitational fields due to the Solar System masses, in particular to account for the off-diagonal terms of the IAU metric. Then, Relativistic Astrometry implies a fully general-relativistic analysis of the light trajectory, from the observational data back to the positions of light-emitting stars.[3] Since Gaia is implementing absolute Relativistic Astrometry for the first time, inside the Gaia consortium for the Gaia data processing and analysis (DPAC) there exist two GR models, which set up two independent astrometric solutions for the celestial sphere. Among the six DPAC centers across Europe, the only one specialized in the treatment and validation of the satellite astrometric data is run by ALTEC (located at Turin) under the scientific supervision of the astromeric group INAF-OATo for ASI. The DPCT hosts the systems of the Astrometric Verification Unit (AVU), which is in charge, for DPAC, of the verification, through the Global Sphere Reconstruction (GSR), of the absolute astrometry achieved through the baseline astrometric model. The adoption of these two models applied to the same set of data, besides to be an independent verification tool to guarantee the Gaia scientific outputs (for example to control systematics), are in itself a GR test.[4] Discrepancies that cannot be fixed by the models deserve to be investigated as possible GR shortcomings.

2. Gravitational Astrometry at Milky Way Scale

For the Gaia-like observer the weak gravitational regime turns out to be "strong" when one has to perform high accurate measurements. The position and velocity data, comprising the outputs of the Gaia mission, are fully GR compliant. Given a relativistic approach for the data analysis and processing, any subsequent exploitations should be consistent with the precepts of the theory underlying the astrometric model. Therefore, a fully relativistic model for the MW structure should be applied as well.

A GR structure of MW can assure a coherent laboratory for Local Cosmology, in particular for testing how well distances and kinematics at the scale of the MW disk compare with the Λ-CDM model predictions based on the Concordance Cosmological Model.[2]

Although the Λ-CDM considers homogeneous and isotropic solutions of the Einstein Equations (EE), in the most advanced simulations Λ-CDM cosmology assumes an average FRLW evolution while growth in structure is treated by Newtonian N-body simulations. Ray-tracing as true observables from Gaia can provide constraints on the parameters included in the simulations and the use of Gaia data must be parallel with the utilisation of the most advanced cosmological simulations with baryonic matter (gas and stars). In such a context, flat galactic rotation curves, a longest outstanding problem for astronomy, provide the main observational support to the hypothesis of a surrounding dark matter. The simplest explanation is that galaxies contain far more mass than can be accounted by the bright stellar objects residing in the galactic disk. Adding a surrounding "dark matter" halo allows a good fit to data.

On the other hand, stellar kinematics, as tracer of gravitational potential, is the most reliable observable for gauging different matter contributions. Rotation curves (RC) are distinctive features of spiral galaxies like our Milky Way, a sort of a kinematical/dynamical signature, like the HR diagram for the astrophysical content. And since Gaia by routinely scanning individual sources throughout the whole sky directly measures the (relativistic) kinematics of the stellar component, the rotation curve of the MW lends itself as a first test for a GR Galaxy with Gaia data. This seems to contradict the common assumption that at MW scale the relativistic effects are usually negligible and locally Newton approximation for the gravitational potential is retained valid at each point. In fact, the dynamics of galaxies is usually treated by considering the Newtonian limit of EE, in practice it boils down to solving Poisson's equation in order to derive the velocities tracing the observed RC. However, if one supposes a MW background geometry due a flat Minkowskian metric plus small perturbations as done for the Gaia relativistic models, the typical velocity of stars in our Galaxy is $v_{Gal} = 250$ km/s, thus the lowest order of accuracy of the perturbation terms to be retained for an hypothetical pN Galaxy metric is $(v_{Gal}/c)^2 \approx 100$mas and $(v_{Gal}/c)^3 \approx 120\mu$as. Since the individual DR2 astrometric error is $\leq 100\mu$as throughout most of its magnitude range,[16] "weak" relativistic effect could be relevant for a Gaia-like observer. This indicates that is worth investigating the small curvature limit in GR at MW scale, bearing in mind that it may not coincide with the Newtonian regime. To answer one needs to compare classical and GR models for the MW that derive from different field equations.

3. Classical and General Relativistic Models for the Milky Way

The classical model (MWC) for the MW structure takes into account several substructures, comprising a bulge, a thin and thick disc, and an halo. For the bulge one can adopt a Plummer density profile[5]

$$\rho_b = \frac{3b_b^2 M_b}{4\pi(r^2 + b_b^2)^{5/2}}, \quad (1)$$

where, in cylindrical coordinates, the bulge spherical radius is $r = \sqrt{R^2 + z^2}$, with $b_b = 0.3$ kpc the Plummer radius and M_b is the total bulge mass.

As for the thin and thick MW disks, one can consider a double-component stellar disk modelled as two Miyamoto-Nagai potentials. This function is also approximated with a double exponential disk as in McMillan[6] and Korol et al.[7] The most general description[5,8,9] is expressed in the form

$$\rho_d(R,z) = \frac{M_d b_d^2}{4\pi} \frac{\left[a_d R^2 + (a_d + 3\sqrt{z^2 + b_d^2})(a_d + \sqrt{z^2 + b_d^2})^2\right]}{\left[R^2 + (a_d + \sqrt{z^2 + b_d^2})^2\right]^{5/2} (z^2 + b_d^2)^{3/2}}, \quad (2)$$

where M_d is the total (thin or thick) disk mass, a and b are the scale–length and scale–height, $b_{td} = 0.25$ kpc and $b_{Td} = 0.8$ kpc the thin and thick disk scale–heights, respectively.

Finally, for the MWC, a standard Navarro-Frank-White (NFW) model describes the DM halo (McMillan[6], Bovy[8], Navarro et al.[10])

$$\rho_h(r) = \rho_0^{halo} \frac{1}{(r/A_h)(1 + r/A_h)^2}, \quad (3)$$

where ρ_0^{halo} is the DM halo density scale and A_h its (spherical) scale radius.

Each component contributes to define the potential in the Poisson's equation

$$\nabla^2 \Phi = 4\pi G \rho_{tot} = 4\pi G(\rho_b + \rho_{td} + \rho_{Td} + \rho_h) \quad (4)$$

from which the velocity profile is derived

$$V^2 = R\left(d\Phi_{tot}/dR\right). \quad (5)$$

On the other hand, Einstein's equation is in general very difficult to solve analytically, making it even the more difficult to detail a metric for the whole Galaxy as a multi-structured object. As first attempt, we adopted in Crosta et al.[11] an axisymmetric and stationary Galactic metric-disk and a simple relativistic model suitable to represent the Galactic disk as dust in equilibrium at a large distance from the centre.[12]

As well known, in a stationary and axisymmetric space-time there exist two commuting killing vector fields, k^α (time-like) and m^α (always zero on the axis of symmetry) and a coordinate system $\{t, \phi, r, z\}$ adapted to the symmetries,[13,14] whose line element for a rotating perfect fluid takes the form:

$$ds^2 = -e^{2U}(dt + Ad\phi)^2 + e^{2U}\left(e^{2\gamma}(dr^2 + dz^2) + Wd\phi^2\right), \quad (6)$$

where e^{2U}, $e^{2\gamma}$ are conformal factors and U, A, W depend only on coordinates $\{r, z\}$. The time coordinate t (time-like far enough from the metric source) spans in the range $[-\infty, +\infty]$ and ϕ is the azimuthal angular coordinate in the range $[0, 2\pi]$.[13] For the general dust solution[14] we have[a]:

$$-e^{2U} = (k|k), \quad -Ae^{2U} = (k|m), \quad e^{-2U}W^2 - A^2 e^{2U} = (m|m). \quad (7)$$

In addition

$$m^\alpha = \partial_\phi^\alpha, \quad k^\alpha = \partial_t^\alpha, \quad \partial_t g_{ij} = \partial_\phi g_{ij} = 0, \quad g_{\phi a} = g_{ta} = 0, \quad (8)$$

where $a = r, z$. Because of the two dimensional Laplace equation one can choose $W = r^2$. For rigidly rotating dust (i.e. shearfree and expansionfree) $U = 0$ and there exist a time-like Killing vector (linear combination of k^α and m^α with constant coefficient) parallel to the four-velocity of the fluid u^α, i.e. the co-rotating one chosen by Balasin and Grumiller,[12] proportional to ∂_t^α.[14] Then, by setting $e^{2\gamma} \equiv e^\nu$, $N = -A$ and $e^{2U} = 1$, eq. (6) becomes the line element adopted by Balasin and Grumiller[12]:

$$ds^2 = g_{\alpha\beta}dx^\alpha dx^\beta = -dt^2 + 2Nd\phi dt + (r^2 - N^2)d\phi^2 + e^\nu(dr^2 + dz^2). \quad (9)$$

Such a model may serve as a crude model for galaxies with the stars considered as dust grains. A rigidly rotating disk of dust is the universal limit of rigidly rotating perfect fluid configurations where the pressure-to-energy-density ratio vanishes. The dust assumptions implies that the masses inside a large portion of the Galaxy interact only gravitationally and reside far from the central bulge region. As a matter of fact, stellar encounters become effective below the parsec scale, on the other hand the Galaxy could be considered globally isolated around 25 kpc where flaring effects emerge, indicating the onset of external gravitational perturbations.

Given a stationary and axisymmetric space-time, the unit tangent vector field of a general spatially circular orbit can be expressed as

$$u^\alpha = \Gamma(k^\alpha + \beta m^\alpha), \quad (10)$$

where β is the constant angular velocity (with respect to infinity) and Γ the normalization factor. Equation (10) represents a class of observers that includes static ones ($\beta = 0$), and can be parametrized either by β or equivalently by the linear velocity, say ζ, with respect to the ZAMOs (Z^α), the locally non-rotating observer with zero angular momentum as:

$$u^\alpha = \gamma\left(e_{\hat{0}}^\alpha + \zeta^{\hat{\phi}} e_{\hat{\phi}}^\alpha\right), \quad (11)$$

where $\gamma = -(u|Z)$ is the Lorentz factor, $e_{\hat{0}}^\alpha$ is the unit normal to the t=constant hypersurfaces, and $e_{\hat{\phi}}^\alpha$ the ϕ unit direction of the orthonormal frame adapted to the ZAMOs. ZAMO frames, indeed, have a non-zero angular velocity with respect to flat infinity and move on worldlines orthogonal to the hypersurfaces t=constant.

---

[a]Symbol (|) stands for the scalar product relative to the chosen metric.

The line element (9) can be rewritten in terms of the lapse $M = r/\sqrt{(r^2 - N^2)}$ and the shift factor $M^\phi = N/(r^2 - N^2)$ as follows

$$ds^2 = -M^2 dt^2 + (r^2 - N^2)\left(d\phi + M^\phi dt\right)^2 + e^\nu (dr^2 + dz^2), \qquad (12)$$

where

$$Z^\alpha = (1/M)(\partial_t - M^\phi \partial_\phi). \qquad (13)$$

Then,[15]

$$\zeta^{\hat{\phi}} = \frac{\sqrt{g_{\phi\phi}}}{M}(\beta + M^\phi). \qquad (14)$$

In order to trace the relativistic velocity profile from Gaia data, one has to consider that the local (static) barycentric observer as defined in the Barycentric Celestial Reference System (BCRS)[3] reduces to be $\propto \partial_t^\alpha$ far away from the Solar System.

In such a context the spatial velocity of the co-rotating dust of the BG model ($\beta = 0$) turns out to be proportional to the off-diagonal term of the chosen metric, indicated with N, which could imply gravitational dragging, namely

$$|V(r,z)| \equiv \zeta^{\hat{\phi}} = \frac{N(r,z)}{r} \propto g_{0\phi}. \qquad (15)$$

The metric function N has been determined by Balasin and Grummiller by solving the set of the Einstein field equations and results as

$$N(r,z) = V_0(R_{out} - r_{in}) + \frac{V_0}{2}\sum_{\pm}\left(\sqrt{(z \pm r_{in})^2 + r^2} - \sqrt{(z \pm R_{out})^2 + r^2}\right), \qquad (16)$$

which is limited by the constraint $|z| < r_{in}$ and depends only on parameters V_0, R_{out}, r_{in}, corresponding, respectively, to the flat regime velocity, the extension of the MW disk and the bulge radius.

Finally, the velocity profiles on the equatorial plane is

$$V^{BG}(R) = \frac{V_0}{R}\left(R_{out} - r_{in} + \sqrt{r_{in}^2 + R^2} - \sqrt{R_{out}^2 + R^2}\right). \qquad (17)$$

4. Testing the Geometry-Driven Rotation Curve of the Milky Way with Gaia DR2

To study if the flatness of the MW RC is geometry driven, we selected stars from the Gaia DR2 archive[16] according to the following strict criteria: i) a complete Gaia DR2 astrometric dataset; ii) parallaxes good to 20%; iii) Gaia-measured velocity along the line of sight, namely radial velocity, with better than 20% uncertainties; iv) materialization of the sample by means of a cross-matched entry in the 2MASS catalog.[17] These steps allow to reconstruct a proper 6D phase-space location occupied by each individual star as derived by the same observer.

The requirements above left us with a very homogenous sample of 5277 early type stars and 325 classical type I Cepheids, where 99.4% of the sample span in a range of 11 kpc and is below 1 kpc from the galactic plane (a characteristic scale height for the validity of the BG-RC model). To date it represents the best angular-momentum sustained stellar population of the Milky Way that better traces its observed RC. The quantities extracted from the Gaia DR2 archive are transformed from their natural ICRS reference frame to its galactocentric cylindrical counterpart.[18]

Since the parameter space is too large, a simple nonlinear fit could not be adequate, the Markov Chain Monte Carlo method to determine the unknown parameters and their uncertainties was used.[11] There are several literature works providing the parameter values for each component. For the fit the more recent ones were adopted. In the following tables the best fit estimates as the median of the posteriors and their 1σ level credible interval are reported.

Table 1. Parameters of BG's model.[11] θ, σ_θ^- and σ_θ^+ are the mean and the 1σ credible interval limits from the posteriors of the parameters.

BG model	θ	σ_θ^-	σ_θ^+
r_{in} [kpc]	0.39	-0.25	+0.36
R_{out} [kpc]	47.87	-14.80	+23.96
V_0 [km/s]	263.10	-16.44	+25.93
e^{ν_0}	0.083	-0.014	+0.014

Table 2. Parameters of the MWC model.[11] θ, σ_θ^- and σ_θ^+ are the mean and the 1σ credible interval limits from the posteriors of the parameters.

MWC model	θ	σ_θ^-	σ_θ^+
$M_b[10^{10}M_\odot]$	1.0	-0.4	+0.4
$M_{td}[10^{10}M_\odot]$	3.9	-0.4	+0.4
$M_{Td}[10^{10}M_\odot]$	4.0	-0.5	+0.5
a_{td}[kpc]	5.2	-0.5	+0.5
a_{Td}[kpc]	2.7	-0.4	+0.4
$\rho_0^{halo}[M_\odot pc^{-3}]$	0.009	-0.003	+0.004
A_h [kpc]	17	-3	+4

In figure 1, the red and blue curves show the best fit to the BG and MWC models, respectively. For the likelihood analysis reported in Crosta et al.[11] the two models appear almost identically consistent with the data, indicating that weak fields in GR can drive the MW rotation curve as the classical dark-matter-based analogue.

The fitted value r_{in}= 0.39 kpc, besides being quite close to the value adopted for the Plummer radius (b_b = 0.3 kpc), provides an independent measurements of the radial size of the MW bulge directly from the velocity data. The least constrained parameter of the BG model is the radial extension of the MW disk, as expected due to the limited radial coverage of the Gaia-only velocity data used.

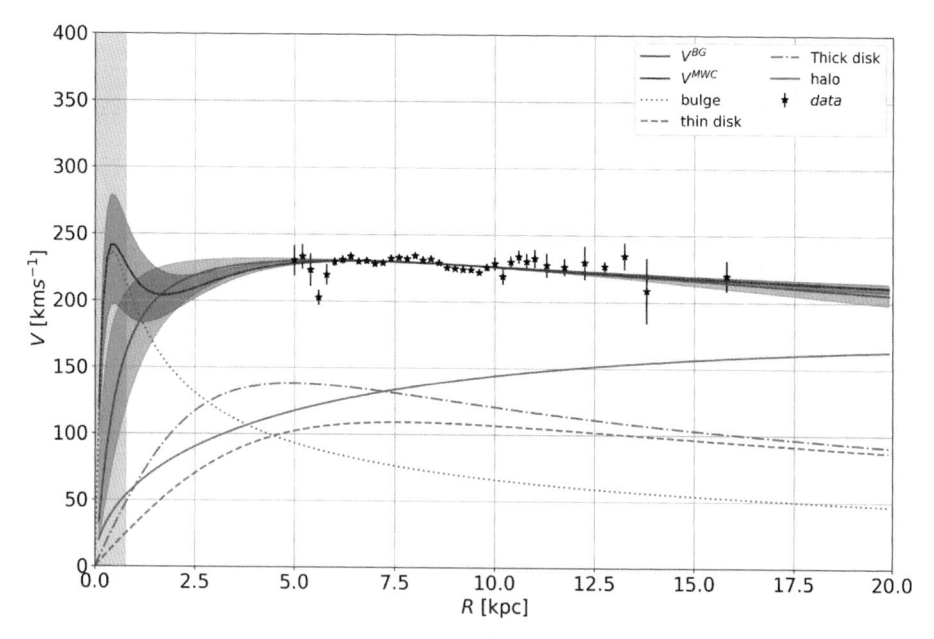

Fig. 1. From M. Crosta, M. Giammaria, M.G. Lattanzi and E. Poggio.[11] The azimuthal velocity profile of the MW as derived from the sample of disk tracers selected from the Gaia DR2. The black starred symbols represent the median values within a radial bin of about 0.2 kpc. The corresponding error bars are computed via bootstrapping. The other grey curves represent the kinematical substructures that contribute to the MWC model, in particular the grey solid line shows the contribution of the NFW halo. The coloured areas represent the reliability intervals of the fitted curves; note that for $R < 5$ kpc both the classical and the relativistic curves are very uncertain because of the lack of data in that region. The grey vertical band represents twice the value of r_{in} estimated with the BG model.

Differently form Balasin and Grummiller, in Crosta et al.[11] also the metric factor $e^{-\nu}$ was estimated via the Einstein equation for the density

$$\rho(R,z) = e^{-\nu(R,z)} \frac{1}{8\pi R^2} [(\partial_R N(R,z))^2 + (\partial_z N(R,z))^2]. \quad (18)$$

Figure 2 two shows that the two models provide a similar baryonic mass distribution in the Galactic disk over the radial range explored by the Gaia data.

From the fit of the data the local relativistic baryonic matter density results $\rho(R = R_\odot, z = 0) \equiv \rho_\odot = 0.083 \pm 0.006 \, M_\odot pc^{-3}$ that is in agreement with independent current estimates.[19–21] Note that, differently form the classical approach, the local mass density was used as the observed datum at Sun position in the likelihood function.

Finally, in order to disentangle the gravitational dragging component, which has not newtonian counterpart, we compared: i) the MWC baryonic-only contribution with the effective Newtonian profile V_{eN}^{BG}, which was calculated by implementing the BG density profile as described in Binney and Tremaine[22] and Almeida et al.[23];

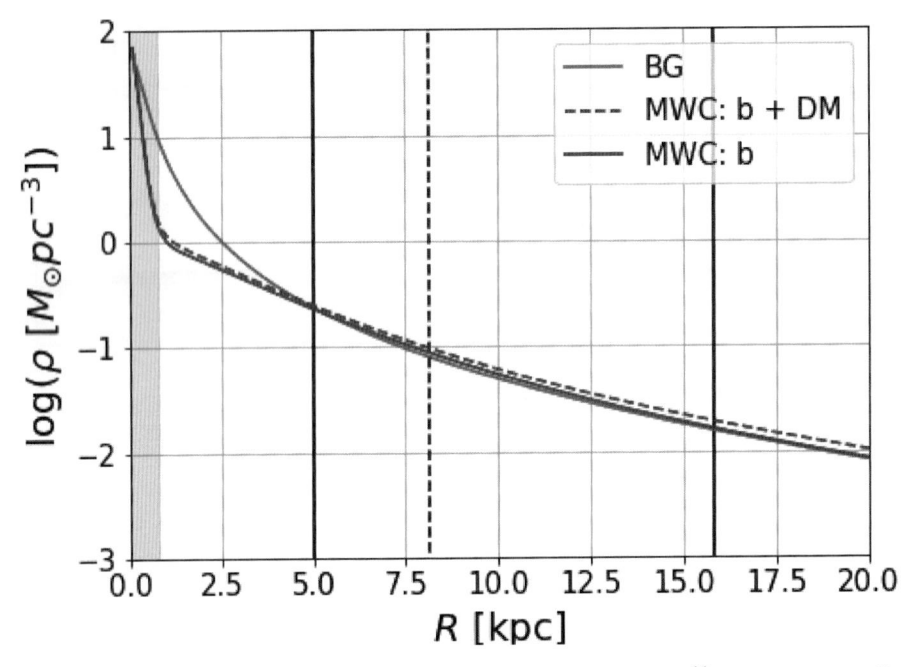

Fig. 2. From M. Crosta, M. Giammaria, M.G. Lattanzi and E. Poggio.[11] The density profile of the MW at $z = 0$ derived from 100 random draws from the posterior distribution of the fit. The red solid line is the BG model, while the blue dashed line represents the total matter contribution for the MWC model (i.e. the sum of the bulge and the two disks as the baryonic counterpart, plus the dark matter halo). The blue solid line shows the contribution of the sole baryonic matter. The vertical black solid lines limit the range of our data, while the vertical black dashed line indicates the Sun position in the Galaxy. Finally, the grey vertical band represents twice the value of r_{in} estimated with the BG model.

ii) the MWC dark matter-only contribution with the "dragging curve" traced by subtracting the effective component V^{BG}_{eN} to the total V^{BG}. More precisely, this last step implied a minimization procedure to get the effective BG disk half-thickness $|z|_{eff}$, that yields $|z|_{eff} = 0.215$ kpc (very close to the value of adopted for the classical thin disc), namely

$$(V^{BG}_{drag}(R_i; |z|_{eff})) = \sqrt{(V^{BG}(R))^2 - (V^{BG}_{eN}(R; |z|_{eff}))^2}. \qquad (19)$$

The results are illustrated in figure 3. Over the range covered by the Gaia data, the relativistic "dragging" component overlaps the one due to the halo in the MWC models. For R ≤ 5 kpc (the region we cannot constrain with the Gaia data at the moment), the two effective Newtonian velocities differ sharply. This could indicate the breaking point for the direct applicability of the BG model to the Milky Way, as it calls for a more suitable relativistic description of its central regions.

Despite the above limitations, the results points clearly to the possibility that a gravitational "dragging-like" effect due to the geometry background could sustain a flat RC.

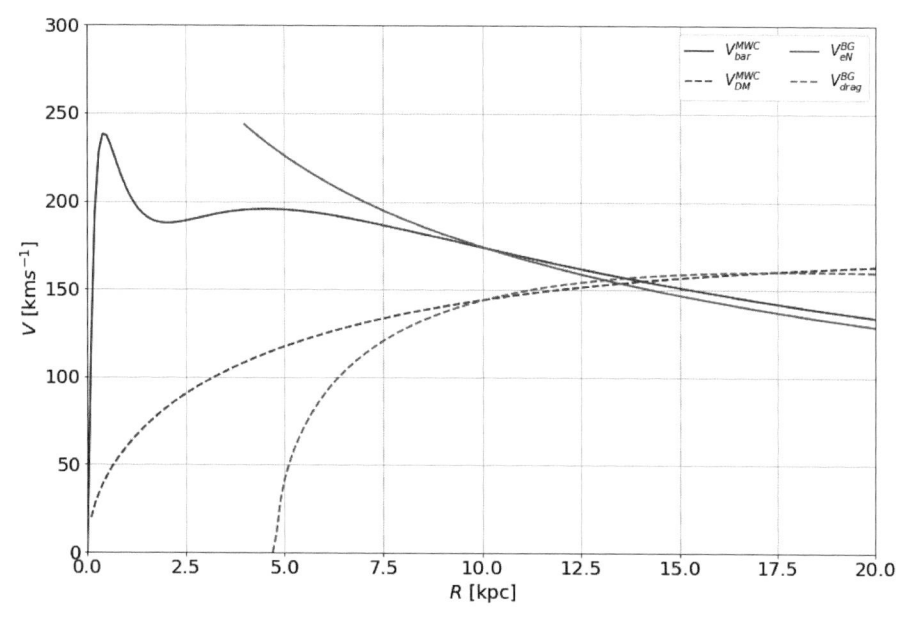

Fig. 3. From M. Crosta, M. Giammaria, M.G. Lattanzi and E. Poggio.[11] Red and blue colors refer to the BG and MWC model, respectively. Solid lines represent the relativistic effective Newtonian rotation curve, V_{eN}^{BG}, and its analogue for the MWC model, as contributed by the total of baryonic mass. The dashed lines show the MWC halo component alone, and the gravitational dragging contribution to V^{BG}, V_{drag}^{BG}, obtained by subtracting V_{eN}^{BG} from V^{BG} itself.

5. Concluding Remarks and Future Perspectives

By setting a coherent GR framework, one can effectively establish to what extent the MW structure is dictated by the standard theory of gravity. The paper Crosta et al.[11] explored the weak relativistic regime of Einstein's equation for the galactic dynamics and gives a possible interpretation of the MW RC as traced by the Gaia data by considering the background curvature, in some respects how space tells mass to move. If we look at DM proprieties, it does not absorb or emit light but it exerts and responds only to the gravity force; it enters the calculation as extra mass (halo) required to justify the flat galactic rotational curves. A gravitational dragging "DM-like" effect driving the MW velocity rotation curve could imply that geometry - unseen but perceived as manifestation of gravity according to Einstein's equation - is responsible of the flatness at large Galactic radii. In spite of some inadequacies, the simplified BG model adopted was proven also to be quite useful to estimate the (external) radial size of the Galactic bulge and the disc thickness at radial distances R $\geq$4 kpc. Obviously, more data and much improved mathematical models are necessary to confirm such a scenario.

For the observational side the sample size will increases from current 6000 to more than 100 thousands upper main sequence disc stars, with the addition of early-type B stars, in perspective of the full Gaia Data Release 3 expected in 2022.[24] Also data from spectroscopic surveys (e.g. SDSS, APOGEE, LAMOST, RAVE, GES - Gaia ESO Survey, GALAH) will be merged.

For the theoretical side, the findings described in the previous section push on the fully use of Einstein's theory, point the lack of mathematical solutions for GR Galactic models and state the need to develop more complex background "geometries" to account for the MW multi-structures in concomitance of the incoming and increasingly accurate Gaia data releases along with other Galactic observations targeting the Galactic center. One attempt could be to study, e.g., the class of Lewis and Papapetrou metrics to encompass all the different MW structures and consider different conformal factors to be fitted with the Gaia data (as was done for the density in the BG model). Once a MW geometry is provided, one can extend it to other similar galaxies and include a fully GR kinematics.

With more physically appropriate metrics, along with adequate solution, the Galaxy can play a reference role for other galaxies, much like the Sun for stellar models.

Acknowledgements

This contribution has made use of data products from: the ESA Gaia mission (gea.esac.esa.int/archive/), funded by national institutions participating in the Gaia Multilateral Agreement; and the Two Micron All Sky Survey (2MASS,www.ipac.caltech.edu/2mass).

References

1. Gaia Collaboration, Prusti, T., de Bruijne, J. H. J., Brown, A. G. A., Vallenari, A., Babusiaux, C. , Bailer-Jones, C. A. L., Bastian, U., Biermann, M., Evans, D. W. and et al., The Gaia mission, *A&A*, **595**, pp. A1 (2016).
2. M. G. Lattanzi, Astrometric cosmology, in *Memorie della Societá Astronomica Italiana*, **83**, p.1033 (2012), https://ui.adsabs.harvard.edu/abs/2012MmSAI..83.1033L.
3. M. Crosta, A. Geralico, M. G. Lattanzi, A. Vecchiato, General relativistic observable for gravitational astrometry in the context of the Gaia mission and beyond, *Phys. Rev. D*, **96**,104030 (2017).
4. M. Crosta, Astrometry in the 21st century. From Hipparchus to Einstein, *Nuovo Cimento Rivista Serie*, **42**, 10 (2019).
5. E. Pouliasis, P. Di Matteo, & M. Haywood, A Milky Way with a massive, centrally concentrated thick disc: New Galactic mass models for orbit computations, *A&A*, **598**, A66 (2017).
6. P. J. McMillan, The mass distribution and gravitational potential of the Milky Way, *MNRAS*, **465**, 76-94 (2017).
7. V. Korol, E. M. Rossi, and E. Barausse, A multimessenger study of the Milky Way's stellar disc and bulge with LISA, Gaia, and LSST, *MNRAS*, **483**, 5518-5533 (2019).
8. J. Bovy, Galpy: A python Library for Galactic Dynamics, *ApJ*, **216**, 29 (2015).
9. D. A. Barros, J. R. D. Lepine, & W. S. Dias, Models for the 3D axisymmetric gravitational potential of the Milky Way galaxy - A detailed modelling of the Galactic disk, *A&A*, **593**, A108 (2016).

10. J. F. Navarro, C. S. Frenk, and S. D. M. White, The Structure of Cold Dark Matter Halos, *ApJ*, **462**, 563 (1996).
11. M. Crosta, M. Giammaria, M. G. Lattanzi, and E. Poggio, On testing CDM and geometry-driven Milky Way rotation curve models with Gaia DR2, *MNRAS*, **496**, Issue 2 (2020).
12. H. Balasin, & D. Grumiller, Non-Newtonian behavior in weak field general relativity for extended rotating sources, *Int. Journal of Mod. Phys. D*, **17**, 475 (2008).
13. F. de Felice & J. S. Clarke, Relativity on curved manifolds (Cambridge Monographs on Mathematical Physics, Cambridge University Press, 1990).
14. H. Stephani, D. Kramer, M. Maccallum, C. Hoenselaers, and E. Herlt, Exact Solutions of Einstein's Field Equations. Second edition (Cambridge Monographs on Mathematical Physics, Cambridge University Press, 2009).
15. F. de Felice & D. Bini, Classical Measurements in Curved Space-Times (Cambridge Monographs on Mathematical Physics, Cambridge University Press, 2010)
16. Gaia Collaboration, A. G. A. Brown, A. Vallenari, T. Prusti, J. H. J. de Bruijne, C. Babusiaux, C. A. L. Bailer-Jones et al., Gaia Data Release 2. Summary of the contents and survey properties, *A&A*, **616**, pp. A1(2018).
17. M. F. Skrutskie et al., The two micron all sky survey (2MASS), *AJ*, **131**, 1163 (2006).
18. F. Mignard et al., Gaia Data Release 2. The celestial reference frame (Gaia-CRF2), *A&A*, **616**, id.A14 (2018).
19. S. Garbari, C. Liu, J. I. Read, G. Lake G., A new determination of the local dark matter density from the kinematics of K dwarfs, *MNRAS*, **425**, 1445 (2012).
20. O. Bienaymé et al., Weighing the local dark matter with RAVE red clump stars, *A&A*, **571**, A92 (2014).
21. C. F. McKee, A. Parravano, D. J. Hollenbach, Stars, Gas, and Dark Matter in the Solar Neighborhood, *ApJ*, **814**, 13 (2015).
22. J. Binney & S. Tremaine, Galactic Dynamics, 2nd ed. (Princeton, NJ: Princeton Univ. Press, 2008).
23. A. O. F. de Almeida, O. F. Piattella, D. C. Rodrigues, A method for evaluating models that use galaxy rotation curves to derive the density profiles, *MNRAS*, **462**, Issue 3 (2016).
24. Details for the Data Release Scenario: http://www.cosmos.esa.int/web/gaia/release.

Spinning cylinders in general relativity: A canonical form for the Lewis metrics of the Weyl class

L. Filipe O. Costa* and José Natário[†]

GAMGSD, Departamento de Matemática, Instituto Superior Técnico, Universidade de Lisboa, Lisboa, 1049-001, Portugal
* E-mail: lfilipecosta@tecnico.ulisboa.pt
† E-mail: jnatar@math.ist.utl.pt

N. O. Santos

Sorbonne Université, UPMC Université Paris 06, LERMA, UMRS8112 CNRS, Observatoire de Paris-Meudon, 5, Place Jules Janssen, F-92195 Meudon Cedex, Paris, F-92195, France
E-mail: Nilton.Santos@obspm.fr

In the main article [CQG **38** (2021) 055003], a new "canonical" form for the Lewis metrics of the Weyl class has been obtained, depending only on three parameters — Komar mass and angular momentum per unit length, plus the angle deficit — corresponding to a coordinate system fixed to the "distant stars" and an everywhere timelike Killing vector field. Such form evinces the local but non-global static character of the spacetime, and striking parallelisms with the electromagnetic analogue. We discuss here its generality, main physical features and important limits (the Levi-Civita static cylinder, and spinning cosmic strings). We contrast it on geometric and physical grounds with the Kerr spacetime — as an example of a metric which is locally non-static.

Keywords: Gravitomagnetism; 1+3 quasi-Maxwell formalism; Sagnac effect; gravitomagnetic clock effect; synchronization gap; local and global staticity; Levi-Civita solution; cosmic strings.

1. Introduction

The general stationary solution of the vacuum Einstein field equations with cylindrical symmetry are the Lewis metrics[1–4]

$$ds^2 = -f(dt + Cd\varphi)^2 + r^{(n^2-1)/2}(dr^2 + dz^2) + \frac{r^2}{f}d\varphi^2 \ ; \tag{1}$$

$$f = ar^{1-n} - \frac{c^2 r^{n+1}}{n^2 a} \ ; \qquad C = \frac{cr^{n+1}}{naf} + b \ , \tag{2}$$

usually interpreted as describing the exterior gravitational field produced by infinitely long rotating cylinders. They divide into two classes: (i) the Weyl class, when all the constants n, a, b, and c are real; (ii) the Lewis class, for n imaginary [implying in turn c real and a and b complex, in order for the line element (1) to be real[3,4]].

In the main article, Ref. 5, we have shown that the Weyl class metrics can be written in the "canonical" form

$$ds^2 = -\frac{r^{4\lambda_m}}{\alpha}\left(dt - \frac{j}{\lambda_m - 1/4}d\phi\right)^2 + r^{4\lambda_m(2\lambda_m-1)}(dr^2 + dz^2) + \alpha r^{2(1-2\lambda_m)}d\phi^2 ,$$

depending only on three parameters with a clear physical significance: the Komar mass (λ_m) and angular momentum (j) per unit z-length, plus the parameter α governing the angle deficit. This form allows for a transparent comparison with the Levi-Civita non-rotating cylinder — archetype of the contrast between local and global staticity — which Ref. 5 discusses in detail both on physical and geometrical grounds. Therein its matching to the van Stockum[6] cylinder in star fixed coordinates is also shown. Here we revise some main features of the solution, focusing on its generality [and redundancies of the more usual form (1)-(2)], notable limits, and physical properties, with special attention to those less developed in Ref. 5. Addressing the question posed to us in the discussion following the presentation of this work at MG16,[7] we focus here on its comparison with a non-static (globally and locally) stationary solution, exemplified by the Kerr spacetime.

2. Stationary spacetimes and levels of gravitomagnetism

The line element $ds^2 = g_{\alpha\beta}dx^\alpha dx^\beta$ of a stationary spacetime can generically be written as

$$ds^2 = -e^{2\Phi}(dt - \mathcal{A}_i dx^i)^2 + h_{ij}dx^i dx^j , \tag{3}$$

where $e^{2\Phi} = -g_{00}$, $\Phi \equiv \Phi(x^j)$, $\mathcal{A}_i \equiv \mathcal{A}_i(x^j) = -g_{0i}/g_{00}$, and $h_{ij} \equiv h_{ij}(x^k) = g_{ij} + e^{2\Phi}\mathcal{A}_i\mathcal{A}_j$. Observers of 4-velocity $u^\alpha = e^{-\Phi}\partial_t^\alpha \equiv e^{-\Phi}\delta_0^\alpha$, whose worldlines are tangent to the timelike Killing vector field ∂_t, are *at rest* in the coordinate system of (3). They are dubbed "static" or "laboratory" observers. The quotient of the spacetime by their worldlines yields a 3-D Riemannian manifold Σ with metric h_{ij} (called the "spatial metric"), which measures the spatial distances between neighboring laboratory observers.[8] It is identified in spacetime with the *space projector* with respect to u^α, $h_{\alpha\beta} \equiv u_\alpha u_\beta + g_{\alpha\beta}$. Let $U^\alpha = dx^\alpha/d\tau$ be the 4-velocity of a test point particle in geodesic motion. The space components of the geodesic equation $DU^\alpha/d\tau = 0$ yield[5,8–11]

$$\frac{\tilde{D}\vec{U}}{d\tau} = \gamma\left[\gamma\vec{G} + \vec{U} \times \vec{H}\right] ; \quad \vec{G} = -\tilde{\nabla}\Phi ; \quad \vec{H} = e^\Phi \tilde{\nabla} \times \vec{\mathcal{A}} , \tag{4}$$

where $\gamma = -U^\alpha u_\alpha$ is the Lorentz factor between U^α and u^α, $\tilde{\nabla}$ denotes covariant differentiation with respect to the spatial metric h_{ij} (i.e., the Levi-Civita connection of Σ, $\tilde{\nabla}_j X^i = X^i{}_{,j} + \Gamma(h)^i_{jk}X^k$, for some spatial vector $\vec{X}$), $\tilde{D}/d\tau \equiv U^i \tilde{\nabla}_i$, so that $\tilde{D}\vec{U}/d\tau$ describes the acceleration of the 3-D curve obtained by projecting the timelike geodesic onto the space manifold Σ, being $\vec{U}$ its tangent vector. The latter is identified in spacetime with the projection of U^α onto Σ: $(\vec{U})^\alpha = h^\alpha{}_\beta U^\beta$ [so its space components equal those of U^α, $(\vec{U})^i = U^i$]. The spatial vectors $\vec{G}$ and $\vec{H}$ (living on Σ) are dubbed, respectively, "gravitoelectric" and "gravitomagnetic" fields [or, jointly, "gravitoelectromagnetic" (GEM) fields]. These play in Eq. (4) roles analogous to those of the electric ($\vec{E}$) and magnetic ($\vec{B}$) fields in the Lorentz force equation, $DU^i/d\tau = (q/m)[\gamma \vec{E} + \vec{U} \times \vec{B}]^i$, and are identified in spacetime, respectively, with minus the acceleration and twice the vorticity of the laboratory observers:

$$G^\alpha = -\nabla_{\mathbf{u}} u^\alpha \equiv -u^\alpha_{;\beta} u^\beta \ ; \qquad H^\alpha = \epsilon^{\alpha\beta\gamma\delta} u_{\gamma;\beta} u_\delta \ . \tag{5}$$

They motivate also dubbing the scalar Φ and the vector $\vec{A}$ gravitoelectric and gravitomagnetic potentials, respectively.

Other realizations of the analogy arise in the equations of motion for a "gyroscope" (i.e., a spinning pole-dipole particle) in a gravitational field and a magnetic dipole in a electromagnetic field. According to the Mathisson-Papapetrou equations,[12,13] under the Mathisson-Pirani spin condition,[14] the spin vector S^α of a gyroscope of 4-velocity U^α is Fermi-Walker transported along its center of mass worldline, $DS^\alpha/d\tau = S^\mu a_\mu U^\alpha$, where $a^\alpha \equiv DU^\alpha/d\tau$. If the gyroscope's center of mass is at rest in the coordinate system of (3) ($U^\alpha = u^\alpha$) the space part of this equation yields[5]

$$\frac{d\vec{S}}{d\tau} = \frac{1}{2}\vec{S} \times \vec{H} \ , \tag{6}$$

which is analogous to the precession of a magnetic dipole in a magnetic field, $D\vec{S}/d\tau = \vec{\mu} \times \vec{B}$. When the electromagnetic field is non-homogeneous, a force is also exerted on the magnetic dipole, covariantly described by $DP^\alpha/d\tau = B^{\beta\alpha}\mu_\beta$,[14,15] where μ^β is the magnetic dipole moment 4-vector, and $B_{\alpha\beta} = \star F_{\alpha\mu;\beta} U^\mu$ ($F^{\alpha\beta} \equiv$ Faraday tensor, $\star \equiv$ Hodge dual) is the "magnetic tidal tensor" as measured by the particle. A covariant force is likewise exerted on a gyroscope in a gravitational field (the "spin-curvature" force[12–15]), which can be written in the remarkably similar form[14]

$$\frac{DP^\alpha}{d\tau} = -\mathbb{H}^{\beta\alpha} S_\beta; \qquad \mathbb{H}_{\alpha\beta} \equiv \star R_{\alpha\mu\beta\nu} U^\mu U^\nu = \frac{1}{2}\epsilon_{\alpha\mu}{}^{\lambda\tau} R_{\lambda\tau\beta\nu} U^\mu U^\nu . \tag{7}$$

Here $\mathbb{H}_{\alpha\beta}$ is the "gravitomagnetic tidal tensor" (or "magnetic part" of the Riemann tensor) as measured by the particle, playing a role analogous to that of $B_{\alpha\beta}$ in electromagnetism. For a particle at rest in a stationary field in the form (3), it is related to the gravitomagnetic field $\vec{H}$ by the expression[11]

$$\mathbb{H}_{ij} = -\frac{1}{2}\left[\tilde{\nabla}_j H_i + (\vec{G} \cdot \vec{H})h_{ij} - 2G_j H_i\right] \ . \tag{8}$$

In the linear regime, $\mathbb{H}_{ij} \approx H_{i,j}$, and so one can say that (comparing to $\vec{H}$) $\mathbb{H}_{\alpha\beta}$ is essentially a quantity one order higher in differentiation of $\vec{A}$.

2.1. Sagnac effect

By contrast with classical electromagnetism (where only the curl of the magnetic vector potential, $\nabla \times \vec{A} = \vec{B}$, manifests physically), and more like in quantum theory (where $\vec{A}$ manifests itself in the so-called Aharonov-Bohm effect[16]), in General Relativity there are also gravitational effects governed by the gravitomagnetic vector potential $\vec{\mathcal{A}}$ (or 1-form $\mathcal{A}$). One of them is the Sagnac effect, consisting of the difference in arrival times of light-beams propagating around a spatially closed path in opposite directions. In flat spacetime, where the concept was first introduced (see e.g. Refs. 17, 18), the time difference is originated by the rotation of the apparatus with respect to global inertial frames (thus to the "distant stars"), see Fig. 1 in Ref. 5. In a gravitational field, however, it arises also in apparatuses which are fixed relative to the distant stars (i.e., to *asymptotically* inertial frames), Fig. 1(a) below, signaling frame-dragging.[5, 18–22] In both cases the effect can be read off from the spacetime metric (3), encompassing the flat Minkowski metric written in a rotating coordinate system, as well as arbitrary stationary gravitational fields. Along a photon worldline, $ds^2 = 0$; by (3), this yields two solutions, the future-oriented one being $dt = \mathcal{A}_i dx^i + e^{-\Phi} dl$, where $dl = \sqrt{h_{ij} dx^i dx^j}$ is the spatial distance element. Consider photons constrained to move within a closed loop C in the space manifold Σ; for instance, an optical fiber loop, as depicted in Fig. 1 (a). Using the + (-) sign to denote the anti-clockwise (clockwise) directions, the coordinate time it takes for a full loop is, respectively, $t_\pm = \oint_{\pm C} dt = \oint_C e^{-\Phi} dl \pm \oint_C \mathcal{A}_i dx^i$; therefore, the Sagnac *coordinate* time delay Δt_S (Δt in the notation of Ref. 5) is

$$\Delta t_S \equiv t_+ - t_- = 2 \oint_C \mathcal{A}_i dx^i = 2 \oint_C \mathcal{A} , \qquad (9)$$

translating, in the observer's proper time, to $\Delta \tau_S = e^\Phi \Delta t_S$. We can thus cast gravitomagnetism into the three distinct levels in Table 1, corresponding to different orders of differentiation of $\mathcal{A}$ (the first one being $\mathcal{A}$ itself).

2.2. Synchronization gap

Another physical process where $\mathcal{A}$ manifests is in the synchronization of the clocks carried by the "laboratory observers" (i.e., tangent to the Killing vector field ∂_t). Consider a curve $x^\alpha(\lambda)$ of tangent $dx^\alpha/d\lambda$ which is spatially closed (i.e., its projection onto Σ yields a closed curve C, so that after each loop it re-intersects the worldline of the original observer). Along $x^\alpha(\lambda)$, the synchronization through Einstein's light signaling procedure[8, 21] amounts to the condition that the curve be orthogonal (at every point) to ∂_t^α, that is, $g_{0\beta} dx^\beta / d\lambda = 0 \Leftrightarrow dt = \mathcal{A}_i dx^i$. This curve will thus re-intersect the worldline of the original observer at a coordinate time $t_f = t_i + \Delta t_{\text{sync}}$, where[8]

$$\Delta t_{\text{sync}} = \oint_C \mathcal{A}_i dx^i = \oint_C \mathcal{A} \quad (= \Delta t_S / 2) . \qquad (10)$$

The observer will then find that his clock is not synchronized with his preceding neighbor's by a time gap (as measured in his proper time) $\Delta\tau_{\text{sync}} = e^{\Phi}\Delta t_{\text{sync}}$, corresponding, in coordinate time, to an interval Δt_{sync} [which is one half the Sagnac time delay Δt_S along such loop, Eq. (9)]. Only when $\Delta t_{\text{sync}} = 0$ the observers are able to fully synchronize their clocks along a closed loop.

2.3. *Gravitomagnetic clock effect*

As is well known, in the field of a spinning body the periods of co- and counter-rotating circular geodesics differ; such an effect has been dubbed[23–26] gravitomagnetic "clock effect". The corresponding angular velocities read (see e.g. Sec. 3.1 of Ref. 5)

$$\Omega_{\text{geo}\pm} = \frac{-g_{0\phi,r} \pm \sqrt{g_{0\phi,r}^2 - g_{\phi\phi,r}g_{00,r}}}{g_{\phi\phi,r}} \quad (11)$$

and thus the difference between their periods, $\Delta t_{\text{geo}} = 2\pi(\Omega_{\text{geo}+}^{-1} + \Omega_{\text{geo}-}^{-1}) = -4\pi g_{0\phi,r}/g_{00,r}$, is[5,27]

$$\Delta t_{\text{geo}} = \Delta t_S + \Delta t_H; \quad \Delta t_S = 4\pi \mathcal{A}_\phi; \quad \Delta t_H = -2\pi \frac{\star H_{r\phi}}{G_r e^{\Phi}}, \quad (12)$$

where $\star H_{jk} \equiv \epsilon_{ijk}H^i$ is the 2-form dual to the gravitomagnetic field $\vec{H}$, such that $\star H_{r\phi} = \sqrt{h}H^z$ in cylindrical coordinates, and $\star H_{r\phi} = -\sqrt{h}H^\theta$ in spherical coordinates. Here h is the determinant of the space metric h_{ij} in (3). Hence, the effect consists of the sum of two contributions of different origin, corresponding to two distinct levels of gravitomagnetism in Table (1): the Sagnac time delay Δt_S around the circular loop, governed by $\mathcal{A}$, cf. Eq. (9), plus the term Δt_H due to the gravitomagnetic force $\gamma \vec{U} \times \vec{H}$ in Eq. (4) (which has a direct electromagnetic counterpart, see Sec. 3.1 in Ref. 5; cf. also Ref. 26).

The delay (12) corresponds to orbital periods (in coordinate time) as seen by the "laboratory" observers, at rest in the coordinates of (3). Other observers (e.g. rotating with respect to the former) will measure different periods since, from their point of view, the closing of the orbits occurs at different points. An *observer-independent* akin effect[25,28] can however be derived, based on the proper times (τ_+ and τ_-) measured by each orbiting particle between the events where they meet, see Fig. 1 (b). Set a starting meeting point at $\phi_+ = \phi_- = 0, t = 0$; the next meeting point is defined by $\phi_+ = 2\pi + \phi_-$. Since $\phi_\pm = \Omega_{\text{geo}\pm}t$, the meeting point occurs at a coordinate time $t = 2\pi/(\Omega_{\text{geo}+} - \Omega_{\text{geo}-})$. Hence,

$$\tau_\pm = \frac{t}{U_\pm^0} = \frac{2\pi(U_\pm^0)^{-1}}{\Omega_{\text{geo}+} - \Omega_{\text{geo}-}}; \quad \Delta\tau \equiv \tau_+ - \tau_- = 2\pi\frac{(U_+^0)^{-1} - (U_-^0)^{-1}}{\Omega_{\text{geo}+} - \Omega_{\text{geo}-}}. \quad (13)$$

3. Artificial features of the usual form of the Weyl class metric

In the case of the static Levi-Civita cylinder, which follows from (1)-(2), with n and a real, by making[a] $b = 0 = c$, we have[b] $\Phi = 2\lambda_m \ln(r) + const.$, $\mathbf{G} = -2\lambda_m/r d\mathbf{r}$, $\mathcal{A} = 0 = \vec{H}$, where $\lambda_m = (1-n)/4$. This exactly matches the electromagnetic counterparts for an infinite static charged cylinder, if ones identifies λ_m with minus the charge per unit z-length. (λ_m being actually the Komar mass per unit z- length, as we shall see in Sec. 4.3). However, in the general case $b \neq 0 \neq c$, we have

- Φ, $\mathcal{A}$, and $\vec{G}$ complicated [Eqs. (43) of Ref. 5], and very different from the electromagnetic counterparts for a infinitely long spinning charged cylinder (in the inertial rest frame);
- $\vec{H}$ and $\mathbb{H}_{\alpha\beta}$ both *non-zero* [and complicated, Eqs. (43) and (45) of Ref. 5], at odds with the electromagnetic analogue.

These features are somewhat unexpected given the similarities with the electromagnetic analogue in the static case, and given that this metric is known to be *locally static*. The situation resembles more the electromagnetic analogue as seen from a rotating frame. Moreover,

- ∂_t ceases to be time-like for $r^{2n} > a^2 n^2/c^2 \Rightarrow$ no observers at rest are possible past this radius

which is, again, reminiscent of a rigidly rotating frame in flat spacetime where, past a certain value of r, the observers would be superluminal. The question then arises, can the metric, in the usual form (1)-(2) given in the literature, be actually written in some trivially rotating coordinate system? We will next show this to be the case.

4. The "canonical" form of the Weyl class metric

4.1. *"Star-fixed" coordinates: the metric with only three parameters*

An analysis of the curvature invariants [cubic and quadratic, Eqs. (39)-(41) and (50) of Ref. 5] reveals that the Weyl class metric (i.e., with n real) is a "purely electric" Petrov type I spacetime.[5,29,30] This means that, at each point, there is an (unique) observer for which the gravitomagnetic tidal tensor vanishes, $\mathbb{H}_{\alpha\beta} = 0$. These observers have 4-velocity of the form $U^\alpha = U^t(\partial_t^\alpha + \Omega \partial_\phi^\alpha)$, with *constant* angular velocity Ω given by

$$\Omega = \frac{c}{n-bc} \quad \text{or} \quad \Omega = -\frac{1}{b}, \tag{14}$$

the first (second) value yielding a time-like U^α if $a > 0$ ($a < 0$). Thus, by performing a coordinate rotation at constant angular velocity

$$\phi = \varphi - \Omega t, \tag{15}$$

---
[a] We shall see that the condition $c = 0$ is actually not necessary, cf. Eqs. (16)-(18).
[b] Taking $a > 0$, so that t is the temporal coordinate.

one switches to a coordinate system where these observers are at rest, and the metric takes the form

$$ds^2 = -\frac{r^{1-s}}{\alpha}(dt + \bar{C}d\phi)^2 + r^{(s^2-1)/2}(dr^2 + dz^2) + \alpha r^{1+s}d\phi^2, \tag{16}$$

with, for $\Omega = c/(n - bc)$,

$$s = n \; ; \qquad \alpha = \frac{\bar{C}^2}{ab^2} \; ; \qquad \bar{C} = b\frac{n - bc}{n} = b\frac{s - bc}{s}, \tag{17}$$

and, for $\Omega = -1/b$,

$$s = -n \; ; \qquad \alpha = -ab^2 \; ; \qquad \bar{C} = -b\frac{n - bc}{n} = b\frac{s - bc}{s} \tag{18}$$

Equation (16) shows that the metric depends only on three effective parameters: α, s, and $\bar{C}$, manifesting a redundancy in the original four parameters [different values of (n, a, b, c) yielding the same values of $(s, \alpha, \bar{C})$ correspond to the same physical solution]. The two values (14) for the angular velocity Ω are two equivalent paths of reaching (16), and manifest a particular case of the redundancy: two sets of parameters (a_1, b_1, c_1, n_1) and (a_2, b_2, c_2, n_2), with $a_1 > 0$ and $a_2 < 0$, such that the values of $(s, \alpha, \bar{C})$ are the same. There is one special case excluded from each of the transformations (14)-(15); namely, $bc = n$ for the first value of Ω, and $b = 0$ for the second; they are however redundant, as both lead to the Levi-Civita line-element[c] (26).

Observe that the Killing vector field ∂_t is, in (16), *everywhere time-like* ($g_{00} < 0$ for all r). Therefore, observers of 4-velocity $u^\alpha = (-g_{00})^{1/2}\partial_t^\alpha$, at rest in the coordinates of (16), exist everywhere (even for arbitrarily large r). As we shall see in Sec. (4.4) below, ∂_t is actually tangent to inertial observers at infinity, hence the reference frame associated to the coordinate system in (16) is asymptotically inertial, and thus fixed to the "distant stars".

4.2. Symmetry under swap of time and angular coordinates

In the transformation (15) one assumes, as is usual practice, that φ is an angular coordinate, ranging $[0, 2\pi]$, and t the time coordinate [which in turn implies $\alpha > 0$ and thus $a > 0$ in case (17), and $a < 0$ in case (18)]. Such assumption is however not necessary to reach (16). Indeed, swapping $t \leftrightarrow \varphi$ in (1), again leads to (16), as we shall now show. Substituting, in (1), $\varphi \to t'$, $t \to \varphi'$, the time-like observers measuring vanishing gravitomagnetic tidal tensor have now angular velocity $\Omega' = 1/\Omega$, where Ω is given by (14), and $\Omega' = (n-bc)/c$ yields a time-like U^α if $a > 0$, and likewise $\Omega' = -b$ for $a < 0$. Applying the transformation $\phi' = \varphi' - \Omega' t' = \varphi' - t'/\Omega$ to such line element leads to a primed version of (16),

$$ds^2 = -\frac{r^{1-s}}{\alpha}(dt' + \bar{C}d\phi')^2 + r^{(s^2-1)/2}(dr^2 + dz^2) + \alpha r^{1+s}d\phi'^2 \tag{19}$$

---

[c]That it is so for $b = 0$ can be immediately seen by substituting in (16)-(17), yielding (26); likewise, that it is so for $n = bc$ can be seen by substituting $n \to bc$ in the expression for $\bar{C}$ in (18).

with, for $\Omega' = (n-bc)/c$, the identifications $s = n$, $\alpha = c^2/(an^2)$, $\bar{C} = c/n$; and, for $\Omega' = -b$, the identifications $s = -n$, $\alpha = -a$, $\bar{C} = -c/n$. This is a natural result. Equations (1)-(2) are just a general solution of the vacuum Einstein field equations with three commuting Killing vector fields, one time-like and two spacelike,[4,31] having no information on global aspects of the coordinates; it is thus natural that one be free to choose the angular coordinate rendering the axial symmetry.

One must note, however, that the metric in star fixed coordinates (16) does not preserve such symmetry. The coordinate rotation (15), with the identification $\varphi = \varphi + 2\pi$, breaks that symmetry by implicitly choosing ϕ (and φ) as a periodic coordinate, and t non-periodic. Indeed, substituting in (16) $\phi \to t'$, $t \to \phi'$, leads to (19) with $\phi' \leftrightarrow t'$ swapped:

$$ds^2 = -\frac{r^{1-s}}{\alpha}(\bar{C}dt' + d\phi')^2 + r^{(s^2-1)/2}(dr^2 + dz^2) + \alpha r^{1+s}dt'^2 ; \qquad (20)$$

forcing now on it the identification $(t', \phi') = (t', \phi' + 2\pi)$ (i.e, taking ϕ' to be periodic), makes it become the Levi-Civita metric in a rotating coordinate system, immediately diagonalizable through the coordinate rotation $\phi'' = \phi' + \bar{C}t$. This occurs because, by overriding the original identifications $(t, \phi) = (t, \phi + 2\pi)$, the geometry was *globally* (albeit not locally) changed. Indeed such transformation (with such identifications) is not a global diffeomorphism, as can be seen e.g. from the fact the ordered pairs $\mathcal{P}_1$: (t, ϕ) and $\mathcal{P}_2$: $(t, \phi + 2\pi)$, which represented the same event in the original metric (16), are mapped into the two different events $\mathcal{P}'_1$: (t', ϕ') and $\mathcal{P}'_2$: $(t' + 2\pi, \phi')$ in the metric (20). The transformation $(t', \phi') = (\phi, t)$, followed by $\phi'' = \phi' + \bar{C}t$, actually amounts to (76) of Ref. 5 which, as shown therein, corresponds to the "famous"[2,4] transformation that takes the Weyl class metric into the static Levi-Civita one.

4.3. *The metric in terms of physical parameters — "canonical" form*

The fact that in Eq. (16) the Killing vector field $\xi^\alpha = \partial_t^\alpha$ is everywhere time-like, tangent to inertial observers at infinity, and appropriately normalized,[5] allows for defining a corresponding Komar integral on simply connected tubes $\mathcal{V}$ of unit z-length parallel to the z-axis, having a physical interpretation of "active" gravitational mass per unit z-length, as discussed in Secs. 5.2.1 and 2.4 of Ref. 5 (cf. also Refs. 32–35). It is given by

$$\lambda_m = \frac{1}{8\pi}\int_{\partial \mathcal{V}} \star d\boldsymbol{\xi} = \frac{1}{8\pi}\int_\mathcal{S} (\star d\boldsymbol{\xi})_{\phi z} d\phi dz = \frac{1-s}{4} ,$$

where $\partial \mathcal{V} = \mathcal{S} \cup \mathcal{B}_1 \cup \mathcal{B}_2$ is the tube's boundary, $\mathcal{S}$ its lateral surface, parameterized by $\{\phi, z\}$, and $\mathcal{B}_1$ and $\mathcal{B}_2$ its bases, lying on the planes orthogonal to the z-axis and parameterized by $\{r, \phi\}$, and in the second and third equalities we noticed that $(\star d\boldsymbol{\xi})_{r\phi} = 0$ and $(\star d\boldsymbol{\xi})_{\phi z} = 1 - s$. Likewise, the Komar integral associated with the axial symmetry Killing vector field $\zeta^\alpha = \partial^\alpha_\phi$ has the interpretation of the spacetime's angular momentum per unit z-length,

$$j = -\frac{1}{16\pi}\int_{\partial\mathcal{V}} \star d\zeta = -\frac{1}{16\pi}\int_S (\star d\zeta)_{\phi z} d\phi dz = \frac{s\bar{C}}{4}$$

where we in the second equality we noticed that $(\star\zeta)_{r\phi} = 0$. It follows that (16) can be re-written as

$$ds^2 = -\frac{r^{4\lambda_m}}{\alpha}\left(dt - \frac{j}{\lambda_m - 1/4}d\phi\right)^2 + r^{4\lambda_m(2\lambda_m-1)}(dr^2 + dz^2) + \alpha r^{2(1-2\lambda_m)}d\phi^2 .$$

(21)

4.4. Physical properties; gravitomagnetism

For $\alpha > 0$ [so that t in Eq. (21) is a temporal coordinate], the metric can be put in the form (3), with

$$e^{2\Phi} = \frac{r^{4\lambda_m}}{\alpha} \quad\Rightarrow\quad \Phi = 2\lambda_m \ln(r) + K \; ; \qquad \boldsymbol{\mathcal{A}} = -\frac{4j}{1-4\lambda_m}d\phi \; ; \qquad (22)$$

$$h_{ij}dx^i dx^j = r^{4\lambda_m(2\lambda_m-1)}(dr^2 + dz^2) + \alpha r^{2(1-2\lambda_m)}d\phi^2 \qquad (23)$$

[with $K \equiv -\ln(\alpha)/2$]. The gravitoelectric and gravitomagnetic 1-forms/fields read, cf. Eqs. (4),

$$\mathbf{G} = -\frac{2\lambda_m}{r}dr \; ; \qquad \vec{H} = \mathbf{H} = 0 \; . \qquad (24)$$

Thus Φ, $\mathbf{G}$ and $\mathbf{H} = 0$ match their electromagnetic counterparts for a spinning charged cylinder (as viewed from the inertial rest frame, see e.g. Sec. 4 in Ref. 5) identifying the Komar mass with *minus* the charge, $\lambda_m \leftrightarrow -\lambda$; the gravitomagnetic potential 1-form $\boldsymbol{\mathcal{A}} = \mathcal{A}_\phi d\phi$ also resembles the magnetic potential 1-form $\mathbf{A} = \mathsf{m}d\phi$. The cylinder's rotation does not manifest in the inertial forces (nor in the tidal forces, as shown in Sec. 5.2.3 of Ref. 5); the only inertial force acting on test particles is the gravitoelectric (Newtonian-like) force $m\vec{G}$, independent of j. Thus, particles dropped from rest or in initial radial motion move along radial straight lines, cf. Eq. (4); and circular geodesics have a *constant* speed given by $v_{\text{geo}} = \sqrt{\lambda_m/(1/2 - \lambda_m)}$, being thus possible when $0 \leq \lambda_m < 1/4$ (it is when $\lambda_m > 0$ that $\vec{G}$ is attractive, and they become null for $\lambda_m = 1/4$). The vanishing of $\vec{H}$ means also that gyroscopes at rest in the coordinates of (21) do not precess, the components of their spin vector $\vec{S}$ remaining constant, cf. Eq. (6). Since $\vec{G} \stackrel{r\to\infty}{\to} \vec{0}$, it follows moreover that the reference frame associated to the coordinate system in (21) is *asymptotically* inertial, thus one can take it as the rest frame of the "distant stars" ("star-fixed" frame).

The only surviving gravitomagnetic object is thus the gravitomagnetic 1-form $\boldsymbol{\mathcal{A}}$, corresponding to the first level in Table 1. One of its physical manifestations is the

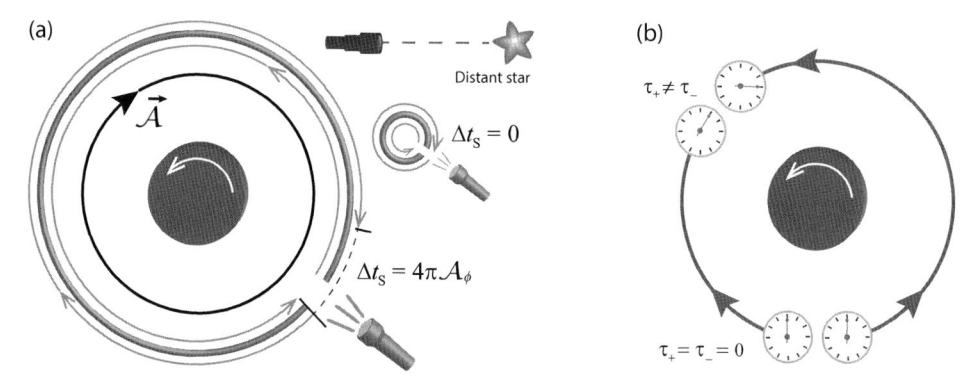

Fig. 1. (a) Sagnac effect around spinning cylinders: a flashlight sends light beams propagating in opposite directions along optical fiber loops fixed with respect to the "distant stars" (i.e., to the asymptotic inertial frame at infinity). In each loop C, the difference in beam arrival times is $\Delta t_S = 2 \oint_C \mathcal{A}$; since $\mathcal{A}$ is a closed form ($\mathbf{d}\mathcal{A} = 0$), the effect vanishes for all loops not enclosing the cylinder, and has the same value (25) for all loops enclosing it (the co-rotating beam arriving first). (b) Frame independent gravitomagnetic clock effect: a pair of clocks in oppositely rotating circular geodesics around a cylinder; when the cylinder spins ($j \neq 0$) the clocks measure different proper times between the events where they meet, $\tau_+ > \tau_-$.

Sagnac effect: consider, as depicted in Fig. 1(a) optical fiber loops fixed with respect to the distant stars, i.e., at rest in the coordinate system of (21). The difference in arrival times for light beams propagating in opposite directions along any of such loops is given by the circulation of $\mathcal{A}$ along the loop, c.f. Eq. (9). Observe that $\mathcal{A}$ is a closed form, $\mathbf{d}\mathcal{A} = 0$ (since $\mathcal{A}_\phi$ is constant), defined in a space manifold Σ homeomorphic to $\mathbb{R}^3 \backslash \{r = 0\}$. By the Stokes theorem, this means[5] that the effect vanishes along any loop which does not enclose the central cylinder (or the axis $r = 0$), such as the small loop in Fig. 1 (a), and has the same nonzero value

$$\Delta t_S = 4\pi \mathcal{A}_\phi = -\frac{4\pi j}{1/4 - \lambda_m} \qquad (25)$$

along any loop enclosing the cylinder, regardless of its shape; for instance, the large circular loop depicted in Fig. 1(a). It is worth noticing that this mirrors the situation for the Aharonov-Bohm effect around spinning charged cylinders, which is likewise independent of the shape of the paths; the two effects are actually described by formally analogous equations[d].

The apparatus above makes use of a star-fixed reference frame, which is physically realized by aiming telescopes at the distant stars.[36,37] It is possible, however (still based on the Sagnac effect) to detect the cylinder's rotation in a more local way, without the need for setting up a specific frame; only not with a single loop, as along a single loop the effect can always be made to vanish by spinning it with some angular velocity. In particular, for a concentric circular loop, the effect

---

[d]Re-writing (9) in terms of the half-loop phase delay $\Delta \varphi = (E/\hbar) \Delta t_S / 2 = (2\pi E/\hbar) \mathcal{A}_\phi$ and identifying $\{E, \mathcal{A}_\phi\} \leftrightarrow \{q, A_\phi\}$, where $E \equiv$ photon's energy, see Sec. 4.1 in Ref. 5.

vanishes if it has zero angular momentum, i.e., if it comoves with the zero angular momentum observers (ZAMOs) of the same radius. The angular velocity of such observers, Eq. (69) of Ref. 5, is however r-dependent; hence, considering instead a "coil" of optical loops, as depicted in Fig. 4 of Ref. 5, provides a frame-independent (thought) experiment to detect the cylinder's rotation, since it is impossible to make the effect vanish simultaneously in every loop when $j \neq 0 \Leftrightarrow \mathcal{A} \neq 0$.

4.4.1. Observer-independent gravitomagnetic clock effect

Another consequence of the vanishing of $\vec{H}$ is that the gravitomagnetic clock effect in Eq. (12) reduces to the Sagnac time delay, $\Delta t_{\text{geo}} = \Delta t_S = 4\pi \mathcal{A}_\phi$; hence, all that was said above about beams in optical loops around the cylinder, applies as well to pairs of particles in oppositely rotating circular geodesics (the co-rotating geodesics having thus shorter periods). It is however actually possible to detect the cylinder's rotation using only *one pair* of particles (i.e., a pair of clocks), through the difference in the proper times (τ_+ and τ_-) measured by each of them between the events where they meet, see Fig. 1 (b). From Eqs. (13) and (11), with $U_\pm^0 = (-g_{00} - 2\Omega_{\text{geo}\pm} g_{0\phi} - \Omega_{\text{geo}\pm}^2 g_{\phi\phi})^{-1/2}$, we have

$$\Delta \tau \equiv \tau_+ - \tau_- = \frac{8\pi j r^{2\lambda_m}}{\sqrt{\alpha(1-4\lambda_m)(1-2\lambda_m) + 8\lambda_m j^2 r^{8\lambda_m - 2}\alpha^{-1}(1/4 - \lambda_m)^{-1}}} \quad (> 0)$$

(this result is mentioned in main paper,[5] though without presenting it explicitly). Hence, when $j \neq 0$, the proper times measured by each clock differ when they meet, the co-rotating clock measuring a longer time.

4.5. Important limits: Levi-Civita static cylinder and cosmic strings

It is immediate to obtain important limits from the canonical form (21). Taking the limit $j \to 0$ yields the Levi-Civita metric[2-4]

$$ds^2 = -\frac{r^{4\lambda_m}}{\alpha} dt^2 + r^{4\lambda_m(2\lambda_m - 1)}(dr^2 + dz^2) + \alpha r^{2(1-2\lambda_m)} d\phi^2 \ . \tag{26}$$

The inertial fields $\vec{G}$ and $\vec{H} = 0$, as well as the spatial metric h_{ij}, remain the same as in (21) (the same applying to the tidal fields/forces, see Sec. 5.2.3 in Ref. 5). They differ only in the gravitomagnetic potential 1-form $\mathcal{A} = -4j/(1-4\lambda_m)\mathbf{d}\phi$, governing global physical effects such as the Sagnac effect and synchronization gap (10) in loops around the cylinder, and the gravitomagnetic clock effect, which are all zero for the static metric (26), see Figs. 1-2.

The limit $\lambda_m \to 0$ yields

$$ds^2 = -\frac{1}{\alpha}[dt + 4jd\phi]^2 + dr^2 + dz^2 + \alpha r^2 d\phi^2 \tag{27}$$

which is the metric of a spinning cosmic string[2, 38, 39] of *Komar* angular momentum per unit length j and angle deficit $2\pi(1 - \alpha^{1/2}) \equiv 2\pi\delta$. In this case the spacetime is locally flat ($R_{\alpha\beta\gamma\delta} = 0$) for $r \neq 0$. All the GEM inertial fields vanish, $\vec{G} = \vec{H} = 0$ (and the same for the tidal fields), thus there are no gravitational forces of any kind. Global gravitational effects however subsist, governed by $\boldsymbol{\mathcal{A}} = -4j\mathrm{d}\phi$ and α. The non-vanishing gravitomagnetic potential 1-form $\boldsymbol{\mathcal{A}}$ means that a Sagnac effect remains, thus the apparatuses manifesting the source's rotation discussed in Sec. 4.4 apply here as well. The same applies to the synchronization of clocks: observers at rest in the coordinates of (27) (which are in this case inertial observers) can synchronize their clocks along closed loops not enclosing the string (i.e., the axis $r = 0$), but are unable to do so for loops enclosing it. As for the gravitomagnetic clock effect, it does not apply here, as circular geodesics do not exist (since there is no gravitational attraction, $\vec{G} = 0$). The angle deficit generates double images of objects located behind the string,[40,41] and a holonomy[41,42] along closed (in spacetime or only spatially) loops around the string. Namely, vectors parallel transported along such loops turn out rotated by an angle $-2\pi\alpha^{1/2}$ (i.e, $2\pi\delta$) about the z-axis when they return to the initial position — an effect which is independent of the shape of the loop and of j; see Sec. 5.2.4 of Ref. 5. One thus can say that the metric (27) possesses two holonomies: a spatial holonomy governed by α, which is the same for spinning or non-spinning strings, plus a synchronization holonomy (Sec. 5.3.3 of Ref. 5) that arises in the spinning case.

4.6. *Summary of "canonical" features*

We argue Eq. (21) to be the most natural, or *canonical*, form for the metric of a Weyl class rotating cylinder for the following reasons:

- the Killing vector field ∂_t is (for $\alpha > 0$) everywhere time-like (i.e., $g_{00} < 0$ for all r), therefore physical observers $u^\alpha = (-g_{00})^{-1/2}\partial_t^\alpha$, at rest in the coordinates of (21), exist everywhere.
- The associated reference frame is *asymptotically* inertial, and thus fixed with respect to the "distant stars" (Sec. 4.4).
- A conserved Komar mass per unit length (λ_m) can be defined from ∂_t which matches its expected value from the gravitational field $\vec{G}$ and potential Φ in Sec. 4.4 (see also Sec. 5.2.1 of Ref. 5), and also that of the Levi-Civita static cylinder (26).
- It is irreducibly given in terms of three parameters with a clear physical interpretation: the Komar mass (λ_m) and angular momentum (j) per unit length, plus the parameter α governing the angle deficit of the spatial metric h_{ij}.
- The GEM fields are strikingly similar to the electromagnetic analogues — the electromagnetic fields of a rotating cylinder as measured in the inertial rest frame (namely $\boldsymbol{\mathcal{A}} = \mathcal{A}_\phi \mathrm{d}\phi$; $\mathcal{A}_\phi \equiv$ constant, $\vec{H} = \mathbb{H}_{\alpha\beta} = 0$, and Φ and $G_{,i}$ match the electromagnetic counterparts identifying the Komar mass per unit length λ_m with the minus charge per unit length λ, cf. Sec. 4 of Ref. 5).

- It is immediate from it to obtain the two important limits: spinning cosmic string ($\lambda_m = 0$), and Levi-Civita static solution (evincing that $j = 0$ is the necessary and *sufficient* condition).
- The GEM inertial fields and tidal tensors are the *same* as those of the Levi-Civita static cylinder (just like the electromagnetic forces produced by a charged spinning cylinder are the same as by a static one).
- It is obtained from a simple rigid rotation of coordinates, Eq. (15), which is a well-defined *global* coordinate transformation (Sec. 4.1).
- It makes immediately transparent the locally static but globally stationary nature of the metric (see Sec. 5 below).
- It has a smooth matching to the van Stockum interior solution (corresponding to a cylinder of rigidly rotating dust) *written in star-fixed coordinates* (Sec. 5.4.2 of Ref. 5).

We conclude that the Lewis metric in its usual form (1)-(2) indeed possesses a trivial coordinate rotation [of angular velocity $-\Omega$, equivalently given by either of Eqs. (14)], which has apparently gone unnoticed in the literature, and causes the artificial features listed in Sec. 3. As shown in Sec. 5.4 of Ref. 5, such rotation has a simple interpretation when the solution is matched to the van Stockum interior solution (corresponding to a rigidly rotating cylinder of dust): the coordinate system in (1)-(2) is *rigidly comoving* with the cylinder.

5. Contrast with a locally (and globally) *non-static* solution — the Kerr spacetime

Question by O. Semerák: *you were comparing the results for the (rotating) Weyl class Lewis metric with the static case; how about the comparison with Kerr, which is different because there the vorticity should contribute to the gravitomagnetic field?*

The contrast with the Kerr spacetime is indeed instructive. In what pertains to gravitomagnetism, it fundamentally differs from the Weyl class cylindrical metrics (rotating or non-rotating) in two mains aspects: it is not locally static, and its Riemann tensor is not (except at the equatorial plane) "purely electric".[29]

Staticity.— a spacetime is static[43] within some region *iff* a time-like Killing vector field ξ^α exists which is proportional to the gradient of some (single-valued) function ψ, $\xi_\alpha = \eta \partial_\alpha \psi$. Locally, this condition is equivalent to the integral lines of ξ^α having no vorticity, i.e., being hypersurface orthogonal (globally, however, the vorticity-free condition is not sufficient[43,44]). One can show (Proposition 5.1 in Ref. 5) that, in the GEM framework, local staticity amounts to the existence of a coordinate system where the metric takes the stationary form (3) with $\mathcal{A}$ closed ($d\mathcal{A} = 0$); and global staticity to $\mathcal{A}$ being moreover an *exact* form (in a globally well defined coordinate system).

The Weyl class Lewis metric (21) is locally static since $d\mathcal{A} = 0$; but, unless $j = 0 \Rightarrow \mathcal{A} = 0$ (Levi-Civita static cylinder), *not* globally static, since $\mathcal{A} = \mathcal{A}_\phi d\phi$ is not an exact form. This means that the Killing vector field ∂_t is hypersurface orthogonal but (unless $j = 0$) such hypersurfaces are not of global simultaneity, see Fig. 2 (a)-(b). In the case of the Kerr spacetime, $d\mathcal{A} \neq 0$, so it is not globally static; no hypersurface orthogonal time-like Killing vector field exists, the only Killing vector field which is time-like at infinity being ∂_t in Boyer-Lindquist coordinates, whose integral lines are well known to have vorticity. Geometrically, this means that the distribution of hyperplanes orthogonal to ∂_t (i.e., the hyperplanes of *local* simultaneity,[21] or local rest spaces of the "laboratory" observers) is not integrable, see Fig. 2 (c). On top of this, outside the equatorial plane, $R_{\alpha\beta\gamma\delta}$ is not purely electric (see Sec. V.C of Ref. 29), thus no observers exist measuring a vanishing gravitomagnetic tidal tensor $\mathbb{H}_{\alpha\beta}$.

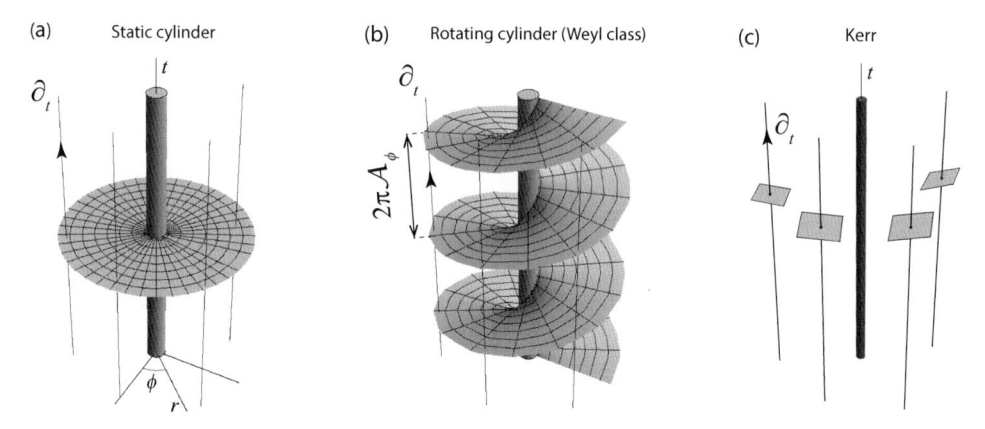

Fig. 2. (a)-(b): In the Weyl class Lewis metrics (21) the Killing vector field ∂_t is hypersurface orthogonal; such hypersurface is of global simultaneity (a plane, in a t, r, ϕ plot) for a non-spinning (Levi-Civita) cylinder, and of local but *non-global* simultaneity (the helicoid $t - \mathcal{A}_\phi \phi = const.$) in the spinning case. (c) In the Kerr spacetime ∂_t is not hypersurface orthogonal, i.e., the distribution of hyperplanes orthogonal to ∂_t (hyperplanes of *local* simultaneity) is not integrable. In (a) observers of worldlines tangent to ∂_t ("laboratory observers") are able to globally synchronize their clocks. In (b) they are unable to synchronize their clocks *around* the cylinder: each 2π turn along the helicoid leads to a different event in time, the jump between turns being the synchronization gap $\Delta t_{\text{sync}} = 2\pi \mathcal{A}_\phi$. In (c) the laboratory observers are (generically) unable to synchronize their clocks along any spatially closed loop, $\Delta t_{\text{sync}} = \oint \mathcal{A} \neq 0$.

Physically, this means that whereas for the Weyl class spinning cylinder (21) only the first level of gravitomagnetism in Table 1 is non-zero, in the Kerr spacetime all the three levels are non-zero. Therein it is thus possible to detect the source's rotation in a more local way (i.e., not needing experiments on loops around the source): in a reference frame fixed to the distant stars, due to the non-zero gravitomagnetic field $\vec{H}$, test particles in geodesic motion will appear to be deflected by a gravitomagnetic (or Coriolis) force $\gamma \vec{U} \times \vec{H}$, cf. Eq. (4), causing e.g. their orbits to precess (Lense-Thirring precession[36]), and gyroscopes will as well be seen to precess, cf. Eq. (6). The non-vanishing $\mathbb{H}_{\alpha\beta}$ means moreover that gyroscopes at rest (or generically moving) will be acted by a force (7).

Table 1. Gravitomagnetic effects present in the Weyl class Lewis metrics and in the Kerr spacetime, as measured in star-fixed reference frames (canonical and Boyer-Lindquist coordinate systems, respectively), split by levels of gravitomagnetism, corresponding to orders of differentiation of $\mathcal{A}$.

Level of Gravitomagnetism		Lewis-Weyl	Kerr
Governing object	Physical effect		
$\vec{\mathcal{A}}$ (gravitomagnetic vector potential)	• Sagnac effect • Synchronization gap	✓ (global effects)	✓ (global *and* local)
$\vec{H}$ (gravitomagnetic field $= e^\phi \nabla \times \vec{\mathcal{A}}$)	• gravitomagnetic force $m\gamma \vec{U} \times \vec{H}$ • gyroscope precession $d\vec{S}/d\tau = \vec{S} \times \vec{H}/2$ • local Sagnac effect in light gyroscope	✗	✓
$\vec{H} + \vec{\mathcal{A}}$	• Gravitomagnetic "clock" effect	• co-rotating geodesic has *shorter* period	• co-rotating geodesic has *longer* period
$\mathbb{H}_{\alpha\beta}$ (gravitomag. tidal tensor $\sim \partial_i \partial_j \mathcal{A}_k$)	• Force on gyroscope $DP^\alpha/d\tau = -\mathbb{H}^{\beta\alpha} S_\beta$	✗	✓

Even in what pertains to the first level of gravitomagnetism (governed by $\mathcal{A}$), present in both, they substantially differ. The fact that $d\mathcal{A} = 0$ in the Lewis-Weyl metric means that a Sagnac effect (9) arises only on loops enclosing the cylinder (as discussed in Sec. 4.4), and is independent of the shape of the loop; and similarly for the synchronization of clocks: the laboratory observers are able to synchronize their clocks along spatially closed loops that do not enclose the cylinder [in other words, closed in spacetime synchronization curves exist along the helicoid of Fig. 2 (b)]; it is only on loops around the cylinder that a synchronization gap (10) arises, see Fig. 2 (b). In the Kerr spacetime, by contrast, since $d\mathcal{A} \neq 0$, the Sagnac effect depends on the shape of the loop, and is generically non-zero (regardless of the loop enclosing or not the axis). The laboratory observers are likewise unable to synchronize their clocks around generic closed loops.

Another interesting contrast is in the gravitomagnetic clock effect (12). Around the spinning cylinder (21), since $\vec{H} = 0$, it reduces to the Sagnac time-delay (25), and thus the co-rotating geodesic has a shorter period. In the case of the Kerr spacetime, by contrast, the term Δt_H of (12) is not zero,

$$\Delta t_{\text{geo}} = \Delta t_S + \Delta t_H = 4\pi \frac{J}{M}; \quad \Delta t_S = -\frac{8\pi J}{r - 2M} (<0); \quad \Delta t_H = \frac{4\pi J r}{M(r - 2M)} (>0),$$

and is actually dominant,[27] so it is the other way around: the co-rotating orbit has a longer period, $\Delta t_{\text{geo}} = 4\pi J/M > 0$. The physical interpretation of $\Delta t_H > 0$ is that the gravitomagnetic force $\gamma \vec{U} \times \vec{H}$ in Eq. (4) is repulsive (attractive) for co- (counter-) rotating geodesics, see Fig. 1(b) of Ref. 27.

References

1. T. Lewis, Some special solutions to the equations of axially symmetric gravitational fields, *Proc. Roy. Soc. Lond.* **A136**, 179 (1932).
2. M. F. A. da Silva, L. Herrera, F. M. Paiva and N. O. Santos, The parameters of the Lewis metric for the Weyl class, *General Relativity and Gravitation* **27**, 859 (Aug 1995).
3. M. F. A. da Silva, L. Herrera, F. M. Paiva and N. O. Santos, On the parameters of Lewis metric for the Lewis class, *Class. Quant. Grav.* **12**, 111 (1995).
4. J. B. Griffiths and J. Podolsky, *Exact Space-Times in Einstein's General Relativity*, Cambridge Monographs on Mathematical Physics (Cambridge University Press, Cambridge, 2009).
5. L. F. O. Costa, J. Natário and N. O. Santos, Gravitomagnetism in the Lewis cylindrical metrics, *Class. Quant. Grav.* **38**, p. 055003 (2021).
6. W. J. van Stockum, IX. The Gravitational Field of a Distribution of Particles Rotating about an Axis of Symmetry, *Proceedings of the Royal Society of Edinburgh* **57**, 135 (1938).
7. Gravitomagnetism in the Lewis cylindrical metrics, *Invited talk at the parallel session "Dragging is never draggy: MAss and CHarge flows in GR", sixteenth Marcel Grossmann Meeting (MG16), July 5-10 2021* (https://youtu.be/ho31IgLNxu8).
8. L. D. Landau and E. M. Lifshitz, *The classical theory of fields; 4rd ed.*, Course of theoretical physics, Vol. 2 (Butterworth-Heinemann, Oxford, UK, 1975), Trans. from the Russian.
9. D. Lynden-Bell and M. Nouri-Zonoz, Classical monopoles: Newton, NUT space, gravomagnetic lensing, and atomic spectra, *Rev. Mod. Phys.* **70**, 427 (Apr 1998).
10. R. T. Jantzen, P. Carini and D. Bini, The Many faces of gravitoelectromagnetism, *Annals Phys.* **215**, 1 (1992).
11. L. F. O. Costa and J. Natário, Gravito-electromagnetic analogies, *General Relativity and Gravitation* **46**, p. 1792 (2014).
12. M. Mathisson, Neue mechanik materieller systemes, *Acta Phys. Polon.* **6**, p. 163 (1937), [*Gen. Relativ. Gravit.* **42**, 1011 (2010)].
13. A. Papapetrou, Spinning test particles in general relativity. 1., *Proc. Roy. Soc. Lond.* **A209**, 248 (1951).
14. L. F. O. Costa, J. Natário and M. Zilhão, Spacetime dynamics of spinning particles: Exact electromagnetic analogies, *Phys. Rev. D* **93**, p. 104006 (2016).
15. W. G. Dixon, A covariant multipole formalism for extended test bodies in general relativity, *Il Nuovo Cimento* **34**, p. 317 (1964).
16. Y. Aharonov and D. Bohm, Significance of electromagnetic potentials in the quantum theory, *Phys. Rev.* **115**, 485 (Aug 1959).
17. E. J. Post, Sagnac effect, *Rev. Mod. Phys.* **39**, 475 (Apr 1967).
18. E. Kajari, M. Buser, C. Feiler and W. P. Schleich, Rotation in relativity and the propagation of light, in *Proceedings of the International School of Physics "Enrico Fermi", Course CLXVIII*, (IOS Press, Amsterdam, 2009).
19. A. Ashtekar and A. Magnon, The Sagnac effect in general relativity, *J. Math. Phys.* **16**, 341 (1975).
20. A. Tartaglia, General relativistic corrections to the Sagnac effect, *Phys. Rev. D* **58**, p. 064009 (1998).
21. E. Minguzzi, Simultaneity and generalized connections in general relativity, *Class. Quant. Grav.* **20**, 2443 (2003).
22. M. L. Ruggiero, Sagnac Effect, Ring Lasers and Terrestrial Tests of Gravity, *Galaxies* **3**, 84 (2015).

23. J. Cohen and B. Mashhoon, Standard clocks, interferometry, and gravitomagnetism, *Physics Letters A* **181**, 353 (1993).
24. W. B. Bonnor and B. R. Steadman, The gravitomagnetic clock effect, *Classical and Quantum Gravity* **16**, p. 1853 (1999).
25. D. Bini, R. T. Jantzen and B. Mashhoon, Gravitomagnetism and relative observer clock effects, *Class. Quant. Grav.* **18**, 653 (2001).
26. L. Iorio, H. I. M. Lichtenegger and B. Mashhoon, An Alternative derivation of the gravitomagnetic clock effect, *Class. Quant. Grav.* **19**, 39 (2002).
27. L. F. O. Costa and J. Natário, Frame-Dragging: Meaning, Myths, and Misconceptions, *Universe* **7**, p. 388 (2021).
28. A. Tartaglia, Detection of the gravitomagnetic clock effect, *Class. Quant. Grav.* **17**, 783 (2000).
29. L. F. O. Costa, L. Wylleman and J. Natário, Gravitomagnetism and the significance of the curvature scalar invariants, *Phys. Rev. D* **104**, p. 084081 (2021).
30. C. B. G. McIntosh, R. Arianrhod, S. T. Wade and C. Hoenselaers, Electric and magnetic Weyl tensors: Classification and analysis, *Classical and Quantum Gravity* **11**, 1555 (jun 1994).
31. M. A. H. MacCallum and N. O. Santos, Stationary and static cylindrically symmetric Einstein spaces of the Lewis form, *Classical and Quantum Gravity* **15**, p. 1627 (1998).
32. W. B. Bonnor, Solution of Einstein's equations for a line-mass of perfect fluid, *Journal of Physics A: Mathematical and General* **12**, 847 (1979).
33. W. Israel, Line sources in general relativity, *Phys. Rev. D* **15**, 935 (Feb 1977).
34. L. Marder, Gravitational Waves in General Relativity. I. Cylindrical Waves, *Proceedings of the Royal Society of London Series A* **244**, 524 (1958).
35. D. Lynden-Bell and J. Bičák, Komar fluxes of circularly polarized light beams and cylindrical metrics, *Phys. Rev. D* **96**, p. 104053 (2017).
36. I. Ciufolini and J. A. Wheeler, *Gravitation and Inertia* (Princeton Series in Physics, Princeton, NJ, 1995).
37. I. Ciufolini, Dragging of inertial frames, *Nature* **449**, 41 (2007).
38. A. Barros, V. B. Bezerra and C. Romero, Global aspects of gravitomagnetism, *Mod. Phys. Lett.* **A18**, 2673 (2003).
39. B. Jensen and H. H. Soleng, General-relativistic model of a spinning cosmic string, *Phys. Rev. D* **45**, 3528 (May 1992).
40. M. Hindmarsh and T. Kibble, Cosmic strings, *Rept. Prog. Phys.* **58**, 477 (1995).
41. L. H. Ford and A. Vilenkin, A gravitational analogue of the Aharonov-Bohm effect, *Journal of Physics A: Mathematical and General* **14**, 2353 (1981).
42. M. Nouri-Zonoz and A. Parvizi, Gaussian curvature and global effects: Gravitational Aharonov-Bohm effect revisited, *Phys. Rev. D* **88**, p. 023004 (2013).
43. J. Stachel, Globally stationary but locally static space-times: A gravitational analog of the Aharonov-Bohm effect, *Phys. Rev. D* **26**, 1281 (1982).
44. W. B. Bonnor, The rigidly rotating relativistic dust cylinder, *Journal of Physics A: Mathematical and General* **13**, p. 2121 (1980).

Magnetized black holes: The role of rotation, boost, and accretion in twisting the field lines and accelerating particles*

Ondřej Kopáček and Vladimír Karas

*Astronomical Institute, Czech Academy of Sciences,
Boční II 1401, CZ-141 00 Prague, Czech Republic
E-mail: kopacek@ig.cas.cz, vladimir.karas@asu.cas.cz
http://astro.cas.cz*

Combined influence of rotation of a black hole and ambient magnetic fields creates conditions for powerful astrophysical processes of accretion and outflow of matter which are observed in many systems across the range of masses; from stellar-mass black holes in binary systems to supermassive black holes in active galactic nuclei. We study a simplified model of outflow of electrically charged particles from the inner region of an accretion disk around a spinning (Kerr) black hole immersed in a large-scale magnetic field. In particular, we consider a non-axisymmetric magnetosphere where the field is misaligned with the rotation axis. In this contribution we extend our previous analysis of acceleration of jet-like trajectories of particles escaping from bound circular orbits around a black hole. While we have previously assumed the initial setup of prograde (co-rotating) orbits, here we relax this assumption and we also consider retrograde (counter-rotating) motion. We show that the effect of *counter-rotation may considerably increase the probability of escape from the system, and it allows more efficient acceleration of escaping particles to slightly higher energies compared to the co-rotating disk.*

Keywords: Black holes, magnetosphere, non-axisymmetry, dynamics of ionized matter, acceleration of particles

1. Introduction

In this contribution we further study astrophysically relevant class of escaping (jet-like accelerated) trajectories in a dynamical system of a magnetized rotating black hole. Electrically charged particles following such orbits may escape the attraction of the black hole in a collimated outflow and they may be accelerated to very high energies. In Paper I[1] we adopted a simple axisymmetric model consisting of a rotating black hole in an asymptotically uniform magnetic field aligned with the rotation axis. Initially neutral particles are supposed to follow circular orbits in the equatorial plane (and freely fall below ISCO). At a particular ionization radius, these particles obtain electric charge and their dynamics changes due to the presence of electromagnetic field, and escape from the accretion disk along high-velocity jet-like trajectories becomes possible. However, the efficiency of the acceleration process remains only moderate in the axisymmetric setup.[1]

---

*Based on an invited contribution at 16th Marcel Grossmann Meeting, Session PT5 "Dragging is never draggy: MAss and CHarge flows in GR" (id. #393), 5–10 July 2021.

In Paper II[2] we relax the assumption of the perfect spin-magnetic alignment and consider a generalized non-axisymmetric model. The effect of non-axisymmetry in electro-vacuum magnetospheres of compact objects is known to introduce dynamically relevant features like magnetic null-points,[3] and breaking the axial symmetry also appears to strongly affect the acceleration process in the current model. In particular, the number of escaping orbits generally increases and acceleration to ultrarelativistic energies becomes possible in the oblique magnetosphere.[2,4] Furthermore,[5] by employing a boost transformation of the system into a frame in translation motion, we explored the electromagnetic aspects of the linear (kick) velocity of the black hole. Refer to enlightening discussions by various authors[6,7] and see also the relevant context of these solutions.[8]

In the above-mentioned previous papers, we numerically studied escaping orbits and we assessed in detail the role of a broad variety of parameters of the model. Nevertheless, the assumption that initially neutral matter co-rotates with the central black hole, was adopted in all previous analyses. Here we relax this assumption and we also consider counter-rotating (retrograde) circular orbits as an initial setup of neutral particles. We compare the both cases (of co-rotating vs. counter-rotating) in terms of the efficiency of the formation and acceleration of the individual trajectories and the emerging outflow.

The role of counter-rotation in processes of accretion and outflow near compact objects has been only partially explored in the literature and various relevant aspects of accretion of counter-rotating matter has been studied. In particular, high-resolution hydrodynamic simulations suggest that counter-rotating structure may largely increase the accretion rate.[9] Moreover, general relativistic magnetohydrodynamic (GRMHD) simulations show that accretion of counter-rotating matter may produce conditions for highly efficient jet launching.[10] We also note that counter-rotating high-velocity outflows are indeed reported in various systems, such as the spiral galaxy NGC 1068.[11]

The paper is organized as follows. In Section 2 we specify the employed model of oblique black hole magnetosphere, we review the equations of motion and describe the charging process of initially neutral matter. Jet-like trajectories of charged particles escaping from counter-rotating orbits are discussed in Section 3 with the focus on the direct comparison with the co-rotating analogues. Results are summarized and briefly discussed in Section 4. As the initial setup of the model investigated in the present paper is analogous to that of Papers I and II, we refer to the more complete introduction and references presented therein.

2. Model specification

We consider a spacetime around a rotating, axially-symmetric, uncharged black hole of mass M and spin a described by the Kerr metric, which may be expressed in Boyer–Lindquist coordinates $x^\mu = (t, r, \theta, \varphi)$ as follows:[12,13]

$$ds^2 = -\frac{\Delta}{\Sigma}[dt - a\sin\theta\, d\varphi]^2 + \frac{\sin^2\theta}{\Sigma}[(r^2 + a^2)d\varphi - a\, dt]^2 + \frac{\Sigma}{\Delta}dr^2 + \Sigma d\theta^2, \quad (1)$$

where $\Delta(r) \equiv r^2 - 2Mr + a^2$ and $\Sigma(r,\theta) \equiv r^2 + a^2\cos^2\theta$. Roots of $\Delta(r)$ locate the outer (+) and the inner (-) horizons as: $r_\pm = M \pm \sqrt{M^2 - a^2}$. Geometrized units are used throughout the paper; values of basic constants (gravitational constant G, speed of light c, Boltzmann constant k, and Coulomb constant k_C) therefore equal unity, $G = c = k = k_C = 1$.

The black hole is supposed to be weakly magnetized by an external, asymptotically uniform magnetic field with an asymptotic strength B which has an arbitrary inclination (angle α) with respect to the rotation axis. Vector potential $A_\mu = (A_t, A_r, A_\theta, A_\varphi)$ of a corresponding test-field solution is given as:[14]

$$A_t = \frac{B_z a M r}{\Sigma}(1 + \cos^2\theta) - B_z a + \frac{B_x a M \sin\theta \cos\theta}{\Sigma}(r\cos\psi - a\sin\psi), \quad (2)$$

$$A_r = -B_x(r - M)\cos\theta\sin\theta\sin\psi, \quad (3)$$

$$A_\theta = -B_x a(r\sin^2\theta + M\cos^2\theta)\cos\psi - B_x(r^2\cos^2\theta \quad (4)$$
$$- Mr\cos 2\theta + a^2\cos 2\theta)\sin\psi,$$

$$A_\varphi = B_z \sin^2\theta\left[\frac{1}{2}(r^2 + a^2) - \frac{a^2 M r}{\Sigma}(1 + \cos^2\theta)\right] \quad (5)$$
$$- B_x \sin\theta\cos\theta\left[\Delta\cos\psi + \frac{(r^2 + a^2)M}{\Sigma}(r\cos\psi - a\sin\psi)\right],$$

where B_z denotes the component parallel to the rotation axis, while B_x corresponds to the perpendicular component, i.e., $B_z = B\cos\alpha$ and $B_x = B\sin\alpha$. Setting $B_x = 0$ reduces the above vector potential A_μ to the axisymmetric solution[15] employed in Paper I. Azimuthal coordinate ψ of Kerr ingoing coordinates is expressed in Boyer–Lindquist coordinates as follows:

$$\psi = \varphi + \frac{a}{r_+ - r_-}\ln\frac{r - r_+}{r - r_-}. \quad (6)$$

The Hamiltonian $\mathcal{H}$ of a particle of electric charge q and rest mass m in the field A_μ and metric $g^{\mu\nu}$ is defined as:[12]

$$\mathcal{H} = \tfrac{1}{2}g^{\mu\nu}(\pi_\mu - qA_\mu)(\pi_\nu - qA_\nu), \quad (7)$$

where π_μ is the generalized (canonical) momentum. The equations of motion are expressed as:

$$\frac{dx^\mu}{d\lambda} \equiv p^\mu = \frac{\partial \mathcal{H}}{\partial \pi_\mu}, \quad \frac{d\pi_\mu}{d\lambda} = -\frac{\partial \mathcal{H}}{\partial x^\mu}, \quad (8)$$

where $\lambda \equiv \tau/m$ is dimensionless affine parameter (τ denotes the proper time). Employing the first equation we obtain the kinematical four-momentum as: $p^\mu = \pi^\mu - qA^\mu$, and the conserved value of the Hamiltonian is therefore given as: $\mathcal{H} = -m^2/2$. System is stationary and the time component of canonical momentum π_t is therefore an integral of motion which equals (negatively taken) energy of the test particle $\pi_t \equiv -E$. In the rest of paper we switch to specific quantities $E/m \to E$,

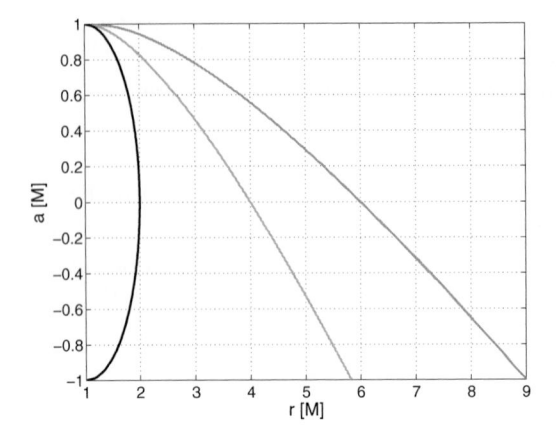

Fig. 1. Position of the black hole's outer horizon (black), marginally bound circular orbit (cyan) and ISCO (green). Negative spin values correspond to the counter-rotating orbits.

$q/m \to q$ which corresponds to setting the rest mass of the particle $m = 1$ in the formulas.

As an initial configuration of electrically neutral particles, we consider circular Keplerian orbits specified by the values of constants of motion, i.e., by specific energy E_{Kep} and specific angular momentum L_{Kep} given as follows:[16]

$$E_{\text{Kep}} = \frac{r^2 - 2Mr \pm a\sqrt{Mr}}{r\sqrt{r^2 - 3Mr \pm 2a\sqrt{Mr}}}, \quad L_{\text{Kep}} = \frac{\pm\sqrt{M}(r^2 + a^2 \mp 2a\sqrt{Mr})}{\sqrt{r(r^2 - 3Mr \pm 2a\sqrt{Mr})}}, \quad (9)$$

where the upper signs are valid for the prograde (co-rotating) orbits and the lower ones for the retrograde (counter-rotating) orbits. Circular geodesics remain stable only above the innermost stable circular orbit (ISCO):

$$r_{\text{ISCO}} = M\left(3 + Z_2 \mp \sqrt{(3 - Z_1)(3 + Z_1 + 2Z_2)}\right), \quad (10)$$

where $Z_1 \equiv 1 + \left(1 - \frac{a^2}{M^2}\right)^{1/3}\left[\left(1 + \frac{a}{M}\right)^{1/3} + \left(1 - \frac{a}{M}\right)^{1/3}\right]$ and $Z_2 \equiv \sqrt{\frac{3a^2}{M^2} + Z_1^2}$. Positions of the ISCO and marginally bound circular orbit[16] are plotted in Fig. 1.

Below ISCO the geodesics are supposed to turn into freely falling inspirals maintaining the energy and angular momentum corresponding to the ISCO radius, i.e., the particles keep $E = E_{\text{Kep}}(r_{\text{ISCO}})$ and $L = L_{\text{Kep}}(r_{\text{ISCO}})$ during their infall while the radial velocity u^r is obtained from the normalization condition $u^\mu u_\mu = -1$.

In our model, we suppose that initially neutral elements undergo a sudden charging process (e.g., due to photoionization) at a given radius r_0 and obtain specific electric charge q. While the change of the rest mass m is considered as negligible, the particle dynamics changes due to the presence of the electromagnetic field.[17]

In particular, the conserved value of energy is modified as:
$$E = E_{\text{Kep}} - qA_t, \qquad (11)$$
while the values of spatial components of canonical momentum are changed as:
$$\pi_r = \pi_r^0 + qA_r, \quad \pi_\theta = qA_\theta, \quad \pi_\varphi = L_{\text{Kep}} + qA_\varphi, \qquad (12)$$
where π_r^0 is zero for particles ionized above/at ISCO and for infalling particles with ionization radius $r_0 < r_{\text{ISCO}}$ the value is calculated from the normalization condition.

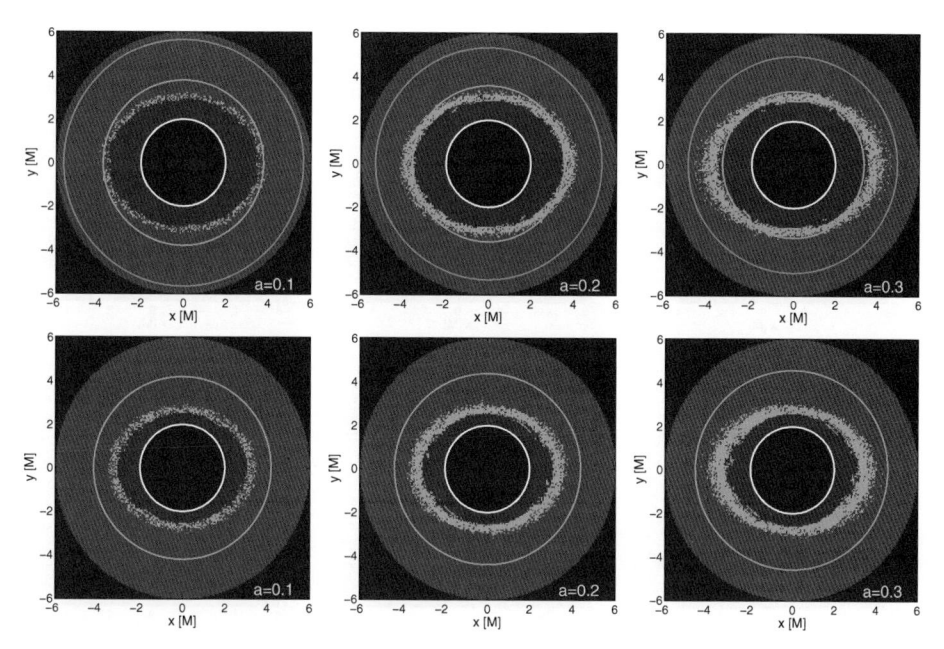

Fig. 2. Comparison of initially co-rotating orbits (upper row) with counter-rotating orbits (lower row). Color-coding: blue for plunging orbits, red for stable ones, and yellow for escaping trajectories. The green circle denotes the ISCO, the cyan circle marks the radius of the marginally bound orbit and the white one shows the ergosphere. The inner black region marks the horizon of the black hole. The parameters of the system are $\alpha = 35°$ and $qB = -5\,M^{-1}$. The magnetic field is inclined in the positive x-direction.

3. Escape zones

The dynamics of initially neutral particles on stable circular orbits (above ISCO) or on a plunging trajectory (below ISCO) changes abruptly as they obtain the electric charge and become affected by the electromagnetic field given by Eqs. (2)-(5). As a result, some stable particles may become plunging, while some plunging trajectories are stabilized by the field. Moreover, it appears that particles may also become unbound and escape to infinity in jet-like trajectories.

We have previously analyzed escaping particles in this model and, in particular, in Paper I[1] we considered the axisymmetric system ($B_x = 0$), while in the Paper II[2] the general non-axisymmetric configuration was studied. We have used the method of effective potential to find the necessary conditions for the escape of particles. It appears that for the parallel orientation of the spin axis z and magnetic field component B_z, only negatively charged particles may escape (while positively charged escape for the anti-parallel orientation). Non-zero spin a and B_z are required for the escape and final Lorentz factor γ is found to be an increasing function of the spin, specific charge $|q|$ and $|B_z|$ while it decreases with the ionization radius r_0.

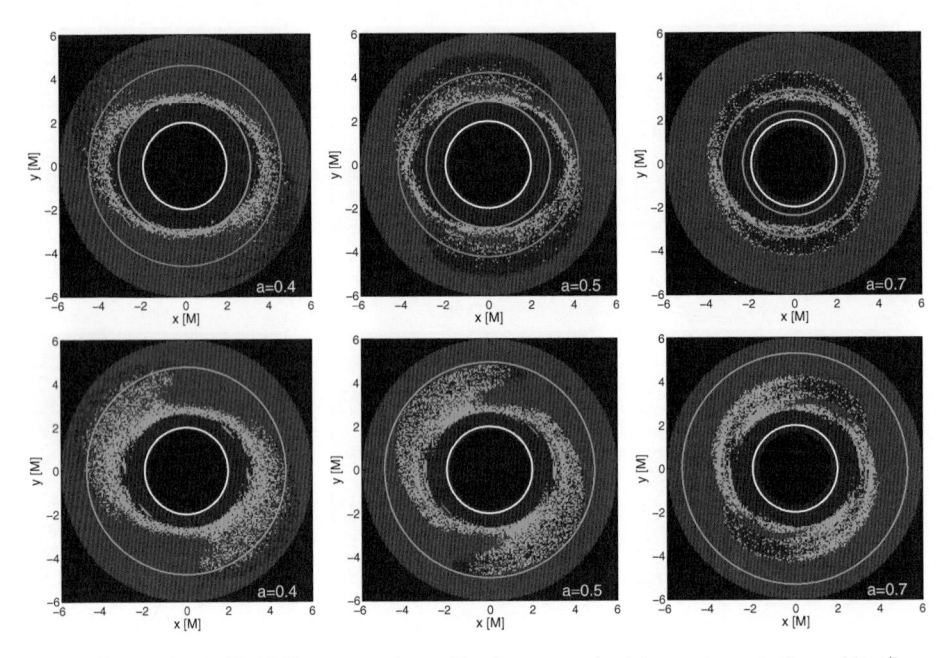

Fig. 3. Comparison of initially co-rotating orbits (upper row) with counter-rotating orbits (lower row). The color-coding and parameters as in Fig. 2.

However, as the above conditions are necessary but not sufficient, we need to investigate the dynamic system numerically in order to determine which particles actually follow the escaping trajectories. Initial locations of escaping particles form *escape zones* whose emergence and evolution with respect to the parameters of the system was discussed in our previous papers.[1,2,4] Efficiency of the acceleration mechanism was quantified by the final Lorentz factor of escaping particles leading to the conclusion that also ultrarelativistic velocities with very high energies may be achieved within the non-axisymmetric model.

In this contribution, we extend the previous discussion and consider a modified setup. In particular, here we suppose that the initially neutral matter may follow counter-rotating geodesics, i.e., unlike the previous papers, here we also consider the lower signs in Eqs. (9) and (10). The ISCO of counter-rotating orbits is located generally farther from the horizon compared to the co-rotating ones (see Fig. 1). In particular, no stable retrograde circular orbits around rotating black hole are allowed for $r \leq 6\,M$ and the ISCO location grows with the spin up to $r_{\mathrm{ISCO}} = 9\,M$ for the maximally rotating black hole with $a = M$.

We assume that below ISCO the initially neutral particle falls freely towards the horizon keeping the energy and angular momentum corresponding to the ISCO radius, while the radial velocity is computed from the normalization condition. At the ionization radius r_0 the particle obtains the electric charge and its dynamics changes due to magnetic field. Three main scenarios may occur then; the particle plunges into the horizon, follows the stable orbit around the black hole or escapes to infinity.

Analogously to our previous studies, we adopt the visual representation of resulting orbits in escape boundary plots in which we assign blue dots to plunging orbits, red dots to stable orbits and yellow dots to escaping ones. In Figs. 2-4 we compare the co-rotating setup (upper rows) with the counter-rotating case (bottom rows) in a series of escape boundary plots for a particular set of parameters ($qB = -5\,M^{-1}$ and $\alpha = 35°$) with varying values of spin. In Fig. 2 we observe that for low spins the both cases do not differ significantly. Corresponding escape zones have comparable shapes and sizes regardless the sense of revolution. However, if we consider moderate values of spin, the situation changes and significant differences between the escape zones in co-rotating and counter-rotating disks arise as shown in Fig. 3. Most importantly, we observe that the number of escaping trajectories is substantially higher for counter-rotating orbits forming considerably larger escape zones. The tendency of more rapid rotation to favorize the escape from counter-rotating orbits is confirmed in Fig. 4, where we notice that high spin allows only narrow escape zones in the co-rotating disk while counter-rotating zones become significantly wider. Also, these plots exhibit clear signatures of a transition from the regular to chaotic system in agreement with previous studies of similarly perturbed black hole systems.[2,18–20]

Another convenient way to visualize the escape zones is to fix the initial value of the azimuthal angle φ_0 and plot the trajectories in the $r_0 \times a$ plane (ionization radius vs. spin) using the same color-coding of trajectories as in Figs. 2-4. The angle φ is measured anticlockwise from the positive direction of x-axis (which is the direction of the field inclination). In particular, we choose the value $\varphi_0 = 135°$ for which the structure of the escape zone seems especially complex. In Fig. 5 we present the resulting plots for several values of magnetization parameter qB and compare co-rotating escape zones (left column) with the counter-rotating zones (right column). It confirms that counter-rotating orbits are generally more prone to escape regardless the value of qB while the both cases differ most significantly for rapidly rotating black holes.

Previous analysis in Papers I and II shows that spin parameter is an important factor for the acceleration of escaping particles. In particular, it appears that final

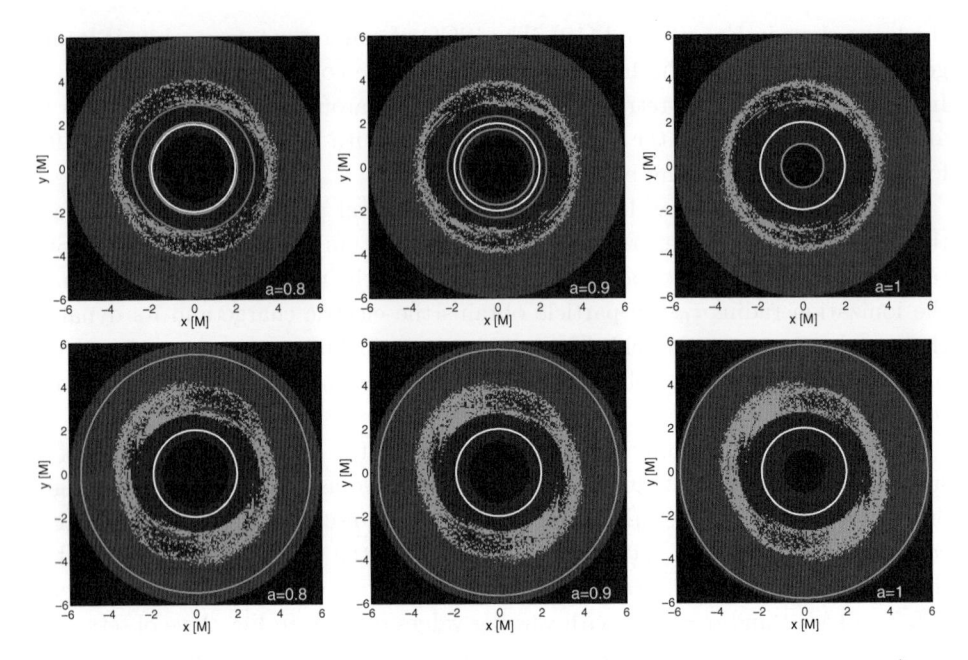

Fig. 4. Comparison of initially co-rotating orbits (upper row) with counter-rotating orbits (lower row). The color-coding and parameters as in Fig. 2.

value of γ for the fixed qB grows with the spin and decreases with the ionization radius r_0. Maximally accelerated particles are thus expected to originate from the inner edge of the escape zone near maximally rotating black hole with spin $a = M$.

In Fig. 5 we observe that counter-rotating escape zones for high spins are considerably wider compared to co-rotating ones and, moreover, we notice that counter-rotating zones are located closer to the horizon. We thus expect that particles escaping from counter-rotating orbits could reach slightly higher energies. This is indeed the case as shown in Fig. 6 where the final values of the Lorentz factor are encoded with the color-scale. For this particular set of parameters ($qB = -20\,M^{-1}$, $\varphi_0 = 135°$) we find that maximally accelerated counter-rotating particle reaches $\gamma_{\max} = 8.1$ being launched from $r_0 = 2.3\,M$ while for the co-rotating disk we find $\gamma_{\max} = 7.3$ for the particle escaping from $r_0 = 2.5\,M$.

4. Conclusions

We have numerically analyzed a simplified model of the outflow of electrically charged particles from the inner region of the accretion disk near a weakly magnetized rotating black hole. Stable circular orbits (freely falling below ISCO) of initially neutral particles were perturbed by the ionization process occuring in the non-axisymmetric magnetosphere. As a result, the escaping jet-like trajectories may be realized for some range of parameters and acceleration to high energies becomes

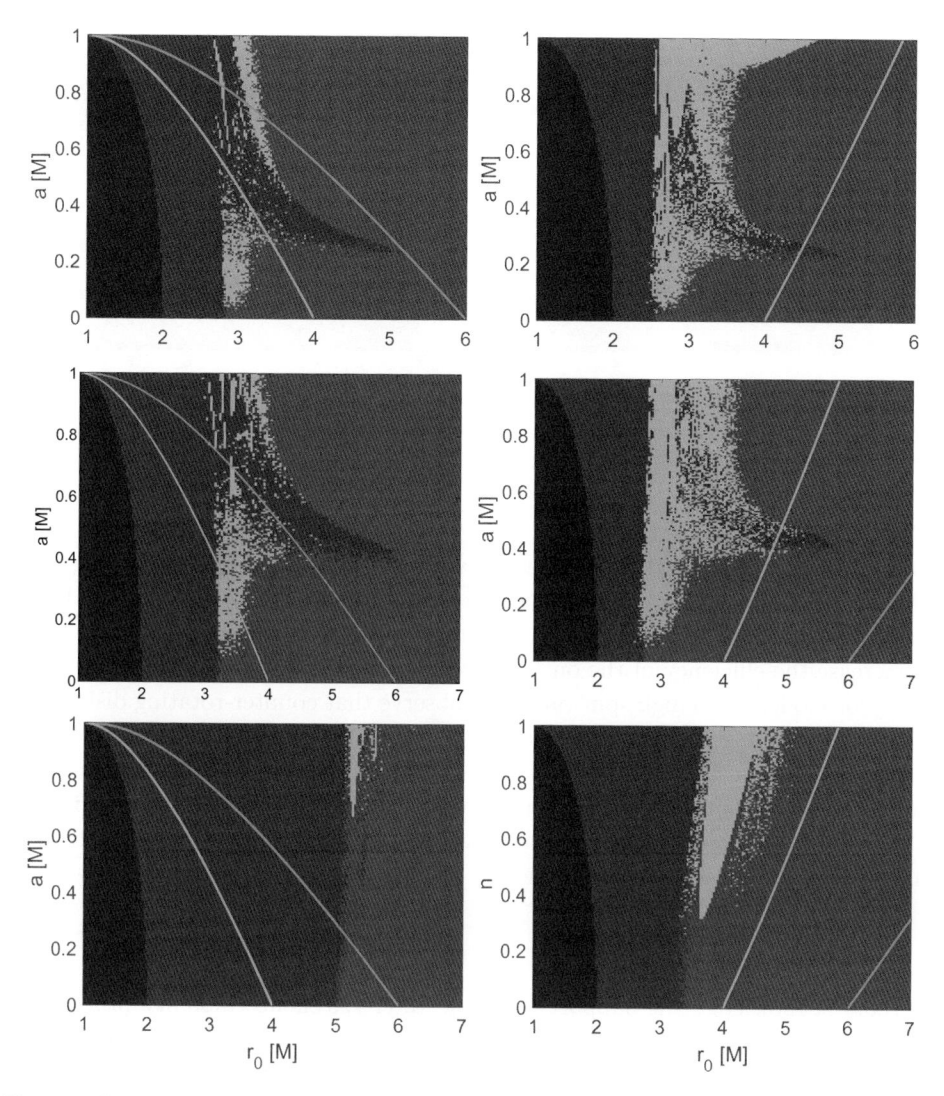

Fig. 5. Comparison of escape zones in co-rotating (left panels) and counter-rotating disks (right panels) for several values of magnetization parameter: $qB = -M^{-1}$ (bottom panels), $qB = -5\,M^{-1}$ (middle panels) and $qB = -10\,M^{-1}$ (upper panels). The inclination of the field is $\alpha = 35°$ and $\varphi_0 = 135°$. The color-coding as in Fig. 2.

possible. While we have previously studied various aspects of given model and investigated the formation of escape zones in detail,[1,2] we have assumed the initial setup of co-rotating accretion disk. In particular, the neutral particles above ISCO were supposed to follow prograde circular orbits and freely fall below ISCO.

In this contribution we have generalized the previous analysis by considering also counter-rotating (retrograde) Keplerian orbits as an initial setup of neutral

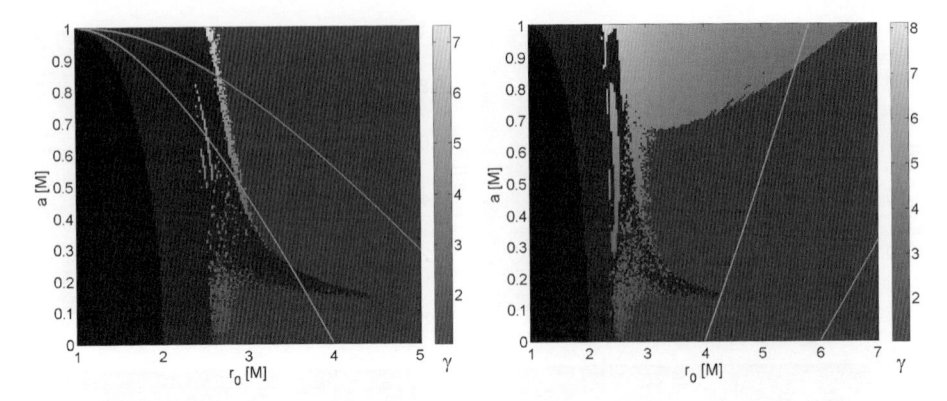

Fig. 6. Final Lorentz factor γ of escaping particles is encoded with the colorscale comparing the co-rotating (left) and the counter-rotating disks (right) while other parameters remain fixed as: $\alpha = 35°$ and $qB = -20\,M^{-1}$.

matter. We have studied the escape zones emerging in the counter-rotating disks which were directly compared with the corresponding co-rotating versions. Based on the analyzed set of escape zones we may conclude that counter-rotation tends to increase the efficiency of the outflow. While its effect becomes negligible for low spins, for moderate to high spin values we observe that counter-rotating disks allow the formation of significantly wider escape zones compared to their co-rotating analogues. The position of the zone is also affected as counter-rotating zones are shifted towards the horizon which makes the acceleration process more efficient. Although the difference is rather small, we observe that counter-rotating particles may be accelerated to higher energies.

Acknowledgements

Authors acknowledge the support from the Inter-Excellence mobility program in science of the Czech Ministry of Education, Youth and Sports (projects ref. 8JCH 1080 and LTC 18058). OK has been supported by the project "Lumina Quaeruntur" (ref. LQ100032102) of the Czech Academy of Sciences. VK thanks the Czech Science Foundation grant "Mass and charge currents in general relativity and astrophysics" (ref. 21-11268S).

References

1. O. Kopáček and V. Karas, Near-horizon Structure of Escape Zones of Electrically Charged Particles around Weakly Magnetized Rotating Black Hole, *The Astrophysical Journal* **853**, p. 53 (January 2018).
2. O. Kopáček and V. Karas, Near-horizon Structure of Escape Zones of Electrically Charged Particles around Weakly Magnetized Rotating Black Hole. II. Acceleration and Escape in the Oblique Magnetosphere, *The Astrophysical Journal* **900**, p. 119 (September 2020).

3. O. Kopáček, T. Tahamtan and V. Karas, Null points in the magnetosphere of a plunging neutron star, *Physical Review D* **98**, p. 084055 (October 2018).
4. V. Karas and O. Kopáček, Near horizon structure of escape zones of electrically charged particles around weakly magnetized rotating black hole: Case of oblique magnetosphere, *Astronomische Nachrichten* **342**, 357 (January 2021).
5. V. Karas, O. Kopáček and D. Kunneriath, Influence of frame-dragging on magnetic null points near rotating black holes, *Classical and Quantum Gravity* **29**, p. 035010 (February 2012).
6. V. Karas, O. Kopáček and D. Kunneriath, Magnetic Neutral Points and Electric Lines of Force in Strong Gravity of a Rotating Black Hole, *International Journal of Astronomy and Astrophysics* **3**, 18 (January 2013).
7. A. Abdujabbarov, N. Dadhich and B. Ahmedov, Electromagnetic field around boosted rotating black hole, *arXiv:1810.08066* (October 2018).
8. E. Gallo and T. Mädler, Comment on "Boosted Kerr black holes in general relativity", *Physical Review D* **101**, p. 028501 (January 2020).
9. S. Dyda, R. V. E. Lovelace, G. V. Ustyugova, M. M. Romanova and A. V. Koldoba, Counter-rotating accretion discs, *Monthly Notices of the Royal Astronomical Society* **446**, 613 (January 2015).
10. S. Koide, D. L. Meier, K. Shibata and T. Kudoh, General Relativistic Simulations of Early Jet Formation in a Rapidly Rotating Black Hole Magnetosphere, *The Astrophysical Journal* **536**, 668 (June 2000).
11. C. M. V. Impellizzeri, J. F. Gallimore, S. A. Baum, M. Elitzur, R. Davies, D. Lutz, R. Maiolino, A. Marconi, R. Nikutta, C. P. O'Dea and E. Sani, Counter-rotation and High-velocity Outflow in the Parsec-scale Molecular Torus of NGC 1068, *The Astrophysical Journal Letters* **884**, p. L28 (October 2019).
12. C. W. Misner, K. S. Thorne and J. A. Wheeler, *Gravitation* 2017.
13. R. P. Kerr, Gravitational Field of a Spinning Mass as an Example of Algebraically Special Metrics, *Physical Review Letters* **11**, 237 (September 1963).
14. J. Bičák and V. Janiš, Magnetic fluxes across black holes, *Monthly Notices of the Royal Astronomical Society* **212**, 899 (February 1985).
15. R. M. Wald, Black hole in a uniform magnetic field, *Physical Review D* **10**, 1680 (September 1974).
16. J. M. Bardeen, W. H. Press and S. A. Teukolsky, Rotating Black Holes: Locally Nonrotating Frames, Energy Extraction, and Scalar Synchrotron Radiation, *The Astrophysical Journal* **178**, 347 (December 1972).
17. Z. Stuchlík and M. Kološ, Acceleration of the charged particles due to chaotic scattering in the combined black hole gravitational field and asymptotically uniform magnetic field, *European Physical Journal C* **76**, p. 32 (January 2016).
18. V. Karas and D. Vokrouhlický, Chaotic motion of test particles in the Ernst spacetime, *General Relativity and Gravitation* **24**, 729 (July 1992).
19. P. S. Letelier and W. M. Vieira, Chaos in black holes surrounded by gravitational waves, *Classical and Quantum Gravity* **14**, 1249 (May 1997).
20. V. Witzany, O. Semerák and P. Suková, Free motion around black holes with discs or rings: Between integrability and chaos - IV, *Monthly Notices of the Royal Astronomical Society* **451**, 1770 (August 2015).

Spinning particle:
Is Newton-Wigner the only way?

V. Witzany

*School of Mathematics and Statistics, University College Dublin,
Belfield, Dublin 4, Ireland*
E-mail: vojtech.witzany at ucd.ie

A rapidly spinning compact object couples to an ambient curved background via the so-called spin-curvature coupling. In expressing this, one has to deal with the ambiguity of the definition of the center of mass of the body. What is worse, in a Hamiltonian formalism, this choice corresponds to an unphysical "parasitic" degree of freedom in the dynamical system. A solution to this is to apply a Hamiltonian constraint on the system and to obtain a set of brackets where the center-of-mass degree of freedom is erased from the algebra. I report on my progress in this procedure in the case of the so-called Tulczyjew-Dixon (or "covariant") supplementary spin condition and in my effort to cover the resulting phase space with canonical coordinates.

Keywords: Equations of motion – Classical relativity – Spinning bodies – Two-body problem – Gravitational waves

1. Introduction: Motion of spinning particle

Notation and convention: I use the $G = c = 1$ geometrized units and a $(-+++)$ metric signature. Greek indices $\mu, \nu, ...$ run from 0 to 3, and Einstein summation convention is assumed.

When the surface of a given body is rotating at relativistic speeds, it will couple to any curved space-time background by the so-called *spin-curvature coupling*. This effect is an important ingredient for the relativistic two-body problem and, in particular, for the modelling of gravitational waves from compact binaries.

To understand how the spin-curvature coupling arises, imagine a compact object such as a neutron star moving in an ambient curved space-time background where, in order to treat the problem step by step, we will for now understand the compact object exclusively as a "test" object. When the variability length, or the curvature scale of the background is much longer than the size of the body, it is meaningful to construct a set of Riemann normal coordinates X^μ with respect to the background geometry centred on the body. The coordinate acceleration of individual elements of the body caused by the background gravitational field then is $\sim \Gamma^\mu{}_{\nu\kappa} U^\nu U^\kappa$, where $\Gamma^\mu{}_{\nu\kappa}$ are Christoffel symbols of the background and U^ν the four-velocity of the body elements, both expressed in the local frame.

Let us now assume that the body is approximately rigidly rotating with respect to the time-foliation by the Riemann normal coordinates $X^0 = \text{const.}$. We can then formally write $U^i = (\vec{\omega} \times \vec{X})^i$ ($i = 1, 2, 3$) where $\vec{\omega}$ is some angular velocity vector. Then let us further assume that we are comparing relative accelerations on the constant-time slice $X^0 = 0$ in the Riemann normal frame so that we obtain

$$\delta a^\mu \sim \Gamma^\mu{}_{\nu\kappa} U^\nu U^\kappa \sim R^\mu{}_{0j0} X^j + R^\mu{}_{0ji} X^j (\vec{\omega} \times \vec{X})^i + \dots, \quad (1)$$

where $R_{\mu\nu\kappa\lambda}$ is the Riemann tensor along the wordline of the particle and the three dots denote higher-order terms in the size of the body. Now by averaging over $\vec{X}$, we see that we are able to choose a centre of coordinates such that the first, dipole-type term vanishes. However, the second term cannot be reduced by any coordinate shift. If we then take any system of particles, be it dust or a body held together by some force, we always see that the centre of mass of this system is subject to a residual *spin-curvature force*.

1.1. Mathisson-Papapetrou-Dixon equations

Procedures such as the one sketched above were carried out in various degrees of generality by Mathisson,[1] Papapetrou[2] and Dixon[3] to derive the equations of motion of extended bodies in curved space-time

$$\frac{DP_\mu}{d\tau} = -\frac{1}{2} R_{\mu\nu\kappa\lambda} \dot{x}^\nu S^{\kappa\lambda} + \dots, \quad (2)$$

$$\frac{DS^{\mu\nu}}{d\tau} = 2P^{[\mu} \dot{x}^{\nu]} + \dots, \quad (3)$$

where $x^\nu(\tau)$ is a referential position within the body, P_μ its momentum, and $S^{\kappa\lambda}$ has the general meaning of an angular momentum or "gravitomagnetic dipole" about its own center of mass. The parameter chosen here is proper time τ, but the equations can be parametrized by any other parameter. It should be noted that even though P_μ has the meaning of the overall linear momentum of the system, it may not be strictly true that the word-line is chosen so that $\dot{x}^\nu \propto P^\nu$.[4]

The three dots in the equation above denote higher-order terms corresponding to the interactions of the higher-order multipoles with the background curvature. The ability to discard higher-order terms is possible only for compact objects, for many astrophysical bodies the spin-curvature term is vastly sub-dominant. However, one can also easily show that even for compact objects, the spin-curvature coupling is suppressed to the 1.5 post-Newtonian order on the level of the equations of motion of binaries, and to linear order in the mass ratio. Thus, there is a limit to the applicability of the discussion of the strictly "test-particle" motion and at some point cross-reaction with other "non-test" effects cannot be ignored any more.

1.2. The ambiguity of x^ν and $S^{\kappa\lambda}$

As discussed at length in the literature the procedure of finding a center of mass for a rotating body is ambiguous.[4,5] In particular, the result depends on the slicing (the frame) we choose for the worldtube of the body. This is an issue even in flat space-time, where one is free to transform to another center of mass and angular-momentum tensor by the shifts[6]

$$x'^\mu = x^\mu + \delta x^\mu, \quad S'^{\nu\kappa} = S^{\nu\kappa} + P^\nu \delta x^\kappa - P^\kappa \delta x^\nu, \tag{4}$$

where δx^μ is some shift vector. This worldline shifting has a natural covariant extension to curved space-time by using Synge's world functions, but the overall physical content of the ambiguity is the same in both cases.[7]

A way to fix this "gauge freedom" of the worldline and the angular-momentum tensor is to choose a so-called *supplementary spin condition* of the form $S^{\mu\nu}V_\nu = 0$ with V_ν some time-like vector. The vector V^μ then has the meaning of the frame in which the center of mass and angular momentum are measured. When chosen judiciously, the supplementary condition eliminates all the nonphysical degrees of freedom from the system and one is left with only the physical ones to be evolved. Sometimes the choice of V^ν is implicit; the vector V^ν refers to the quantities it is supposed to fix (such as $x^\nu, S^{\kappa\lambda}$). In such cases one often ends up in a system where the non-physical degrees of freedom are not entirely constrained.[4,5,8,9]

2. Hamiltonian formalism

There is a range of reasons to use the Hamiltonian formalism, for the spinning-particle motion, from efficient numerical methods,[9] through perturbation theory,[10] to the use of the results in the so-called Effective-one-body model for relativistic binaries.[7,11] Let us now briefly summarize the Hamiltonians introduced by Witzany et al. in a previous work.[9] Consider the three covariant Hamiltonians corresponding to different choice of the frame V^ν:

$$V^\nu \text{ parallel transported along } x^\nu(\tau): \tag{5}$$

$$H_{\text{KS}} = \frac{1}{2m} g^{\mu\nu} P_\mu P_\nu, \tag{6}$$

$$V^\nu \propto P^\nu: \tag{7}$$

$$H_{\text{TD}} = \frac{1}{2\mathcal{M}} \left(g^{\mu\nu} - \frac{4 S^{\nu\gamma} R^\mu{}_{\gamma\kappa\lambda} S^{\kappa\lambda}}{4\mathcal{M}^2 + R_{\chi\eta\omega\xi} S^{\chi\eta} S^{\omega\eta}} \right) P_\mu P_\nu, \tag{8}$$

$$V^\nu = \dot{x}^\nu: \tag{9}$$

$$H_{\text{MP}} = \frac{1}{2m} g^{\mu\nu} P_\mu P_\nu, \tag{10}$$

where $m = -\dot{x}^\nu P_\nu$, $\mathcal{M} = \sqrt{-P^\nu P_\nu}$ are mass parameters with slightly different meanings but all corresponding roughly to the mass of the spinning body.[9,12]

The equations of motion are obtained with the use of the Poisson bracket

$$\{x^\mu, P_\nu\} = \delta^\mu_\nu, \quad \{x^\mu, S^{\kappa\lambda}\} = 0, \quad \{x^\mu, x^\nu\} = 0, \tag{11}$$

$$\{P_\mu, P_\nu\} = -\frac{1}{2} R_{\mu\nu\kappa\lambda} S^{\kappa\lambda}, \tag{12}$$

$$\{S^{\mu\nu}, P_\kappa\} = -\Gamma^\mu{}_{\lambda\kappa} S^{\lambda\nu} - \Gamma^\nu{}_{\lambda\kappa} S^{\mu\lambda}, \tag{13}$$

$$\{S^{\mu\nu}, S^{\kappa\lambda}\} = g^{\mu\kappa} S^{\nu\lambda} - g^{\mu\lambda} S^{\nu\kappa} + g^{\nu\lambda} S^{\mu\kappa} - g^{\nu\kappa} S^{\mu\lambda}, \tag{14}$$

There is a set of canonical coordinates that reduce the Poisson brackets to the simple canonical form, these were also discussed by Witzany et al.[9]

2.1. *Hunting down degrees of freedom*

Amongst the choices for the supplementary conditions discussed above, only the so-called Tulczyjew-Dixon or "covariant" supplementary spin condition $V^\nu \propto P^\nu$ constrains the gauge freedom fully. This can be seen, in particular, by counting the degrees of freedom in phase space within the Hamiltonian formalism. A covariant formalism for a spinning particle parametrized by proper time τ should then not have more than 4 orbital degrees of freedom (corresponding to the 4 space-time coordinates), and a *single* degree of freedom corresponding to the spin sector (recall that each degree of freedom corresponds to a pair of canonically conjugate coordinates). If a larger number degrees of freedom crops up in the system of evolution equations, there are necessarily nonphysical or gauge-type degrees of freedom left in the system.

This being said, the issue with the Hamiltonian H_{TD} presented in equation (8) is the following. The supplementary spin condition $S^{\mu\nu} P_\nu = 0$ is only an *integral of motion* of H_{TD} when used along with the brackets (11)-(14). This means that in a numerical evolution one finds initial data such that $S^{\mu\nu} P_\nu = 0$ initially and then evolves them – the system consequently conserves the supplementary condition up to numerical noise.

Nevertheless, what one *cannot* do is to assume $S^{\mu\nu} P_\nu = 0$ as an identity to reduce the number of degrees of freedom that are evolved numerically while respecting the geometric structure of the problem.[9] That, is the system still keeps an additional gauge degree of freedom in the numerical evolution, even though it stays zero up to numerical error. Is there perhaps a way to obtain just the minimal Hamiltonian system without this redundant degree of freedom?

Efforts of this type have actually been carried out perturbatively with the use of the so-called Newton-Wigner supplementary spin condition $V^\mu \propto P^\mu/\mathcal{M} + \xi^\mu(x^\nu)$, where $\xi^\mu(x^\nu)$ is a fixed time-like vector field.[7,8] As such, this supplementary spin condition is necessarily non-covariant and refers to an additional fixed structure on the background. In other words, the vector $\xi^\mu(x^\nu)$ defines a privileged observer frame and the dynamics are in some sense defined with respect to this privileged frame. This impression is even more strengthened by the fact that the constraint procedure of the algebra (11)-(14) by the Newton-Wigner condition seems to be necessarily coupled to a constraint procedure on the time parameter. To rephrase this, the Newton-Wigner condition forces one's hand into an explicit 3+1 formalism – and covariance is lost.

2.2. Dirac constraint procedure

Let me now sketch the Dirac constraint procedure for the Tulczyjew-Dixon constraint $S^{\mu\nu}P_\nu = 0$ applied to the Poisson bracket (11)-(14). This should serve as a covariant counter-example to the procedures using the Newton-Wigner condition.

It was already shown in the paper by Witzany et al.[9] that one can add the Tulczyjew-Dixon Lagrangian-constraint term to the "minimal" Hamiltonian (6), solve for the Lagrange multiplier, and the resulting Hamiltonian gives the correct Mathisson-Papapetrou-Dixon equations for the motion of the body under the Tulczyjew-Dixon supplementary spin condition. The resulting Hamiltonian is actually $H_{\rm TD}$ presented in eq. (8). That is, we already *know* that applying the constraint $S^{\mu\nu}P_\nu = 0$ as a Lagrangian constraint to the system will lead to the correct dynamics, one only needs to figure out the correct *Dirac bracket* corresponding to this constraint.

Let me now briefly summarize the Dirac constraint procedure.[13,14] One starts with a set of n independent constraints $\Phi_a = 0$, $a = 1...n$ with a Poisson bracket $\{\Phi_a, \Phi_b\} = C_{ab}$, where one assumes the matrix C to be invertible, $\exists (C^{-1})^{bc} : C_{ab}(C^{-1})^{bc} = \delta_a^c$. Then we define the Dirac bracket $[,]$ for any phase-space functions A, B as

$$[A, B] = \{A, B\} - \{A, \Phi_a\}(C^{-1})^{ab}\{\Phi_b, B\}. \tag{15}$$

Now it is easy to see that this bracket fulfils the Jacobi identity and that $[\Phi_c, A] = 0$ for any A when evaluated on the $\Phi_a = 0$ hypersurface in phase space. As a result, the set of constraints $\Phi_a = 0$ can then be used as an *identity* on phase space in the sense that its use will commute with the Dirac bracket. In particular, it can be shown that the system with a given Hamiltonian and a Dirac bracket is equivalent to the system with the same Hamiltonian and a Lagrangian-constraint term.[13,14]

Now to the specific case of the constraint $S^{\mu\nu}P_\nu = 0$. Even though there are 4 components to this equation, not all of them are linearly independent. For instance, independently on whether the constrain is fulfilled or not, it holds that $P_\mu(S^{\mu\nu}P_\nu) = 0$, and $w_\mu(S^{\mu\nu}P_\nu) = 0$, where $w_\mu = \epsilon_{\mu\rho\sigma\chi}S^{\rho\sigma}P^\chi$ and $\epsilon_{\mu\rho\sigma\chi}$ is the Levi-Civita pseudo-tensor. As such, there are only *two* non-trivial constraints on the system hidden in the formula $S^{\mu\nu}P_\nu = 0$. Nevertheless, as already shown partially by Witzany et al.,[9] one can proceed in a covariant fashion by defining

$$C^{\mu\nu} = \{S^{\mu\kappa}P_\kappa, S^{\nu\lambda}P_\lambda\} = -\tilde{\mathcal{M}}^2 S^{\mu\nu}, \tag{16}$$

$$\tilde{\mathcal{M}}^2 \equiv -P_\lambda P^\lambda + \frac{1}{4}R_{\gamma\rho\sigma\chi}S^{\gamma\rho}S^{\sigma\chi}, \tag{17}$$

$$C^\dagger_{\kappa\lambda} = -\frac{1}{\tilde{\mathcal{M}}^2 S^2}S_{\kappa\lambda}, \tag{18}$$

where $S^2 \equiv S^{\mu\nu}S_{\mu\nu}/2$. The matrix $C^\dagger_{\kappa\lambda}$ is then a pseudo-inverse of $C^{\mu\nu}$ on the non-trivial sub-spaces of the constraint (specifically, $C^{\mu\nu}C^\dagger_{\nu\lambda}$ projects out the sub-spaces $\sim P_\mu, w_\mu$ discussed above). One can then covariantly define the Dirac bracket using the original Poisson bracket (11)-(14) as

$$[A,B] = \{A,B\} - \{A, S^{\mu\nu}P_\nu\}C^\dagger_{\mu\kappa}\{S^{\kappa\lambda}P_\lambda, B\}. \qquad (19)$$

The resulting brackets for $P_\mu, x^\nu, S^{\kappa\lambda}$ are now straightforward to compute and they contain various orders of new spin and curvature terms as compared to the original brackets. (The full expressions and simplified bases will be reported on elsewhere.)

2.3. *The zeroth-order problem*

The bracket (19) is essentially what we have been looking for: only a minimal number of degrees of freedom is left in the phase space and one can happily evolve them in the Hamiltonian formalism defined by the Dirac bracket and the minimal Hamiltonian (6). In particular, it is advantageous to define the spin vector

$$s^\lambda \equiv \frac{1}{2\mathcal{M}} \epsilon^{\lambda\gamma\rho\sigma} S_{\gamma\rho} P_\sigma, \qquad (20)$$

$$\Rightarrow S^{\mu\nu} = \frac{1}{\mathcal{M}} \epsilon^{\mu\nu\kappa\lambda} P_\kappa s_\lambda, \qquad (21)$$

where the second equality applies on the $S^{\mu\nu}P_\nu = 0$ hypersurface. This vector partially reduces the number of the many dependent components of the tensor $S^{\mu\nu}$, but not fully, since it also holds that $s^\mu P_\mu = 0$.

Now one would like to transform to canonical coordinates so that the bracket (19) reduces to a simple form. One soon realizes that one of the biggest obstacles is the *zeroth-order problem*. That is, even in flat space-time $R_{\mu\nu\kappa\lambda} = 0$ and Minkowski coordinates, the bracket is quite non-trivial. Specifically, it reduces in the pure Minkowski case to

$$[x^\mu, P_\nu] = \delta^\mu_\nu, \quad [P_\mu, P_\nu] = 0, \quad [P_\mu, s^\lambda] = 0, \qquad (22)$$

$$[x^\mu, x^\nu] = \frac{1}{\mathcal{M}^3} \epsilon^{\mu\nu\kappa\lambda} P_\kappa s_\lambda, \qquad (23)$$

$$[x^\mu, s^\nu] = \frac{P^\mu s^\nu - s^\mu P^\nu}{\mathcal{M}}, \qquad (24)$$

$$[s^\mu, s^\nu] = -\frac{1}{\mathcal{M}} \epsilon^{\mu\nu\kappa\lambda} P_\kappa s_\lambda. \qquad (25)$$

There is no obvious and/or elegant way to cover this Dirac algebra with canonical coordinates.

2.4. *Is Newton-Wigner the only way?*

The difficulty with Poisson brackets of spinning systems in flat space-time was already the concern of the works of Newton and Wigner,[15] even though there the motivation was the quantum analogue of this problem for the commutation relations of operators. Jordan[16] proved that the Newton-Wigner basis of positions and spins is the only basis such that the position "transforms as a position should". (For a review and a classical rederivation, see the recent paper by Schwartz and Giulini.[17])

The results on the Newton-Wigner basis can be rephrased in the context of this work as follows. Consider any physical Dirac-constraint procedure that 1) reduces the unphysical spin degrees of freedom, 2) forces the time parametrization to be coordinate time $t = x^0$ (by using the $P^\mu P_\mu = -\mathcal{M}^2$ on-shell constraint[13,18]), and 3) parametrizes the phase-space in terms of variables $X^i, P_j, \tilde{S}^k$ such that P_j are spatial components of P_μ and such that the final bracket is

$$[X^i, X^j]' = 0, \tag{26}$$
$$[X^i, P_j]' = \delta^i_j, \tag{27}$$
$$[X^i, \tilde{S}^j]' = 0, \tag{28}$$
$$[\tilde{S}^j, P_i]' = 0, \tag{29}$$
$$[\tilde{S}^i, \tilde{S}^j]' = \epsilon^{ijk} \tilde{S}^k, \tag{30}$$

where ϵ^{ijk} is the permutation symbol. Then (up to singular systems), the variables $X^i, P_j, \tilde{S}^k$ are *necessarily* the Newton-Wigner variables with $\xi^\mu = \delta^\mu_0$.

One conclusion of this theorem is that if one was to cover the algebra (22)-(25) with coordinates X^μ canonically conjugate to P_μ and two other canonically conjugate coordinates on the spin sector of the phase space, then these would necessarily be Newton-Wigner variables when reduced to spatial sections. Even this result would be interesting, since it would "covariantize" the Newton-Wigner prescription. Of course, it is also possible to construct canonical coordinates that do not have $\sim P_\mu$ as canonical variables, but these seem to almost always violate manifest rotational and/or translational invariance of the dynamics.

3. Summary and Outlooks

I have shown that capturing the spin-curvature coupling of a test body on a curved background in a covariant Hamiltonian formalism – while eliminating redundant degrees of freedom – is a non-trivial matter. This matter is also far from closed. In the future, I hope to find a set of "covariant Newton-Wigner variables" for the brackets (22)-(25) and formulate a (possibly implicit) iteration problem to canonicalize the full curved-spacetime brackets (19). These should provide a first, truly general basis for the canonical treatment of spinning test particles in general relativity (but see also the work of Steinhoff in the ADM formalism[19]).

This result should then have obvious pay-offs for the relativistic two-body problem and gravitational-wave modelling. For example, the procedure of Vines et al.[7] suggests that the minimally coupled spinning particle (that is, with no additional multipoles) under the Tulczyjew-Dixon condition represents a "test Kerr black hole" on the curved background, since its effective quadrupole in the Newton-Wigner variables matches the Hansen multipole of a Kerr black hole.[20] Does this apply at all orders? A more general and robust formalism is needed for an answer. The question of the minimally coupled particle is all the more interesting due to the fact that the motion of a spining test particle under the Tulzcyjew-Dixon condition is integrable at $O(S)$ in Kerr space-time,[10,21,22] but apparently non-integrable at $O(S^2)$.[23] This then naturally ties-in to the important question of the integrability and smoothness of gravitational-wave inspirals and our ability to efficiently generate predictions for them.[24,25]

Acknowledgements

I would like to thank to thank Oldřich Semerák for organizing this interesting parallel session. This work was supported by European Union's Horizon 2020 research and innovation programme under grant agreement No 894881.

References

1. M. Mathisson, Neue mechanik materieller systemes, *Acta Phys. Polon.* **6**, 163 (1937).
2. A. Papapetrou, Spinning test-particles in general relativity. I, *Proc. Roy. Soc. Lond.* **A209**, 248 (1951).
3. W. Dixon, A covariant multipole formalism for extended test bodies in general relativity, *Il Nuovo Cimento (1955-1965)* **34**, 317 (1964).
4. L. F. O. Costa and J. Natário, Center of mass, spin supplementary conditions, and the momentum of spinning particles, in *Equations of Motion in Relativistic Gravity*, (Springer, 2015) pp. 215–258.
5. L. F. O. Costa, G. Lukes-Gerakopoulos and O. Semerák, On spinning particles in general relativity: Momentum-velocity relation for the Mathisson-Pirani spin condition, *Phys. Rev.* **D97**, p. 084023 (2018).
6. K. Kyrian and O. Semerák, Spinning test particles in a kerr field–ii, *Mon. Not. Roy. Astron. Soc.* **382**, p. 1922 (2007).
7. J. Vines, D. Kunst, J. Steinhoff and T. Hinderer, Canonical Hamiltonian for an extended test body in curved spacetime: To quadratic order in spin, *Phys. Rev.* **D93**, p. 103008 (2016).
8. E. Barausse, E. Racine and A. Buonanno, Hamiltonian of a spinning test particle in curved spacetime, *Phys. Rev.* **D80**, p. 104025 (2009), [Erratum: Phys. Rev.D85,069904(2012)].
9. V. Witzany, J. Steinhoff and G. Lukes-Gerakopoulos, Hamiltonians and canonical coordinates for spinning particles in curved space-time, *Classical and Quantum Gravity* **36**, p. 075003 (2019).
10. V. Witzany, Hamilton-Jacobi equation for spinning particles near black holes, *Physical Review D* **100**, p. 104030 (2019).
11. E. Barausse and A. Buonanno, Improved effective-one-body Hamiltonian for spinning black-hole binaries, *Phys. Rev. D* **81**, p. 084024 (April 2010).
12. O. Semerák, Spinning test particles in a Kerr field—I, *Monthly Notices of the Royal Astronomical Society* **308**, 863 (1999).
13. P. A. M. Dirac, *Lectures on quantum field theory* (Yeshiva Univ., 1966).

14. A. Hanson, T. Regge and C. Teitelboim, *Constrained Hamiltonian Systems* (Accademia Nazionale dei Lincei, 1976).
15. T. D. Newton and E. P. Wigner, Localized States for Elementary Systems, *Rev. Mod. Phys.* **21**, 400 (1949).
16. T. F. Jordan, Simple derivation of the Newton-Wigner position operator, *Journal of Mathematical Physics* **21**, 2028 (1980).
17. P. K. Schwartz and D. Giulini, Classical perspectives on the Newton–Wigner position observable, *International Journal of Geometric Methods in Modern Physics* **17**, p. 2050176 (2020).
18. A. J. Hanson and T. Regge, The Relativistic Spherical Top, *Annals Phys.* **87**, p. 498 (1974).
19. J. Steinhoff, Canonical formulation of spin in general relativity, *Annalen der Physik* **523**, 296 (2011).
20. R. O. Hansen, Multipole moments of stationary space-times, *J. Math. Phys.* **15**, 46 (1974).
21. R. Rüdiger, Conserved quantities of spinning test particles in general relativity. I, *Proceedings of the Royal Society of London. A. Mathematical and Physical Sciences* **375**, 185 (1981).
22. R. Rüdiger, Conserved quantities of spinning test particles in general relativity. II, *Proceedings of the Royal Society of London. A. Mathematical and Physical Sciences* **385**, 229 (1983).
23. O. Zelenka, G. Lukes-Gerakopoulos, V. Witzany and O. Kopáček, Growth of resonances and chaos for a spinning test particle in the schwarzschild background, *Physical Review D* **101**, p. 024037 (2020).
24. E. E. Flanagan and T. Hinderer, Transient resonances in the inspirals of point particles into black holes, *Physical review letters* **109**, p. 071102 (2012).
25. G. Lukes-Gerakopoulos and V. Witzany, Non-linear effects in EMRI dynamics and their imprints on gravitational waves, *arXiv:2103.06724, to appear in "Handbook of Gravitational Wave Astronomy"* (Eds. C. Bambi, S. Katsanevas, and K. Kokkotas; Springer, Singapore) (2021).

Gravitomagnetic resonance and gravitational waves

Matteo Luca Ruggiero

Politecnico di Torino, Torino - Italy and INFN, Laboratori Nazionali di Legnaro, Legnaro - Italy
E-mail: matteo.ruggiero@polito.it

Antonello Ortolan

INFN, Laboratori Nazionali di Legnaro, Legnaro - Italy

We show that using Fermi coordinates it is possible to describe the gravitational field of a wave using a gravitoelectromagnetic analogy. In particular, we show that using this approach, a new phenomenon, called gravitomagnetic resonance, may appear. We describe it both from classical and quantum viewpoints, and suggest that it could in principle be used as the basis for a new type of gravitational wave detectors.

Keywords: Gravitomagnetism; gravitational waves; gravitomagnetic resonance

1. Introduction

General Relativity (GR) is the best model that we have to understand gravitational interactions, and its predictions were verified with great accuracy during last century, even though we know that there are difficulties to explain, in the general relativistic framework, observations on galactic and cosmological scales, without claiming the existence of *dark components*.[1,2] Remarkably, GR not only predicts corrections to known Newtonian effects such as in the case of perihelion advance, but there are general relativistic effects without Newtonian counterparts: for instance, this is the case of gravitational waves and the so-called gravitomagnetic effects produced by mass currents.

As for gravitational waves, the first indirect evidence of their existence came from the observation of the binary pulsar B1913+16, whose orbital parameters are modified by the emission of gravitational waves.[3,4] It took about 100 years after the publication of Einstein's theory of gravity to obtain, in 2015, the first direct detection of gravitational waves,[5] which was the beginning of gravitational wave astronomy.

It is well known[6] that Einstein equations, in weak-field approximation (small masses, low velocities), can be written in analogy with Maxwell equations for the electromagnetic field, where the mass density and current play the role of the charge density and current, respectively; more in general, both the inertial and curvature effects in the vicinity of a given world-line, can be dealt with using a gravitoelectromagnetic formalism.[7,8] These gravitomagnetic effects are very small if compared to the gravitoelectric ones, originating from mass density and, consequently, it is very difficult to measure them. Nonetheless, there have been various attempts and proposals: we remember the LAGEOS tests around the Earth,[9,10] the subsequent

LARES mission,[11,12] and the recent measurements performed with laser-tracked satellites.[13] A comprehensive analysis of the Lense-Thirring effect in the solar system can be found in Ref. 14. The mission Gravity Probe B[15] was launched to measure the precession of orbiting gyroscopes.[16] There have been other proposals, such as LAGRANGE, which exploit spacecrafts located in the Lagrangian points of the Sun-Earth system,[17] or the use of satellites around the Earth.[18] In addition, we mention the GINGER experiment, which aims to measure gravitomagnetic effects in a terrestrial laboratory by using an array of ring lasers.[19–22]

Recently, the gravitomagnetic effects connected with the passage of a gravitational wave were analyized:[23] this should not be surprising, since a gravitational wave transports angular momentum. In particular, these effects can be easily understood by using Fermi coordinates on the basis of a gravitoelectromagnetic analogy.[8] Here, we review this approach and suggest how it could be possible to detect the effects due to the magnetic-like part of a plane gravitational wave. The plan of the paper is as follows: in Section 2 we review Fermi coordinates and the definition of local spacetime metric, then we use this approach to study the effect of a plane gravitational wave in Section 3. Conclusions are in Section 4.

2. Local spacetime metric in Fermi coordinates

If we consider the world-line of a given observer, which ideally constitutes our laboratory frame, it is possible to write the expression of the local spacetime metric in its vicinity, using Fermi coordinates. This expression depends both on the background spacetime and on the properties of the world-line. Fermi coordinates in the vicinity of an arbitrary accelerated world-line with rotating tetrads were studied in Refs. 24–26, and the general expression of the line element, up to quadratic displacements $|X^i|$ from the reference world-line, turns out to be

$$ds^2 = -\left[\left(1 + \frac{\mathbf{a} \cdot \mathbf{X}}{c^2}\right)^2 - \frac{1}{c^2}(\mathbf{\Omega} \wedge \mathbf{X})^2 + R_{0i0j}X^i X^j\right]c^2 dT^2 +$$
$$+ \left[\frac{1}{c}(\mathbf{\Omega} \wedge \mathbf{X})_i - \frac{4}{3}R_{0jik}X^j X^k\right]cdT dX^i + \left(\delta_{ij} - \frac{1}{3}R_{ikjl}X^k X^l\right)dX^i dX^j. \quad (1)$$

Here, $\mathbf{X}$ is the position vector in the Fermi frame. We see that in the line element (1) there are both the gravitational effects, deriving from the curvature tensor, and the inertial effects, due to world-line acceleration $\mathbf{a}$ and the tetrad rotation $\mathbf{\Omega}$.

The metric (1) can be written in terms of the gravitoelectromagntic potentials $(\Phi, \mathbf{A})$ (see Refs. 7, 8), neglecting the terms g_{ij} related to the spatial curvature:

$$ds^2 = -\left(1 - 2\frac{\Phi}{c^2}\right)c^2 dT^2 - \frac{4}{c}(\mathbf{A} \cdot d\mathbf{X})dt + \delta_{ij}dX^i dX^j, \quad (2)$$

where

$$\Phi(T, \mathbf{X}) = \Phi^I(\mathbf{X}) + \Phi^C(T, \mathbf{X}), \quad \mathbf{A}(T, \mathbf{X}) = \mathbf{A}^I(\mathbf{X}) + \mathbf{A}^C(T, \mathbf{X}), \quad (3)$$

In particular, in the gravitoelectric potential $\Phi(T, \mathbf{X})$

$$\Phi^I(\mathbf{X}) = -\mathbf{a} \cdot \mathbf{X} - \frac{1}{2}\frac{(\mathbf{a} \cdot \mathbf{X})^2}{c^2} + \frac{1}{2}\left[|\mathbf{\Omega}|^2|\mathbf{X}|^2 - (\mathbf{\Omega} \cdot \mathbf{X})^2\right] \quad (4)$$

is the *inertial* contribution, while

$$\Phi^C(T, \mathbf{X}) = -\frac{1}{2}R_{0i0j}(T)X^i X^j \quad (5)$$

is the *curvature* contribution. As for the gravitomagnetic potential $\mathbf{A}(T, \mathbf{X})$, we may distinguish the *inertial* contribution

$$A^I_i(\mathbf{X}) = -\left(\frac{\mathbf{\Omega} c}{2} \wedge \mathbf{X}\right)_i, \quad (6)$$

and the *curvature* contribution:

$$A^C_i(T, \mathbf{X}) = \frac{1}{3}R_{0jik}(T)X^j X^k. \quad (7)$$

The gravitoelectric and gravitomagnetic fields $\mathbf{E}$ and $\mathbf{B}$ are defined in terms of the potentials by

$$\mathbf{E} = -\nabla\Phi - \frac{1}{c}\frac{\partial}{\partial T}\left(\frac{1}{2}\mathbf{A}\right), \quad \mathbf{B} = \nabla \times \mathbf{A}. \quad (8)$$

which, up to up to linear order in $|X^i|$, can be written as

$$\mathbf{E}^I = \mathbf{a}\left(1 + \frac{\mathbf{a} \cdot \mathbf{X}}{c^2}\right) + \mathbf{\Omega} \wedge (\mathbf{\Omega} \wedge \mathbf{X}), \quad E^C_i(T, \mathbf{X}) = c^2 R_{0i0j}(T)X^j. \quad (9)$$

and

$$\mathbf{B}^I = -\mathbf{\Omega} c, \quad B^C_i(T, \mathbf{R}) = -\frac{c^2}{2}\epsilon_{ijk}R^{jk}{}_{0l}(T)X^l. \quad (10)$$

In summary, the gravitoelectricmagnetic fields are written in the form

$$\mathbf{E} = \mathbf{E}^I + \mathbf{E}^C, \quad \mathbf{B} = \mathbf{B}^I + \mathbf{B}^C. \quad (11)$$

In addition, the analogy with electromagnetism can be exploited to describe the motion of free test masses; in particular, the motion of free test masses *relative* to a reference mass, at rest at origin of the Fermi frame, is determined by the geodesics of the metric (1). The latter can be written in the form of a Lorentz-like force equation[7]

$$m\frac{d^2\mathbf{X}}{dT^2} = -m\mathbf{E} - 2m\frac{\mathbf{V}}{c} \times \mathbf{B} \quad (12)$$

up to linear order in the particle velocity $\mathbf{V} = \frac{d\mathbf{X}}{dT}$ (which is the *relative velocity* with respect to the reference mass). Moreover, the evolution equation of classical spinning particle with spin $\mathbf{S}$ in an external gravitomagnetic field $\mathbf{B}$ is

$$\frac{d\mathbf{S}}{dT} = \frac{1}{c}\mathbf{B} \times \mathbf{S}, \quad (13)$$

in analogy with the corresponding equation for a charged spinning test particle in a magnetic field.[7]

In the following Section we will apply this formalism to plane gravitational waves.

3. Gravitomagnetic resonance due to the passage of a gravitational wave

Gravitomagnetic effects deriving from the passage of the gravitational wave can be in principle detected by using devices such as the heterodyne antenna (see e.g. Ref. 8) or studying the perturbations of planetary motion.[27] Here, we focus on a different approach, that is based on the fulfilment of a *resonance condition*.[28]

We consider a spinning particle interacting with the gravitatomagnetic field a plane wave. In the Fermi frame, where the spacetime metric is written in the form (1), we consider coordinates T, X, Y, Z with a set of unit vectors $\{\mathbf{u}_X, \mathbf{u}_Y, \mathbf{u}_Z\}$; the direction of propagation of the wave is the X axis. In this case, for a circularly polarized wave, the components of the gravitomagnetic field deriving from the spacetime curvature (and, hence, connected to the passage of the wave) can be written in the form[8]

$$B_X^C = 0, \quad B_Y^C = -\frac{A\omega^2}{2}\left[-\cos(\omega T)Y + \sin(\omega T)Z\right],$$

$$B_Z^C = -\frac{A\omega^2}{2}\left[\sin(\omega T)Y + \cos(\omega T)Z\right], \tag{14}$$

where A is the amplitude and ω the frequency of the wave. In order to study the interaction with a spinning particle, we consider a frame clockwise rotating in the YZ plane with the wave frequency ω; then, the corresponding basis vectors are $\mathbf{u}_{X'} = \mathbf{u}_X$, $\mathbf{u}_{Y'}(T) = \cos(\omega T)\mathbf{u}_Y - \sin(\omega T)\mathbf{u}_Z$ and $\mathbf{u}_{Z'}(T) = \sin(\omega T)\mathbf{u}_Y + \cos(\omega T)\mathbf{u}_Z$. As a consequence, the gravitomagnetic field is written as

$$\mathbf{B}^C(T) = \frac{A\omega^2}{2}\left[Y\mathbf{u}_{Y'}(T) - Z\mathbf{u}_{Z'}(T)\right] \tag{15}$$

Notice that $\mathbf{B}^C$ is a *static field* in the rotating frame that we have considered.

Let us consider the spin evolution equation (13); the total gravitomagnetic field is $\mathbf{B} = \mathbf{B}^I + \mathbf{B}^C$, where $\mathbf{B}^I = -\Omega c$ and it is simply proportional to the rotation rate Ω of the frame. We suppose that Ω is constant and it is in the direction of propagation of the wave: then, we may write $\mathbf{B}^I = -B^I \mathbf{u}_X$ where $B^I = \Omega c$. As a consequence, the spin evolution equation turns out to be

$$\frac{d\mathbf{S}}{dT} = \frac{1}{c}\left[\mathbf{B}^C(T) + \mathbf{B}^I\right] \times \mathbf{S}. \tag{16}$$

If we consider the frame co-rotating with $\mathbf{B}^C(T)$, since $\boldsymbol{\omega} = -\omega \mathbf{u}_X$ is the rotation rate, the time derivatives in the two frames are related by

$$\frac{d\mathbf{S}}{dT} = \left(\frac{d\mathbf{S}}{dT}\right)_{rot} + \boldsymbol{\omega} \times \mathbf{S} = \left(\frac{d\mathbf{S}}{dT}\right)_{rot} - \omega \mathbf{u}_{X'} \times \mathbf{S}. \tag{17}$$

Then, from Eqs. (16) and (17) we get

$$\left(\frac{d\mathbf{S}}{dT}\right)_{rot} = \left[\Delta\omega \mathbf{u}_{X'} + \frac{1}{c}\mathbf{B}^C\right] \times \mathbf{S} = \frac{1}{c}\mathbf{B}_{eff} \times \mathbf{S}, \qquad (18)$$

where we set $\omega - \frac{1}{c}B^I = \omega - \Omega = \Delta\omega$ and $\frac{1}{c}B^C = \omega^*$ (see below).

Then, according to Eq. (18), we may say that the spinning particle undergoes a precession determined by the static effective gravitomagnetic field $\mathbf{B}_{eff} = c\left[\Delta\omega \mathbf{u}_{X'} + \frac{1}{c}\mathbf{B}^C\right]$. Accordingly, we see that when $\Delta\omega \simeq 0$, i.e. in *resonance* condition, the spin precession is around the direction of $\mathbf{B}^C$, which is in any case in the YZ plane, so the precession may flip the spin completely. In summary, the *gravitomagnetic resonance* is obtained when the rotation rate of the frame is equal to the frequency of the gravitational wave. It is important to remember that all precessions are referred to a reference spinning particle,[23] at the origin of the Fermi frame so, in any case, we are talking about a *relative precession*.

Actually, the above description, which is analogous to the classical dynamics of a magnetic moment in a magnetic field, can be translated into quantum terms for a two-level system,[28] taking into account the Hamiltonian description of the interaction of the spin of intrinsic particles in a gravitational field.[7,29–31] As a consequence, we may introduce a probability transition for spinning particles in the field of a gravitational wave. Let us suppose that $|g>$ and $|e>$ are the two eigenvectors, respectively of the ground and excited states, of the projection of the spinning particle along the X axis. If we suppose that a spin is, at $t = 0$, in the ground state $|g>$, the probability of transition to the excited state $|e>$ at time t is given by Rabi's formula

$$P_{g \to e}(T) = \frac{(\omega^*)^2}{(\omega^*)^2 + \Delta\omega^2} \sin^2\left(\sqrt{(\omega^*)^2 + \Delta\omega^2}\frac{T}{2}\right). \qquad (19)$$

Again, at resonance, i.e. when $\Delta\omega = 0$, or $\omega = \Omega$, even a weak gravitational field can reverse the direction of the spin: the probability of transition is equal to 1 *independently of the strength of the gravitomagnetic field*, for $T = \frac{2n+1}{(\omega^*)}\pi$.

Let us add a comment on how the resonance condition could be achieved without requiring the physical rotation of our reference frame. In fact, if we consider charged spinning particles, we may get an equivalent situation by using a true magnetic field, on the basis of Larmor theorem, which states the equivalence between a system of electric charges in a magnetic field and the same system rotating with the Larmor frequency. So a magnetic field can be used to produce the gravitomagnetic field $\mathbf{B}^I$.

4. Conclusions

We have seen that, using Fermi coordinates, it is possible to emphasize the gravitomagnetic effects connected to the passage of a gravitational wave. Current detectors such as LIGO and VIRGO can detect only the interaction of a system of masses with the electric-like component of the field, so we discussed the possibility of detecting the interaction of a suitable probe with the magnetic-like component of the wave field. In particular, we considered the interaction of the wave with a spinning particle, both using a classical and a quantum approach, and we showed that in analogy with what happens in electromagnetism, a gravitational magnetic resonance phenomenon may appear when the reference frame rotates along the direction of propagation of the wave and the rotation rate is equal to the wave frequency. Actually, since it is not possible to have physical rotations for arbitrary frequencies, we pointed out that an equivalent situation can be obtained by using a true magnetic field, on the basis of the Larmor theorem. As for the detection of this effect, we imagine not to detect the modification of a single spinning particle, rather to consider a great number of identical particles. For instance, the precession induced by the gravitational wave can modify the magnetization of a macroscopical sample which, in turn, can be detected by measuring the differences in the magnetic field produced.

References

1. C. M. Will, Was Einstein Right? A Centenary Assessment, in *General Relativity and Gravitation. A Centennial Perspective*, eds. A. Ashtekar, B. K. Berger, J. Isenberg and M. MacCallum (Cambridge University Press, Cambridge, jul 2015).
2. I. Debono and G. F. Smoot, General Relativity and Cosmology: Unsolved Questions and Future Directions, *Universe* **2**, p. 23 (2016).
3. R. Hulse and J. Taylor, Discovery of a pulsar in a binary system, *Astrophys. J. Lett.* **195**, L51 (1975).
4. J. M. Weisberg and J. H. Taylor, Relativistic binary pulsar B1913+16: Thirty years of observations and analysis, *ASP Conf. Ser.* **328**, p. 25 (2005).
5. B. P. Abbott, R. Abbott, T. Abbott, M. Abernathy, F. Acernese, K. Ackley, C. Adams, T. Adams, P. Addesso, R. Adhikari *et al.*, Observation of gravitational waves from a binary black hole merger, *Physical review letters* **116**, p. 061102 (2016).
6. M. L. Ruggiero and A. Tartaglia, Gravitomagnetic effects, *Nuovo Cim.* **B117**, 743 (2002).
7. B. Mashhoon, Gravitoelectromagnetism: A Brief review, in *The Measurement of Gravitomagnetism: A Challenging Enterprise*, ed. L. Iorio (Nova Science, New York, 2003)
8. M. L. Ruggiero and A. Ortolan, Gravito-electromagnetic approach for the space-time of a plane gravitational wave, *Journal of Physics Communications* **4**, p. 055013 (may 2020).
9. I. Ciufolini and E. C. Pavlis, A confirmation of the general relativistic prediction of the lense–thirring effect, *Nature* **431**, p. 958 (2004).
10. I. Ciufolini, E. C. Pavlis, J. Ries, R. Koenig, G. Sindoni, A. Paolozzi and H. Newmayer, Gravitomagnetism and its measurement with laser ranging to the lageos satellites and grace earth gravity models, in *General Relativity and John Archibald Wheeler*, eds. I. Ciufolini and R. A. Matzner (Springer, 2010) pp. 371–434.
11. I. Ciufolini, A. Paolozzi, E. Pavlis, J. Ries, V. Gurzadyan, R. Koenig, R. Matzner, R. Penrose and G. Sindoni, Testing general relativity and gravitational physics using the lares satellite, *The European Physical Journal Plus* **127**, p. 133 (2012).
12. I. Ciufolini, A. Paolozzi, E. C. Pavlis, R. Koenig, J. Ries, V. Gurzadyan, R. Matzner, R. Penrose, G. Sindoni, C. Paris *et al.*, A test of general relativity using the lares and

lageos satellites and a grace earth gravity model, *The European Physical Journal C* **76**, p. 120 (2016).
13. D. Lucchesi, M. Visco, R. Peron, M. Bassan, G. Pucacco, C. Pardini, L. Anselmo and C. Magnafico, A 1% measurement of the gravitomagnetic field of the earth with laser-tracked satellites, *Universe* **6**, p. 139 (2020).
14. L. Iorio, H. I. M. Lichtenegger, M. L. Ruggiero and C. Corda, Phenomenology of the Lense-Thirring effect in the Solar System, *Astrophys. Space Sci.* **331**, 351 (2011).
15. C. F. Everitt, D. DeBra, B. Parkinson, J. Turneaure, J. Conklin, M. Heifetz, G. Keiser, A. Silbergleit, T. Holmes, J. Kolodziejczak *et al.*, Gravity probe b: Final results of a space experiment to test general relativity, *Physical Review Letters* **106**, p. 221101 (2011).
16. L. I. Schiff, Possible new experimental test of general relativity theory, *Physical Review Letters* **4**, p. 215 (1960).
17. A. Tartaglia, D. Lucchesi, M. L. Ruggiero and P. Valko, How to use the Sun–Earth Lagrange points for fundamental physics and navigation, *Gen. Rel. Grav.* **50**, p. 9 (2018).
18. M. L. Ruggiero and A. Tartaglia, Test of gravitomagnetism with satellites around the earth, *The European Physical Journal Plus* **134**, p. 205 (2019).
19. F. Bosi, G. Cella, A. Di Virgilio, A. Ortolan, A. Porzio, S. Solimeno, M. Cerdonio, J. Zendri, M. Allegrini, J. Belfi *et al.*, Measuring gravitomagnetic effects by a multi-ring-laser gyroscope, *Physical Review D* **84**, p. 122002 (2011).
20. M. L. Ruggiero, Sagnac effect, ring lasers and terrestrial tests of gravity, *Galaxies* **3**, 84 (2015).
21. A. Di Virgilio, M. Allegrini, A. Beghi, J. Belfi, N. Beverini, F. Bosi, B. Bouhadef, M. Calamai, G. Carelli, D. Cuccato *et al.*, A ring lasers array for fundamental physics, *Comptes Rendus Physique* **15**, 866 (2014).
22. A. Tartaglia, A. Di Virgilio, J. Belfi, N. Beverini and M. L. Ruggiero, Testing general relativity by means of ring lasers, *Eur. Phys. J. Plus* **132**, p. 73 (2017).
23. D. Bini, A. Geralico and A. Ortolan, Deviation and precession effects in the field of a weak gravitational wave, *Phys. Rev. D* **95**, p. 104044 (May 2017).
24. W.-T. Ni and M. Zimmermann, Inertial and gravitational effects in the proper reference frame of an accelerated, rotating observer, *Physical Review D - Particles and Fields* **17**, p. 1473 (March 1978).
25. W.-Q. Li and W.-T. Ni, Coupled inertial and gravitational effects in the proper reference frame of an accelerated, rotating observer, *Journal of Mathematical Physics* **20**, 1473 (July 1979).
26. K.-P. Marzlin, Fermi coordinates for weak gravitational fields, *Phys. Rev. D* **50**, 888 (Jul 1994).
27. L. Iorio and M. L. Ruggiero, Perturbations of the orbital elements due to the magnetic-like part of the field of a plane gravitational wave, *IJMPD (to appear)* (2021).
28. M. L. Ruggiero and A. Ortolan, Gravitomagnetic resonance in the field of a gravitational wave, *Phys. Rev. D* **102**, p. 101501 (Nov 2020).
29. B. Mashhoon, Gravitational couplings of intrinsic spin, *Classical and Quantum Gravity* **17**, 2399 (jun 2000).
30. F. W. Hehl and W.-T. Ni, Inertial effects of a dirac particle, *Physical Review D* **42**, p. 2045 (1990).
31. L. Ryder, Relativistic treatment of inertial spin effects, *Journal of Physics A: Mathematical and General* **31**, p. 2465 (1998).

Studying the EPRL spinfoam self-energy

Pietropaolo Frisoni

Department of Physics and Astronomy, Western University,
London, Ontario, Canada
E-mail: pfrisoni@uwo.ca

I present some recent progresses in the study of the EPRL self-energy amplitude.[1] New numerical methods allow to analyze how the divergence scales, for which previous works only provided bounds spanning more than 9 orders of magnitude. I discuss the role that the Immirzi parameter plays in the asymptotic behavior, and the dependence of the scaling on some boundary data. Finally, I discuss the dynamical expectation values of some relevant geometric boundary observables.

Keywords: Spinfoam; self energy; infrared divergences; HPC; LQG.

1. Introduction

The spinfoam formalism is an attempt to define the dynamics of loop quantum gravity in an explicitly Lorentz covariant way.[2,3] It defines transition amplitudes for spinnetwork states of the canonical theory in a form of a sum (or equivalently a refinement[4]) over all the possible two-complexes having the chosen spinnetwork as boundary. This is equivalent to a sum over histories of quantum geometries providing in this way a regularised version of the quantum gravity path integral.

The state of the art of the spinfoam approach to LQG is currently the model proposed by Engle, Pereira, Rovelli and Livine (EPRL),[5,6] independently developed by Freidel and Krasnov[7] and extended to arbitrary spinnetwork states.[8,9] I assume that the reader is familiar with the EPRL-FK[a] model, and refer to the original literature[10–13] and existing reviews (e.g.[2,14–16]) for the details on how it encodes the covariant dynamics of Loop Quantum Gravity.

The EPRL model presents infrared divergences, which have a similar structure to the UV divergences in the Feynman expansion of a standard quantum field theory. The presence of divergences require a renormalization procedure. This is an important open direction of investigation in the theory, since their study and understanding is important in the definition of the continuum limit. A number of questions are still open, for example regarding the proper normalisation of the n point functions and similar.[14] Divergences have been the subject of many studies following different investigation strategies: via refining of the 2-complex as proposed in,[17–19] or via a resummation, defined for instance using group field theory/random tensor models as proposed in.[20–23] The properties of these divergences have been studied

---
[a]From now on I will call it just EPRL for notation convenience.

in the context of the Ponzano-Regge model of 3d quantum gravity and discrete BF theory,[24,25] group field theory[26] and EPRL model: with both Euclidean[27,28] and Lorentzian signature.[29]

Analytic estimates of divergences in the Lorentzian EPRL model[29] and[30] are based on two different methods. In[29] the "self-energy" amplitude is considered, finding a logarithmic divergence $\log K$ as a *lower bound*, where K is an artificial cut-off on the internal $SU(2)$ spins associated with the faces of the diagrams (the need to introduce a cut-off is justified by the fact that the sum on the internal spins is unbounded). The computation is rather involved and relies on the techniques developed for the asymptotic analysis of the vertex amplitude of the model.[31] This approach requires an independent study of each geometrical sector and the logarithmic divergence is obtained by looking at the non-degenerate geometries. On the other hand, in[30] is proposed an algorithm to systematically determine the potential infrared divergence for all spinfoam diagrams. The approach is based on the hypothesis that the dominant contribution to the divergence scaling of the amplitude comes from the uniform scaling of all the spins and that there is no interference between various terms of the sum. This leads to an *upper bound* on the divergence proportional to K^9.

These two bounds are therefore remarkably different, leading a window of possibilities which spans several orders of magnitude, and it is necessary to find methods of investigation that can help clarify the question. Here I report the results of a numerical study[1] regarding the scaling of the self-energy amplitude, which also investigates the dependence on the Immirzi parameter and some other boundary data. In particular, the numerical estimates confirm both the two bounds previously found.

For the numerical calculation of the EPRL vertex amplitudes, the "sl2cfoam-next" library was used.[32] All computations were performed on Compute Canada's Cedar and Graham clusters (www.computecanada.ca). The plots were made with julia[33] and Mathematica.[34] Here I present a summary of the results obtained. The interested reader can find further details and analysis, including explicit formulas for the $SU(2)$ invariant symbols and the booster functions, in the full analysis.[1]

The paper is organized as follows. In section 2 I describe the triangulation used to study the self-energy amplitude. In section 3 the amplitude is derived in the purely $SU(2)$ BF model. This intermediate step allows to compare the numerical results with the analytical ones present in the literature. In section 4 the EPRL amplitude is derived from the BF model. In section 5 I perform the numerical analysis of the EPRL self-energy amplitude. Finally, in section 6, I report the results of the dynamical expectation value of the boundary angle operators.

2. Self-energy diagram

I consider bubbles, studying one of the most elementary diagrams appearing in the self-energy amplitude.[29,30] Since the associated divergence can be viewed as the one

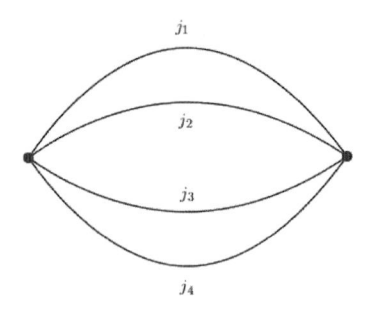

Fig. 1. Boundary graph of the spinfoam associated with the self-energy amplitude. In blue are highlighted the two four valent nodes, corresponding to the two tetrahedra in the dual triangulation. The nodes are joined by all the links. The boundary spins are denoted with j_f, where $f = 1, ..., 4$.

related to a particularly simple triangulation, from a computational point of view it turns out to be the one of the simplest divergence to deal with. The triangulation is formed by two 4-simplices joined by four tetrahedra. The associated two-complex turns out to be composed by two vertices, four edges, six internal faces (one per couple of edges) and four external faces (one per edge). The boundary of the dual triangulation is formed by two tetrahedra joined by all the faces, therefore the boundary graph consists in two four valent nodes connected by all the links (see Fig. 1).

The kinematical Hilbert space of LQG at fixed graph Γ, with L links and N nodes, is:

$$\mathcal{H}_\Gamma = L_2\left[SU(2)^L/SU(2)^N\right] \qquad (1)$$

For the self-energy diagram, we have $L = 4$, $N = 2$ and the corresponding graph[b] Γ is represented in Figure 1. Since the self-energy spinfoam graph is entirely symmetrical and has two nodes, I shall use the $+$ and $-$ symbols as labels for the latter. I use the same symbols to distinguish the corresponding intertwiners $i_\pm$, i.e. the invariant $SU(2)$ tensors associated with each node. The intertwiner space of a 4-valent node is denoted as:

$$\mathcal{I}_4 = Inv\left[V^{j_1} \otimes V^{j_2} \otimes V^{j_3} \otimes V^{j_4}\right] \qquad (2)$$

where V^{j_i} is the irreducible representation of spin j_i. I consider the recoupling base (j_1, j_2) for the intertwiner space (2). That is, I fix a pairing of the links at each node and I choose the basis that diagonalises the modulus square of the sum of the $SU(2)$ generators in the pair (j_1, j_2). A basis for the Hilbert space (1) is given by the spin-network states $|j_l, i_\pm\rangle$, where the j_l's are the spin associated with each link of the graph, $l = 1...4$, and the $i_\pm$'s are a basis in the corresponding intertwiners space (2) according to the recoupling scheme. The spin-network states are interpreted

---

[b]From now on, I will drop the explicit dependence on Γ.

as quantum tetrahedra or, if the node have valence higher than 4, as quantum polyhedra.[c, 35, 36] The corresponding discrete geometry, in which the shared faces between the tetrahedra must have the same area but nor necessarily the same shape or orientation, is called *twisted geometry*.[37]

I shall focus on the subspaces $\mathcal{H}_j$ of (1) such that all spins are the same $j_l = j$, for which the basis states are denoted as

$$|j, i_\pm\rangle \equiv \bigotimes_\pm |i_\pm\rangle = |i_+\rangle \otimes |i_-\rangle \qquad (3)$$

The explicit dependence on j can be dropped in the notation, since all the spins have the same value.

3. Derivation of the BF spinfoam amplitude

I start deriving the formula for the spinfoam transition amplitude associated to the triangulation described in section 2. The strategy chosen to derive the self-energy EPRL amplitude consists in starting from the corresponding amplitude for the BF model, for which it is possible to compare our numerical computations with the exact estimate of the amplitude's divergence,[30] since in the pure $SU(2)$ model one can isolate the divergent factor. Then, I include the contribution of the booster functions (see[38]), as they encode all the details of the EPRL model. This process serves to facilitate the derivation and, at the same time, make sure that the phases and normalization factors are correct.

3.1. *Numerical scaling of the BF amplitude*

The BF self-energy amplitude is written as:

$$W_{BF}(j, S_+, S_-) = \sum_{j_{ab}} \prod_{(a,b)} (2j_{ab} + 1) \{15j\}^2 \qquad (4)$$

where the algebric notation $\{15j\}^2$ refers to the spinfoam in Figure 2. For the algebraic expression of the $SU(2)$ $\{15j\}$ invariant quantities, I refer to.[1, 39] In (4), $(a, b) = (23, 24, 25, 35, 45, 34)$ are the labels which denote the spins attached to the 6 internal faces of the spinfoam, while the dependence on the 4 boundary spins is denoted with $j \equiv j_f$ with $f = 1...4$. In (4), the parameters specifying the boundary tetrahedra are generically denoted with S. The sums over the internal faces (explicitly highlighted in red) are unbounded: this is precisely the way in which the bubble's divergence manifests itself. Strictly speaking, the dimensional factor of the boundary faces should be taken into account in the expression for the amplitude, but this is a constant overall factor that can be ignored in the analysis, since it does not affect the scaling of the divergence. The 4-simplices are labeled in the following

---

[c]At least to some extent, since the Heisenberg uncertainty principle prevent us from determining the full geometry of the polyhedra. Thus, the interpretation of a spinnetwork state as a sharp polyhedron fails.

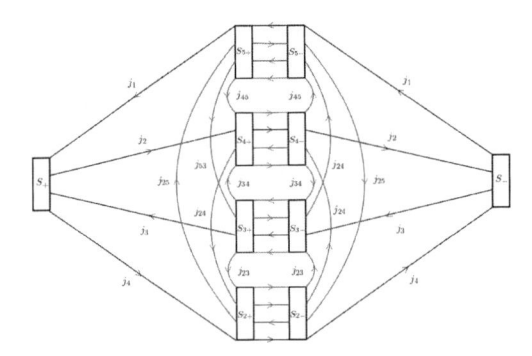

Fig. 2. Spinfoam corresponding to the BF self-energy amplitude. The two $\{15j\}$ symbols are graphically represented in order to highlight the bulk contractions.

way. The subscripts $+$ and $-$ distinguish the tetrahedra belonging to one vertex amplitude from those of the other, while the numeric subscripts distinguish the ones belonging to the same vertex. The two boundary tetrahedra, on the "opposite sides" of the spinfoam, are only labeled with $+$ and $-$ subscripts according the notation introduced in 2. The internal faces, dual to triangles, are labeled by two points indicating the tetrahedra attached to them, while the spins attached to the boundary links are labeled according to Figure 1.

In order to study numerically the scaling behavior of the amplitude, I impose an arbitrary cutoff K on the spin's values of the 6 internal faces. This allows to estimate the divergence scaling without performing an infinite number of sums. By doing so, the amplitude acquires an *artificial* dependence also on K. From now on, I refer to K as the "bulk spins cut-off".

I perform the integration over $SU(2)$ and obtain:

$$W_{BF}(j,i;K) = (-1)^{2(i_+ + i_-)} \sum_{j_{ab}} \prod_{(a,b)} (2j_{ab}+1) \sum_{i_e} \prod_e (2i_e+1) \{15j\}^2 \quad (5)$$

I denoted with $i \equiv (i_+, i_-)$ the dependence on the intertwiners at the two nodes in the recoupling base (j_1, j_2), and the phase $(-1)^{2(i_+ + i_-)}$ comes from the fact that I changed the orientation of the line represented by the boundary intertwiners, according to our convention for the $\{15j\}$ symbol, following the rules of the $SU(2)$ graphical calculus.[40]

In passing from (4) to (5), I attached an intertwiner i_e with $e = 2, ..., 5$ to each edge. Therefore, each edge carries a boundary spin, three face spins and an intertwiner. Triangular inequalities constrain the intertwiner to assume values in an interval centered on a face spin, implying that, for a fixed value of the spins on the faces, the sums over these intertwiners are bounded. I choose the spinnetwork boundary state with fixed spins and intertwiners and analyze the bubble's divergence with it, since the contraction of the amplitude with less trivial boundary states (for example, coherent states) requires to compute all the possible amplitudes

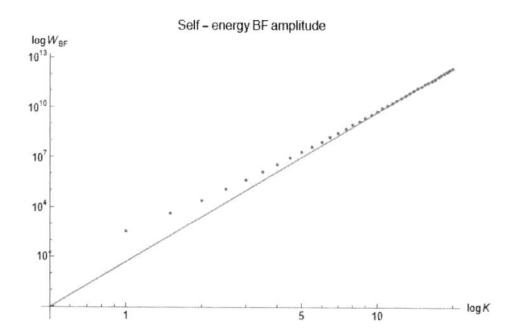

Fig. 3. Logarithmic plot of the BF self-energy amplitude scaling. The points computed with (5) are fitted with the curve $W_{BF} = 4.8 * K^9$, and the latter is shifted so that the last point coincides with the end of the curve. Notice that the divergence scaling is reached for very low values of the bulk spins cutoff K.

obtained by varying independently the intertwinwers i_+, i_-, thus increasing the computational complexity. The computation with other choices of boundary states are considered in.[1]

As previously stated, I only consider equilateral boundary spins configuration, that is, the spins $j \equiv j_f = j_1...j_4$ have all the same value[d]. In fixing the boundary state entirely, that is, both the boundary spins and the intertwiners, the amplitude turns out to depend only on 6 parameters, namely the 4 spins $j \equiv j_f$ and the 2 intertwinwers $i \equiv (i_+, i_-)$. To further minimize the computational time, I fix the spins of the boundary faces to their minimum non-trivial value $j = \frac{1}{2}$. Notice that the value of the boundary spins j and intertwiners i is not relevant, since in the BF model the amplitude must be independent of the values of the latter. Computing the amplitude (5) numerically, for different values of K, I verify that it correctly reproduces the divergent scaling derived in,[30] as shown in Figure 3:

$$W_{BF}(j, i, K) \propto K^9. \tag{6}$$

4. From BF to EPRL

In the BF model it is possible to isolate the divergent factor, but the aim is to use the numerical tools to study the EPRL model, where only analytical estimates of the lower[29] and upper bounds[30] on the scaling of the bubble's divergence are available in the literature. The picture is therefore not clear, especially considering that these two limits differ greatly. In fact, while the lower bound is logarithmically divergent in the cutoff K over the $SU(2)$ representation spins, the upper bound turns out to be K^9.

---

[d]Notice that, by doing so, each boundary intertwiner assumes a range of possible integer values ranging from 0 to $2j + 1$, so the overall phase of the amplitude is always unitary.

The crucial point of the passage from BF to EPRL model lies in the expression of the EPRL vertex amplitude. Since the reader may be unfamiliar with such amplitude form, I briefly underline the essential ideas, referring to the original paper[38] for an accurate description.

4.1. *EPRL vertex amplitude*

The EPRL vertex amplitude is built from the topological $SL(2,\mathbb{C})$ spinfoam vertex amplitude by imposing, weakly, the simplicity constraints. This results in a restriction of the unitary irreducible representations in the principal series.[10,41] In order to evaluate it in its original form, one should perform four group integrals (one of the original five integrals is redundant and has to be removed to guarantee finiteness[42]). Each group integral is, in general, a six dimensional unbounded highly oscillating integral for which numerical integration methods are not easy to implement efficiently. To get around this computational hurdle, an alternative form for the amplitude has been derived, resulting in a superposition of $SU(2)$ $\{15j\}$ symbols weighted by one booster functions B_4 per edge in the considered vertex.

$$A_v(j_f, i_e, \gamma) = \lim_{\Delta l \to \infty} \sum_{l_f=j_f}^{j_f+\Delta l} \sum_{k_e} \prod_e (2k_e+1) B_4(j_f, l_f; i_e, k_e; \gamma) \{15j\}_{j_f, i_1}(l_f, k_e) \tag{7}$$

For the explicit formulas of the booster functions B_4, I refer to.[1,38,43] In[1] it is also introduced a convenient graphical notation which combines the $SU(2)$ graphical calculus with algebraic formulas to define the quantities involved. Notice that in (7) the dimensional factors attached to the boundary intertwiners i_e and to the boundary spins j_f are neglected, since I assume the latter to be determined by the boundary spinnetwork state, so that they turn out to be constant. In less trivial spinfoams, as in the self-energy case, there are typically more vertex amplitudes glued together. This implies that dimensional factors of bulk spins and intertwiners must be taken into account, as did for the BF self-energy amplitude (5), in which the elementary vertex amplitude is represented by a single $SU(2)$ invariant $\{15j\}$ symbol. The key conceptual step to obtain the expression (7), starting from the integral representation over $SL(2,C)$, is to decompose each $SL(2,C)$ integral h according to the Cartan decomposition:

$$h = u e^{(\frac{r\sigma_3}{2})} v^{-1}, \tag{8}$$

where u and v are $SU(2)$ arbitrary rotations and $r \in [0, \infty)$ is the rapidity parameter of a boost along the z axis. The compact integrals, resulting from the above parameterization, are then evaluated exactly composing the $SU(2)$ invariants in the amplitude (7). This decomposition introduces a summation over a set of auxiliary spins l_f for each face involving the vertex (excluding the gauge fixed one), for a total of 6 distinct l_f, with lower bound $l_f \geq j_f$, and a set of auxiliary intertwiners k_e for each edge in the vertex (excluding the gauge fixed one) for a total of 4, which can assume all the values compatible with triangular inequalities. Finally, the "Y-map" imposes that the polyhedron shared by two adjacent polytopes lives in the same space-like hyperplane.[16,44,45]

The Y-map is present only on one side of each booster function, namely the one reaching out to the next vertex: the group elements joining at the vertex are instead multiplied together without the latter. Because of this, an infinite sum appears on the auxiliary spins l_f and the EPRL model is, in principle, recovered only in the limit in which this sum becomes infinite. The full EPRL amplitude is well defined,[42] as the summations over the l_f are convergent. Nevertheless, in order to perform a numerical evaluation of the amplitude, we need to introduce a homogeneous cut-off[e] Δl on the auxiliary spins l_f. In the following, I will refer to the cutoff Δl as the number of *shell*.

Beside the numerical precision with which the single terms that contribute to the vertex amplitude are computed, notice that this is the only approximation on which this method is based. If the convergence in the sum over the auxiliary spins l_f is sufficiently good, then we obtain a reasonable estimate of the EPRL model. As originally shown in,[38] the largest contributions to the booster functions come from configurations with $l_f = j_f$, namely the minimal admissible values for the l_f spins. The EPRL model defined with the approximation $l_f = j_f$ is usually called "simplified model". Even if the convergence of the amplitude (7) as a function of Δl is assured,[46,47] it is not possible to have a unique prescription to set the optimal Δl to get an acceptable convergence, since it depends on the details of data such as the face spins j_f and the Immirzi parameter. Furthermore, the convergence strongly depends on the structure of the 2-complex, and there is still no method that allows to estimate the error made in truncating the sum over the auxiliary spins. In section 5.1, I describe a numerical property of the convergence that allows extrapolating the limit $\Delta l \to \infty$ for the self-energy.

4.2. *EPRL self-energy amplitude*

According the procedure described above, starting from the BF amplitude (5), I attach a booster function between the bulk intertwiners, choosing the boundary intertwiners $i \equiv (i_+.i_-)$ as the gauge fixed ones in the two vertex amplitudes which form the self-energy spinfoam, which is the most convenient choice from a computational point of view. Here I consider the case[1] in which the two boundary intertwiners have the same value. When this happens, the fully algebraic compact

---

[e] The nature of this cut-off is obviously completely different from the K cutoff on the internal faces of self-energy amplitude introduced in section 3.1 for the BF amplitude.

expression of amplitude becomes[f]:

$$W(j,i,\gamma;K,\Delta l) = \sum_{j_{ab}}^{K} \prod_{(a,b)} (2j_{ab}+1) \sum_{i_e} A_v(j,j_{ab},i,i_e,\gamma;\Delta l)^2 \qquad (9)$$

where $q = 2,...5$, and the EPRL vertex amplitude is defined in (7). The EPRL self-energy amplitude (9) is the main object of our analysis. The dependence on the Immirzi parameter γ is "hidden" inside the booster functions, which appear in the definition of the single vertex amplitude (7). In the EPRL self-energy amplitude (9) I explicitly emphasized the *artificial* dependence on the two cut-off K and Δl. I shall always consider the two boundary intertinwers $i \equiv (i_+.i_-)$ to have the same value. When this is the case, the asymptotic divergence scaling remains essentially[g] unchanged by modifying the value of the intertwiners. Since it is necessary to choose a specific value of i for the computations, in the following I use $i = (0,0)$ by default. This completes the derivation of amplitude we considered in,[1] and now I describe the numerical results obtained.

5. Divergence analysis

The amplitude (9) has been studied numerically. Recalling that the analysis must be limited to a small number of parameters' configurations, the goal of the latter consists in answering the following question (for further numerical studies I refer again to,[1] which addresses more questions), for which there are currently no analytical methods of investigation: what is the exact asymptotic scaling of the EPRL divergence, and is there a dependence on the Immirzi parameter?

The logical step is to proceed in the same way as we did with the BF amplitude (5), that is, fix the boundary state entirely to the lowest value $j = 0.5$, and compute the amplitude as a function of the cut-off K on the internal faces. It is reasonable to do so using several different values of the Immirzi parameter γ. However, compared to the purely $SU(2)$ case, the EPRL amplitude (9) has an additional cut-off Δl necessary to truncate the sum on the auxiliary spins l_f in the single vertex amplitudes (7) which constitute self-energy. This fact makes the EPRL analysis much more complicated due to the reasons explained in section 4. In section 5.1 I present a property of the convergence which allows to extrapolate the limit $\Delta l \to \infty$. Since for computations it is necessary to select a specific value of the Immirzi parameter, I first illustrate the divergence scaling extrapolation algorithm by selecting a specific value for the latter. The analysis for different γ values is similar.

The result of the computation of the amplitude (9), for increasing values of Δl and K, is shown in Figure 4. From a simple qualitative analysis we infer that the convergence is faster for a reduced bulk spins cutoff, while it becomes slower

---

[f] In the following omit the EPRL subscript for the amplitude, since every time I write W (without the BF subscript) I always implicitly refer to the EPRL model.
[g] A part from irrelevant numerical fluctuations.

Self-energy amplitude (j = 0.5, i = 0, γ = 1)

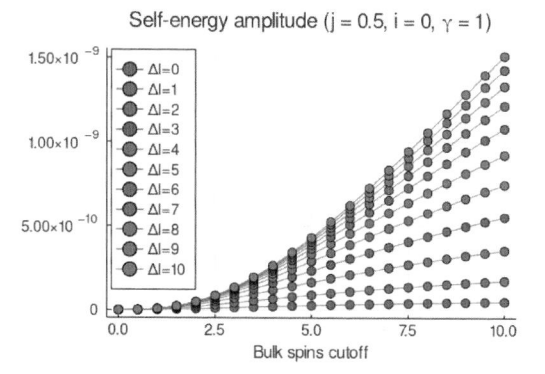

Fig. 4. Divergence of the EPRL self-energy amplitude (9) computed numerically. All boundary spins $j \equiv j_f$, where $f = 1...4$, are equal to $\frac{1}{2}$, while boundary intertwiners i_+, i_- are both set to zero. The plots with i_+, i_- equal to 1 are identical.

as K increases. Strictly speaking, the numerically computed curves turn out to be a *lower bound* to the EPRL divergence, since the latter is recovered only in the limit $\Delta l \to \infty$. Since further increasing numerically the parameter Δl requires exponentially increasing the computation times, it is necessary to introduce an algorithm for extrapolating the above limit.

5.1. *Extrapolation algorithm for the amplitude*

In order to derive the full EPRL amplitude, we study the convergence of (9) in the parameter Δl based on the data of Figure 4, and we extrapolate infinite shell limit based on this trend. In order to do so, we plot the ratios of the differences between adjacent curves of Figure 4, at fixed K, as a function of Δl. That is, we study the function:

$$f(K, \Delta l, \gamma) \equiv \frac{W(K, \Delta l + 2, \gamma) - W(K, \Delta l + 1, \gamma)}{W(K, \Delta l + 1, \gamma) - W(K, \Delta l, \gamma)}. \tag{10}$$

The result is shown in Figure 5. Numerical data shows that the convergence of (9) in the shell parameter Δl, for each bulk spins cut-off K, is such that the function (10) is first a decreasing function of Δl, then it remains constant in the convergence phase. Therefore, it exists an integer N such that:

$$W(K, \Delta l + 1, \gamma) - W(K, \Delta l, \gamma) \approx (c_{K,\gamma})^{\Delta l} \quad \text{for} \quad \Delta l \geq N \tag{11}$$

where the coefficient $c_{K,\gamma}$ is roughly equal to function (10) for the highest number of shells computed numerically. So, if the amplitude has been calculated up to N shells, we approximate the coefficient $c_{K,\gamma}$ as:

$$c_{K,\gamma} \equiv f(K, N-2, \gamma). \tag{12}$$

For the extrapolation of the EPRL amplitude we used $N = 10$, even if Figure 5 shows that property (11) becomes evident even for lower values. Once the convergence is

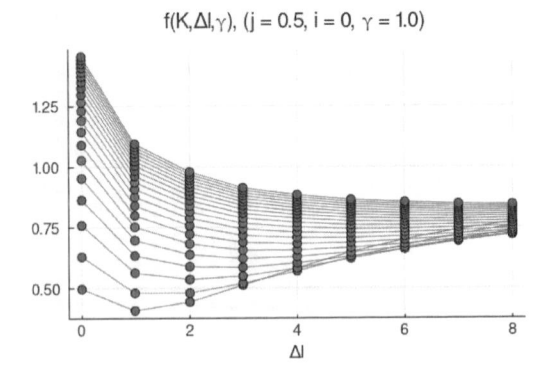

Fig. 5. Plot of the function $f(K, \Delta l, \gamma)$ defined as in (10). I plot the values of K between $\frac{1}{2}$ and 10 in ascending order from bottom to top.

reached, that is, when $\frac{W(K,\Delta l+1,\gamma)}{W(K,\Delta l,\gamma)} \approx 1$, function (10) shows some slight fluctuations by further increasing the shells[h]. This is evident for low bulk spins cut-off values, where convergence in Δl is extremely fast, as shown in Figure 5. Property (11) allows to obtain a good estimate of the EPRL curve by using the equation:

$$W(K,\gamma) \equiv \lim_{\Delta l \to \infty} W(K,\Delta l,\gamma) \approx W(K, N-1, \gamma) + \frac{W(K,N,\gamma) - W(K,N-1,\gamma)}{1 - c_{K,\gamma}} \quad (13)$$

Equation (13) is obtained by using the known limit of the geometric series:

$$\sum_{l=N}^{\infty} (c_{K,\gamma})^l = \frac{(c_{K,\gamma})^N}{1 - c_{K,\gamma}} \approx \frac{W(K,N,\gamma) - W(K,N-1,\gamma)}{1 - c_{K,\gamma}} \quad (14)$$

where in the second passage we used the property (11). In Figure 7 we plot the EPRL amplitude extrapolated with equation (13) along with the curves in Figure 4.

Let's discuss the above extrapolation scheme:

- Extrapolating the limit $\Delta l \to \infty$ of (9) for low values of the bulk spins cut-off K, for which a good convergence in the auxiliary spin sum has already been reached numerically, equation (13) provides a value which essentially coincides with the last computed point. This happens because, despite the fluctuations of function (10) for low K, the difference $W(K, N, \gamma) - W(K, N-1, \gamma)$ is extremely small. Therefore, the only relevant contribution to the extrapolated amplitude comes from the computed one, which is a good approximation of the EPRL model.
- For each bulk spins cut-off value K, the corresponding EPRL amplitude is extrapolated *independently* from the other values the latter. By doing so,

---

[h] As we shall see, this fluctuations are not relevant.

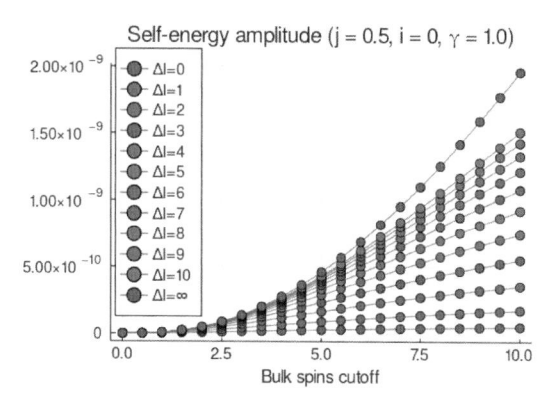

Fig. 6. EPRL asymptotic scaling curve extrapolated with the equation (13), plotted together with those computed numerically, that is, the curves of Figure 4. Notice that for $K \leq 4$, where the convergence is reached numerically, the extrapolated point essentially coincides with the last computed one.

we actually see that the resulting amplitude can be approximated extremely well by a polynomial fit $W(K, \gamma) = a + bK^c$ as a function of the bulk spins cut-off K.

- The specific properties of the convergence in the auxiliary spins sum of the single vertex amplitude (7) are still unexplored. It is possible that property (11) also manifests for spinfoam amplitudes defined on a more elaborate 2-complex with respect to the triangulation described in section 2. If this would be the case, the above extrapolation scheme could allow to obtain a good estimate of the EPRL model by using a negligible amount of computational resources compared to that necessary to reach a good approximation by using solely numerical techniques.

- In order to apply equation (13) it is necessary to know $W(K, N, \gamma)$, $W(K, N-1, \gamma)$, $W(K, N-2, \gamma)$. That is, only three amplitudes must be computed numerically (for N sufficiently high). Despite this, we still opted to compute all the amplitudes $W(K, \Delta l, \gamma)$ for $\Delta l = 0, 1...N$. This was done both to test property (11) and, on the other hand, to estimate the effectiveness of the extrapolation with a qualitative comparison between all the numerically calculated amplitudes and the extrapolated one. Furthermore, since the curves in Figure 5 are not exactly constant, that is, they start to increase when $\frac{W(K,\Delta l+1,\gamma)}{W(K,\Delta l,\gamma)} \approx 1$, the extrapolated curve is an approximation, which improves by increasing N in equation (13). Therefore, the higher is the number of shells computed numerically, the better is the approximation represented by the extrapolated amplitude. In[1] we discuss this in more detail and we also provide further numerical confirmation of the effectiveness of this extrapolation algorithm.

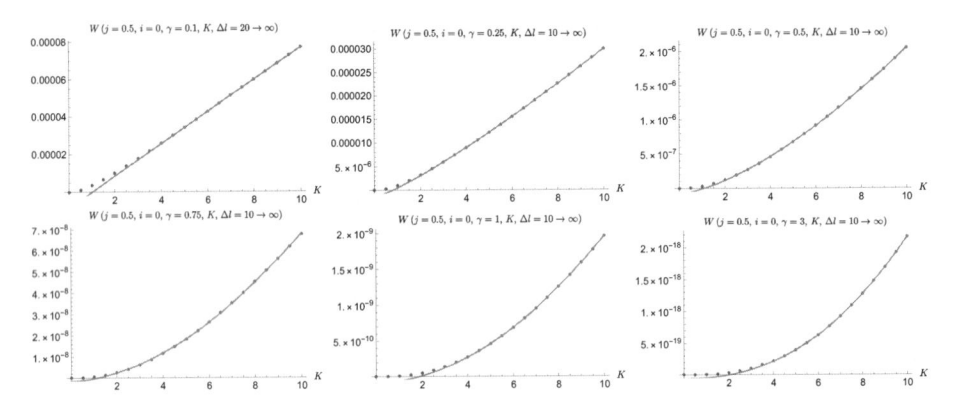

Fig. 7. EPRL asymptotic scaling curve extrapolated with the equation (13), plotted together with those computed numerically, that is, the curves of Figure 4. Notice that for $K \leq 4$, where the convergence is reached numerically, the extrapolated point essentially coincides with the last computed one.

5.2. Scaling of the divergence and role of the Immirzi parameter

Using the above scheme in,[1] we study the scaling of the asymptotic divergence of the EPRL self-energy amplitude for 9 different values of the Immirzi parameter. We choose an approximately uniform sampling of γ between 0.1 and 10, arguing that a significant effect of the latter in the scaling should occur in a range which spans two orders of magnitude. We fit the curves with a function:

$$W(K, \gamma) = a + bK^c \tag{15}$$

where a, b, c are real coefficients. The values[i] of $W(K, \gamma)$ are shown in table 1.

Table 1. Fit coefficients table

	$W(K,\gamma) = a + bK^c$	$(j = 0.5, i = 0)$, $K \in [0, 10]$	
Immirzi parameter	a	b	c
$\gamma = 0.1$	$-3.0884 * 10^{-6}$	$6.0304 * 10^{-6}$	1.1
$\gamma = 0.25$	$-1.58614 * 10^{-6}$	$1.9783 * 10^{-6}$	1.2
$\gamma = 0.5$	$-7.5523 * 10^{-8}$	$6.7306 * 10^{-8}$	1.5
$\gamma = 0.75$	$-1.7153 * 10^{-9}$	$1.10779 * 10^{-9}$	1.8
$\gamma = 1$	$-8.6894 * 10^{-11}$	$2.5801 * 10^{-11}$	1.9
$\gamma = 3$	$-6.0026 * 10^{-20}$	$1.1186 * 10^{-20}$	2.3
$\gamma = 5$	$-4.5405 * 10^{-25}$	$1.0642 * 10^{-25}$	2.3
$\gamma = 7.5$	$-2.35075 * 10^{-29}$	$8.25374 * 10^{-30}$	2.3
$\gamma = 10$	$-1.7872 * 10^{-32}$	$9.2770 * 10^{-33}$	2.3

---

[i]Recall that we neglected all the dimensional factors which, in the amplitude (9), are constant as a function of K.

The analysis of the scaling shows that the amplitude is strongly suppressed as γ increases. Moreover, the divergence turns out to be well fitted by a linear scaling when the Immirzi parameter is small enough, while for $\gamma \geq 1$ the curve is approximated by a quadratic function in the range $K \in [0, 10]$. Unfortunately, the huge computation cost required by increasing the bulk spins cut-off in the divergence analysis prevents us from testing the divergence for $K > 10$. It is possible that the divergence scaling is actually independent of the Immirzi parameter, and that the different asymptotic trends, as γ varies, are only an effect of the fact that the range of the bulk spins cut-off K is too small. On the other hand, it is also possible that the Immirzi parameter plays an effective role in modifying the asymptotic scaling of self-energy amplitude. This deserves future investigations.

In any case, the numerically observed scaling in the range $K \in [0, 10]$, with boundary parameters $j = 0.5, i = 0$ falls within the upper and lower bounds present in the literature. In particular, unlike the BF self-energy divergence (see equation (3)), the role of the destructive interference between the oscillations of the booster functions $B_4(j_f, l_f; i, k)$ and the $\{15j\}$ symbols in the sum over the bulk spins j_{ab} implies that the divergence is considerably dumped. This was not expected, since it has been shown that in the three-dimensional EPRL model, the upper bound provided by the algorithm proposed in[30] provides an excellent estimate of the divergence.

6. Boundary observables

In this section we compute some spinfoam boundary observables. We focus on the normalized dynamical expectation value of geometrical operators, that is:

$$\langle O \rangle = \frac{\langle W | O | \Psi \rangle}{\langle W | \Psi \rangle} \qquad (16)$$

where the bra W contains the propagator, namely the dynamics, while the ket Ψ turns out to be the tensor product of the *in* and *out* states of the LQG Hilbert space. With the term "propagator" we refer to the square matrices (they are such since the self-energy triangulation has two boundary tetrahedra) in which the element a, b corresponds to the EPRL self-energy amplitude with $a = i_+, b = i_-$. The observable O therefore contains the dynamic correlations.

The booster function $B_4(j_f, l_f; i, k)$ are interpreted as a quantum tetrahedron being boosted among adjacent frames: the two sets j_f and l_f describe the four areas of the tetrahedron in the two frames connected by a boost, and the two intertwiners i and k describe the quantum intrinsic shape of the tetrahedron.[48] Therefore, the expectation values (16) of geometric operators describing boundary tetrahedra should be equivalent with respect to the $SU(2)$ model. From a numerical point of view it is an excellent check, especially considering that numerical calculations carried out with the EPRL model are still in their primordial stages,[30, 43, 47] and, as far as we know, there are no such numerical computations (ie dynamic expectation value of geometric operators) with spinfoams more complicated than those consisting of a single vertex amplitude[49] which used these specific techniques.

In[1] we find that the boundary observables are not affected in any way by the presence of the spinfoam divergence in the bulk. Furthermore, while in the divergence analysis we see an important contribution due to the number of shells Δl of the amplitude (9), for the observables there is no trace of a dependence in that sense[j]. In fact, an excellent approximation of the correct geometric value is obtained with the approximation $\Delta l = 0$. The fact that the number of shells is completely irrelevant in the computation of geometric boundary observables allows them to be computed very fast.

6.1. Angles

The shape of the tetrahedra in twisted geometry is measured by the angle operator:

$$A_{ab}|i_\pm\rangle = \cos(\theta_{ab})|i_\pm\rangle \tag{17}$$

which is interpreted as the cosine of the external dihedral angle between the faces a and b of the tetrahedron defined on the nodes $\pm$. The spinnetwork basis states diagonalize the dihedral angle θ_{ab} between faces a and b. The equation for measuring the dihedral angle $\cos(\theta_{ab})$ of $|i_\pm\rangle$ in terms of intertwiner spin $i_\pm$ was derived in[49] and it reads:

$$\cos(\theta_{ab}) = \frac{i_+(i_+ + 1) - j_a(j_a + 1) - j_b(j_b + 1)}{2\sqrt{j_a(j_a + 1)j_b(j_b + 1)}}. \tag{18}$$

We consider the expectation value (16) of the angle operator (17) in any of the two (equal) boundary regular tetrahedra of the triangulation using the spinnetwork state. According to the recoupling basis (j_1, j_2), we focus on the angle between faces 1 and 2. The expectation value can be computed as:

$$\frac{\langle W|A_{12}|W\rangle}{\langle W|W\rangle} = \frac{\sum_{i_\pm} [W(j,i,K)]^2 \cos(\theta_{12})}{\sum_{i_\pm} [W(j,i,K)]^2}. \tag{19}$$

Carrying out the numerical computation of (19), we obtain a value that is in agreement with the geometric value of the external angle of a regular tetrahedron up to the tenth significant digit, as shown in Figure 8. This is consistent with the fact that we are looking at the only angle which is completely sharp, while the others turn out to be spread. In fact, according to the Heisenberg uncertainty principle, since different angle operators do not commute, only one of the dihedral angles can be determined. We also analyzed the boundary states of the self-energy amplitude by using the Livine-Speziale coherent intertwiners, which allow to define a superposition of spin-network states peaked on a classical geometry with minimal

---

[j]At least for the ones that we computed.

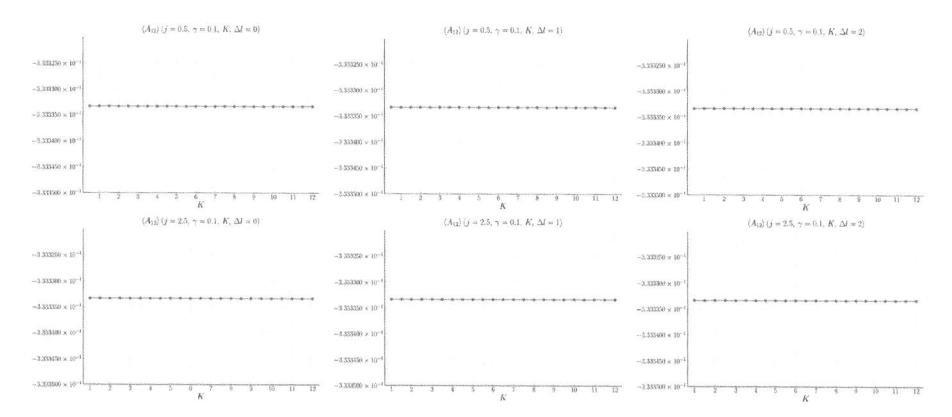

Fig. 8. Dynamic expectation value of the cosine of the external dihedral angle operator (19). We plot the angle for different values of Δl, showing that an excellent agreement with the value $-0.\bar{3}$ is obtained with the approximation $\Delta l = 0$. We used $\gamma = 0.1$.

spread. A wave packet peaked on a classical triangulated geometry, that can be viewed as a coherent state in the Hilbert space (1), is obtained by combining coherent intertwiners at each node. In this case, all the dihedral angles are minimally spread around the classical values, and this is exactly what we verify numerically. The plots obtained are qualitatively identical to those in Figure 8, except that the computed value of the angle is approximately[k] that of the external dihedral angle of a regular tetrahedron. This is due to the fact that the square modulus of the coefficients of the coherent states, in the spin-intertwiner basis, turns out to be a a distribution centered around the value of the intertwiner which determines the semiclassical value of the dihedral angle, and the width of the distribution is much higher as the spins are low. For the computation of the volumes, we refer to.[1]

7. Conclusions

I have presented the application[1] of new computational techniques applied to the study of the infrared divergence represented by the self-energy EPRL amplitude. The divergence scaling obtained falls within the upper and lower bounds in the literature. Particular emphasis was placed on the role of the Immirzi parameter in the asymptotic divergence. I presented the extrapolation method introduced to overcome the computational cost represented by the convergence in the shell parameter Δl, which can potentially be used in other contexts. The analysis of the boundary angles shows that the latter are finite and consistent with classical geometry, despite the divergence in the bulk, and that the approximation represented by the shells does not play any relevant role in the dynamical expectation values of the latter.

---

[k]Up to the first 2 significant digits.

We thank all the collaborators of this work, in particular Francesco Gozzini, without whom this would not have been possible, as well as Carlo Rovelli for useful discussions and comments. I explicitly thank my supervisor Francesca Vidotto for the constant support and for an accurate review in the drafting of this paper. I also thank Pietro Dona for countless contributions in various stages of.[1] Finally, we also thanks the Compute Canada staff for their help in using the Graham and Cedar clusters. This work is supported by the NSERC Discovery Grant.

References

1. P. Frisoni and Others, Numerical analysis of the EPRL spin foam self-energy, *in preparation* (2021).
2. A. Perez, The Spin-Foam Approach to Quantum Gravity, *Living Reviews in Relativity* **16** (2013).
3. C. Rovelli, D. Colosi, L. Doplicher, W. Fairbairn, L. Modesto and K. Noui, Background independence in a nutshell, *arXiv.org* **gr-qc** (2004).
4. C. Rovelli and M. Smerlak, In quantum gravity, summing is refining, *Class. Quant. Grav.* **29**, p. 55004 (2012).
5. R. Pereira, Lorentzian LQG vertex amplitude, *Class. Quant. Grav.* **25**, p. 85013 (2008).
6. J. Engle, R. Pereira and C. Rovelli, Flipped spinfoam vertex and loop gravity, *arXiv.org* **gr-qc** (2007).
7. L. Freidel, Reconstructing AdS/CFT (2008).
8. Y. Ding, M. Han and C. Rovelli, Generalized Spinfoams (2010).
9. W. Kaminski, M. Kisielowski and J. Lewandowski, Spin-Foams for All Loop Quantum Gravity, *Class. Quant. Grav.* **27**, p. 95006 (2010).
10. J. Engle, E. Livine, R. Pereira and C. Rovelli, LQG vertex with finite Immirzi parameter, *Nucl. Phys.* **B799**, 136 (2008).
11. E. R. Livine and S. Speziale, A new spinfoam vertex for quantum gravity, *Phys. Rev.* **D76**, p. 84028 (2007).
12. E. R. Livine and S. Speziale, Consistently Solving the Simplicity Constraints for Spinfoam Quantum Gravity, *Europhys. Lett.* **81**, p. 50004 (2008).
13. L. Freidel and K. Krasnov, A New Spin Foam Model for 4d Gravity, *Class. Quant. Grav.* **25**, p. 125018 (2008).
14. C. Rovelli and F. Vidotto, *Covariant Loop Quantum Gravity* (Cambridge University Press, Cambridge, 2015).
15. C. Rovelli, Zakopane lectures on loop gravity, *arXiv.org* **gr-qc** (2011).
16. P. Doná and S. Speziale, Introductory lectures to loop quantum gravity, in *TVC 79. Gravitation: théorie et expérience*, eds. A. Bounames and A. Makhlouf (Hermann, 2013).
17. B. Dittrich, The continuum limit of loop quantum gravity - A framework for solving the theory (2016).
18. B. Dittrich, S. Mizera and S. Steinhaus, Decorated tensor network renormalization for lattice gauge theories and spin foam models, *New Journal of Physics* **18**, p. 053009 (May 2016).
19. B. Bahr and S. Steinhaus, Investigation of the spinfoam path integral with quantum cuboid intertwiners, *Physical Review D* **93** (May 2016).
20. V. Bonzom, R. Gurau and V. Rivasseau, Random tensor models in the large N limit: Uncoloring the colored tensor models, *Physical Review D* **85** (Apr 2012).

21. D. Benedetti and R. Gurau, Phase transition in dually weighted colored tensor models, *Nuclear Physics B* **855**, p. 420–437 (Feb 2012).
22. S. Carrozza, D. Oriti and V. Rivasseau, Renormalization of a su(2) tensorial group field theory in three dimensions, *Communications in Mathematical Physics* **330**, p. 581–637 (Mar 2014).
23. J. B. Geloun, T. A. Koslowski, D. Oriti and A. D. Pereira, Functional renormalization group analysis of rank-3 tensorial group field theory: The full quartic invariant truncation, *Physical Review D* **97** (Jun 2018).
24. V. Bonzom and M. Smerlak, Bubble divergences from twisted cohomology (2010).
25. V. Bonzom and M. Smerlak, Bubble divergences: sorting out topology from cell structure (2011).
26. A. Baratin, S. Carrozza, D. Oriti, J. Ryan and M. Smerlak, Melonic phase transition in group field theory, *Letters in Mathematical Physics* **104**, p. 1003–1017 (May 2014).
27. C. Perini, C. Rovelli and S. Speziale, Self-energy and vertex radiative corrections in LQG, *Phys. Lett.* **B682**, 78 (2009).
28. T. Krajewski, J. Magnen, V. Rivasseau, A. Tanasa and P. Vitale, Quantum Corrections in the Group Field Theory Formulation of the EPRL/FK Models, *Phys. Rev.* **D82**, p. 124069 (2010).
29. A. Riello, Self-Energy of the Lorentzian EPRL-FK Spin Foam Model of Quantum Gravity, *Phys. Rev.* **D88**, p. 24011 (2013).
30. P. Donà, Infrared divergences in the EPRL-FK Spin Foam model, *Class. Quant. Grav.* **35**, p. 175019 (2018).
31. J. W. Barrett, R. J. Dowdall, W. J. Fairbairn, F. Hellmann and R. Pereira, Lorentzian spin foam amplitudes: Graphical calculus and asymptotics, *Classical and Quantum Gravity* **27** (2010).
32. F. Gozzini, A high-performance code for eprl spin foam amplitudes (2021), *In preparation*.
33. J. Bezanson, A. Edelman, S. Karpinski and V. B. Shah, Julia: A fresh approach to numerical computing, *SIAM review* **59**, 65 (2017).
34. W. R. Inc., Mathematica, Version 12.2 Champaign, IL, 2020.
35. E. Bianchi and Y. Ding, Lorentzian spinfoam propagator, *Phys. Rev.* **D86**, p. 104040 (2012).
36. E. Bianchi and H. M. Haggard, Discreteness of the volume of space from Bohr-Sommerfeld quantization (2011).
37. L. Freidel and S. Speziale, Twisted geometries: A geometric parametrisation of SU(2) phase space, *Phys. Rev.* **D82**, p. 84040 (2010).
38. S. Speziale, Boosting Wigner's nj-symbols, *Journal of Mathematical Physics* **58** (sep 2017).
39. A. P. Yutsin, I. B. Levinson and V. V. Vanagas, *Mathematical Apparatus of the Theory of Angular Momentum* (Israel Program for Scientific Translation, Jerusalem, Israel, 1962).
40. V. D. Aleksandroviic, A. N. Moskalev and K. V. Kel'manoviic, *Quantum theory of angular momentum: Irreducible tensors, spherical harmonics, vector coupling coefficients, 3nj symbols* (World Scientific, 1988).
41. J. Engle, R. Pereira and C. Rovelli, The loop-quantum-gravity vertex-amplitude, *Phys. Rev. Lett.* **99**, p. 161301 (2007).
42. J. Engle and R. Pereira, Regularization and finiteness of the Lorentzian LQG vertices, *Phys. Rev.* **D79**, p. 84034 (2009).
43. P. Donà, M. Fanizza, G. Sarno and S. Speziale, Numerical study of the Lorentzian Engle-Pereira-Rovelli-Livine spin foam amplitude, *Physical Review D* **100** (Mar 2019).

44. E. Bianchi, P. Donà and S. Speziale, Polyhedra in loop quantum gravity, *Physical Review D* **83** (2011).
45. P. Donà, M. Fanizza, G. Sarno and S. Speziale, Su(2) graph invariants, Regge actions and polytopes, *Classical and Quantum Gravity* **35** (2018).
46. P. Donà and G. Sarno, Numerical methods for EPRL spin foam transition amplitudes and Lorentzian recoupling theory, *General Relativity and Gravitation* **50** (2018).
47. P. Donà, M. Fanizza, G. Sarno and S. Speziale, Numerical study of the lorentzian engle-pereira-rovelli-livine spin foam amplitude, *Physical Review D* **100** (2019).
48. P. Dona and S. Speziale, Asymptotics of lowest unitary SL(2,C) invariants on graphs (Jul 2020).
49. F. Gozzini and F. Vidotto, Primordial fluctuations from quantum gravity (2019).

A spin foam framework for the black-to-white hole transition

Farshid Soltani

Department of Physics and Astronomy, The University of Western Ontario,
London, Ontario N6A 3K7, Canada
E-mail: fsoltan2@uwo.ca

Black holes formation and evolution have been extensively studied at the classical level. However, not much is known regarding the end of their lives, a phase that requires to consider the quantum nature of the gravitational field. A black-to-white hole transition can capture the physics of this phenomenon, in particular the physics of the residual small black holes at the end of the Hawking evaporation. This work shows how the spin foam formalism is able to describe this non-perturbative phenomenon. A thorough examination of the black hole spacetime region in which quantum effects cannot be neglected indicates that the scenario in which the black hole geometry undergoes a quantum transition in a white hole geometry is natural and conservative. This quantum transition is then studied using the spin foam formalism and the resulting transition amplitude is explicitly computed.

Keywords: Black holes, white holes, black-to-white hole transition, loop quantum gravity, spin foam formalism.

1. Introduction

The exterior region of a black hole is described extraordinarily well by general relativity. Its interior region, on the other hand, is not and it is thus not known what happens inside a black hole. The reason for this breakdown of predictability is the presence of a spacetime singularity in the interior of a black hole: since the quantum nature of the gravitational field cannot be neglected in the vicinity of a spacetime singularity, the classical theory cannot be trusted in this region. Although effective black hole models exhibiting a non-singular interior have been extensively studied in the literature, a non-singular black hole interior consisting of a black hole geometry that undergoes a quantum transition in a white hole geometry was proposed for the first time in Ref. 1.

A different open question concerning black holes is what happens at the end of their life. Working in semiclassical gravity, Hawking[2] famously showed that black holes evaporate and are thus not eternal. However, since the quantum nature of the gravitational field near the horizon can no longer be neglected when the horizon reaches Planckian size (or possibly even before then[1]), the end of the evaporation process of a black hole is a quantum gravity phenomenon. A very natural and conservative scenario for the end of the life of a black hole is the black-to-white hole transition.

The aim of this work is to report in a concise and coherent fashion the results obtained in Refs. 3 and 4. The black hole spacetime region in which quantum effects cannot be neglected is analyzed in detail and it is shown to be actually composed of three physically independent subregions, with one of them being a region surrounding the black hole horizon at the end of the evaporation process. As a consequence, the last stage of the life of a black hole can be studied focusing solely on this region. Independent analyses of the three separate quantum regions consistently point toward a black-to-white hole transition. The last stage of the life of a black hole in this scenario, that is the quantum region where the black hole horizon undergoes a quantum transition in a white hole horizon, is then studied using the spin foam formalism[5,6] (also known as covariant loop quantum gravity) and a concrete spin foam framework for the black-to-white hole transition is developed.

The discussion is here limited to the case of a Schwarzschild black hole. See however Ref. 7 for a generalization of the black-to-white hole geometry to the case of a charged black hole.

2. The three quantum regions of a black hole spacetime

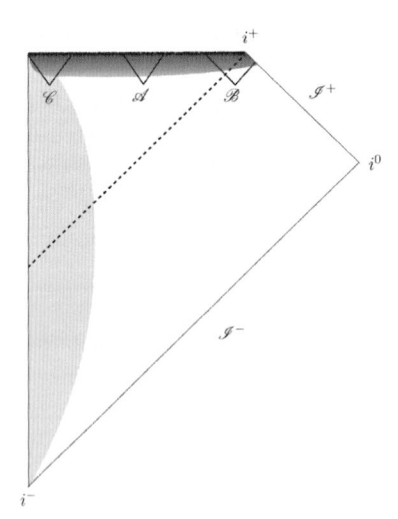

The conformal diagram of the spacetime describing the formation of a black hole by gravitationally collapsed matter and its subsequent evaporation is reported in Fig. 1. The light grey region represents the interior of the collapsing matter, the dashed line represents the apparent horizon of the black hole and the dark grey region represents the spacetime region where the quantum nature of the gravitational field cannot be neglected and where consequently the classical (or semiclassical) theory can no longer be trusted.

Fig. 1. Conformal diagram of the spacetime describing the formation of a black hole by gravitationally collapsed matter and its subsequent evaporation.

The quantum region can be divided[8] in three different subregions: region $\mathscr{C}$, where the collapsing matter reaches Planckian density; region $\mathscr{B}$, where the horizon reaches Planckian size at the end of the evaporation process; region $\mathscr{A}$, where the curvature reaches Planckian scale but the spacetime events belong neither to region $\mathscr{B}$ nor to region $\mathscr{C}$. In order to prove that these subregions are physically independent from each other, it is sufficient to show that their spatial separation is considerable. In the classical theory the principle of locality assures that two events whose separation is spacelike and significant cannot be causally connected. Furthermore, although the quantum theory may alter the causal structure of spacetime, quantum fluctuations cannot causally connect widely spacelike-separated events.

A rough estimate of the distance $d_{\mathscr{BC}}$ between regions $\mathscr{B}$ and $\mathscr{C}$ is[3]

$$d_{\mathscr{BC}} \sim \ell_{\text{Pl}} \left(\frac{m_0}{m_{\text{Pl}}}\right)^{\frac{10}{3}}, \qquad (1)$$

where m_0 is the initial mass of the black hole before the start of the evaporation process and ℓ_{Pl} and m_{Pl} are respectively the Planck length and the Planck mass. For a stellar black hole this distance is

$$d_{\mathscr{BC}}(m_0 = M_\odot) \sim 10^{75} \text{ light years}. \qquad (2)$$

Regions $\mathscr{B}$ and $\mathscr{C}$ are thus spacelike separated and considerably distant from each other. It follows that regions $\mathscr{B}$ and $\mathscr{C}$ are physically independent from each other and they can thus be studied separately. Furthermore, since region $\mathscr{A}$ contains spacetime events that are physically independent from region $\mathscr{B}$ as well as spacetime events that are physically independent from region $\mathscr{C}$, the physics of region $\mathscr{A}$ must be independent from the physics of both region $\mathscr{B}$ and region $\mathscr{C}$. However, since region $\mathscr{A}$ contains spacetime events that are causally connected to region $\mathscr{B}$ as well as spacetime events that are causally connected to region $\mathscr{C}$, the physics of both region $\mathscr{B}$ and region $\mathscr{C}$ depend on the physics of region $\mathscr{A}$. These three quantum regions will be now analyzed separately.

2.1. *Region $\mathscr{A}$*

Since the physics of region $\mathscr{A}$ does not depend on the quantum gravity regime of the collapsing matter (region $\mathscr{C}$) or on the last stage of the life of the black hole (region $\mathscr{B}$), it can be studied in the context of an eternal (Schwarzschild) black hole.

The effort to understand the physics of region $\mathscr{A}$ has led to the development of several effective models (see Refs. 9–11 and references therein) that describe the internal region of an eternal black hole using techniques developed in the framework of loop quantum cosmology. Although the specifics of these models are different, they all exhibit a regular interior region where the trapped region of the black hole makes a smooth transition in an anti-trapped region bounded by a future horizon describing the interior of a white hole. This result, besides supporting the conjecture that classical curvature singularities are not a true physical prediction of the theory but rather an indication that the classical theory can no longer be trusted, is the first evidence suggesting a black-to-white hole transition.

Interestingly, a hint of the same result can be found also at the classical level. It can indeed be shown[12,13] that, using specific coordinate systems, the geodesics in the interior region of a black hole can be naturally continued across the curvature singularity into the interior region of a white hole. The resulting geometry is still singular, but now it is geodesically complete and it can be interpreted as the classical limit of the quantum geometry of the effective models.

2.2. Region $\mathscr{C}$

The physics of region $\mathscr{C}$ is independent from the physics of region $\mathscr{B}$ and it can thus be studied neglecting the evaporation process of the black hole. However, it is not independent from the physics of region $\mathscr{A}$ and its analysis must be consistent with the scenario emerging from the investigation of region $\mathscr{A}$.

The study of the classical physics of the collapsing matter is a hard task. The analysis of its quantum gravity regime is even trickier. In Ref. 14 it was hypothesized that, in analogy with the cosmological singularity resolution in loop quantum cosmology,[15] the collapsing matter bounces due to a quantum-gravitational repulsion effect. This possibility, that will be assumed to accurately represent the physics of region $\mathscr{C}$ in the following, is consistent with the physics of region $\mathscr{A}$. A qualitative conformal diagram of the spacetime emerging from this partial analysis (region $\mathscr{B}$ still needs to be discussed) can be found in Fig. 2(a).

This scenario is further corroborated by several independent quantum descriptions of the phenomenon (see e.g. Refs. 16–19). Although these models use different techniques and focus on different aspects of the phenomenon, they all predict that the collapsing matter undergoes a bounce. This is a strong indication of the general validity of the scenario.

2.3. Region $\mathscr{B}$

The conformal diagram in Fig. 2(a) represents the black hole spacetime that emerges taking into account the quantum physics of regions $\mathscr{A}$ and $\mathscr{C}$. It is however immediate to see that this spacetime does not represent properly the physics of region $\mathscr{B}$. While the black hole evaporation process takes a finite amount of time to shrink the horizon to the Planck scale, in Fig. 2(a) region $\mathscr{B}$ is reached only asymptotically. The physics of region $\mathscr{B}$ thus need to be properly modified whilst remaining consistent with the scenario emerging from regions $\mathscr{A}$ and $\mathscr{C}$.

A scenario that is often considered for the end of the life of a black hole is the complete evaporation of the black hole. Having spent time investigating regions $\mathscr{A}$ and $\mathscr{C}$ separately, it is now easy to see that a complete evaporation of the black hole, besides being an ad hoc assumption with no foundation in any quantum gravity model, is hardly consistent with the global picture of the spacetime in Fig. 2(a).

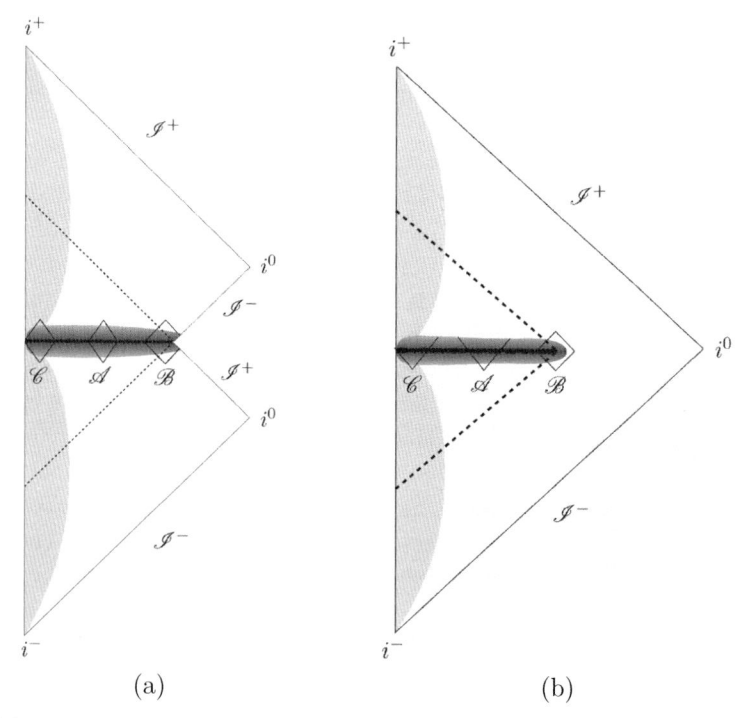

Fig. 2. (a) Qualitative conformal diagram of the black hole spacetime emerging from the analysis of regions $\mathscr{A}$ and $\mathscr{C}$. (b) Conformal diagram of the spacetime describing the black-to-white hole transition.

The most natural and conservative scenario for the end of the life of a black hole consistent with the physics of region $\mathscr{A}$ and region $\mathscr{C}$ is a quantum transition of the black hole horizon in a white hole horizon. The conformal diagram of the spacetime describing the complete black-to-white hole transition can be found in Fig. 2(b). The purpose of this work is to complete the analysis of region $\mathscr{B}$ by investigating its quantum physics using the spin foam approach.

The conformal diagram in Fig. 2(b) describes a physical phenomenon only if there exists a classical metric that satisfies the Einstein field equations and that covers the whole diagram except for the quantum region. This metric exists and it has been explicitly constructed in Refs. 1, 20, 21. This is an extraordinary result from the point of view of the classical theory and it provides yet another strong evidence in favor of the black-to-white hole transition scenario.

3. The black-to-white hole transition

In order to investigate in detail the physics of region $\mathscr{B}$ of the black-to-white hole spacetime it is necessary to specify its boundary $\Sigma := \partial \mathscr{B}$ and to compute the classical geometry that the black-to-white hole metric induces on it. This boundary geometry represents the outcome of the quantum transition taking place in region $\mathscr{B}$ and it thus uniquely defines the quantum boundary state for the transition. The boundary Σ can be chosen freely as long as it bounds the entirety of the quantum subregion.

As a first approximation, the presence of the Hawking radiation near region $\mathscr{B}$ is neglected. Its inclusion is left for future work. The metric around region $\mathscr{B}$ is thus taken to be the Schwarzschild metric up to quantum corrections from region $\mathscr{A}$. The main quantum correction that the physics of region $\mathscr{A}$ induces on the boundary between regions $\mathscr{A}$ and $\mathscr{B}$ is the absence of the classical singularity. The black hole interior can be foliated with surfaces of topology $S^2 \times \mathbb{R}$. If one angular dimension is suppressed, these surfaces can be seen as long cylinders of different radii and heights. Closer is the singularity, smaller is the radius of the cylinder. In the classical theory the foliation ends at the singularity, where the cylinder has a null radius. In the quantum theory the cylinder radius shrinks (black hole geometry) until it reaches a minimum value r_* (smooth transition from black to white hole geometry) and then starts to increase again (white hole geometry). The presence of this minimum radius r_* in the effective geometry of region $\mathscr{A}$ has a significant impact on the physics of region $\mathscr{B}$.

Having neglected Hawking radiation, the physics of region $\mathscr{B}$ must be invariant under time-reversal. Accordingly, the boundary Σ can be decomposed as $\Sigma = \Sigma^p \cup \Sigma^f$, where the past surface Σ^p and the future surface Σ^f are equal up to time reflection. This means that to completely define Σ it is sufficient to only specify Σ^p. A convenient choice of Σ^p is reported in Fig. 3 and it can be constructed as follows. Let S_+ and S_- be the points in the conformal diagram of Schwarzschild spacetime defined by the ingoing Eddington-Finkelstein coordinates $S_+ = (v_+, r_+)$ and $S_- = (v_-, r_-)$. The point S_+ is taken to be on the surface of

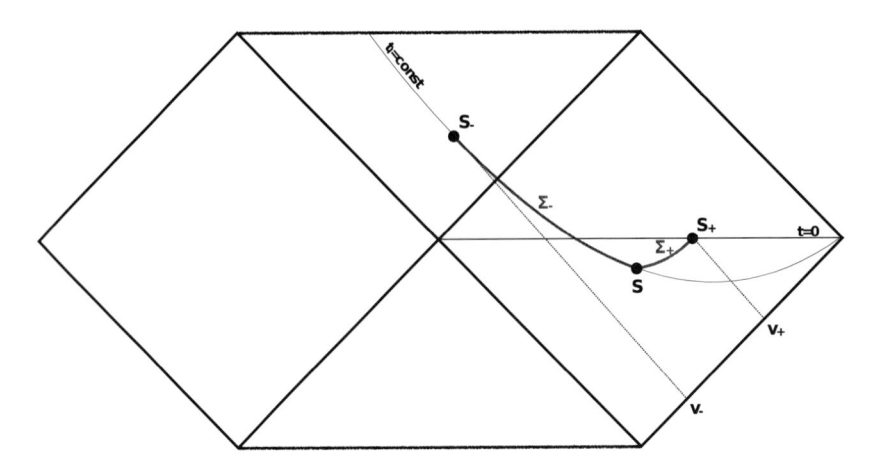

Fig. 3. The past portion $\Sigma^p = \Sigma^p_+ \cup \Sigma^p_-$ of the boundary Σ.

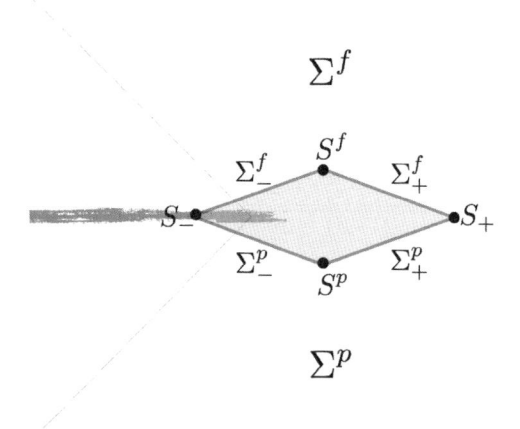

Fig. 4. Portion of the conformal diagram of the black-to-white hole transition depicting region $\mathscr{B}$ and its boundary Σ.

constant Schwarzschild time $t = 0$, thus fixing the value of v_+ in terms of r_+ (or viceversa), and the point S_- is taken to be on the surface of constant Schwarzschild radius $r = r_*$, thus fixing the value of r_- to be the minimum radius r_* characterizing the effective geometry of region $\mathscr{A}$. The values of r_+ and v_- can be chosen freely as long as they define a boundary Σ that bounds the entirety of the quantum subregion. Let then Σ_-^p be the surface of constant Lemaitre time coordinate

$$t_L := t + 2\sqrt{2mr} + 2m \log \left| \frac{\sqrt{r/2m} - 1}{\sqrt{r/2m} + 1} \right| \tag{3}$$

passing by S_-, where m is the mass of the black hole at the moment in which the quantum transition of the horizon takes place, and Σ_+^p be the surface of equation

$$v - \beta r = \text{const}, \tag{4}$$

where β is an arbitrary constant in $\mathbb{R}$, passing by S_+. Given the point S^p of their intersection, the past boundary Σ^p is defined to be the union of the portion of the surface Σ_-^p bounded by S_- and S^p and the portion of the surface Σ_+^p bounded by S_+ and S^p. Requiring the normal to Σ^p to be continuous at S^p uniquely fixes the value of β. The surface Σ^f is defined as the time-reversal of Σ^p. The portion of the conformal diagram of the black-to-white hole transition depicting region $\mathscr{B}$ and its boundary Σ can be found in Fig. 4.

The intrinsic and the extrinsic geometry of Σ_+^p and Σ_-^p can be straightforwardly computed from their definition. The line element ds_+^2 on Σ_+^p reads

$$ds_+^2 = \beta \left(2 - \beta \left(1 - \frac{2m}{r} \right) \right) dr^2 + r^2 \, d\Omega^2 \tag{5}$$

and the line element ds_-^2 on Σ_-^p reads
$$ds_-^2 = dr^2 + r^2 \, d\Omega^2, \tag{6}$$
where $d\Omega^2$ is the line element of the two-sphere. Let $k_{ij}^{\pm}$ be the extrinsic curvature tensor of $\Sigma_{\pm}^p$. Then it can be shown that
$$k_+ := k_{ij}^+ \, dx^i \, dx^j = \frac{m\beta^{3/2}(r(3-\beta)+2m\beta)}{\sqrt{r^5(r(2-\beta)+2m\beta)}} \, dr^2 - \frac{r(1-\beta)+2m\beta}{\sqrt{\beta(2-(1-2m/r)\beta)}} \, d\Omega^2 \tag{7}$$
and
$$k_- := k_{ij}^- \, dx^i \, dx^j = \frac{m}{2r^3} \, dr^2 - \sqrt{2mr} \, d\Omega^2, \tag{8}$$
where x^i, $i = 1, 2, 3$, are coordinates on Σ^p.

The geometry of Σ is thus completely determined by four parameters: the mass m of the black hole at the moment in which the quantum transition of the horizon takes place; the external asymptotic (retarded) time $v = v_+ - v_-$ it takes for the transition to happen; the minimal external radius r_+ for which the classical theory can still be trusted; the minimal internal radius r_- (it is important to stress that r is a temporal coordinate in the interior region of the black hole) reached by the black hole interior in region $\mathcal{A}$.

Each set of data $(m, v, r_{\pm})$ corresponds to a different outcome of the quantum transition taking place in region $\mathcal{B}$. This means that each set of data $(m, v, r_{\pm})$ uniquely defines a different quantum boundary state $\Psi(m, v, r_{\pm})$ for the transition. Given the boundary state Ψ, any sufficiently developed tentative theory of quantum gravity should be able to assign a transition amplitude $W(m, v, r_{\pm}) \equiv W\left[\Psi(m, v, r_{\pm})\right]$ to it. The transition amplitude for the phenomenon can then be used to analyze the physics of region $\mathcal{B}$.

The next section is devoted to the computation of the transition amplitude $W(m, v, r_{\pm})$ for the black-to-white hole transition using the spin foam approach.

4. Spin foam framework

The spin foam formalism[5,6] is a tentative path integral quantization of general relativity. The current state of the art is the EPRL-KKL spin foam model.[22–24] The theory is regularized and concretely defined in the discrete setting. The boundary Σ of a generic quantum region is discretized by a graph Γ with a finite number of nodes and a boundary Hilbert space $\mathcal{H}_\Gamma$ is assigned to it. The latter is the space of SU(2) spin-networks on Γ. Namely, the boundary Hilbert space is $\mathcal{H}_\Gamma := L^2\left[\text{SU}(2)^L/\text{SU}(2)^N\right]_\Gamma$, where N and L are respectively the total number of nodes and links in Γ. A boundary state is then given by a square integrable function $\psi(\{h_\ell\})$ that is gauge invariant at every node $n \in \Gamma$. Each $h_\ell \in \text{SU}(2)$ can be seen as the holonomy of the Ashtekar-Barbero connection along the link $\ell \in \Gamma$. The interior of the quantum region is then discretized by a two-complex $\mathcal{C}$ ($\partial \mathcal{C} \equiv \Gamma$) with a finite number of vertices.

Let f, e, v ∈ $\mathcal{C}$ denote respectively a face, an edge and a vertex in $\mathcal{C}$. To each internal oriented edge $\mathcal{C} \ni e := (v, v')$ having source in v and target in v' are assigned two SL(2, $\mathbb{C}$) elements $g_{ve} = g_{ev}^{-1}$ and $g_{ev'} = g_{v'e}^{-1}$. The oriented edge $e^{-1} := (v', v)$ is the edge e with opposite orientation. To each boundary edge $E \in \mathcal{C}$, that is an edge linking an internal vertex $v \in \mathcal{C}$ and a node $n \in \Gamma$, is assigned an SL(2, $\mathbb{C}$) element $g_{vn} = g_{nv}^{-1}$. A face $f := (e_1, \ldots, e_n)$ is the oriented face bounded by the edges $e_1, \ldots, e_n$. The orientation of the face is given by the ordering of the edges. For easier reading, the latters are written oriented accordingly to the orientation that the face induces on them. An internal face $f \in \mathcal{B} := \mathcal{C}/\Gamma$ is a face bounded by vertices and internal edges. A boundary face $F \in \Gamma$ is a face containing a link $\ell \in \Gamma$ in its boundary. Finally, a face $f \ni e$ is a face f containing the edge e in its boundary, a face $f \ni v$ is a face f containing the vertex v in its boundary and an edge $e \ni v$ is an edge e containing the vertex v in its boundary.

Given an arbitrary boundary state $\psi \in \mathcal{H}_\Gamma$, the theory assigns to it the amplitude

$$W_\mathcal{C}[\psi] = \int_{SU(2)} \prod_{\ell \in \Gamma} dh_\ell \, W_\mathcal{C}(\{h_\ell\}) \, \psi(\{h_\ell\}), \qquad (9)$$

where the two-complex amplitude $W_\mathcal{C}(\{h_\ell\})$ can be defined in terms of elementary face amplitudes as

$$W_\mathcal{C}(\{h_\ell\}) = \int_{SL(2,\mathbb{C})} \left[\prod_{v \in \mathcal{C}} \prod_{e \ni v}' dg_{ve} \right] \left[\prod_{f \in \mathcal{B}} A_f(\{g_{ve}\}) \right] \left[\prod_{F \in \Gamma} A_F(\{g_{ve}\}, h_{\ell_F}) \right]. \qquad (10)$$

The product $\prod'_{e \ni v}$ stands for the product over all the edges $e \ni v$ except one (which can be chosen arbitrarily at each vertex), ℓ_F is the unique link in Γ that belongs to the boundary face $F \in \Gamma$ and the face amplitudes $A_f(\{g_{ve}\})$ and $A_F(\{g_{ve}\}, h_{\ell_F})$ are given by[a]

$$A_f(\{g_{ve}\}) := \sum_{j_f} d_{j_f} \text{Tr} \left[D_\gamma^{(j_f)}(g_{ev}g_{ve'}) \cdots D_\gamma^{(j_f)}(g_{e^{(n)}v^n}g_{v^{(n)}e}) \right], \qquad (11)$$

$$A_F(\{g_{ve}\}, h_{\ell_F}) := \sum_{j_F} d_{j_F} \text{Tr} \left[D_\gamma^{(j_F)}(g_{n_tv}g_{ve'}) \cdots D_\gamma^{(j_F)}(g_{e^{(n)}v^n}g_{v^{(n)}n_s}) D^{(j_F)}(h_{\ell_F}) \right]. \qquad (12)$$

The matrix $D^{(j)}$ is the Wigner D-matrix of the d_j-dimensional $(d_j = 2j+1)$ representation of SU(2). The matrix $D_\gamma^{(j)}$ is the $d_j \times d_j$ matrix $[D_\gamma^{(j)}]_{mn}(g) = D_{jm\,jn}^{(\gamma j,j)}(g)$, $g \in SL(2,\mathbb{C})$, where $D_{lm\,jn}^{(\rho,k)}$ are the matrix elements of the (ρ, k) unitary representation of the principal series of SL(2, $\mathbb{C}$) in the basis labeled by the eigenfunctions of L^2 and L_z. The nodes n_s and n_t are respectively the source and the

---

[a]For the sake of simplicity, the orientation of every edge in each face is assumed to be the one induced from the face orientation. Since however this kind of orientation cannot be implemented consistently throughout the whole two-complex, in actual computations the orientation of the edges needs to be taken into account properly.

target of the link ℓ_F and γ is the Barbero-Immirzi parameter. The value of the label (n) in $v^{(n)}$ and $e^{(n)}$ is fixed for each face by the topology of the two-complex $\mathcal{C}$.

4.1. *Discretization of region* $\mathcal{B}$

In order to exploit the spin foam formalism to analyze the physics of region $\mathcal{B}$, the latter needs to be properly discretized. There is no unique or right way to perform the discretization. However, in order to get simpler and clearer calculations throughout the spin foam analysis it is particularly useful to preserve as much symmetries as possible during the procedure. In this subsection the combinatorial definition of both the cellular decomposition discretizing region $\mathcal{B}$ and its dual two-complex are given. Although the combinatorial definition of these objects is compact and complete, it does not convey as much geometrical insight as graphical representations do. For this reason, the interested reader is strongly encouraged to look at the graphical representations reported in Refs. 3 and 4.

As it can be seen from Fig. 4, the topology of region $\mathcal{B}$ is $S^2 \times [0,1] \times [0,1]$ and the topology of Σ is $S^2 \times S^1$. The geometry of Σ has two symmetries: the spherical $SO(3)$ symmetry and the Z_2 time-reversal symmetry that exchanges p and f. There is also an additional topological Z_2 symmetry that exchanges $+$ and $-$. Since however the geometry of S_+ and S_- is different, this is not a symmetry of the geometry of Σ. Although the topology of Σ is not easy to discretize while preserving its symmetries, the discretization presented in this subsection is able to accomplish this task.

Before introducing the discretization, it is useful to fix some notational conventions. Let a, b, c, d be indices taking values in the set $\{1, 2, 3, 4\}$, t be an index taking values in the set $\{p, f\}$ and ϵ be an index taking values in the set $\{+, -\}$. If the same expression contains several indices a, b, c, d, they are assumed to be all different from each other. The order of two consecutive indices is not important and the exchange of these indices results in the same element. If however two indices are separated by a comma, the exchange of these indices results in a different element.

Let p_a^+ be four points on S_+ and p_a^- be four points on S_-. The three-dimensional triangulation discretizing Σ is then defined by the points p_a^ϵ, the segments s_{ab}^ϵ and $s_{a,b}^t$, the triangles L_a^ϵ and $L_{a,b}^{t\epsilon}$, the tetrahedra $N_a^{t\epsilon}$ and N_{ab}^t, and their boundary relations:

$$\partial s_{ab}^\epsilon = (p_a^\epsilon, p_b^\epsilon); \tag{13}$$

$$\partial s_{a,b}^t = (p_a^-, p_b^+)^t; \tag{14}$$

$$\partial L_a^\epsilon = (s_{bc}^\epsilon, s_{cd}^\epsilon, s_{db}^\epsilon); \tag{15}$$

$$\partial L_{a,b}^{t+} = (s_{cd}^+, s_{a,c}^t, s_{a,d}^t); \tag{16}$$

$$\partial L_{a,b}^{t-} = (s_{cd}^-, s_{c,a}^t, s_{d,a}^t); \tag{17}$$

$$\partial N_a^{t\epsilon} = (L_{a,b}^{te}, L_{a,c}^{te}, L_{a,d}^{te}, L_a^\epsilon); \tag{18}$$

$$\partial N_{ab}^t = (L_{a,b}^{t+}, L_{b,a}^{t+}, L_{c,d}^{t-}, L_{d,c}^{t-}). \tag{19}$$

Besides being a three-dimensional object of its own, this triangulation serves as the boundary of the cellular decomposition discretizing region $\mathcal{B}$. This four-dimensional cellular decomposition is defined by the two-dimensional surfaces $f_{a,b}$, the three-dimensional cells $e_{a,b}^\epsilon$, the four-dimensional cells v_a^ϵ and v_{ab}, and their boundary relations:

$$\partial f_{a,b} = (s_{a,b}^p, s_{a,b}^f); \tag{20}$$

$$\partial e_{a,b}^\epsilon = (L_{a,b}^{pe}, L_{a,b}^{fe}, f_{a,c}, f_{a,d}); \tag{21}$$

$$\partial v_a^\epsilon = (N_a^{pe}, N_a^{fe}, e_{a,b}^\epsilon, e_{a,c}^\epsilon, e_{a,d}^\epsilon); \tag{22}$$

$$\partial v_{ab} = (N_{ab}^p, N_{ab}^f, e_{a,b}^+, e_{b,a}^+, e_{c,d}^-, e_{d,c}^-). \tag{23}$$

Note that this cellular decomposition is not a triangulation.

The spin foam formalism is defined using the discrete object dual to the cellular decomposition. The graph Γ dual to the three-dimensional triangulation of Σ is defined as

Nodes $\quad n_a^{te}$ and $n_{ab}^t;$ (24)

Links $\quad \ell_a^\epsilon = (n_a^{pe}, n_a^{fe});$ (25)

$\quad \ell_{a,b}^{t+} = (n_{ab}^t, n_a^{t+});$ (26)

$\quad \ell_{a,b}^{t-} = (n_{cd}^t, n_a^{t-}).$ (27)

The two-complex $\mathcal{C}$, whose boundary $\partial\mathcal{C}$ is Γ, dual to the four-dimensional cellular decomposition of region $\mathcal{B}$ is defined as

Vertices $\quad v_a^\epsilon$ and $v_{ab};$ (28)

Edges $\quad E_a^{te} = (v_a^\epsilon, n_a^{te});$ (29)

$\quad E_{ab}^t = (v_{ab}, n_{ab}^t);$ (30)

$\quad e_{a,b}^+ = (v_a^+, v_{ab});$ (31)

$\quad e_{a,b}^- = (v_a^-, v_{cd});$ (32)

Faces $\quad F_a^\epsilon = (\ell_a^\epsilon, (E_a^{fe})^{-1}, E_a^{pe});$ (33)

$\quad F_{a,b}^{t+} = (\ell_{a,b}^{t+}, (E_a^{t+})^{-1}, e_{a,b}^+, E_{ab}^t);$ (34)

$\quad F_{a,b}^{t-} = (\ell_{a,b}^{t-}, (E_a^{t-})^{-1}, E_{a,b}^-, E_{cd}^t);$ (35)

$\quad f_{a,b} \stackrel{c \leq d}{=} (e_{a,c}^+, (e_{b,d}^-)^{-1}, e_{b,c}^-, (e_{a,d}^+)^{-1}).$ (36)

The orientation of each element of the two-complex can be easily read from this combinatorial definition.

It is interesting to analyze how many of the topological symmetries of region $\mathcal{B}$ are preserved under this discretization. The spherical SO(3) symmetry of region $\mathcal{B}$ is discretized to a tetrahedral symmetry of the two-complex, which is realized as an even permutation of the indices a, b, c, d. The Z_2 time-reversal symmetry that exchanges the indices p and f and the Z_2 symmetry that exchanges the indices $+$ and $-$ are instead preserved exactly.

4.2. Discrete geometrical data and boundary state

The continuous geometry of Σ is approximated by the assignment of discrete geometrical data to the triangulation discretizing Σ (or equivalently to is dual graph Γ). There is once again no unique or right way to do it. Different assignments of discrete geometrical data simply define different approximations of the same continuous geometry. The discrete geometry presented in this subsection preserves the two geometrical symmetries of the continuous geometry of Σ.

To preserve the Z_2 time-reversal symmetry is sufficient to firstly construct the discrete geometrical data for the triangulation discretizing Σ^p and then to define the discrete geometrical data for the triangulation discretizing Σ^f as their time reversal. The sphere S_+ (S_-) in Σ is discretized by the tetrahedron bounded by the four triangles $\{L_a^+\}$ ($\{L_a^-\}$) in the triangulation. In order to preserve as much symmetry as possible in the discretization process of the geometry, the same area $a_+ = \pi r_+^2$ ($a_- = \pi r_-^2$), which is one fourth of the area of the sphere S_+ (S_-), is assigned to each triangle L_a^+ (L_a^-).

The continuous intrinsic geometry of Σ^p is specified by the line element

$$ds^2 = f^2(r)\, dr^2 + r^2\, d\Omega^2, \tag{37}$$

in which $f^2(r) = \beta\,(2 - \beta\,(1 - 2m/r))$ on Σ_+^p and $f^2(r) = 1$ on Σ_-^p. To begin with, this line element is approximated with

$$ds^2 = \xi^2\, dr^2 + r^2\, d\Omega^2, \tag{38}$$

where ξ is a constant that is fixed by requiring the volume of Σ^p computed with the line element in Eq. (38) to coincide with the volume of Σ^p computed with the line element in Eq. (37). This condition uniquely fixes the value of ξ in terms of the four parameters $(m, v, r_\pm)$ characterizing the continuous geometry of Σ^p. Requiring the discrete geometrical data to preserve the topological tetrahedral symmetry of the triangulation of Σ, the same area A_+ (A_-) must be assigned to each triangle $L_{a,b}^{p+}$ ($L_{a,b}^{p-}$). The line element in Eq. (38) is then used to compute the value of $A_\pm$, which is

$$A_\pm = \pi r_\pm^2 \sqrt{\frac{\xi^2}{18}\left(1 - 3\frac{r_\mp}{r_\pm}\right)^2 + \frac{2}{3}}. \tag{39}$$

The symmetry conditions together with the values of the areas $a_\pm$ and $A_\pm$ completely define the discrete intrinsic geometry of the triangulation of Σ. Analogously, the discrete extrinsic geometry of the triangulation is completely defined by the assignment of the extrinsic angles $\theta_\pm$ between $N_a^{p\pm}$ and $N_a^{f\pm}$ at $L_a^\pm$ and the extrinsic angles $\Theta_\pm$ between $N_a^{p\pm}$ and $N_{a,b}^p$ at $L_{a,b}^{p\pm}$.

Let $n_\mu^{t\epsilon}$ be the normal one-form of Σ_ϵ^t. From the definition of $\theta_\pm$ it follows that

$$\cos(\theta_\pm) = \left(g^{\mu\nu}\, n_\mu^{f\pm}\, n_\nu^{p\pm}\right)\Big|_{S_\pm}, \tag{40}$$

where $g^{\mu\nu}$ is the inverse of the metric tensor defined by the line element in Eq. (37), giving

$$\cos(\theta_+) = \frac{1 + \left[(1 - 2m/r_+)\beta - 1\right]^2}{|\beta(\beta - 2 - 2m\beta/r_+)|(1 - 2m/r_+)} \tag{41}$$

and

$$\cos(\theta_-) = \frac{1 + 2m/r_-}{1 - 2m/r_-}. \tag{42}$$

The angles $\Theta_\pm$ represent a discrete approximation of the continuous extrinsic curvature of $\Sigma_\pm$. A convenient discretization that preserves the symmetries of the triangulation is

$$\Theta_\pm = \frac{1}{12} \int_{\Sigma_\pm^p} (k^\pm)^i{}_i, \tag{43}$$

where $k_{ij}^\pm$ is the extrinsic curvature tensor of $\Sigma_\pm^p$ defined in Eqs. (7) and (8).

The discrete geometry of the triangulation of Σ has thus been explicitly constructed in terms of the four parameters $(m, v, r_\pm)$ characterizing the continuous geometry of Σ. From the point of view of the dual graph Γ, the discrete geometry consists in the assignment of an area and an angle to each link of Γ. The area assigned to each link represents the area of the triangle that is dual to the link and the angle assigned to each link represents the extrinsic curvature between the two tetrahedra that share the triangle dual to the link. This geometrical data uniquely specifies an extrinsic coherent state[5] $\Psi_{BW} = \Psi_{BW}(a_\pm, \theta_\pm, A_\pm, \Theta_\pm) = \Psi_{BW}(m, v, r_\pm) \in \mathcal{H}_\Gamma$ that is peaked on the discrete classical geometry defined by $(a_\pm, \theta_\pm, A_\pm, \Theta_\pm)$. The boundary state $\Psi_{BW} \in \mathcal{H}_\Gamma$ is the quantum state representing the outcome of the transition taking place in region $\mathscr{B}$.

4.3. *Transition amplitude*

Having explicitly constructed the two-complex discretizing region $\mathscr{B}$ and the boundary state describing the outcome of the quantum transition, the spin foam transition amplitude for the black-to-white hole transition can be readily computed using the formulas in Eqs. (9) and (10).

The assignment of group elements to the edges and the links of the two-complex $\mathcal{C}$ is:

$$\ell_a^\epsilon \longleftrightarrow h_a^\epsilon \in \mathrm{SU}(2); \tag{44}$$

$$\ell_{a,b}^{te} \longleftrightarrow h_{a,b}^{te} \in \mathrm{SU}(2); \tag{45}$$

$$E_a^{te} \longleftrightarrow g_a^{te} \in \mathrm{SL}(2,\mathbb{C}); \tag{46}$$

$$E_{ab}^t \longleftrightarrow g_{ab}^t \in \mathrm{SL}(2,\mathbb{C}); \tag{47}$$

$$e_{a,b}^\epsilon \longleftrightarrow g_{a\to b}^\epsilon, g_{a\leftarrow b}^\epsilon \in \mathrm{SL}(2,\mathbb{C}). \tag{48}$$

The group elements $g^\epsilon_{a\leftrightarrow b}$ are assigned to the two oriented half-edges of $e^\epsilon_{a,b}$. The element $g^\epsilon_{a\to b}$ is assigned to the oriented half-edge with source in the source of $e^\epsilon_{a,b}$ and target in the center of $e^\epsilon_{a,b}$. The element $g^\epsilon_{a\leftarrow b}$ is assigned to the oriented half-edge with source in the target of $e^\epsilon_{a,b}$ and target in the center of $e^\epsilon_{a,b}$. Carefully considering the topology and the orientation pattern of the two-complex, the elementary face amplitudes (see Eqs. (11) and (12)) for $\mathcal{C}$ can be computed:

$$A^\epsilon_a(\{g^{te}_a\}, h^\epsilon_a) = \sum_j d_j \, \mathrm{Tr}\left[D^{(j)}_\gamma\left((g^{fe}_a)^{-1} g^{pe}_a\right) D^{(j)}(h^\epsilon_a)\right], \qquad (49)$$

$$A^{t+}_{a,b}(g^{t+}_a, g^t_{ab}, g^+_{a\leftrightarrow b}, h^{t+}_{a,b}) = \sum_j d_j \, \mathrm{Tr}\left[D^{(j)}_\gamma\left((g^{t+}_a)^{-1} g^+_{a\to b}\right) D^{(j)}_\gamma\left((g^+_{a\leftarrow b})^{-1} g^t_{ab}\right)\right.$$
$$\left. \times D^{(j)}(h^{t+}_{a,b})\right], \qquad (50)$$

$$A^{t-}_{a,b}(g^{t-}_a, g^t_{cd}, g^-_{a\leftrightarrow b}, h^{t-}_{a,b}) = \sum_j d_j \, \mathrm{Tr}\left[D^{(j)}_\gamma\left((g^{t-}_a)^{-1} g^-_{a\to b}\right) D^{(j)}_\gamma\left((g^-_{a\leftarrow b})^{-1} g^t_{cd}\right)\right.$$
$$\left. \times D^{(j)}(h^{t-}_{a,b})\right], \qquad (51)$$

$$A_{a,b}(\{g^+_{a\leftrightarrow c}\}, \{g^-_{b\leftrightarrow c}\}) \stackrel{c\leq d}{=} \sum_j d_j \, \mathrm{Tr}\left[D^{(j)}_\gamma\left((g^+_{a\to d})^{-1} g^+_{a\to c}\right) D^{(j)}_\gamma\left((g^+_{a\leftarrow c})^{-1} g^-_{b\leftarrow d}\right)\right.$$
$$\left. \times D^{(j)}_\gamma\left((g^-_{b\to d})^{-1} g^-_{b\to c}\right) D^{(j)}_\gamma\left((g^-_{b\leftarrow c})^{-1} g^+_{a\leftarrow d}\right)\right]. \qquad (52)$$

The two-complex transition amplitude $W_\mathcal{C}(\{h_\ell\})$ can then be written as

$$W_\mathcal{C}(\{h^\epsilon_a\}, \{h^{te}_{a,b}\}) = \int_{SL(2,\mathbb{C})} \prod_{\epsilon a} \mathrm{d}g^{pe}_a \prod_{a<b} \mathrm{d}g^p_{ab} \prod_{\epsilon ab} \mathrm{d}g^\epsilon_{a\leftrightarrow b}$$
$$\times \prod_{\epsilon a} A^\epsilon_a(\{g^{te}_a\}, h^\epsilon_a) \prod_{ab} A_{a,b}(\{g^+_{a\leftrightarrow c}\}, \{g^-_{b\leftrightarrow c}\})$$
$$\times \prod_{tab} A^{t+}_{a,b}(g^{t+}_a, g^t_{ab}, g^+_{a\leftrightarrow b}, h^{t+}_{a,b})$$
$$\times \prod_{tab} A^{t-}_{a,b}(g^{t-}_a, g^t_{cd}, g^-_{a\leftrightarrow b}, h^{t-}_{a,b}). \qquad (53)$$

Since Eq. (10) dictates to drop one integration per vertex, the integration over the $\{g^{fe}_a\}$ and $\{g^f_{ab}\}$ variables has been dropped.

Finally, the black-to-white hole transition amplitude $W(m, v, r_\pm)$ is

$$W(m, v, r_\pm) = W[\Psi_{BW}] = \int_{SU(2)} \prod_{\epsilon a} \mathrm{d}h^\epsilon_a \prod_{teab} \mathrm{d}h^{te}_{a,b} \, W_\mathcal{C}(\{h^\epsilon_a\}, \{h^{te}_{a,b}\})$$
$$\times \Psi_{BW}(\{h^\epsilon_a\}, \{h^{te}_{a,b}\}). \qquad (54)$$

This expression contains the whole physics of the phenomenon. Its investigation is currently ongoing and it will be reported elsewhere.

5. Summary and outlook

The quantum region of a black hole spacetime can be divided in three different subregions: region $\mathscr{C}$, where the collapsing matter enters its quantum gravity regime; region $\mathscr{B}$, where the horizon reaches Planckian size at the end of the evaporation process; region $\mathscr{A}$, where the curvature reaches Planckian scale independently from region $\mathscr{B}$ and region $\mathscr{C}$. The principle of locality demands that these regions are independent from each other and that they can subsequently be studied separately. The evidence in favor of the black-to-white hole transition scenario resulting from the separate analysis of the physics of these regions is overwhelming.

Focusing on the black-to-white hole horizon transition in region $\mathscr{B}$, that is the last stage of the life of a black hole in this scenario, the physics of the boundary of the quantum region is completely determined by four parameters: the mass m of the black hole at the moment in which the transition takes place; the external asymptotic (retarded) time v it takes for the transition to happen; the minimal external radius r_+ for which the classical theory can still be trusted; the minimal internal radius r_- reached by the black hole interior in region $\mathscr{A}$.

The spin foam formalism provides a clear framework to study this scenario. However, since the theory is properly defined in the discrete setting, to compute the transition amplitude for the phenomenon the physics of region $\mathscr{B}$ needs to be appropriately discretized. From a practical point of view the discretization needs to be both sufficiently refined to capture the relevant degrees of freedom of the phenomenon and sufficiently simple for the transition amplitude to be explicitly computed and analyzed. In this work a convenient discretization that preserves the symmetries of the continuous geometry is explicitly constructed and the resulting transition amplitude $W(m, v, r_\pm)$ is computed. Although the two-complex $\mathcal{C}$ discretizing region $\mathscr{B}$ is rather complicated, its high degree of symmetry allows the transition amplitude to be expressed in a remarkably compact way. Due to the severe complexity of spin foam amplitudes, an analytical study of the transition amplitude $W(m, v, r_\pm)$ for the black-to-white hole transition is not feasible at this point. On the other hand, recent developments[25-28] in the numerical computation of spin foam amplitudes and the high degree of symmetry of the constructed discretization should allow a numerical investigation of the transition amplitude.

In this work the black hole lifetime is assumed to be of the order of the evaporation process (although the constructed framework can describe also smaller timescales). This choice is motivated by the analysis of the black-to-white hole transition performed in Refs. 29 and 30, where, neglecting Hawking radiation, the lifetime of the black hole was estimated to be much longer of the evaporation process, thus proving that the assumption of neglecting Hawking radiation was not justified. However, due to the use of a fairly coarse discretization and of several rough approximations it is unclear whether this result is reliable. Furthermore, recent results[17] seems to support the black hole lifetime of the order m_0^2 heuristically suggested in Ref. 1. The numerical analysis of the transition amplitude $W(m, v, r_\pm)$

computed in this work may provide an estimation of the black-to-white hole transition timescales and improve the understanding of its phenomenology.[31–34]

References

1. H. M. Haggard and C. Rovelli, Black hole fireworks: Quantum-gravity effects outside the horizon spark black to white hole tunneling, *Physical Review D* **92** (2015).
2. S. W. Hawking, Black hole explosions?, *Nature* **248** (1974).
3. F. D'Ambrosio, M. Christodoulou, P. Martin-Dussaud, C. Rovelli and F. Soltani, End of a black hole's evaporation, *Physical Review D* **103** (2021).
4. F. Soltani, C. Rovelli and P. Martin-Dussaud, End of a black hole's evaporation. II., *Physical Review D* **104** (2021).
5. C. Rovelli and F. Vidotto, *Covariant Loop Quantum Gravity* (Cambridge University Press, 2015).
6. A. Perez, The spin-foam approach to quantum gravity, *Living Reviews in Relativity* **16** (2013).
7. A. Rignon-Bret and C. Rovelli, Black to white transition of a charged black hole (2021).
8. E. Bianchi, M. Christodoulou, F. D'Ambrosio, H. M. Haggard and C. Rovelli, White holes as remnants: A surprising scenario for the end of a black hole, *Classical and Quantum Gravity* **35** (2018).
9. A. Corichi and P. Singh, Loop quantization of the Schwarzschild interior revisited, *Classical and Quantum Gravity* **33** (2016).
10. A. Ashtekar, J. Olmedo and P. Singh, Quantum transfiguration of Kruskal black holes, *Physical Review Letters* **121** (2018).
11. R. Gambini, J. Olmedo and J. Pullin, Spherically symmetric loop quantum gravity: Analysis of improved dynamics, *Classical and Quantum Gravity* **37** (2020).
12. K. Peeters, C. Schweigert and J. W. van Holten, Extended geometry of black holes, *Classical and Quantum Gravity* **12** (1995).
13. F. D'Ambrosio and C. Rovelli, How information crosses Schwarzschild's central singularity, *Classical and Quantum Gravity* **35** (2018).
14. C. Rovelli and F. Vidotto, Planck stars, *International Journal of Modern Physics D* **23** (2014).
15. A. Ashtekar, T. Pawlowski and P. Singh, Quantum nature of the big bang, *Physical Review Letters* **96** (2006).
16. P. Hajicek and C. Kiefer, Singularity avoidance by collapsing shells in quantum gravity, *International Journal of Modern Physics D* **10** (2001).
17. J. G. Kelly, R. Santacruz and E. Wilson-Ewing, Black hole collapse and bounce in effective loop quantum gravity, *Classical and Quantum Gravity* **38** (2020).
18. W. Piechocki and T. Schmitz, Quantum Oppenheimer-Snyder model, *Physical Review D* **102** (2020).
19. J. Münch, Effective quantum dust collapse via surface matching, *Classical and Quantum Gravity* **38** (2021).
20. C. Rovelli and P. Martin-Dussaud, Interior metric and ray-tracing map in the firework black-to-white hole transition, *Classical and Quantum Gravity* **35** (2018).
21. P. Martin-Dussaud and C. Rovelli, Evaporating black-to-white hole, *Classical and Quantum Gravity* **36** (2019).
22. J. Engle, E. Livine, R. Pereira and C. Rovelli, LQG vertex with finite Immirzi parameter, *Nuclear Physics B* **799** (2008).

23. W. Kamiński, M. Kisielowski and J. Lewandowski, Spin-foams for all loop quantum gravity, *Classical and Quantum Gravity* **27** (2010).
24. Y. Ding, M. Han and C. Rovelli, Generalized spinfoams, *Physical Review D* **83** (2011).
25. P. Donà and G. Sarno, Numerical methods for EPRL spin foam transition amplitudes and Lorentzian recoupling theory, *General Relativity and Gravitation* **50** (2018).
26. P. Donà, M. Fanizza, G. Sarno and S. Speziale, Numerical study of the lorentzian Engle-Pereira-Rovelli-Livine spin foam amplitude, *Physical Review D* **100** (2019).
27. F. Gozzini, A high-performance code for EPRL spin foam amplitudes (2021).
28. P. Frisoni, Studying of the EPRL self-energy, in *16th Marcel Grossmann Meeting on Recent Developments in Theoretical and Experimental General Relativity, Astrophysics, and Relativistic Field Theories*, 2021.
29. M. Christodoulou, C. Rovelli, S. Speziale and I. Vilensky, Planck star tunneling time: An astrophysically relevant observable from background-free quantum gravity, *Physical Review D* **94** (2016).
30. M. Christodoulou and F. D'Ambrosio, Characteristic time scales for the geometry transition of a black hole to a white hole from spinfoams (2018).
31. A. Barrau, C. Rovelli and F. Vidotto, Fast radio bursts and white hole signals, *Physical Review D* **90** (2014).
32. A. Barrau, B. Bolliet, F. Vidotto and C. Weimer, Phenomenology of bouncing black holes in quantum gravity: A closer look, *Journal of Cosmology and Astroparticle Physics* **2016** (2016).
33. A. Barrau, B. Bolliet, M. Schutten and F. Vidotto, Bouncing black holes in quantum gravity and the Fermi gamma-ray excess, *Physics Letters B* **772** (2017).
34. C. Rovelli and F. Vidotto, Small black/white hole stability and dark matter, *Universe* **4** (2018).

Holographic properties of the bulk-to-boundary transmission of information in regions of quantum space

Eugenia Colafranceschi

School of Mathematical Sciences, University of Nottingham,
Nottingham NG7 2RD, United Kingdom
E-mail: eugenia.colafranceschi@nottingham.ac.uk

We show that quantum gravity states associated to open spin network graphs implicitly define maps from the bulk to the boundary of the corresponding region of quantum space. Employing random tensor network techniques, we then investigate under which conditions the flow of information from the bulk to the boundary is an isometric map, which is a necessary condition for holography.

Keywords: Holography; Spin Networks; Random Tensor Networks.

1. Introduction

Over the past two decades, quantum information has been playing an increasingly prominent role in quantum gravity.[1] A crucial factor in this is the relation between entanglement and geometry, which has been highlighted by various results in different quantum gravity contexts. As an example, within the AdS/CFT correspondence,[2] which describes quantum gravity in asimptotically anti-de Sitter (AdS) spacetime in terms of a conformal field theory (CFT) living on its boundary, the Ryu-Takayanagi (RT) formula[3,4] relates the entanglement entropy of the boundary CFT in a subregion to the area of a codimension-2 surface in the dual bulk spacetime. The entanglement-geometry relation pointed out by the RT formula is further strengthened by the observation that entanglement (of boundary degrees of freedom) is a necessary condition for the connectivity of the dual spacetime.[5,6] More generally, quantum correlations are assumed to be at the origin of spacetime geometry in all those approaches to quantum gravity that regard spacetime as emerging from fundamental quantum entities.[7] This aspect is particularly emphasised in the approach we adopt here, group field theories[8–10] (GFT), where discrete geometries arise as pattern of entanglement among space quanta. Specifically, the GFT quanta are fundamental simplices dual to spin network vertices, which upon becoming entangled (in their edge degrees of freedom) form spin network graphs dual to simplicial complexes. In this respect, GFT realises what the aforementioned results suggest: the idea of *quantum spacetime as a geometric representation of entanglement*.

Remarkably, a geometric representation of entanglement is the key feature of a quantum information tool, tensor networks[11–13] (TN), which consists in a decomposition of many-body wave-functions (specifically, of their entanglement structure) into interconnected (one-body) tensors. This feature has been largely exploited in the AdS/CFT correspondence, starting from Ref. 14, which showed that the entanglement renormalization of CFT boundary states carries out a TN decomposition of the latter, with the possibility to interpret the emerging network as (a spatial slice of) AdS spacetime (upon definition of a metric from combinatorial ingredients). Exactly-solvable models of the AdS/CFT correspondence have then been constructed through perfect[15] and random[16] tensors.

However, in these works (and others of similar nature) tensor networks, which *a priori* have nothing to do with gravity, are provided with a spatiotemporal interpretation by defining a metric on the network through combinatorial elements. We make a change of perspective[17] here, in which (suitably generalised) tensor networks are identified, through the match with the GFT formalism, with a quantum gravity language, where the "bodies" of the many-body system are quanta of space, and link-entanglement expresses adjacency relations between them; in other terms, the GFT-generalised tensor networks naturally carry a quantum-geometry interpretation. This identification leads to the possibility of using tensor network techniques in a full quantum gravity context, to study entanglement-based properties of spin network states, which are of interest to a wider part of the quantum gravity community (as they enter other approaches as well, such as loop quantum gravity, spinfoam models and lattice quantum gravity).

On this ground, we look at what is supposed to be a constitutive feature of quantum gravity, originally prompted by the Bekenstein-Hawking area law for the black hole entropy: holography. The holographic principle,[18,19] of which the AdS/CFT correspondence is a realization, argues that the three-dimensional world is the holographic image of data living on a two-dimensional space. Crucially, certain classes of tensor networks turn out to possess holographic features[20] (and have in fact been largely employed in the AdS/CFT context, as recalled earlier). Within the perspective change mentioned above, we thus exploit tensor network methods to highlight properties of spin network states that are related to holography.

We specifically look at the transmission of information from the bulk to the boundary of an open spin network graph (where the bulk is made by the intertwiner degrees of freedom associated to the vertices, and the boundary by spin degrees of freedom on open links of the graph), pointing out that every spin network state can be seen as a map between these two sets. As we shall see, the map then turns out to be an isometry (which is a necessary condition for an holographic bulk-to-boundary transmission of information) if and only if the reduced bulk state has maximum entanglement entropy. Assuming a random distribution of weights associated to the individual spin network vertices, we carry out the entropy calculation via random tensor network techniques, and thereby manage to highlight the properties of spin network graphs that favour in them an holographic behaviour. The results reported here have been obtained as part of the work presented in Ref. 21.

2. Quantum space from spin network entanglement graphs

The GFT models for quantum gravity[8–10] are quantum field theories defined on d copies of a group G, whose fundamental excitations are $(d-1)$-simplices (to be understood as quanta of space), decorated by group variables (one for each face) that capture their geometric properties. In the model of 4D quantum gravity, $d=4$ and the usual choice for the group is $G=SU(2)$; the space quanta are then quantized tetrahedra. In a dual picture, the fundamental $(d-1)$-simplex is represented as a d-valent vertex, with an edge dual to each face and carrying the corresponding geometric data, i.e. a spin network vertex.

As we are going to detail in the following, spatial geometries, in the form of simplicial complexes dual to spin network graphs, arise in GFT from the gluing of fundamental simplices/spin-network vertices, given by entanglement of their edge degrees of freedom.

2.1. Combinatorial structure of spin network graphs

We start by introducing some combinatorics notions needed to construct spin network states in the GFT framework.

Let $V=\{1,...,N\}$ be a set of vertices. The d lines departing from a vertex are distinguished by a "colour" $i=1,...,d$, and the i-th line of a vertex v is denoted as e_v^i. In graph theory, a connectivity pattern among N vertices is encoded in a $N \times N$ matrix A, called *adjacency matrix*, such that its element A_{vw} is equal to 1 or 0 if, respectively, vertices v and w are connected or not by a link. To include the information of the colour labelling the links between vertices, we can use a $(N \cdot d) \times (N \cdot d)$ generalised adjacency matrix; we also assume that vertices can be connected only along edges of the same colour. Then:

- e_v^i and e_w^i form a link, denoted by e_{vw}^i, if and only if $A_{(v-1)\cdot d+i,(w-1)\cdot d+i} = 1$
- e_v^i is an open edge if and only if $A_{(v-1)\cdot d+i,(w-1)\cdot d+i} = 0 \ \forall \ w \in V$

The connectivity pattern defined by the adjacency matrix A, also called *graph*, is indicated as γ; the two notions A and γ thus contain the same information. Given the graph γ, we denote as L the set of internal links: $L = \{e_{vw}^i | A_{(v-1)\cdot d+i,(w-1)\cdot d+i} = 1\}$, and as $\partial\gamma$ the set of boundary links: $\partial\gamma = \{e_v^i | A_{(v-1)\cdot d+i,(w-1)\cdot d+i} = 0 \ \forall \ w \in V\}$. We also call E the set of all edges of the graph: $E = L \cup \partial\gamma$.

2.2. Spin network entanglement graphs

The d-valent vertices introduced above, dressed with group geometric data, are spin network vertices dual to $(d-1)$-simplices, representing fundamental excitations of the GFT field. In particular, each line e_v^i of a vertex v, corresponding to a face of the dual simplex, is decorated with a group variable g_v^i, and the complete set $g_v^1, ..., g_v^d$ specifies the geometry of the $(d-1)$-simplex up to global action of the group G; the associated Hilbert space is thus given by $\mathcal{H}_v = L^2(G^d/G)$.

A spin network graph (dual to a simplicial complex) can be constructed out of a set $V = \{1, ..., N\}$ of vertices by correlating their edge degrees of freedom (which graphically amounts to gluing their open edges); the corresponding state thus lives in a subspace of the Hilbert space associated to the set of (a priori, open) vertices $\mathcal{H}_V = \bigotimes_{v=1}^{N} \mathcal{H}_v$. In particular, invariance of the state under right action of the group on the variables g_v^i and g_w^i implies that e_v^i and e_w^i are glued together to form a link e_{vw}^i, which carries the element $g_{vw}^i = g_v^i (g_w^i)^{-1}$. The wavefunction ψ_γ associated with a graph γ can thus be obtained by a generic $\psi \in \mathcal{H}_V$ as follows:

$$\psi_\gamma(..., g_{vw}^i = g_v^i(g_w^i)^{-1}, ...) = \int dh\; \psi(..., g_v^i h, ..., g_w^i h, ...) \tag{1}$$

and pertains to the Hilbert subspace $\mathcal{H}_\gamma = L^2(G^E/G^V) \subseteq \mathcal{H}_V$. Note that, although GFT and LQG associate the same set of states to a given graph γ (namely, the ones of $\mathcal{H}_\gamma$), the nature of such states in the two theories is radically different.[22] In fact, the GFT ones live in a Hilbert space ($\mathcal{H}_V$) which describes a collection of possibly disconnected vertices; the graph structure, and hence the simplicial complex associated with it, is not given *a priori*, but emerges from the particular form of the state (specifically, from its entanglement structure, as explained below).

By the Peter-Weyl theorem, the single-vertex Hilbert space can be decomposed into irreducible representations j of $SU(2)$ (spin network representation):

$$\mathcal{H}_v = \bigoplus_{\vec{j}_v} \left(\mathcal{I}^{\vec{j}_v} \otimes \bigotimes_{i=1}^{d} V^{j_v^i} \right) \tag{2}$$

where $\vec{j}_v = j_v^1, ..., j_v^d$ are the $SU(2)$ representations associated to the edges $e_v^1, ..., e_v^d$ of vertex v, V^j is the space carrying the representation j, and $\mathcal{I}^{\vec{j}} = \text{Inv}_{SU(2)}\left[V^{j^1} \otimes ... \otimes V^{j^d}\right]$ is the space of d-valent intertwiners recoupling spins $j^1, ..., j^d$. A basis state for Eq. (2) is denoted by $|\vec{j}_v \vec{n}_v \iota_v\rangle$, where $\vec{n}_v = n_v^1, ..., n_v^d$ with n_v^i quantum number (spin projection) labelling a basis of $V^{j_v^i}$, and $\iota_v \in \mathcal{I}^{\vec{j}_v}$.

In the spin network basis, gluing vertices corresponds to imposing maximal entanglement between edge spins:

$$|\psi_\gamma\rangle = \left(\bigotimes_{e_{vw}^i \in L} \langle e_{vw}^i | \right) |\psi\rangle \tag{3}$$

where $|e_{vw}^i\rangle$ is a maximally entangled state of spins associated to e_v^i and e_w^i. The entanglement pattern of a state thus constitutes the graph dual to the simplicial complex the state represents. For this reason we refer to states like that in Eq. (3) as *entanglement graphs*.

Denoting by J an assignment of spins to all edges of γ, i.e. $J = \{j_e | e \in E\}$, the Hilbert subspace of $\mathcal{H}_V$ associated to γ can be written as follows:

$$\mathcal{H}_\gamma = \bigoplus_{J} \left(\bigotimes_v \mathcal{I}^{\vec{j}_v} \otimes \bigotimes_{e \in \partial \gamma} V^{j_e} \right) \tag{4}$$

It is clear from Eq. (4) that we can identify, for each graph, two different sets of degrees of freedom: intertwiners attached to the vertices, which we refer to as *bulk degrees of freedom*, and spin projections attached to the boundary edges, the *boundary degrees of freedom*. Note that the two sets are not independent, as intertwiners also recouple spins that pertain to the boundary; however, as can be easily seen from Eq. (4), they can be considered independent within each fixed-spin subspace of the direct sum.

2.2.1. *Classes of spin network entanglement graphs as tensor networks*

A tensor network[11–13] is, formally, a set of tensors whose indices are contracted according to a certain patter; when each tensor accounts for the state of a quantum system (say a "particle"), the tensor network is a many-body wavefunction. Its peculiarity (underlying the efficiency of this quantum information tool) is that the network represents the skeleton of quantum correlations (typically, entanglement) among the individual particles. This recalls the GFT graphs, which represent the entanglement structure of a many-vertex state. Let us illustrate the analogy with an example: consider a set of *open* vertices in the factorized state $\bigotimes_v |f_v\rangle \in \mathcal{H}_V$, where

$$|f_v\rangle = \bigoplus_{\vec{j}_v} \sum_{\vec{n}_v \vec{\iota}_v} (f_v)^{\vec{j}_v}_{\vec{n}_v \vec{\iota}_v} |\vec{j}_v \vec{n}_v \vec{\iota}_v\rangle \tag{5}$$

is the generic state of vertex v, and glue them according to a given combinatorial pattern γ:

$$|\phi_\gamma\rangle = \left(\bigotimes_{e^i_{vw} \in L} \langle e^i_{vw}| \right) \bigotimes_v |f_v\rangle \tag{6}$$

In the case where every f_v is picked on specific values $\vec{j}_v$ of the edge spins, the state of Eq. (6) is an ordinary tensor network, specifically a PEPS, having j_e with $e \in E$ as bond dimensions[13]:

$$(\phi_\gamma)^{\{j_e \in E\}}_{\{n_e \in \partial\gamma\}\{\iota_v \in V\}} = (f_1)^{\vec{j}_1}_{\vec{n}_1 \vec{\iota}_1} \cdots (f_N)^{\vec{j}_N}_{\vec{n}_N \vec{\iota}_N} \prod_{e^i_{vw} \in L} \delta_{j^i_v j^i_w} \delta_{n^i_v n^i_w} \tag{7}$$

In the more general case where every f_v runs over all possible values of the edge spins, Eq. (6) corresponds to a generalised tensor network, whose bond dimensions are dynamical variables. For a detailed discussion on the analogy between GFT entanglement graphs and tensor networks see Ref. 17.

3. Bulk-to-boundary transmission of information

3.1. *Spin network entanglement graphs as bulk-to-boundary maps*

By considering a bipartition of the degrees of freedom of an entanglement graph (like the one in Eq. (3)) into *bulk* (intertwiners on vertices, collectively indicated as $\dot{\gamma}$)

and *boundary* (spin projections on open edges), we can regard it as a map between these two sets. Such a viewpoint is quite natural when we consider an entanglement graph with fixed spins $J = \{j_e | e \in E\}$, whose Hilbert space factorizes, as can be seen from Eq. (4), into a bulk space $\mathcal{H}_{\hat{\gamma}}(J) = \bigotimes_v \mathcal{I}^{\vec{j}_v}$ and a boundary space $\mathcal{H}_{\partial\gamma}(J_\partial) = \bigotimes_{e \in \partial\gamma} V^{j_e}$, where $J_\partial = \{j_e | e \in \partial\gamma\} \subset J$ is the set of spins on the boundary edges. In particular, to every state $|\psi_\gamma\rangle \in \mathcal{H}_\gamma(J) = \mathcal{H}_{\hat{\gamma}}(J) \otimes \mathcal{H}_{\partial\gamma}(J_\partial)$ we can associate a map $M[\psi_\gamma] : \mathcal{H}_{\hat{\gamma}}(J) \to \mathcal{H}_{\partial\gamma}(J_\partial)$ acting as follows:

$$M[\psi_\gamma]: \quad |\zeta\rangle \in \mathcal{H}_{\hat{\gamma}}(J) \quad \to \quad \langle\zeta|\psi_\gamma\rangle = |\psi_{\partial\gamma}(\zeta)\rangle \in \mathcal{H}_{\partial\gamma}(J_\partial) \tag{8}$$

In the more general case of $|\psi_\gamma\rangle$ spreading over all possible values of the edge spins we can still define an associated bulk-to-boundary map $M[\psi_\gamma]$: by embedding the graph Hilbert space $\mathcal{H}_\gamma$, which is given by Eq. (4), into $\mathcal{H}_{\hat{\gamma}} \otimes \mathcal{H}_{\partial\gamma}$, where

$$\mathcal{H}_{\hat{\gamma}} = \bigoplus_J \mathcal{H}_{\hat{\gamma}}(J), \tag{9}$$

$$\mathcal{H}_{\partial\gamma} = \bigoplus_{J_\partial} \mathcal{H}_{\partial\gamma}(J_\partial), \tag{10}$$

we can regard Eq. (9) as *bulk input space* and Eq. (10) as *boundary output space*, and define the map action similarly to the fixed-spin case.

3.2. *Isometry condition*

A necessary condition for the bulk and boundary information in $|\psi_\gamma\rangle$ to be holographically related is that the map $M[\psi_\gamma]$ is an isometry. As we are going to show, this property can be verified by studying the entanglement entropy of the reduced bulk state. We focus, for simplicity, on the spin-fixed case. Let $\{|\vec{\iota} = \iota_1...\iota_N\rangle\}$ be a basis of $\mathcal{H}_{\hat{\gamma}}(J)$; by writing the state $|\psi_\gamma\rangle$ in terms of the corresponding map (denoted with M only, for brevity),

$$|\psi_\gamma\rangle = \sum_{\vec{\iota}} (M \otimes \mathbb{I}) |\vec{\iota}\rangle \otimes |\vec{\iota}\rangle, \tag{11}$$

we obtain the following expression for the (normalised) reduced bulk state:

$$\rho_{\hat{\gamma}} = \text{Tr}_{\partial\gamma}\left(\frac{|\psi_\gamma\rangle\langle\psi_\gamma|}{D_{\hat{\gamma}}}\right) = \frac{1}{D_{\hat{\gamma}}} \sum_{\vec{\iota}\vec{\iota}'} (M^\dagger M)^*_{\vec{\iota}\vec{\iota}'} |\vec{\iota}\rangle\langle\vec{\iota}'| \tag{12}$$

where $D_{\hat{\gamma}} = \prod_v D_{\vec{j}_v}$ is the dimension of the bulk, with $D_{\vec{j}_v}$ dimension of the intertwiner at vertex v. From Eq. (12) we can easily see that the isometry condition $M^\dagger M = \mathbb{I}$ translates into the requirement that the bulk state is maximally mixed, i.e. $\rho_{\hat{\gamma}} = \frac{\mathbb{I}}{D_{\hat{\gamma}}}$, namely that it has maximum entropy.

4. Investigating holography in spin networks via random tensor networks

We focus on states having the form

$$|\phi_\gamma\rangle = \left(\bigotimes_{e \in L}\langle e|\right) \bigotimes_v |f_v\rangle, \qquad (13)$$

with the single-vertex wavefunctions $f_1, ..., f_N$ chosen randomly according to a uniform probability distribution, corresponding to a random tensor network; moreover, we assume that in γ each vertex has at most one boundary edge.

Our goal is to identify the combinatorial and dimensional features of $|\phi_\gamma\rangle$ that make the corresponding bulk-to-boundary map isometric; to accomplish this, we check under which conditions the reduced bulk state has maximum entropy.

4.1. Rényi-2 entropy of random tensor networks

We start by illustrating how to compute the average Rényi-2 entropy of a generic region of the entanglement graph in Eq. (13), consisting of a boundary portion $A \in \partial\gamma$ and a bulk portion $\Omega \in \dot{\gamma}$, under the assumption that the random wavefunctions f_v are picked on specific values of the edge spins. Through the replica trick, and in the large-spins regime, the average Rényi-2 entropy of $\rho_{A \cup \Omega}$, where $\rho = |\phi_\gamma\rangle\langle\phi_\gamma|$, is given by

$$\overline{S_2(\rho_{A\cup\Omega})} \approx -\log\left(\frac{\overline{Z_1}}{\overline{Z_0}}\right) \qquad (14)$$

with

$$\overline{Z_0} = \text{Tr}\left[\rho_L^{\otimes 2} \bigotimes_v \overline{\rho_v^{\otimes 2}}\right], \quad \overline{Z_1} = \text{Tr}\left[\rho_L^{\otimes 2} \bigotimes_v \overline{\rho_v^{\otimes 2}} \, \mathcal{S}_{A\cup\Omega}\right], \qquad (15)$$

where $\rho_L = \bigotimes_{e \in L} |e\rangle\langle e|$ and $\rho_v = |f_v\rangle\langle f_v|$, the average $\overline{\rho_v^{\otimes 2}}$ is computed by randomizing over vertex wavefunctions with a uniform probability measure, and $\mathcal{S}_{A\cup\Omega}$ is the copy-swap operator on $A \cup \Omega$. The characterizing aspects of the calculation are summarized hereafter. The randomization over vertex wavefunctions yields, by the Schur's lemma, a linear combination of the identity and the copy-swap operator for each vertex v; the quantities $\overline{Z_1}$ and $\overline{Z_0}$ thus involve a sum of 2^N terms, and can be written as partition functions for configurations of two-level spins, $\sigma_v = \pm 1$ with $v = 1, ..., N$, controlling the presence ($\sigma = -1$) or absence ($\sigma_v = +1$) of a copy-swap operator for each vertex v in all terms of the resulting sum. Such partition functions also depend on two-level "pinning fields": boundary fields, $\mu_e = \pm 1$ with $e \in \partial\gamma$, each one controlling the presence ($\mu_e = -1$) or absence ($\mu_e = +1$) of a copy-swap operator on the corresponding boundary edge e, potentially contained in $\mathcal{S}_A$; and bulk fields, $\nu_v = \pm 1$ with $v = 1, ..., N$, each one controlling the presence ($\nu_v = -1$)

or absence ($\nu_v = +1$) of a copy-swap operator on the corresponding vertex v, potentially deriving from $\mathcal{S}_\Omega$. As a result, $\overline{Z_0}$ and $\overline{Z_1}$ turn out to be particular values of the partition function

$$\overline{Z}(\vec{\mu}, \vec{\nu}) = \sum_{\vec{\sigma}} e^{-\mathcal{A}[\vec{\mu},\vec{\nu}](\vec{\sigma})} \tag{16}$$

where

$$\mathcal{A}[\vec{\mu}, \vec{\nu}](\vec{\sigma}) = -\frac{1}{2} \sum_{e^i_{vw} \in L} (\sigma_v \sigma_w - 1) \log d_{j^i_{vw}} - \frac{1}{2} \sum_{e \in \partial\gamma} (\sigma_v \mu_e - 1) \log d_{j_e}$$
$$- \frac{1}{2} \sum_v (\sigma_v \nu_v - 1) \log D_{\vec{j}_v} + k \tag{17}$$

is an Ising-type action (k is a constant), having a parametric dependence on the pinning fields $\vec{\mu} = \{\mu_e | e \in \partial\gamma\}$ and $\vec{\nu} = \{\nu_v | v \in V\}$; specifically, $\overline{Z_0}$ is given by Eq. (16) with all pinning fields pointing up (i.e. $\mu_e = +1$ for all e, and $\nu_v = +1$ for all v), while $\overline{Z_1}$ corresponds to the case in which the pinning fields within $A \cup \Omega$ are flipped down (i.e. $\mu_e = -1$ if and only if $e \in A$, and $\nu_v = -1$ if and only if $v \in \Omega$). By defining the free energies $F_0 = -\log \overline{Z_0}$ and $F_1 = -\log \overline{Z_1}$, the average Rényi-2 entropy is then given by $\overline{S_2(\rho_{A\cup\Omega})} = F_1 - F_0$.

We consider the large-spins regime (corresponding to a low-temperature regime of the Ising model), in which the partition functions are estimated by the contribution of the configuration $\vec{\sigma}$ that minimizes the action, i.e.

$$F(\vec{\mu}, \vec{\nu}) = -\log \overline{Z}(\vec{\mu}, \vec{\nu}) \approx \min_{\vec{\sigma}} \mathcal{A}[\vec{\mu}, \vec{\nu}](\vec{\sigma}) \tag{18}$$

Note that F_0 is independent of the particular reduction of ρ we want to compute the entropy of; in fact, all pinning fields in $\overline{Z_0}$ take the "neutral value" $+1$. In the low-temperature regime all Ising spins get aligned with them, reaching the all-up configuration that minimizes $\mathcal{A}_0$, which takes the value $\mathcal{A}_{0\min} = k$. Therefore, from Eq. (18), $F_0 = k$. Since what matters is the difference $F_1 - F_0$, the constant k can be set equal to zero, and the calculation of $\overline{S_2(\rho_{A\cup\Omega})}$ thus be reduced to that of F_1 via Eq. (18), with $k = 0$ in the action.

4.2. Checking the isometry condition for bulk-to-boundary maps

We exploit the above technique to compute the average Rényi-2 entropy of the reduced bulk state: $\overline{S_2(\rho_{\dot\gamma})}$. This requires setting $A = \emptyset$ and $\Omega = \dot\gamma$; the partition function $\overline{Z_1}$ is thus given by Eq. (16) with all boundary fields $\vec{\mu}$ equal to $+1$, and all bulk fields $\vec{\nu}$ equal to -1.

4.2.1. Homogeneous case

In the homogeneous case, i.e. when all spins on the graph take the same value j, the quantity $\log d_j = \beta$ plays the role of inverse Ising temperature, as can be seen by expressing the action as $\mathcal{A}(\vec{\sigma}) = \beta H(\vec{\sigma})$, with

$$H(\vec{\sigma}) = -\frac{1}{2}\left[\sum_{e^i_{vw}\in L}(\sigma_v\sigma_w - 1) + \sum_{e\in\partial\gamma}(\sigma_v - 1) + \frac{\log D_j}{\beta}\sum_v(\sigma_v\nu_v - 1)\right], \quad (19)$$

where D_j is the dimension of an intertwiner recoupling d j-spins; we then obtain, for the partition function of Eq. (16), the form $\overline{Z} = \sum_{\vec{\sigma}} e^{-\beta H(\vec{\sigma})}$ (we removed the dependence on $\vec{\mu}$, $\vec{\nu}$ for brevity).

In the range $\beta \gg 1$ we have that $\overline{Z} \approx \exp\{-\beta\min_{\vec{\sigma}} H(\vec{\sigma})\}$, and the free energy is thus given by $F \approx \beta\min_{\vec{\sigma}} H(\vec{\sigma})$. In this range the maximum value of the entropy is obtained when the free energy F_1 is estimated through the configuration with all Ising spins pointing up (in short, $\vec{\sigma} = \uparrow$); in fact,

$$\overline{S_2(\rho_{\hat{\gamma}})} = F_1 - F_0 \approx \beta H_1(\vec{\sigma} = \uparrow) = \log(D_j^N), \quad (20)$$

which is the maximum entropy the reduced bulk state can have, as D_j^N is the bulk dimension in the homogeneous case.

Based on this consideration, we can translate the isometry condition into the requirement of stability of the all-up configuration:

$$H_1(\vec{\sigma}) > H_1(\vec{\sigma} = \uparrow) \quad \forall \vec{\sigma} \quad (21)$$

By inserting Eq. (19) into Eq. (21), and denoting by $X(\vec{\sigma})$ the region that, for a given configuration $\vec{\sigma}$, contains the Ising spins that point down (i.e. $\sigma_v = -1$ if and only if $v \in X(\vec{\sigma})$), the stability condition of Eq. (21) can be written as follows:

$$|\partial X(\vec{\sigma})|\log d_j > |X(\vec{\sigma})|\log D_j \quad \forall \vec{\sigma} \quad (22)$$

We are interested in graphs made of 4-valent vertices; in that case $D_j = d_j = 2j+1$, and Eq. (22) becomes

$$|\partial X(\vec{\sigma})| > |X(\vec{\sigma})| \quad \forall \vec{\sigma}, \quad (23)$$

which cannot be satisfied for $\vec{\sigma} = \downarrow$, as $X(\vec{\sigma} = \downarrow) = \dot{\gamma}$ and every vertex has at most one boundary link. This implies that no bulk-to-boundary map associated to an homogeneous graph, made of 4-valent vertices and with at most one boundary link for each vertex, can be an isometry.

4.2.2. *Inhomogeneous case*

In the generic, inhomogeneous case, we can still put in evidence the parameter $\beta = \log d_j$, where j is now the average spin, and write the partition function as $\overline{Z} = \sum_{\vec{\sigma}} e^{-\beta H(\vec{\sigma})}$ with

$$H(\vec{\sigma}) = -\frac{1}{2}\sum_{e^i_{vw}\in L}(\sigma_v\sigma_w - 1)\frac{\log d_{j^i_{vw}}}{\beta} - \frac{1}{2}\sum_{e\in\partial\gamma}(\sigma_v - 1)\frac{\log d_{j_e}}{\beta}$$

$$-\frac{1}{2}\sum_v(\sigma_v\nu_v - 1)\frac{\log D_{\vec{j}_v}}{\beta} \quad (24)$$

Similarly to the homogeneous case, when the partition function $\overline{Z_1}$ is dominated by the all-up configuration, and so $F_1 \approx \beta H_1(\vec{\sigma} = \uparrow)$, the entropy takes its maximum value: $\overline{S_2(\rho_{\vec{\gamma}})} = \log\left(\prod_v D_{\vec{j}_v}\right)$. We can therefore express the isometry condition of the bulk-to-boundary map as stability condition of the $\vec{\sigma} = \uparrow$ configuration; by making use of the $\vec{\sigma}$-dependent region $X(\vec{\sigma})$ previously defined, that takes the following form:

$$\sum_{e \in \partial X(\vec{\sigma})} \log d_{j_e} > \sum_{v \in X(\vec{\sigma})} \log D_{\vec{j}_v} \quad \forall \vec{\sigma} \quad (25)$$

Let us now focus on graphs with 4-valent vertices. By renaming the spins of every vertex with labels a, b, c, d according to their increasing order, i.e. $j^a \leq j^b \leq j^c \leq j^d$, we can write the intertwiner dimension as follows: $D_{j^a j^b j^c j^d} = \min\{j^a + j^d, j^b + j^c\} - \Delta + 1$, where $\Delta = j^d - j^a$ is the difference between the maximum and the minimum spin[a]. Equation (25) then becomes

$$\sum_{e \in \partial X(\vec{\sigma})} \log d_{j_e} > \sum_{v \in X(\vec{\sigma})} \log\left(\min\{j_v^a + j_v^d, j_v^b + j_v^c\} - \Delta_v + 1\right) \quad \forall \vec{\sigma} \quad (26)$$

To highlight the trend of the isometric character of the map as a function of Δ, we consider the scenarios corresponding to the extreme values of Δ:

(i) $\Delta_v = 0 \ \forall v$: homogeneous case, the bulk-to-boundary map is not an isometry
(ii) $\Delta_v = j_v^b + j_v^c - 1 \ \forall v$: the stability condition becomes

$$\sum_{e \in \partial X(\vec{\sigma})} \log d_{j_e} > |X(\vec{\sigma})| \log 2 \quad \forall \vec{\sigma} \quad (27)$$

which is satisfied for sufficiently high values of the edge spins.

5. Conclusions and outlook

We investigated the holographic features of spin networks by regarding them as emerging from the entanglement of individual vertices, in the group field theory approach to quantum gravity. This enabled us to highlight the entanglement structure of spin network states, and write them in the language of tensor networks. Based on this correspondence, we showed that spin networks naturally define bulk-to-boundary maps, whose properties can efficiently be investigated via tensor network techniques. Specifically, we used the latter to identify which (entanglement-induced) features of a spin network can give rise to an isometric mapping of quantum data from the bulk to the boundary, which is the pre-condition for an holographic behaviour. In the case of graphs made of four-valent vertices (which is the interesting one for 4D quantum gravity) we found that homogeneity of the spin assignment to the spin network prevents the latter to be an isometric bulk-to-boundary map,

---

[a]Note that $\Delta \leq j^b + j^c$; however, since for $\Delta = j^b + j^c$ the intertwiner degree of freedom is suppressed, in the following we assume $\Delta \leq j^b + j^c - 1$.

while increasing the range of spins attached to each vertex favours the attainment of the isometry condition. The results presented here are part of Ref. 21, which also contains an extension of the above analysis to states involving spin superposition, with randomization diagonal with respect to the sum over spins. Importantly, a full generalization to the case of spin superposition, as well as graph superposition, is crucial for a promotion of our results to the dynamical level, since both features can be produced by the quantum dynamics.

Besides contributing to the understanding of the entanglement origin of holography in quantum gravity, our work is meant to be the starting point of a research direction that exploits quantum information techniques in a quantum gravity framework having a purely information-theoretic characterisation, i.e. the one in which spin networks are regarded as generalised tensor networks in the group field theory formalism for quantum gravity. In fact, we have recently used the techniques presented here to study how the boundary entropy depends on the bulk entanglement, specifically that determining the graph connectivity (internal-link entanglement) and that among intertwiner degrees of freedom[23]; in particular, we have analysed under which conditions the latter gives rise to a black hole-like region, analogously to what has been shown in Ref. 16. These methods and results, combined with the typicality approach to the study of the local behaviour of spin networks,[24,25] should pave the way for an information-theoretic characterization of black hole horizons and thus provide important insights into the structure of quantum black holes.

References

1. X.-L. Qi, Does gravity come from quantum information?, *Nature Phys.* **14**, 984 (2018).
2. J. M. Maldacena, The Large N limit of superconformal field theories and supergravity, *Int. J. Theor. Phys.* **38**, 1113 (1999).
3. S. Ryu and T. Takayanagi, Holographic derivation of entanglement entropy from AdS/CFT, *Phys. Rev. Lett.* **96**, p. 181602 (2006).
4. S. Ryu and T. Takayanagi, Aspects of Holographic Entanglement Entropy, *JHEP* **08**, p. 045 (2006).
5. M. Van Raamsdonk, Comments on quantum gravity and entanglement (7 2009).
6. M. Van Raamsdonk, Building up spacetime with quantum entanglement, *Gen. Rel. Grav.* **42**, 2323 (2010).
7. D. Oriti, Levels of spacetime emergence in quantum gravity (7 2018).
8. D. Oriti, The microscopic dynamics of quantum space as a group field theory, 257 (10 2011).
9. T. Krajewski, Group field theories, *PoS* **QGQGS2011**, p. 005 (2011).
10. S. Carrozza, Flowing in Group Field Theory Space: A Review, *SIGMA* **12**, p. 070 (2016).
11. S.-J. Ran, E. Tirrito, C. Peng, X. Chen, L. Tagliacozzo, G. Su and M. Lewenstein, Lecture Notes of Tensor Network Contractions, *arXiv e-prints* (August 2017).
12. D. Perez-Garcia, F. Verstraete, M. M. Wolf and J. I. Cirac, Matrix Product State Representations, *arXiv e-prints* (August 2006).
13. R. Orús, A practical introduction to tensor networks: Matrix product states and projected entangled pair states, *Annals of Physics* **349**, 117 (2014).

14. B. Swingle, Entanglement Renormalization and Holography, *Phys. Rev. D* **86**, p. 065007 (2012).
15. W. Helwig, W. Cui, A. Riera, J. I. Latorre and H.-K. Lo, Absolute Maximal Entanglement and Quantum Secret Sharing, *Phys. Rev. A* **86**, p. 052335 (2012).
16. P. Hayden, S. Nezami, X.-L. Qi, N. Thomas, M. Walter and Z. Yang, Holographic duality from random tensor networks, *JHEP* **11**, p. 009 (2016).
17. E. Colafranceschi and D. Oriti, Quantum gravity states, entanglement graphs and second-quantized tensor networks, *JHEP* **07**, p. 052 (2021).
18. G. 't Hooft, Dimensional reduction in quantum gravity, *Conf. Proc. C* **930308**, 284 (1993).
19. L. Susskind, The World as a hologram, *J. Math. Phys.* **36**, 6377 (1995).
20. I. Cirac, D. Perez-Garcia, N. Schuch and F. Verstraete, Matrix Product States and Projected Entangled Pair States: Concepts, Symmetries, and Theorems (11 2020).
21. E. Colafranceschi, G. Chirco and D. Oriti, Holographic maps from quantum gravity states as tensor networks (5 2021).
22. D. Oriti, Group field theory as the 2nd quantization of Loop Quantum Gravity, *Class. Quant. Grav.* **33**, p. 085005 (2016).
23. G. Chirco, E. Colafranceschi and D. Oriti, in preparation.
24. F. Anzà and G. Chirco, Fate of the Hoop Conjecture in Quantum Gravity, *Phys. Rev. Lett.* **119**, p. 231301 (2017).
25. F. Anzà and G. Chirco, Typicality in spin-network states of quantum geometry, *Phys. Rev. D* **94**, p. 084047 (2016).

Minimal length discretization and properties of modified metric tensor and geodesics

Abdel Nasser Tawfik

Egyptian Center for Theoretical Physics (ECTP), Cairo, Egypt
World Laboratory for Cosmology and Particle Physics (WLCAPP), Cairo, Egypt
E-mail: atawfik@cern.ch

Fady T. Farouk, F. Salah Tarabia and Muhammad Maher

Helwan University, Faculty of Science, Physics Department, 11792 Ain Helwan, Cairo, Egypt

> We argue that the minimal length discretization generalizing the Heisenberg uncertainty principle, in which the gravitational impacts on the non–commutation relations are thoughtfully taken into account, radically modifies the spacetime geometry. The resulting metric tensor and geodesic equation combine the general relativity terms with additional terms depending on higher–order derivatives. Suggesting solutions for the modified geodesics, for instance, isn't a trivial task. We discuss on the properties of the resulting metric tensor, line element, and geodesic equation.
>
> *Keywords*: Quantum gravity, Noncommutative geometry, Relativity and gravitation, Line element, Metric tensor, Geodesic equation, Generalized uncertainty principle

1. Introduction

Suggesting a consistent theory for quantum gravity is an ultimate goal of recent research aiming at unifying quantum mechanics (QM) with the theory of general relativity (GR). The quantum nature of gravity is still an open question in physics. It turns to form an enigma occupying the minds of many physicists for many decades, for instance, so–far there is no scientific explanation for the origin of the gravitational fields and how particles behave inside them! This makes the gravity fundamentally different from the other fources of nature. There were various attempts to reconcile some principles of GR in a quantum framework.[1,2] The quantum gravity - on one hand - is conjectured to add new elements to GR and QM. On the other hand, the Einstein field equations combine classical geometry with quantum stress–energy–momentum tensor! For QM, we recall the possible modification in the Heisenberg uncertainty principle due to gravitational effects[a], known as generalized uncertainty princile (GUP).[3,4] The present work introduces some insights on the possible impacts of GUP on the metric tensor and the geodesic equation and their properties.

Couple decades ago, the line element modification and the gravity quantization have been suggested in litrature.[5–7] A review of these models could be found in Refs.[8–10]. An extended class of the metric tensors which are functions of a field of an

---
[a] They weren't taken into considration in the original Heisenberg uncertainty principle.

internal vectors $y^\alpha(x)$, $g_{\mu\nu}(x^\alpha \cdot y^\alpha(x))$, was also discussed in litrature.[11] Accordingly, the origin of the gravitational field of spin-1 massless particle could be determined.[11] Regarding the equivalence principle of gravitationan and enirtial mass in extended gravity and non–geodesic motion, a machian request was scratched,[12] where a direct coupling between the Ricci curvature scalar and the matter Lagrangian could be fixed in cosmological observations.[12]

The present script aims at tackling the long–standing essential puzzle that the Einstein field equations relate *non–quantized* semi–Riemannian geometry expressed in Ricci and Einstein tensors, which are basically depending on the metric tensor $g_{\mu\nu}(x^\alpha)$, with the *full–quantized* stress–energy-momentum tensor $T_{\mu\nu}$.[13] The approach applied here is the finite minimal length uncertainty obtained from GUP. GUP was inspired by black hole physics, doubly special relativity, and string theory.[3,4] It is worthy highligting that GUP is comparable with the Planck length, where quantum fluctuations in *quasi–quantized* manifold likely emerge.[14–16]

The modifications in the metric tensor and geodesic equation due to GUP shall be introduced. Accordingly, we believe that the present study offers a theoretical framework for the observations that the universe acceleratingly expands. Alongside forces deriving this type of expansion, such as dark energy[16] and cosmological constant,[17] we suggest that it might be also originated to interdependence of GR on QM, especially at the Planck scale.

The present paper is organized as follows. Section 2 reviews the generalized uncertainly principle and minimal length uncertainty. The discretized metric tensor and its properties shall be discussed in section 3. The discretized geodesic equation and its properties shall be introduced in section 4. Section 5 is devoted to the final conclusions.

2. Generalized uncertainly principle and minimal length uncertainty

The Heisenberg uncertainty principle (HUP) is a recipe on how the uncertainties are constrained in the quantum non–commutation relations of length and momentum operators, for instance. This was originally suggested in absence of any gravitational field. Analyzing HUP in gravitational fields comes up with modifications, know as GUP. Such a phenomenological aspect can be originated in black hole physics, doubly special relativity, and string theory.[3,4] Phenomenology because so–far there is no theoretical explanation of the gravitational fields origin making gravity substantially different from the other three forces of nature. A finite minimal length was suggested as,[18]

$$\Delta x\, \Delta p \geq \frac{\hbar}{2}\left[1 + \beta(\Delta p)^2\right], \qquad (1)$$

where Δx and Δp are length and momentum uncertainties, respectively. $\beta = \beta_0(\ell_p/\hbar)^2 = \beta_0/(m_p c)^2$, is the GUP parameter with $\ell_p = \sqrt{\hbar G/c^3} = 1.977 \times 10^{-16}$ GeV^{-1} the Planck length and $m_p = \sqrt{\hbar c/G} = 1.22 \times 10^{19}$ GeV/c^2 the

Planck mass. An upper bound on β_0 is based on astronomical observations, such as, $\beta_0 \lesssim 5.5 \times 10^{60}$ based on recent gravitational waves observations. From Eq. (1), then the minimum length uncertainty reads

$$\Delta x_{\min} \approx \hbar\sqrt{3\beta_0} = \ell_p\sqrt{\beta_0}. \tag{2}$$

The experimental estimations[19] of β_0 range from $\sim 10^{21}$ to $\sim 10^{39}$. Another GUP approach motivated by quantum deformation of the Pioncarre algebra[20,21] suggests that the minimal length associated with is given as

$$\Delta x_{\min} \simeq \frac{\hbar G}{\gamma_0} = \frac{\ell_p^2}{\gamma_0}, \tag{3}$$

where γ_0 is photon's wavelength sent from infinity to be absorbed in a black hole. Its experimental estimations[19] range from $\sim 10^{26}$ to $\sim 10^{34}$.

The UV/IR correspondence can be applied on various phenomena in which short and long distance physics play a characterized role. For example, gravity[22] and the *"deformed"* commutation relations have features of UV/IR correspondence.[23] Therefore, we assume that the minimal length discretization could be analyzed from the UV/IR correspondence.[10] Indeed, Δx rapidly increases (IR) as the Δp increases beyond the Planck scale (UV).[24–26]

Analogous to expression (1), the canonical non–commutation relation of length and momentum quantum operators is given as

$$[\hat{x}_i, \hat{p}_j] \geq \delta_{ij} i\hbar \left(1 + \beta p^2\right), \tag{4}$$

where $p^2 = g_{ij} p^{0i} p^{0j}$ and g_{ij} is Minkowski spacetime metric tensor, for instance $(-,+,+,+)$. Both length and momentum operators, respectively, read

$$\hat{x}_i = \hat{x}_{0i}(1 + \beta p^2), \tag{5}$$
$$\hat{p}_j = \hat{p}_{0j}, \tag{6}$$

in which $\hat{x}_{0i}$ and $\hat{p}_{0j}$ can be derived from the corresponding non–communitation relation,

$$[\hat{x}_{0i}, \hat{p}_{0j}] = \delta_{ij} i\hbar. \tag{7}$$

3. Discretized metric tensor and its properties

With the quantum non–commutation operations discussed in section 2 the four–dimensional Minkowskian manifold of the line element can be given as

$$ds^2 = g_{\mu\nu} dx^\mu dx^\nu, \tag{8}$$

where μ, ν, and $\lambda = 0, 1, 2, 3$. This could be extended to eight–dimensional spacetime tangent bundle with coordinates $x^A = (x^\mu(\zeta^a), \beta \dot{x}^\mu(\zeta^a))$, where $\dot{x}^\mu = dx^\mu/d\zeta^\mu$.[27] Obviously, the line element reads

$$d\tilde{s}^2 = g_{AB} dx^A dx^B, \tag{9}$$

where $x^A = x^A(\zeta^\mu)$, $g_{AB} = g_{\mu\nu} \otimes g_{\mu\nu}$, and the indices A and $B = 0, 1, \ldots, 7$. With some assumptions and approximations, this manifold could be reformulated as an effective four-dimensional spacetime manifold,

$$\tilde{g}_{\mu\nu} = g_{AB} \frac{\partial x^A}{\partial \zeta^\mu} \frac{\partial x^B}{\partial \zeta^\nu} \simeq g_{ab} \left[\frac{\partial x^a}{\partial \zeta^\mu} \frac{\partial x^b}{\partial \zeta^\nu} + \beta \frac{\partial \dot{x}^a}{\partial \zeta^\mu} \frac{\partial \dot{x}^b}{\partial \zeta^\nu} \right] \simeq \left(1 + \beta \ddot{x}^\lambda \ddot{x}_\lambda\right) g_{\mu\nu}. \tag{10}$$

$\ddot{x}^\mu = \partial \dot{x}^\mu / \partial \zeta^\mu$ is four-dimensional acceleration. The indices a, and $b = 0, 1, \ldots, 7$.

It is now proper to highlight a number of the discretized metric tensor properties. First, we distinguish between flat and curved spacetime:

- For flat spacetime, $g_{\mu\nu} = \eta_{\mu\nu}$ and the modified metric tensor reads

$$\tilde{g}_{\mu\nu} \simeq \eta_{\mu\nu} + \beta \ddot{x}^\lambda \ddot{x}_\lambda \eta_{\mu\nu} \simeq \eta_{\mu\nu} + h_{\mu\nu}, \tag{11}$$

where $h_{\mu\nu} = \beta \ddot{x}^\lambda \ddot{x}_\lambda \eta_{\mu\nu}$. The quantum fluctuations from which the minimal length uncertainty likely emerges are compassed in $h_{\mu\nu}$. In other words, both GR metric tensor and this modified one are only distinguishable, at finite $h_{\mu\nu}$.

- For curved spacetime, the modified metric tensor reads

$$\tilde{g}_{\mu\nu} \simeq g_{\mu\nu} + \beta \ddot{x}^\lambda \ddot{x}_\lambda g_{\mu\nu}. \tag{12}$$

Again, $\beta \ddot{x}^\lambda \ddot{x}_\lambda g_{\mu\nu}$ represents the minimal length contributions.

The $\tilde{g}_{\mu\nu}$, Eq. (12), seems to play the same role as that of $g_{\mu\nu}$, namely it turns a covariant tensor into a contravariant tensor and vice versa. $\tilde{g}_{\mu\nu}$ is apparently symmetric in its indices μ and ν as its components are likely equal upon exchanging the indices. The $\tilde{g}_{\mu\nu}$ symmetric properties are invariant upon basis transformation only if its indices are of the same type; variant or covariant. For spacetime represented by a four-dimensional differentiable manifold $\mathcal{M}$, the metric tensor, $\tilde{g}_{\mu\nu}$, Eq. (12), is covariant, second-degree, symmetric on $\mathcal{M}$. Such manifold is Lorentzian. In local coordinates x^μ, the metric can be expressed in dx^μ (one-form gradients of the scalar coordinate fields x^μ), and the coefficients $\tilde{g}_{\mu\nu}$ (16 real-valued functions). If the local coordinates are specified, the metric can be written as a 4×4 symmetric matrix with the coefficients $\tilde{g}_{\mu\nu}$. If the matrix is non-singular having non-vanishing determinant, $\tilde{g}_{\mu\nu}$ is non-degenerate. The Lorentzian signature of $\tilde{g}_{\mu\nu}$ obviously implies that the matrix has one negative and three positive eigenvalues. Under a change of the local coordinates $x^\mu \to x^{\bar{\mu}}$, we obtain

$$\tilde{g}_{\bar{\mu}\bar{\nu}} = \frac{\partial x^\alpha}{\partial x^{\bar{\mu}}} \frac{\partial x^\beta}{\partial x^{\bar{\nu}}} \tilde{g}_{\alpha\beta} = \Theta^\alpha_{\bar{\mu}} \Theta^\beta_{\bar{\nu}} \tilde{g}_{\alpha\beta} \tag{13}$$

If dx^μ are regarded as the components of an infinitesimal coordinate displacement four-vector, the metric determines the invariant square of an infinitesimal line element. Also, it is apparent that the principle of the general covariance is satisfied even in absence of gravitational effects on the modified Minkowski metric. Then, the modified four–dimensional line element can be expressed as

$$d\tilde{s}^2 = g_{\mu\nu}\left(dx^\mu dx^\nu + \beta^2 d\dot{x}^\mu\, d\dot{x}^\nu\right) = ds^2 + \beta^2 \ddot{x}^\lambda \ddot{x}_\lambda\, ds^2, \qquad (14)$$

and $d\tilde{s}^2$ manifests the causal structure of the spacetime. Only timelike four–dimensional line element, $d\tilde{s}^2 < 0$, can physically covered by a massive object. If $d\tilde{s}^2 = 0$ the line element is lightlike (covered by massless photon). On the other hand, for $d\tilde{s}^2 > 0$, the four–dimensional line element is an incremental proper length, i.e., spacelike.

4. Discretized geodesic equation and its properties

The properties of the manifold including geodesics in GR $[\ddot{x}^\mu + \Gamma^\mu_{\alpha\beta}\dot{x}^\mu \dot{x}^\nu = 0$ with $\dot{x}^\mu = \partial x^\mu / \partial s$, Christopher symbols $\Gamma^\mu_{\alpha\beta} = (g^{\mu\gamma}/2)(\partial g_{\gamma\alpha}/\partial x^\beta) + \partial g_{\gamma\beta}/\partial x^\alpha - \partial g_{\alpha\beta}/\partial x^\gamma)$, and s is a scalar parameter of motion such as a proper time] can be generalized. For example, the notion of a "*straight line*" is to be generalized to "*curved spacetime*". The consequences of the length discretization or minimal length uncertainty based on GUP, generalize the world line of a free particle. GR assumes that gravity couldn't be regarded as a force but it should be emerged from "*classical*" curved spacetime geometry and "*quantized*" stress–energy–momentum tensor is causing the "*classical*" spacetime curvature. The approach utilized here is discretized minimal length, which modifies both metric tensor and line element.

As discussed in Ref.[10], using the variational principle and extremization of the path s_{AB}, the geodesic equation could be derived as follows.

- In flat spacetime (Minkowski space)

$$\beta \mathcal{L}\frac{d^2\dot{x}^\mu}{ds^2} - \frac{dx^\mu}{ds} + c = 0. \qquad (15)$$

Even if β, the GUP parameter vanishes, the geodesic equation reduces to that of a straight line, at constant velocity, i.e., both β terms disappear.
- and in curved spacetime

$$\frac{d^2 x^\eta}{ds^2} + \Gamma^\eta_{\mu\nu}\frac{dx^\mu}{ds}\frac{dx^\nu}{ds} = \beta\frac{d}{ds}\left(\mathcal{L}\frac{d^3 x^\eta}{ds^3}\right)$$
$$+ \beta g^{\eta\alpha} g_{\mu\nu,\alpha}\frac{d^2 x^\mu}{d^2 s}\frac{d^2 x^{nu}}{ds^2}$$
$$+ \beta \mathcal{L} g^{\eta\alpha} g_{\mu\alpha,\gamma}\left[\frac{dx^\gamma}{ds}\frac{d^2 \dot{x}^\mu}{ds^2} + \frac{d}{ds}\left(\frac{dx^\gamma}{ds}\frac{d\dot{x}^\mu}{ds}\right)\right]$$
$$+ \beta \mathcal{L} g^{\eta\alpha} g_{\mu\alpha,\gamma,\delta}\frac{dx^\delta}{ds}\frac{dx^\gamma}{ds}\frac{d\dot{x}^\mu}{ds}, \qquad (16)$$

where the proper time can be deduced from the Lagrangian, $\tau = \int \mathcal{L}(s, \dot{x}, \ddot{x})\, ds$,

$$\frac{\partial \tau}{\partial s} = \mathcal{L}(s, \dot{x}, \ddot{x}) = -\left[g_{\mu\nu}\left(\frac{dx^\mu}{ds}\frac{dx^\nu}{ds} + \beta \frac{d\dot{x}^\mu}{ds}\frac{d\dot{x}^\nu}{ds} \right) \right]^{1/2},$$

$$\Gamma^\eta_{\mu\nu} = \frac{1}{2} g^{\eta\alpha}\left[g_{\mu\alpha,\nu} - g_{\alpha\nu,\mu} + g_{\mu\nu,\alpha} \right],$$

$$g_{\mu\nu,\alpha} = \frac{\partial g_{\mu\nu}}{\partial x^\alpha},$$

$$g_{\mu\alpha,\gamma,\delta} = \frac{\partial}{\partial x^\delta}\left(\frac{\partial g_{\mu\alpha}}{\partial x^\gamma} \right).$$

The β–terms in Eq. (16) distinguish this expression of discretized geodesics from the GR geodesics,

$$\frac{d^2 x^\mu}{ds^2} + \Gamma^\mu_{\alpha\beta}\frac{dx^\mu}{ds}\frac{dx^\nu}{ds} = 0, \qquad (17)$$

which could be solved when, for instance, assuring that the proper time reads $ds^2 = g_{\mu\nu} dx^\mu dx^\nu$. Under the condition that

$$g_{\mu\nu}\frac{dx^\mu}{ds}\frac{dx^\nu}{ds} = \epsilon, \qquad (18)$$

where $\epsilon = 0$ for photon and $\epsilon = 1$ for massive particles, the geodesic equation is supplemented. For conserved energy and angular momentum the geodesic equation can be expressed as an ordinary first–order differential equation.[28]

Solving the discretized geodesic equation, Eq. (16), is not a trivial task, because of the finite terms in rhs, which encompass higher–order derivatives.

5. Conclusions

The approach of minimal length uncertainty conserves both Christoffel connection[b] and the equivalence principle of the gravitational and inertial mass. They are not affected. This allows to recover any violations in the equivalence principle, especially as a possible reason of quantum gravity. We highlight that this conclusion contradicts previous studies.[29,30] The reason could be the rigorous procedure implemented in the present study. We have first determined the modified metric tensor. Accordingly, we have obtained the modified line element. Both are key principles of the proposed theory of discretized geometry. We could also derive the corresponding geodesics, in which the appearance of higher–order derivatives substantially distinguishes this expression from the GR geodesics.

The modification to the line element is summarized in the term $\beta^2 \ddot{x}^\lambda \ddot{x}_\lambda$, which highlights the essential contributions added by the acceleration of the test particle.

---

[b]The metric connection characterizes the affine connection to a manifold provided with the metric. This allows lengths, for instance, to be measured on that manifold.

We conclude that the length discretization ensures that the line element wouldn't only expand but apparently accelerates. The metric tensor is also modified by the term $\beta \ddot{x}^\lambda \ddot{x}_\lambda$. The properties of the modified metric tensor has been elaborated.

We find that the modified geodesics is not only providing the acceleration of a test particle inside the gravitational field. Higher–order derivatives are also present,[31] namely the jerk, $\dddot{x}^\mu$, which in turn is derived from the time derivative of the acceleration. In contract to GR geodesics, solving the modified geodesics isn't a trivial task. The corresponding differential equations are complex and non–linear.

Acknowledgments

AT is very grateful to organizers of sixteenth Marcel Grossmann meeting - MG16 for their kind invitation and financial support!

References

1. C. Rovelli and L. Smolin, Loop Space Representation of Quantum General Relativity, *Nucl. Phys. B* **331**, 80 (1990).
2. J. F. Donoghue, General relativity as an effective field theory: The leading quantum corrections, *Phys. Rev. D* **50**, 3874 (1994).
3. A. N. Tawfik and A. M. Diab, Generalized Uncertainty Principle: Approaches and Applications, *Int. J. Mod. Phys. D* **23**, p. 1430025 (2014).
4. A. N. Tawfik and A. M. Diab, Review on Generalized Uncertainty Principle, *Rept. Prog. Phys.* **78**, p. 126001 (2015).
5. A. Feoli, G. Lambiase, G. Papini and G. Scarpetta, Schwarzschild field with maximal acceleration corrections, *Phys. Lett. A* **263**, 147 (1999).
6. S. Capozziello, A. Feoli, G. Lambiase, G. Papini and G. Scarpetta, Massive scalar particles in a modified Schwarzschild geometry, *Phys. Lett. A* **268**, 247 (2000).
7. V. Bozza, A. Feoli, G. Lambiase, G. Papini and G. Scarpetta, Maximal acceleration effects in Kerr space, *Phys. Lett. A* **283**, 53 (2001).
8. P. O. Hess, M. Schafer and W. Greiner, *Pseudo-complex General Relativity* (Springer, Heidelberg, 2015).
9. P. Hess, Alternatives to Einstein's General Relativity Theory, *Prog. Part. Nucl. Phys.* **114**, p. 103809 (2020).
10. A. N. Tawfik, A. M. Diab, S. Shenawy and E. A. El Dahab, Consequences of minimal length discretization on line element, metric tensor and geodesic equation, *Astron. Nachr.* **342**, 54 (2021).
11. C. G. Oliveira, On the properties of an extended class of metric tensors in relativity, *Int. J. Theor. Phys.* **24**, p. 1081 (1985).
12. I. Licata, C. Corda and E. Benedetto, A machian request for the equivalence principle in extended gravity and nongeodesic motion, *Grav. Cosmol.* **22**, 48 (2016).
13. H. Stephani, D. Krämer, M. MacCallum, C. Hoenselaers and E. Herlt, *Exact solutions of Einstein's field equations; 2nd ed.* (Cambridge Univ. Press, Cambridge, 2003).
14. F. Karolyhazy, Gravitation and quantum mechanics of macroscopic objects, *Nuovo Cimento (Italy) Divided into Nuovo Cimento A and Nuovo Cimento B* **(10), 42A** (1966).
15. A. Tawfik and A. Diab, Emergence of cosmic space and minimal length in quantum gravity: A large class of spacetimes, equations of state, and minimal length approaches, *Indian J. Phys.* **90**, 1095 (2016).

16. A. N. Tawfik and E. A. El Dahab, Review on Dark Energy Models, *Grav. Cosmol.* **25**, 103 (2019).
17. P. Peebles and B. Ratra, The Cosmological Constant and Dark Energy, *Rev. Mod. Phys.* **75**, 559 (2003).
18. A. Kempf, G. Mangano and R. B. Mann, Hilbert space representation of the minimal length uncertainty relation, *Phys. Rev. D* **52**, 1108 (1995).
19. D. Gao and M. Zhan, Constraining the generalized uncertainty principle with cold atoms, *Phys. Rev. A* **94**, p. 013607 (2016).
20. M. Maggiore, A Generalized uncertainty principle in quantum gravity, *Phys. Lett. B* **304**, 65 (1993).
21. M. Maggiore, Quantum groups, gravity and the generalized uncertainty principle, *Phys. Rev. D* **49**, 5182 (1994).
22. M. G. Jackson, Gravity from a modified commutator, *Int. J. Mod. Phys. D* **14**, 2239 (2005).
23. M. Jackson, Gravity from a modified commutator, *International Journal of Modern Physics D* **14**, 2239 (2005).
24. J. M. Maldacena, The Large N limit of superconformal field theories and supergravity, *Int. J. Theor. Phys.* **38**, 1113 (1999).
25. S. Gubser, I. R. Klebanov and A. M. Polyakov, Gauge theory correlators from non-critical string theory, *Phys. Lett. B* **428**, 105 (1998).
26. E. Witten, Anti-de Sitter space and holography, *Adv. Theor. Math. Phys.* **2**, 253 (1998).
27. H. E. Brandt, Causal Domain of Minkowski-spacetime Tangent Bundle, *Found. Phys. Lett.* **13**, 581 (2000).
28. E. Hackmann and C. Lammerzahl, Complete Analytic Solution of the Geodesic Equation in Schwarzschild- (Anti-) de Sitter Spacetimes, *Phys. Rev. Lett.* **100**, p. 171101 (2008).
29. S. Ghosh, Quantum Gravity Effects in Geodesic Motion and Predictions of Equivalence Principle Violation, *Class. Quant. Grav.* **31**, p. 025025 (2014).
30. F. Scardigli and R. Casadio, Is the equivalence principle violated by generalized uncertainty principles and holography in a brane-world?, *Int. J. Mod. Phys. D* **18**, 319 (2009).
31. D. Eager, A.-M. Pendrill and N. Reistad, Beyond velocity and acceleration: Jerk, snap and higher derivatives, *European Journal of Physics* **37**, p. 065008 (oct 2016).

The structure of the multiverse from the entanglement entropy

Samuel Barroso Bellido

Institute of Physics, University of Szczecin
Wielkopolska 15, 70-451 Szczecin, Poland
E-mail: samuel.barroso-bellido@usz.edu.pl

Third quantization of canonical quantum gravity allows us to consider the multiverse as the playground of a field theory of universes. In the scenario where two universes are created by analogy with pair production in quantum field theory, we analyze the entanglement entropy between them and get some conclusions about the structure of the multiverse.

Keywords: Multiverse, Entanglement Entropy, Third Quantization

1. What is Time and Space?

Canonical quantum gravity[1,2] is one of the most natural ways to venture in search of a theory which combines gravity and the quantum world. Even though it is an old topic, there are several fundamental problems one needs to sort out to get satisfactory predictions from it.[3,4] However, the theory has got quite important results we should not ignore.[2,5]

This approach to a quantum theory of gravity predicts the existence of a wave function of the universe, which describes the universe as a whole.[6,7] It is defined by the Wheeler-DeWitt equation

$$\mathcal{H}\Psi = 0, \qquad (1)$$

where $\mathcal{H}$ is the Hamiltonian which considers all possible degrees of freedom from fields and gravity, and Ψ is such wave function. To assume a homogeneous and isotropic universe where there is a limited number of fields, is the simplest way to reduce the complexity of the calculations. Then, the Hamiltonian is quantized by replacement of the momenta by their associated operators, and the wave function of the universe is found solving the differential equation (1).

For instance, let us choose the proper factor ordering for the scale factor a, and the parametrization $\alpha = \ln(a)$, to write its associated momentum as[2]

$$p_a^2 = -\frac{1}{a}\frac{\partial}{\partial a}\left(a\frac{\partial}{\partial a}\right) = -e^{-2\alpha}\frac{\partial^2}{\partial \alpha^2}. \qquad (2)$$

A single scalar field is going to be quantized as usual by

$$p_\phi^2 = -\frac{\partial^2}{\partial \phi^2}. \qquad (3)$$

Thus, the Wheeler-DeWitt equation (1) has the shape of a wave equation

$$\left[\frac{\partial^2}{\partial \alpha^2} - \frac{\partial^2}{\partial \phi^2} + f(\alpha, \phi, ...)\right] \Psi(\alpha, \phi) = 0, \qquad (4)$$

where $f(\alpha, \phi, ...)$ contains the information of the curvature of the universe, the cosmological constant, and so on.

In this theory, *time* is not present. Usually, the scale factor, or a function like α, is the variable which replaces time, but it is an arbitrary choice that leads to physical and even philosophical problems.[8] Since the scale factor as a function of time is not an isomorphism, it is not a well-behaved parametrization of time. Expanding and contracting phases of a closed universe will be described by the same scale factor at two different times, and so big bang and big crunch will have no differences at all. In a practical sense, our universe has never gone through a phase of contraction,[9] and it looks like it will never be in such phase.[10] Hence, the parametrization could still be valid for realistic purposes. On the contrary, *space* is replaced by the scalar field, the one which has the opposite sign in the hyperbolic differential equation (4).

Third quantization of canonical quantum gravity[11-14] is the next step behind a more essential description. By means of it, our universe is seen as one of many universes of a multiverse, where a full quantum field theory takes place, the wave function of the universe plays now the role of an operator over vectors of a Fock space, and annihilation and creation operators can also be defined.

One might expect the number of universes from this picture to be infinite. All of them interacting under the rules of the field theory. Therefore, pair creation of universes is somewhat natural in this picture,[15] as it is in quantum electrodynamics, and two universes can be seen as particle and antiparticle, born at the same time and space in the multiverse (whether *time* and *space* exist or not), being entangled since then.[16] One of those two universes could be our universe. We need to assume that the moment we know as the origin of our universe is the same as that precise moment when our universe is created. Thereafter, we have not notice much difference from what the classical theory of gravity tells us,[17] so we can say that there has not been any interaction with any other universe, and therefore the trajectory through the multiverse has been unaffected. According to this, the pair has *always* been a pair, and the number of universes of this subsystem of the multiverse, has always been constant since its origin.

When considering a curved background, third quantization suffers from the lack of definition of particle as in quantum field theory in curved spacetimes,[18] and so the number of universes is variable. In general, the number of universes appears to be infinite with a certain distribution of modes,[19-21] which are defined by the proper Fock space. To solve this, we turn to an invariant representation[22,23] in which the number operator remains constant, and so the number of universes.

The quantum state at the birth of the pair[24-26] is going to be denoted by $|00\rangle$, which is the same in the natural description due to the diagonal Hamiltonian and in the invariant representation we would like to work with. The Bogoliubov transformation between both representations at different time lets us to write the density operator $\rho = |00\rangle_{\text{inv}}\langle 00|$ in terms of the vectors of the diagonal representation, where $|00\rangle_{\text{inv}}$ is the vacuum state in the invariant representation. Finally, the entanglement entropy as the von Neumann entropy of the bipartite system is found tracing out the degrees of freedom of one of the two universes.

2. How is the Multiverse?

First of all, the quantum field theory we are used to, is not in perfect harmony with third quantization picture. By ordinary field theory, we states that fundamental particles are really fundamental, and so, they have no internal structure.

In the third quantization picture, particles are universes where we could be living *in*, where all laws of Physics seem to be satisfied. They have an internal structure. As far as it seems, we have no idea about how this multiverse really affects the internal structure of the universes. It is, for example, how the interactions between universes in the multiverse could change the dynamics of our universe. Some attempts have been done previously,[27] but it is not conclusive since the power spectrum of the cosmic microwave background is only affected by an interacting multiverse in the low multipoles interval.

The multiverse is a *place* where time and space are not well defined. We can imagine a particle and antiparticle distancing one from the other, since our laboratory is a *place* where they can be moving away. A pair of universes could have not that place to move freely. Assuming the existence of such place could be imprudent.

When an electron and a positron are created from a virtual photon, their spins are entangled. At that moment, the entanglement[28] is maximum, and it can only be reduced or removed naturally by decoherence. The entanglement cannot be increased naturally in any case after they start to travel freely. For the case in which there is not environment with which the particles can interact, the entanglement must be constant.

For most of the models where there are critical points along the classical evolution, the entanglement entropy of a pair of universes has been found[25, 26] to be high or divergent at the initial singularity (when they are created), and divergent at those critical points of the expansion of each universe. It implies that the quantum entanglement of the pair is high at their origin, and at the moment when the expansion of the universes is maximum or minimum.

If such notion of usual space is present in this kind of multiverse, where the universes move and interact, the rules of entanglement should be different from the ones we know from our experiments. It must allow the possibility for the entanglement to increase naturally, such that at the maximum of the expansion of the universes, the entanglement is high again. Alternatively, the multiverse might not be a *place* like the ordinary one we are used to.

Somehow, if we consider the entanglement to work like in our laboratories, the structure of this multiverse cannot be seen as a laboratory where entangled particles run away from each other, otherwise the entanglement would be constant or vanishing while time goes by. And perhaps, the problem is not only about the space but also the time. If a time-like variable exists for the multiverse, we cannot tell what it is, or how it is intermingled with the spatial variable.

3. Conclusions

The results of the entanglement entropy of the multiverse, assuming that third quantization is correct, indicate that the multiverse is a different *space* from the one we know from the experience in our universe, or maybe it is the *time* the one which is different, or both at the same time. Here, when we talk about time we mean any notion of time, whether it is the usual time, thermodynamic entropy, or any other physical variable which controls the regular arrow of time.

There could be another possibility where the quantum entanglement works differently in the multiverse than into the universes. In such case, the relationship between both behaviors is unknown. Furthermore, taking for granted that the laws of Physics are satisfied anywhere else could be mistaken. If they hold, we know that the sweet spot where our universe is to let life occurs[29] is highly unlikely. If the rest of the universes exist, and the fundamental constants are different from the ones in our universe, it is expected not to harbor life or, more importantly, avoid immediate recollapse after creation.[30] Indeed, for inflation to occur and let the universe expands, the initial conditions of a universe must also satisfy some requirements, otherwise that universe would recollapse and disappear. There is not much doubt then, that whenever we are able to check the presence of other universes, we would better believe in the possibility that there are different laws of Physics out there.

The manner in which the actual theory of quantum gravity describes this kind of multiverse is in terms of the *internal* degrees of freedom of the universes, like the scale factor or the fields. It could not be the appropriate way to do it, since they have not a good definition out of each universe, and so either space and time.

The emergence of a universe which is exact to ours is probabilistic as long as we are assuming a full quantum behavior of the multiverse. The curvature, the cosmological constant, and the rest of the characteristics of a universe are subject to the probabilistic rules of the multiverse. Therefore, the chance for the existence of a universe like ours cannot be far from null.

There is, of course, the possibility that third quantization picture is not correct at all and the multiverse, as it is described by it, is not realistic. Nevertheless, our results could also be showing that third quantization is unavoidably wrong. If our results are correct, then canonical quantum gravity is correct and the third quantization picture is wrong, or both are wrong. The interpretation of third quantization scenario is also a bit odd, and many improvements can be done behind a more strict field theory of universes.

At present, there seems not to be a way out of our ignorance when multiverse comes in context. We are making so many assumptions when we talk about the multiverse that the most likely outcome seems to be reasonably incorrect. The remaining work for us is to check whether our theories are, by coincidence, in agreement with the observations or not. The cosmic microwave background is still effectively blind to the effects of the entanglement and other interactions in the multiverse, whatever the kind of multiverse is analyzed.[31–35] So, we may wait for a future discovery of the cosmic neutrino background, or the spectrum of the primordial gravitational waves to confirm that some of the theories fit to the observations. Up to that day and even later, the multiverse will remain an unsolvable mystery.

Acknowledgments

This work was supported by the Polish National Research and Development Center (NCBR) project "UNIWERSYTET 2.0. – STREFA KARIERY", POWR.03.05.00-00-Z064/17-00 (2018-2022).

References

1. B. S. DeWitt, Quantum theory of gravity. I. the canonical theory, *Phys. Rev.* **160**, 1113 (1967).
2. C. Kiefer, *Quantum gravity* (2004).
3. C. J. Isham, Canonical quantum gravity and the problem of time, *NATO Sci. Ser. C* **409**, 157 (1993).
4. C. Kiefer, Conceptual Problems in Quantum Gravity and Quantum Cosmology, *ISRN Math. Phys.* **2013**, p. 509316 (2013).
5. C. Rovelli, Notes for a brief history of quantum gravity, in *9th Marcel Grossmann Meeting on Recent Developments in Theoretical and Experimental General Relativity, Gravitation and Relativistic Field Theories (MG 9)*, 6 2000.
6. J. B. Hartle and S. W. Hawking, Wave function of the universe, *Phys. Rev. D* **28**, 2960 (Dec 1983).
7. A. Vilenkin, Quantum creation of universes, *Phys. Rev. D* **30**, 509 (Jul 1984).
8. L. Mersini-Houghton and R. Vaas (eds.), *The Arrows of Time: A Debate in Cosmology* (Springer, 2012).
9. S. Weinberg (ed.), *Cosmology* (Oxford University Press, 2008).
10. D. Rubin and B. Hayden, Is the expansion of the universe accelerating? All signs point to yes, *The Astrophysical Journal* **833** (2016).
11. M. McGuigan, Third quantization and the wheeler-dewitt equation, *Phys. Rev. D* **38**, 3031 (Nov 1988).
12. A. Hosoya and M. Morikawa, Quantum Field Theory of Universe, *Phys. Rev. D* **39** (1989).
13. S. B. Giddings and A. Strominger, Baby Universes, Third Quantization and the Cosmological Constant, *Nucl. Phys. B* **321**, 481 (1989).
14. A. Strominger and J. R. Ellis, Third quantization [and discussion], *Philosophical Transactions of the Royal Society of London. Series A, Mathematical and Physical Sciences* **329**, 395 (1989).
15. M. McGuigan, Universe creation from the third-quantized vacuum, *Phys. Rev. D* **39**, 2229 (Apr 1989).
16. S. J. R. Pérez, Inter-universal entanglement, in *Open Questions in Cosmology*, ed. G. J. Olmo (IntechOpen, Rijeka, 2012)

17. L. Perivolaropoulos and F. Skara, Challenges for ΛCDM: An update (2021).
18. N. D. Birrell and P. C. W. Davies, *Quantum Fields in Curved Space*, Cambridge Monographs on Mathematical Physics (Cambridge Univ. Press, Cambridge, UK, 2 1984).
19. X. Yingming and L. Liao, Third quantization of a solvable model in quantum cosmology in brans-dicke theory, *Chinese Physics Letters* **8**, 52 (Jan 1991).
20. L. O. Pimentel and C. Mora, Third quantization of brans–dicke cosmology, *Physics Letters A* **280**, 191 (2000).
21. A. Balcerzak and K. Marosek, Emergence of multiverse in third quantized varying constants cosmologies, *The European Physical Journal C* **79** (07 2019).
22. H. R. Lewis and W. B. Riesenfeld, An exact quantum theory of the time-dependent harmonic oscillator and of a charged particle in a time-dependent electromagnetic field, *Journal of Mathematical Physics* **10**, 1458 (1969).
23. S. Robles-Pérez, Invariant vacuum, *Physics Letters B* **774**, 608 (2017).
24. S. Robles-Pérez and P. F. González-Díaz, Quantum state of the multiverse, *Phys. Rev. D* **81**, p. 083529 (Apr 2010).
25. S. Robles-Pérez, A. Balcerzak, M. P. Dąbrowski and M. Krämer, Interuniversal entanglement in a cyclic multiverse, *Phys. Rev. D* **95**, p. 083505 (Apr 2017).
26. A. Balcerzak, S. Barroso-Bellido, M. P. Dąbrowski and S. Robles-Pérez, Entanglement entropy at critical points of classical evolution in oscillatory and exotic singularity multiverse models, *Phys. Rev. D* **103**, p. 043507 (Feb 2021).
27. M. Bouhmadi-López, M. Krämer, J. Morais and S. Robles-Pérez, The interacting multiverse and its effect on the cosmic microwave background, *Journal of Cosmology and Astroparticle Physics* **2019**, 057 (Feb 2019).
28. R. Horodecki, P. Horodecki, M. Horodecki and K. Horodecki, Quantum entanglement, *Rev. Mod. Phys.* **81**, 865 (Jun 2009).
29. *Science and Ultimate Reality: Quantum Theory, Cosmology, and Complexity* (Cambridge University Press, 2004).
30. A. Vilenkin, Boundary conditions in quantum cosmology, *Phys. Rev. D* **33**, 3560 (Jun 1986).
31. S. Kanno, Cosmological implications of quantum entanglement in the multiverse, *Physics Letters B* **751**, 316 (2015).
32. W. H. Kinney, Limits on entanglement effects in the string landscape from planck and BICEP/keck data, *Journal of Cosmology and Astroparticle Physics* **2016**, 013 (Nov 2016).
33. E. D. Valentino and L. Mersini-Houghton, Testing predictions of the quantum landscape multiverse 1: The starobinsky inflationary potential, *Journal of Cosmology and Astroparticle Physics* **2017**, 002 (Mar 2017).
34. E. D. Valentino and L. Mersini-Houghton, Testing predictions of the quantum landscape multiverse 2: The exponential inflationary potential, *Journal of Cosmology and Astroparticle Physics* **2017**, 020 (Mar 2017).
35. E. Di Valentino and L. Mersini-Houghton, Testing predictions of the quantum landscape multiverse 3: The hilltop inflationary potential, *Symmetry* **11** (2019).

Effective field theory from relativistic Generalized Uncertainty Principle

Vasil N. Todorinov*, Saurya Das, and Pasquale Bosso

Department of Physics & astronomy, University of Lethbridge,
Lethbridge, AB T1K 3M4, Canada
* E-mail: v.todorinov@uleth.ca
https://www.ulethbridge.ca

Theories of Quantum Gravity predict a minimum measurable length and a corresponding modification of the Heisenberg Uncertainty Principle to the so-called Generalized Uncertainty Principle (GUP). However, this modification is usually formulated in non-relativistic language, making it unclear whether the minimum length is Lorentz invariant. We have formulated a Relativistic Generalized Uncertainty Principle, resulting in a Lorentz invariant minimum measurable length and the resolution of the composition law problem. This proved to be an important step in the formulation of Quantum Field Theory with minimum length. We derived the Lagrangians consistent with the existence of minimal length and describing the behaviour of scalar, spinor, and U(1) gauge fields. We calculated the Feynman rules (propagators and vertices) associated with these Lagrangians. Furthermore, we calculated the Quantum Gravity corrected scattering cross-sections for a lepton-lepton scattering. Finally, we compared our results with current experiments, which allowed us to improve the bounds on the scale at which quantum gravity phenomena will become relevant.

Keywords: Quantum Gravity: Quantum Gravity Phenomenology, Effective Field theory, Generalized Uncertainty Principle

1. Introduction

The quantization of gravity is one of the major outstanding problems of fundamental physics. The family of theories tackling this problem is known as Quantum Gravity (QG). This family is home to a large diversity of ideas and approaches to the problem. The most prevalent members of the family, namely String Theory, Loop Quantum Gravity in addition to models such as Doubly-Special Relativity theories as well as many others, agree on the existence of a minimum measurable length or a similar scale in spacetime. The minimum length is usually considered to be the proportional to the Planck length, $\ell_{Pl} = 10^{-35}m$, and it signifies the scale at which quantum gravity effects would manifest. Currently, we have no access to energy regimes anywhere close to the Planck scale, therefore all theories of QG lack a direct experimental confirmation. The field of Quantum Gravity Phenomenology (QGP) tackles this problem by using the existing theories to make models in order of finding low energy remnants of QG phenomena in already existing experiments.

As we already mentioned, one phenomenon that most theories of QG agree on is the existence of a minimum measurable length, which is in direct contradiction with the Heisenberg uncertainty principle (HUP), since the latter allows for infinitely small uncertainties in position. The solution is the introduction of a new model which deforms the HUP in order to accommodate for a minimal uncertainty in position. The deformed HUP is known as Generalized Uncertainty Principle (GUP), and was first introduced by Kempf, Mangano, and Mann in 1995.[1] One of the possible position-momentum commutators corresponding to a GUP model has the following form

$$[x_i, p_j] = i\hbar \delta_{ij}(1 + \beta_1 p^2) + i\hbar \beta_2 p_i p_j ,\qquad(1)$$

where $\beta_1 = \beta_1^*(\ell_{\text{Pl}}/\hbar)^2$, $\beta_2 = \beta_2^*(\ell_{\text{Pl}}/\hbar)^2$, and β_1^*, β_2^* are numerical coefficients. The GUP model has been successful in modeling a wide array of corrections to quantum mechanical phenomena,[1-58] and has provided compelling bound on the minimum length scale, by comparing the result to existing experimental data.

However, the model introduced by Eq. (1) has two shortcomings:

- The position-momentum commutator and the corresponding uncertainty relation are not Lorentz covariant, and therefore the resulting minimum length is frame dependent,
- *Composition Law Problem*: Energies and momenta do not sum up linearly.[59]

The composition law problem arises due to the fact that deformation of the HUP is done through a generalization of the momentum operator. Namely terms of higher order in momentum are added in order to deform the commutator. This leads to a deformation of the Einstein dispersion relation of the form

$$E^2 = p^2 c^2 + m^2 c^4 \;\rightarrow\; E^2 = p^2 c^2 + m^2 c^4 + \mathcal{O}(p^4). \qquad(2)$$

Consequently one can show that if there are terms of higher than second order in momentum in the dispersion relation, for a composite system moving in the same speed the energies and momenta do not sum up linearly,

$$\vec{p}_3 \neq \vec{p}_2 + \vec{p}_1 \qquad E_3 \neq E_1 + E_2 .\qquad(3)$$

It is important to note that solutions of this problem have been developed, some examples are.[60, 61]

Such problems prevents us to apply the GUP models to Relativistic Quantum Mechanics and Quantum Field Theory, which essentially restricts the energy regimes in which we can search for the remnants of QG effects, by preventing us from using the highest energy experiments currently available, *i.e.* LHC.

In the following sections, we will address these problems by extending the GUP up to second order in Planck length, to relativistic regimes (RGUP), we will explore the deformations of the Lorenz group and symmetries associated with it, and we will obtain Lagrangians allowing for the existence of minimum length for fields of spin-$0, 1/2, 1$.

2. Relativistic Generalized Uncertainty Principle[62]

Inspired by,[63] we will use the most general form of quadratic GUP algebra and extend it to a covariant expression in Minkowski spacetime with the following signature $\{-,+,+,+\}$. The particular form obtained for the commutator is as follows

$$[x^\mu, p^\nu] = i\hbar \left(1 + (\varepsilon - \kappa)\gamma p^\rho p_\rho\right)\eta^{\mu\nu} + i\hbar(\beta + 2\varepsilon)\gamma p^\mu p^\nu, \quad (4)$$

where $\mu, \nu \in \{0, 1, 2, 3\}$. For convenience it is useful to separate the dimensionality of the corrections into a dimensionful parameter γ, with the dimension of inverse momentum, and dimensionless parameters κ, β and ϵ (and also ξ in Eq. (7) below). The scale of the QG effects γ is defined as $\gamma = \frac{1}{(cM_{Pl})^2} = \frac{\ell_{Pl}^2}{\hbar^2}$, where M_{Pl} is the Planck mass, and ℓ_{Pl} is the Planck length. The minimum length we can obtain from the algebra Eq. (4) is of the order of the Planck length. Important to note is that Eq. (4) reduces in the non-relativistic ($c \to \infty$) limit to the one proposed in.[1] Furthermore, in the non-relativistic ($c \to \infty$), and non-GUP limit ($\gamma \to 0$) limit, Eq. (4) reduces to the standard Heisenberg algebra. We can clearly see from the commutator Eq. (4) that while x^μ and p^ν are the physical position and momentum, they are no longer canonically conjugate variables. Therefore, we introduce two auxiliary 4-vectors, x_0^μ and p_0^ν which are canonically conjugate, such that

$$p_0^\mu = -i\hbar \frac{\partial}{\partial x_{0\,\mu}}, \qquad [x_0^\mu, p_0^\nu] = i\hbar\eta^{\mu\nu}. \quad (5)$$

Then we assume that the physical position and momentum are both functions of the auxiliary ones,

$$x^\mu = x^\mu(x_0, p_0), \quad p^\mu = p^\mu(x_0, p_0). \quad (6)$$

By expanding Eq. (6) in Taylor series, which we truncate up to first order in the QG scale γ, and imposition of commutativity in momentum space $[p_\mu, p_\nu] = 0$, we can write the general expressions of the physical position and momentum are as follows

$$x^\mu = x_0^\mu - \kappa\gamma p_0^\rho p_{0\rho} x_0^\mu + \beta\gamma p_0^\mu p_0^\rho x_{0\rho} + \xi\hbar\gamma p_0^\mu, \quad (7)$$

$$p^\mu = p_0^\mu \left(1 + \varepsilon\gamma p_0^\rho p_{0\rho}\right). \quad (8)$$

Using Eqs. (7) and (8), we can calculate the following expression for the position-position commutator

$$[x^\mu, x^\nu] = i\hbar\gamma \frac{-2\kappa + \beta}{1 + (\varepsilon - \kappa)\gamma p^\rho p_\rho} \left(x^\mu p^\nu - x^\nu p^\mu\right). \quad (9)$$

Therefore as in,[1] in this case as well we arrive at a non-commutative spacetime.

We also note that the last two terms in Eq. (7) introduce a preferred direction of p_0^μ and therefore break isotropy of spacetime. Since this violates the principles of relativity, we will assume that $\beta = \xi = 0$ from now on.

2.1. Lorentz and Poincaré algebra

Using Eqs. (7) and (8), we now construct the generators of the Lorentz group

$$M^{\mu\nu} = p^\mu x^\nu - p^\nu x^\mu = [1 + (\varepsilon - \kappa)\gamma p_0^\rho p_{0\,\rho}]\tilde{M}^{\mu\nu}, \tag{10}$$

where $\tilde{M}^{\mu\nu} = p_0^\mu x_0^\nu - p_0^\nu x_0^\mu$ is the Lorentz generators constructed from the canonical variables x_0 and p_0. The commutator representative of the Poincaré algebra for the physical operators can then be calculated

$$[x^\mu, M^{\nu\rho}] = i\hbar[1 + (\varepsilon - \kappa)\gamma p^\rho p_\rho](x^\nu \delta^{\mu\rho} - x^\rho \delta^{\mu\nu}) + i\hbar 2(\varepsilon - \kappa)\gamma p^\mu M^{\nu\rho} \tag{11a}$$

$$[p^\mu, M^{\nu\rho}] = i\hbar[1 + (\varepsilon - \kappa)\gamma p^\rho p_\rho](p^\nu \delta^{\mu\rho} - p^\rho \delta^{\mu\nu}), \tag{11b}$$

$$[M^{\mu\nu}, M^{\rho\sigma}] = i\hbar(1 + (\varepsilon - \kappa)\gamma p^\rho p_\rho)(\eta^{\mu\rho} M^{\nu\sigma} - \eta^{\mu\sigma} M^{\nu\rho} - \eta^{\nu\rho} M^{\mu\sigma} + \eta^{\nu\sigma} M^{\mu\rho}). \tag{11c}$$

From Eqs. (11a,11b,11c), we can see that on the line $\varepsilon = \kappa$ in the parameter space, one has a non-trivial RGUP with an *unmodified* Poincaré algebra. On this line in parameter space, the RGUP algebra and the non-commutativity of spacetime coming from Eqs. (4) and (9) takes this form:

$$[x^\mu, p^\nu] = i\hbar(\eta^{\mu\nu} + 2\kappa\gamma p^\mu p^\nu), \tag{12}$$

$$[x^\mu, x^\nu] = -2i\hbar\kappa\gamma(x^\mu p^\nu - x^\nu p^\mu), \tag{13}$$

where $\kappa > 0$. We notice that for any one-dimensional spatial component, Eq. (12) mirrors the one obtained in.[1] Eqs. (12) and (13) have similarities to the ones proposed in.[53]

2.2. Lorentz invariant minimum length and the Composition Law Problem

The main reason for extending GUP to relativistic frameworks is to make its minimum uncertainty in position Lorentz invariant, or in other words to make a minimum length frame independent. In relativistic QM, position and momentum are promoted to operators and the Lorentz transformations Λ are represented by a unitary operator $U(p^\nu, M^{\rho\sigma})$, i.e. $U^* = U^{-1}$, where p^ν is the generator of translation and $M^{\rho\sigma}$ is the generator of rotations of the Poincaré group. The position and momentum in this case transform as follows

$$x'^\mu = U(p^\nu, M^{\rho\sigma}) x^\mu U^{-1}(p^\nu, M^{\rho\sigma}), \tag{14}$$

$$p'^\mu = U(p^\nu, M^{\rho\sigma}) p^\mu U^{-1}(p^\nu, M^{\rho\sigma}). \tag{15}$$

The operator $U(p^\nu, M^{\rho\sigma})$ can be expressed from the generators of the Poincaré algebra as

$$U(p^\nu, M^{\rho\sigma}) = \exp[ia_\nu p^\nu] \exp\left[i\frac{\omega_{\rho\sigma} M^{\rho\sigma}}{2}\right], \tag{16}$$

where the coordinate system is translated by a vector a_μ and is rotated by $\omega_{\rho\sigma}$.

The position-momentum commutator transforms as follows

$$[x'^\mu, p'^\nu] = U[x^\mu, p^\nu]U^{-1}. \tag{17}$$

Substituting $[x^\mu, p^\nu]$ for its expression as given in Eq. (4), we get

$$[x'^\mu, p'^\nu] = U\left\{i\hbar\left(1 + (\varepsilon - \kappa)\gamma p^\rho p_\rho\right)\eta^{\mu\nu} + i\hbar(\beta + 2\varepsilon)\gamma p^\mu p^\nu\right\}U^{-1} \tag{18a}$$
$$= i\hbar\left(1 + (\varepsilon - \kappa)\gamma p'^\rho p'_\rho\right)\eta^{\mu\nu} + i\hbar(\beta + 2\varepsilon)\gamma U p^\mu U^{-1} U p^\nu U^{-1} \tag{18b}$$
$$= i\hbar\left(1 + (\varepsilon - \kappa)\gamma p'^\rho p'_\rho\right)\eta^{\mu\nu} + i\hbar(\beta + 2\varepsilon)\gamma p'^\mu p'^\nu. \tag{18c}$$

Therefore, the commutator between position and momentum has the same form in every frame. Then, we can safely conclude that every frame will observe the same minimum measurable length.

For the composition law problem, we need to find the dispersion relation and see if it is quadratic or it has terms of higher order in momentum. As we know, the dispersion relation is connected to the Casimir invariants of the Poincaré algebra. In the unmodified case, there are two Casimir invariants: the momentum squared $p_0^\mu p_{0\mu}$; and the physical Pauli-Lubanski vector squared $\tilde{W}^\mu \tilde{W}_\mu$, where

$$\tilde{W}_\mu \equiv \frac{1}{2}\varepsilon_{\mu\nu\rho\sigma}\tilde{M}^{\nu\rho}p_0^\sigma. \tag{19}$$

In our case, both the Poincare algebra and the momentum and Pauli-Lubanski vectors are deformed. However, by taking the commutator between the physical momentum squared $p^\mu p_\mu$ and all the other generators of the algebra, it can easily be shown that it is a Casimir invariant of the modified Poincaré algebra presented in Eq. (11). This can be repeated for the Pauli-Lubanski vector squared as well.

This shows that our dispersion relation can be written as

$$p_\mu p^\mu = -m^2 c^4. \tag{20}$$

As we can see, the dispersion relation is quadratic in the physical momentum which means that energies and momenta sum up linearly as they should. It is important to note that due to the fact that the physical momentum is a polynomial of the auxiliary one, the resulting equations of motion will be of higher than second order.

3. Effective Quantum Field Theory with Minimum Length[64,65]

Having cleared up the frame dependence and the composition law problem for our model, we can proceed to apply it to quantum field theory.

In the general case, the commutation relation we get for the position-position operator depends on the momentum. Therefore, it does not form an algebra and it cannot be represented by a smooth Lie manifold. For that reason we have chosen for further calculations to fix the model by making $\kappa = 0$ and $\epsilon = \gamma_0$. We can redefine the RGUP parameter as follows

$$\gamma = \frac{\gamma_0}{(M_{\text{Pl}}c)^2}. \tag{21}$$

In this particular model, the physical position and momentum take the form

$$x^\mu = x_0^\mu, \qquad (22a)$$
$$p^\mu = p_0^\mu \left(1 + \gamma p_0^\rho p_{0\rho}\right). \qquad (22b)$$

From now on, the results will be presented in natural units, i.e. $c = \hbar = 1$. With the parameters redefined as such, the position-momentum commutator is

$$[x^\mu, p^\nu] = i \left(1 + \gamma p^\rho p_\rho\right) \eta^{\mu\nu} + 2i \gamma p^\mu p^\nu. \qquad (23)$$

The Poincaré group corresponding to the RGUP above is represented by the following algebra

$$[x^\mu, M^{\nu\rho}] = i[1 + \gamma p^\rho p_\rho] \left(x^\nu \delta^{\mu\rho} - x^\rho \delta^{\mu\nu}\right) + i2\gamma p^\mu M^{\nu\rho}, \qquad (24a)$$
$$[p^\mu, M^{\nu\rho}] = i[1 + \gamma p^\rho p_\rho] \left(p^\nu \delta^{\mu\rho} - p^\rho \delta^{\mu\nu}\right), \qquad (24b)$$
$$[M^{\mu\nu}, M^{\rho\sigma}] = i \left(1 + \gamma p^\rho p_\rho\right) \left(\eta^{\mu\rho} M^{\nu\sigma} - \eta^{\mu\sigma} M^{\nu\rho} - \eta^{\nu\rho} M^{\mu\sigma} + \eta^{\nu\sigma} M^{\mu\rho}\right). \qquad (24c)$$

It is important to note that the deformed Poincaré algebra presented above has the same irreducible representations, and therefore describes the same particles as the standard Poincaré algebra. This feature can be seen derived in Appendix B. As we already showed, the physical momentum squared is a Casimir invariant of the modified Poincaré algebra presented above in Eq. (24). Therefore, the Einstein dispersion relation for our case is

$$p^\mu p_\mu = -m^2, \qquad (25)$$

where p_μ is the physical momentum, the differential form of which is an equation of motion for any Lagrangian describing a boson field. The Dirac equations i.e., the equations of motion describing the dynamics of fermion fields, can also be easily derived. Starting from the dispersion relation Eq. (25) and expressing it in terms of the auxiliary variables defined in Eq. (22a), we get the modified Klein-Gordon equation in its differential form

$$\left[\partial_\mu \partial^\mu \left(1 + \gamma \partial_\nu \partial^\nu\right)^2 + m\right] \phi = 0. \qquad (26)$$

Similarly, the differential form of the Dirac equation is shown to be

$$(\tau^\mu p_\mu - m)\psi = \left[\tau^\mu p_{0\,\mu}(1 + \gamma p_{0\rho} p_0^\rho) - m\right]\psi = 0, \qquad (27)$$

where τ^μ are the Dirac matrices and ψ is a Dirac spinor. We can show that as part of the Lorentz group the generators of the Clifford algebra $Cl_{(3,1)}(\mathbb{R})$, if the Casimir is preserved then the properties of the Clifford algebra will remain unchanged, as well. This is true in our case, thus,

$$\left[i\tau^\mu \partial_\mu (1 + \gamma \partial_\rho \partial^\rho)^2 - m\right] \psi = 0, \qquad (28)$$

and its Dirac conjugate are the equations of motion for the RGUP-QED Lagrangian.

4. RGUP Modified Lagrangians

In the previous section, we established the modified equations of motion for the scalar, vector, and spinor fields. Note that the equations of motion are differential equations of higher than second order. Therefore, the Lagrangians corresponding to these equations of motion need to have higher than second derivative. The methodology of working with higher derivative Lagrangians

$$L = L(\phi, \dot{\phi}, \ddot{\phi}, \ldots, \overset{(n)}{\phi}), \tag{29a}$$

$$\mathcal{L} = \mathcal{L}(\phi, \partial_{\mu_1}\phi, \partial_{\mu_1}\partial_{\mu_2}\phi, \ldots, \partial_{\mu_1}\ldots\partial_{\mu_n}\phi), \tag{29b}$$

is given by the Ostrogradsky method.[66–68] The Euler-Lagrange equations for theories with higher derivatives will have the form:

$$\frac{dL}{dq} - \frac{d}{dt}\frac{dL}{d\dot{q}} + \frac{d^2}{dt^2}\frac{dL}{d\ddot{q}} + \ldots + (-1)^n \frac{d^n}{dt^n}\frac{dL}{d(d^n q/dt^n)} = 0, \tag{30}$$

which in the case of fields is

$$\frac{\partial\mathcal{L}}{\partial\phi} - \partial_\mu \frac{\partial\mathcal{L}}{\partial(\partial_\mu\phi)} + \partial_{\mu_1}\partial_{\mu_2}\frac{\partial\mathcal{L}}{\partial(\partial_{\mu_1}\partial_{\mu_2}\phi)} + \ldots + (-1)^m \partial_{\mu_1}\ldots\partial_{\mu_m}\frac{\partial\mathcal{L}}{\partial(\partial_{\mu_1}\ldots\partial_{\mu_m}\phi)} = 0. \tag{31}$$

The Ostrogradsky method allows us to reconstruct the Lagrangian describing the dynamics of scalar and spinor fields from their equations of motion.

4.1. Scalar field Lagrangian

We begin by assuming the most general form of higher derivative Lagrangian, which is one order higher than the equations of motion

$$\mathcal{L} = \frac{1}{2}\partial_\mu\phi\partial^\mu\phi + \gamma\left(C_1\,\partial_\mu\partial^\mu\phi\,\partial_\nu\partial^\nu\phi + C_2\,\partial_\mu\phi\,\partial^\mu\partial_\nu\partial^\nu\phi + C_3\,\partial_\nu\partial^\nu\partial^\mu\phi\,\partial_\mu\phi\right)$$
$$+ \gamma^2\left(C_4\,\partial_\mu\partial^\mu\partial_\nu\phi\,\partial^\nu\partial_\rho\partial^\rho\phi + C_5\,\partial_\mu\partial^\mu\partial_\nu\partial^\nu\phi\,\partial_\rho\partial^\rho\phi + C_6\,\partial_\mu\partial^\mu\partial_\nu\partial^\nu\partial_\rho\phi\,\partial^\rho\phi\right.$$
$$\left.+ C_7\,\partial_\mu\partial^\mu\phi\,\partial_\nu\partial^\nu\partial_\rho\partial^\rho\phi + C_8\,\partial_\mu\phi\,\partial^\mu\partial_\nu\partial^\nu\partial_\rho\partial^\rho\phi\right) + C_9 m^2\phi^2, \tag{32}$$

where $\partial_\mu = \partial/\partial x^\mu$. Using the Euler-Lagrange equation prescribed by the Ostrogradsky method Eq. (30), we obtain the following Lagrangian

$$\mathcal{L}_{\phi,\mathbb{R}} = \frac{1}{2}\partial_\mu\phi\partial^\mu\phi - \frac{1}{2}m^2\phi^2 + \gamma\,\partial_\nu\partial^\nu\partial^\mu\phi\,\partial_\mu\phi + \frac{\gamma^2}{2}\partial_\mu\phi\,\partial^\mu\partial_\nu\partial^\nu\partial_\rho\partial^\rho\phi, \tag{33}$$

As for the Lagrangian for a complex scalar field ϕ, we generalize Eq. (33) by including additional terms obtaining

$$\mathcal{L}_{\phi,\mathbb{C}} = \frac{1}{2}(\partial_\mu\phi)^\dagger\partial^\mu\phi - \frac{1}{2}m^2\phi^\dagger\phi + \gamma\left[(\partial_\nu\partial^\nu\partial^\mu\phi)^\dagger\partial_\mu\phi + \partial_\nu\partial^\nu\partial^\mu\phi\,(\partial_\mu\phi)^\dagger\right]$$
$$+ \frac{\gamma^2}{2}\left[(\partial_\mu\phi)^\dagger\partial^\mu\partial_\nu\partial^\nu\partial_\rho\partial^\rho\phi + \partial_\mu\phi\,(\partial^\mu\partial_\nu\partial^\nu\partial_\rho\partial^\rho\phi)^\dagger\right], \tag{34}$$

such that hermiticity is restored, i.e. $\mathcal{L}^\dagger_{\phi,\mathbb{C}} = \mathcal{L}_{\phi,\mathbb{C}}$. Furthermore, it is worth noticing that Eq. (34) is consistent with Eq. (55) in[42] up to a numerical factor.

4.2. Spinor field Lagrangian

The first step in the derivation of the spinor field Lagrangian is to assume a general form of the Lagrangian, where the order of derivatives is determined by the order of the equation of motion Eq. (28). Moreover, an assumption is made that different terms will be multiplied by an arbitrary numerical coefficient

$$\mathcal{L}_\psi = \bar{\psi} \left[iC_1 \tau^\mu \partial_\mu (1 + C_2 \gamma \partial_\rho \partial^\rho) - C_3 m \right] \psi. \tag{35}$$

Next step is to prove that it has Eq. (28) as an equation of motion. Applying the Ostrogradsky method, one gets the following equations of motion for the field and its complex conjugate

$$C_1 i \tau^\mu \partial_\mu \psi + C_1 C_2 \gamma \partial_\rho \partial^\rho \psi - C_3 m \psi = 0, \tag{36}$$

$$C_1 i \tau^\mu \partial_\mu \bar{\psi} + C_1 C_2 \gamma \partial_\rho \partial^\rho \bar{\psi} - C_3 m \bar{\psi} = 0. \tag{37}$$

The equations of motion obtained through the Ostrogradsky method from Eq. (35) need to be identical to Eq. (28), which is obtained from the dispersion relation. Therefore, the Lagrangian corresponding to the QFT spinor with minimum length will be of the form

$$\mathcal{L}_\psi = \bar{\psi} \left[i \tau^\mu \partial_\mu (1 - \gamma \partial_\rho \partial^\rho) - m \right] \psi. \tag{38}$$

4.3. $U(1)$ gauge field theory

The gauge field Lagrangian is obtained in a different way. The Ostrogradsky method is not utilized in this case. The derivation is done by firstly assuming that the vector boson A^μ obeys the ususal $U(1)$ gauge symmetries. For the equations of motion, we assume that they have the same RGUP corrections as the KG equation of the form Eq. (26)

$$\partial_\mu F^{\mu\nu} = \partial_\mu \partial^\mu A^\nu + 2\gamma \partial_\mu \partial^\mu \partial_\rho \partial^\rho A^\nu = 0. \tag{39}$$

Defining the standard gauge invariant field strength tensor as

$$F_0^{\mu\nu} = \partial^\mu A^\nu - \partial^\nu A^\mu, \tag{40}$$

one can express the RGUP modified field strength tensor in terms of the standard one up to first order in γ, as follows:

$$F^{\mu\nu} = F_0^{\mu\nu} + 2\gamma \partial_\rho \partial^\rho F_0^{\mu\nu}. \tag{41}$$

Then Eq. (39) can be rewritten as

$$\partial_\mu F^{\mu\nu} = \partial_\mu F_0^{\mu\nu} + 2\gamma \partial_\rho \partial^\rho \partial_\mu F_0^{\mu\nu} + \gamma^2 \partial_\sigma \partial^\sigma \partial_\rho \partial^\rho \partial_\mu F_0^{\mu\nu}. \tag{42}$$

A test of gauge invariance of $F^{\mu\nu}$ is carried through by considering the following gauge transformation of the four-potential

$$A^\mu \to A'^\mu = A^\mu + \partial^\mu \Lambda, \tag{43}$$

and the field strength tensor is shown to be gauge invariant. Thus, up to first order in the RGUP parameter γ, the gauge field Lagrangian reads

$$\mathcal{L}_A = -\frac{1}{4} F^{\mu\nu} F_{\mu\nu} = -\frac{1}{4} F_0^{\mu\nu} F_{\mu\nu 0} - \frac{\gamma}{2} F_{\mu\nu 0} \partial_\rho \partial^\rho F_0^{\mu\nu} . \tag{44}$$

Notice that both the field tensor in Eq. (41) and the gauge field Lagrangian Eq. (44) are invariant under $U(1)$ gauge transformations.

5. Feynman Rules

We use the Lagrangians derived above to formulate a RGUP deformed scalar and spinor electrodynamics. This is achieved by minimally coupling the lepton to the gauge fields. The Feynman rules, consisting of the propagators and vertices for both cases, are calculated using the standard methodology, which can be found in any QFT textbook.

5.1. Propagators

The Feynman propagator for the scalar field with a minimum length is the Green's function of the the modified KG equation in Eq. (26)

$$\left[\partial_\mu \partial^\mu (1 + \gamma \partial_\nu \partial^\nu) + (mc)^2\right] G(x - x') = -i\delta(x - x') . \tag{45}$$

Expressing the Green's function $G(x - x')$ in terms of its Fourier transform

$$G(x - x') = \int \frac{d^4 p_0}{(2\pi)^4} \tilde{G}(p_0) e^{-i p_0 \cdot (x - x')} , \tag{46}$$

and substituting it in Eq. (45), we get

$$\int \frac{d^4 p_0}{(2\pi)^4} \tilde{G}(p_0) \left[-p_0^2(1 - \gamma p_0^2) + (mc)^2\right] e^{-i p_0 \cdot (x - x')} = -i \int \frac{d^4 p_0}{(2\pi)^4} e^{-i p_0 \cdot (x - x')} . \tag{47}$$

The Fourier transform of the Feynman propagator is

$$\tilde{G}(p_0) = \frac{-i}{-p_0^2(1 + \gamma p_0^2) + (mc)^2} , \tag{48}$$

while the propagator itself is

$$G(x - x') = \int \frac{d^4 p_0}{(2\pi)^4} \frac{-i}{-p_0^2(1 + \gamma p_0^2) + (mc)^2} e^{-i p_0 \cdot (x - x')} . \tag{49}$$

With the exception of a little trick consisting of multiplying both sides by

$$[\tau^\mu p_{0\,\mu}(1 - \gamma p_{0\rho} p_0^\rho) + m] , \tag{50}$$

we find the Dirac field propagator in the same way

$$G(x - x') = \int \frac{d^4 p_0}{(2\pi)^4} \frac{-i \left[\tau^\mu p_{0\,\mu}(1 + \gamma p_{0\rho} p_0^\rho) + m\right]}{p_0^\mu p_{0\,\mu}(1 + \gamma p_{0\rho} p_0^\rho)^2 - m^2} e^{-i p_0 \cdot (x - x')} . \tag{51}$$

Again, the gauge field propagator can be treated in a similar manner. And the Feynman propagator is found to be

$$G(x - x') = \int \frac{d^4 q_0}{(2\pi)^4} \frac{-i}{-q_0^2 + 2\gamma q_0^4} e^{-i q_0 \cdot (x - x')}, \qquad (52)$$

where q_0 is the auxiliary four-momentum of the gauge field.

This construction assumes that one can define Dirac delta functions in position space, and the minimal length arises when one tries to localize the fields.

5.2. Vertices

The complete set of Feynman rules for the system requires the calculation of the vertices for the charged and gauge fields. Starting from the Lagrangian in Eq. (34), one introduces the minimal coupling as follows

$$\partial_\mu \to D_\mu = \partial_\mu - ieA_\mu, \qquad (53)$$

where A_μ is the four-potential or the gauge field.

Replacing partials in Eq. (34) by covariant derivatives, the full action of the minimally coupled complex scalar field and the gauge field is obtained. The action reads as follows

$$\int \mathcal{L} d^4 x = \int [\mathcal{L}_A + \mathcal{L}_{\phi,\mathbb{C}}] \, d^4 x = \int \left\{ \frac{1}{2} (D_\mu \phi)^\dagger D^\mu \phi - \frac{1}{2} m^2 \phi^\dagger \phi \right.$$
$$- \frac{1}{4} F^{\mu\nu} F_{\mu\nu} + \gamma \left[(D_\nu D^\nu D^\mu \phi)^\dagger D_\mu \phi + D_\nu D^\nu D^\mu \phi (D_\mu \phi)^\dagger \right]$$
$$\left. + \frac{\gamma^2}{2} \left[(D_\mu \phi)^\dagger D^\mu D_\nu D^\nu D_\rho D^\rho \phi + D_\mu \phi (D^\mu D_\nu D^\nu D_\rho D^\rho \phi)^\dagger \right] \right\} d^4 x. \qquad (54)$$

By expanding the Lagrangian we get a very rich theory

$$\mathcal{L} = \frac{1}{2} (\partial_\mu \phi)^\dagger \partial^\mu \phi - ieA^\mu \left[\phi^\dagger \partial_\mu \phi - \phi (\partial_\mu \phi)^\dagger \right] - \frac{1}{2} m^2 \phi^\dagger \phi + e^2 A_\mu A^\mu \phi^\dagger \phi$$
$$- \frac{1}{4} F^{\mu\nu} F_{\mu\nu} \gamma \left\{ (\partial_\nu \partial^\nu \partial^\mu \phi)^\dagger \partial_\mu \phi + \partial_\nu \partial^\nu \partial^\mu \phi (\partial_\mu \phi)^\dagger - \frac{1}{4} F^{\mu\nu} F_{\mu\nu} \partial_\mu \partial_\nu F^{\mu\nu} \right.$$
$$- ie \left\{ (\partial_\nu \partial^\nu A^\mu) \left[\phi^\dagger \partial_\mu \phi - \phi (\partial_\mu \phi)^\dagger \right] + 2 \partial_\nu A^\mu \left[(\partial^\nu \phi)^\dagger \partial_\mu \phi - \partial^\nu \phi (\partial_\mu \phi^\dagger) \right] \right.$$
$$+ A^\mu \left[(\partial_\nu \partial^\nu \phi)^\dagger \partial_\mu \phi - \partial_\nu \partial^\nu \phi (\partial_\mu \phi^\dagger) \right] \right\} + e^2 \left\{ A^\nu (\partial_\nu A_\mu) \left[(\partial^\mu \phi)^\dagger \phi + (\partial^\mu \phi) \phi^\dagger \right] \right.$$
$$+ 2 A^\nu A_\mu \left[(\partial^\mu \phi)^\dagger \partial_\nu \phi + (\partial^\mu \phi) (\partial_\nu \phi)^\dagger \right] + A^\nu A_\nu \left[(\partial^\mu \phi)^\dagger \partial_\mu \phi + (\partial^\mu \phi) (\partial_\mu \phi)^\dagger \right]$$
$$- 2 A^\mu A^\nu \left[\phi^\dagger \partial_\nu \partial_\mu \phi + \phi (\partial_\nu \partial_\mu \phi)^\dagger \right] + 2 A^\mu (\partial_\nu \partial^\nu A_\mu) \phi^\dagger \phi$$
$$+ A^\mu (\partial^\nu A_\mu) \left[\phi^\dagger \partial_\nu \phi + \phi (\partial_\nu \phi)^\dagger \right] + A^\mu A_\mu \left[\phi^\dagger \partial_\nu \partial^\nu \phi + \phi (\partial_\nu \partial^\nu \phi)^\dagger \right] \right\}$$
$$+ ie^3 \left\{ A_\mu A_\nu A^\nu \left[\phi (\partial^\mu \phi)^\dagger - \phi^\dagger \partial^\mu \phi \right] + 2 A^\mu A_\mu A^\nu \left[\phi^\dagger \partial_\nu \phi - \phi (\partial_\nu \phi)^\dagger \right] \right\}$$
$$+ 2 e^4 A^\mu A_\mu A^\nu A_\nu \phi^\dagger \phi \right\} + \mathcal{O}(\gamma^2). \qquad (55)$$

The above expression contains all terms relevant to Feynman diagrams predicted by the usual scalar Quantum Electrodynamics (QED) Lagrangian with the addition of RGUP corrections. By counting the fields in each term, it is easy to see that up to 6-point vertices (2 scalar and 4 gauge) are allowed. This Lagrangian contains 74 Feynman diagrams, with coupling constants classified by powers of the fine structure constant α and the minimum length parameter γ, see Table 1. It is also worth mentioning that in the low energy limit $\gamma \to 0$ we recover the usual Lagrangian for a complex scalar fields.

Table 1. Classification of the Feynman vertices arising from Eq. (55) in terms of the powers of the coupling constants: α the fine structure constant; γ the minimum length coefficient.

	Powers of γ			
Powers of α	$\alpha^{1/2}$	$\alpha^{1/2}\gamma$	$\alpha^{1/2}\gamma^2$	$\alpha^{1/2}\gamma^3$
	α	$\alpha\gamma$	$\alpha\gamma^2$	$\alpha\gamma^3$
	N/A	$\alpha^{3/2}\gamma$	$\alpha^{3/2}\gamma^2$	$\alpha^{3/2}\gamma^3$
	N/A	$\alpha^2\gamma$	$\alpha^2\gamma^2$	$\alpha^2\gamma^3$
	N/A	$\alpha^{5/2}\gamma$	$\alpha^{5/2}\gamma^2$	$\alpha^{5/2}\gamma^3$
	N/A	$\alpha^3\gamma$	$\alpha^3\gamma^2$	$\alpha^3\gamma^3$

Similar procedure is done for the Dirac field Lagrangian the full RGUP-QED action reads

$$S = \int \mathcal{L}\, d^4x = \int [\mathcal{L}_A + \mathcal{L}_\psi]\, d^4x$$
$$= \int \bar{\psi}\left[i\tau^\mu D_\mu \psi - \gamma \bar{\psi} i\tau^\mu D_\mu D_\nu D^\nu \psi - \frac{1}{4}F^{\mu\nu}F_{\mu\nu}\right] d^4x. \qquad (56)$$

We can read off the vertices after we expand the covariant derivatives in the minimally coupled modified Dirac field Lagrangian Eq. (38)

$$\mathcal{L}_\psi = i\bar{\psi}\tau^\mu \partial_\mu \psi + i\gamma\bar{\psi}\tau^\mu \partial^\rho \partial_\rho \partial_\mu \psi - m\bar{\psi}\psi$$
$$- e\left[\bar{\psi}\tau^\mu A_\mu \psi - 2\gamma\bar{\psi}\tau^\mu (\partial_\mu A^\rho) \partial_\rho \psi - 2\gamma\bar{\psi}\tau^\mu A^\rho \partial_\mu \partial_\rho \psi - \gamma\bar{\psi}\tau^\mu A_\mu \partial^\rho \partial_\rho \psi\right]$$
$$- ie^2\gamma\left[2\bar{\psi}\tau^\mu A_\mu A^\rho \partial_\rho \psi + 2\bar{\psi}\tau^\mu (\partial_\mu A^\rho) A_\rho \psi - \bar{\psi}\tau^\mu A^\rho A_\rho \partial_\mu \psi\right]$$
$$- e^3\gamma\bar{\psi}\tau_\mu A^\mu A^\rho A_\rho \psi. \qquad (57)$$

Up to five particle vertices allowed, they include always two fermions and from one to three gauge bosons. Furthermore, the coupling constants for each vertex are a product of powers of the electronic charge e and the RGUP coefficient γ. In fact, the power of the electronic charge determines how many bosons couple to the vertex and the power of γ is 0 for the usual terms and 1 for the RGUP corrections terms. As before we can classify the coupling constants in Table 2.

Table 2. Classification of the coupling constants in Eq. (57) in terms of the powers: α the fine structure constant; γ the minimum length coefficient.

	Powers of γ	
	$\alpha^{1/2}$	$\alpha^{1/2}\gamma$
Powers of α	N/A	$\alpha\gamma$
	N/A	$\alpha^{3/2}\gamma$

6. RGUP Corrections to QED Scattering Amplitudes

The calculations for the scattering amplitudes can be quite cumbersome so we will not present them in full here. If the reader is interested the full calculations are presented in.[64,65,69]

The particular case we will be studying is an electron-muon scattering. We made this choice to avoid mass degeneracies which will complicate our calculations without helping in clarifying the concept. First when calculating the scattering amplitudes the focus will be on the 3-point vertices, containing up to first order the RGUP coefficient γ. This approximation is justified by the fact that the 3-point vertices will have the largest contribution to the scattering amplitudes.

In brief, we begin by calculating the transition amplitudes for a single three legged vertex. For the scalar field we get

$$T_{fi} = -i \int eA^\mu \left[\phi_f^\dagger \partial_\mu \phi_i - \phi_f \partial_\mu \phi_i^\dagger \right] d^4x$$
$$-i \int e\gamma A^\mu \left[4\partial_\nu \partial^\nu \phi^\dagger \partial_\mu \phi + 4\partial^\nu \phi^\dagger \partial_\nu \partial_\mu \phi + \phi^\dagger \partial_\nu \partial^\nu \partial_\mu \phi - 4\partial_\nu \partial^\nu \phi \partial_\mu \phi^\dagger \right.$$
$$\left. - 4\partial^\nu \phi \partial_\nu \partial_\mu \phi^\dagger - \phi \partial_\nu \partial^\nu \partial_\mu \phi^\dagger \right] d^4x . \tag{58a}$$

In the QED case we get for the different components

$$T_{fi} = i \int e\bar{\psi}_f \tau^\mu A_\mu \psi_i \, d^4x + i \int 2e\gamma \partial_\rho \bar{\psi}_f \tau^\rho A^\mu \partial_\mu \psi_i \, d^4x ,$$
$$- i \int e\gamma \bar{\psi} \tau^\mu A_\mu \partial^\rho \partial_\rho \psi \, d^4x . \tag{59a}$$

The separation in different terms is purely for convenience.

We then couple two Feynman vertices thorough a gauge boson A^μ, and isolate the modified invariant amplitude squared

$$|\mathfrak{M}_{\text{Scalar}}|^2 = 4\pi\alpha \frac{3 + \cos\theta}{1 - \cos\theta} \left[1 + 8\gamma E^2 (1 - \cos\theta) \right] , \tag{60a}$$

$$|\mathfrak{M}_{\text{spinor}}|^2 = 32\pi^2 \epsilon_0^2 \alpha \left[\frac{t^2 + u^2}{s^2} + \frac{1}{2}\gamma(m_e^2 + m_{\text{muon}}^2) \frac{tu - u^2}{s^2} \right] , \tag{60b}$$

where s, t, u are the Mandelstam variables given by

$$s = (k+k')^2 = (p+p')^2 \approx 2k \cdot k' \approx 2p \cdot p', \tag{61a}$$

$$t = (k-p)^2 = (p'-k')^2 \approx -2k \cdot p \approx -2k' \cdot p', \tag{61b}$$

$$u = (k-p')^2 = (p-k') \approx -2k \cdot p' \approx -2p \cdot k'. \tag{61c}$$

From here, it is easy to calculate the RGUP scaled transition rates, from which we can isolate a formula for the differential cross-ectons for both cases. For the scalar fields, the differential cross-section is

$$\left.\frac{d\sigma}{d\Omega}\right|_{CM} = \frac{1}{4s}\alpha^2 \left(\frac{3+\cos\theta}{1-\cos\theta}\right)^2 \left[1 + 16\gamma E^2(1-\cos\theta)\right], \tag{62}$$

and for the spinors

$$\left.\frac{d\sigma}{d\Omega}\right|_{CM} = \frac{\alpha^2}{4s}\left[\frac{1}{2}\left(1+\cos^2\theta\right) + \frac{1}{4}\gamma(m_e^2 + m_{\text{muon}}^2)\left(\cos\theta + \cos^2\theta\right)\right]. \tag{63}$$

As one can see from the differential cross-section for the scalar fields Eq. (62), the magnitude og QG effects depends on the energy of the scattering squared, and it will be largest for the backscattering. We can see that this is also the case in the spinor case Eq. (63). It is interesting to note that for the spinor case the corrections depend on the mass squared of the particles involved. This suggests that minimum length effects on scattering amplitudes may be measurable for electromagnetic scattering of heavier systems, such as scattering of heavy ions. Applied to existing data from the Xe-Xe scattering observed in the ATLAS experiment, the order of magnitude of the corrections is $\gamma m_{\text{Xe}}^2/4 \sim 10^{-34}$.[70] The respective upper bounds on the RGUP parameter are then set to be $\gamma_0 < 10^{34}$.

7. Conclusion

In this work we have extended the Generalized Uncertainty Principle to relativistic framework. This leads to the solution of two major problems: the dependence of the minimum measurable length on the frame of reference; and the composition law problem. This allowed us to extend the reach of GUP from experiments and effects in Quantum Mechanics into Quantum Fired Theory. We achieved that through the formulation of Effective Field Theory with minimum length. Further, we were able to calculate the scattering amplitudes for high-enegy scattering of scalar and spinor particles. Comparing our results to data collecd in the ATLAS experiments, we were able to obtain bounds on the RGUP parameters, *i.e.* $\gamma_0 < 10^{34}$. This bound does not seem impressive on the first glance, however, it is sixteen orders of magnitude improvement compared to previous results from purely quadratic GUP models.

Additionally, we have already been able to obtain RGUP modified action for a spin-2 particle, and through the classical limit connect it to quadratic gravity, allowing us to test our ideas into fields like cosmological inflation.

The results presented here provide a valuable step to extend the reach of Quantum Gravity Phenomenology to the most highly energetic earthbound experiments like LHC. For example, we need to generalize the results here for the gauge group of the Standard Model $U(1)\otimes SU(2)\otimes SU(3)$. Additionally, the gauge field Lagrangian can be used to calculate corrections to phenomena in classical electrodynamics and light propagation, amongst others, like cosmology with weakly self-interacting photons, gravitational waves, and Higgs mechanism and mass.

Appendix A. Ostrogradsky Method and Vacuum Instability

The Ostrogradsky method is a mathematical constructions allowing one to work with higher derivative Lagrangians.[66–68] One of the major issues with it, is the instability of the Hamiltonian, arising when one considers higher than second order derivative. The instability for the particular case presented in here is discussed in the following appendix. We show that the Hamiltonian for a scalar field is positively defined in sub Planckian regimes, thus fixing the applicable domain for our Effective field theory.

We from the equation of motion for the real scalar field, obtained from the modified dispersion relation which corresponds to the Casimir operator of the modified Poincaré group defined in[62]

$$p_0^\rho p_{0\rho}(1 + 2\alpha\gamma^2 p_0^\sigma p_{0\sigma}) = -(mc)^2 . \tag{A.1}$$

The Lagrangian for a real scalar field is derived by assuming the most general form of the Lagrangian, and applying the Ostrogradsky method to obtain its equations of motion and comparing to Eq. (A.1). The form of the Lagrangian is

$$\mathcal{L}_{\phi,\mathbb{R}} = \frac{1}{2}\partial_\mu\phi\partial^\mu\phi - \frac{1}{2}m^2\phi^2 + \gamma\partial_\nu\partial^\nu\partial^\mu\phi\partial_\mu\phi . \tag{A.2}$$

The generalized coordinates are defined as

$$q_1 \equiv \phi \quad q_2 \equiv \partial_\mu\partial^\mu\phi . \tag{A.3}$$

The generalized momenta are then derived as

$$\pi_\rho^{\mu\rho} = \frac{\partial\mathcal{L}}{\partial(\partial_\mu\partial_\rho\partial^\rho\phi)} = 2\gamma\partial^\mu\phi , \tag{A.4a}$$

$$\pi^\mu = \frac{\partial\mathcal{L}}{\partial(\partial_\mu\phi)} - \partial_\sigma\partial^\sigma\pi_\rho^{\mu\rho} = \partial^\mu\phi . \tag{A.4b}$$

The Hamiltonian density is then obtained using the Ostrogradsky Legendre transformations

$$\mathcal{H} = \pi^\mu\partial_\mu\phi + \pi_\rho^{\mu\rho}\partial_\sigma\partial^\sigma\partial_\mu\phi - \frac{1}{2}\pi^\mu\pi_\mu - \pi_\rho^{\mu\rho}\partial^\sigma\partial_\sigma\pi_\mu + \frac{1}{2}m\phi^2 \tag{A.5a}$$

$$= \frac{1}{2}\pi^\mu\pi_\mu + \frac{1}{2}m^2\phi^2 . \tag{A.5b}$$

We can easily see that the above is positive definite. However, we can also see that the correction terms cancel, the Quantum Gravity corrections are hidden in the dispersion relation of ϕ. The field ϕ is solution of Eq. (A.1) which has four different solutions all containing Quantum Gravity corrections. The calculation above is done in the framework of De Donder Weyl Covariant Hamiltonian Formulation of Field Theory.

Considering the same definition of generalized coordinates presented in Eq. (A.3), one can derive the field momenta outside of the De Donder Weyl formulation as

$$\pi_\rho^\rho = \frac{\partial \mathcal{L}}{\partial(\partial_\rho \partial^\rho \phi)} = 2\gamma\dot\phi, \tag{A.6a}$$

$$\pi = \frac{\partial \mathcal{L}}{\partial(\dot\phi)} - \partial_\sigma \partial^\sigma \pi_\rho^\rho = \dot\phi. \tag{A.6b}$$

Performing the Legendre transformation the Hamiltonian density is obtained as

$$\mathcal{H} = \pi\dot\phi + \pi_\rho^\rho \partial_\sigma \partial^\sigma \dot\phi - \frac{1}{2}\pi\pi - \pi_\rho^\rho \partial^\sigma \partial_\sigma \pi + \frac{1}{2}m\phi^2$$
$$+ \frac{1}{2}(\nabla\phi)\cdot(\nabla\phi) + \gamma(\nabla\phi)\cdot(\partial_\sigma \partial^\sigma \nabla\phi) \tag{A.7}$$

$$= \frac{1}{2}\pi\pi + \frac{1}{2}m\phi^2 + \frac{1}{2}(\nabla\phi)\cdot(\nabla\phi) + \gamma(\nabla\phi)\cdot(\partial_\sigma \partial^\sigma \nabla\phi). \tag{A.8}$$

We can not be sure if he Hamiltonian density is positive definite. This is due to the fact that one is not sure of the sign of the term proportional to $\gamma = \frac{\gamma_0}{(M_{Pl}\,c)^2}$. If one assumes that γ_0 is of the order one, the coefficient is $\gamma \sim 10^{-38}$. Therefore, for energies smaller than the Planck energy $E < E_{Pl}$, the leading order terms in Eq. (A.7) are several orders of magnitude bigger than the quantum gravity corrections, which means that the Hamiltonian density on the whole is positive definite and does *not* have Ostrogradsky instability. Conclusion about the positive definition of the Hamiltonian for energies bigger than the Planck energy $E > E_{Pl}$ cannot be drawn. Making the QFT presented here an effective theory.

Appendix B. Modified Poincaré Algebra Representations

Let us explore the RGUP modified Poincaré algebra. The physical position x_μ and momentum p_μ are functions of the auxiliary ones represented as

$$x^\mu = x_0^\mu \tag{B.1a}$$
$$p^\mu = p_0^\mu \left(1 + \gamma p_0^\rho p_{0\rho}\right). \tag{B.1b}$$

While the Lorentz generators are defined as

$$M^{\mu\nu} = p^\mu x^\nu - p^\nu x^\mu = [1 + \gamma p_0^\rho p_{0\,\rho}]\,\tilde M^{\mu\nu}, \tag{B.2}$$

where it is wort mentioning that all the results are truncated to first order in the RGUP parameter γ. The modified Poincaré algebra is then calculated to be

$$[x^\mu, M^{\nu\rho}] = i\hbar[1 + \gamma p^\rho p_\rho](x^\nu \delta^{\mu\rho} - x^\rho \delta^{\mu\nu}) + i\hbar 2\gamma p^\mu M^{\nu\rho} \tag{B.3a}$$

$$[p^\mu, M^{\nu\rho}] = i\hbar[1 + \gamma p^\rho p_\rho](p^\nu \delta^{\mu\rho} - p^\rho \delta^{\mu\nu}), \tag{B.3b}$$

$$[M^{\mu\nu}, M^{\rho\sigma}] = i\hbar(1 + \gamma p^\rho p_\rho)(\eta^{\mu\rho} M^{\nu\sigma} - \eta^{\mu\sigma} M^{\nu\rho} - \eta^{\nu\rho} M^{\mu\sigma} + \eta^{\nu\sigma} M^{\mu\rho}). \tag{B.3c}$$

We can show that the physical rotations J_i and boosts K_i are as follows

$$J_i = \frac{1}{2}\varepsilon_{imn} M^{mn} = \frac{1}{2}(1 + \gamma p^\rho p_\rho)\varepsilon_{imn} \tilde{M}^{mn} \tag{B.4a}$$

$$K_i = M_{0i} = (1 + \gamma p^\rho p_\rho)\tilde{M}_{0i}, \tag{B.4b}$$

The algebra for which is

$$[J_i, J_j] = -i\varepsilon_{ijk}(1 + \gamma p^\rho p_\rho) J^k, \tag{B.5a}$$

$$[K_i, K_j] = i\varepsilon_{ijk}(1 + \gamma p^\rho p_\rho) J^k, \tag{B.5b}$$

$$[J_i, K_j] = i\varepsilon_{ijk}(1 + \gamma p^\rho p_\rho) K^k. \tag{B.5c}$$

Once again we can define new set of this time physical operators A_i and B_i

$$A_i = \frac{1}{2}(J_i + iK_i) = \frac{1}{2}(1 + \gamma p^\rho p_\rho)\left(\tilde{J}_i + i\tilde{K}_i\right) \tag{B.6a}$$

$$B_i = \frac{1}{2}(J_i - iK_i) = \frac{1}{2}(1 + \gamma p^\rho p_\rho)\left(\tilde{J}_i - i\tilde{K}_i\right). \tag{B.6b}$$

Which form the following algebra

$$[A_i, A_j] = -i\varepsilon_{ijk}(1 + \gamma p^\rho p_\rho) A^k, \tag{B.7a}$$

$$[B_i, B_j] = -i\varepsilon_{ijk}(1 + \gamma p^\rho p_\rho) B^k, \tag{B.7b}$$

$$[A_i, B_j] = 0. \tag{B.7c}$$

We notice that once again this algebra is equivalent to $SU(2) \otimes SU(2)$ algebra. The irreducible representation of which are scalar $(0,0)$, spinors/fermions $(0,1/2)$ and $(1/2,0)$, vector bosons/ photons $(1/2,1/2)$, and potentially gravitons $(1,1)$. We have taken two things in consideration: First that the modified Poincaré algebra has both the auxiliary momentum squared $p_{0\mu} p_0^\mu$ and the physical momentum squared $p_\mu p^\mu$ as Casimir invariants; And second that those quantities are scalars and therefore modify the structure constants of the algebra without actually changing its physical properties.

References

1. A. Kempf, G. Mangano and R. B. Mann, Hilbert space representation of the minimal length uncertainty relation, *Phys. Rev. D* **52**, 1108 (1995).
2. R. J. Adler and D. I. Santiago, On gravity and the uncertainty principle, *Mod. Phys. Lett. A* **14**, p. 1371 (April 1999).
3. R. J. Adler, P. Chen and D. I. Santiago, The generalized uncertainty principle and black hole remnants, *Gen. Relat. Grav.* **33**, p. 2101–2108 (Dec 2001).

4. A. F. Ali, S. Das and E. C. Vagenas, A proposal for testing Quantum Gravity in the lab, *Phys. Rev. D* **84**, p. 044013 (2011).
5. A. F. Ali and B. Majumder, Towards a cosmology with minimal length and maximal energy, *Class. Quant. Grav.* **31**, p. 215007 (Oct 2014).
6. A. F. Ali, M. Faizal and M. M. Khalil, Short distance physics of the inflationary de sitter universe, *JCAP* **2015**, p. 025–025 (Sep 2015).
7. A. Alonso-Serrano, M. P. Dabrowski and H. Gohar, Generalized uncertainty principle impact onto the black holes information flux and the sparsity of hawking radiation, *Phys. Rev. D* **97** (Feb 2018).
8. D. Amati, M. Ciafaloni and G. Veneziano, Can spacetime be probed below the string size?, *Phys. Lett. B* **216**, 41 (January 1989).
9. G. Amelino-Camelia, Testable scenario for relativity with minimum length, *Phys. Lett. B* **510**, p. 255–263 (Jun 2001).
10. G. Amelino-Camelia, Relativity in spacetimes with short-distance structure governed by an observer-independent (planckian) length scale, *Int. J. Mod. Phys. D* **11**, p. 35–59 (Jan 2002).
11. G. Amelino-Camelia, Quantum-Spacetime phenomenology, *Living Rev. Relativ.* **16**, p. 5 (June 2013).
12. P. Bargueño and E. C. Vagenas, Semiclassical corrections to black hole entropy and the generalized uncertainty principle, *Phys. Lett. B* **742**, p. 15–18 (Mar 2015).
13. C. Bambi and F. R. Urban, Natural extension of the generalised uncertainty principle, *Class. Quant. Grav.* **25**, p. 095006 (September 2007).
14. M. Bawaj and et al., Probing deformed commutators with macroscopic harmonic oscillators, *Nature Communications* **6** (Jun 2015).
15. M. Bojowald and A. Kempf, Generalized uncertainty principles and localization of a particle in discrete space, *Phys. Rev. D* **86**, p. 085017 (December 2011).
16. B. Bolen and M. Cavagliá, (anti-)de sitter black hole thermodynamics and the generalized uncertainty principle, *Gen. Relat. Grav.* **37**, 1255 (July 2005).
17. P. Bosso and S. Das, Generalized uncertainty principle and angular momentum, *Ann. of Phys.* **383**, 416 (2017).
18. P. Bosso, S. Das and R. B. Mann, Potential tests of the Generalized Uncertainty Principle in the advanced LIGO experiment, *Phys. Lett. B* **785**, 498 (2018).
19. P. Bosso, Rigorous Hamiltonian and Lagrangian analysis of classical and quantum theories with minimal length, *Phys. Rev. D* **97**, p. 126010 (2018).
20. P. Bosso and O. Obregón, Minimal length effects on quantum cosmology and quantum black hole models, *Class. Quant. Grav.* **37**, p. 045003 (2020).
21. D. J. Burger and et al, Towards the Raychaudhuri equation beyond general relativity, *Phys. Rev. D* **98** (Jul 2018).
22. P. Bushev and et al, Testing the generalized uncertainty principle with macroscopic mechanical oscillators and pendulums, *Phys. Rev. D* **100**, p. 066020 (2019).
23. S. Capozziello, G. Lambiase and G. Scarpetta, Generalized uncertainty principle from quantum geometry, *Int. J. Theor. Phys.* **39**, 15 (2000).
24. R. Casadio and F. Scardigli, Generalized uncertainty principle, classical mechanics, and general relativity, *Phys. Lett. B* **807**, p. 135558 (Aug 2020).
25. L. N. Chang and et al, On the Minimal Length Uncertainty Relation and the Foundations of String Theory, *Adv. High Energy Phys.* **2011**, p. 493514 (2011).
26. J. L. Cortes and J. Gamboa, Quantum uncertainty in doubly special relativity, *Phys. Rev. D* **71**, p. 065015 (2005).
27. R. N. Costa Filho and et al, Extended uncertainty from first principles, *Phys. Lett. B* **755**, 367 (April 2016).

28. M. P. Dabrowski and F. Wagner, Extended Uncertainty Principle for Rindler and cosmological horizons, *Eur. Phys. J. C* **79**, p. 716 (2019).
29. M. P. Dabrowski and F. Wagner, Asymptotic generalized extended uncertainty principle, *Eur. Phys. J. C* **80**, p. 676 (June 2020).
30. S. Das and E. C. Vagenas, Universality of Quantum Gravity Corrections, *Phys. Rev. Lett.* **101**, p. 221301 (2008).
31. S. Das and E. C. Vagenas, Phenomenological Implications of the Generalized Uncertainty Principle, *Can. J. Phys.* **87**, 233 (2009).
32. S. Das, E. C. Vagenas and A. F. Ali, Discreteness of Space from GUP II: Relativistic Wave Equations, *Phys. Lett. B* **690**, 407 (2010), [Erratum: Phys. Lett. B 692, 342–342 (2010)].
33. S. Das and R. Mann, Planck scale effects on some low energy quantum phenomena, *Phys. Lett. B* **704**, 596 (2011).
34. S. Das, M. P. G. Robbins and M. A. Walton, Generalized Uncertainty Principle Corrections to the Simple Harmonic Oscillator in Phase Space, *Can. J. Phys.* **94**, 139 (2016).
35. S. Das, S. S. Haque and B. Underwood, Constraints and horizons for de sitter with extra dimensions, *Phys. Rev. D* **100** (Aug 2019).
36. A. Das, S. Das and E. C. Vagenas, Discreteness of space from gup in strong gravitational fields, *Phys. Lett. B* **809**, p. 135772 (Oct 2020).
37. A. Garcia-Chung and et al, Propagation of quantum gravity-modified gravitational waves on a classical FLRW spacetime, *Phys. Rev. D* **103**, p. 084053 (2021).
38. S. B. Giddings, Black holes and other clues to the quantum structure of gravity, *Galaxies* **9**, p. 16 (December 2020).
39. B. Hamil, M. Merad and T. Birkandan, Applications of the extended uncertainty principle in AdS and ds spaces, *Eur. Phys. J. Plus* **134**, p. 278 (June 2019).
40. S. Hossenfelder, Interpretation of quantum field theories with a minimal length scale, *Phys. Rev. D* **73**, p. 105013 (2006).
41. S. Hossenfelder, Minimal Length Scale Scenarios for Quantum Gravity, *Living Rev. Rel.* **16**, p. 2 (2013).
42. M. Kober, Gauge Theories under Incorporation of a Generalized Uncertainty Principle, *Phys. Rev. D* **82**, p. 085017 (2010).
43. K. Konishi, G. Paffuti and P. Provero, Minimum physical length and the generalized uncertainty principle in string theory, *Phys. Lett. B* **234**, 276 (1990).
44. M. Maggiore, A generalized uncertainty principle in quantum gravity, *Phys. Lett. B* **304**, 65 (1993).
45. M. Maggiore, Quantum groups, gravity, and the generalized uncertainty principle, *Phys. Rev. D* **49**, 5182 (May 1994).
46. F. Marin *et al.*, Gravitational bar detectors set limits to Planck-scale physics on macroscopic variables, *Nature Phys.* **9**, 71 (2013).
47. C. A. Mead, Observable consequences of Fundamental-Length hypotheses, *Phys. Rev.* **143**, 990 (March 1966).
48. H. Moradpour, S. Aghababaei and A. H. Ziaie, A note on effects of generalized and extended uncertainty principles on jüttner gas, *Symmetry* **13**, p. 213 (January 2021).
49. J. R. Mureika, Extended uncertainty principle black holes, *Phys. Lett. B* **789**, 88 (February 2019).
50. Y. S. Myung, Y.-W. Kim and Y.-J. Park, Black hole thermodynamics with generalized uncertainty principle, *Phys. Lett. B* **645**, p. 393–397 (Feb 2007).
51. M.-I. Park, The generalized uncertainty principle in (A)dS space and the modification of hawking temperature from the minimal length, *Phys. Lett. B* **659**, 698 (January 2008).

52. F. Scardigli, Generalized uncertainty principle in quantum gravity from micro - black hole gedanken experiment, *Phys. Lett. B* **452**, 39 (April 1999).
53. H. S. Snyder, Quantized space-time, *Phys. Rev.* **71**, 38 (Jan 1947).
54. M. Sprenger, P. Nicolini and M. Bleicher, Neutrino oscillations as a novel probe for a minimal length, *Class. Quant. Grav* **28**, p. 235019 (Nov 2011).
55. L. Sriramkumar and S. Shankaranarayanan, Path integral duality and Planck scale corrections to the primordial spectrum in exponential inflation, *JHEP* **12**, p. 050 (2006).
56. D. J. Stargen, S. Shankaranarayanan and S. Das, Polymer quantization and advanced gravitational wave detector, *Phys. Rev. D* **100** (Oct 2019).
57. L. Tedesco, Fine structure constant, domain walls, and generalized uncertainty principle in the universe, *Int. J. Math. and Math. S.* **2011** (2011).
58. B. Wang, C. Long, Z. Long and T. Xu, Solutions of the schrödinger equation under topological defects space-times and generalized uncertainty principle, *Eur. Phys. J. Plus* **131**, p. 378 (2016).
59. S. Hossenfelder, The Soccer-Ball Problem, *SIGMA* **10**, p. 074 (2014).
60. G. Amelino-Camelia, Planck-scale soccer-ball problem: A case of mistaken identity, *Entropy* **19**, p. 400 (2017).
61. M. J. Lake, A Solution to the Soccer Ball Problem for Generalized Uncertainty Relations, *Ukr. J. Phys.* **64**, 1036 (2019).
62. V. Todorinov, P. Bosso and S. Das, Relativistic generalized uncertainty principle, *Ann. Phys.* **405**, 92 (October 2018).
63. C. Quesne and V. Tkachuk, Lorentz-covariant deformed algebra with minimal length, *Czech. J. Phys.* **56**, 1269 (2006).
64. P. Bosso, S. Das and V. Todorinov, Quantum field theory with the generalized uncertainty principle i: Scalar electrodynamics, *Ann. Phys.* **422**, p. 168319 (May 2020).
65. P. Bosso, S. Das and V. Todorinov, Quantum field theory with the generalized uncertainty principle II: Quantum electrodynamics, *Ann. Phys.* **424**, p. 168350 (May 2020).
66. J. Pons, Ostrogradski Theorem for Higher Order Singular Lagrangians, *Lett. Math. Phys.* **17**, p. 181 (1989).
67. R. P. Woodard, Ostrogradsky's theorem on Hamiltonian instability, *Scholarpedia* **10**, p. 32243 (2015).
68. F. de Urries and J. Julve, Ostrogradski formalism for higher derivative scalar field theories, *J. Phys. A* **31**, 6949 (1998).
69. V. Todorinov, Relativistic Generalized Uncertainty Principle and Its Implications (2020).
70. P. Balek, Charged-hadron suppression in Pb+Pb and Xe+Xe collisions measured with the ATLAS detector, *Nucl. Phys. A* **982**, 571 (2019).

Stelle gravity as the limit of quantum gravity with maximal momentum

V. Nenmeli* and S. Shankaranarayanan[†]

Department of Physics, Indian Institute of Technology Bombay,
Mumbai, Maharashtra, 400076, India
*vijay.nenmeli@iitb.ac.in
[†]*shanki@phy.iitb.ac.in*

V. Todorinov* and S. Das[†]

Theoretical Physics Group and Quantum Alberta, Department of Physics and Astronomy,
University of Lethbridge, 4401 University Drive,
Lethbridge, Alberta, T1K 3M4, Canada
*v.todorinov@uleth.ca
[†]*saurya.das@uleth.ca*

Many quantum gravity theories predict several interesting phenomenological features such as minimal length scales and maximal momenta. Generalized uncertainty principles (GUPs), which are extensions of the standard Heisenberg uncertainty principle, have proven very useful in modelling the effects of such features on physics at sub-Planck energy scales. In this talk, we use a GUP modelling maximal momentum to establish a correspondence between the GUP modified dynamics of a massless spin 2 field and Stelle gravity with suitably constrained parameters. Thus, Stelle gravity can be regarded as the classical manifestation of the imposition of a momentum cutoff at the quantum gravity level. We then study the applications of Stelle gravity to cosmology. Specifically, we analytically show that Stelle gravity, when applied to a homogeneous, isotropic background, leads to inflation with exit. Lastly, using numerical simulations and data from CMB observations, we obtain strong bounds on the GUP parameter. Unlike previous works which fixed only upper bounds for GUP parameters, we show that we can bound the GUP parameter from above and from below.

Keywords: Generalized Uncertainty Principles, Quadratic Gravity, Inflation, Based on [1]

1. Introduction

Generalized Uncertainty Principles (GUPs) are phenomenological tools used to model generic features of Quantum Gravity theories such as minimal measurable length-scales[2] and maximal momentum.[3] Since GUPs have traditionally been formulated in non-covariant settings, they have primarily been used for computing Planck scale corrections to classical and quantum *mechanics*. Studying corrections to quantum *field theory* necessitates the use of a covariant GUP. Recently, Todorinov et al. introduced a class of such GUPs, and their effects on relativistic quantum mechanics were elucidated.[4] Following this, the authors considered a covariant, maximal momentum GUP modeled by the modified commutator (we set $\hbar = c = 1$)

$$[x^\mu, p^\nu] = i\eta^{\mu\nu}(1 - \gamma p^\sigma p_\sigma) - 2i\gamma p^\mu p^\nu \qquad (1)$$

and studied the effects of this RGUP on free spin-0,[5] spin-1/2[6] and spin-1 fields. Combining these observations, the corrections to scalar and spinor electrodynamics were also obtained.[5,6] A natural follow-up would be to study the effects of GUPs on spin-2 fields (and, by extension, General Relativity). We would then have a complete lexicon detailing the effects of GUPs on all the "basic" quantum fields. Practically, such a study would also allow us to study deviations from General Relativity (GR) in the strong-field regime.

2. Computing RGUP Corrections — An Overview

From the RGUP (1), it is clear that the position and momentum operators are no longer canonically conjugate. The introduction of a "canonical" 4-momentum p_0^μ satisfying $[x^\mu, p_0^\nu] = i\eta^{\mu\nu}$ simplifies calculations considerably. The "physical" 4-momentum p^μ can be expressed in terms of p_0^μ as[5,6]

$$p^\mu = p_0^\mu(1 - \gamma p_{0\nu} p_0^\nu). \qquad (2)$$

We can break down the procedure followed for computing RGUP corrections to QED into stages:

- A. Compute the RGUP modified Poincare algebra and show that $p^\mu p_\mu$ is a Casimir operator.
- B. Starting with the free field equations for spin-0, spin-1/2 and spin-1, obtain the modified EOM by replacing the canonical 4-momentum by the physical 4-momentum.
- C. Using the Ostrogradsky approach, find actions that yield the modified EOM.
- D. Minimally couple the matter and gauge field actions to obtain the modified QED action.
- E. Compute corrections to cross-sections arising from additional interaction terms and compare with existing high-energy experiments.

When computing corrections to the spin-2 field, our aim is not to evaluate cross-sections but to search for modifications to GR. Hence, the procedure we must follow is slightly different. As with QED, we proceed with finding the GUP-modified EOM for the spin-2 field. After this, however, to connect our results to GR, we search for modified gravity theories *whose EOM, in the linear limit, match the GUP modified spin-2 field equations*. We then claim that this modified gravity theory can be regarded as the classical limit of spin-2 theory with the imposition of a maximal momentum scale.

3. RGUP Corrections to the Spin-2 Field

While the spin-2 field equations can be obtained by simply linearizing the Einstein field equations, the RGUP corrections to the EOM seem more natural if we instead begin with a field theoretical approach. Such an approach was first outlined by Gupta[7] and popularized by Feynman[8] and can be summarized as follows:

A. The Lagrangian for the *free* spin-2 field must be bilinear in the field, $h_{\mu\nu}$, and its derivatives. The relevant bilinears are easily listed out.
B. Since the gravitational force is long range, the mediating gauge bosons must be massless. Thus, we may assume that the Lagrangian has no mass term and is strictly a function of field derivatives.
C. We can construct a *minimal* list by identifying pairs of bilinears that differ by surface terms. We can thus fix the action up to undetermined coefficients. In particular, we have

$$\mathcal{L} = a h_{\mu\nu,\sigma} h^{\mu\nu,\sigma} + b h_{\mu\nu}{}^{,\nu} h^{\mu\sigma}{}_{,\sigma} + c h_{\mu\nu}{}^{,\nu} h^{\sigma}{}_{\sigma,\mu} + d h_{\mu}{}^{\mu}{}_{,\sigma} h^{\nu}{}_{\nu}{}^{,\sigma} \quad (3)$$

D. If matter-gravity interactions were present, we would presumably have an interaction term of the form $\lambda h_{\mu\nu} T^{\mu\nu}$. By adding such a term to the above action and appealing to energy-momentum conservation (i.e. $T^{,\nu}_{\mu\nu} = 0$), we get

$$(2a+b)\Box h_{\mu\nu}{}^{,\nu} + (b+c) h^{;\nu\sigma}_{\nu\sigma}{}_{,\mu} + (c+2d)\Box h_{\nu}{}^{\nu}{}_{,\mu} = 0 \quad (4)$$

which fixes the coefficients.

Thus, up to an irrelevant scale factor, we see that the Lagrangian for the free spin-2 field is given by

$$\mathcal{L}_{free} = \frac{1}{2} h_{\mu\nu,\sigma} h^{\mu\nu,\sigma} - h_{\mu\nu}{}^{,\nu} h^{\mu\sigma}{}_{,\sigma} + h_{\mu\nu}{}^{,\nu} h^{\sigma}{}_{\sigma,\mu} - \frac{1}{2} h_{\mu}{}^{\mu}{}_{,\sigma} h^{\nu}{}_{\nu}{}^{,\sigma} \quad (5)$$

The EOM are obtained from the resulting action by variation

$$-G^L_{\mu\nu} = \Box h_{\mu\nu} - h_{\mu\sigma,\nu}{}^{\sigma} - h_{\nu\sigma,\mu}{}^{\sigma} + h_{\sigma,\mu\nu}{}^{\sigma} + \eta_{\mu\nu} h^{;\sigma\rho}_{\sigma\rho} - \eta_{\mu\nu} \Box h_{\sigma}{}^{\sigma} = 0, \quad (6)$$

where $G^L_{\mu\nu}$ is the linearized Einstein tensor. The RGUP modified EOM are obtained from the position space representation of (2) (i.e. $\partial_\mu \to \partial_\mu(1-\gamma\Box)$). We have

$$G^L_{\mu\nu} + \gamma \mathcal{G}_{\mu\nu} = 0, \quad (7)$$

where

$$\mathcal{G}_{\mu\nu} = \Box^2 h_{\mu\nu} - \Box h_{\mu\sigma,\nu}{}^{,\sigma} - h_{\nu\sigma\mu}{}^{,\sigma}. + \Box h_{\sigma,\mu\nu}{}^{,\sigma} + \eta_{\mu\nu} h^{;\sigma\rho}_{\sigma\rho} - \eta_{\mu\nu} \Box^2 h^{\sigma}_{\sigma}. \quad (8)$$

4. Stelle Gravity and GUP modified GR

The Einstein-Hilbert action describing the most general quadratic gravity theory (Stelle gravity) is[9]

$$S_{Stelle} = \int d^4x \sqrt{-g} [\frac{1}{2\kappa^2} R - \alpha R_{\mu\nu} R^{\mu\nu} + \beta R^2]. \quad (9)$$

By studying static, localized and isotropic solutions in the linear limit, it was shown[9] that the resultant theory contains two extra gauge bosons with masses $\frac{1}{\sqrt{2\alpha}\kappa}$ and

$\frac{1}{\sqrt{4(3\beta-\alpha)\kappa}}$. where $\kappa^2 = 1/8\pi G$. To avoid tachyonic instabilities, α and β must satisfy

$$3\beta \geq \alpha \geq 0. \tag{10}$$

The EOM for Stelle gravity are

$$\frac{1}{2\kappa^2}G_{\mu\nu} + (\alpha - 2\beta)R_{;\mu\nu} - \alpha\Box R_{\mu\nu} - \left(\frac{\alpha}{2} - 2\beta\right)g_{\mu\nu}\Box R - 2\alpha R^{\rho\sigma}R_{\mu\rho\nu\sigma} \tag{11}$$
$$+ 2\beta R R_{\mu\nu} + \frac{1}{2}g_{\mu\nu}(\alpha R^{\rho\sigma}R_{\rho\sigma} - \beta R^2) = 0.$$

To first order in $h_{\mu\nu} \equiv g_{\mu\nu} - \eta_{\mu\nu}$ (where $\eta_{\mu\nu}$ is the Minkowski metric), we have

$$\frac{1}{2\kappa^2}G^L_{\mu\nu} - (\alpha - 2\beta)(\Box h^\lambda_{\lambda,\mu\nu} - h^{\lambda,\rho}_{\rho,\lambda\mu\nu}) + \frac{\alpha}{2}(\Box^2 h_{\mu\nu} + \Box h^\lambda_{\lambda,\mu\nu} - \Box h^\lambda_{\mu,\lambda\nu} - \Box h^\lambda_{\nu,\lambda\mu})$$
$$+ \left(\frac{\alpha}{2} - 2\beta\right)\eta_{\mu\nu}(\Box^2 h^\lambda_\lambda - \Box h^{\lambda\rho}_{,\lambda\rho}) = 0. \tag{12}$$

It is easy to show that (12) match (7) perfectly when $\alpha = 2\beta = \gamma/\kappa^2$. From (10), this means that we must have $\gamma \geq 0$. Thus, we may claim that $\alpha = 2\beta$ Stelle gravity is a modified gravity theory modelling maximal momentum. Note, however, that it is by no means the *unique* modified gravity theory modelling maximal momentum. This is because the effects of curvature terms of order at least three will not appear in the linear regime. Thus, a more precise statement would be that $\alpha = 2\beta$ Stelle gravity is the *minimally modified, metric-only* theory of gravity which models the effects of maximal momentum.

There are two further points worthy of notice. First, it has been shown[10,11] that Stelle Gravity (and thus GUP modified gravity) does not contain malicious ghosts. Second, when $\alpha = 2\beta$, the additional gauge bosons mentioned earlier have *equal* masses. In this sense, GUP modified GR is a *degenerate* theory.

5. Applications to Cosmology

It is well known that quantum corrections to GR can lead to inflation. A natural question to ask is whether we can obtain inflation from GUP modified GR. To answer this, we compute the EOM for *generic* Stelle gravity (with parameters α and β) in an FRW background. We assume a flat background although the results can be extended. In terms of the Hubble parameter $H(t) \equiv \dot{a}(t)/a(t)$, we have

$$H^2 - 4\lambda[\dot{H}^2 - 2H\ddot{H} - 6H^2\dot{H}] = 0 \tag{13}$$

and

$$3H^2 + 2\dot{H} + \lambda\left[18H^2\dot{H} + 9\dot{H}^2 + 12H\ddot{H} + 2\dddot{H}\right] = 0 \tag{14}$$

where the arguments have been suppressed and $\lambda \equiv (3\beta - \alpha)/\kappa^2$. From these equations, it is clear that the *qualitative* dependence of the solutions is *independent* of the parameter values. Thus, we can qualitatively study the dynamics of *any* Stelle gravity theory by observing the dynamics of one particular case. Moreover, since Stelle gravity with $\alpha = 0$ corresponds to the Starobinsky action[12] which is a well studied inflationary model, it is clear that *any* Stelle gravity theory and in particular GUP modified GR leads to inflation.

6. Numerics

We can also graphically verify the existence of inflation with exit. To do so, we would like to numerically solve the EOM and study the properties of the resulting solutions. While there are apparently two equations, (13) and (14), the two are completely equivalent as they are related via the Bianchi identities. Therefore, it is preferable to solve (13) as it is second order in time as opposed to (14) which is third order. However, the large scale of H during inflation and the small scale of γ make it difficult to solve (13) numerically. We, therefore, define the following dimensionless variables:

$$s = \frac{t}{\sqrt{\gamma}}; \quad b(s) = \ln\left(\frac{H(s)}{H_{inf}}\right); \quad U = \sqrt{\gamma} H_{inf} \quad (15)$$

where H_{inf} is a constant denoting the energy scale during inflation. In terms of the new dynamical variable $b(s)$, (13) is transformed to:

$$1 + 2\dot{b}(s)^2 + 4\ddot{b}(s) + 12U e^{b(s)} \dot{b}(s) = 0 \quad (16)$$

While γ and H_{inf} are respectively small and large, their composition, U, is not too large or too small. Additionally, since $b(s)$ is clearly $\mathcal{O}(1)$ during inflation, solving (16) is quite tractable. Figure 1a depicts the variation of the scale factor $a(s)$ with s, the rescaled cosmic time, for various values of U. The existence of inflection points graphically demonstrates the existence of inflation with exit. Figure 1b shows the variation of the slow roll parameter $\epsilon(s)$ with s for various values of U. The necessary condition for inflation is $\epsilon < 1$. Such behaviour is evident from the graphs, along with a crossover to $\epsilon > 1$, which shows the exit from inflation.

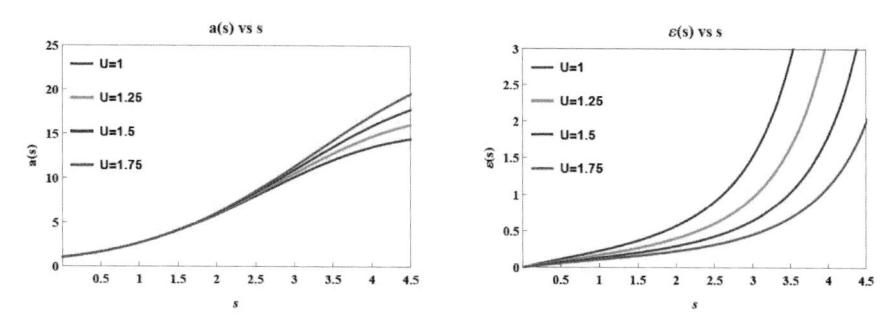

Fig. 1. (a) Variation of a with s. (b) Variation of ϵ with s.

7. Parameter Estimation

The fact that GUP modified GR predicts inflation means that we should able to constrain the GUP parameter γ using the existing constraints on inflation. These constraints stem from theoretical considerations and CMB observations. To do this, we plot the variation of s_0, the exit time (defined as the value of s when $\epsilon = 1$), with U. We see that $s_0 = U$ holds as an order of magnitude relation. This observation can be used to constrain the GUP parameter. Define $t_0 = s_0\sqrt{\gamma}$, $\gamma_0 = \gamma/l_{Pl}^2$ and $\alpha = t_0/l_{Pl}$. t_0 is simply the exit time is units of cosmic time while α is the exit time in units of Planck time/Planck length (l_{Pl}) and γ_0 is the ratio of two energy scales - the Planck scale and the GUP energy scale. We now have

$$s_0 = \frac{\alpha l_{Pl}}{\sqrt{\gamma}} = \frac{\alpha}{\gamma_0}. \tag{17}$$

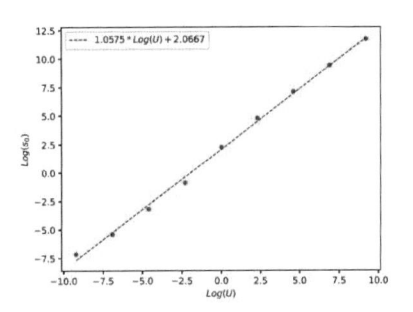

Fig. 2. Variation of s_0 with U.

Since $s_0 \sim U$, we can replace the former with the latter in (17). Simplifying, we get

$$\gamma_0 = \frac{\alpha}{H_{inf} l_{Pl}}. \tag{18}$$

Note that the right hand side is now a function of constants and known parameters. From PLANCK data,[13] we have $H_{inf} \leq 10^{-4} M_{Pl}$. We take $H_{inf} = 10^{-5} M_{Pl}$ which also coincides from the GUT scale. Typically, $\alpha \in (10^9 - 10^{12})$, but we stretch these bounds to $(10^6 - 10^{15})$ to account for errors stemming from the "hand-waving" nature of the argument. Substituting these bounds in (18) and utilizing the additional constraint that the GUP energy scale must exceed the CERN energy scale $\sim 10 TeV$, we obtain the following bounds

$$10^{10} \leq \gamma_0 \leq 10^{15} \tag{19}$$

or

$$10^{-28} GeV^{-2} \leq \gamma \leq 10^{-23} GeV^{-2}. \tag{20}$$

In addition to being among the most stringent bounds available (which is expected since, unlike most constraining procedures, the one used above involved inflation and hence the strong gravity regime), our bounds are double-sided. To our knowledge, this is the first time double-sided bounds have been obtained for GUP parameters.

8. Conclusions and Future Prospects

One expects that the imposition of a maximal momentum scale at the quantum level leads to modifications to GR at the classical level. In this proceeding, we have shown that $\alpha = 2\beta$ Stelle gravity can be regarded as the minimal extension of GR that can model maximal momentum. We have also shown that GUP modified GR leads to inflation and used this feature to obtain some of the best-known bounds on GUP parameters. We reiterate that our bounds possess a unique feature - they are double-sided. Using the GUP-Stelle Gravity correspondence, we can study the effects of maximal momentum scales on gravitational systems by studying these systems using $\alpha = 2\beta$ Stelle gravity. Additionally, we believe that approaches similar to the one outlined in this proceeding can be used to study the effects of other Planck scale phenomena at the classical level.

GUP modified GR is degenerate. It is not clear what the origins or the implications of this degeneracy are. These are currently being looked into. Finally, it is worth pondering over whether we can extend the GUP used above to construct a two-parameter GUP that "corresponds," in the classical limit, to *generic* Stelle gravity.

References

1. V. Nenmeli, S. Shankaranarayanan, V. Todorinov and S. Das, Maximal Momentum GUP leads to quadratic gravity, *Physics Letters* **B821**, 136621 (2021).
2. A. Kempf, G. Mangano and R. B. Mann, Hilbert space representation of the minimal length uncertainty relation, *Physical Review D* **52**, 1108 (1995).
3. P. Pedram, A Higher Order GUP with Minimal Length Uncertainty and Maximal Momentum, *Physics Letters* **B714**, 317 (2012).
4. V. Todorinov, P. Bosso and S. Das, Relativistic Generalized Uncertainty Principle, *Annals of Physics* **405**, 92 (2018).
5. P. Bosso, V. Todorinov and S. Das, Quantum field theory with the generalized uncertainty principle I: Scalar electrodynamics, *Annals of Physics* **422**, 168319 (2020).
6. P. Bosso, V. Todorinov and S. Das, Quantum field theory with the generalized uncertainty principle II: Quantum Electrodynamics, *Annals of Physics* **424**, 168350 (2020).
7. S. N. Gupta, Gravitation and Electromagnetism, *Physical Review D* **96**, 1683 (1954).
8. R. P. Feynman, *The Feynman Lectures on Gravitation*, 1st edn. (CRC Press, 2003)
9. K. S. Stelle, Classical gravity with higher derivatives, *General Relativity and Gravitation* **9**, 353 (1978).
10. E. T. Tomboulis, Unitarity in Higher Derivative Quantum Gravity, *Physical Review Letters* **52**, 1173 (1984).
11. I. Antoniadis and E. T. Tomboulis, Gauge invariance and unitarity in higher-derivative quantum gravity, *Physical Review D* **33**, 2756 (1986).
12. A. A. Starobinsky, A new type of isotropic cosmological models without singularity, *Physics Letters* **B91**, 99 (1980).
13. Y. Akrami and Others, Planck 2018 results. X. Constraints on inflation, *Astronomy and Astrophysics Supplement Series* **641**, A10 (2020).

Baryon asymmetry and minimum length

Saurya Das* and Mitja Fridman[†]

Theoretical Physics Group and Quantum Alberta, Department of Physics and Astronomy, University of Lethbridge, 4401 University Drive, Lethbridge, Alberta, T1K 3M4, Canada
* E-mail: saurya.das@uleth.ca
[†] E-mail: fridmanm@uleth.ca

Gaetano Lambiase

Dipartimento di Fisica E.R. Caianiello, Universita di Salerno, Via Giovanni Paolo II, 132 - 84084 Fisciano, Salerno, Italy & INFN - Gruppo Collegato di Salerno, Italy
E-mail: lambiase@sa.infn.it

Elias C. Vagenas

Theoretical Physics Group, Department of Physics, Kuwait University, P.O. Box 5969, Safat 13060, Kuwait
E-mail: elias.vagenas@ku.edu.kw

We study Quantum Gravity effects in cosmology, and in particular that of the Generalized Uncertainty Principle on the Friedmann equations. We show that the Quantum Gravity induced variations of the energy density and pressure in the radiation dominated era provide a viable explanation of the observed baryon asymmetry in the Universe.

Keywords: Quantum Gravity, Quantum Gravity Phenomenology, Minimal Length, Cosmology, Baryon Asymmetry.

1. Introduction

So far there are two successful theories which describe the world around us. Quantum theory, which describes interactions on the smallest scales on one hand and General Relativity, which describes gravitational interactions on large scales on the other hand.[1,2] There is no straightforward way to combine these two theories to describe physics in a regime, where both contribute, which is why we need a theory of Quantum Gravity (QG). Several QG theories have been proposed, but there is no direct experimental evidence yet to verify them. However, phenomenologists have a good intuition what fundamental concepts the regime of QG may imply on physics.[3–11] One such concept is the existence of a minimal measurable length, predicted by all or most models of QG. A natural way to incorporate minimal length in our considerations is to modify the Heisenberg uncertainty principle.[12–30] The modified Heisenberg uncertainty principle is called the Generalized Uncertainty Principle (GUP) and in the commutator form it reads as[21]

$$[x_i, p_j] = i\hbar \left(\delta_{ij} - \alpha \left(p\delta_{ij} + \frac{p_i p_j}{p} \right) + \beta \left(p^2 \delta_{ij} + 3 p_i p_j \right) \right) \qquad (1)$$

where $\alpha \equiv \alpha_0/(M_Pc)$, $\beta \equiv \beta_0/(M_Pc)^2$, α_0, β_0 are the dimensionless linear and quadratic GUP parameters and $M_P = \sqrt{\hbar c/G}$ is the Planck mass. This phenomenological model describes a length scale $\alpha_0 \ell_P$ and $\sqrt{\beta_0} \ell_P$ between the electroweak scale, i.e., $\ell_{EW} \approx 10^{-18}$ m, and the Planck scale, i.e., $\ell_P = \sqrt{\hbar G/c^3} \approx 10^{-35}$ m. We apply the GUP to quantum quantum mechanical and gravitational systems and predict deviations from standard theory, which we hope experiments can detect now or in the future, or provide explanations for observed phenomena, as in the case of this work, namely the observed baryon asymmetry that is observed in the Universe.

The asymmetry between matter and anti-matter has been an unsolved problem in physics for a long time. Standard theories such as quantum theory and general relativity suggest that there is no reason why the asymmetry between matter and anti-matter in the Universe should exist.[31] This means there should be an equal amount of matter as there is anti-matter in the Universe, while observations show a very large asymmetry. To explain this observed asymmetry we have to satisfy the so-called Sakharov conditions[32]:

1) violation of baryon number B,
2) violation of C and CP symmetries and
3) deviation from thermal equilibrium.

If a proposed mechanism is able to satisfy the above three Sakharov conditions, then it may be possible to explain the origin of the observed baryon asymmetry in the Universe. The mechanism we use is an interaction term from supergravity theories which couples the baryon current and space-time to satisfy the first two Sakharov conditions, and the holographic principle with the thermodynamics of horizons to derive the GUP-modified Friedmann equations, which satisfy the third Sakharov condition. Several proposals how GUP modifies the Friedmann equations have been presented so far.[33–36] In this way we provide a viable explanation of the observed baryon symmetry in the Universe using the GUP.

The paper is structured as follows. In section 2 we modify the Bekenstein-Hawking entropy using GUP, then in section 3, by using the holographic principle we modify the Friedmann equations, and in section 4 by using these modified Friedmann equations we attempt to explain the observed baryon symmetry in the Universe. In section 5 we summarize the work with concluding remarks.

2. Modified Bekenstein-Hawking entropy

In order to modify the Friedmann equations, using the holographic principle, we need to modify the Bekenstein-Hawking entropy formula, since the Friedmann equations can be derived from the first law of thermodynamics, which requires the change in entropy. The holographic principle makes it possible to write a d-dimensional theory on a $d-1$ dimensional boundary.[37,38] We can re-write the GUP from Eq. (1) in the usual form[39] (where $\langle p \rangle = 0$)

$$\Delta x \Delta p \gtrsim \left[1 - \alpha \Delta p + 4\beta \Delta p^2\right], \tag{2}$$

where we have set the numerical prefactor to be $\mathcal{O}(1)$.[40–42]

When a particle with energy E gets absorbed by a horizon, the horizon area changes by $\Delta A_{min} \geq 8\pi \ell_P^2 E \Delta x$, where Δx is the uncertainty in position of the absorbed particle.[43,44] To obtain the energy of the particle E, we solve the quadratic equation for Δp from Eq. (2) and obtain the expression

$$E = \Delta p \gtrsim \frac{\Delta x + \alpha}{8\beta}\left(1 - \sqrt{1 - \frac{16\beta}{\Delta x^2 + 2\alpha \Delta x + \alpha^2}}\right), \qquad (3)$$

where we chose the negative solution, since we want to obtain the smallest change in area of the apparent horizon and this solution reduces to the standard Heisenberg uncertainty for $\alpha, \beta \longrightarrow 0$. The position uncertainty Δx is the diameter of the observable Universe $\Delta x = 2r_S$, where r_S is the Schwarzschild radius. The square of Δx is then related to the area of the apparent cosmic horizon as $\Delta x^2 = A/\pi$. Plugging all of the above in the change in ΔA_{min}, we get

$$\Delta A_{min} \simeq \lambda \frac{\ell_P^2(A + \alpha\sqrt{\pi}A^{1/2})}{\beta}\left(1 - \sqrt{1 - \frac{16\pi\beta}{A + 2\alpha\sqrt{\pi}A^{1/2} + \alpha^2\pi}}\right), \qquad (4)$$

where λ is determined by the Bekenstein-Hawking entropy formula $b/\lambda = 2\pi$. Here $b = \Delta S_{min} = \ln 2$ is the minimal increase in entropy, corresponding to one bit of information.[35]

The Bekenstein-Hawking entropy was first introduced for a black hole, but the holographic principle suggests that it can be used for any horizon. Therefore we can write it for a cosmic horizon in the same way[45,46]

$$S = \frac{A}{4G} = \frac{A}{4\ell_P^2}. \qquad (5)$$

If we introduce some modification to the Heisenberg uncertainty principle or we modify the entropy in any other way, the only variable in this equation, the area, gets modified.[33] The Bekenstein-Hawking entropy then reads $S = \frac{f(A)}{4\ell_P^2}$. Since the first law of thermodynamics includes a differential of entropy, it useful to calculate its derivative

$$\frac{dS}{dA} = \frac{f'(A)}{4\ell_P^2}. \qquad (6)$$

On the other hand, the above derivative can be written using the minimal change in entropy ΔS_{min} and ΔA_{min}

$$\frac{dS}{dA} = \frac{\Delta S_{min}}{\Delta A_{min}} = \frac{\beta^*}{8\ell_P^2\left(A + \alpha^* A^{1/2} - \sqrt{A^2 + 2\alpha^* A^{3/2} + (\alpha^{*2} - \beta^*)A}\right)}, \qquad (7)$$

where $\alpha^* = \sqrt{\pi}\alpha$ and $\beta^* = 16\pi\beta$. By comparing Eqs. (6) and (7) we can read out what $f'(A)$ is

$$f'(A) = \frac{1}{2}\frac{\beta^*}{\left(A + \alpha^* A^{1/2} - \sqrt{A^2 + 2\alpha^* A^{3/2} + (\alpha^{*2} - \beta^*)A}\right)}. \qquad (8)$$

To obtain the modified Bekenstein-Hawking entropy we must integrate Eq. (6) over area A, from A to ∞, using $f'(A)$ from Eq. (8). The exact GUP-modified Bekenstein-Hawking entropy then reads

$$S = \frac{1}{8\ell_P^2} \left[A\left(1 + \sqrt{1 + 2\alpha^* \frac{1}{A^{1/2}} + (\alpha^{*2} - \beta^*)\frac{1}{A}}\right) \right.$$
$$+ \alpha^* A^{1/2}\left(2 + \sqrt{1 + 2\alpha^* \frac{1}{A^{1/2}} + (\alpha^{*2} - \beta^*)\frac{1}{A}}\right)$$
$$\left. - \beta^* \ln\left(1 + \frac{A^{1/2}}{\alpha^*}\left(1 + \sqrt{1 + 2\alpha^* \frac{1}{A^{1/2}} + (\alpha^{*2} - \beta^*)\frac{1}{A}}\right)\right)\right], \quad (9)$$

where we obtain the standard result from Eq.(5) for $\alpha^*, \beta^* \longrightarrow 0$.

3. Modified Friedmann Equations

The Friedmann equations describe the evolution of a dynamical Universe and provide the foundations for the standard model of cosmology. They can be derived in different ways. The most common is by solving the Einstein equations in $(n+1)$-dimensional space-time for a FLRW metric

$$ds^2 = h_{cd}dx^c dx^d + \tilde{r}^2 d\Omega_{n-1}^2, \quad (10)$$

where $x^c = (t, r)$, $\tilde{r} = a(t)r$, $h_{cd} = \text{diag}(-1, a^2/(1 - kr^2))$, $d\Omega_{n-1}$ is the angular part of the $(n-1)$-dimensional sphere, $a = a(t)$ is the scale factor, r is the comoving radius and k is the spatial curvature constant. Indices c and d only take values 0 and 1. The other way to derive the Friedmann equations is using the holographic principle, which takes advantage of the thermodynamics of horizons.

To generalize the Friedmann equations to include minimum length effects we derive the same from the first law of thermodynamics, with the difference of using the modified Bekenstein-Hawking entropy, derived in the previous section. The first law of thermodynamics for the content inside an apparent horizon is given by[33-36]

$$dE = TdS + WdV, \quad (11)$$

where E is the energy contained inside the apparent horizon, given by $E = \rho V$, V is the volume of an n-dimensional sphere, given by $V = \Omega_n \tilde{r}_A^n$, with $\Omega_n = \frac{\pi^{n/2}}{\Gamma(n/2+1)}$ which has an area of $A = n\Omega_n \tilde{r}_A^{n-1}$), T is the Hawking temperature given by[47,48]

$$T = \frac{\kappa}{2\pi} = -\frac{1}{2\pi \tilde{r}_A}\left(1 - \frac{\dot{\tilde{r}}_A}{2H\tilde{r}_A}\right), \quad (12)$$

dS is the differential of the Bekenstein-Hawking entropy given by Eq. (6), and W is the work density which reads as[49]

$$W = -\frac{1}{2}T^{cd}h_{cd} = \frac{1}{2}(\rho - p). \quad (13)$$

In the above T^{cd} is a projection of the energy-momentum tensor $T_{\mu\nu} = (\rho+p)u_\mu u_\nu + pg_{\mu\nu}$ on the $t-r$ subspace. What remains is to differentiate the energy and volume, write everything in terms of dA, and plug the above equations in the first law of thermodynamics from Eq. (11). From here we derive the first Friedmann equation

$$-\frac{8\pi G}{n-1}(\rho+p) = \left(\dot{H} - \frac{k}{a^2}\right)f'(A). \tag{14}$$

By using the continuity equation $\dot{\rho} + nH(\rho+p) = 0$, originating from the conservation of energy $T^{\mu\nu}{}_{;\nu} = 0$, with Eq.(14) and integrating it, one obtains the second Friedmann equation

$$-\frac{8\pi G}{n(n-1)}\rho = \frac{(n\Omega_n)^{\frac{n+1}{n-1}}}{n(n-1)\Omega_n}\int f'(A)\frac{dA}{A^{\frac{n+1}{n-1}}}. \tag{15}$$

By setting $f'(A) = 1$ ($f(A) = A$ in standard theory) we obtain the standard Friedmann equations as we expect. However, to obtain GUP corrections to the Friedmann equations, we plug $f'(A)$ from Eq. (8) in Eqs. (14) and (15). Both of the Friedmann equations have exact solutions in $n=3$, which read as

$$-4\pi G(\rho+p) = \left(\dot{H} - \frac{k}{a^2}\right)$$

$$\times \frac{\beta^*}{8\pi}\frac{\left(H^2 + \frac{k}{a^2}\right)}{1 + \frac{\alpha^*}{(4\pi)^{1/2}}\left(H^2 + \frac{k}{a^2}\right)^{1/2} - \sqrt{1 + \frac{2\alpha^*}{(4\pi)^{1/2}}\left(H^2 + \frac{k}{a^2}\right)^{1/2} + \frac{(\alpha^{*2}-\beta^*)}{4\pi}\left(H^2 + \frac{k}{a^2}\right)}} \tag{16}$$

and

$$\frac{8\pi G}{3}(\rho - \Lambda) = \frac{1}{2}\left(H^2 + \frac{k}{a^2}\right) + \frac{\alpha^*}{3(4\pi)^{1/2}}\left(H^2 + \frac{k}{a^2}\right)^{3/2} + \frac{2\pi(\alpha^{*2} + 2\beta^*)}{3(\alpha^{*2} - \beta^*)^2}$$

$$+ \left[\frac{1}{3}\left(H^2 + \frac{k}{a^2}\right) + \frac{(4\pi)^{1/2}\alpha^*}{6(\alpha^{*2}-\beta^*)}\left(H^2 + \frac{k}{a^2}\right)^{1/2} - \frac{2\pi(\alpha^{*2}+2\beta^*)}{3(\alpha^{*2}-\beta^*)^2}\right]$$

$$\times \sqrt{1 + \frac{2\alpha^*}{(4\pi)^{1/2}}\left(H^2 + \frac{k}{a^2}\right)^{1/2} + \frac{(\alpha^{*2}-\beta^*)}{4\pi}\left(H^2 + \frac{k}{a^2}\right)}$$

$$+ \frac{2\pi\alpha^*\beta^*}{(\alpha^{*2}-\beta^*)^{5/2}}\ln\left[1 + \frac{(\alpha^{*2}-\beta^*)}{(4\pi)^{1/2}(\alpha^* + \sqrt{\alpha^{*2}-\beta^*})}\left(H^2 + \frac{k}{a^2}\right)^{1/2}\right]$$

$$+ \frac{\sqrt{\alpha^{*2}-\beta^*}}{\alpha^* + \sqrt{\alpha^{*2}-\beta^*}}$$

$$\times \left(\sqrt{1 + \frac{2\alpha^*}{(4\pi)^{1/2}}\left(H^2 + \frac{k}{a^2}\right)^{1/2} + \frac{(\alpha^{*2}-\beta^*)}{4\pi}\left(H^2 + \frac{k}{a^2}\right)} - 1\right)\bigg],$$

$$\tag{17}$$

where

$$A = 4\pi \tilde{r}_A^2 = \frac{4\pi}{H^2 + \frac{k}{a^2}} \qquad (18)$$

was used. We are interested in the radiation dominated era, since the baryon asymmetry was frozen in at that epoch. In that epoch the small cosmological constant Λ can be ignored, since $\rho \gg \Lambda$ and the curvature constant can be set to $k = 0$, which is consistent with the observations which show a flat Universe. The modified Friedmann equations then get simplified to

$$-4\pi G (\rho + p) = \frac{\beta^* \dot{H}}{8\pi} \frac{H^2}{1 + \frac{\alpha^*}{(4\pi)^{1/2}} H - \sqrt{1 + \frac{2\alpha^*}{(4\pi)^{1/2}} H + \frac{(\alpha^{*2} - \beta^*)}{4\pi} H^2}} \qquad (19)$$

and

$$\frac{8\pi G}{3} \rho = \frac{1}{2} H^2 + \frac{\alpha^*}{3(4\pi)^{1/2}} H^3 + \frac{2\pi(\alpha^{*2} + 2\beta^*)}{3(\alpha^{*2} - \beta^*)^2}$$

$$+ \left[\frac{1}{3} H^2 + \frac{(4\pi)^{1/2} \alpha^*}{6(\alpha^{*2} - \beta^*)} H - \frac{2\pi(\alpha^{*2} + 2\beta^*)}{3(\alpha^{*2} - \beta^*)^2} \right]$$

$$\times \sqrt{1 + \frac{2\alpha^*}{(4\pi)^{1/2}} H + \frac{(\alpha^{*2} - \beta^*)}{4\pi} H^2}$$

$$+ \frac{2\pi \alpha^* \beta^*}{(\alpha^{*2} - \beta^*)^{5/2}} \ln \left[1 + \frac{(\alpha^{*2} - \beta^*)}{(4\pi)^{1/2}(\alpha^* + \sqrt{\alpha^{*2} - \beta^*})} H \right]$$

$$+ \frac{\sqrt{\alpha^{*2} - \beta^*}}{\alpha^* + \sqrt{\alpha^{*2} - \beta^*}} \left(\sqrt{1 + \frac{2\alpha^*}{(4\pi)^{1/2}} H + \frac{(\alpha^{*2} - \beta^*)}{4\pi} H^2} - 1 \right) \right]. \qquad (20)$$

The Taylor expansions of the above modified Friedmann equations up to first order in α^* and β^* turn out to be

$$-4\pi G (\rho + p) = \dot{H} \left(1 + \frac{\alpha^*}{2\sqrt{\pi}} H - \frac{\beta^*}{16\pi} H^2 \right) \qquad (21)$$

and

$$\frac{8\pi G}{3} \rho = H^2 \left(1 + \frac{\alpha^*}{3\sqrt{\pi}} H - \frac{\beta^*}{32\pi} H^2 \right). \qquad (22)$$

The above simplified equations are used to study the breaking of thermal equilibrium in the radiation dominated era, which satisfies one of the Sakharov conditions.

4. Gravitational Baryogenesis

To provide an explanation for the observed baryon asymmetry in the Universe, all Sakharov conditions must be satisfied. Theories of supergravity introduce an extra interaction term to the action which couples the baryon current and space-time[50]

$$\frac{1}{M_*^2} \int d^4 x \sqrt{-g} \, J^\mu \partial_\mu R, \qquad (23)$$

and thus violates the C, CP and CPT symmetries. In the above M_* is the cutoff scale characterizing the effective theory.[51] The magnitude of M_* is chosen to be in the regime of the Grand Unified Theories (GUT), where interactions which violate the baryon number exist. The term in Eq. (23) therefore satisfies the first two Sakharov conditions. We can see that the integrand from Eq. (23) reduces to

$$\frac{1}{M_*^2} J^\mu \partial_\mu R = \frac{1}{M_*^2}(n_B - n_{\bar{B}})\dot{R} , \qquad (24)$$

where n_B ($n_{\bar{B}}$) is the baryon (anti-baryon) number density. In the above equation only the time derivative survives, since the spatial derivative of the Ricci scalar vanishes $\nabla R = 0$ for the FLRW metric from Eq. (10). Because the integrand from Eq. (24) corresponds to the energy density term of the grand canonical ensemble, we can read the chemical potential for baryons and anti-baryons from it as

$$\mu_B = -\mu_{\bar{B}} = -\frac{\dot{R}}{M_*^2} . \qquad (25)$$

To study the baryon asymmetry, we need a suitable variable, which parametrizes this asymmetry. Following Ref.[52], the baryon asymmetry parameter is defined as

$$\eta \equiv \frac{n_B - n_{\bar{B}}}{n_\gamma} \simeq 7\frac{n_B - n_{\bar{B}}}{s} , \qquad (26)$$

where the photon number density n_γ and the entropy density s are related by a constant factor $n_\gamma \simeq s/7$ since the epoch of $e^\pm$ annihilation. For relativistic particles, the entropy density turns out to be[52]

$$s = \frac{2\pi^2 g_*}{45} T^3 \qquad (27)$$

and the baryon number density[52]

$$n_B - n_{\bar{B}} = \frac{g_b}{6}\mu_B T^2 . \qquad (28)$$

In the above equations $g_* \approx 106$ is the number of degrees of freedom for particles which contribute to the entropy of the universe and $g_b \sim \mathcal{O}(1)$ is the number of intrinsic degrees of freedom for baryons.[52] Plugging Eqs. (25), (27) and (28) in Eq. (26) the baryon asymmetry parameter reads

$$\eta \simeq -\frac{105\, g_b}{4\pi^2 g_*} \frac{\dot{R}}{M_*^2 T}\bigg|_{T_D} . \qquad (29)$$

The above parameter is evaluated at some decoupling temperature T_D. This decoupling temperature represents the energy scale at which the baryon violating interactions freeze out and go out of equilibrium. The baryon number is conserved below this temperature for all future epochs.

Next, we use the modified Friedmann equations which turn out to break thermal equilibrium. To see that they indeed break thermal equilibrium, we write the energy density and pressure as their equilibrium values plus some small variations

$$\rho = \rho_0 + \delta\rho, \qquad p = p_0 + \delta p . \qquad (30)$$

If there is no variations $\delta\rho = \delta p = 0$, we have thermal equilibrium and no baryon asymmetry is produced due to the third Sakharov condition. We require some variations $\delta\rho, \delta p \neq 0$ to deviate from the thermal equilibrium. To obtain non-vanishing variations we plug the energy density and pressure from Eq. (30) into the modified Friedman equations from Eqs. (21) and (22) to express $\delta\rho$ and δp in terms of the GUP parameters and the equation of state $p_0 = w\rho_0$. The variations then read

$$\delta\rho = \frac{\alpha^*}{3}\sqrt{\frac{8G}{3}}\rho_0^{3/2} - \frac{\beta^*}{12}G\rho_0^2 \tag{31}$$

and

$$\delta p = \frac{\alpha^*}{6}\sqrt{\frac{8G}{3}}(1+3w)\rho_0^{3/2} - \frac{\beta^*}{12}G(1+2w)\rho_0^2, \tag{32}$$

We can see if there is no GUP corrections $\alpha^*, \beta^* = 0$, we get no variations in the energy density and pressure and thermal equilibrium is preserved.

The trace of the Einstein equations give us the Ricci scalar $R = -8\pi G T_g = -8\pi G (\rho - 3p)$, where we plug in the energy density and pressure from Eq. (30) with their respective variations from Eqs. (31) and (32). We compute its time derivative, use the continuity equation for $n = 3$ and evaluate the whole expression in the radiation-dominated era with $w = 1/3$, where the baryon violating interactions froze out. The time derivative of the Ricci scalar then reads

$$\dot{R} = -\alpha^* \frac{256}{3}\pi^{3/2} G^2 \rho_0^2 + \beta^* 8 \left(\frac{8\pi}{3}\right)^{3/2} G^{5/2} \rho_0^{5/2}. \tag{33}$$

We can see that the above derivative would also vanish if there would be no GUP corrections because every term is proportional to α^* or β^*. We plug Eq. (33) in Eq. (29) and use the equilibrium energy density for relativistic particles[52]

$$\rho_0 = \frac{\pi g_*}{30}T^4, \tag{34}$$

to obtain the expression for the predicted baryon asymmetry

$$\eta = \alpha_0 \frac{112\,\pi^2 g_* g_b}{45}\left(\frac{T_D}{M_P}\right)^7\left(\frac{M_P}{M_*}\right)^2 - \beta_0 \frac{896\sqrt{5}\,\pi^3 g_*^{3/2} g_b}{675}\left(\frac{T_D}{M_P}\right)^9\left(\frac{M_P}{M_*}\right)^2, \tag{35}$$

where we expressed the gravitational constant in terms of the Planck mass, i.e., M_P, as $G = 1/M_P^2$. From the above we can see that the baryon asymmetry is dependent on α_0 and β_0 parameters and the scales M_* and T_D.

To compare Eq. (35) to the observed baryon asymmetry we plug in the suggested values for $M_* = M_P/\sqrt{8\pi}$, the reducep Planck mass and $T_D = M_I \sim 2 \times 10^{16}$ GeV which corresponds to the tensor mode fluctuations in the inflationary scale.[53] We then obtain

$$\eta = \alpha_0\, 2.08 \times 10^{-15} - \beta_0\, 2.16 \times 10^{-19}, \tag{36}$$

where we can see the baryon asymmetry vanishes for $\alpha_0, \beta_0 \longrightarrow 0$. If $\alpha_0, \beta_0 \neq 0$ the baryon asymmetry is explained by the existence of a minimal length scale.

We compare the predicted baryon asymmetry from Eq. (36) to the observational bounds $5.7 \times 10^{-11} \lesssim \eta \lesssim 9.9 \times 10^{-11}$.[54] By doing this we can fix the GUP parameters to their actual values for different models:

- Only linear GUP ($\beta_0 = 0$): $2.74 \times 10^4 \lesssim \alpha_0 \lesssim 4.76 \times 10^4$
- Only quadratic GUP ($\alpha_0 = 0$): $-4.58 \times 10^8 \lesssim \beta_0 \lesssim -2.64 \times 10^8$
- Linear and Quadratic GUP ($\beta_0 = -\alpha_0^2$): $1.21 \times 10^4 \lesssim \alpha_0 \lesssim 1.71 \times 10^4$ and $-2.92 \times 10^8 \lesssim \beta_0 \lesssim -1.46 \times 10^8$
- Linear and Quadratic GUP: $\alpha_0 \gtrsim 4.81 \times 10^3$ and $\beta_0 \lesssim -1.48 \times 10^8$

We can see that the GUP parameters should have values $\alpha_0 \approx 10^4$ and $\beta_0 \approx -10^8$, which suggest a new length scale of $\ell_{new} = \alpha_0 \ell_P \sim \sqrt{-\beta_0} \ell_P \approx 10^{-31}$ m.

5. Conclusion

With this work we test the fundamental physics of nature. More specifically, how the minimal length can affect phenomena on large scales such as in this case, the baryon asymmetry in the Universe, which is still a problem in physics up to this day. The mechanism which we propose satisfies all Sakharov conditions and thus offers a viable explanation of the observed baryon asymmetry in the Universe. We used an interaction term which couples the baryon current and space-time to satisfy the first two Sakharov conditions, and using the holographic principle we modified the Bekenstein-Hawking entropy and the Friedmann equations to break thermal equilibrium and thus satisfying the third and last Sakharov condition. The modified Friedmann equations can also be used more broadly in cosmology and can provide a very rich phenomenology.

Our findings suggest that minimal length effects could have been the cause for generating the observed baryon symmetry. Our work does not constrain the GUP parameters to an improved upper bound because, but rather fixes the values of the GUP parameters α_0 and β_0 and thus sets the new length scale to be $\ell_{new} = \alpha_0 \ell_P \sim \sqrt{-\beta_0} \ell_P \approx 10^{-31}$ m.

We noticed that the quadratic GUP parameter turns out to be negative. This is consistent with other cosmological studies using quadratic GUP,[55] non-trivial structures of space-time[8,16,55–57] and a crystal lattice considerations with GUP.[56] This can suggest that space-time can have a granular structure at the Planck scale.[27,58–60]

References

1. A. Zeilinger, Rev. Mod. Phys. **71**, S288-S297 (1999).
2. C. M. Will, Living Rev. Rel. **17**, 4 (2014) [arXiv:1403.7377 [gr-qc]].
3. J. Magueijo, Phys. Rev. D **73**, 124020 (2006) [arXiv:gr-qc/0603073 [gr-qc]].
4. A. Hamma and F. Markopoulou, New J. Phys. **13**, 095006 (2011) [arXiv:1011.5754 [gr-qc]].

5. M. M. Dos Santos, T. Oniga, A. S. Mcleman, M. Caldwell and C. H. T. Wang, J. Plasma Phys. **79**, 437 (2013) [arXiv:1301.0494 [quant-ph]].
6. A. Feller and E. R. Livine, Class. Quant. Grav. **33**, no. 6, 065005 (2016) [arXiv:1509.05297 [gr-qc]].
7. I. Danshita, M. Hanada and M. Tezuka, PTEP **2017**, no. 8, 083I01 (2017) [arXiv:1606.02454 [cond-mat.quant-gas]].
8. L. Buoninfante, G. G. Luciano and L. Petruzziello, Eur. Phys. J. C **79**, no. 8, 663 (2019) [arXiv:1903.01382 [gr-qc]].
9. M. Blasone, G. Lambiase, G. G. Luciano, L. Petruzziello and F. Scardigli, Int. J. Mod. Phys. D **29**, no. 2, 2050011 (2020) [arXiv:1912.00241 [hep-th]].
10. T. W. van de Kamp, R. J. Marshman, S. Bose and A. Mazumdar, Phys. Rev. A **102**, no. 6, 062807 (2020) [arXiv:2006.06931 [quant-ph]].
11. S. A. Haine, New J. Phys. **23**, no. 3, 033020 (2021) [arXiv:1810.10202 [quant-ph]].
12. M. Maggiore, Phys. Lett. B **304**, 65-69 (1993) [arXiv:hep-th/9301067 [hep-th]].
13. M. Maggiore, Phys. Lett. B **319**, 83-86 (1993) [arXiv:hep-th/9309034 [hep-th]].
14. M. Maggiore, Phys. Rev. D **49**, 5182-5187 (1994) [arXiv:hep-th/9305163 [hep-th]].
15. F. Scardigli, Phys. Lett. B **452**, 39-44 (1999) [arXiv:hep-th/9904025 [hep-th]].
16. A. Kempf, G. Mangano and R. B. Mann, Phys. Rev. D **52**, 1108-1118 (1995) [arXiv:hep-th/9412167 [hep-th]].
17. F. Scardigli and R. Casadio, Class. Quant. Grav. **20**, 3915-3926 (2003) [arXiv:hep-th/0307174 [hep-th]].
18. S. Das and E. C. Vagenas, Can. J. Phys. **87**, 233-240 (2009) [arXiv:0901.1768 [hep-th]].
19. A. F. Ali, S. Das and E. C. Vagenas, "The Generalized Uncertainty Principle and Quantum Gravity Phenomenology" [arXiv:1001.2642 [hep-th]].
20. S. Basilakos, S. Das and E. C. Vagenas, JCAP **09**, 027 (2010) [arXiv:1009.0365 [hep-th]].
21. A. F. Ali, S. Das and E. C. Vagenas, Phys. Rev. D **84**, 044013 (2011) [arXiv:1107.3164 [hep-th]].
22. I. Pikovski, M. R. Vanner, M. Aspelmeyer, M. S. Kim and C. Brukner, Nature Phys. **8**, 393-397 (2012) [arXiv:1111.1979 [quant-ph]].
23. F. Scardigli and R. Casadio, Eur. Phys. J. C **75**, no. 9, 425 (2015) [arXiv:1407.0113 [hep-th]].
24. F. Scardigli, G. Lambiase and E. Vagenas, Phys. Lett. B **767**, 242-246 (2017) [arXiv:1611.01469 [hep-th]].
25. S. P. Kumar and M. B. Plenio, Phys. Rev. A **97**, no. 6, 063855 (2018) [arXiv:1708.05659 [quant-ph]].
26. D. Amati, M. Ciafaloni and G. Veneziano, Phys. Lett. B **197**, 81 (1987); D. J. Gross and P. F. Mende, Phys. Lett. B **197**, 129-134 (1987); D. Amati, M. Ciafaloni and G. Veneziano, Phys. Lett. B **216**, 41-47 (1989); K. Konishi, G. Paffuti and P. Provero, Phys. Lett. B **234**, 276-284 (1990); S. Capozziello, G. Lambiase and G. Scarpetta, Int. J. Theor. Phys. **39**, 15-22 (2000) [arXiv:gr-qc/9910017 [gr-qc]].
27. A. Das, S. Das and E. C. Vagenas, Phys. Lett. B **809**, 135772 (2020) [arXiv:2006.05781 [gr-qc]].
28. G. Lambiase and F. Scardigli, Phys. Rev. D **97**, no. 7, 075003 (2018) [arXiv:1709.00637 [hep-th]].
29. A. Iorio, G. Lambiase, P. Pais and F. Scardigli, Phys. Rev. D **101**, no. 10, 105002 (2020) [arXiv:1910.09019 [hep-th]].
30. L. Petruzziello, Class. Quant. Grav. **38**, no. 13, 135005 (2021) [arXiv:2010.05896 [hep-th]]; G. G. Luciano and L. Petruzziello, Eur. Phys. J. Plus **136**, no. 2, 179 (2021).

31. L. Canetti, M. Drewes and M. Shaposhnikov, New J. Phys. **14**, 095012 (2012) [arXiv:1204.4186 [hep-ph]].
32. A. D. Sakharov, Pisma Zh. Eksp. Teor. Fiz. **5**, 32-35 (1967).
33. R. G. Cai, L. M. Cao and Y. P. Hu, JHEP **08**, 090 (2008) [arXiv:0807.1232 [hep-th]].
34. T. Zhu, J. R. Ren and M. F. Li, Phys. Lett. B **674**, 204-209 (2009) doi:10.1016/j.physletb.2009.03.020 [arXiv:0811.0212 [hep-th]].
35. A. Awad and A. F. Ali, JHEP **06**, 093 (2014) [arXiv:1404.7825 [gr-qc]].
36. S. Giardino and V. Salzano, Eur. Phys. J. C **81**, no. 2, 110 (2021) [arXiv:2006.01580 [gr-qc]].
37. G. 't Hooft, Conf. Proc. C **930308**, 284-296 (1993) [arXiv:gr-qc/9310026 [gr-qc]].
38. L. Susskind, J. Math. Phys. **36**, 6377-6396 (1995) [arXiv:hep-th/9409089 [hep-th]].
39. P. Bosso and S. Das, Annals Phys. **383**, 416-438 (2017) [arXiv:1607.01083 [gr-qc]].
40. A. J. M. Medved and E. C. Vagenas, Phys. Rev. D **70**, 124021 (2004) [arXiv:hep-th/0411022 [hep-th]].
41. G. Amelino-Camelia, M. Arzano and A. Procaccini, Phys. Rev. D **70**, 107501 (2004) [arXiv:gr-qc/0405084 [gr-qc]].
42. L. J. Garay, Int. J. Mod. Phys. A **10**, 145-166 (1995) [arXiv:gr-qc/9403008 [gr-qc]].
43. D. Christodoulou, Phys. Rev. Lett. **25**, 1596-1597 (1970).
44. D. Christodoulou and R. Ruffini, Phys. Rev. D **4**, 3552-3555 (1971).
45. J. D. Bekenstein, Phys. Rev. D **7**, 2333-2346 (1973).
46. S. W. Hawking, Phys. Rev. D **13**, 191-197 (1976).
47. R. G. Cai and S. P. Kim, JHEP **02**, 050 (2005) [arXiv:hep-th/0501055 [hep-th]].
48. R. G. Cai, L. M. Cao and Y. P. Hu, Class. Quant. Grav. **26**, 155018 (2009) [arXiv:0809.1554 [hep-th]].
49. S. A. Hayward, Class. Quant. Grav. **15**, 3147-3162 (1998) [arXiv:gr-qc/9710089 [gr-qc]].
50. H. Davoudiasl, R. Kitano, G. D. Kribs, H. Murayama and P. J. Steinhardt, Phys. Rev. Lett. **93**, 201301 (2004) [arXiv:hep-ph/0403019 [hep-ph]].
51. N. Azhar, A. Jawad and S. Rani, Phys. Dark Univ. **32**, 100815 (2021); H. Davoudiasl, Phys. Rev. D **88**, 095004 (2013) [arXiv:1308.3473 [hep-ph]]; S. D. Odintsov and V. K. Oikonomou, EPL **116**, no. 4, 49001 (2016) [arXiv:1610.02533 [gr-qc]]; S. D. Odintsov and V. K. Oikonomou, Phys. Lett. B **760**, 259-262 (2016) [arXiv:1607.00545 [gr-qc]]; V. K. Oikonomou and E. N. Saridakis, Phys. Rev. D **94**, no. 12, 124005 (2016) [arXiv:1607.08561 [gr-qc]]; S. Bhattacharjee and P. K. Sahoo, Eur. Phys. J. C **80**, no. 3, 289 (2020) [arXiv:2002.11483 [physics.gen-ph]]; E. H. Baffou, M. J. S. Houndjo, D. A. Kanfon and I. G. Salako, Eur. Phys. J. C **79**, no. 2, 112 (2019) [arXiv:1808.01917 [gr-qc]]; M. P. L. P. Ramos and J. Páramos, Phys. Rev. D **96**, no. 10, 104024 (2017) [arXiv:1709.04442 [gr-qc]]; M. Fukushima, S. Mizuno and K. i. Maeda, Phys. Rev. D **93**, no. 10, 103513 (2016) [arXiv:1603.02403 [hep-ph]]; H. M. Sadjadi, Phys. Rev. D **76**, 123507 (2007) [arXiv:0709.0697 [gr-qc]].
52. E. W. Kolb and M. S. Turner, "The Early Universe," Front. Phys. **69**, 1-547 (1990).
53. W. H. Kinney, E. W. Kolb, A. Melchiorri and A. Riotto, Phys. Rev. D **74**, 023502 (2006) [arXiv:astro-ph/0605338 [astro-ph]].
54. J. M. Cline, "Baryogenesis," [arXiv:hep-ph/0609145 [hep-ph]]; A. D. Dolgov, "CP violation in cosmology," [arXiv:hep-ph/0511213 [hep-ph]]; A. Riotto, "Theories of baryogenesis," [arXiv:hep-ph/9807454 [hep-ph]]; A. Riotto and M. Trodden, Ann. Rev. Nucl. Part. Sci. **49**, 35-75 (1999) [arXiv:hep-ph/9901362 [hep-ph]]; M. Yoshimura, J. Korean Phys. Soc. **29**, S236 (1996) [arXiv:hep-ph/9605246 [hep-ph]]; G. Lambiase, S. Mohanty and A. R. Prasanna, Int. J. Mod. Phys. D **22**, 1330030 (2013) [arXiv:1310.8459 [hep-ph]].

55. V. Nenmeli, S. Shankaranarayanan, V. Todorinov and S. Das, Phys. Lett. B **821**, 136621 (2021) [arXiv:2106.04141 [gr-qc]].
56. P. Jizba, H. Kleinert and F. Scardigli, Phys. Rev. D **81**, 084030 (2010) [arXiv:0912.2253 [hep-th]].
57. T. Kanazawa, G. Lambiase, G. Vilasi and A. Yoshioka, Eur. Phys. J. C **79**, no. 2, 95 (2019).
58. A. F. Ali, S. Das and E. C. Vagenas, Phys. Lett. B **678**, 497-499 (2009) [arXiv:0906.5396 [hep-th]].
59. S. Das, E. C. Vagenas and A. F. Ali, Phys. Lett. B **690**, 407-412 (2010) [erratum: Phys. Lett. B **692**, 342-342 (2010)] [arXiv:1005.3368 [hep-th]].
60. S. Deb, S. Das and E. C. Vagenas, Phys. Lett. B **755**, 17-23 (2016) [arXiv:1601.07893 [gr-qc]].

On quantum gravity and quantum gravity phenomenology

Douglas Edmonds

Department of Physics, Penn State Hazleton, Hazleton, PA, 18202, U.S.A.
E-mail: bde12@psu.edu

Djordje Minic[*] and Tatsu Takeuchi

Department of Physics, Virginia Tech, Blacksburg, VA 24061, U.S.A.
[*] Talk given by D.M. at the 16th Marcel Grossmann Meeting
E-mail: dminic@vt.edu, takeuchi@vt.edu

This article summarizes a new approach to quantum gravity based on the concepts of modular spacetime, Born geometry, and metastring theory and their applications to quantum gravity phenomenology. In particular, we discuss a new understanding of dark matter in terms of metaparticles (zero modes of the metastring) and its relation to dark energy (the curvature of dual spacetime) in view of the actual astronomical observations.

Keywords: Quantum Gravity, Quantum Spacetime, Dark Matter, Dark Energy.

1. Introduction and summary

In this paper we review recent work[1–10] on quantum foundations of quantum mechanics (QM), quantum field theory (QFT), and quantum gravity (in the guise of metastring theory) as well as unique implications for the problems of dark matter and dark energy.[11,12] This generic formulation of quantum gravity implies a radiatively stable positive cosmological constant (dark energy)[11] in the observed classical spacetime, and metaparticle quanta (the zero modes of the metastring) representing the natural quanta of dark matter[12] (correlated to dark energy and visible matter). The logic of our story is very similar to the path that leads from the Minkowski geometry of special relativity via relativistic non-gravitational field theory to a dynamical spacetime of general relativity. In this paper, we start with a hidden geometry in quantum theory (Born geometry) and proceed to its dynamical implementation in quantum gravity (formulated as a metastring theory) with implications for QFT (formulated in a way that takes into account the hidden Born geometry) with implications for the observed world: metaparticles as dark matter quanta, and dark energy emerging from the geometry of the dual spacetime. In some sense, this is a sharpening of the modern approaches to non-perturbative quantum physics,[13] using a simple but crucial insight about a completeness of quantum kinematics of discretized physical systems.[14]

In particular, in Ref. 5 we demonstrated that any quantum theory is endowed with a generic quantum polarization associated with modular spacetime.[4] The generic polarization manifestly realizes quantum non-locality, associated with the quantum superposition principle, that is consistent with causality, and reveals a novel geometry structure, called Born geometry,[1,2] which unifies symplectic (ω), orthogonal (η), and conformal geometries (H). Born geometry is fundamental for a particular quantum theory that consistently propagates in this geometry – this turns out to be string theory formulated in a generalized-geometric and intrinsically non-commutative, doubled, chiral phase-space-like form (called metastring theory).[3,6–8] The zero modes of the metastring correspond to metaparticles that explicitly realize the geometry of modular spacetime,[9] and as such, could be considered as an explicit prediction of the modular representation of quantum theory. The metaparticles[10] are quanta of a modular generalization of quantum fields, the low energy remnants of metastring fields. From this new viewpoint[1–10] quantum gravity is essentially defined as "gravitization of the quantum," that is, as a theory of a dynamical Born geometry. As such it incorporates the concept of Born reciprocity[15] as a covariant implementation of T-duality, the fundamental relation between short and long distance physics in string theory, as well as the new idea of relative (or observer dependent) locality.[16]

In what follows, we start with a discussion of quantum theory via quantum (modular) spacetime and then comment on QFT in this approach, and then move on to quantum gravity and its phenomenology in the context of dark matter and dark energy and the actual astronomical observations.

2. Quantum theory and quantum spacetime

The fundamental reason for the existence of modular polarizations in quantum theory is as follows.[5] If one imagines that a quantum system is formulated on a lattice, as assumed in the modern (Wilsonian) non-perturbative approaches,[13] then a theorem due to Zak[14] states that a complete set of quantum numbers needed to describe any quantum system would require both quantum numbers associated with the lattice and its inverse. This is easy to see by realizing that non-commuting Hermitian operators, such as coordinates and momenta $[\hat{q}, \hat{p}] = i\hbar$, when exponentiated, together with the appropriate lattice spacing a and its inverse $2\pi\hbar/a$, commute, that is,

$$\left[\exp\left(\frac{i}{\hbar} \hat{q} \frac{2\pi\hbar}{a}\right), \exp\left(\frac{i}{\hbar} \hat{p} a\right) \right] = 0. \quad (1)$$

Such unitary observables were labeled as "modular" by Aharonov.[17] These variables are purely quantum in the sense that their formal $\hbar \to 0$ limit is singular. Also, even though their commutators are zero, the associated Poisson brackets are non-zero, as these are unitary (phase) variables. Finally, the classical limit is defined by starting with a modular formulation and defining an appropriate "extensification,"[5] with, in principle, many classical limits. These purely quantum variables also appear in the context of QFT.

Thus we concentrate on a complete set of unitary operators as opposed to a complete set of Hermitian operators. Let us examine the simplest example of the $\hat{q}$ and $\hat{p}$ operators. The commuting subalgebra of the original non-commuting $[\hat{q}, \hat{p}] = i\hbar$ algebra can be completely described by self-dual lattices (endowed with the natural symplectic form (ω) coming from the commutator bracket). These in turn represent a discretization of a (covariant) phase space defined by q and p, and when lifted to the original non-commutative algebra, require extra data associated with the lift that is described by a doubly orthogonal ($O(d,d)$, where d denotes the spacetime dimension) metric η (a symmetric counterpart of the antisymmetric ω associated with $Sp(2d)$ transformations). Finally, in order to define the vacuum state on this self-dual lattice, we need a conformal structure $O(2, 2(d-1))$.[5] This triplet of structures defines Born geometry[1,2] associated with the modular representation of quantum theory.[5] Born geometry captures quantum non-locality that is consistent with causality, given the quantum nature of the unitary operators and the fact that the triple intersection of $Sp(2d)$, $O(d,d)$ and $O(2, 2(d-1))$ gives the Lorentz group.[6]

Let us formalize these insights about the hidden quantum spacetime geometry of quantization.[5] We start with the Heisenberg (or Weyl-Heisenberg) group, which is generated, on the level of the corresponding algebra, by the familiar position $\hat{q}^a$ and momentum $\hat{p}_b$ operators: $[\hat{q}^a, \hat{p}_b] = i\hbar \delta^a_b$. It will be convenient to introduce a length scale λ and a momentum scale ϵ, with $\lambda\epsilon = \hbar$. Also, let us introduce the notation $\hat{x}^a \equiv \hat{q}^a/\lambda$, $\hat{\tilde{x}}_a \equiv \hat{p}_a/\epsilon$ so that $[\hat{x}^a, \hat{\tilde{x}}_b] = i\delta^a_b$, and let us define

$$\mathbb{X}^A \equiv (x^a, \tilde{x}_a)^T, \quad [\hat{\mathbb{X}}^a, \hat{\mathbb{X}}^b] = i\omega^{AB}, \quad \text{with} \quad \frac{1}{2}\omega_{AB} dX^A dX^B = \frac{1}{\hbar} dp_a \wedge dq^a, \quad (2)$$

where $\omega_{AB} = -\omega_{BA}$ is the canonical symplectic form on phase space $\mathcal{P}$. The Heisenberg group $H_\mathcal{P}$ is generated by Weyl operators[18] $W_\mathbb{K} \equiv e^{2\pi i \omega(\mathbb{K}, \mathbb{X})}$, where $\mathbb{K}$ stands for the pair $(\tilde{k}, k)$ and $\omega(\mathbb{K}, \mathbb{K}') = k \cdot \tilde{k}' - \tilde{k} \cdot k'$. These form a central extension of the translation algebra, $W_\mathbb{K} W_{\mathbb{K}'} = e^{2\pi i \omega(\mathbb{K}, \mathbb{K}')} W_{\mathbb{K}+\mathbb{K}'}$. The projection $\pi : H_\mathcal{P} \to \mathcal{P}$ (where $\pi : W_\mathbb{K} \to \mathbb{K}$) defines a line bundle over $\mathcal{P}$ (in principle a covariant phase space of quantum probes). In this formulation, states are sections of degree one, $W_{\mathbb{K}'} \Phi(\mathbb{K}) = e^{2\pi i \omega(\mathbb{K}, \mathbb{K}')} \Phi(\mathbb{K} + \mathbb{K}')$.

Using notions of non-commutative algebra and non-commutative geometry[19] (such as the theorem of Gelfand-Naimark[20]), we can say that a Lagrangian submanifold (a half-dimensional submanifold of phase space upon which the symplectic form pulls back to zero) is a maximally commutative subgroup of the Heisenberg group. If we accept this notion of a Lagrangian, then the quantum regime is very different from the classical regime. In particular the vanishing Poisson bracket $\{f(q), g(p)\} = 0$ requires either f or g to be constant. However, the vanishing commutator $[f(\hat{q}), g(\hat{p})] = 0$ requires only that the functions be commensurately periodic:

$$e^{i\alpha \hat{p}} e^{i\beta \hat{q}} = e^{i\hbar\alpha\beta} e^{i\beta \hat{q}} e^{i\alpha \hat{p}}, \qquad \alpha\beta = 2\pi/\hbar. \quad (3)$$

Similar considerations led Aharonov to introduce *modular variables* to describe purely quantum phenomena such as interference.[21]

Modular variables are described in great detail in Ref. 21, where one can find detailed references on this subject. The modular variables, denoted $[\hat{q}]$ and $[\hat{p}]$, are defined modulo a length scale R (the slit spacing being a natural choice) as

$$[\hat{p}]_{2\pi\hbar/R} = \hat{p} \bmod (2\pi\hbar/R), \qquad [\hat{q}]_R = \hat{q} \bmod (R). \tag{4}$$

They play a central role in understanding interference in terms of operators (and not states). The shift operator $e^{iR\hat{p}/\hbar} = e^{iR[\hat{p}]/\hbar}$ shifts the position of a particle state (say an electron in the double-slit experiment) by distance R and is a function of the modular momenta (see also Ref. 22). These modular variables (the main examples being the Aharonov-Bohm and Aharonov-Casher phases[21]) satisfy non-local operator equations of motion. For example, given the Hamiltonian $\hat{H} = \hat{p}^2/2m + V(\hat{q})$, the Heisenberg equation of motion for the shift operator is

$$e^{-iR\hat{p}/\hbar} \frac{d}{dt} e^{iR\hat{p}/\hbar} = -\frac{iR}{\hbar}\left(\frac{V(\hat{q}+R) - V(\hat{q})}{R}\right). \tag{5}$$

Modular variables are fundamentally non-local in a non-classical sense, since we see here that their evolution depends on the value of the potential at distinct locations. Remarkably, thanks to the uncertainty principle, this dynamical non-locality does not lead to a violation of causality.[21] One of the characteristic features of these variables is that they do not have classical analogues; indeed, the limit $\hbar \to 0$ of $[p]_{\hbar/R}$ is ill-defined. Also, modular variables capture entanglement of continuous q, p variables. When exponentiated (i.e., when understood as Weyl operators) the modular variables naturally commute. In other words, given $[\hat{x}^a, \hat{\tilde{x}}_b] = i\delta^a_b$ we find[5] $[e^{2\pi i \hat{x}}, e^{2\pi i \hat{\tilde{x}}}] = 0$. Thus, the quantum algebra of modular variables possesses more commutative directions than the classical Poisson algebra, since the Poisson bracket of modular variables does not vanish, $\{e^{2\pi i x}, e^{2\pi i \tilde{x}}\} \neq 0$.

2.1. Modular spacetime as quantum spacetime and Born geometry

In this view of quantum theory we have a structure analogous to a Brillouin cell in condensed matter physics. The volume and shape of the cell are given by λ and ϵ (i.e. $\hbar$ and G (or α')). The uncertainty principle is implemented in a subtle way: we can specify a point in a modular cell, but if so, we cannot say *which* cell we are in. This means that there is a more general notion of quantization.[5] Instead of selecting a classical polarization L (the arguments of the wave function, or the arguments of a local quantum field) we choose a *modular polarization*. In terms of the Heisenberg group, all that is happening is that in order to have a commutative algebra, we need only $\omega(\mathbb{K}, \mathbb{K}') \in 2\mathbb{Z}$, and $W_\mathbb{K} W_{\mathbb{K}'} = e^{2\pi i \omega(\mathbb{K},\mathbb{K}')} W_{\mathbb{K}+\mathbb{K}'} = W_{\mathbb{K}'} W_{\mathbb{K}'}$. This defines a lattice Λ in phase space $\mathcal{P}$. Finally, we specify a "lift" of the lattice from the phase space $\mathcal{P}$ to the Heisenberg group $H_\mathcal{P}$.

Maximally commuting subgroups $\hat{\Lambda}$ of the Heisenberg group correspond to lattices that are integral and self-dual with respect to ω.[23] Given W_λ, where $\lambda \in \Lambda$, there is a lift to $\hat{\Lambda}$ which defines "modular polarization," $U_\lambda = \alpha(\lambda) W_\lambda$, where $\alpha(\lambda)$

satisfies the co-cycle condition $\alpha(\lambda)\,\alpha(\mu)\,e^{\pi i \omega(\lambda,\mu)} = \alpha(\lambda+\mu)$, with $\lambda, \alpha \in \Lambda$. One can parametrize a solution to the co-cycle condition by introducing a symmetric bilinear from $\eta(\mathbb{K}, \mathbb{K}') = k \cdot \tilde{k}' + \tilde{k} \cdot k'$ and setting $\alpha_\eta(\lambda) \equiv e^{i\frac{\pi}{2}\eta(\lambda,\lambda)}$. Finally, when we choose a classical Lagrangian L there exists a special translation-invariant state that we associate with the vacuum, which we interpret as "empty space." In modular quantization there is no such translation-invariant state because of the lattice structure. The best we can do is to choose a state that minimizes an "energy," which requires the introduction of another symmetric bilinear form that we call, again suggestively, H. This means that we are looking for operators such that

$$[\hat{\mathbb{P}}_A, \Phi] = \frac{i}{2\pi}\partial_A \Phi, \quad \text{and} \quad \Phi(\hat{\mathbb{X}} + \lambda) = \Phi(\hat{\mathbb{X}}), \tag{6}$$

where the modular observables $\Phi(\hat{\mathbb{X}} + \lambda) = \Phi(\hat{\mathbb{X}})$ are generated by the lattice observables U_λ with $\lambda \in \Lambda$. Translation invariance would be the condition $\hat{\mathbb{P}}|0\rangle = 0$. Since this is not possible, the next natural choice is to minimize the translational energy. Therefore, we pick a positive definite metric H_{AB} on $\mathcal{P}$, and we define[5] $\hat{E}_H \equiv H^{AB}\hat{\mathbb{P}}_A\hat{\mathbb{P}}_B$, and demand that $|0\rangle_H$ be the ground state of $\hat{E}_H$. This is indeed the most natural choice and it shows that we cannot fully disentangle kinematics (i.e., the definition of translation generators) from dynamics. In the Schrödinger case, since the translation generators commute, the vacuum state $\hat{E}|0\rangle = 0$ is also the translation-invariant state and it carries no memory of the metric H needed to define the energy. In our context, due to the non-commutativity of translations, the operators $\hat{E}_H$ and $\hat{E}_{H'}$ do not commute. Thus, the vacuum state depends on H, in other words $|0\rangle_H \neq |0\rangle_{H'}$, and it also possesses a non-vanishing zero point energy.

Therefore, modular quantization involves the introduction of three quadratic forms (ω, η, H), called *Born geometry*,[1,2] which underlies the geometry of modular variables. As we will see, in the context of metastring theory, a choice of polarization is a choice of a spacetime within $\mathcal{P}$ but the most general choice is a *modular polarization* that we have discussed above. From the foundational quantum viewpoint, Born geometry (ω, η, H) arises as a parametrization of such quantizations, which results in a notion of quantum spacetime, that we call *modular spacetime*. In particular, a one-dimensional modular line is a two-dimensional torus that is compact and not simply connected. Finally, large spacetimes of canonical general relativity (and its extensions, like string theory) result as a "many-body" phenomenon through a process of tensoring (entangling) unit modular cells, which we refer to as "extensification."[5] Note that the Lorentz group (in d spacetime dimensions) lies at the intersection of the symplectic, neutral and doubly orthogonal groups,[5]

$$O(1, d-1) = Sp(2d) \cap O(d, d) \cap O(2, 2(d-1)), \tag{7}$$

which sheds new light on the origin of quantum theory through compatibility of the causal (Lorentz) structure and non-locality captured by the discreteness of quantum spacetime. Note that relative (observer-dependent) locality[16] is needed to resolve the apparent contradiction between discreteness of quantum spacetime and Lorentz symmetry.

One can pass from a classical polarization (such as the Schrödinger representation) to a modular polarization via the Zak transform.[14] Note that, there is a connection on the line bundle over phase space that has unit flux through a modular cell. (This is very similar to Integer Quantum Hall effect.) A modular wave function is quasi-periodic

$$\Psi(x+a, \tilde{x}) = e^{2i\pi a \tilde{x}} \Psi(x, \tilde{x}), \quad \Psi(x, \tilde{x}+\tilde{a}) = \Psi(x, \tilde{x}). \tag{8}$$

The quasi-periods correspond to the tails of an Aharonov-Bohm[24] potential attached to a unit flux. In particular, vacuum states must have at least one zero in a cell, which leads to theta functions (the Zak transforms of Gaussians).

2.2. *A comment on quantum field theory and quantum spacetime*

A few general comments about QFT in the modular form are in order, following the general modular formulation of any quantum theory. The modular polarization of QFT reveals new structures and sheds new light on both the short distance (UV) and long distance (IR) physics of quantum fields, and the continuum limit of QFTs which is self-dual with respect to the UV and IR properties (resembling some crucial properties of non-commutative field theories[25]). In particular, the modular representation of QFT introduces dual "electric" and "magnetic" variables, which are non-commuting in general. This extends our results in the context of the 2d conformal field theory formulation of string theory in which the non-commutativity of such "electric" and "magnetic" variables has been explicitly demonstrated.[7,8]

The general modular representation can be defined in terms of the Zak transform of a Schrödinger representation (*i.e.*, wave functions). Given a square normalizable wave function $\psi(x)$ belonging to a Hilbert space, one defines the modular representation as the lattice Fourier transform (or Zak transform)

$$\psi_a(x, \tilde{x}) \equiv \sqrt{a} \sum_n e^{-2\pi i n \tilde{x}} \psi(a(x+n)), \tag{9}$$

where $x \equiv q/a$, $\tilde{x} \equiv p/b$, with $ab = 2\pi\hbar$. Note that if $\psi(x)$ is a Gaussian, its Zak transform, the modular $\psi_a(x, \tilde{x})$, is given by the doubly-periodic theta function associated with the lattice. (The inverse Zak transform

$$\Phi(x+n) \equiv \frac{1}{\sqrt{a}} \int_0^1 d\tilde{x}\, e^{2\pi i n \tilde{x}} \Phi_a(a^{-1}x, \tilde{x}), \tag{10}$$

illustrates that the usual Schrödinger representation is truly singular, and thus not generic.)

Now if one second quantizes $\psi(x)$, one naturally ends up with a quantum field operator $\phi(x)$. Similarly, the second quantization of the modular $\psi_a(x, \tilde{x})$ would lead to a modular quantum field operator $\phi(x, \tilde{x})$, $\phi(x) \to \phi(x, \tilde{x})$. The excitations of such modular quantum fields are non-local in general, and will be discussed below as *metaparticles*. Note that the usual wave functional approach to QFT defined in terms of functionals $\Psi[\phi(x)]$ should be now defined in terms of wave functionals of modular fields $\Psi[\phi(x,\tilde{x})]$. However, now we have more freedom in the general modular polarization. The dual momenta p and $\tilde{p}$ (to x and $\tilde{x}$ respectively) lead, via the canonical minimal-coupling prescription, not only to the usual fields ϕ but also to their duals $\tilde{\phi}$ (see below). This procedure defines the modular polarization of QFT in terms of the functional Zak transform of the original wave functional, $\Psi[\phi(x)] \to \Psi[\phi(x,\tilde{x}), \tilde{\phi}(x,\tilde{x})]$. For example, the Gaussian wave functionals with non-trivial kernels (such as the ones found in the context of non-trivial interacting theories like 2+1 and 3+1 dimensional Yang Mills theory[26]) would be mapped into functional theta functions.

The non-perturbative formulation is defined in a symmetric, self-dual way with respect to the double RG flows (as in non-commutative field theory[25]) with full spacetime covariance, and should be important not only for quantum non-locality of QFT, but also in the realms of strong coupling and deep infrared.

3. Quantum gravity and dynamical quantum (modular) spacetime

The unexpected outcome of this new view of the foundations of quantum theory is that this fundamental geometry of quantum theory can be realized in the context of metastring theory, in which this Born geometry (given by ω, η and H) is "gravitized" (i.e. dynamical). At the classical level, metastring theory[1-10] can be thought of as a formulation of string theory in which the target space is doubled in such a way that T-duality acts linearly on the coordinates. This doubling means that momentum and winding modes appear on an equal footing. In this formulation, T-duality exchanges the Lagrangian sub-manifold with its image under $J = \eta^{-1}H$. Classical metastring theory is defined by the action[3,27]

$$\hat{S} = \frac{1}{4\pi}\int_\Sigma d^2\sigma \left(\partial_\tau \mathbb{X}^A(\eta_{AB}+\omega_{AB})(\mathbb{X})\partial_\sigma \mathbb{X}^B - \partial_\sigma \mathbb{X}^A H_{AB}(\mathbb{X})\partial_\sigma \mathbb{X}^B\right), \quad (11)$$

where $\mathbb{X}^A$ are dimensionless coordinates on phase space and the fields η, H, ω are all dynamical (i.e., in general dependent on $\mathbb{X}$) phase space fields ($\mathbb{X}^A \equiv (x^a, \tilde{x}_a)^T$). In the context of a flat metastring we have constant η_{AB}, H_{AB}, and ω_{AB} :

$$\eta_{AB} \equiv \begin{pmatrix} 0 & \delta \\ \delta^T & 0 \end{pmatrix}, \quad H_{AB} \equiv \begin{pmatrix} h & 0 \\ 0 & h^{-1} \end{pmatrix}, \quad \omega_{AB} \equiv \begin{pmatrix} 0 & \delta \\ -\delta^T & 0 \end{pmatrix}, \quad (12)$$

where δ^μ_ν is the d-dimensional identity matrix, and $h_{\mu\nu}$ is the d-dimensional Lorentzian metric. The Polyakov string[28] is obtained in a singular limit of zero ω after integrating over $\tilde{x}$. (For a phase space structure of the canonical string see Ref. 29 and references therein.)

3.1. *Non-commutativity and non-associativity in quantum gravity*

The metastring formulation points to an unexpected fundamental non-commutativity of closed string theory, that we address in what follows. The string commutation relations[7,8] state $[\mathbb{X}^A(\sigma), \mathbb{X}^B(\sigma')] = 2i\lambda^2 \left[\pi \omega^{AB} - \eta^{AB}\theta(\sigma - \sigma')\right]$, where $\theta(\sigma)$ is the staircase distribution, i.e., a solution of $\theta'(\sigma) = 2\pi\delta(\sigma)$; it is odd and quasi-periodic with period 2π. Following standard practice, all indices are raised and lowered using η and η^{-1}. The momentum density operator is given by

$$\mathbb{P}_A(\sigma) = \frac{1}{2\pi\alpha'}\, \eta_{AB}\, \partial_\sigma \mathbb{X}^B(\sigma)\,, \qquad (13)$$

and the previous commutation relation implies that it is conjugate to $\mathbb{X}^A(\sigma)$. The two-form ω appears when one integrates this canonical commutation relation to include the zero-modes, the integration constant being uniquely determined by worldsheet causality. Denoting by $(\hat{\mathbb{X}}, \hat{\mathbb{P}})$ the zero mode components of the string operators $\mathbb{X}(\sigma)$ and $\mathbb{P}(\sigma)$, we have $[\hat{\mathbb{P}}_A, \hat{\mathbb{P}}_B] = 0$, $[\hat{\mathbb{X}}^A, \hat{\mathbb{P}}_B] = i\hbar\delta^A{}_B$, and $[\hat{\mathbb{X}}^A, \hat{\mathbb{X}}^B] = 2\pi i \lambda^2 \omega^{AB}$. This is a deformation of the doubled Heisenberg algebra involving the string length λ as a deformation parameter. Note that under a constant B-field transformation $\mathbb{X} = (x^a, \tilde{x}_a) \mapsto (x^a, \tilde{x}_a + B_{ab}x^b)$, the trivial symplectic form $\omega(\mathbb{K},\mathbb{K}') = k\cdot \tilde{k}' - \tilde{k}\cdot k'$ is mapped onto $\omega(\mathbb{K},\mathbb{K}') = k_a \tilde{k}'^a - k'_a \tilde{k}^a - 2B_{ab}\tilde{k}^a \tilde{k}'^b$, and the commutators read

$$\left[\hat{x}^a, \hat{x}^b\right] = 0\,, \quad \left[\hat{x}^a, \hat{\tilde{x}}_b\right] = 2\pi i \lambda^2 \delta^a{}_b\,, \quad \left[\hat{\tilde{x}}_a, \hat{\tilde{x}}_b\right] = -4\pi i \lambda^2 B_{ab}\,. \qquad (14)$$

We see that the effect of the B-field is to render the dual coordinates non-commutative (and that the B-field originates from the symplectic structure ω). This implies a new view of the axion in four spacetime dimensions. The β-transformation on the other hand corresponds to the map $(x^a, \tilde{x}_a) \mapsto (x^a + \beta^{ab}\tilde{x}_b, \tilde{x}_a)$. Equivalently, it has the effect of mapping the symplectic structure to $\omega(\mathbb{K},\mathbb{K}') = k_a \tilde{k}'^a - k'_a \tilde{k}^a + 2\beta^{ab}k_a k'_b$, and yields commutation relations

$$\left[\hat{x}^a, \hat{x}^b\right] = 4\pi i \lambda^2 \beta^{ab}\,, \quad \left[\hat{x}^a, \hat{\tilde{x}}_b\right] = 2\pi i \lambda^2 \delta^a{}_b\,, \quad \left[\hat{\tilde{x}}_a, \hat{\tilde{x}}_b\right] = 0\,. \qquad (15)$$

Dramatically, the coordinates that are usually thought of as the spacetime coordinates have become themselves non-commutative. Since this is the result of an $O(d,d)$ transformation it can be thought of in similar terms as the B-field; these are related by T-duality. We are familiar with the B-field background because we have, in the non-compact case, a fixed notion of locality in the target-space theory. However, in the non-geometric β-field background, we do not have such a notion of locality but we can access it through T-duality. However, this background does lead to non-commutative field theory, and one can place a bound on the minimal length λ of $O(10\,\text{TeV})$, which is the current high-energy limit for probing the continuum structure of spacetime. (Similarly, this background can be used to argue for an effective minimal-length extension of commutation relations.[30] For astrophysical probes of the minimal length, see Ref. 31.)

Note that the dilaton can be understood as coming from the volume of phase space.[32] In general, for varying B-backgrounds we encounter non-associativity as well,[33] and the proper closure of such non-commutative and non-associative structure is ensured by the equations of motion. Here we remark that fundamental non-associativity can be related to the robustness of the Standard Model (SM) gauge group.[34] Similarly, fundamental non-commutativity can be related to the underlying non-commutative nature of the SM and its phenomenology.[19,35]

3.2. *Non-perturbative formulation of quantum gravity*

The metastring offers a new view on the fundamental question of a non-perturbative formulation of quantum gravity.[1–10] The worldsheet can be made modular in our formulation, with the doubling of τ and σ, so that $\mathbb{X}(\tau, \sigma)$ can be in general viewed as an infinite-dimensional matrix (the matrix indices coming from the Fourier components of the doubles of τ and σ). Then the corresponding metastring action reads as

$$\int \mathrm{Tr}\Big[\partial_\tau \mathbb{X}^A \partial_\sigma \mathbb{X}^B (\omega_{AB} + \eta_{AB}) - \partial_\sigma \mathbb{X}^A H_{AB} \partial_\sigma \mathbb{X}^B\Big] d\tau d\sigma , \qquad (16)$$

where the trace is over the matrix indices. One can associate partonic degrees of freedom with matrix entries. A non-perturbative quantum gravity follows by replacing the σ-derivative with a commutator involving one extra $\mathbb{X}^{26}$:

$$\partial_\sigma \mathbb{X}^A \to \big[\mathbb{X}^{26}, \mathbb{X}^A\big] , \qquad (17)$$

with $A = 0, 1, 2, \ldots, 25$. The resulting matrix-model form of the above metastring action is

$$\int \mathrm{Tr}\Big(\partial_\tau \mathbb{X}^a \big[\mathbb{X}^b, \mathbb{X}^c\big] \eta_{abc} - H_{ac}\big[\mathbb{X}^a, \mathbb{X}^b\big]\big[\mathbb{X}^c, \mathbb{X}^d\big] H_{bd}\Big) d\tau , \qquad (18)$$

with $a, b, c = 0, 1, 2, \ldots, 25, 26$, where the first term is of a Chern-Simons form and the second of the Yang-Mills form. η_{abc} contains both ω_{AB} and η_{AB}. This defines a non-perturbative quantum gravity viewed as "a gravitization of the quantum."[10]

This formulations invokes the IIB matrix model,[36] which describes N D-instantons (and is by T-duality related to the Matrix model of M-theory[37]). Given our new viewpoint we suggest a new covariant non-commutative matrix-model formulation of string theory as a theory of quantum gravity, by writing in the large N limit $\partial_\sigma \mathbb{X}^C = [\mathbb{X}, \mathbb{X}^C]$ (and similarly for $\partial_\tau \mathbb{X}^B$) in terms of commutators of two (one for $\partial_\sigma \mathbb{X}^C$ and one for $\partial_\tau \mathbb{X}^C$) extra $N \times N$ matrix-valued chiral $\mathbb{X}$'s. Notice that, in general, we do not need an overall trace, and so the action can be viewed as a matrix, rendering the entire non-perturbative formulation as purely quantum in the sense of the original matrix formulation of QM:

$$\mathbb{S}_{\mathrm{ncF}} = \frac{1}{4\pi}\big[\mathbb{X}^a, \mathbb{X}^b\big]\big[\mathbb{X}^c, \mathbb{X}^d\big] f_{abcd} , \qquad (19)$$

where instead of 26 bosonic $\mathbb{X}$ matrices we have 28, with supersymmetry emerging in 10(+2) dimensions from this underlying bosonic formulation. (This is a non-commutative matrix-model formulation of F-theory.) By T-duality, the new covariant M-theory matrix model is

$$\mathbb{S}_{\mathrm{ncM}} = \frac{1}{4\pi} \int_\tau \Big(\partial_\tau \mathbb{X}^i \big[\mathbb{X}^j, \mathbb{X}^k\big] g_{ijk} - \big[\mathbb{X}^i, \mathbb{X}^j\big]\big[\mathbb{X}^k, \mathbb{X}^l\big] h_{ijkl}\Big), \qquad (20)$$

with 27 bosonic X matrices, with supersymmetry emerging in 11 dimensions. In this approach, holography[38] (such as AdS/CFT[39] or dS/CFT[40]), which can be viewed as a "quantum Jarzynski equality on the space of geometrized RG flows,"[41] is emergent in a particular "extensification" of quantum spacetime. The relevant information about ω_{AB}, η_{AB}, and H_{AB} is now contained in the new dynamical backgrounds f_{abcd} in F-theory, and g_{ijk} and h_{ijkl} in M-theory. This offers a new formulation of covariant Matrix theory in the M-theory limit,[42] which is essentially a partonic formulation; strings emerge from partonic constituents in a certain limit. This new matrix formulation is fundamentally bosonic (*i.e*, supersymmetry is emergent only in a specific limit) and thus it is reminiscent of bosonic M-theory.[43] The relevant backgrounds g_{ijk} and h_{ijkl} should be determined by the matrix RG equations. Also, there are lessons here for the new concept of "gravitization of quantum theory" as well as the idea that dynamical Hilbert spaces, or 2-Hilbert spaces (here represented by matrices), are fundamentally needed in quantum gravity.[44]

This matrix-like formulation should be understood as a general non-perturbative formulation of string theory. In this partonic formulation closed strings are collective excitations, in turn constructed from the product of open string fields. The observed classical spacetime emerges as an "extensification"[1–10] in a particular limit, out of the basic building blocks of quantum spacetime. Their remnants can be found in the low energy bi-local quantum fields, with bi-local (metaparticle) quanta, to which we now turn.

4. Quantum gravity, metastrings, metaparticles and dark matter

The above manifestly T-duality covariant formulation of closed strings (i.e. metastring theory) implies intrinsic non-commutativity of zero-modes. It is thus instructive to formulate a particle-like limit of the metastring that we call the *metaparticle*.[7–9] The theory of metaparticles (the low energy remnants of the metastring, and as such, the low energy remnants (predictions) of quantum gravity) is defined by the following world-line action[7–9]

$$S \equiv \int_0^1 d\tau \left[p\dot{x} + \tilde{p}\dot{\tilde{x}} + \lambda^2 p\dot{\tilde{p}} - \frac{N}{2}\left(p^2 + \tilde{p}^2 + m^2\right) + \tilde{N}\left(p\tilde{p} - \mu\right) \right]. \quad (21)$$

Here the signature $(+, -, \cdots, -)$ and the contraction of indices are implicitly assumed. At the classical level, theory of metaparticles is a worldline theory with the usual reparameterization invariance and two additional features.[9] The first new feature is the presence of an additional local symmetry, which from the string point of view corresponds to the completion of worldsheet diffeomorphism invariance. From the particle worldline point of view, this symmetry is associated with an additional local constraint. The second new feature is the presence of a non-trivial symplectic form on the metaparticle phase space, also motivated by string theory.[7,8] Because of its interpretation as a particle model on Born geometry, associated with the modular representation of quantum theory, the spacetime on which the metaparticle propagates is ambiguous, with different choices related by T-duality. The attractive feature of this model include worldline causality and unitarity, as well as an explicit mixing of widely separated energy-momentum scales. The metaparticle propagator follows from the world line path integral defined by the above action and it has the following form in momentum space[9]:

$$G(p,\tilde{p};p_i,\tilde{p}_i) \sim \delta^{(d)}(p-p_i)\delta^{(d)}(\tilde{p}-\tilde{p}_i)\frac{\delta(p\cdot\tilde{p}-\mu)}{p^2+\tilde{p}^2+m^2-i\varepsilon}. \qquad (22)$$

The canonical particle propagator is a highly singular $\tilde{p} \to 0$ (and $\mu \to 0$) limit of this expression. This propagator also predicts the following dispersion relation (in a particular gauge[9]) that can be tested in various experiments and with various probes: $E_p^2 + (\mu^2/E_p^2) = \vec{p}^2 + m^2$. This formulation is fully compatible with Lorentz covariance, and is a direct consequence of the consistency of quantum theory and a minimal length (and thus Born geometry). In a cosmological context, one can use this dispersion relation to put a bound on μ for the case of neutrinos, which turns out to be close to the energy scale of dark energy.[45] In general, for each particle at energy E there exists a dual particle at energy μ/E. This is in complete analogy of the well-known prediction of antiparticles in the union of special relativity and quantum theory.

Note that the usual particle limit is obtained, at least classically, by taking $\mu \to 0$ and $\tilde{p} \to 0$. Given the form of the above Lagrangian, the metaparticle looks like two particles that are entangled through a Berry-phase-like $p_\mu \dot{\tilde{p}}^\mu$ factor. The metaparticle is fundamentally non-local, and thus it should not be associated with effective local field theory. In particular, by looking at the metaparticle constraints $p^2 + \tilde{p}^2 = m^2$ and $p\tilde{p} = \mu$, we note that the momenta p and $\tilde{p}$ can be, in principle, widely separated. For example, if m is of the order of the Planck energy, and μ of the order of TeV^2 (which can be considered a characteristic particle physics scale), then the p can be of the order of the Planck energy, and the $\tilde{p}$ of the vacuum energy scale. Thus metaparticle theory can naturally relate widely separated scales, which transcends the usual reasoning based on Wilsonian effective field theory (and should be relevant for the naturalness and hierarchy problems).

We can also discuss the background fields that couple to the metaparticle quanta. Following the well-known procedure of introducing background fields in the case of particles, by shifting the canonical momentum by a gauge field we may try to extend the gauging procedure to the metaparticle counterpart. There is a possible ambiguity in this gauging which depends on which configuration variables one decides to work with. If one takes $(x,\tilde{x})$ as configuration variables, one obtains a gauging which could also be motivated by the presence of a "stringy gauge field" in metastring theory,[3] $p_\mu \to p_\mu + A_\mu(x,\tilde{x})$ and $\tilde{p}^\mu \to \tilde{p}^\mu + \tilde{A}^\mu(x,\tilde{x})$. The generic prediction here is the existence of a dual field $\tilde{A}$, which is correlated (entangled), with the original A field. Thus the entire SM would have a dual SM (which we propose, describes the dark matter sector).

We expect that the correct field theoretic description of the metaparticle is in terms of the above general non-commutative (modular) field theory $\Phi(x,\tilde{x})$ limit of the metastring.[1–10] Such an effective non-commutative field theory is similar in spirit to Ref. 25. Also, we note that the concept of metaparticles might be argued from the compatibility of the quantum spacetime that underlies the generic representations of quantum theory, as discussed in Ref. 5, and thus the metaparticle might be as ubiquitous as the concept of antiparticles which is demanded by the compatibility of relativity and quantum theory. The metaparticles also provide a natural route to the problem of dark matter. To lowest (zeroth) order of the expansion in the non-commutative parameter λ, the effective action for the SM matter Lagrangian (L_m) and their duals (that could be interpreted as the dark matter Lagrangian L_{dm}) takes the form

$$S_{\text{eff}} = -\iint \sqrt{g(x)\tilde{g}(\tilde{x})} \left[L_m(A(x,\tilde{x})) + \tilde{L}_{dm}(\tilde{A}(x,\tilde{x})) + \cdots \right], \tag{23}$$

where we have included the non-dynamical gravitational background. Note that after integrating over the "hidden variable" parameters $\tilde{x}$, we obtain an effective theory of visible and dual (dark) matter in the observed spacetime x:

$$S_{\text{eff}} = -\int \sqrt{g(x)} \left[L_m(A(x)) + \tilde{L}_{dm}(\tilde{A}(x)) + \cdots \right]. \tag{24}$$

Thus, the metaparticle can be understood as a generic message of string theory/quantum gravity for low energy physics. Like their visible particle cousins, dark matter quanta should be detectable through their particular metaparticle correlation/entanglement to visible matter. This is a Berry-phase-like effect that comes from a fully covariant description, and is uniquely different from the usual effective field theory interaction terms between visible and dark matter particles. We will discuss the observable consequences of this view of dark matter in the last section.

5. Quantum gravity, dark matter and dark energy

We now explain how the generalized geometric formulation of string theory discussed above provides for an effective description of dark energy that is consistent with de Sitter spacetime. This is essentially due to the theory's chirally and non-commutatively doubled realization of the target space, and the stringy effective action on the doubled non-commutative spacetime $(x^a, \tilde{x}^a)$:

$$S_{\text{eff}}^{nc} = \iint \text{Tr} \sqrt{g(x,\tilde{x})} \left[R(x,\tilde{x}) + L_m(x,\tilde{x}) + \cdots \right], \tag{25}$$

where the ellipses denote higher-order curvature terms induced by string theory, and L_m is the matter Lagrangian. S_{eff}^{nc} clearly expands into numerous terms with different powers of λ, which upon $\tilde{x}$-integration and from the x-space vantage point produce various effective terms. To lowest (zeroth) order of the expansion in the non-commutative parameter λ of S_{eff}^{nc} takes the form:

$$S_d = -\iint \sqrt{-g(x)} \sqrt{-\tilde{g}(\tilde{x})} \left[R(x) + \tilde{R}(\tilde{x}) \right], \tag{26}$$

a result which was first obtained almost three decades ago, effectively neglecting ω_{AB} by assuming that $[\hat{x}^a, \hat{\tilde{x}}_b] = 0$.[46] In this leading limit, the $\tilde{x}$-integration in the first term defines the gravitational constant G, and in the second term produces a *positive* cosmological constant $\Lambda > 0$. In particular, we are lead to the following low-energy effective action valid at long distances of the observed accelerated universe (focusing on the relevant 3+1-dimensional spacetime X, of the $+---$ signature):

$$S_{\text{eff}} = \frac{-1}{8\pi G} \int_X \sqrt{-g}(\Lambda + \tfrac{1}{2}R + \mathcal{O}(R^2)), \tag{27}$$

with Λ the positive cosmological constant (corresponding to the scale of 10^{-3} eV) and the $\mathcal{O}(R^2)$ denote higher order corrections (which are also required by the sigma model of string theory[47]).

It also follows from this construction that the weakness of gravity is determined by the size of the canonically-conjugate dual space, while the smallness of the cosmological constant is given by its curvature. Given this action, we may proceed reinterpreting Ref. 46. Integrate out the dual spacetime coordinates and write the effective action as

$$\overline{S} \sim \tilde{V} \int_X \sqrt{-g(x)} R(x) + \cdots, \quad \text{where} \quad \tilde{V} = \int_{\tilde{X}} \sqrt{-\tilde{g}(\tilde{x})}, \tag{28}$$

and then relate the dual spacetime volume to the observed spacetime volume as $\tilde{V} \sim V^{-1}$ (T-duality). This produces an "intensive" effective action[46]:

$$\overline{S} = \frac{\int_X \sqrt{-g(x)}\,(R(x) + L_m(x))}{\int_X \sqrt{-g(x)}} + \cdots. \tag{29}$$

By concentrating on the classical description first (we discuss below quantum corrections and the central role of intrinsic non-commutativity in string theory) we obtain the Einstein equations[46]

$$R_{ab} - \frac{1}{2}R g_{ab} + T_{ab} + \frac{1}{2}\overline{S}\, g_{ab} = 0, \quad \text{with} \quad T_{ab} \stackrel{\text{def}}{=} \frac{\partial L_m}{\partial g^{ab}} - \frac{1}{2} L_m\, g_{ab}. \tag{30}$$

We emphasize that our reinterpretation of Ref. 46 does not follow the original presentation and intention. In particular, we directly relate the intensive action to the cosmological constant, $\overline{S} \sim \Lambda$. Note that this new approach to the question of dark energy (viewed as a cosmological constant) in quantum gravity is realized in certain stringy-cosmic-string-like toy models,[48] which can be viewed as illustrative of a generic non-commutative phase of F-theory.[49] In particular, a "see-saw" formula is directly realized in Ref. 48 as $M_\Lambda \sim M^2/M_P$, where M_Λ is the dark energy scale, M_P the Planck scale, and M an intermediate scale coming from the matter sector (such as the Higgs scale).

Note that, in general, to lowest (zeroth) order of the expansion in the non-commutative parameter λ, S_{eff}^{nc} takes the following form (that also includes the matter sector and its dual)[50]:

$$S_d = -\iint \sqrt{g(x)\tilde{g}(\tilde{x})} \left[R(x) + \tilde{R}(\tilde{x}) + L_m(A(x,\tilde{x})) + \tilde{L}_{dm}(\tilde{A}(x,\tilde{x})) \right]. \tag{31}$$

Here, A denotes the usual SM fields, and $\tilde{A}$ denotes their duals. Note that after integrating over the dual spacetime, and after taking into account T-duality, the intensive action now reads

$$\overline{S} = \frac{\int_X \sqrt{-g(x)}\big(R(x) + L_m(x) + \tilde{L}_{dm}(x)\big)}{\int_X \sqrt{-g(x)}} + \cdots . \tag{32}$$

The proposal here is that the dual sector (as already indicated in the previous section) should be interpreted as the dark matter sector, which is correlated to the visible sector via the dark energy sector, as discussed in Ref. 12. (The radiative stability of this construction has been discussed in Ref. 50, which also addresses the hierarchy problem.) We emphasize the unity of the description of the entire dark sector based on the properties of the dual spacetime. Note that one can also discuss statistical effects in this view of dark energy and, in particular, provide an explicit formula for a dynamical form of dark energy[51] that can be compared to cosmological observations.

6. Coda: Quantum gravity phenomenology and the real world

In conclusion, we discuss the implications of our new view on dark matter and dark energy in the context of actual astronomical observations.

6.1. *Observational issues*

The above metaparticle-like dark matter quanta are by construction correlated to visible matter and have been discussed in the literature as Modified dark matter (MDM).[12] MDM is, at the moment, a phenomenological model of dark matter inspired by gravitational thermodynamics. For an accelerating Universe with positive cosmological constant Λ, certain phenomenological considerations lead to the emergence of a critical acceleration parameter related to Λ. This "fundamental acceleration" is just the value of Λ expressed as acceleration $\sim cH_0$, where H_0 is the Hubble constant, and thus, is of the order of 10^{-10}m/s^2. Appearance of this acceleration scale in the data is an expected manifestation of MDM, and its existence is observationally supported as discussed below. The resulting MDM mass profiles, which are sensitive to Λ, are consistent with observational data at both the galactic and cluster scales. In particular, the same critical acceleration appears both in the galactic and cluster data fits based on MDM.[12] Furthermore, using some robust qualitative arguments, MDM appears to work well on cosmological scales. If the quanta of MDM are metaparticles, this may explain why, so far, dark matter detection experiments have failed to detect dark matter particles. In particular, the natural model for MDM quanta could be provided by the metaparticle realizations of the SM particles, associated with bi-local extensions of all SM fields. Thus the baryonic matter described by the SM fields (the A backgrounds in the above discussion) would have natural cousins (the $\tilde{A}$ backgrounds in the above discussion) in the dark matter sector, which in turn would be sensitive to the dark energy modeled by the cosmological constant $\Lambda \sim 1/H_0^2$, that is, the curvature of the dual spacetime, which is radiatively stable and related to the Planck energy and the characteristic energy scale of the visible sector $M_\Lambda \sim M^2/M_P$.

The importance of the fundamental acceleration 10^{-10}m/s^2 is manifest in the empirically established baryonic Tully-Fisher[53] (BTF), and baryonic Faber-Jackson[54] (BFJ) relations. The BTF relation refers to the observed correlation between the total baryonic mass of spiral galaxies M_{bar} and the rotational velocity in the flat part of the rotation curve v_{flat} of the form $M_{\text{bar}} \sim v_{\text{flat}}^4$. The slope of the BTF relation gives the fundamental acceleration $v_{\text{flat}}^4/(GM_{\text{bar}}) \sim 10^{-10}$m/s^2. The relation for elliptical galaxies and other pressure supported systems that parallels the BTF for spirals is the BFJ relation between M_{bar} and the line-of-sight velocity dispersion σ of the form $M_{\text{bar}} \sim \sigma^n$. When fit to data of various pressure supported systems, the best fit to the power n was found to be anywhere from about 3 to 5 depending on the scale of the systems considered. However, when the data for globular clusters, elliptical galaxies, galaxy clusters, etc. are all analyzed together, the preferred power is $n = 4$, though the data does show considerable scatter around this line.[52,55,56] Furthermore, the slope of the $n = 4$ BFJ fit again gives the fundamental acceleration $\sigma^4/(GM_{\text{bar}}) \sim 10^{-10}$m/s^2.

According to the ΛCDM model of cosmology, our Universe started out with almost uniform distributions of cold dark matter (CDM) and baryonic matter. Consequently, a correlation between the total dark matter and total baryonic matter in a region surrounding a galaxy is to be expected in the ΛCDM model. However, given that galaxies are thought to have gone through various phases including starbursts, emission of gasses, and multiple mergers during their evolutionary histories, a dynamic correlation such as the BTF and BFJ relations involving the fundamental acceleration scale is surprising. The question is: what do these correlations imply on the nature of dark matter? What type of dark matter would be able to explain these relations?

6.2. Analogy with turbulence

Given that the temperature fluctuations in the Cosmic Microwave Background have been observed to be scale invariant,[57] and assuming that dark matter (whether traditional or metaparticle) is collisionless, then an analogy with Kolmogorov's theory of turbulence may be instructive.[58]

In the so-called inertial range of the turbulent fluid, *i.e.* at length scales L where the viscosity of the fluid can be neglected, the dynamics of vortices is determined solely by the rate of energy dissipation ε, and if one writes $\langle \text{KE} \rangle = \int dk\, E(k)$, where $\langle \text{KE} \rangle$ is the mean turbulent kinetic energy of the flow and $k = 2\pi/L$ is the wave number, simple dimensional analysis yields the famous Kolmogorov scaling relation $E(k) \propto \varepsilon^{2/3} k^{-5/3}$, which has been confirmed experimentally. The length scale η

below which viscous effects become important, called the Kolmogorov microscale, is the boundary of the inertial region. Again, from dimensional analysis, it is argued that $\eta \propto (\nu^3/\varepsilon)^{1/4}$, where ν is the kinematic viscosity. Essentially, the scale η is determined by the competition between ε and ν. Note that this argument assumes that there is no other dimension-ful scale in the problem other than these two parameters.

In the case of structure formation in a statistically self-similar (*i.e.* scale invariant) Universe, the two competing effects would be attraction due to gravity, parametrized by G, and the speed of the expansion of the Universe $H(z) = \dot{a}/a$, where z is the redshift. The scale of the structures that form at redshift z should be determined by G and $H(z)$. Now, consider the size $R_{\rm vir}$ of a virialized structure of total mass M. We expect $\langle v^2 \rangle \sim \sigma^2 \sim GM/R_{\rm vir}$. The gravitational acceleration at the edge of this structure is $a_{\rm vir} = GM/R_{\rm vir}^2 \sim \sigma^4/(GM)$. Thus, the scale of the structure $R_{\rm vir}$ can be characterized by this acceleration scale $a_{\rm vir}$. From dimensional analysis a la Kolmogorov we expect $a_{\rm vir} \sim \sigma^4/(GM) \propto cH(z)$, which is analogous to the $n = 4$ FJ relation except 1) M is the sum of the dark matter mass and the baryonic mass, 2) dark matter halos are not necessarily virialized, 3) the proportionality constant may not be order one, 4) the z dependence of $H(z)$ suggests that $\sigma^4/(GM)$ will depend on the redshift z at which the structures formed, and 5) in actuality, there are many other scales present. Nevertheless, this simple handwaving argument does suggest a possible path toward the BFJ, or a BFJ-like relation. Note also that metaparticle quanta are sensitive to both the UV (G, the Planck scale) and the IR ($H(z)$), suggesting that they may provide the linchpin connecting those scales, and the crucial ingredient in constructing a dark matter model that could realize this scenario.

One intriguing prediction of the above discussion is the possible z-dependence of $\sigma^4/(GM)$. Replacing M by $M_{\rm bar}$ should not erase this dependence. Dimensionally, $\sigma^4/(GM_{\rm bar})$ should scale as $(1+z)$. Galaxy clusters have formed recently ($z<1$), galaxies have started to form at around $z \sim 10$, and globular clusters at around $z \sim 10^{2.59}$ So if $\sigma^4/(GM_{\rm bar})$ is around $10^{-10}\,\mathrm{m/s^2}$ for galaxy clusters, it should be around $10^{-9}\,\mathrm{m/s^2}$ for galaxies, and $10^{-8}\,\mathrm{m/s^2}$ for globular clusters. In Fig. 1 we plot $\sigma^4/(GM_{\rm bar})$ for a variety of structures. As can be seen, the galaxy cluster data points are clustered around $10^{-10}\,\mathrm{m/s^2}$, while the galaxy data points are spread out in both directions and go up as far as $\sim 10^{-9}\,\mathrm{m/s^2}$, and the globular cluster data are spread out even further and go up as far as $\sim 10^{-8}\,\mathrm{m/s^2}$. One interpretation of this result is that galaxies and globular clusters started out with characteristic accelerations of $O(10^{-9}\,\mathrm{m/s^2})$ and $O(10^{-8}\,\mathrm{m/s^2})$, respectively, but have migrated to lower values as they went through various stages of evolution, resulting in distributions centered around $10^{-10}\,\mathrm{m/s^2}$ (in the log scale). This possibility had not been manifest in previous BFJ analyses which had always plotted σ^4 against $M_{\rm bar}$, demonstrating that a simple change of perspective can open up new vistas.

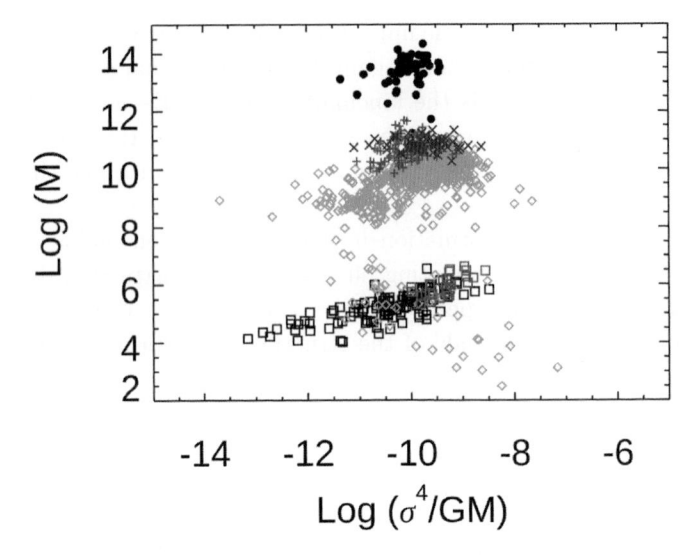

Fig. 1. The virial acceleration for structures spanning about 10 decades of scale $M/M_\odot = 10^{4\sim 14}$. The data points are: • galaxy clusters,[60] + elliptical galaxies,[61,62] × elliptical galaxies,[63,64] ◇ elliptical, dwarf elliptical, and dwarf spheroidal galaxies,[65] □ Milky Way globular clusters,[66] □ M31 (Andromeda) globular clusters.[67]

6.3. Closing remarks

In this paper, we propose that the BFJ relation could be explained by metaparticle-based, or similar MDM models. We are, however, mindful that it could well be explained by more conventional means. Indeed, Kaplinghat and Turner[68] have provided a scenario on how the BTF relation may emerge from ΛCDM, though we are unaware of a similar work on the BFJ relation. MDM models, though suggestive, are lacking in similar concrete scenarios that would connect the models to the BFJ relation; a direction of research we intend to pursue.

This concludes our presentation of the new approach to quantum gravity (based on modular spacetime, Born geometry and metastring theory) and quantum gravity phenomenology in the context of dark matter and dark energy and actual astronomical observations.

Acknowledgements

We are grateful to L. Freidel, R. G. Leigh, J. Kowalski-Glikman, P. Berglund, T. Hübsch, D. C. Dai, D. Stojkovic, J. H. Simonetti, M. Kavic and V. Jejjala for discussions. The research of DM and TT is supported in part by the US Department of Energy (DE-SC0020262). DM also thanks the Julian Schwinger Foundation, and TT the NSF (PHY-1413031) for support.

References

1. L. Freidel, R. G. Leigh and D. Minic, Phys. Lett. B **730**, 302 (2014).
2. L. Freidel, R. G. Leigh and D. Minic, Int. J. Mod. Phys. D **23**, 1442006 (2014).
3. L. Freidel, R. G. Leigh and D. Minic, JHEP **1506**, 006 (2015).
4. L. Freidel, R. G. Leigh and D. Minic, Int. J. Mod. Phys. D **24**, 1544028 (2015).
5. L. Freidel, R. G. Leigh and D. Minic, Phys. Rev. D **94**, 104052 (2016).
6. L. Freidel, R. G. Leigh and D. Minic, J. Phys. Conf. Ser. **804**, 012032 (2017).
7. L. Freidel, R. G. Leigh and D. Minic, JHEP **1709**, 060 (2017).
8. L. Freidel, R. G. Leigh and D. Minic, Phys. Rev. D **96**, 066003 (2017).
9. L. Freidel, J. Kowalski-Glikman, R. G. Leigh and D. Minic, Phys. Rev. D **99**, 066011 (2019).
10. L. Freidel, R. G. Leigh and D. Minic, Int. J. Mod. Phys. A **34**, 1941004 (2019), D. Minic, arXiv:2003.00318 [hep-th].
11. P. Berglund, T. Hubsch and D. Minic, Phys. Lett. B **798**, 134950 (2019); Int. J. Mod. Phys. D **28**, 1902003 (2019); JHEP **1912**, 166 (2019) [JHEP **2019**, 166 (2020)].
12. C. M. Ho, D. Minic and Y. J. Ng, Phys. Lett. B **693**, 567 (2010); Gen. Rel. Grav. **43**, 2567 (2011) [Int. J. Mod. Phys. D **20**, 2887 (2011)]; Phys. Rev. D **85**, 104033 (2012), D. Edmonds, D. Farrah, C. M. Ho, D. Minic, Y. J. Ng and T. Takeuchi, Astrophys. J. **793**, 41 (2014); Int. J. Mod. Phys. A **32**, 1750108 (2017), D. Edmonds, D. Farrah, D. Minic, Y. J. Ng and T. Takeuchi, Int. J. Mod. Phys. D **27**, 1830001 (2017).
13. K. G. Wilson and J. B. Kogut, Phys. Rept. **12**, 75 (1974); K. G. Wilson, Rev. Mod. Phys. **47**, 773 (1975).
14. J. Zak, Phys. Rev. **168**, 686 (1968); Phys. Rev. Lett. **19**, 1385 (1967).
15. M. Born, Nature 136 (1935) 952; Rev. Mod. Phys. 21 (1949) 463.
16. G. Amelino-Camelia, L. Freidel, J. Kowalski-Glikman and L. Smolin, Phys. Rev. D **84**, 084010 (2011).
17. Y. Aharonov, A. Petersen and H. Pendleton, Int. J. Theor. Phys. **2**, 213 (1969).
18. H. Weyl, *The theory of groups and quantum mechanics* (Dover, New York, 1931).
19. A. Connes, *Noncommutative Geometry* (Academic Press, San Diego, 1994); A. Connes and M. Marcolli, *Noncommutative Geometry, Quantum Fields and Motives* (AMS, 2007).
20. I. M. Gelfand, and M. A. Naimark, *Mat. Sbornik* **12** 197 (1943).
21. Y. Aharonov, and D. Rohrlich, *Quantum Paradoxes: Quantum Theory for the Perplexed* (Wiley, New York, 2005).
22. L. N. Chang, Z. Lewis, D. Minic and T. Takeuchi, Mod. Phys. Lett. B **27**, 1350064 (2013); J. Phys. A **46**, 065304 (2013); J. Phys. A **46**, 485306 (2013); Int. J. Mod. Phys. A **29**, 1430006 (2014); AIP Conf. Proc. **1508**, no. 1, 502 (2012), L. N. Chang, D. Minic and T. Takeuchi, J. Phys. Conf. Ser. **1275**, no. 1, 012036 (2019).
23. G. Mackey, *Annals Math.* **55** 101 (1952); *Acta Math.* **99** 265 (1958).
24. Y. Aharonov and D. Bohm, Phys. Rev. **115**, 485 (1959).
25. M. R. Douglas and N. A. Nekrasov, Rev. Mod. Phys. **73**, 977 (2001); R. J. Szabo, Phys. Rept. **378**, 207 (2003); H. Grosse and R. Wulkenhaar, Commun. Math. Phys. **256**, 305 (2005).
26. D. Karabali, C. J. Kim and V. P. Nair, Phys. Lett. B **434**, 103 (1998), R. G. Leigh, D. Minic and A. Yelnikov, Phys. Rev. Lett. **96**, 222001 (2006); Phys. Rev. D **76**, 065018 (2007), L. Freidel, R. G. Leigh and D. Minic, Phys. Lett. B **641**, 105 (2006), L. Freidel, R. G. Leigh, D. Minic and A. Yelnikov, AMS/IP Stud. Adv. Math. **44**, 109 (2008).

27. A. A. Tseytlin, Nucl. Phys. B **350** 395 (1991); Phys. Lett. B **242** 163 (1990), R. Floreanini, and R. Jackiw, Phys. Rev. Lett. **59** 1873 (1987), W. Siegel, Phys. Rev. D **47** 5453 (1993); Phys. Rev. D **48**, 2826 (1993) C. Hull, and B. Zwiebach, JHEP **0909** 099 (2009), O. Hohm, C. Hull and B. Zwiebach, JHEP **1007**, 016 (2010), O. Hohm, D. Lust and B. Zwiebach, Fortsch. Phys. **61**, 926 (2013).
28. J. Polchinski, *String theory. Vol. 1: An introduction to the bosonic string* (Cambridge University Press, 1998), M. B. Green, J. H. Schwarz and E. Witten, *Superstring theory: Volume 1* (Cambridge University Press, 1987); A. M. Polyakov, *Gauge Fields and Strings* (Harwood, 1987).
29. D. Minic, J. Polchinski and Z. Yang, Nucl. Phys. B **369**, 324 (1992); J. Polchinski, "What is string theory?", hep-th/9411028.
30. See, for example, L. N. Chang, Z. Lewis, D. Minic and T. Takeuchi, Adv. High Energy Phys. **2011**, 493514 (2011) and references therein.
31. M. Kavic, D. Minic and J. Simonetti, Int. J. Mod. Phys. D **17**, 2495 (2009); Int. J. Mod. Phys. D **27**, 1847007 (2018), J. H. Simonetti, M. Kavic, D. Minic, U. Surani and V. Vijayan, Astrophys. J. **737**, L28 (2011), D. C. Dai, D. Minic and D. Stojkovic, Phys. Rev. D **98**, 124026 (2018), D. C. Dai, D. Minic, D. Stojkovic and Changbo Fu, arXiv:2002.08178 [hep-th], J. H. Simonetti, M. J. Kavic, D. Minic, D. Stojkovic and D. C. Dai, arXiv:2007.12184 [gr-qc].
32. E. Boffo and P. Schupp, JHEP **2001**, 007 (2020)
33. M. Gunaydin and D. Minic, Fortsch. Phys. **61**, 873 (2013); R. J. Szabo, PoS CORFU **2018**, 100 (2019), and references therein.
34. M. Gunaydin and F. Gursey, Phys. Rev. D **9**, 3387 (1974).
35. U. Aydemir, D. Minic and T. Takeuchi, Phys. Lett. B **724**, 301 (2013); U. Aydemir, D. Minic, C. Sun and T. Takeuchi, Phys. Rev. D **91**, 045020 (2015); Int. J. Mod. Phys. A **31**, 1550223 (2016); Mod. Phys. Lett. A **31**, 1650101 (2016); JHEP **1809**, 117 (2018).
36. N. Ishibashi, H. Kawai, Y. Kitazawa, and A. Tsuchiya, Nucl. Phys. **B498** (1997) 467.
37. T. Banks, W. Fischler, S. H. Shenker, and L. Susskind, Phys. Rev. **D55** (1997) 5112.
38. G. 't Hooft, Conf. Proc. C **930308**, 284 (1993); L. Susskind, J. Math. Phys. **36**, 6377 (1995).
39. J. M. Maldacena, Int. J. Theor. Phys. **38**, 1113 (1999) [Adv. Theor. Math. Phys. **2**, 231 (1998)], S. S. Gubser, I. R. Klebanov and A. M. Polyakov, Phys. Lett. B **428**, 105 (1998), E. Witten, Adv. Theor. Math. Phys. **2**, 253 (1998).
40. A. Strominger, JHEP **0110**, 034 (2001), E. Witten, hep-th/0106109, V. Balasubramanian, J. de Boer and D. Minic, Class. Quant. Grav. **19**, 5655 (2002) [Annals Phys. **303**, 59 (2003)]; Phys. Rev. D **65**, 123508 (2002), V. Balasubramanian, P. Horava and D. Minic, JHEP **0105**, 043 (2001).
41. D. Minic and M. Pleimling, Phys. Lett. B **700**, 277 (2011), N. Gray, D. Minic and M. Pleimling, Int. J. Mod. Phys. A **28**, 1330009 (2013), V. Balasubramanian, E. G. Gimon, D. Minic and J. Rahmfeld, Phys. Rev. D **63**, 104009 (2001).
42. D. Minic, hep-th/9909022; hep-th/0009131, H. Awata, M. Li, D. Minic and T. Yoneya, JHEP **0102**, 013 (2001), D. Minic and H. C. Tze, Phys. Lett. B **536**, 305 (2002); Phys. Rev. D **68** 061501 (2003); Phys. Lett. B **581**, 111 (2004); V. Jejjala, M. Kavic, and D. Minic, Int. J. Mod. Phys. A **22** 3317 (2007); D. Minic, T. Takeuchi and C. H. Tze [arXiv:2012.06583 [hep-ph]].
43. G. T. Horowitz and L. Susskind, J. Math. Phys. **42**, 3152 (2001). See also F. Englert, H. Nicolai and A. Schellekens, Nucl. Phys. B **274**, 315 (1986); J. J. Atick and E. Witten, Nucl. Phys. B **310**, 291 (1988); R. Penrose, Phil. Trans. Roy. Soc. Lond. A **373**, 20140237 (2015).

44. D. Minic, Phys. Lett. B **442**, 102 (1998), T. Banks and W. Fischler, hep-th/0102077, V. Balasubramanian, J. de Boer and D. Minic, gr-qc/0211003.
45. L. Freidel, J. Kowalski-Glikman, R. G. Leigh and D. Minic, arXiv:2104.00802 [gr-qc].
46. A. A. Tseytlin, Phys. Rev. Lett. **66**, 545 (1991).
47. D. H. Friedan, Ann. Phys. **163** (1985) 318–419; Phys. Rev. Lett. **45**, 1057 (1980).
48. P. Berglund, T. Hübsch, and D. Minic, JHEP **09** (2000) 015; JHEP **02** (2001) 010; JHEP **01** (2001) 041; Phys. Lett. B **512** (2001) 155–160; Phys. Lett. B **534** (2002) 147–154; Phys. Rev. D **67** (2003) 041901.
49. C. Vafa, Nucl. Phys. B **469** no. 3, (1996) 403–415.
50. P. Berglund, T. Hübsch, and D. Minic, LHEP **2021**, 186 (2021); arXiv:2109.01122 [hep-th], V. Jejjala, R. G. Leigh, and D. Minic, Phys. Lett. B **556** (2003) 71–79.
51. V. Jejjala, M. Kavic and D. Minic, Adv. High Energy Phys. **2007**, 21586 (2007), V. Jejjala, M. Kavic, D. Minic and T Takeuchi, arXiv:2011.08852 [hep-th].
52. D. Edmonds, D. Minic and T. Takeuchi, Int. J. Mod. Phys. D **29**, 2043030 (2020); arXiv:2009.12915 [astro-ph.CO].
53. R. B. Tully and Fisher, J. R., Astron. Astrophys. **54** (3): 661-673 (1977).
54. S. M. Faber and R. E. Jackson, Astrophys. J. **204**, 668-683 (1976).
55. R. T. Farouki, S. L. Shapiro and M. J. Duncan, Astrophys. J. **265**, 597 (1983).
56. R. H. Sanders, Astron. Astrophys. **284**, L31 (1994).
57. N. Aghanim et al. [Planck], Astron. Astrophys. **641**, A6 (2020) [erratum: Astron. Astrophys. **652**, C4 (2021)].
58. U. Frisch, *Turbulence: The Legacy of Kolmogorov* (Cambridge University Press, 1996).
59. G. Bothun, *Modern Cosmological Observations and Problems* (CRC Press, 1st ed., 1998)
60. Y. Y. Zhang, et al., Astron. Astrophys. **526**, 105 (2011).
61. M. Cappellari, et al., Mon. Not. Roy. Astron. Soc. **432**, 1709 (2013).
62. M. Cappellari, et al., Mon. Not. Roy. Astron. Soc. **432**, 1862 (2013).
63. S. Beli, A. B. Newman, and R. S. Ellis, Astrophys. J. **783**, 117 (2014).
64. S. Beli, A. B. Newman, and R. S. Ellis, Astrophys. J. **799**, 206 (2015).
65. J. Dabringhausen and M. Fellhauer, Mon. Not. Roy. Astron. Soc. **460**, 4492 (2016).
66. H. Baumgardt and M. Hilker, Mon. Not. Roy. Astron. Soc. **478**, 1520 (2018).
67. J. Strader, et al., Astron. J. **138**, 547 (2009).
68. M. Kaplinghat and M. Turner, Astrophys. J. Lett. **569**, L19-L22 (2002).

WKB approach to the gravity-matter dynamics: A cosmological implementation

G. Maniccia[1,2,*] and G. Montani[1,3,†]

[1] *Department of Physics, "La Sapienza" University of Rome, P.le A. Moro 5, 00185 Roma, Italy*
[2] *INFN Section of Rome, Piazzale Aldo Moro 2, 00185 Roma, Italy*
[3] *ENEA, C.R. Frascati, Via E. Fermi 45, 00044 Frascati (Roma), Italy*
[*] *E-mail: giulia.maniccia@uniroma1.it*
[†] *E-mail: giovanni.montani@enea.it*

The problem of time emerging in the canonical quantization procedure of gravity signals a necessity to properly define a relational time parameter. Previous approaches, which are here briefly discussed, make use of the dependence of the quantum system on semi-classical gravitational variables in order to define time. We show that such paths, despite the following studies, lead to a non-unitary evolution. We propose a different model for the quantization of the gravity-matter system, where the time parameter is defined via an additional term, i.e. the kinematical action, which acts as a clock for quantum matter. The procedure here used implements a Born-Oppenheimer-like separation of the system, which maintains covariance under the foliation of the gravitational background and keeps the correct classical limit of standard quantum field theory on a fixed background. It is shown with a WKB expansion that quantum gravity corrections to the matter dynamics arise at the next order of expansion, and such contributions are unitary, signaling a striking difference from previous proposals. Applications to a cosmological model are presented and the analogies of the kinematical term with an incoherent dust are briefly discussed.

Keywords: Quantum Gravity; Quantum Field Theory; Born-Oppenheimer approach; Cosmology.

1. Introduction

A suitable quantum description of the gravity-matter system is necessary in order to describe the Universe and its early phases. An important requirement for this purpose is the quantization of the gravitational field, which has opened a debate leading to many approaches and outcomes. The first candidate for this procedure is the Dirac prescription,[1] which leads however to the problem of time[2]: the Universe wave function does not evolve on time, hence a probabilistic interpretation is not clear. For this reason a different clock must be introduced[2,3]: essentially, we have to define a *relational time*[4] in order to describe the quantum system dynamics, adopting a subpart of the system as a clock through carefully chosen boundary conditions.

A first step in this path was proposed in,[5] by separating the system into a semiclassical component and the purely quantum sector due to their different energy scales, in analogy with the Born-Oppenheimer approximation.[6] The external time was introduced via the dependence of the quantum subsystem on the semiclassical variables and, with a Wentzel-Kramer-Brillouin expansion[7] (WKB) in the Planck constant, the limit of standard quantum field theory on curved background was recovered at the first order, together with a positive-semidefinite probability density under certain conditions (see the original article[5] for such discussion).

Other models,[8–10] which differ for the choice of expansion parameter and initial conditions, have been studied focusing on the next order of expansion. The work[8] in particular dealt with computing quantum gravity induced corrections to the quantum matter dynamics, finding that non-unitary terms emerge. The workaround,[10] proposed to avoid such troublesome feature, cannot be applied in many contexts due to the strict initial requirements (see discussion in[11]). The work[9] followed more closely a Born-Oppenheimer approach on the problem, in order to define a conserved probability density; also in this case, however, it can be shown via the WKB expansion that the Hamiltonian operator describing the system dynamics is not unitary at the next order.[11]

Here we shall present a different implementation of the gravity-matter system, that ensures the standard limit of quantum field theory on curved background, with an expansion parameter proportional to the squared Planck mass (symbolizing the energy scale of gravity). The time parameter will not be linked to the dependence of the quantum sector on the semiclassical variables, but instead arise from an additional Hamiltonian term, i.e. the *kinematical action*,[12] that reinstates covariance of the theory in Arnowitt-Deser-Misner (ADM) variables[13] for assigned foliations. This term, together with the definition of the deformation vector, will allow us to obtain a functional Schrödinger equation for the quantum matter sector and, at the next order, a unitary dynamics including quantum gravity corrections.

An application will be shown for the case of the homogeneous free massless scalar field in a spatially flat Friedmann-Lemaitre-Robertson-Walker background, representing the inflaton field during the de Sitter phase; in this case such quantum gravity corrections indeed modify the Hamiltonian spectrum, with non-vanishing but small contributions due to the perturbative nature of the approach.

An important analogy is also discussed, linking the introduction of the *kinematical action* to the frame fixing procedure using Gaussian coordinates,[14] that emerge as a fluid term (more specifically, an incoherent dust) in the action, and showing how the two procedures are related.

The structure of the paper is the following. In Sec. 2 we will briefly introduce the WKB expansion of the gravity-matter system, discussing the mentioned approaches in literature and their outcomes. In Sec. 3 we propose a model constructing the time parameter from the kinematical action and show that its WKB expansion gives a unitary dynamics for the quantum matter sector at the order next to standard quantum field theory. In Sec. 4 the procedure is applied to a case representing the homogeneous inflaton field, in order to analyze the outcome in a cosmological view. In Sec. 5 the analogy of such construction with the frame-fixing procedure is presented. Sec. 6 contains the conclusive remarks.

2. Main features of the WKB expanded gravity-matter system

The starting point for the study of quantum gravity effects is the quantization of the gravitational field. It is known that, following the Dirac prescription,[1] one finds a time-independent Schrödinger equation which describes no evolution in time: the equation, known as the Wheeler-DeWitt[3] equation, is the essence of the so-called problem of time.[2] Then, in order to overcome such problem, one has to define a relational time parameter,[4] meaning that a selected subsystem must be chosen as a new, different clock to describe the evolution.

Let us briefly recall how this critical result emerges. We start with the foliation of space-time proposed by Arnowitt, Deser and Misner[13]: we identify 3d hypersurfaces immersed in the 4d spacetime environment by using some parametric equations, and derive the induces properties of such hypersurfaces from the environment ones. We label the induced 3d metric with the tensor h_{ij}, and the normal vector field with n^μ. Using these variables, one can compute the Hamiltonian formalism of the gravitational field, finding primary and secondary constraints on the wave function of the system.[15] It follows that the wave function depends only on the equivalence class of the induced geometries $\{h_{ij}\}$, and on the matter fields ϕ_a if present. Due to the superHamiltonian constraint, the action of the superHamiltonian on the system wave function must vanish:

$$H\Psi = \left(-\frac{2\hbar^2\kappa}{\sqrt{h}}\nabla_g^2 - \frac{\sqrt{h}\,R^{(3)}}{2\kappa} - \frac{\hbar^2}{2\sqrt{h}}\nabla_m^2 + u(h_{ij}, \phi_a)\right)\Psi = 0 \qquad (1)$$

where h refers to the determinant of the induced metric, $R^{(3)}$ to its curvature, κ is the Einstein coefficient $\kappa = 8\pi G/c^3$ and $u(h_{ij}, \phi_a)$ is the total potential energy of the matter fields. The gradients ∇_g and ∇_m indicate respectively the derivatives with respect to the gravitational and matter variables.

This result is troublesome since it implies the problem of time,[2] where the associated Schrödinger equation states that the Universe wave function does not evolve in time at all. It follows that another time parameter[4] should be implemented in order to describe a non-trivial, meaningful dynamics.

A semiclassical approach can be implemented in this sense. By following the Wentzel-Kramer-Brillouin expansion,[7] we write the system wave function as the complex exponential $e^{iS/\hbar}$ and expand it with a chosen parameter, examining the dynamics order by order. The choice of parameter will determine the range of validity: it can be chosen as the Planck constant $\hbar$, or related to the inverse of the Einstein coefficient κ, i.e. proportional to the square of the reduced Planck mass (here labeled m_{Pl}):

$$M \equiv \frac{1}{4c^2\kappa} = \frac{c\,(m_{\text{Pl}})^2}{4\hbar}. \qquad (2)$$

Although different parameters can be implemented, these two cases present interesting results and therefore will be discussed in this paper.

The works under examination[5,8] differ from each other in few but fundamental starting hypotheses; let us briefly discuss them in the following.

2.1. *Expansion in* $\hbar$

In the $\hbar \to 0$ expansion,[5] the variables are separated into semiclassical c and quantum ones q, so that Eq. (1) reads

$$\left(-\hbar^2 \nabla_c^2 + U_c(c) - \hbar^2 \nabla_q^2 + U_q(c,q)\right) \Psi(c,q) = 0, \tag{3}$$

where the operator H_c is obtained neglecting all the quantum variables and U_c, U_q are respectively the semiclassical and quantum sector potentials.

The first assumption states that the action of the quantum Hamiltonian on the system wave function Ψ is small with respect to the semiclassical one:

$$\frac{\hat{H}_q \Psi}{\hat{H}_c \Psi} = \mathcal{O}(\hbar). \tag{4}$$

Secondly, it is assumed that the semiclassical and quantum subspaces are orthogonal; stronger requirements are needed in order to perform the expansion after the quantum mechanical order $\mathcal{O}(\hbar)$ (see discussion in[11]).

These assumptions allow a clean factorization of the action, which is implemented at each order of expansion after the first one:

$$S_n = \sigma_n(c) + \eta_n(c,q), \quad n \geq 1 \tag{5}$$

so that

$$S = S_0 + P + Q \quad \text{with} \quad P(c) = \sum_{n=1}^{\infty} \hbar^n \sigma_n, \quad Q(c,q) = \sum_{n=1}^{\infty} \hbar^n \eta_n, \tag{6}$$

being the term S_0 at lowest order $\mathcal{O}(\hbar^0)$ purely classical. This factorization is reflected in the wave function:

$$\Psi(c,q) = \psi(c)\chi(c,q) = e^{i(S_0+P)/\hbar} e^{iQ/\hbar}, \tag{7}$$

where the background part $\psi(c)$ is assumed to satisfy the semiclassical part of the Wheeler-DeWitt equation:

$$\left(-\hbar^2 \nabla_c^2 + U_c\right) \psi(c) = 0. \tag{8}$$

Expanding up to order $\hbar$, a functional Schrödinger equation is recovered for the quantum subsystem χ_q in the background given by the semiclassical variables:

$$i\hbar \frac{\partial \chi_1}{\partial \tau} = \hat{H}_q \chi_1, \tag{9}$$

with the following definition of time derivative

$$\frac{\partial}{\partial \tau} = 2 \nabla_c S_0 \cdot \nabla_c. \tag{10}$$

This implementation describes a non-trivial dynamics (Eq. (9)) and allows the definition of a positive-semidefinite probability density, with suitable requirements on the background foliation, so that the standard interpretation of the wave function for a small subsystem of the Universe is recovered.

It shall be noted that in this process the semiclassical variables, from which the time parameter is constructed, have been essentially treated as classical ones. At the next order of expansion $\mathcal{O}(\hbar^2)$, not present in the original work, the quantum properties of the background should start to influence the quantum subsystem. By continuing the calculation,[11] it can be seen that some correction terms to the quantum dynamics emerge:

$$i\hbar \frac{\partial \chi_2}{\partial \tau} = \hat{H}_q \chi_2 - \left(2i\hbar^2 \, \nabla_c \sigma_1 \cdot \nabla_c + \hbar^2 \, \nabla_c^2\right) \chi_2. \tag{11}$$

It is straightforward to prove that these additional terms, which are attributed to the non-purely classical behavior of the background, are not unitary, thus presenting us a crucial point of discussion.

2.2. Expansion in $M \propto G$

The work[8] uses the parameter M defined in Eq. (2) for the expansion. Being it representative of the Planck scale, this choice implies that the lowest order will only see gravity and not the matter sector, describing a vacuum Universe in the limit $M \to \infty$. Eq. (1) becomes then:

$$\left(-\frac{\hbar^2}{2M} \nabla_g^2 + MV(g) + H_m\right) \Psi(g, m) = 0 \tag{12}$$

where H_m contains all the matter terms. The wave function is factorized in a similar matter (see Eqs. (5),(6)) into a gravitational function and a matter one, each expanded with the WKB method:

$$\Psi(g, m) = \psi(g)\chi(m; g) = e^{i(MS_0 + P)/\hbar} e^{iQ/\hbar}, \tag{13}$$

where the action at the lowest order (pure gravity) is of order M.

Similarly, a time-dependent non-trivial Schrödinger equation (see Eq. (9)) for the matter sector is obtained, defining again time from the dependence on the semiclassical gravitational variables:

$$\frac{\partial}{\partial \tau} = \nabla_g S_0 \cdot \nabla_g. \tag{14}$$

The authors also investigate the next order of expansion, finding that the quantum matter dynamics is described by:

$$i\hbar \frac{\partial \chi_2}{\partial \tau} = \hat{H}_q \chi_2 - \left(\frac{i\hbar}{M} \nabla_g \sigma_1 \cdot \nabla_g + \frac{\hbar^2}{2M} \nabla_g^2\right) \chi_2, \tag{15}$$

presenting non-unitary terms.

Cosmological implications of such a result were presented in.[16] A possible workaround for the issue developed by the authors in,[10] which eliminated the non-Hermitian part of the matter Hamiltonian by suitable redefinitions of the wave functions in the product $\Psi = \psi\chi$, is not applicable to many cases (see discussion in[11]) due to the basic assumptions implemented, thus leaving the problem of how to deal with non-unitarity. We stress that both definitions of time (see Eqs. (10), (14)) make use of the dependence of the quantum subsystem on the background semiclassical variables.

It is essential to cite the work,[9] which applied a procedure more similar to the Born-Oppenheimer method, by subtracting to the initial Eq. (1) its average over the quantum function χ. However, once WKB expanded in the M parameter, with a similar time definition as in Eqs. (10), (14), the total quantum Hamiltonian operator still presents a non-unitary morphology.[11]

3. A different definition of time via the kinematical action

We have seen that the previously mentioned definitions of relational time, using the dependence on the semiclassical variables, give a non-unitary matter Hamiltonian operator due to quantum gravitational corrections (Eqs. (11), (15)). This result seems a direct consequence of such construction, even with different expansion parameters (we refer for this point to Ssec. 4.1 of the mentioned article[11]).

For this reason we here propose a different construction, which implements the kinematical action[12] into the theory as a clock for quantum matter.

3.1. *The kinematical action*

The kinematical action, first introduced in,[12] is an additional action term used to ensure some constraint equations of a quantum system, in analogy with a Lagrangian multiplier. We remind that, in the Hamiltonian formalism, gravity presents both primary and secondary constraints[15]; the components of the deformation vector of the ADM splitting[13]

$$N^\mu = \partial_t y^\mu = N n^\mu + N^i b_i^\mu \qquad (16)$$

play the role of the Lagrangian multipliers for the secondary constraints.

When a specific splitting is assigned, however, the components N and N^i still appear in the action of the quantum field theory as multipliers, but their initial meaning as components of the four-vector N^μ is not evident. To recover this, the kinematical action in ADM variables can be inserted:

$$S_k = \int d^4x (p_\mu \partial_t y^\mu - N^\mu p_\mu), \qquad (17)$$

where $y^\mu = y^\mu(x^i; x^0)$ are the coordinates defining the parametric equations of the hypersurfaces, and p^μ are the conjugate momenta. Inserting this term into the action, some additional equations of motion appear by variations of y^μ, p_μ and N^μ:

these equations ensure[12] that the momenta p_μ are trivial and recover the physical meaning of the deformation vector N^μ as in Eq. (16).

Additional contributions also emerge in the Hamiltonian formalism to the superHamiltonian and supermomentum functions:

$$\mathcal{H}^k = n^\mu p_\mu, \tag{18a}$$
$$\mathcal{H}^k_i = b^\mu_i p_\mu \tag{18b}$$

which are linear in the conjugate momenta, a feature which is crucial in order to construct the time parameter of the theory.

3.2. Basic hypotheses and conditions

Let us now start with a Born-Oppenheimer-like separation of the wave function:

$$\Psi(h_a, \phi, y^\mu) = \psi(h_a)\chi(\phi, y^\mu; h_a) \tag{19}$$

where ψ is the slow gravitational sector, and χ the fast quantum one. We are considering the kinematical action as a matter term, regarding its variables as fast. This choice ensures the correct limit at the order of standard quantum theory on curved background.

As stated in,[5] since the matter fields live at an energy scale much lower than the Planck scale, we can reasonably assume that the slow function satisfies the semiclassical Wheeler-DeWitt equation, as in Eq. (8). For the sake of generality, we will not work in the minisuperspace, so that supermomentum constraints are not automatically satisfied. With the same reasoning we assume that the slow function satisfies the gravitational supermomentum constraint:

$$\left[-\frac{\hbar^2}{2M}\left(\nabla_g^2 + g \cdot \nabla_g\right) + MV\right]\psi = 0, \tag{20}$$

$$2i\hbar\, h_i D \cdot \nabla_g \psi = 0. \tag{21}$$

By insertion of the kinematical action, the equations satisfied by the total wave function Ψ are:

$$\left[-\frac{\hbar^2}{2M}\left(\nabla_g^2 + g \cdot \nabla_g\right) + MV - \hbar^2 \nabla_m^2 + U_m\right]\Psi = i\hbar\, n^\mu \frac{\delta}{\delta y^\mu}\Psi, \tag{22}$$

$$\left(2h_i D \cdot \nabla_g - \partial_i\phi \cdot \nabla_m\right)\Psi = i\hbar\, b^\mu_i \frac{\delta}{\delta y^\mu}\Psi. \tag{23}$$

We implement M, defined in Eq. (2), as the expansion parameter, so that the perturbative approach will be valid for fields with small associated energy with respect to the Planckian one. Formally, this property can be stated as the smallness of the ratio

$$\frac{\hat{H}\chi(\phi, y^\mu; h_a)}{\hat{H}\psi(h_a)} = \mathcal{O}\left(\frac{1}{M}\right) \tag{24}$$

and the adiabatic approximation also implies the smallness of the variation of the fast wave function with respect to the slow variables:

$$\frac{\delta}{\delta h_a}\chi(\phi, y^\mu; h_a) \simeq \mathcal{O}\left(\frac{1}{M}\right). \qquad (25)$$

3.3. Emerging dynamics for the gravity-matter system

The model can now be expanded following the WKB method. At the first order $\mathcal{O}(M^1)$, it is clear that only gravitational terms survive, recreating the gravitational Hamilton-Jacobi equation

$$\frac{1}{2}\nabla_g S_0 \cdot \nabla_g S_0 + V = 0 \qquad (26)$$

which ensures the classical limit of General Relativity. This is an intrinsic property of the expansion due to the choice of parameter, which selects the Planck scale.

Following the expansion, at $\mathcal{O}(M^0)$ both the gravitational and the matter sector are present. Making use of the gravitational constraints (20), (21), the equation for the matter wave function at this order (here labeled χ_0) is found:

$$i\hbar\frac{\delta}{\delta\tau}\chi_0 \equiv i\hbar\int_\Sigma d^3x \left(Nn^\mu + N^i b_i^\mu\right)\frac{\delta}{\delta y^\mu}\chi_0 = \hat{H}\chi_0 \qquad (27)$$

where the operator $\hat{H}$ is the matter Hamiltonian up to this order, defined combining both the matter superHamiltonian and supermomentum functions:

$$\hat{H}(\bullet) = \int_\Sigma d^3x \left(N\hat{\mathcal{H}}^m + N^i \hat{\mathcal{H}}_i^m\right)(\bullet). \qquad (28)$$

Eq. (27) has been rewritten as a functional Schrödinger equation through an integration over the spatial hypersurfaces and an appropriate definition of the time derivative, using the definition of the deformation vector (16). The striking difference from previous works is that, in this case, time comes from the kinematical action which plays the role of clock in the theory, instead of the dependence from the slow gravitational variables.

The next order of expansion $\mathcal{O}(\frac{1}{M})$ gives for the matter wave function χ, now enclosing the contributions up to this order, the following:

$$i\hbar\frac{\delta}{\delta\tau}\chi = \hat{H}\chi + \int_\Sigma d^3x \left[N\nabla_g S_0 \cdot (-i\hbar\nabla_g\chi) - 2N^k h_k D \cdot \left(\frac{1}{\chi}(-i\hbar\nabla_g\chi)\right)\chi\right]. \qquad (29)$$

It can be shown[11] that the additional terms in Eq. (29) are unitary. This property, together with the smallness of such contributions coming from the initial adiabatic assumption (25), make this model an acceptable one for investigating quantum gravity effects on the matter dynamics.

4. Dynamics of a cosmological scalar field

Let us now consider an homogeneous Universe filled with a free massless homogeneous scalar field, and with a cosmological constant $\Lambda > 0$, a setup similar to.[16] This model reproduces the inflationary scheme during the de Sitter phase, since the kinetic term of the scalar field stands for the kinetic term of the inflaton one, which can become important towards the Planck scale, and the cosmological constant accounts for the almost constant potential during that phase. We now apply the model described in the previous section to this simple case in order to infer the effect of the corrections computed in Eq. (29) to the Hamiltonian spectrum of the scalar matter field.

The background is given by a Robertson-Walker metric:

$$ds^2 = N^2 dt^2 - a(t)^2 (dx^2 + dy^2 + dz^2) \tag{30}$$

with Ricci scalar:

$$R = \frac{6}{c^2}\left(\frac{\ddot{a}}{a} + \frac{\dot{a}^2}{a^2}\right) \tag{31}$$

where a is the cosmic scale factor. The shift vector N^i (see Eq. (16)) cannot be included in the metric since it would violate isotropy of the model.

Since we are considering the homogeneous case, choosing the ADM foliation such that the normal vector field is $n^\mu = (1,0,0,0)$, it is easy to see that the only surviving contribution of the kinematical conjugate momenta is

$$\hat{p}_0 = i\hbar \frac{\delta}{\delta T} \tag{32}$$

where the constructed time parameter, here labeled as T, coincides with the synchronous time[17] hence $N = 1$.

Following the steps in Sec. 3, the total wave function of the system will satisfy the gravitational superHamiltonian constraint (20) and the total superHamiltonian constraint (22). The second one, after integration over a proper portion of space, i.e. the fiducial volume V_0, gives:

$$(H_{grav} + H_\phi + H_{kin})\Psi = \left(\frac{1}{2V_0 a^3}\pi_\phi^2 - \frac{2\pi G c^2}{3V_0 a}\pi_a^2 + \frac{V_0}{8\pi G}\Lambda a^3 + p_0\right)\Psi \tag{33}$$

and analogously for the gravitational constraint. The contribution of the supermomentum is canceled due to the condition $N^i = 0$.

In order to proceed with the expansion, the Einstein constant has to be rewritten in terms of the chosen parameter M defined in Eq. (2). Then, the system composed of the two constraints can be expanded order by order as presented in Sec. 3.

The gravitational constraint equation gives solutions for the functions S_0, P_1, P_2 of the gravitational wave function up to order $\mathcal{O}(1/M)$, following the separation in Eq. (13). Implementing these solutions, the total constraint gives at order $\mathcal{O}(M^0)$

the ordinary Schrödinger equation for the scalar field:

$$i\hbar \frac{\delta}{\delta T}\chi = \hat{H}\chi \qquad (34)$$

where we have taken $V_0 = 1$.

The corrections emerge at the next order $\mathcal{O}(1/M)$. After plugging the gravitational solutions into the total constraint equation, we switch to the time parameter τ such that $d\tau = \frac{dT}{a^3}$ and we pass to the Fourier space, so that the dynamical equation for the scalar field becomes:

$$i\hbar \frac{\delta \tilde{\chi}}{\delta \tau} = -\frac{\hbar^2}{2}\frac{\delta^2 \tilde{\chi}}{\delta \phi^2} + \hbar \frac{k_a(-\tau)^{7/3}}{3(3\Lambda)^{1/6}}\tilde{\chi}, \qquad (35)$$

where the matter Hamiltonian (given by the standard kinetic term of the free field) is indeed corrected by the additional term related to k_a, which is the eigenvalue of the conjugate momentum π_a of the scale factor a.

The solution for the matter wave function is

$$\tilde{\chi} = e^{-i\frac{\hbar p^2}{2}\tau + i\frac{k_a(-\tau)^{7/3}}{7(3\Lambda)^{1/6}}}, \qquad (36)$$

where p is the conjugate momentum with respect to the scalar field ϕ.

The solution (36) can be used to construct a wave packet and infer the magnitude of the spectrum modifications. It is important to stress that, passing from Eq. (33) to Eq. (35), the momentum k_a and hence the cosmic scale factor maintain their quantum nature: for this reason we do not insert the classical limit $a(T)$ of the background metric, but we leave a as an intrinsic quantum variable. We also remind that, due to the initial assumptions (see in particular Eq. (24)), the range of validity of the expansion is $-\frac{1}{M} < k_a < \frac{1}{M}$.

Numerical analysis of the corrected Hamiltonian spectrum has been computed by considering a Gaussian wave packet in a, ϕ constructed with the solution in Eq. (36). The results of the analysis show small corrections as expected from the hypotheses of the theory, since the quantum contributions are considered of order $\mathcal{O}(1/M)$.

5. Analogy with the frame fixing procedure

An interesting observation should be made regarding the procedure we followed. In a later paper,[14] the authors fix the reference frame of a gravity-matter system by inserting an additional term to the action, which resonates with the kinematical action insertion developed years before from one of the authors.[12] We do not show the detailed calculations here, reporting only the key points of such procedure and why it is connected to this work.

The chosen coordinates for their procedure are the Gaussian ones $g^{00} = 1$, $g^{0i} = 0$, implemented with Lagrange multipliers $\mathcal{M}, \mathcal{M}_i$ into the action with an additional term, that is written in a parametrized form as:

$$S^F = \int_\Sigma d^4x \left[-\frac{1}{2}\mathcal{M}\sqrt{-g}(g^{\alpha\beta}\partial_\alpha T \partial_\beta T - 1) + \mathcal{M}_i \sqrt{-g}(g^{\alpha\beta}\partial_\alpha T \partial_\beta X^i) \right], \quad (37)$$

where X^i, T are the Gaussian coordinates and x^α are the new variables ("parameters") associated to the metric $g_{\alpha\beta}$, so that coordinate transformations on the x^α are allowed.

The authors prove that such term (37), corresponding to the choice of reference system, materializes into the theory as a fluid, more precisely as an incoherent dust with energy tensor:

$$T^{\alpha\beta} = \mathcal{M} U^\alpha U^\beta \quad \text{with } U^\alpha = g^{\alpha\beta}\partial_\beta T \quad (38)$$

and with positive-definite energy as long as $\mathcal{M} \geq 0$.

Again, going to the order of quantum matter, a Schrödinger equation emerges with time coinciding with the parameter T of the Gaussian frame. This means that the emergent fluid plays the role of clock for quantum matter, in a way which is very similar to the kinematical action implementation.

Starting from the action with the "emergent fluid term", we can implement the same WKB expansion as explained in Sec. 3. We obtain that, in the minisuperspace, such procedure gives at the order $\mathcal{O}(1/M)$ quantum gravity corrections which are isomorphic to those of Eq. (29).

This result has an immediate explanation. In the minisuperspace, one can choose the ADM foliation such that $n^\mu = (1, \vec{0})$, consequently the parametric equations in (17) give $y^0 = T$, $y^i = X^i$; this means that their time derivative becomes

$$\partial_t y^\mu \to \partial_t y^0 = \dot{T} = \frac{\delta T}{\delta t} \quad (39)$$

It is clear that, in the minisuperspace and with a specific foliation, the kinematical action exactly reduces to the "reference fluid" emerging from the Gaussian reference frame fixing of Eq. (37). In this sense, the two implementations are equivalent.

6. Concluding remarks

The semiclassical WKB expansions of the gravity-matter system presented in the works here cited[5,8–10] encounter some problems when the canonical quantization procedure is applied and a time parameter is recovered from the dependence of the quantum system on the semiclassical variables. We have shown that the expansion performed in[5] with parameter $\hbar$ describes a non-unitary quantum matter dynamics at the next order, as seen in Eq. (11). A similar result already emerged in the work,[8] see Eq. (15), which was later modified with an *ad-hoc* procedure[10]; however the basic assumptions of that workaround cannot be satisfied in many cosmological models, thus requiring a different procedure.

Even dealing with an approach more similar to the Born-Oppenheimer one,[9] after the WKB expansion, it seems that non-unitary terms for the matter sector dynamics do not emerge, but the theory cannot be set by means of a general Hilbert product (see discussion in[11]).

The previous results signal a necessity to define the relational time in a different way, not using the dependence from the gravitational variables, which have an intrinsic quantum component due to the WKB limit. For this reason a different construction of the gravity-matter system has been implemented, where both the WKB expansion and the adiabatic approximation have been used, but with the core difference that time has been constructed from the the kinematical action. The utility of such term, defined in Eq. (17), in quantum field theory on a given background is to recover covariance under ADM foliation, since the deformation vector is assigned due to an *a priori* choice of the reference system.

Thanks to the additional contributions (see Eqs. (18a)-(18b)) coming from the kinematical action, we have recovered a dynamics described by linear constraints in the conjugate momenta (Eqs. (22), (23)) and covariant under choice of an ADM foliation. The momenta p_μ associated to the kinematical variables y^μ, after the quantization procedure, are a strong candidate for the definition of a time parameter.

By performing the WKB expansion in the parameter M defined in (2), we have obtained at the highest order the Hamilton-Jacobi equation (26) for gravity, which is equivalent to the Einstein equations in vacuum.[15] At the next order, with the definition in Eq. (27), we have recovered at the zero-th order a functional Schrödinger equation which corresponds standard quantum field theory. Finally, at order $\mathcal{O}(1/M)$, the corrections arising from quantum gravity to the quantum matter sector dynamics have been computed, showing that the additional terms in Eq. (29) are unitary. Although the obtained corrections are small by construction, they suggest a new investigation tool to evaluate how a non-standard dynamics of quantum field theory behaves, when examining energies small with respect to the Planck scale. We have shown in Sec. 4 that such modifications give a non-zero contribution to the Hamiltonian spectrum of the scalar matter field in a cosmological setting.

We have shown in Sec. 5 the comparison between the kinematical action insertion and the reference frame fixing procedure.[14] Setting the problem in the minisuperspace and choosing a specific ADM foliation, the parametric equations giving the kinematical variables directly correspond to the Gaussian coordinates of the frame fixing procedure. Then, it is clear that the kinematical action in this case is equivalent to the choice of the reference system, that clearly emerges as a fluid in the theory. This analogy provides a starting point for a deeper understanding and future analysis on the presented model.

References

1. P. A. M. Dirac, *Lectures on Quantum Mechanics* (Dover Publications, 2001), first published 1964.
2. C. J. Isham, Canonical quantum gravity and the problem of time, *Integrable Systems, Quantum Groups, and Quantum Field Theories. NATO ASI Series (Series C: Mathematical and Physical Sciences)* **409** (1992).

3. B. S. DeWitt, Quantum theory of gravity. I. the canonical theory, *Phys. Rev.* **160**, 1113 (August 1967).
4. C. Rovelli, Time in quantum gravity: An hypothesis, *Phys. Rev. D* **43**, 442 (January 1991).
5. A. Vilenkin, Interpretation of the wave function of the universe, *Phys. Rev. D* **39**, 1116 (February 1989).
6. D. Prasad Datta, Notes on the Born-Oppenheimer approach in a closed dynamical system, *Classical and Quantum Gravity* **14**, 2825 (October 1997).
7. L. D. Landau and E. M. Lifshitz, *Quantum mechanics: Non-relativistic theory*, Course on Theoretical Physics, Vol. 3, 3 edn. (Pergamon Pr, 1981).
8. C. Kiefer and T. P. Singh, Quantum gravitational corrections to the functional Schrödinger equation, *Phys. Rev. D* **44**, 1067 (August 1991).
9. C. Bertoni, F. Finelli and G. Venturi, The Born-Oppenheimer approach to the matter-gravity system and unitarity, *Classical and Quantum Gravity* **13**, 2375 (September 1996).
10. C. Kiefer and D. Wichmann, Semiclassical approximation of the Wheeler-DeWitt equation: Arbitrary orders and the question of unitarity, *General Relativity and Gravitation* **50**, p. 66 (May 2018).
11. F. Di Gioia, G. Maniccia, G. Montani and J. Niedda, Nonunitarity problem in quantum gravity corrections to quantum field theory with Born-Oppenheimer approximation, *Phys. Rev. D* **103**, p. 103511 (May 2021).
12. K. V. Kuchař, Canonical methods of quantization, in *Oxford Conference on Quantum Gravity* (Clarendon Press, Oxford, January 1980).
13. R. L. Arnowitt, S. Deser and C. W. Misner, Republication of: The dynamics of general relativity, *General Relativity and Gravitation* **40**, 1997 (September 2008).
14. K. V. Kuchař and C. G. Torre, Gaussian reference fluid and interpretation of quantum geometrodynamics, *Phys. Rev. D* **43**, 419 (January 1991).
15. F. Cianfrani, O. M. Lecian, M. Lulli and G. Montani, *Canonical Quantum Gravity* (World Scientific, 2014).
16. D. Brizuela, C. Kiefer and M. Krämer, Quantum-gravitational effects on gauge-invariant scalar and tensor perturbations during inflation: The slow-roll approximation, *Phys. Rev. D* **94**, p. 123527 (December 2016).
17. G. Montani, Canonical quantization of gravity without "frozen formalism", *Nuclear Physics B* **634**, p. 370–392 (Jul 2002).

Natural evidence for fuzzy sphere noncommutative geometry: Super-Chandrasekhar white dwarfs

Surajit Kalita

Department of Physics, Indian Institute of Science, Bangalore-560012, India
E-mail: surajitk@iisc.ac.in

T. R. Govindarajan

The Institute of Mathematical Sciences, Chennai-600113, India
E-mail: trg@imsc.res.in

Banibrata Mukhopadhyay

Department of Physics, Indian Institute of Science, Bangalore-560012, India
E-mail: bm@iisc.ac.in

Noncommutative geometry is one of the quantum gravity theories, which various researchers have been using to describe different physical and astrophysical systems. However, so far, no direct observations can justify its existence, and this theory remains a hypothesis. On the other hand, over the past two decades, more than a dozen overluminous type Ia supernovae have been observed, which indirectly predict that they originate from white dwarfs with super-Chandrasekhar masses $2.1 - 2.8\,M_\odot$. In this article, we discuss that considering white dwarfs as squashed fuzzy spheres, a class of noncommutative geometry, helps in accumulating more mass than the Chandrasekhar mass-limit. The length-scale beyond which the effect of noncommutativity becomes prominent is an emergent phenomenon, which depends only on the inter-electron separations in the white dwarf.

Keywords: Noncommutative geometry, white dwarfs, type Ia supernova, mass-limit.

1. Introduction

Noncommutative geometry, a theory of quantum gravity, has been used for many decades to explain physical systems. Riemann quoted in 1854 that "*... it seems that empirical notions on which the metrical determinations of space are founded, the notion of a solid body and a ray of light cease to be valid for the infinitely small. We are therefore quite at liberty to suppose that the metric relations of space in the infinitely small do not conform to hypotheses of geometry; and we ought in fact to suppose it, if we can thereby obtain a simpler explanation of phenomena ...*". In 1930s, Bronstein, using Heisenberg uncertainty principle and the features of Einstein's general relativity (GR), first argued that gravitational dynamics does not allow to measure arbitrarily small spacetime distances, concluding that the notions of classical Riemannian geometry should be duly modified. The formalism of a fuzzy sphere, first introduced in 1992,[1] was later modified to show equivalence between noncommutativity (NC) and Landau levels in the presence of magnetic fields.[2] Moreover, NC alters the spacetime metric,[3] which results in shifting the event horizon and removing the essential singularity at the center of a black hole.[4] etc. Unfortunately, there is no direct way to confirm the existence of NC like most of the other quantum gravity formalism, which compels it to remain a hypothesis.

In astrophysics, a white dwarf (WD) is the end state of a star with mass $\lesssim (10\pm2)\,M_\odot$. Chandrasekhar showed that the maximum mass of a carbon-oxygen non-magnetized and non-rotating WD is about $1.4\,M_\odot$.[5] Above this mass-limit, they burst out to produce type Ia supernovae (SNe Ia) with nearly similar luminosities. However, observations of various peculiar over-luminous SNe Ia, such as SN 2003fg, SN 2006gz, SN 2007if, SN 2009dc, and many more, suggested that they were originated from super-Chandrasekhar WDs with mass $2.1-2.8\,M_\odot$.[6,7] Over the years, different models including rotation, magnetic fields, modified gravity, ungravity effects, generalized Heisenberg uncertainty principle, to name a few, have been proposed to explain these massive WDs. However, since these super-Chandrasekhar WDs have not been observed directly, no one can single out the correct theory so far.

This article shows that the squashed fuzzy sphere algebra can quantize the energy dispersion relation, which further alters the equation of state (EoS) of the degenerate electrons present in a WD, resulting in the increase in mass of the WD beyond the Chandrasekhar mass-limit. It also discusses that the length-scale below which NC is prominent depends on the inter-electron separation. Hence, the inference of super-Chandrasekhar WDs can indirectly predicts the existence of NC in high-density regimes.

2. Squashed fuzzy sphere and equation of state

The formalism of a fuzzy sphere is analogous to the angular momentum algebra in ordinary quantum mechanics, where the position coordinates mimic the angular momentum variables. In an N-dimensional irreducible representation of $SU(2)$ group, the commutation relation for the coordinates of fuzzy sphere, X_i ($i=1,2,3$), is given by[1]

$$[X_i, X_j] = i\frac{k\hbar}{r}\epsilon_{ijk}X_k, \qquad (1)$$

where $k = 2r^2/\hbar\sqrt{N^2-1}$, $\hbar = h/2\pi$, h is the Planck constant and r the radius of the fuzzy sphere.

A squashed fuzzy sphere is a simple geometrical construction obtained from the fuzzy sphere by projecting all the points to an equatorial plane as shown in Figure 1. The equatorial plane can be in any direction, and for illustration, we show the $X_1 - X_2$ plane. Using the above relation, the commutation relation for this squashed fuzzy sphere is given by[2]

$$[X_1, X_2] = \pm i\frac{k\hbar}{r}\sqrt{r^2 - X_1^2 - X_2^2}. \qquad (2)$$

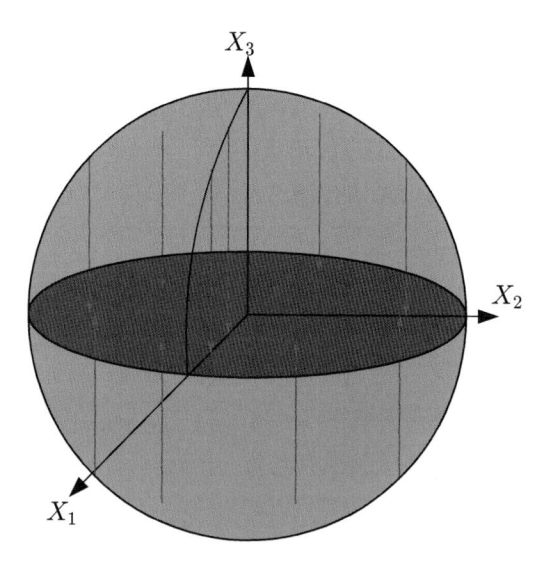

Fig. 1. An illustrative diagram of a squashed fuzzy sphere which is obtained by projecting all the points of the fuzzy sphere on an equatorial plane.

Note that NC vanishes at the surface of the sphere. The square of the quantized energies in a squashed fuzzy sphere, obtained from the Dirac operator, is given by[8]

$$E_{l,m}^2 = \frac{2\hbar c^2}{k\sqrt{N^2-1}} \{l(l+1) - m(m\pm 1)\}, \qquad (3)$$

where c is the speed of light and l, m are the quantum numbers with l taking all the integer values from 0 to $N-1$ and m taking all the integer values from $-l$ to l. Moreover, the relations between the Cartesian and spherical polar coordinates are $X_1 = r\sin\theta\cos\phi$ and $X_2 = r\sin\theta\sin\phi$. Therefore, from Equation (2), the squashed fuzzy sphere algebra in spherical polar coordinates is given by

$$[\sin\theta\cos\phi, \sin\theta\sin\phi] = \pm i\frac{k\hbar}{r^2}\cos\theta. \qquad (4)$$

A squashed fuzzy sphere is such that it actually provides a NC between its azimuthal and polar coordinates at the surface of the fuzzy sphere. This is because the squashed plane in a fuzzy sphere can be any of its equatorial planes and there is no particular direction for it, which means that the squashed fuzzy sphere has a rotational symmetry about the equatorial plane. There is no NC along the r-direction and an electron with mass m_e does not experience NC along the radial direction. Defining p_r to be the momentum of the electron in r-direction, considering Equation (3), we obtain the total energy dispersion relation in the squashed fuzzy sphere as[8]

$$E^2 = p_r^2 c^2 + m_e^2 c^4 \left[1 + \{l(l+1) - m(m\pm 1)\}\frac{2\hbar}{m_e^2 c^2 k\sqrt{N^2-1}}\right]. \qquad (5)$$

In the large N limit, this expression reduces to[8]

$$E^2 = p_r^2 c^2 + m_e^2 c^4 \left(1 + 2\nu \frac{2\hbar}{m_e^2 c^2 k}\right), \qquad \nu \in \mathbb{Z}^{0+}. \tag{6}$$

It is evident that $1/k$ behaves as the strength of NC. Note that a similar dispersion relation occurs in the case of a planar NC.[9] We can assume a series of concentric squashed fuzzy spheres, such that at the surface of each spheres, the above relation is valid. Nevertheless, $k \propto r^2$ and hence $1/k$ decreases from center to the surface. Now, applying simple statistical mechanics techniques, we obtain the EoS for the degenerate electrons present in a WD, given by[8,10]

$$\text{pressure} \quad \mathcal{P} = \frac{2\rho^{2/3}}{\xi h \mu_e^{2/3} m_p^{2/3}} \sum_{\nu=0}^{\nu_{max}} g_\nu \left\{ p_F E_F - \left(m_e^2 c^3 + 2\nu \frac{2\hbar c}{k}\right) \ln\left(\frac{E_F + p_F c}{\sqrt{m_e^2 c^4 + 2\nu \frac{hc^2}{\pi k}}}\right) \right\}, \tag{7}$$

$$\text{density} \quad \rho = \frac{64 \mu_e m_p (2\nu_{max} + 1)^3 p_F^3}{\xi^3 h^3}, \tag{8}$$

where $\xi = kh \left(\rho/\mu_e m_p\right)^3$, m_p is the mass of the proton, μ_e is the mean molecular weight per electron, g_ν is the degeneracy factor, and p_F and E_F are respectively the Fermi momentum and Fermi energy of the electron gas. ξ needs to be chosen appropriately such that at the low-density limit, EoS is same as the Chandrasekhar's EoS, where NC is almost negligible. Figure 2 shows EoS for the degenerate electrons when they occupy different energy levels. It is evident that if the electrons occupy more levels, it tends to the Chandrasekhar's EoS and NC is not prominent in that density regime.

3. Stellar structure model

To obtain the stellar structure of any compact object in GR, one needs to solve the Tolman-Oppenheimer-Volkoff or TOV equations along-with EoS of the constituent particles. The TOV equations for a non-rotating and non-magnetized star are given by[11]

$$\begin{aligned}\frac{d\mathcal{M}}{dr} &= 4\pi r^2 \rho, \\ \frac{d\mathcal{P}}{dr} &= -\frac{G}{r^2}\left(\rho + \frac{\mathcal{P}}{c^2}\right)\left(\mathcal{M} + \frac{4\pi r^3 \mathcal{P}}{c^2}\right)\left(1 - \frac{2G\mathcal{M}}{c^2 r}\right)^{-1},\end{aligned} \tag{9}$$

where $\mathcal{M}$ is the mass of the star inside a volume of radius r and G is Newton's gravitational constant. Note that NC affects the microscopic physics, while TOV equations describe the pressure and mass balances, which are macroscopic physics. Hence, in a semi-classical approach, TOV equations remain unchanged to that for the classical GR formalism. Figure 3 shows the mass–radius relation for the WDs

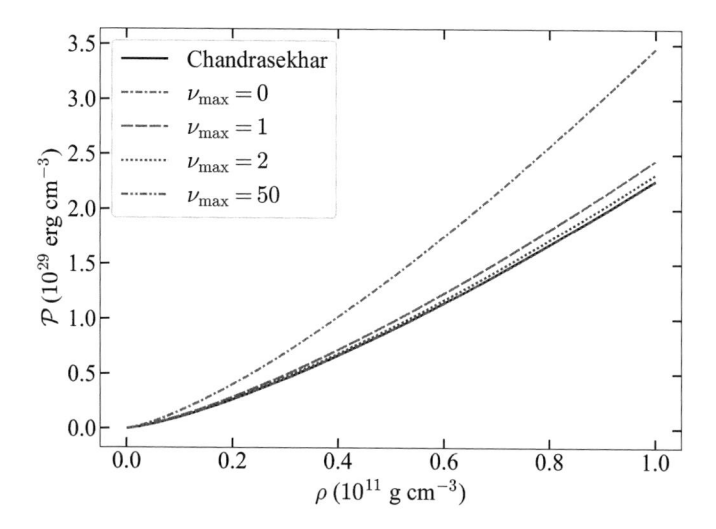

Fig. 2. EoS for degenerate electrons in a squashed fuzzy sphere with various $\nu_{\max}$ along with the Chandrasekhar's EoS. $\nu_{\max} = 0$ means electrons occupy only the ground energy level, $\nu_{\max} = 1$ means they occupy both ground and first energy levels, and so on. Chandrasekhar's EoS corresponds to $\nu_{\max} \to \infty$.

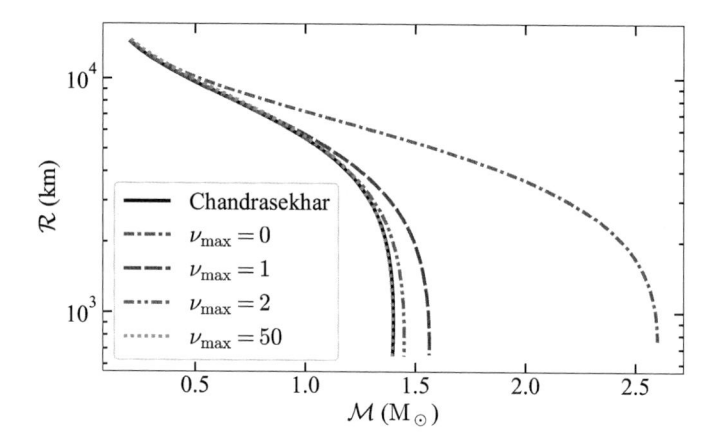

Fig. 3. Mass–radius relations of the WDs in the presence of NC when various energy levels are occupied.

in the presence of NC for various $\nu_{\max}$ along with the Chandrasekhar's mass–radius relation, which corresponds to $\nu_{\max} \to \infty$. It is evident from the figure that a non-rotating and non-magnetized WD can have a limiting mass of about $2.6\,M_\odot$ if all the electrons occupy the ground level. The mass-limit decreases when more energy levels are filled, and finally coincides with the Chandrasekhar's original mass–radius curve when many levels are occupied furnishing a limiting mass of about $1.4\,M_\odot$.

3.1. Length scale in noncommutative geometry

It is understood from Equation (6) that NC is prominent if $2\hbar \gtrsim m_e^2 c^2 k$, which implies that the system length-scale $\mathcal{L} \lesssim \mathcal{L}_{\text{eff}} = \lambda_e/\sqrt{\pi\xi}$ with λ_e being the Compton wavelength of the electron.[8] In the case of degenerate electrons, $\mathcal{L}$ is the inter-electron separations. It is evident from this expression that for the prominence of NC, $\mathcal{L}$ does not need to be the Planck scale $\mathcal{L}_P$ as opposed to the general belief. Rather it depends upon the system's length-scale. Indeed Salecker and Wigner showed that the new uncertainty in length-scale for a system has to be $\delta \sim (\mathcal{L}\mathcal{L}_P^2)^{1/3}$, and one needs to consider δ as the quantum measurement of length.[12] Hence, for a WD, one can expect to observe a significant NC effect depending on the inter-electron separation, even though it is far from the Planck scale. In extremely high densities with inter-electron distance much less than the Compton wavelength, one can expect certain features of NC becomes prominent. One such feature is the notion of statistics, which needs localization of particles, gets distorted and can affect physical systems, such as the mass-limit of the WD.

4. Conclusions

We have demonstrated that NC may have a prominent effect in a system whose length-scale is greater than $\mathcal{L}_P$. Whether NC has a significant effect or not depends upon the system's length-scale, and we show that it is an emergent phenomenon. We have used the formalism of a squashed fuzzy sphere where NC is at the surface of the sphere, i.e., between the azimuthal and polar coordinates. We have obtained the energy dispersion relation for this formalism and found that it is very similar to that for the Landau levels in the presence of magnetic fields. Hence, one may assume that NC mimics the internally generated magnetic field. It has a significant effect in a WD if the inter-electron separation is nearly less than one-tenth of the Compton wavelength of electrons. Such prominent NC may provide a super-Chandrasekhar limiting mass $2.6\,M_\odot$ and it can explain the formation of peculiar over-luminous SNe Ia. In the future, if gravitational wave detectors detect these massive WDs directly, it can confirm the existence of NC more firmly.[13]

References

1. J. Madore, The fuzzy sphere, *Classical and Quantum Gravity* **9**, 69 (Jan 1992).
2. S. Andronache and H. C. Steinacker, The squashed fuzzy sphere, fuzzy strings and the Landau problem, *Journal of Physics A Mathematical General* **48**, p. 295401 (Jul 2015).
3. V. P. Nair, *Noncommutative Mechanics, Landau Levels, Twistors, and Yang-Mills Amplitudes*, in Lecture Notes in Physics, Berlin Springer Verlag, ed. S. Bellucci 2006, p. 97.
4. R. Kumar and S. G. Ghosh, Accretion onto a noncommutative geometry inspired black hole, *European Physical Journal C* **77**, p. 577 (Sep 2017).
5. S. Chandrasekhar, The Maximum Mass of Ideal White Dwarfs, *ApJ* **74**, p. 81 (July 1931).

6. D. A. Howell, M. Sullivan, P. E. Nugent, R. S. Ellis, A. J. Conley, D. Le Borgne, R. G. Carlberg, J. Guy, D. Balam, S. Basa, D. Fouchez, I. M. Hook, E. Y. Hsiao, J. D. Neill, R. Pain, K. M. Perrett and C. J. Pritchet, The type Ia supernova SNLS-03D3bb from a super-Chandrasekhar-mass white dwarf star, *Nature* **443**, 308 (September 2006).
7. R. A. Scalzo, G. Aldering, P. Antilogus, C. Aragon, S. Bailey, C. Baltay, S. Bongard, C. Buton, M. Childress, N. Chotard, Y. Copin, H. K. Fakhouri, A. Gal-Yam, E. Gangler, S. Hoyer, M. Kasliwal, S. Loken, P. Nugent, R. Pain, E. Pécontal, R. Pereira, S. Perlmutter, D. Rabinowitz, A. Rau, G. Rigaudier, K. Runge, G. Smadja, C. Tao, R. C. Thomas, B. Weaver and C. Wu, Nearby Supernova Factory Observations of SN 2007if: First Total Mass Measurement of a Super-Chandrasekhar-Mass Progenitor, *ApJ* **713**, 1073 (April 2010).
8. S. Kalita, T. R. Govindarajan and B. Mukhopadhyay, Super-Chandrasekhar limiting mass white dwarfs as emergent phenomena of noncommutative squashed fuzzy spheres, *International Journal of Modern Physics D*, (in press) (November 2021).
9. S. Kalita, B. Mukhopadhyay and T. R. Govindarajan, Significantly super-Chandrasekhar mass-limit of white dwarfs in noncommutative geometry, *International Journal of Modern Physics D* **30**, p. 2150034 (April 2021).
10. D. Lai and S. L. Shapiro, Cold Equation of State in a Strong Magnetic Field: Effects of Inverse beta -Decay, *ApJ* **383**, p. 745 (December 1991).
11. L. Ryder, *Introduction to General Relativity* (Cambridge University Press, 2009).
12. H. Salecker and E. P. Wigner, Quantum Limitations of the Measurement of Space-Time Distances, *Physical Review* **109**, 571 (Jan 1958).
13. S. Kalita, B. Mukhopadhyay, T. Mondal and T. Bulik, Timescales for Detection of Super-Chandrasekhar White Dwarfs by Gravitational-wave Astronomy, *ApJ* **896**, p. 69 (June 2020).

A model of polymer gravitational waves: Theory and some possible observational consequences

Angel Garcia-Chung

Departamento de Física, Universidad Autónoma Metropolitana - Iztapalapa,
San Rafael Atlixco 186, Ciudad de México 09340, México
E-mail: alechung@xanum.uam.mx

James B. Mertens

Department of Physics and McDonnell Center for the Space Sciences, Washington University,
St. Louis, MO 63130, USA
E-mail: jmertens@wustl.edu

Saeed Rastgoo

Department of Physics and Astronomy, York University
4700 Keele Street, Toronto, Ontario M3J 1P3 Canada
E-mail: srastgoo@yorku.ca

Yaser Tavakoli

School of Astronomy, Institute for Research in Fundamental Sciences (IPM), P. O. Box
19395-5531, Tehran, Iran
E-mail: yaser.tavakoli@guilan.ac.ir

Paulo Vargas Moniz

Departamento de Fisica, Centro de Matematica e Aplicações: CMA-UBI, Universidade da Beira
Interior, 6200 Covilhã, Portugal
E-mail: pmoniz@ubi.pt

We propose a polymer quantization scheme to derive the effective propagation of gravitational waves on a classical Friedmann-Lemaitre-Robertson-Walker (FLRW) spacetime. These waves, which may originate from a high energy source, are a consequence of the dynamics of the gravitational field in a linearized low-energy regime. A novel method of deriving the effective Hamiltonian of the system is applied to overcome the challenge of polymer quantizing a time-dependent Hamiltonian. Using such a Hamiltonian, we derive the effective equations of motion and show that (i) the form of the waves is modified, (ii) the speed of the waves depends on their frequencies, and (iii) quantum effects become more apparent as waves traverse longer distances.

Keywords: Quantum gravity, gravitational waves

1. Introduction

Recent discovery of gravitational waves (GWs) and the rapid increase in the sensitivity of GWs observatories has opened up a great opportunity in connecting theory and phenomenology with experiment in precision cosmology, black hole physics and quantum gravity among other fields. In particular we are now becoming more hopeful about the observation of signatures of quantum gravity in GWs emitted from black hole mergers and high redshift regions of the cosmos.

There have been numerous studies connecting theories of quantum gravity with potential observations regarding the structure of quantum spacetime. In particular, in Loop Quantum Gravity (LQG),[1] there have been studies to understand the consequence of nonpertubative quantization in propagation of Gamma Ray Bursts (GRBs), other matter fields, and GWs on cosmological or black holes spacetimes (for some examples see, Refs. [2–31] and references within).

In this work we consider GWs as effective perturbations propagating on a classical FLRW cosmological spacetime. The effective form of such waves is derived by applying the techniques of polymer quantization[32–36] to the classical perturbations. Such a quantization is a representation of the classical algebra on a Hilbert space that is unitarily inequivalent to the usual Schrödinger representation. In it, operators are regularized and written in a certain exponential form. In such theories, the infinitesimal generators corresponding to some of the operators do not exist on the Hilbert space. As a consequence, the conjugate variables to those operators only admit finite transformations. Thus, the dynamics of the theory leads to the discretization of the spectrum of the conjugate operators (for more details and some examples of polymer quantization applied to particles and path integral formulation of black holes, see Refs. [34, 35, 37–39]).

In the model we present in this paper, the Hamiltonian is time-dependent and directly polymer quantizing it proves to be quite challenging. Hence, we apply a novel method based on the use of extended phase space, to overcome this issue (see Ref. [40]). The Hamiltonian in the extended phase space is rendered time independent by applying a certain canonical transformation and then polymer quantized using some of techniques developed in the literature.[35,41,42] After that, the effective version of this quantum Hamiltonian is made time-dependent again by applying the inverse of the above-mentioned canonical transformation. Finally the system is re-expressed in the usual non-extended phase space. Using this modified Hamiltonian, we derive the effective equations of motion of polymerized GWs and show that i) the form of the waves is modified, ii) the speed of the waves depends on their frequencies, and iii) the quantum effects are amplified by the distance/time the waves travel.

This paper is organized as follows: in Sec. 2, we derive the classical Hamiltonian of perturbations on an FLRW classical background. In Sec. 3, this time-dependent Hamiltonian is turned into a polymer effective time-dependent Hamiltonian by applying a certain method that is inspired by an approach used to deal with time-dependent Harmonic oscillators. Using this Hamiltonian, we then derive the effective equations of motion. In Sec. 4, we study the behavior of the solutions in both nonperturbative and perturbative regimes and show that quantum gravitational effects induce certain imprints on the waveform, frequency, and speed of GWs. Finally, in Sec. 5 we present our concluding remarks.

2. Hamiltonian formalism for GWs

We start with a spacetime manifold $M = \mathbb{T}^3 \times \mathbb{R}$ with a spatial 3-torus topology[a], equipped with coordinates $x^j \in (0, \ell)$ and a temporal coordinate $x^0 \in \mathbb{R}$. The background metric $\mathring{g}_{\mu\nu}$ is then perturbed by a small perturbation $h_{\mu\nu}$ such that the full metric $g_{\mu\nu}$ can be written as

$$g_{\mu\nu} = \mathring{g}_{\mu\nu} + h_{\mu\nu}. \tag{1}$$

GWs are the result of the weak-field approximation to the Einstein field equations for the above metric. As is well-known, a wave traveling along, say, the x^3 direction, can be separated into two polarization scalar modes $h_+(x)$ and $h_\times(x)$ as

$$h_{ij}(x) = h_+(x) e_{ij}^+ + h_\times(x) e_{ij}^\times, \tag{2}$$

where

$$e^+ = \begin{pmatrix} 1 & 0 \\ 0 & -1 \end{pmatrix} \quad \text{and} \quad e^\times = \begin{pmatrix} 0 & 1 \\ 1 & 0 \end{pmatrix}. \tag{3}$$

We would like to study the dynamics of the perturbations on a homogeneous, isotropic universe described by the FLRW metric

$$\mathring{g}_{\mu\nu} dx^\mu dx^\nu = -N^2(x^0) d(x^0)^2 + a^2(x^0) d\mathbf{x}^2, \tag{4}$$

where x^0 is an arbitrary time coordinate, $N(x^0)$ is the lapse function which depends on the choice of x^0, and $d\mathbf{x}^2 = \sum_i^3 d(x^i)^2$ is a unit 3-sphere. To obtain a Hamiltonian which resembles the Hamiltonian of a Harmonic oscillator, we introduce a new field

$$h_\sigma(x^0, \mathbf{x}) = \frac{a^2 \sqrt{\kappa}}{\ell^{3/2}} \sum_{\mathbf{k}} \mathcal{A}_{\sigma,\mathbf{k}}(x^0) e^{i\mathbf{k}\cdot\mathbf{x}} \tag{5}$$

which together with its conjugate momentum $\mathcal{E}_{\sigma,\mathbf{k}}$ constitute a canonically conjugate pair

$$\{\mathcal{A}_{\lambda,\mathbf{k}}, \mathcal{E}_{\lambda',\mathbf{k}'}\} = \delta_{\mathbf{k}\mathbf{k}'} \delta_{\lambda\lambda'}. \tag{6}$$

Here ℓ is the result of our quantization on a lattice which corresponds to an upper limit on the momenta involved. The above canonical pair allow us to write the Hamiltonian of the system as

$$H = \frac{N}{2a^3} \sum_{\sigma=+,\times} \sum_{\mathbf{k}} [\mathcal{E}_{\sigma,\mathbf{k}}^2 + k^2 a^4 \mathcal{A}_{\sigma,\mathbf{k}}^2] =: \sum_{\sigma=+,\times} \sum_{\mathbf{k}} H_{\sigma,\mathbf{k}}(x^0), \tag{7}$$

where N is the lapse. It is clear that this last equation represents the Hamiltonian of a set of decoupled harmonic oscillators with a time-dependent frequency $\omega^2 = k^2 a^4$, due to time dependence of $a(t)$.

At this point, we choose the harmonic time gauge where $N(x^0 = \tau) = a^3(\tau)$ to get rid of the factor a^{-3} in front of Eq. (7). Hence, the Hamiltonian of the

---

[a]To avoid a discussion of boundary conditions on fields (generated by perturbations), we will assume that the spatial 3-manifold is $\mathbb{T}^3$.

perturbations (for a fixed mode **k** and a fixed polarization σ) over the FLRW background in harmonic time becomes

$$H_{\sigma,\mathbf{k}}(\tau) = \frac{1}{2}\left[\mathcal{E}_{\sigma,\mathbf{k}}^2 + k^2 a^4 \mathcal{A}_{\sigma,\mathbf{k}}^2\right]. \tag{8}$$

3. Polymer quantization and the effective Hamiltonian

The time-dependence of this Hamiltonian (8) makes deriving its effective polymer corrections quite complicated. This is because its polymer quantization will yield a time-dependent quantum pendulum-type system whose solutions are mathematically difficult to treat. In order to circumvent this issue, we will apply a procedure based on the extended phase space formalism (more details in Ref. [40]). The idea is to first lift the (action of the) system

$$S = \int \left\{ p\frac{dq}{dt} - H(t) \right\} dt, \tag{9}$$

with time-dependent Hamiltonian of the form

$$H(t) = \frac{1}{2m}p^2 + \frac{1}{2}m\omega(t)^2 q^2, \tag{10}$$

to the extended phase space (EPS). In accordance with Dirac's formalism, the system is now described by the extended action

$$S = \int \left\{ p\frac{dq}{d\tau} + p_t \frac{dt}{d\tau} - \lambda\phi \right\} d\tau, \tag{11}$$

where

$$\phi = p_t + H(t) \approx 0, \tag{12}$$

is a first class constraint ensuring the compatibility of the two actions (9) and (11) on the constrained surface $\phi = 0$, λ is a Lagrange multiplier, and p_t is the momentum conjugate to t. This is step (1) in Fig. 1. In step (2) in Fig. 1, we apply a canonical transformation

$$Q = \frac{1}{\rho(t)}q, \tag{13}$$

$$T = \int \frac{1}{\rho^2(t)} dt, \tag{14}$$

$$P = \rho(t)p - m\dot{\rho}(t)q, \tag{15}$$

$$P_T = \rho^2(t)p_t + \rho(t)\dot{\rho}(t)\, q\, p - \frac{m}{2}q^2\left[\dot{\rho}^2(t) + \frac{W^2}{\rho^2(t)} - \omega^2(t)\rho^2(t)\right], \tag{16}$$

in the extended phase space which removes the time dependency of the Hamiltonian $H(t)$ in ϕ. Here, W is the time-independent frequency of the time-independent

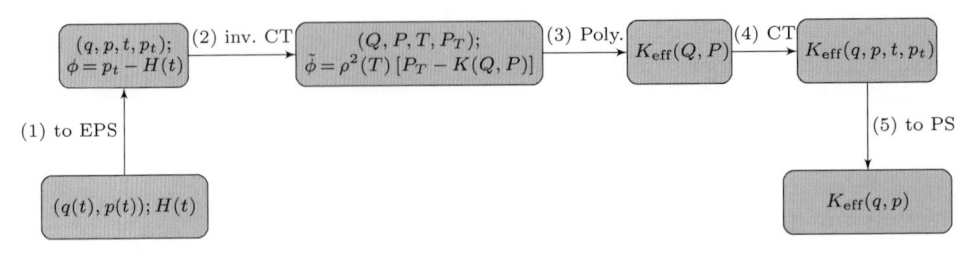

```
(1) (q,p,t,p_t);      (2) inv. CT    (Q,P,T,P_T);        (3) Poly.   K_eff(Q,P)   (4) CT   K_eff(q,p,t,p_t)
    φ = p_t − H(t)  ────────────▶   φ̃ = ρ²(T)[P_T − K(Q,P)] ────────▶              ────────▶
```

(1) to EPS ↓   ↓ (5) to PS

(q(t), p(t)); H(t)   K_eff(q, p)

Fig. 1. Schematics of the derivation of a time-dependent effective Hamiltonian constraint. Here "EPS" means extended phase space, "inv. CT" denotes inverse canonical transformation, "Poly." means the process of polymer quantization and getting an effective polymer Hamiltonian from there, "CT" denotes the canonical transformation, and "PS" means the nonextended phase space. The lower row corresponds to the usual phase space, while the upper row corresponds to the extended phase space.

system and ρ is an auxiliary variable to be determined by the specific properties of the system, more precisely by ω and W. After this step the action becomes

$$S = \int \left\{ P \frac{dQ}{d\tau} + P_T \frac{dT}{d\tau} - \lambda \tilde{\phi} \right\} d\tau, \tag{17}$$

where, the first class constraint now reads

$$\tilde{\phi} = \rho^2(T)[P_T + K] \approx 0, \tag{18}$$

and the corresponding Hamiltonian K appearing in it is

$$K = \frac{1}{2m} P^2 + \frac{1}{2} m W^2 Q^2. \tag{19}$$

Moreover, the auxiliary equation used to fix $\rho(t)$ becomes

$$\ddot{\rho}(t) + \omega^2(t)\rho(t) = \frac{W^2}{\rho^3(t)}. \tag{20}$$

This time-independent harmonic oscillator can now be polymer quantized[35,41,42] as in step (3) of Fig. 1. We then perform the inverse canonical transformations above in step (4) of Fig. 1. Finally, in step (5) of Fig. 1, we apply the inverse of the canonical transformations above and solve the constraint. This yields the polymer effective Hamiltonian on the usual phase space, where now the Hamiltonian is not just effective but also time-dependent.

By applying this method to our Hamiltonian (7), we obtain an effective polymer Hamiltonian with polymer $\mathcal{E}_{\sigma,\mathbf{k}}$ and discrete spectra for $\mathcal{A}_{\sigma,\mathbf{k}}$ as

$$H_{\text{eff}}^{(\mathcal{E})} = \sum_{\sigma=+,\times} \sum_{\mathbf{k}\in\mathscr{L}} \left\{ \frac{2}{\mu^2 \rho^2} \sin^2\left(\frac{\mu(\rho\mathcal{E}_{\sigma,\mathbf{k}} - \dot{\rho}\mathcal{A}_{\sigma,\mathbf{k}})}{2}\right) + \frac{\dot{\rho}\mathcal{A}_{\sigma,\mathbf{k}}\mathcal{E}_{\sigma,\mathbf{k}}}{\rho} + \frac{\mathcal{A}_{\sigma,\mathbf{k}}^2}{2}\left[\omega^2 - \frac{\dot{\rho}^2}{\rho^2}\right] \right\}, \tag{21}$$

where μ is called the polymer parameter that sets the scale for which the quantum gravity effects become important, and we have set $\hbar = 1$. The corresponding equations of motion read

$$\frac{d\mathcal{A}_{\sigma,\mathbf{k}}}{dt} = \frac{1}{\rho}\frac{\sin\left(\mu\left(\rho\mathcal{E}_{\sigma,\mathbf{k}} - \dot{\rho}\mathcal{A}_{\sigma,\mathbf{k}}\right)\right)}{\mu} + \frac{\dot{\rho}}{\rho}\mathcal{A}_{\sigma,\mathbf{k}}, \tag{22}$$

$$\frac{d\mathcal{E}_{\sigma,\mathbf{k}}}{dt} = \frac{\dot{\rho}}{\rho^2}\frac{\sin\left(\mu\left(\rho\mathcal{E}_{\sigma,\mathbf{k}} - \dot{\rho}\mathcal{A}_{\sigma,\mathbf{k}}\right)\right)}{\mu} + \left(\frac{\dot{\rho}}{\rho}\right)^2\mathcal{A}_{\sigma,\mathbf{k}} - \omega^2\mathcal{A}_{\sigma,\mathbf{k}} - \frac{\dot{\rho}}{\rho}\mathcal{E}_{\sigma,\mathbf{k}}. \tag{23}$$

These equations are nonlinear in both $\mathcal{A}_{\sigma,\mathbf{k}}$ and $\mathcal{E}_{\sigma,\mathbf{k}}$, and their $\mu \to 0$ limit matches the classical equations of motion as expected. Also notice that in our case, ρ controls the background geometry such that a time-dependent ρ corresponds to a time-dependent background geometry and a constant ρ corresponds to the flat spacetime.

4. Perturbative and nonperturbative numerical solutions

We will now solve Eqs. (22)–(23) for specific field-space configurations, both perturbatively, and numerically and nonperturbatively for both time-dependent and time-independent backgrounds.

4.1. *Time-independent background*

For a time-independent background, for which $\rho = 1$ and $\dot{\rho} = \ddot{\rho} = 0$, we can obtain full nonpertubative numerical solutions for $\mathcal{A}(t)$ as seen in Fig. 2. We can also obtain a perturbative solution

$$\mathcal{A}(t) \simeq \mathcal{E}_I \sin\left[(1 - (\mathcal{E}_I k\mu)^2/16)kt\right]$$
$$- \frac{\mathcal{E}_I^3 k^2 \mu^2}{16} \sin^2\left[(1 - (\mathcal{E}_I k\mu)^2/16)kt\right] \cos\left[(1 - (\mathcal{E}_I k\mu)^2/16)kt\right]. \tag{24}$$

This solution can exhibits a frequency shift of order μ^2, and a cubic correction term. The cubic term can also be rewritten, and thought of, as an introduction of higher harmonics using angle identities. In observations, the frequency shift may be more important to account for than the excited harmonics. This is because the frequency shift can manifest as a phase shift that has considerable time to develop as the wave traverses cosmological distances. In Fig. 2 we demonstrate this, comparing the perturbative solution to the exact and classical ones for the time-independent case.

We can also analyze the above perturbative solutions and obtain some insight into the speed of propagation of the waves. For that, we note that the dominant contributions to Eq. (24) can be written as

$$\mathcal{A}(t) \simeq \mathcal{E}_I \sin\left[\left(1 - \left(\frac{\mathcal{E}_I k\mu}{4}\right)^2\right)kt\right]. \tag{25}$$

Comparing with the classical solution where we identify $ka^2 = \omega_c$, with ω_c being the classical angular speed, we notice that up to first order the polymer angular speed is

$$\omega_\mu^{(\mathcal{E})} \simeq \omega_c \left[1 - k^2 \left(\frac{\mathcal{E}_I \mu}{4}\right)^2\right]. \tag{26}$$

Although this is a perturbative and approximate result and even though we have neglected higher harmonics in Eq. (24), the above equation reveal a curious phenomenon. Noting that $\omega_c = ka^2$ and with the group velocity being

$$v = \frac{d\omega_{\text{poly}}}{d(ka^2)} \tag{27}$$

with ω_{poly} being either $\omega_\nu^{(\mathcal{A})}$ or $\omega_\nu^{(\mathcal{E})}$, we obtain

$$v_\mu^{(\mathcal{E})} \simeq 1 - k^2 \left(\frac{\mathcal{E}_I \mu}{4}\right)^2. \tag{28}$$

where $v_\mu^{(\mathcal{E})}$ is the velocity of the effective waves. One can see from Eq. (28) that the group velocity of the waves is slower than the speed of light by a factor of $k^2 \left(\frac{\mathcal{E}_I \mu}{4}\right)^2$, and it also depends on the initial momentum $\mathcal{E}_I$ of the waves and the polymer parameter μ due to the factor $k^2 \left(\frac{\mathcal{E}_I \mu}{4}\right)^2$. More importantly, the deviation from the speed of light also depends on the modes k. Hence, waves with larger k (i.e., larger energies) have a lower speed compared to the ones with smaller k and are more affected by the quantum structure of spacetime. Also, notice that this case leads to the violation of Lorentz symmetry as can be seen by squaring both sides of Eq. (26). Of course, due to the sheer smallness of the expected value of μ, and the appearance of their squares in the above expressions, these effects are very small, but a highly energetic phenomenon with a large $\mathcal{E}_I$ may help to amplify it to an extent that future observatories can detect it. We should emphasize that the presence of the violation of the Lorentz symmetry in this case, as seen from the above results, is a consequence of the polymer quantization and, in particular, this model, and is not a direct consequence of LQG.

4.2. Time-independent background

For the case of a time-dependent background, we can obtain a solution in one of two ways: directly integrating the EOMs, or using the canonical transformation in Eqs. (13)–(16). In either case, we will need to obtain a solution for ρ by solving Eq. (20). In general, this choice determines whether the mode amplitude will be purely decaying or will contain oscillatory behavior. Here we will seek purely growing solutions for ρ, choosing initial conditions such that oscillatory behavior is minimized; in our case, simply choosing $\rho = 1$ and $\dot\rho = 0$ is sufficient. Choosing a different initial amplitude for ρ is in any case equivalent to rescaling of the scale factor a, polymer scale, momentum, and time coordinate. The full nonperturbative

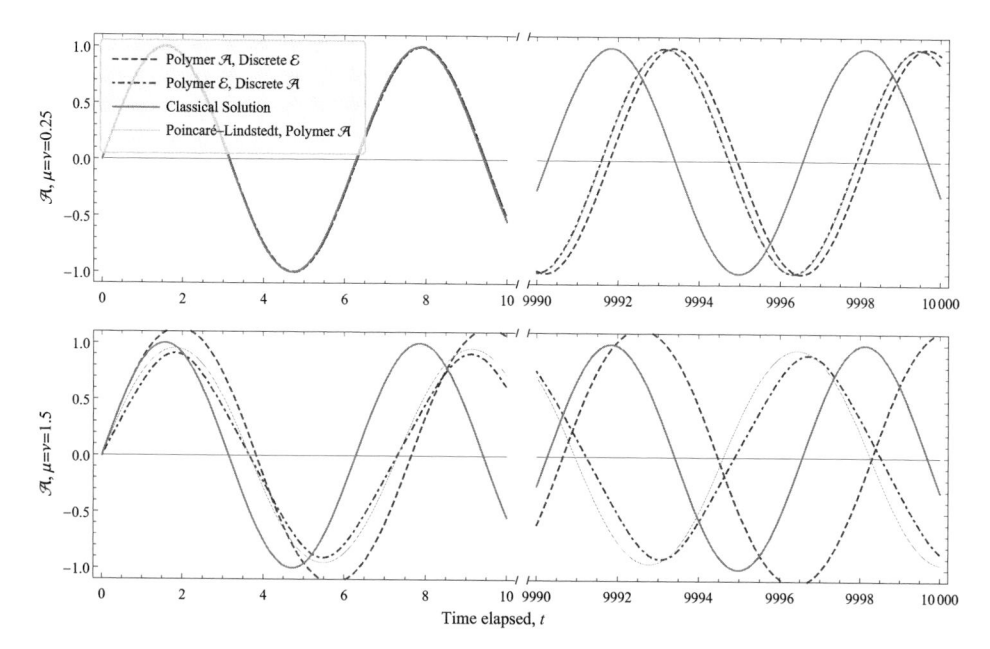

Fig. 2. Time evolution of $\mathcal{A}$ with $\mathcal{A}_I = 0$, $\mathcal{E}_I = 1$, and $k = 1$ for two different choices of μ in the case of a time-independent background spacetime, i.e., ρ = const. Here ν refers to another representation of the polymer quantization in which the momentum $\mathcal{E}$ is discrete, which can be found in our original paper.[31] The solutions are shown at early times, and the axis is broken to show the behavior at a much later time. Solutions can be mapped to different choices of k and $\mathcal{E}_I$, while changing $\mathcal{A}_I = 0$ can be viewed as a phase shift.

solutions are plotted in Fig. 4. We can also obtain a perturbative solution

$$\mathcal{A}(t) \simeq \mathcal{E}_I \rho \sin\left[(1 - (\mathcal{E}_I k \mu)^2/16)kT(t)\right]$$
$$- \frac{\mathcal{E}_I^3 k^2 \mu^2}{16} \rho \sin^2\left[(1 - (\mathcal{E}_I k \mu)^2/16)kT(t)\right] \cos\left[(1 - (\mathcal{E}_I k \mu)^2/16)kT(t)\right], \tag{29}$$

where

$$T(t) = \int_{t_I}^{t} dt' \frac{1}{\rho(t')^2} \tag{30}$$

For GWs emitted at a time much greater than the characteristic wave time scale, i.e., $t_I \gg k^{-1}$, where T_I is the initial time, and for nonoscillatory solutions of ρ, the second-derivative term is small, and solutions to the auxiliary equations are well approximated by a simple power law, $\rho = 1/a$. In Fig. 3 we show the behavior of ρ for several sets of initial conditions, and for a universe with a cosmological constant with $w = -1$, $a \propto t^{1/3}$, and $t_I = 10^3$ (in units of k^{-1}). In subsequent plots we will use initial conditions that do not result in oscillatory behavior.

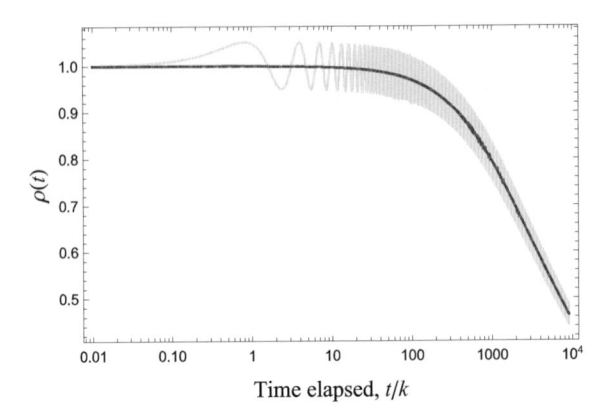

Fig. 3. Evolution of the auxiliary variable $\rho(t)$. The full numerical nonoscillatory solution is shown in solid red, an approximate power-law solution is shown in dashed blue, and a solution with initial conditions that result in oscillatory behavior is shown in light grey.

From the canonical transformation (13)–(15) (or, rather, its inverse), we see that the time-dependent waveform amplitude will pick up an overall factor of ρ relative to the time-independent one, the time coordinate will be altered, and the momentum will be similarly rescaled but will also pick up an additional factor proportional to the wave amplitude. Due to the monotonically decreasing nature of ρ and the smallness of its derivative, this additional factor will be a strongly subdominant contribution. In Fig. 4 we show the final solution for the field $\mathcal{A}(t)$ for this time-dependent background. Somewhat counterintuitively, the frequency is seen to increase at later times; more commonly the frequency is considered to decrease (redshift) with cosmological expansion. This is due to the choice of harmonic slicing we have made, with $N = a^3$ instead of the more commonly used $N = 1$ (synchronous) or $N = a$ (comoving) time coordinate.

5. Discussion and conclusion

In this work we have studied a certain effective form of GWs, considered as quantized perturbations propagating over a classical FLRW spacetime, in order to derive observational signatures to be compared with the results of experiments conducted by GW observatories. We have considered the Hamiltonian of classical gravitational perturbations, a time-dependent Hamiltonian, and have applied the techniques of polymer quantization to it. This polymer quantization was applied to each of the Fourier modes of the GW. A feature of this quantization is that the one-particle Hilbert space is modified and the Lorentz symmetry is no longer present.[38] This modification is "encoded" on the polymer scale μ, which is usually considered to be very small (of the order of the Planck scale). However, our intuition in the present case is that the propagation of the GWs may capture some insights about these modifications despite the small values of the polymer scales.

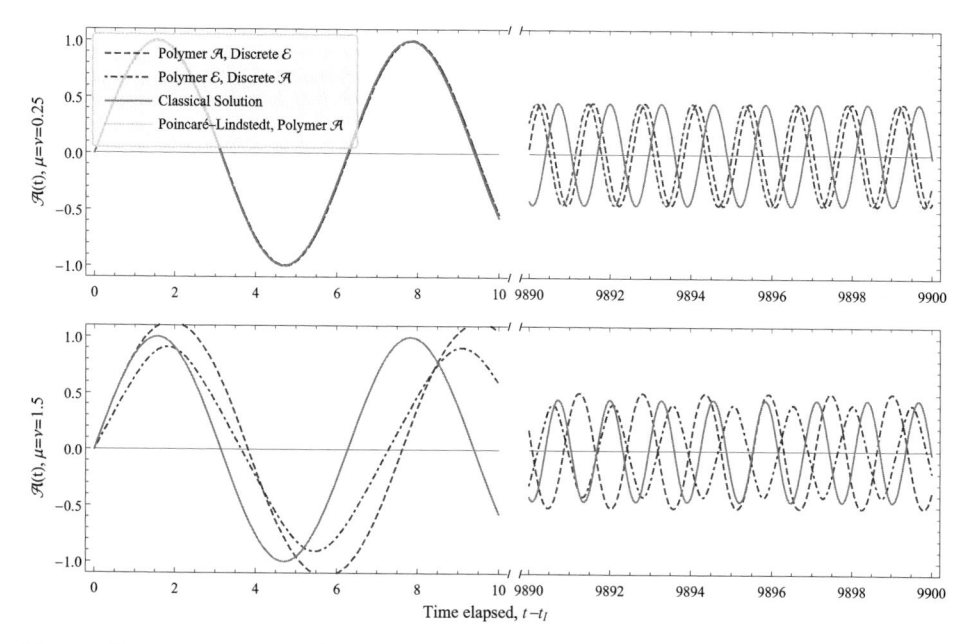

Fig. 4. Time evolution of $\mathcal{A}$ (as in Fig. 2) for two different choices of μ, for the case of a time-dependent background, i.e., $\rho(t)$ as described in the text. The axis is broken to show the behavior at a later time. Again, ν refers to another representation of the polymer quantization in which the momentum $\mathcal{E}$ is discrete, which can be found in our original paper.[31]

After deriving a tine-dependent effective polymer Hamiltonian using a novel approach, we derived both nonperturbative and perturbative analytical expression for the solutions and analyzed them to obtain further insight into the behavior of such waves. As a result, we found the following:

i) The form of the waves is modified. More precisely, there is a phase shift with respect to the classical case. Furthermore, small-amplitude harmonics are excited.

ii) The speed of the waves turns out to be smaller than the speed of light by a factor $k^2 \left(\frac{\mathcal{E}_I \mu}{4}\right)^2$. This factor not only depends on the polymer scale μ and the initial momentum of the perturbations $\mathcal{E}_I$, but also on the wave vector k or, equivalently, the frequency of the waves. Thus, the higher-energy waves show a greater deviation from the classical behavior compared to the low-energy waves.

iii) The modifications to the classical behavior due to quantum effects become increasingly visible as the waves travel: the corrections result in an effective phase shift, which can become of order unity when $\mathcal{E}_I \mu^2 k^3 D_s$ is of order unity for a distance D_s traveled.

In a future work, we will proceed to apply our method to the case where both the background spacetime and the perturbations are effective.

References

1. T. Thiemann, *Modern Canonical Quantum General Relativity*, Cambridge Monographs on Mathematical Physics (Cambridge University Press, 2007).
2. A. Ashtekar, C. Rovelli and L. Smolin, Gravitons and loops, *Phys. Rev. D* **44**, 1740 (1991).
3. M. Varadarajan, Gravitons from a loop representation of linearized gravity, *Phys. Rev. D* **66**, p. 024017 (2002).
4. L. Freidel and L. Smolin, The linearization of the kodama state, *Class. Quant. Grav.* **21**, 3831 (2004).
5. M. Bojowald and G. M. Hossain, Loop quantum gravity corrections to gravitational wave dispersion, *Phys. Rev.* **D77**, p. 023508 (2008).
6. A. Ashtekar, W. Kaminski and J. Lewandowski, Quantum field theory on a cosmological, quantum space-time, *Phys. Rev.* **D79**, p. 064030 (2009).
7. G. M. Hossain, V. Husain and S. S. Seahra, Background independent quantization and wave propagation, *Phys. Rev. D* **80**, p. 044018 (2009).
8. R. Gambini, J. Pullin and S. Rastgoo, Quantum scalar field in quantum gravity: The vacuum in the spherically symmetric case, *Class. Quant. Grav.* **26**, p. 215011 (2009).
9. J. Mielczarek, T. Cailleteau, J. Grain and A. Barrau, Inflation in loop quantum cosmology: Dynamics and spectrum of gravitational waves, *Phys. Rev. D* **81**, p. 104049 (2010).
10. G. Date and G. M. Hossain, Matter in loop quantum gravity, *SIGMA* **8**, p. 010 (2012).
11. R. Gambini, J. Pullin and S. Rastgoo, Quantum scalar field in quantum gravity: The propagator and lorentz invariance in the spherically symmetric case, *Gen. Rel. Grav.* **43**, 3569 (2011).
12. R. Gambini, S. Rastgoo and J. Pullin, Small lorentz violations in quantum gravity: Do they lead to unacceptably large effects?, *Class. Quant. Grav.* **28**, p. 155005 (2011).
13. P. M. Sa and A. B. Henriques, Gravitational wave generation in loop quantum cosmology, *Phys. Rev. D* **85**, p. 024034 (2012).
14. F. Hinterleitner and S. Major, Towards loop quantization of plane gravitational waves, *Class. Quant. Grav.* **29**, p. 065019 (2012).
15. F. Hinterleitner and S. Major, Plane gravitational waves and loop quantization, *J. Phys. Conf. Ser.* **360**, p. 012030 (2012).
16. D. E. Neville, Plane wave holonomies in quantum gravity. i. A model, *Phys. Rev. D* **92**, p. 044005 (2015).
17. D. E. Neville, Plane wave holonomies in quantum gravity. ii. A sine wave solution, *Phys. Rev. D* **92**, p. 044006 (2015).
18. P. A. Höhn, Canonical linearized regge calculus: Counting lattice gravitons with pachner moves, *Phys. Rev. D* **91**, p. 124034 (2015).
19. M. Arzano and G. Calcagni, What gravity waves are telling about quantum spacetime, *Phys. Rev.* **D93**, p. 124065 (2016) [Addendum: *Phys. Rev. D* **94**, no. 4, 049907 (2016)].
20. S. Rastgoo, Y. Tavakoli and J. C. Fabris, Phenomenology of a massive quantum field in a cosmological quantum spacetime, *Annals Phys.* **415**, p. 168110 (2020).
21. A. Dapor, J. Lewandowski and Y. Tavakoli, Lorentz Symmetry in QFT on Quantum Bianchi I Space-Time, *Phys. Rev.* **D86**, p. 064013 (2012).
22. B. Elizaga Navascués, M. Martín-Benito and G. A. Mena Marugán, Hybrid models in loop quantum cosmology, *Int. J. Mod. Phys. D* **25**, p. 1642007 (2016).
23. Y. Bonder, A. Garcia-Chung and S. Rastgoo, Bounds on the polymer scale from gamma ray bursts, *Phys. Rev. D* **96**, p. 106021 (2017).

24. J. Lewandowski, M. Nouri-Zonoz, A. Parvizi and Y. Tavakoli, Quantum theory of electromagnetic fields in a cosmological quantum spacetime, *Phys. Rev.* **D96**, p. 106007 (2017).
25. F. Hinterleitner, Canonical LQG operators and kinematical states for plane gravitational waves (3 2017).
26. A. Dapor and K. Liegener, Modifications to gravitational wave equation from canonical quantum gravity, *Eur. Phys. J. C* **80**, p. 741 (2020).
27. Y. Tavakoli and J. C. Fabris, Creation of particles in a cyclic universe driven by loop quantum cosmology, *Int. J. Mod. Phys.* **D24**, p. 1550062 (2015).
28. G. Calcagni, Quantum gravity and gravitational-wave astronomy (12 2020).
29. G. Calcagni, S. Kuroyanagi, S. Marsat, M. Sakellariadou, N. Tamanini and G. Tasinato, Gravitational-wave luminosity distance in quantum gravity, *Phys. Lett. B* **798**, p. 135000 (2019).
30. G. Calcagni, S. Kuroyanagi, S. Marsat, M. Sakellariadou, N. Tamanini and G. Tasinato, Quantum gravity and gravitational-wave astronomy, *JCAP* **10**, p. 012 (2019).
31. A. Garcia-Chung, J. B. Mertens, S. Rastgoo, Y. Tavakoli and P. Vargas Moniz, Propagation of quantum gravity-modified gravitational waves on a classical FLRW spacetime, *Phys. Rev. D* **103**, p. 084053 (2021).
32. A. Ashtekar, S. Fairhurst and J. L. Willis, Quantum gravity, shadow states, and quantum mechanics, *Class. Quant. Grav.* **20**, 1031 (2003).
33. A. Corichi, T. Vukasinac and J. A. Zapata, Polymer Quantum Mechanics and its Continuum Limit, *Phys. Rev. D* **76**, p. 044016 (2007).
34. H. A. Morales-Técotl, S. Rastgoo and J. C. Ruelas, Path integral polymer propagator of relativistic and nonrelativistic particles, *Phys. Rev. D* **95**, p. 065026 (2017).
35. H. A. Morales-Técotl, D. H. Orozco-Borunda and S. Rastgoo, Polymer quantization and the saddle point approximation of partition functions, *Phys. Rev. D* **92**, p. 104029 (2015).
36. E. Flores-González, H. A. Morales-Técotl and J. D. Reyes, Propagators in Polymer Quantum Mechanics, *Annals Phys.* **336**, 394 (2013).
37. A. A. García-Chung and H. A. Morales-Técotl, Polymer dirac field propagator: A model, *Physical Review D* **89**, p. 065014 (2014).
38. A. Garcia-Chung and J. D. Vergara, Polymer-fourier quantization of the scalar field revisited, *International Journal of Modern Physics A* **31**, p. 1650166 (2016).
39. H. A. Morales-Técotl, S. Rastgoo and J. C. Ruelas, Effective dynamics of the Schwarzschild black hole interior with inverse triad corrections, *Annals Phys.* **426**, p. 168401 (2021).
40. A. Garcia-Chung, D. G. Ruiz and J. D. Vergara, Dirac's method for time-dependent hamiltonian systems in the extended phase space, *arXiv preprint arXiv:1701.07120* (2017).
41. J. A. Austrich-Olivares, A. Garcia-Chung and J. D. Vergara, Instanton solutions on the polymer harmonic oscillator, *Classical and Quantum Gravity* **34**, p. 115005 (2017).
42. H. A. Morales-Técotl, D. H. Orozco-Borunda and S. Rastgoo, Polymerization, the Problem of Access to the Saddle Point Approximation, and Thermodynamics, in *14th Marcel Grossmann Meeting on Recent Developments in Theoretical and Experimental General Relativity, Astrophysics, and Relativistic Field Theories* (World Scientific, Singapore, 2017).

Primordial power spectrum from a matter-ekpyrotic scenario in loop quantum cosmology[1]

Bao-Fei Li[*], Sahil Saini[†] and Parampreet Singh[*]

[*]*Department of Physics and Astronomy, Louisiana State University, Baton Rouge, LA 70803, USA*

[†]*Department of Physics, Guru Jambheshwar University of Science & Technology, Hisar 125001, Haryana, India*

The general matter bounce scenario, including an Ekpyrotic field to avoid anisotropic instabilities, is studied in a loop quantized isotropic and homogeneous FLRW setting. The matter bounce scenario provides a convenient way to include quantum corrections from the bounce in the perturbations originating in the far past, which also produce a scale invariant power spectrum. LQC provides the right setting for studying quantum corrections in a matter bounce scenario as the bounce in LQC occurs entirely due to quantum geometrical effects without needing any exotic matter fields to avoid the singularity. A detailed exploration of this general matter-Ekpyrotic scenario in spatially flat FLRW spacetime in LQC filled with minimally coupled dust and Ekpyrotic scalar field is studied with the help of numerical simulations. Various features of the background dynamics are shown to be robust under variations in initial conditions and choice of parameters. We use the dressed metric approach for the perturbations and obtain a scale invariant power spectrum for modes exiting the horizon in the dust dominated contracting phase. In contrast to previous studies considering a constant equation of state for the Ekpyrotic field, we found that the magnitude of the power spectrum changes during the evolution. The scale invariant section of the power spectrum also undergoes a rapid increase in its magnitude in the bounce regime, while its scale invariance is unaffected. We argue that apart from increasing the magnitude, the bounce regime may only substantially affect the modes outside the scale invariant regime. However, the spectral index is found to be too close to unity, thus inconsistent with the observational constraints, necessitating further modifications of the model.

Keywords: Loop quantum cosmology; bouncing cosmology; primordial power spectrum.

1. Introduction

Early universe cosmology provides one of the most promising avenues to search for signatures of quantum gravity. Singularity free bouncing cosmologies of LQC provide a convenient setting for this. Inflation being the leading model has been studied widely with LQC backgrounds. Since there is no singularity, it is possible to extend the inflationary scenario further back in time upto the Planck regime of the quantum bounce to include quantum gravity signatures. These studies have led to predictions that are in excellent agreement with standard inflation and CMB observations at small angular scales but are closer to observations at larger scales than standard inflation.[2] The quantum bounce which lies to the past of this inflationary regime is a cataclysmic event which changes the course of the evolution of the universe, thus is expected to contribute significantly to the quantum gravity signatures in the early universe. In this regard, it's natural to consider alternatives such as the matter-bounce scenario where the perturbations start out in the far past in the contracting branch, hence getting imprinted by the highly quantum phenomena as they pass through the quantum bounce. Due to a duality between inflation and matter-bounce, a scale invariant spectrum of perturbations is obtained in both of them.[3] An Ekpyrotic field is generally also included to guard against a potential BKL instability which may occur due to unchecked growth of anisotropies during the contracting phase.[4] An Ekpyrotic field is a scalar field with a negative-definite potential, thus having an equation of state larger than unity. As the bounce is approached in the contracting phase, the Ekpyrotic field having an equation of state larger than unity is expected to dominate the anisotropies which evolve as a^{-6}, where a denotes the scale factor.[5] Thus combining these two ingredients we obtain the the matter-Ekpyrotic scenario,[6] in which a scale invariant spectrum is produced by matter perturbations which exit the horizon during the contracting phase.

An important ingredient of the matter-Ekpyrotic scenario is a non-singular bounce which allows the scale invariant perturbations to pass through without changing them substantially. This is where LQC provides an advantageous framework. In LQC, the quantum bounce arises purely due to quantum geometry effects without requiring any exotic matter content violating the weak energy conditions.[7] Thus the marriage of the matter-Ekpyrotic scenario with an LQC bouncing background provides a compelling model for obtaining quantum gravity signatures in the early universe. Using effective dynamics of LQC, a nonsingular model with an Ekpyrotic potential was obtained[8,9] but it was found that a viable cyclic model cannot be realized unless another matter field or anisotropies are present.[10] Previous studies of the matter-Ekpyrotic model in LQC have either restricted to a special case of a constant equation of state for the Ekpyrotic field,[11] or when the general case has been considered,[12] the analysis has been limited to qualitative predictions due to difficulties associated with the deformed algebra approach used for perturbations in dealing with ultraviolet modes near the bounce. Thus a detailed study of the general matter-Ekpyrotic scenario in LQC analyzing the impact of the Ekpyrotic phase and the bounce on the perturbations has been lacking so far. Our work aims to fill this gap and provide a basis for further exploration.

2. Background dynamics of the matter-Ekpyrotic scenario in LQC

LQC uses the techniques of non-perturbative canonical quantization of LQG on symmetry reduced cosmological models such as the isotropic and homogeneous FLRW model. The canonical quantization of gravity in LQG is carried out in terms of the Ashtekar-Barbero connection and their conjugate triads instead of metric variables. The discrete quantum dynamics obtained in LQC is found to be well approximated by a continuum effective description in terms of differential equations on a smooth manifold, giving modified versions of Friedmann and Raychaudhuri equations that include quantum corrections that lead to a singularity free evolution in which the big bang is replaced by a bounce. The effective Hamiltonian describing the dynamics of loop quantized spatially flat FLRW model in terms of symmetry-reduced Ashtekar-Barbero connection and its conjugate triad, namely c and p, is given by[7]

$$\mathcal{H} = -\frac{3v}{8\pi G\gamma^2\lambda^2}\sin^2(\lambda b) + \mathcal{H}_m, \qquad (1)$$

where $\lambda = \sqrt{\Delta}$. Here $\Delta = 4\sqrt{3}\pi\gamma\ell_{\mathrm{Pl}}^2$ is the minimum area eigenvalue in LQG. The matter Hamiltonian $\mathcal{H}_m$ is given by

$$\mathcal{H}_m = \frac{p_\phi^2}{2v} + vU(\phi) + \mathcal{E}_{\mathrm{dust}}, \qquad (2)$$

and the Ekpyrotic potential $U(\phi)$ is taken to be,

$$U(\phi) = \frac{-2u_o}{e^{-\sqrt{\frac{16\pi}{p}}\phi} + e^{\beta\sqrt{\frac{16\pi}{p}}\phi}}, \qquad (3)$$

which has the shape of an asymmetric exponential well. Here u_o, p and β are parameters taking positive values. The potential (3) is negative definite. The width of the potential increases with an increasing p, and the degree of asymmetry is controlled by β.

We obtain the following Hamilton's equations from the above Hamiltonian constraint,

$$\dot{b} = -\frac{3\sin^2(\lambda b)}{2\gamma\lambda^2} - 4\pi G\gamma P, \qquad (4)$$

$$\dot{v} = \frac{3\sin(2\lambda b)}{2\gamma\lambda}v, \qquad (5)$$

$$\dot{\phi} = \frac{p_\phi}{v}, \qquad \dot{p}_\phi = vU_{,\phi}, \qquad (6)$$

where $U_{,\phi}$ stands for the differentiation of the potential with respect to the Ekpyrotic field and P is the isotropic pressure $P = -\frac{\partial \mathcal{H}_m}{\partial v}$. It can be shown that the above equations lead to a following modified Friedmann equation of the form

$$H^2 = \frac{8\pi G}{3}\rho\left(1 - \frac{\rho}{\rho_c}\right), \qquad (7)$$

where $\rho_c = 3/(8\pi G\gamma^2\lambda^2) \approx 0.41\rho_{\mathrm{Pl}}$ is called the critical energy density in LQC. The Hubble rate is generically bounded, and vanishes and turns around when the energy density reaches a maximum ρ_c. This is when the bounce occurs. The matter content satisfies the continuity equation $\dot{\rho} + 3H(\rho + P) = 0$, where ρ and P are given respectively by

$$\rho = \frac{\dot{\phi}^2}{2} + U(\phi) + \frac{\mathcal{E}_{\mathrm{dust}}}{v}, \qquad P = \frac{\dot{\phi}^2}{2} - U(\phi). \qquad (8)$$

We use the above set of equations along with suitable initial conditions provided at the bounce to numerically analyze the background dynamics of this model. We also carry out simulations to study the effect of changes in the potential parameters and the relative proportion of the initial dust energy density compared to the Ekpyrotic field energy density. We find that LQC leads to a non-singular bounce in all cases. Although there can be multiple bounces, we restrict ourselves to the cases with a single bounce to study the evolution of curvature perturbations. As an example, we show here the evolution for the choice of parameters $u_o = 0.75, p = 0.10$ and $\beta = 5.0$ with the following initial conditions:

$$\phi_B = 0, \qquad \mathcal{E}_{dust} = 2.00 \times 10^{-5}, \qquad p_{\phi_B} = 1.50. \qquad (9)$$

The volume at bounce is taken to be unity, while we choose $b_B = \pi/2\lambda$ in order to have the correct classical limit on either side of the bounce. The dust energy density is chosen such that the energy density at the bounce is dominated by the Ekpyrotic field. The initial conditions are taken to satisfy the Hamiltonian constraint which has to be satisfied throughout the evolution. The evolution of the energy densities and the equation of state for these initial conditions is shown in Fig. 1. We note that the contracting phase starts in a dust dominated phase where the total energy density is very small and the universe is classical. Eventually it transitions to a phase dominated by the Ekpyrotic field which lasts through the bounce. Thus we find the equation of state at the bounce is $w_B \approx 5.76$. Thus a distinct phase where $w > 1$ is obtained near the bounce, which is very important to avoid the BKL instability as envisaged. The $w > 1$ regime is obtained only when the scalar field is traversing the very bottom of the potential, and is obtained only for a short duration during the scalar field dominated phase near the bounce. After the bounce the equation of state quickly drops below unity and decreases monotonically as the Ekpyrotic field moves away from the bottom of the potential. We did extensive simulations to study the robustness of the qualitative features of the background dynamics obtained above by varying the parameters of the potential and taking different proportions of the initial dust energy density while still keeping the bounce dominated by Ekpyrotic field. We found that the effect of reducing the proportion of the dust energy density

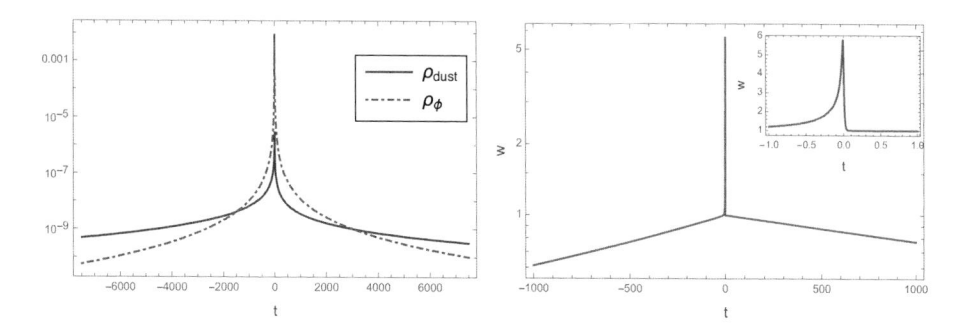

Fig. 1. In the left panel, we see that the energy density of the Ekpyrotic field dominates over the dust energy density in the bounce regime. The right panel shows the behavior of the equation of state when the Ekpyrotic field is dominant and the inset plot depicts the details of the change in the equation of state near the bounce point.

at the bounce has the obvious effect of increasing the duration of Ekpyrotic field dominated regime and the $w > 1$ regime near the bounce. The $w > 1$ regime can also be elongated by widening the potential by increasing p, making it less steep due to which the field takes longer to traverse the bottom of the well. Further, increasing the parameter u_o has effect of increasing both the depth and steepness of the potential. If we increase u_o while keeping the rest of the conditions same, this has the effect of numerically increasing both the kinetic and potential energy of the scalar field at the bounce while keeping the total the same (since the potential is negative-definite, the total energy density is the difference of the numerical values of kinetic and potential energies). Higher kinetic energy means the field climbs out of the well faster, i.e. the duration of the Ekpyrotic field dominated phase is reduced. But a deeper well means that $w > 1$ for most of the duration of this climb. Thus increasing u_o has the effect of decreasing the Ekpyrotic field dominated phase while increasing the $w > 1$ regime. This is illustrated in the following table showing durations of different regimes in the contracting branch (in Planck seconds):

u_o	Ekpyrotic field dominated phase	$w > 1$ regime
1	8.70×10^4	100
0.75	1.50×10^5	65
0.03	3.00×10^5	11
0.008	3.04×10^5	6.5

3. Scalar power spectrum using the dressed metric approach

In this section, we study perturbations around the background spacetime studied in the previous section. As mentioned above, due to the duality with the inflationary epoch,[3] the perturbations in dust matter that exit the horizon during the contracting phase yield a scale invariant spectrum. The dust dominated phase in our background dynamics occurs in the far past, away from the bounce when the universe is classical. Thus we must start perturbations in the far past and then evolve them through the Ekpyrotic phase and the bounce upto the expanding branch.

Since the Ekpyrotic field contributes negligibly to the total energy density in the far past and the equation of state $w \approx 0$, thus we ignore it while considering perturbations in this phase. In this regime the total energy density is far below the Planck density and quantum gravity modifications are negligible. Thus the perturbation equation in terms of the Mukhanov-Sasaki variable also takes its classical form in this phase,

$$v_k'' + \left(k^2 - \frac{z''}{z}\right)v_k = 0, \tag{10}$$

where the prime represents the differentiation with respect to the conformal time. And we choose initial conditions such that, the above state corresponds to the Bunch-Davies vacuum in the asymptotic past:

$$\lim_{\eta \to -\infty} v_k = \frac{e^{-ik\eta}}{\sqrt{2k}}. \tag{11}$$

The above equations are only valid in the matter dominated phase. As perturbations evolve towards the bounce, the Ekpyrotic field starts dominating and the energy density starts increasing towards the Planck scale. Since the Ekpyrotic field dominated phase overlaps with the bounce regime, we cannot use classical equations to describe the perturbations in the Ekpyrotic field dominated phase. Of the various approaches in LQC that consider perturbations in the quantum spacetime, we work with the dressed metric approach.[13] This avoids the Jeans instability encountered near the bounce in the previous study based on deformed algebra approach.[12] In the dressed metric approach, the quantum spacetime is approximated by a differential manifold with a dressed metric for sharply peaked semi-classical states. The effective description of the quantum perturbations is then provided by a Mukhanov-Sasaki variable with an evolution equation of the form

$$v_k'' + \left(k^2 + \Omega^2 - \frac{a''}{a}\right)v_k = 0, \tag{12}$$

where Ω^2 can be written in terms of the background variables as

$$\Omega^2 = 3\kappa \frac{p_\phi^2}{a^4} - 18 \frac{p_\phi^4}{a^6 \pi_a^2} - 12a\frac{p_\phi}{\pi_a}U_{,\phi} + a^2 U_{,\phi\phi}. \tag{13}$$

Here $\kappa = 8\pi G$ and π_a is the conjugate momentum of the scale factor. The required background quantities in the above equations are to be calculated using the effective background dynamics described in section 2. The power spectrum is given by

$$\mathcal{P}_\mathcal{R} = \frac{k^3}{2\pi^2}\frac{|v_k|^2}{z^2}, \tag{14}$$

with $z = a\dot{\phi}/H$. The modes that exit the horizon in the matter-dominated phase of contraction are scale invariant, and it is these modes that will be observable today. However, numerical simulations are important to study the impact of the Ekpyrotic field dominated phase and the bounce on the spectrum of these perturbations. In particular, the scale invariance of spectrum is to be preserved in order to be consistent with observations. Fig. 2 shows the evolution of scalar power spectrum at different stages.

It is clear from the plots that a scale invariant spectrum is already generated at the end of the dust dominated phase during contraction. However, in contrast to previous studies relying on constant equation of state for the Ekpyrotic field,[11] the

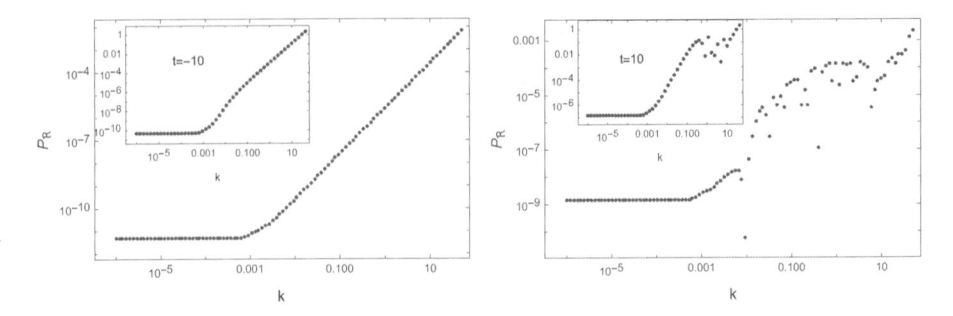

Fig. 2. The power spectra at different times are depicted: in the left panel, the power spectra are evaluated at the transition time from dust dominated to Ekpyrotic field dominated regime in the contracting phase ($t \approx -1.49 \times 10^3$) and at $t = -10$ (in the inset plot); while in the right panel, the power spectra are evaluated at the transition time in the expanding phase ($t \approx 3.02 \times 10^3$) from Ekpyrotic field domination to dust domination and at $t = 10$ (in the inset plot).

magnitude of the scale invariant power spectrum changes over time. Although the scale invariance is preserved through the bounce, a rapid increase in the magnitude of the power spectrum is observed from before the bounce to after the bounce seen by comparing the inset plots. Further, an oscillatory regime reminiscent of inflationary scenarios is seen for $k \geq 10^{-2}$. A comparison of the oscillatory regime at different times as seen in the right panel of Fig. 2 shows that different modes become oscillatory as they exit the horizon in the expanding phase. In contrast to earlier works on the matter-Ekpyrotic scenario in LQC dealing with special cases as well as in contrast to inflationary scenarios, the magnitude of the spectrum in the scale invariant regime gradually decreases as the universe expands. The qualitative behavior of the spectrum remains the same when we vary the proportion of the initial dust energy density relative to the Ekpyrotic field density. However, the range of modes that show scale invariance may get shifted. When the dust energy proportion is decreased, that leads to a shorter duration of dust dominated phase during contraction. Since only those modes that exit during the dust dominated contraction show a scale invariant spectrum, range of modes that show scale invariance is decreased. This may be used to put a constraint on the duration of Ekpyrotic field allowed by observed range of scale invariant modes.

Lastly, in order to compare with observations, we compute the spectral index of the spectrum given by:

$$n_s = 1 + \frac{d \ln P_\mathcal{R}}{d \ln k}. \quad (15)$$

The spectral index is plotted in Fig. 3. We find that the spectral index is larger than unity in the scale invariant regime and is unfavored by recent CMB observations that put tight constraints on the spectral index: $n_s = 0.9649 \pm 0.0042$ (68%CL).[14] We find that this cannot be ameliorated by either changing the parameters of the scalar field potential or changing the proportion of initial dust density to Ekpyrotic field density. Thus making further modifications of this model necessary.

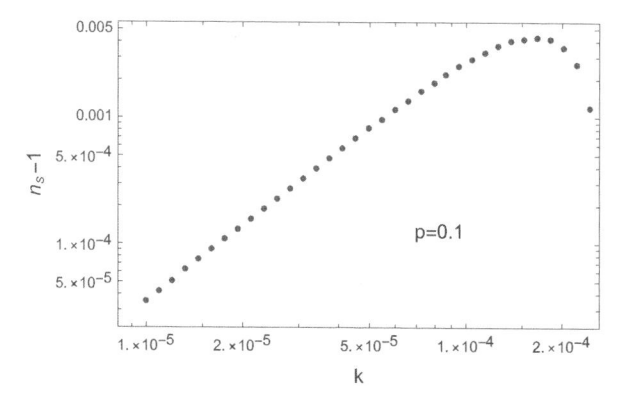

Fig. 3. For the power spectrum displayed in Fig. 2, we evaluate the spectral index n_s at the transition point $t \approx 3.02 \times 10^3$ in the expanding branch and find n_s is larger than unity in the scale invariant regime of the power spectrum.

4. Conclusion

In this paper, we study a general matter-Ekpyrotic scenario in an isotropic and homogeneous FLRW universe in LQC. Using extensive numerical simulations, we establish some general features of the background dynamics and the scalar power spectrum, some of which were not seen in earlier works that either dealt with special cases or were limited to qualitative analysis. A bouncing background cosmology, characteristic of LQC, is obtained where a contracting and an expanding branch connected through a bounce. We find that the background dynamics in each branch is characterized in general by two distinct phases. It starts out in the far past with dust domination and transitions to Ekpyrotic field dominated phase which overlaps with the high energy quantum regime at the bounce. After the bounce there is another transition back to dust dominated universe in the expanding branch. Further we find that the Ekpyrotic field dominated phase generally also contains a phase of ultrastiff equation of state ($w > 1$) leading up to the bounce, which is essential in avoiding the BKL instability. We varied the parameters of the potential and also varied the relative proportion of initial dust density (while keeping it subdominant at the bounce), and found the above mentioned features of the background dynamics to hold in general.

We found that the duration of the Ekpyrotic field dominated phase and the $w > 1$ phase can be increased by increasing the width of the Ekpyrotic field potential or by decreasing the relative proportion of initial dust density. In contrast, increasing the depth of the potential has the effect of shortening the Ekpyrotic field dominated phase while increasing the $w > 1$ phase at the same time.

For the study of comiving curvature perturbations, we give our initial conditions in the far past in the dust-dominated classical phase of the contracting branch in order to include the full effect of the quantum bounce on the power spectrum. We employ the classical Mukhanov-Sasaki equation for the dust-dominated contraction phase as the universe is large and classical in this phase. Since the Ekpyrotic field dominated phase overlaps with the quantum bounce regime, we have employed the dressed metric approach to obtain the effective evolution equation for quantum perturbations on a quantum spacetime in this regime. This is a deliberate choice as previous studies employing the deformed algebra approach have faced difficulty in analyzing ultraviolet modes near the bounce. Using the dressed metric approach for the bounce regime has allowed us to fully explore the scalar power spectrum in the bounce regime.

We found that the perturbation modes exiting the horizon during dust dominated phase have a scale invariant spectrum. These modes then maintain their scale invariance as they pass through the Ekpyrotic field dominated phase, the $w > 1$ phase and the bounce, until they start re-entering the horizon in the expanding branch after which they become oscillatory. However, unlike previous studies considering a constant equation of state for the Ekpyrotic field, the magnitude of the scale invariant modes gradually increases during the Ekpyrotic-field dominated contraction, then rapidly increases during the bounce regime and then gradually decreases as the universe expands. This is also in contrast to inflationary scenarios where the magnitude is frozen after the modes exit the horizon during inflation. Further, the duration of the Ekpyrotic field dominated not only impacts the magnitude of the scale invariant power spectrum, but also impacts the range of comoving modes that lie in the scale invariant part of the spectrum.

We also studied the spectral index of the scale invariant part of the spectrum and found that it is inconsistent with current observational bounds. This is due to the fact that perturbation originating in a purely dust-dominated phase of contraction have an exactly scale invariant spectrum, while the observed spectrum has a slight red tilt. Thus changing potential parameters of the Ekpyrotic field potential has no effect on this feature.

Based on our results, further studies are needed to fully explore the possibilities presented by the matter-Ekpyrotic scenario in LQC. In particular, a lower bound on the minimum number of e-foldings required of the $w > 1$ phase needs to be rigorously established by studying the Ekpyrotic scenario in more general anisotropic spacetimes. Further, a suitable extension of the matter-Ekpyrotic scenario needs to be developed where the perturbations finally exit to a radiation-dominated universe. Bounds on the duration of the Ekpyrotic field dominated phase also needs to be established by employing its impact on the range of scale invariant modes and their magnitude. The issue of the inconsistent spectral index can addressed if instead of sourcing perturbations from a purely dust-dominated phase, we have a matter field with slightly negative equation of state. Although, preliminary studies following these lines have been carried out in the literature in various bouncing cosmologies including those of LQC, but rigorous and extensive studies taking the most general matter-Ekpyrotic scenario need to be done.

References

1. B. F. Li, S. Saini and P. Singh, *Primordial power spectrum from a matter-Ekpyrotic bounce scenario in loop quantum cosmology*, Phys. Rev. D **103**, 066020 (2021).
2. A. Ashtekar, B. Gupt, V. Sreenath, *Cosmic Tango Between the Very Small and the Very Large: Addressing CMB Anomalies Through Loop Quantum Cosmology*, Frontiers in Astronomy & Space Science **8**, 685288 (2021).
3. D. Wands, *Duality invariance of cosmological perturbation spectra*, Phys. Rev. D **60**, 023507 (1999).
4. V. A. Belinsky, I. M. Khalatnikov and E. M. Lifshitz, *Oscillatory approach to a singular point in the relativistic cosmology*, Adv. Phys. **19**, 525 (1970).
5. J. K. Erickson, D. H. Wesley, P. J. Steinhardt and N. Turok, *Kasner and mixmaster behavior in universes with equation of state $w \geq 1$*, Phys. Rev. D **69**, 063514 (2004).
6. Y. F. Cai, D. A. Easson and R. Brandenberger, *Towards a nonsingular bouncing cosmology*, JCAP **1208**, 20 (2012).
7. A. Ashtekar and P. Singh, *Loop Quantum Cosmology: A Status Report*, Class. Quant. Grav. **28**, 213001 (2011).
8. P. Singh, K. Vandersloot, and G. V. Vereshchagin, *Nonsingular bouncing universes in loop quantum cosmology*, Physical Review D **74(4)**, 043510, (2006).
9. M. Bojowald, R. Maartens and P. Singh, *Loop quantum gravity and the cyclic universe*, Phys. Rev. D **70**, 083517 (2004).
10. T. Cailleteau, P. Singh, K. Vandersloot, *Nonsingular Ekpyrotic/cyclic model in loop quantum cosmology*, Phys. Rev. D **80**, 124013, (2009).
11. J. Haro, J. Amoros and L. Salo, *The matter-Ekpyrotic bounce scenario in Loop Quantum Cosmology*, JCAP **09**, 002 (2017).
12. Y. F. Cai and E. Wilson-Ewing, *Non-singular bounce scenarios in loop quantum cosmology and the effective field description.* JCAP **03**, 026 (2014).
13. B. F. Li, P. Singh, A. Wang, *Primordial power spectrum from the dressed metric approach in loop cosmologies*, Phys. Rev. D **100**, 086004 (2020).
14. P. A. R. Ade et al. [Planck Collaboration], *Planck 2018 results. X. Constraints on inflation*, Astron. Astrophys. 641, A10 (2020).

The primordial power spectra in modified loop quantum cosmology

Bao-Fei Li*, Javier Olmedo*, Parampreet Singh* and Anzhong Wang[†,‡]

*Department of Physics and Astronomy, Louisiana State University,
Baton Rouge, LA 70803, USA

[†]Institute for Theoretical Physics & Cosmology, Zhejiang University of Technology,
Hangzhou, 310032, China

[‡]GCAP-CASPER, Department of Physics, Baylor University,
Waco, TX 76798, USA

We review recent developments in the primordial power spectra of two modified loop quantum cosmological models (mLQCs) which originate from the quantization ambiguities while loop quantizing the spatially-flat Friedmann-Lemaître-Robertson-Walker (FLRW) universe. The properties of the background dynamics and the primordial scalar power spectra in two modified models, namely mLQC-I and mLQC-II, are reported. In both models, the inflationary scenario can be naturally extended to the Planck regime when a single scale field is minimally coupled to gravity with an inflationary potential and the big bang singularity is replaced with a quantum bounce. The qualitative difference lies in the behavior of the contracting phase where a quasi de Sitter phase emerges in mLQC-I. When applying the dressed metric approach and the hybrid approach to mLQCs, we find the most distinguishable differences between these models and the standard loop quantum cosmology (LQC) occur in the infrared and intermediate regimes of the power spectra.

Keywords: Loop quantum cosmology; bouncing cosmology; primordial power spectrum.

1. Introduction

Loop quantum cosmology (LQC)[1,2] provides an elegant resolution to the big bang singularity in the standard big bang cosmology by replacing it with a quantum bounce and also naturally extends the inflationary paradigm into the Planck regime. The loop quantization of the spatially flat FLRW spacetime in LQC is based on the homogeneity and isotropy of the spacetime. It has been found that the dynamics of the resulting quantum theory can be well described by the effective dynamics for the states which are sharply peaked around the classical trajectories at late times.[3] However, as is common in any quantum theory, different regularizations of the classical Hamiltonian may give rise to different quantum theory and finally result in distinct physical consequences. So it is important to check the robustness of the theoretical predictions from standard LQC by studying its variants originating from quantization ambiguities. The modified LQC models initially proposed in[4] provide a good platform to investigate the impacts of the quantization prescriptions on the dynamics and the observations.

In standard LQC, when quantizing a spatially flat FLRW universe, the Lorentz term was initially treated in the same way as the Euclidean term since they are proportional to each other at the classical level due to the homogeneity and isotropy of the background spacetime.[5] A separate treatment of these two terms was first implemented in[4] where two modified LQC models, namely mLQC-I and mLQC-II, were proposed due to different regularizations of the Lorentz term. Later, mLQC-I was rediscovered by computing the expectation value of the Hamiltonian constraint in LQG with complexifier coherent state.[6] The right Friedmann and Raychauduri equations of these two models were first reported in,[7,8] and it was found that after taking into account an inflaton field in mLQCs, the inflationary phase turns out to be an attractor in both models.[8] As a result, the inflationary scenario can also be naturally extended to the Planck regime in both models. In the following, assuming the validity of the effective dynamics in mLQCs, we first summarize the main features of the background dynamics of these two mLQCs and their similarities and differences with/from standard LQC. Then we report the results on the numerical simulations of the power spectra in both mLQCs in the dressed metric and the hybrid approaches.

2. The background dynamics in the modified LQC

Although the big bang singularity is resolved and replaced with a quantum bounce in both mLQCs, the differences in the background dynamics between these models are still distinct. Similar to standard LQC, the evolution of the background dynamics in mLQC-II is symmetric with respect to the bounce when gravity is coupled to a massless scalar field. The maximum energy density in mLQC-II is about $1.73 m_{\rm pl}^4$ which is larger than the maximum energy density ($\approx 0.41 m_{\rm pl}^4$) in LQC. It turns out that the evolution of the universe in mLQC-II is similar to that in LQC when gravity is coupled to the same matter content. In contrast, in mLQC-I, the contracting and the expanding phases are no longer symmetric with respect to the bounce point which takes place at the maximum energy density ($\approx 0.097 m_{\rm pl}^4$). A characteristic quasi de Sitter phase quickly emerges in the contracting phase when the universe is evolved backwards from the bounce point. This de Sitter phase is dominated by a Planck-sized effective cosmological constant and the asymptotic forms of the Friedmann and Raychauduri equations reveal a rescaled Newton's constant in the contracting phase as well.[7] As a result, when filled with an inflaton field, the classical universe can only be recovered in the expanding phase of mLQC-I while in the contracting phase, the universe remains quantum with a Planck-scale Hubble parameter.

Meanwhile, the numerical simulations of the background dynamics shows qualitatively similar behavior of the universe in the expanding phase of mLQCs and standard LQC.[9] The initial conditions of the background dynamics which are relevant to CMB data are those dominated by the kinetic energy of the inflaton field at the bounce. For these initial conditions, three distinct phases can be observed in the expanding phase: the bouncing phase with $w \approx 1$ which lasts only a few number of e-foldings, the transient transition phase where the equation of state quickly decreases from positive unity to near negative unity and the slow-roll inflationary phase. These generic features of the background dynamics shared by mLQCs and LQC imply the robustness of the preinflationary dynamics in loop quantizations of the spatially flat FLRW universe and the different regularizations of the Lorentz term in the classical Hamiltonian constraint leave imprints only in the contracting phase.

3. The primordial power spectra in the modified LQC

To compute the primordial power spectra in the mLQCs, one can appeal to the techniques developed in standard LQC where several distinct approaches are widely studied. Among them the most popular ones are the dressed metric approach[10–12] and the hybrid approach.[13–16] We have applied both these approaches to mLQCs and numerically obtained the resulting scalar power spectrum.[17,18] Irrespective of specific model and approach, the power spectrum can be generally divided into three distinctive regimes: the infrared (IR) regime, the intermediate regime and the ultraviolet (UV) regime.

The behavior of the IR regime sensitively depends on the initial states, the specific model and the applied approach. For example, when the fourth-order adiabatic states are employed as the initial states in the contracting phase, the magnitude of the power spectra remains almost constant in LQC and mLQC-II in both dressed metric and hybrid approaches. In contrast, when the second-order adiabatic states are used as the initial states, the magnitude of the power spectra keeps increasing with the comoving wavenumber in LQC and mLQC-II in both approaches. In mLQC-I, the power spectrum in the IR regime strongly relies on the approach we use. In the dressed metric approach, due to the emergent de Sitter phase, the preferred choice of the Bunch-Davies (BD) vacuum state yields a Planck-sized magnitude of the power spectrum in the IR regime. While in the hybrid approach, the effective mass changes so drastically as compared with the one in the dressed metric approach that the adiabatic states can be again chosen as the initial states of the scalar perturbations, leading to a power spectrum whose magnitude is comparable to that of LQC and mLQC-II in the IR regime. From our numerical results, we find the relative difference between LQC and mLQC-II in the IR regime turns out to be less than 40% in the dressed metric approach and less than 50% in the hybrid approach. Due to the similar background dynamics between the LQC and mLQC-II, the relative difference between LQC and mLQC-II is much less than that between LQC(mLQC-II) and mLQC-I.

The power spectrum keeps oscillating throughout the intermediate regime in all of the three models with the dressed metric and the hybrid approaches. This oscillatory behavior is believed to be associated with the bouncing regime where adiabatic conditions are violated for the modes whose comoving wavenumbers are close to the characteristic wavenumber in each model and thus particle creations become appreciable.[19] For the adiabatic initial states and in particular the BD vacuum state in the dressed metric approach of mLQC-I, the magnitude of the power spectrum in this regime is amplified as compared with that in the UV regime. Moreover, the relative difference of the power spectra between different models turns out to be larger than that in the IR regime due to the oscillatory behavior of the power spectra. In particular, the relative difference of the power spectra between LQC and mLQC-II in the intermediate regime can be up to 100% in both approaches and the relative difference between LQC and mLQC-II is also smaller than that between LQC(mLQC-II) and mLQC-I.

Finally, regardless of the initial states, the specific model and approach used to compute the power spectra, we always observe a scale-invariant UV regime whose magnitude agrees with the observations. The relative difference between the magnitudes of the power spectra from three models turns out to be less than 1%. As a result, only the IR and intermediate regimes are mostly affected by the different regularizations of the classical Hamiltonian constraints, there is little impact on the UV regime due to the quantization ambiguities as it should be.

4. Summary

We have studied the background dynamics and the primordial power spectra in mLQCs and compare the results with those from LQC. The background dynamics in mLQC-II is qualitatively similar to that in LQC with a symmetric evolution with respect to the bounce when gravity is minimally coupled to a massless scalar field. An asymmetric evolution is observed only in mLQC-I where the classical limit can only be recovered in the expanding phase and there shows up an emergent de Sitter spacetime in the contracting phase. The difference between the background dynamics also affects the power spectrum in the IR and intermediate regime. From our numerical results, we find the relative difference of the power spectra between LQC and mLQC-II in these two regimes is much smaller than the relative difference between LQC(mLQC-II) and mLQC-I in the dressed metric and hybrid approaches. Moreover, mLQC-I also serves as a good example to explicitly show the differences between the dressed metric and hybrid approaches. In particular, a Planck scale magnitude of the power spectrum in the IR regime of mLQC-I with the dressed metric approach is observed while in the hybrid approach the magnitude of the power spectrum is suppressed in the IR regime of mLQC-I. This difference is completely due to the distinct construction of the Mukhanov-Sasaki equation in each approach which leads to different effective masses. Finally, the power spectrum in the UV regime is found to be consistent with the CMB data in all three models regardless of the approach and the initial states.

References

1. A. Ashtekar and P. Singh, *Loop Quantum Cosmology: A Status Report*, Class. Quant. Grav. **28**, 213001 (2011).

2. I. Agullo and P. Singh, *Loop Quantum Cosmology*, in Loop Quantum Gravity: The First 30 Years, edited by A. Ashtekar and J. Pullin (World Scientific, Singapore, 2017).
3. A. Ashtekar, T. Pawlowski, and P. Singh, *Quantum nature of the Big Bang: Improved dynamics*, Phys. Rev. **D74**, 084003 (2006).
4. J. Yang, Y. Ding and Y. Ma, *Alternative quantization of the Hamiltonian in loop quantum cosmology II: Including the Lorentz term*, Phys. Lett. B**682** (2009) 1.
5. A. Ashtekar, M. Bojowald and J. Lewandowski *Mathematical structure of loop quantum cosmology*, Adv. Theor. Math. Phys. 7:233-268,2003.
6. A. Dapor and K. Liegener, *Cosmological Effective Hamiltonian from full Loop Quantum Gravity Dynamics*, Phys. Lett. B**785** (2018) 506.
7. B.-F. Li, P. Singh, A. Wang, *Towards cosmological dynamics from loop quantum gravity*, Phys. Rev. D**97**, 084029 (2018).
8. B.-F. Li, P. Singh, A. Wang, *Qualitative dynamics and inflationary attractors in loop cosmology*, Phys. Rev. D**98**, 066016 (2018).
9. B.-F. Li, P. Singh, A. Wang, *Genericness of pre-inflationary dynamics and probability of the desired slow-roll inflation in modified loop quantum cosmologies*, Phys. Rev. D**100**, 063513 (2019).
10. I. Agullo, A. Ashtekar and W. Nelson, *Quantum gravity extension of the inflationary scenario*, Phys. Rev. Lett. **109**, 251301 (2012).
11. I. Agullo, A. Ashtekar and W. Nelson, *Extension of the quantum theory of cosmological perturbations to the Planck era*, Phys. Rev. D**87**, 043507 (2013).
12. I. Agullo, A. Ashtekar and W. Nelson, *The pre-inflationary dynamics of loop quantum cosmology: Confronting quantum gravity with observations*, Class. Quantum Grav. **30**, 085014 (2013).
13. L. Castelló Gomar, M. Fernández-Méndez, G. A. Mena Marugan and J. Olmedo, *Cosmological perturbations in hybrid loop quantum cosmology: Mukhanov-Sasaki variables*, Phys. Rev. D**90**, 064015 (2014).
14. M. Fernández-Méndez, G. A. Mena Marugán and J. Olmedo, *Hybrid quantization of an inflationary universe*, Phys. Rev. D**86**, 024003 (2012).
15. M. Fernández-Méndez, G. A. Mena Marugán and J. Olmedo, *Hybrid quantization of an inflationary model: The flat case*, Phys. Rev. D**88**, 044013 (2013).
16. L. Castelló Gomar, M. Martín-Benito, G. A. Mena Marugán, *Gauge-invariant perturbations in hybrid quantum cosmology*, JCAP 1506 (2015) 045.
17. B.-F. Li, P. Singh, A. Wang, *Primordial power spectrum from the dressed metric approach in loop cosmologies*, Phys. Rev. D**100**, 086004 (2020).
18. B.-F. Li, J. Olmedo, P. Singh, and A. Wang, *primordial scalar power spectrum from the hybrid approach in loop cosmologies*, Phys. Rev. D**102**, 126025 (2020).
19. Q. Wu, T. Zhu, and A. Wang, *Nonadiabatic evolution of primordial perturbations and non-Gaussianity in hybrid approach of loop quantum cosmology*, Phys. Rev. D**98**, 103528 (2018).

Primordial perturbations in kinetically dominated regimes of classical and quantum cosmology

B. Elizaga Navascués

JSPS International Research Fellow, Department of Physics, Waseda University, 3-4-1 Okubo, Shinjuku-ku, 169-8555 Tokyo, Japan

R. Jiménez-Llamas and G.A. Mena Marugán[*]

Instituto de Estructura de la Materia, IEM-CSIC, Serrano 121, 28006 Madrid, Spain
[*] E-mail: mena@iem.cfmac.csic.es

There is an increasing interest in very early stages of the Universe in which the energy density of the inflaton could be dominated by its kinetic part. This includes classical inflationary scenarios with deviations from slow-roll regimes that can introduce modifications to the power spectra of the primordial fluctuations. Another example are certain quantum bouncing cosmologies. For instance, this is the typical situation in loop quantum cosmology if quantum corrections may leave observable traces in the power spectra. In models of this type, we discuss the leading-order effects of an inflaton potential on the primordial perturbations. These effects are of two kinds, referred to the case without potential. First, there are changes in the background-dependent mass appearing in the dynamical equations of the perturbations in conformal time. Second, away from conventional slow roll, a Bunch-Davies vacuum may no longer be natural, and possible new choices depend on the potential.

Keywords: Loop Quantum Cosmology, Kinetically Dominated Inflation, Primordial Perturbations

1. Introduction

We live in an era of precision cosmology, in which the technological progress has allowed us to obtain more accurate observations and determine a number of cosmological parameters with a precision of a few percent.[1] This new era opens the possibility of confronting predictions with observations, falsifying cosmological models and gravitational theories that may suggest corrections to general relativity (GR). Although the standard cosmological model, based on GR and an inflationary phase in slow-roll regime, has proved extremely succesful to explain the observations, there exist some anomalies that, at least, point towards the statistical exceptionality of our universe.[2–6] Namely, cosmological data such as those imprinted in the spectrum of anisotropies of the cosmic microwave background (CMB) or the lensing amplitude are not statistically favored within this standard model. These anomalies may be a sign of new physics that modifies in part the paradigms of the model.

A possibility that has attracted a lot of attention lately is the occurrence of kinetically dominated regimes in the very early epochs of the expansion of the Universe, i.e. regimes in which the scalar field that is going to drive the inflationary mechanism displays a period in its evolution in which its energy density is dominated by the kinetic contribution, rather than by a potential. This kinetic dominance would have taken place before slow roll, and the transition between both regimes may cover a part of the inflationary era. Typically, the situations of interest combine this kinetic dominance with a short lived inflation, because it is then that the frequencies that are most affected by the dynamics away from slow roll can overlap at present with the band that is observed in the CMB fluctuations.[7,8] This change in the early dynamics of the primordial fluctuations can leave traces in their amplitude and modify the predictions about their power and other measurable quantities, mostly for modes that in those early moments have (wavelength) scales similar to those of the physical phenomena that modify the standard picture of slow-roll inflation.[8]

Clearly, this type of modifications of the standard model can happen within GR.[7] Most interesting, they can also appear owing to quantum effects, in a quantum description of cosmology. An example that has been studied in some detail in recent years is the case of loop quantum cosmology (LQC).[9,10] In this formalism, the cosmological background spacetime is quantized adopting the techniques of loop quantum gravity,[11] a quantum version of GR that is based on the use of holonomies and fluxes of densitized triads, and that avoids any dependence of the results on fixed spacetime structures. On top of this quantum version of the cosmological background, matter and geometry fluctuations provide the cosmological perturbations that eventually serve as seeds for the anisotropies of the CMB and the formation of large-scale structures. Different approaches have been suggested to deal with these perturbations.[12–16] Among them, here we will consider only two of them, that share the property of preserving the ultraviolet structure of the dynamical equations for the perturbations in GR. The first one is called hybrid LQC, and is based on a simultaneous quantization of the background and the gauge-invariant degrees of freedom of the perturbations, using loop quantization techniques for the former and Fock techniques for the latter.[17–23] We will focus most of our analysis on this quantization proposal. The other approach that we will mention, but will not discuss in detail in our study, is called the dressed-metric proposal.[24–29] In this case, the gauge-invariant perturbations evolve in a kind of mean-field background that is dressed with quantum corrections, in order to take into account the most relevant effects of its quantization in LQC.

Remarkably, in the case of kinetic dominance, both in GR and in LQC, the changes with respect to the standard evolution of slow-roll inflation in Einstein's theory can be encapsulated in modifications of the time-dependent mass that appears in the dynamical equations of the gauge-invariant perturbations.[30] This modified mass captures the change in the behavior of the background as compared to the standard inflationary case. Essentially, these changes incorporate (at most) two characteristic scales: one is the scale of the onset of inflation away from slow roll; the other is the typical scale of the quantum phenomena, if such corrections are present.[22]

The main purpose of this work is to introduce a formalism capable to deal with the changes introduced by a kinetically dominated era in the predictions of the primordial spectrum of the cosmological perturbations. Employing that in this era the energy density of the inflaton is dominated by the kinetic term, the basic idea is to treat the effects of the inflaton potential just as a modification to the free case of a scalar field with vanishing potential, and include them only at leading order. In the next section, we present the theoretical framework within which we will develop this formalism. Section 3 describes the cosmological system that we will consider for our study. In Sec. 4 we provide the dynamical equations of the gauge invariant perturbations, including their modified mass. We then consider the issue of the choice of vacuum state for the perturbations in Sec. 5. The following sections are devoted to calculate the leading-order correction of the potential to the modified mass and the related change in the selection of vacuum state. Section 6 discusses what types of effects can be expected owing to the presence of a potential. Then, we compute these effects in: (a) the geometric terms that provide the modified mass, (b) the evolution of the background state, (c) the modified mass as a whole, combining the two previous types of effects, and (d) the choice of a vacuum. This is carried out, respectively, in Secs. 7, 8, 9, and 10. Finally, in Sec. 11 we discuss our results, and explain their possible use in future works.

2. The framework

We will consider cosmological perturbations in the framework of LQC and in the classical counterpart that corresponds to GR. We will restrict our discussion to the case of scalar perturbations, because tensor perturbations can be treated in a similar and in fact simpler way, since the inflaton potential directly affects the scalar matter content and hence the corresponding scalar perturbations.[19] On the other hand, vector perturbations are pure gauge in the absence of vector matter fields. The scalar perturbative gauge-invariant degrees of freedom of the geometry and the matter content, when the latter is given by a scalar field, can be described e.g. by the so-called Mukhanov-Sasaki (MS) invariant, which can be straightforwardly related to the comoving curvature perturbations for spatially flat cosmologies.[31–33] The Fourier modes of the MS gauge-invariant field satisfy a second-order differential evolution equation that can be written in the form of that of a harmonic oscillator, except for the addition of a time-dependent mass term to the squared frequency (or wavenorm) contribution. It is not difficult to derive the expression of this mass in GR, using cosmological perturbation theory. Moreover, in the considered approaches to LQC, it is possible to prove that the MS modes satisfy a dynamical equation which parallels that of GR except for the modification of the time-dependent mass. In the specific case of hybrid LQC, this modified mass turns out to be given by the ratio of two expectation values of background geometry operators, quantized with loop methods.[19,23] Those expectations values are calculated employing the inner product characteristic of LQC for homogeneous and isotropic spacetimes, that is defined using the discrete measure.[9,10] This is the paradigmatic example that we will analyze in full detail in our discussion.

Nonetheless, the study can be extended without too many complications to the case of dressed-metric LQC, case in which the modified MS mass is also provided by expectation values of geometric operators, but the corresponding expression is different from the hybrid one.[30] Similarly, one can consider the case of hybrid geometrodynamics, in which the background geometry is quantized using geometrodynamics[34,35] and the perturbations using a Fock description, as in hybrid LQC. The modified mass is given again in this alternative quantization by a ratio of two expectation values, but in this case the representation of the geometric operators and the quantum integration measure over the background are not those of LQC, but of geometrodynamics.

An exact treatment of the modified mass in any of these quantization approaches would require numerical simulations to compute the evolution of the quantum state of the background, the action on it of the geometric operators, and the expectation value using the corresponding quantum measure. These numerical simulations would be quite intrincate, because the quantum dynamics in the presence of a potential for the inflaton is extremely nontrivial (actually, it is not even guaranteed that there exists a well-defined self-adjoint operator that generates the background evolution when the potential is not zero and generic). Furthermore, the fact that the quantum background state evolves in time implies that (most of) these numerical simulations have to be repeated at each instant of time in the considered epoch. For instance, the evolution can be described in terms of the inflaton, regarded as an internal time, since this is a good clock when the inflaton energy is kinetically dominated. The need to carry out the calculation of the expectation values for each value of interest of the inflaton complicates enormously the numerical challenges. In addition, the time description in terms of the inflaton has to be re-expressed in terms of a conformal time, which is the one that appears in the MS equation for the perturbations. This change of time involves the computation of additional expectation values,[19,23] as we will see in some detail later in our discussion. Besides, of course, all of these complicated numerical calculations need to be repeated if one changes the potential, e.g. if one wants to consider the effect of different families of potentials in the evolution of the primordial perturbations.

To complicate even more the situation, it is known that the choice of the Bunch-Davies state as a natural vacuum for the perturbations[36] is no longer sustainable away from slow roll.[22,37] The vacuum state should be optimally adapted to the background evolution. When this evolution does not reproduce a de Sitter regime, the validity of the Bunch-Davies vacuum is questionable, especially for modes that are able to feel the change of dynamics. To try to deal with this issue, at least in LQC, several proposals have recently been introduced for the choice of a vacuum of the perturbations. For instance, Ashtekar and Gupt have suggested to identify the vacuum as a state with a maximal classical behavior at the end of inflation among those that, in the genuine quantum regime, have geometric uncertainties compatible with a quantum extension of Penrose's Weyl curvature hypothesis.[38,39] Another interesting proposal, introduced by Martín-de Blas and Olmedo,[20] is to choose a state with a non-oscillating power spectrum at the end of inflation. This proposal was motivated by the finding of states with rapid oscillations superimposed in the spectrum. Typically, an average of these oscillations over phenomenologically realistic frequency bins leads to an enhancement of the power. Recent works have shown that the desirable non-oscillating behavior can be characterized by a suitable asymptotic behavior in the sector of modes with infinitely large wavenumbers.[40,41] From this sector, one would determine the vacuum for all modes by properly extending the asymptotic solution. Moreover, it has been proved that this asymptotic behavior is displayed by positive frequency solutions associated with an asymptotic diagonalization of the Hamiltonian of the perturbations. Namely, by means of that diagonalization one straightfowadly finds a background-dependent frequency that defines the desired solutions, at least in the asymptotic ultraviolet sector. We will focus our discussion on this form of the proposal for the choice of a vacuum for the perturbations, since it can be handled analytically, opposite to the situation found for the alternative form in terms of the absence of oscillations in the spectrum, or for the proposal of Ashtekar and Gupt, which in a way or another require the use of numerical methods to pick out a vacuum solution.

As we have anticipated, the basic idea of our investigation is to approximate the MS mass around its value for a free scalar field and derive the leading-order correction to it owing to the presence of a small but nonzero potential term. This approach to the problem leads to a drastic simplification of the numerical calculations required for a complete study of the evolution of the perturbations, which in any case can be related to the free evolution, that is usually manageable in most of the quantization approaches (sometimes even analytically). Furthermore, as far as kinetic dominance persists in the studied period of time, the analysis can be carried out in a parallel way, if not at once, for any possible inflaton potential.

3. The system

The cosmological system that we will consider in this work is a perturbed flat Friedmann-Lemaître-Robertson-Walker (FLRW) spacetime endowed with a scalar field as matter content. We start with a homogeneous and isotropic FLRW geometry with flat spatial sections and a homogeneous scalar field ϕ provided with a potential $W(\phi)$, which will play the role of an inflaton. In the absence of perturbations, or when their backreaction is negligible, this background is subject to a Hamiltonian constraint of the form[23,42]

$$\hat{\pi}_\phi^2 - \hat{H}_0^{(2)} = 0, \tag{1}$$

where $\hat{\pi}_\phi$ is the momentum operator of the inflaton and $\hat{H}_0^{(2)}$ contains all dependence on the FLRW geometry, namely[a]

$$\hat{H}_0^{(2)} = \left[\hat{H}_0^{(F)}\right]^2 - 2W(\phi)\hat{V}^2, \qquad \hat{H}_0^{(F)} = 2\sqrt{3\pi G}|\pi_V|V. \qquad (2)$$

We have set $\hbar = c = 1$, and G is Newton's constant. The operator $\hat{H}_0^{(F)}$ generates the free evolution, in the absence of potential, and can be interpreted as proportional to the generator of dilations. On the other hand, V is the physical volume of the spatial sections (in principle, we consider them compact, and take the noncompact limit at the end of the calculations about the dynamics of the perturbations[43]). Its momentum is denoted by π_V.

On this background, we introduce perturbations in the geometry and the scalar field, truncating the action of the whole system at quadratic perturbative order, which is the first nontrivial one. As we have said above, we restrict our discussion to scalar perturbations (in the continuous limit[43]) for simplicity. We adopt a canonical set of variables for the background and the perturbations in which the perturbative degrees of freedom correspond to the MS gauge invariant and its momentum, togeteher with a canonical set for the pure gauge sector.[19] The background is still described by suitable variables for the inflaton and the physical volume and their momenta. These variables differ from the original ones by quadratic perturbative corrections[19] but, in order to maintain our notation as simple as possible, we will not introduce new symbols for them and use the ones already introduced.

The resulting system has only one constraint that is not trivial to impose quantum mechanically: the spatial average, or zero-mode, of the Hamiltonian constraint[19] (truncated at quadratic order). We quantize this system and the constraint, and search for physical states by adopting an ansatz of separation of variables. The corresponding wavefunctions depend only on the MS gauge invariant, the background geometry (e.g. the volume), and the inflaton. With our ansatz, the dependence on the MS modes and the FLRW geometry separates in partial wavefunctions, that may all depend on the inflaton, used as a reference variable for the quantum evolution. Moreover, as part of the ansatz, the background state is taken to adopt the expression

$$\chi(V,\phi) = P\left[\exp\left(i\int_{\phi_0}^{\phi} d\tilde\phi\,\hat{H}_0(V,\tilde\phi)\right)\right]\chi_0(V), \qquad (3)$$

where $\chi_0(V)$ is the initial state of the FLRW geometry. In addition, the operator $\hat{H}_0$ is the square root of (the positive part of) $\hat{H}_0^{(2)}$. We will call it the background Hamiltonian. We can understand this operator as a(n approximate) generator of the background evolution. Finally, the symbol P denotes path ordering, since the

---

[a] Actually, we allow some freedom in the factor ordering for the representation of this operator. This will be useful when calculating its square root, to obtain a specially simple operator [see Eq. (14)].

integral in the exponential is defined over the inflaton, and the operator $\hat{H}_0$ depends on it.

Using this ansatz for the physical states, imposing the zero-mode of the Hamiltonian constraint, and assuming that the transitions between different background quantum states mediated by this constraint can be neglected, it is possible to derive a quantum constraint just on the perturbations, that depends on expectation values of geometric operators over the FLRW geometry of the background.[19,23] This constraint on the perturbations implies dynamical equations of the MS type, but with a background-dependent mass that is modified with respect to GR by including quantum effects via expectation values.

4. Modified MS equations

The coefficients of the Fourier expansion (in terms of sines and cosines, for instance) of the MS gauge-invariant field can be treated as time dependent variables $v_{\vec{k},\varepsilon}$, where ε is a dichotomic label that indicates the parity of the mode and $\vec{k}$ is the wavevector, restricted to have a positive first nonvanishing component (in an Euclidean fiducial spatial system of coordinates). We will call k the norm of this wavevector.

In hybrid quantum cosmology, according to the discussion of the previous section, the MS variables satisfy the following dynamical equations:

$$\ddot{v}_{\vec{k},\varepsilon} + \left[k^2 + \frac{\langle \hat{\vartheta}_e^q + (\hat{\vartheta}_o \hat{H}_0)_{sym} \rangle_\chi}{\langle \hat{\vartheta}_e \rangle_\chi} \right] v_{\vec{k},\varepsilon} = 0, \qquad (4)$$

which rule their propagation on the FLRW (quantum) background. The dot denotes the derivative in conformal time η. We will call modified mass the term added to k^2 in the factor between square brackets, and denote it by $s(\eta)$. The geometric operators that appear in this modified mass and have not been defined yet are

$$\hat{\vartheta}_e = \frac{3}{2G} \hat{V}^{2/3}, \qquad (5)$$

$$\hat{\vartheta}_o = \frac{3}{\pi} \sqrt{\frac{3}{\pi G}} \hat{V}^{2/3} (\hat{H}_0^{(F)})^{-1} \hat{\Lambda}_0^{(F)} (\hat{H}_0^{(F)})^{-1} \hat{V}^{2/3} W'(\phi), \qquad (6)$$

$$\hat{\vartheta}_e^q = \frac{1}{2\pi} \left[\frac{\widehat{1}}{V} \right]^{1/3} \hat{H}_0^{(2)} \left(19 - 18 (\hat{H}_0^{(F)})^{-2} \hat{H}_0^{(2)} \right) \left[\frac{\widehat{1}}{V} \right]^{1/3}$$
$$+ \hat{V}^{4/3} \left(\frac{3}{8\pi^2 G} W''(\phi) - \frac{2}{\pi} W(\phi) \right). \qquad (7)$$

The norm of the operator $\hat{\Lambda}_0^{(F)}$ denotes an alternative representation of $\hat{H}_0^{(F)}$ in LQC, obtained with holonomies of double length. Besides, $\left[\widehat{\frac{1}{V}}\right]$ is the so-called inverse volume operator of LQC,[9,23] which is not the inverse of the volume operator $\hat{V}$ at scales of the Planck volume or below. On the other hand, the prime denotes the derivative with respect to the inflaton.

The expectation values that appear in the modified mass have to be computed on the quantum state for the background FLRW geometry, of the form (3) according to our ansatz. In hybrid LQC, one uses for this calculation the discrete inner product characteristic of homogeneous and isotropic LQC. If one considers instead hybrid geometrodynamics (i.e. the combination of geometrodynamics and a Fock quantization of the perturbations), both the representation of all the involved geometric operators and the inner product for the expectation values must be those corresponding to a geometrodynamic quantum cosmology. In the case of the dressed-metric approach to LQC, on the other hand, the modified mass is slightly different, although defined again in terms of expectation values of certain geometric operators.[26] We will not give its expression here, but emphasize that can be handled in a similar way as we will explain for hybrid LQC. Finally, in GR, expectation values become evaluation on classical background trajectories, and operators become phase space functions, with certain subtleties that we will comment later in our analysis.

It is worth emphasizing that the modified MS equations described above dictate the evolution of the gauge-invariant scalar perturbations in conformal time. On the other hand, the evolution of the quantum state (3), as well as the explicit dependence on the potential W of the geometric operators, are in principle described in terms of the inflaton ϕ, that in the kinetic dominated regimes is a good reference variable for the quantum background dynamics. In the derivation of the modified MS equation,[19,23] one finds that the relation between the conformal time η and the inflaton as a dynamical parameter is given by the equation

$$\langle \hat{H}_0 \rangle_\chi d\eta = \langle \hat{\vartheta}_e \rangle_\chi d\phi. \tag{8}$$

This relation is state dependent, but it is well defined because $\hat{H}_0$ is a positive operator (a square root, in fact) and the expectation values translate any operator dependence into one on c-numbers (treating the inflaton as such, and realizing that its momentum does not appear in the considered equation).

5. Vacuum state

The fact that the dynamical equations of the (scalar) primordial gauge-invariant perturbations change with respect to those that would dictate the evolution on a de Sitter background, owing to the modifications suffered by the MS mass, calls for a change as well in the choice of vacuum for those perturbations, from the Bunch-Davies state adopted in the standard situations to a new state that is optimally adapted to the background dynamics. As we have commented in the Introduction, several proposals have been put forward for this choice of vacuum state in LQC. Here we will adhere to a prescription that is based on an asymptotic diagonalization of the Hamiltonian of the perturbations in the sector of infinitely large wavenorms, as a way to select a natural positive frequency in that sector, which can then be extended to all MS modes.[40] We have already commented that this prescription has been shown to select a vacuum with non-oscillating primordial spectrum in the ultraviolet sector.

An important advantage of the asymptotic diagonalization prescription is that it can be handled in an (essentially) analytical way in the asymptotic ultraviolet sector. Let us see this in more detail. Once we are given a (modified) MS mass $s(\eta)$, we can determine a set of positive frequency solutions $\{\mu_k\}$ in the form

$$\mu_k = \frac{1}{\sqrt{-2\Im[h_k]}} e^{i \int_{\eta_0}^{\eta} d\tilde{\eta}\, \Im[h_k]}, \qquad (9)$$

where h_k is a complex solution of the Riccati equation

$$\dot{h}_k = k^2 + s + h_k^2. \qquad (10)$$

The positivity of the frequency would be guaranteed if and only if $\Im[h_k]$, i.e. the imaginary part of h_k, is negative. In the following, we will call h_k the complex frequency function. Note, by the way, that the above set of mode solutions depends only on the wavenorm k, and not on the specific wavevector $\vec{k}$ associated with it. The asymptotic diagonalization prescription selects complex frequencies with the following asymptotic behavior[41]:

$$\frac{1}{h_k} = \frac{i}{k}\left[1 + 2\sum_{n=0}^{\infty} \frac{\gamma_n}{(2ik)^{n+2}}\right], \qquad (11)$$

where the coefficients γ_n are fixed by the recursion relation

$$\gamma_{n+1} = -\dot{\gamma}_n + 4s\left[\gamma_{n-1} + \sum_{l=0}^{n-3} \gamma_l \gamma_{n(l+3)}\right] - \sum_{l=0}^{n-1} \gamma_l \gamma_{n-(l+1)}, \qquad (12)$$

starting with the data $\gamma_0 = s$. So, the complex frequency must behave asymptotically as $-ik$, with all subleading terms forming an asymptotic series in inverse powers of k, and with the coefficient γ_0 of the first term equal to the modified MS mass. This asymptotic behavior should characterize the complex frequency and hence the set of mode solutions that determine the vacuum state.

For completeness, recall that, if the solutions were valid until the end of inflation, the corresponding primordial power spectrum would be proportional to

$$P_v(k,\eta) = -\frac{k^3}{4\pi^2 \Im[h_k](\eta)}. \qquad (13)$$

If our expressions for the mode solutions $\{\mu_k\}$ are applicable only in an interval that does not contain all the inflationary period, then we have to evolve their data until the end of inflation and compute the primordial spectrum there.

6. Corrections produced by the potential

In order to calculate the leading-order effect of the potential in the regime of kinetic dominance, let us first identify the different types of corrections that the potential introduces in comparison to the case of a free evolution. First, the potential modifies the expression of the geometric operators that appear in the MS mass. Besides, it affects the evolution of the quantum background state on which the expectation values are computed, both because the generator of the evolution parametrized by the inflaton is different and because the relation between the inflaton and the conformal time that is used in the MS equation changes. Combining all these corrections one obtains the total change in the modified MS mass. This would complete the corrections to the dynamical equations of the perturbations in the kinetic regime, but we also have to consider the initial conditions for these dynamics, that are determined by the vacuum state. We have already explained that the natural choice of a vacuum changes as well with respect to the Bunch Davies state, away of slow roll, and that the new choice depends on the modified MS mass, and hence displays a dependence on the inflaton potential.

In the following sections, we will consider each of these types of corrections separately.

7. Corrections to the geometric operators in the MS mass

Let us consider the expression of the modified MS mass in Eq. (4). The corrections that the presence of a potential introduce in the geometric operators that appear in this expression are easy to calculate, taking into account that they are at most quadratic in this potential (and its derivatives), except for the dependence that may exist via the operator $\hat{H}_0$. In more detail, the operator $\hat{\vartheta}_e$ that gives the denominator is independent of the potential. Meanwhile, at leading order in this potential the operator $\hat{\vartheta}_e^q$ in the numerator contains a free and a linear contribution. Finally, the remaining operator $\hat{\vartheta}_o$, which is multiplied by $\hat{H}_0$ in the numerator, is linear. As a result, at the leading order in the potential that we are considering, we can approximate $\hat{H}_0$ by its free counterpart $\hat{H}_0^{(F)}$ in the numerator. With this replacement and the linear truncation of $\hat{\vartheta}_e^q$ in the potential, the expression of the modified mass is valid (as far as the geometric operators are concerned) at the studied order.

For later discussion, it is helpful to derive the expression of the background Hamiltonian, expanded in the potential. Clearly, the first term in this expansion is the free Hamiltonian $\hat{H}_0^{(F)}$. With a suitable choice of factor ordering, one can show that[30]

$$\hat{H}_0 = \hat{H}_0^{(F)} - W(\phi)(\hat{H}_0^{(F)})^{-1/2}\hat{V}^2(\hat{H}_0^{(F)})^{-1/2} + O(W^2), \qquad (14)$$

where the symbol $O(W^2)$ denotes terms that are of quadratic or higher order in the potential and its derivatives.

8. Corrections to the background evolution

In order to calculate the effect of the potential in the quantum evolution of the background state, it is especially convenient to adopt an interaction picture,[44] in which the dynamics of the free case is isolated and the contribution of the inflaton potential is viewed as an interaction. Approximating, to leading order in the potential, the interaction part of the background Hamiltonian according to Eq. (14) and expanding to the same order the evolution operator associated with this interaction, it is straightforward to see that

$$\chi(V,\phi) = \left[1 - i \int_{\phi_0}^{\phi} d\tilde{\phi}\, \hat{K}(\phi,\tilde{\phi}) W(\tilde{\phi}) + O(W^2)\right] \chi^{(F)}(V,\phi), \tag{15}$$

$$\hat{K}(\phi,\tilde{\phi}) = \exp[i\hat{H}_0^{(F)}(\phi - \tilde{\phi})](\hat{H}_0^{(F)})^{-1/2} \hat{V}^2 (\hat{H}_0^{(F)})^{-1/2} \exp[-i\hat{H}_0^{(F)}(\phi - \tilde{\phi})], \tag{16}$$

where $\chi^{(F)}(V,\phi)$ is the background state evolved with respect to the inflaton with the free Hamiltonian $\hat{H}_0^{(F)}$, namely

$$\chi^{(F)}(V,\phi) = \exp[i\hat{H}_0^{(F)}(\phi - \phi_0)] \chi_0(V). \tag{17}$$

To express this evolution in terms of the conformal time, we also need to calculate its relation with the inflaton up to the leading-order correction of the potential. Recall that this relation is given by $\langle \hat{H}_0 \rangle_\chi d\eta = \langle \hat{\vartheta}_e \rangle_\chi d\phi$. Substituting the approximate expressions of $\hat{H}_0$ and χ that we have obtained, this equation for the conformal time leads first to the free relation

$$\eta^{(F)}(\phi) = \frac{3}{2G} \int_{\phi_0}^{\phi} d\tilde{\phi}\, \frac{\langle \hat{V}^{2/3} \rangle_{\chi^{(F)}}}{\langle \hat{H}_0^{(F)} \rangle_{\chi^{(F)}}}, \tag{18}$$

with inverse that we call $\phi^{(F)}(\eta)$, and next to a leading-order correction to this free term that we denote by $\eta^{(W)}(\phi)$. The expression of this correction is long but manageable. We do not reproduce it here because its explicit form is not relevant for our discussion.

In practice, we are interested in writing the inflaton as a function of the conformal time, rather than the opposite, because we want to obtain the evolution of the background state in terms of this time within our approximations. With this purpose, we can expand the functional time dependence of the inflaton as the free contribution plus corrections of the potential, in the form $\phi(\eta) = \phi^{(F)}(\eta) + \phi^{(W)}(\eta) + O(W^2)$. From our discussion above, it is then possible to show[30] that the leading-order correction to the inflaton dependence is just the negative of $\eta^{(W)}(\phi)$ mapped under the free relation $\phi^{(F)}$:

$$\phi^{(W)}(\eta) = -\phi^{(F)}\left(\eta^{(W)}(\phi^{(F)}(\eta))\right). \tag{19}$$

9. Total correction to the MS mass

We can now combine the corrections to the geometric operators and the background state that are necessary to compute the modified MS mass. First, we note that at our leading order we can substitute the free relation between the inflaton and the conformal time in all geometric operators, since the the expression of the latter was already linear in the potential as far as the numerator of the MS mass is concerned, whereas the operator in the denominator was free of any explicit inflaton dependence.

On the other hand, let us define the freely evolved background state in conformal time, instead of its counterpart in terms of the inflaton:

$$\tilde{\chi}^{(F)}(V,\eta) = \exp\left[i\hat{H}_0^{(F)}\left(\phi^{(F)}(\eta) - \phi_0\right)\right]\chi_0(V). \tag{20}$$

It is then straightforward to see that

$$\chi(V,\phi(\eta)) = \left[1 + i\hat{J}^{(W)}(\eta) + O(W^2)\right]\tilde{\chi}^{(F)}(V,\eta), \tag{21}$$

$$\hat{J}^{(W)}(\eta) = \hat{H}_0^{(F)}\phi^{(W)}(\eta) - \int_{\phi_0}^{\phi^{(F)}(\eta)} d\tilde{\phi}\,\hat{K}\left(\phi^{(F)}(\eta),\tilde{\phi}\right)W(\tilde{\phi}). \tag{22}$$

With all these ingredients, we get an expansion for the modified MS mass of the form $s(\eta) = s^{(F)}(\eta) + s^{(W)}(\eta) + O(W^2)$. More especifically, the result is

$$s^{(F)} = \frac{G}{3\pi\langle\hat{V}^{2/3}\rangle_{\tilde{\chi}^{(F)}}}\left\langle\left[\frac{\hat{1}}{V}\right]^{1/3}(\hat{H}_0^{(F)})^2\left[\frac{\hat{1}}{V}\right]^{1/3}\right\rangle_{\tilde{\chi}^{(F)}} \tag{23}$$

for the free contribution to the mass, and

$$s^{(W)} = \frac{1}{\langle\hat{V}^{2/3}\rangle_{\tilde{\chi}^{(F)}}}\left(\frac{2\sqrt{3G}}{\pi\sqrt{\pi}}W'\langle(\hat{V}^{2/3}(\hat{H}_0^{(F)})^{-1}\hat{\Lambda}_0^{(F)}(\hat{H}_0^{(F)})^{-1}\hat{V}^{2/3}\hat{H}_0^{(F)})_{sym}\rangle_{\tilde{\chi}^{(F)}}\right.$$

$$+ \left(\frac{1}{4\pi^2}W'' - \frac{4G}{3\pi}W\right)\langle\hat{V}^{4/3}\rangle_{\tilde{\chi}^{(F)}} + \frac{34G}{3\pi}W\left\langle\left[\frac{\hat{1}}{V}\right]^{1/3}\hat{V}^2\left[\frac{\hat{1}}{V}\right]^{1/3}\right\rangle_{\tilde{\chi}^{(F)}}$$

$$\left. + \frac{iG}{3\pi}\left\langle\left[\left[\frac{\hat{1}}{V}\right]^{1/3}(\hat{H}_0^{(F)})^2\left[\frac{\hat{1}}{V}\right]^{1/3},\hat{J}^{(W)}\right]\right\rangle_{\tilde{\chi}^{(F)}} - is^{(F)}\langle[\hat{V}^{2/3},\hat{J}^{(W)}]\rangle_{\tilde{\chi}^{(F)}}\right). \tag{24}$$

In these equations, we have not displayed explicitly the functional dependence on the conformal time to simplify the expressions.

We can particularize these formulas to hybrid LQC by substituting the definitions of the involved geometric operators, that can be found in Refs.[23,30]. Similarly, the particularization to quantum geometrodynamics is quite straightforward, using the operator representation and integration measure over the volume (or the scale factor) that corresponds to this quantization. Several simplifications occur in this case, because the inverse volume operator is in fact the inverse of the operator that represents the volume, and no distinction has to be made between $|\hat{\Lambda}_0^{(F)}|$ and $\hat{H}_0^{(F)}$.

Finally, let us comment that our formulas provide as well the right result for kinetically dominated regimes in GR if the passage to the classical description is carried out correctly. For this, commutators of operators have to be translated into Poisson brackets of phase space functions using Dirac's rule, any other operator has to be translated also into its phase space function counterpart, and the expectation values have to be regarded just as the evaluation on the background classical solution. With this correspondence, one recovers the classical relativistic equations.[30]

10. Corrections to the vacuum

As we have already seen, changes in the MS mass affect the complex frequency h_k that determines the positive frequency solution μ_k corresponding to the vacuum state in the asymptotic diagonalization prescription. We recall that this complex frequency satisfies the Ricatti equation $\dot{h}_k = k^2 + s + h_k^2$ in conformal time, with a fixed, specific asymptotic behavior for unboundedly large wavenorms. Similarly to what we have done with other functions in order to calculate their free part and the leading-order correction of the potential, we expand the complex frequency in the form $h_k = h_k^{(F)} + h_k^{(W)} + O(W^2)$. Then, linearizing the Ricatti equation, we obtain a first-order ordinary differential equation for $h_k^{(W)}$ that admits the general solution

$$h_k^{(W)}(\eta) = \left(C_k^{(W)} + \int_{\eta_0}^{\eta} d\tilde{\eta}\, s^{(W)}(\tilde{\eta}) e^{-I_{h_k}^{(F)}(\tilde{\eta})} \right) e^{I_{h_k}^{(F)}(\eta)}, \tag{25}$$

where

$$I_{h_k}^{(F)}(\eta) = 2 \int_{\eta_0}^{\eta} d\tilde{\eta}\, h_k^{(F)}(\tilde{\eta}) \tag{26}$$

and $C_k^{(W)}$ is any (possibly potential-dependent) constant for each given wavenorm k.

Integrating by parts the above expression and calling $d\tau_k = 2h_k^{(F)}(\eta)d\eta$, we obtain the following alternative form of this general solution:

$$h_k^{(W)}(\eta) = -\sum_{n=0}^{\infty} \frac{d^n}{d\tau_k^n} \left(\frac{s^{(W)}(\eta)}{2h_k^{(F)}(\eta)} \right) + D_k^{(W)} e^{I_{h_k}^{(F)}(\eta)}, \tag{27}$$

where $D_k^{(W)}$ is a constant for each k.

We still have to take into account the asymptotic behavior of the function h_k. With this aim, we expand its asymptotic coefficients γ_n around those of the free case in the form $\gamma_n = \gamma_n^{(F)} + \gamma_n^{(W)} + O(W^2)$. From the asymptotics of the total complex frequency h_k and of its counterpart for the free case with vanishing potential, $h_k^{(F)}$, we then obtain that the leading-order correction must have the asymptotic behavior

$$h_k^{(W)} = \sum_{n=0}^{\infty} \frac{\gamma_n^{(W)}}{(2ik)^{n+1}} \left[1 + 2\sum_{n=0}^{\infty} \frac{\gamma_n^{(F)}}{(2ik)^{n+2}} \right]^{-2}, \tag{28}$$

with $\gamma_0^{(W)} = s^{(W)}$, given by the correction to the MS mass that we have computed in previous sections. The other coefficients $\gamma_n^{(W)}$ for $n \geq 1$ verify a recursion relation that can be derived from the linearization of the known relation for the coefficients γ_n, truncating it at leading order in the potential. For our discussion, the important point about the asymptotic behavior (28) is that it does not contain any oscillating exponential (in fact, the expression can be reformulated as an asymptotic series in inverse powers of k). This result implies that the constant $D_k^{(W)}$ in Eq. (27) must vanish for the solution selected by our asymptotic condition. Hence, we conclude that (asymptotically at least)

$$h_k^{(W)}(\eta) = -\sum_{n=0}^{\infty} \frac{d^n}{d\tau_k^n}\left(\frac{s^{(W)}(\eta)}{2h_k^{(F)}(\eta)}\right). \tag{29}$$

In this way, we have succeeded in obtaining the expression of the leading-order correction to the complex frequency function, and therefore in getting the ingredients necessary to characterize the vacuum state selected by the asymptotic diagonalization prescription at our order of truncation in the potential and its derivatives.

11. Conclusions

In this work, we have considered kinetically dominated regimes in the very early evolution of the Universe. These regimes are attracting an increasing attention, both within GR and within quantum cosmology, as a mechanism to produce modifications in the CMB power spectra and other related cosmological quantities that can alleviate the possible anomalies that have been claimed in the observations, especially when this period of kinetic dominance in the energy density of the scalar field is accompanied with a later epoch of short lived inflation. In general, intricate numerical computations are needed to study these kinetically dominated regimes previous to the slow-roll phase.

The situation is particularly complicated in quantum cosmology, where the background is described quantum mechanically. In many practical situations, this is one of the reasons why most of the analyses carried out so far in LQC have concentrated on the consideration of quantum background states that are peaked on *effective* trajectories,[9] described in the purely homogeneous and isotropic case by a corrected Hamiltonian constraint (with respect to that of GR) that incorporates effects of the quantum geometry. One of the effects that these trajectories incorporate is the existence of the renowned quantum bounce that avoids the cosmological singularity.[9,34,42] For this kind of states, expectation values are replaced with evaluation on the peak trajectories. However, it is not totally clear if this procedure is valid for any kind of geometric operator, like those that appear in the modified MS mass, which are highly nonlinear in the basic variables in which the peak trajectories have been confirmed. Besides, one cannot analyze in this way background states with a more genuine quantum behavior. Both issues are relevant because the modifications in the MS mass produced by the loop quantization are only significant in the regions with important quantum geometry corrections, that would correspond to the bounce in the case of the commented effective description. So, the interest in performing a fully quantum analysis in those regions is clear. In the situations that are phenomenologically appealing, the evolution is indeed kinetically dominated in those regions. A formalism like the one that we have presented, which allows a quantum investigation employing approximations that are based on the kinetic dominance, may therefore be of great help. Notice also that, even if one accepts a simplification of the problem by using some kind of effective description for the background, the discussion would need to be carried out separately for each inflaton potential, with a complicated dynamics that would almost certainly require numerical calculations at some step of the analysis, and that would have to be repeated for any different potential that one considers.

Instead of facing any of the aforementioned, involved and time-consuming, numerical calculations, we have developed a formalism that allows us to study the problem starting from the dynamics of a free scalar field including the effects of a potential as corrections, with an applicability restricted to regimes with kinetic dominance and hence away of the period of slow-roll inflation. More specifically, we have analytically studied the leading-order corrections caused by the inflaton potential, focusing our attention on the case of a hybrid quantization in cosmology, which combines a quantization of the FLRW background with a Fock quantization of the perturbations. These corrections of the potential modify the geometric quantities (operators in general) that provide the modified MS mass in the dynamical equations for the perturbations. They also affect the evolution of the background state, both because they modify the generator of its evolution with respect to the inflaton (that can be used in kinetic dominance as an internal reference variable for the dynamics) and because the relation between the inflaton and the conformal time is changed. More subtle is the effect on the vacuum of the perturbations. Away from slow roll, the choice of a Bunch-Davies state does not seem justified anymore. We have adopted a prescription for the choice of a vacuum that rests on an asymptotic diagonalization of the Hamiltonian of the perturbations, and which has been seen to lead to an asymptotically non-oscillating primordial power spectrum. The vacuum selected with this prescription is characterized by a set of positive frequency solutions, determined by a complex function, which we have called the complex frequency. This function satisfies a Ricatti equation and has to fulfill certain asymptotic conditions. Since this Ricatti equation and also the asymptotics depend on the modifed MS mass, the presence of a potential produces corrections in them, and therefore on the complex frequency, altering the choice of vaccum state.

We have succeeded in calculating all of these leading-order corrections, providing in this way all the ingredients needed to study at that order the evolution of the primordial perturbations and the state that fixes their initial conditions. It is worth remarking that our results can be generalized to other prescriptions in quantum cosmology other than a hybrid quantization. For instance, we have commented that the dressed-metric approach to LQC can be studied in a similar way, with the only difference that the expression of the modified MS mass is not the one that we have considered in detail here.[26] Besides, we have also seen that the results are applicable to the case of GR, with certain rules for the translation of our formulas into the classical case. On the other hand, our results have been derived at leading order in the corrections produced by the potential, but in principle there is no obstruction to extend the analysis to higher orders. The expressions will become much more intrincate, but there is no conceptual obstacle to obtain those corrections, increasing order by order the accuracy of the formalism.

Our treatment opens the possibility of comparing the effects of different potentials without the need of performing explicit calculations for each of them spearately. This is so because the potential appears in our formulas for the corrections in an abstract way, without any requirement about it apart from the validity of the kinetic dominance. It would be very interesting to use this approach and study the different effects that distinct potentials can produce in the primordial power spectra of the perturbations, left as imprints of a kinetically dominated epoch previous to slow roll. Finally, our results make possible the investigation of another very interesting issue, which is extremely relevant to ellucidate whether quantum effects can be detected or not in cosmological observations. This issue is the question of whether the effects of a classical fast-roll period (i.e. an inflationary period that does not satisfy the slow-roll conditions) can be differentiated from the effects of a quantization of the geometry. This question is crucial to answer whether the last of these types of effects has any hope to be observed. Since our formalism is applicable to kinetically dominated regimes both in GR and in the relevant quantum regions of LQC (and other quantum cosmology proposals), it can be used to analyze the effects of these distinct dynamics of the perturbations, studying the differences in the imprints that each of them may eventually leave on the spectra of the primordial perturbations.

Acknowledgments

This work was partially supported by Project. No. MICINN FIS2017-86497-C2-2-P and Project. No. MICINN PID2020-118159GB-C41 from Spain. B.E.N. acknowledges financial support from the Standard Program of JSPS Postdoctoral Fellowships for Research in Japan. The authors are grateful to L. Castelló Gomar, A. García-Quismondo, L. Morala, and S. Prado for discussions.

References

1. B.J.T. Jones, *Precision Cosmology: The First Half Million Years* (Cambridge University Press, Cambridge, England, 2017).
2. E. Di Valentino, A. Melchiorri, and J. Silk, Planck evidence for a closed Universe and a possible crisis for cosmology, *Nature Astron.* **4**, 196 (2019).
3. A. Ashtekar, B. Gupt, D. Jeong, and V. Sreenath, Alleviating the tension in CMB using Planck-scale physics, *Phys. Rev. Lett.* **125**, 051302 (2020).
4. A. Ashtekar, B. Gupt, and V. Sreenath, Cosmic tango between the very small and the very large: Addressing CMB anomalies through Loop Quantum Cosmology, *Front. Astron. Space Sci.* **8**, 685288 (2021).

5. I. Agullo, D. Kranas, and V. Sreenath, Large scale anomalies in the CMB and non-Gaussianity in bouncing cosmologies, *Class. Quantum Grav.* **38**, 065010 (2021).
6. I. Agullo, D. Kranas, and V. Sreenath, Anomalies in the Cosmic Microwave Background and their non-Gaussian origin in Loop Quantum Cosmology, arXiv:2105.12993 (2021).
7. C.R. Contaldi, M. Peloso, L. Kofman, and A.D. Linde, Suppressing the lower multipoles in the CMB anisotropies, *JCAP* **0307**, 002 (2003).
8. I. Agullo and N.A. Morris, Detailed analysis of the predictions of Loop Quantum Cosmology for the primordial power spectra, *Phys. Rev. D* **92**, 124040 (2015).
9. A. Ashtekar and P. Singh, Loop Quantum Cosmology: A status report, *Class. Quantum Grav.* **28**, 213001 (2011).
10. G.A. Mena Marugán, A brief introduction to Loop Quantum Cosmology, *AIP Conf. Proc.* **1130**, 89 (2011).
11. T. Thiemann, *Modern Canonical Quantum General Relativity* (Cambridge University Press, Cambridge, England, 2007).
12. E. Wilson-Ewing, Testing Loop Quantum Cosmology, *Comptes Rendus Phys.* **18**, 207 (2017).
13. M. Bojowald, G. Calcagni, and S. Tsujikawa, Observational constraints on Loop Quantum Cosmology, *Phys. Rev. Lett.* **107**, 211302 (2011).
14. T. Cailleteau, L. Linsefors, and A. Barrau, Anomaly-free perturbations with inverse-volume and holonomy corrections in Loop Quantum Cosmology, *Class. Quantum Grav.* **31**, 125011 (2014).
15. A. Barrau, M. Bojowald, G. Calcagni, J. Grain, and M. Kagan, Anomaly-free cosmological perturbations in effective canonical quantum gravity, *JCAP* **05**, 051 (2015).
16. S. Schander, A. Barrau, B. Bolliet, J. Grain, L. Linsefors, and J. Mielczarek, Primordial scalar power spectrum from the Euclidean Big Bounce, *Phys. Rev. D* **93**, 023531 (2016).
17. M. Fernández-Méndez, G.A. Mena Marugán, and J. Olmedo, Hybrid quantization of an inflationary universe, *Phys. Rev. D* **86**, 024003 (2012).
18. M. Fernández-Méndez, G.A. Mena Marugán, and J. Olmedo, Hybrid quantization of an inflationary model: The flat case, *Phys. Rev. D* **88**, 044013 (2013).
19. L. Castelló Gomar, M. Martín-Benito, and G.A. Mena Marugán, Gauge-invariant perturbations in Hybrid Quantum Cosmology, *JCAP* **06**, 045 (2015).
20. D. Martín de Blas and J. Olmedo, Primordial power spectra for scalar perturbations in Loop Quantum Cosmology, *JCAP* **06**, 029 (2016).
21. L. Castelló Gomar, G.A. Mena Marugán, D. Martín de Blas, and J. Olmedo, Hybrid Loop Quantum Cosmology and predictions for the Cosmic Microwave Background, *Phys. Rev. D* **96**, 103528 (2017).
22. B. Elizaga Navascués, D. Martín de Blas, and G.A. Mena Marugán, The vacuum state of primordial fluctuations in Hybrid Loop Quantum Cosmology, *Universe* **4**, 98 (2018).
23. B. Elizaga Navascués and G.A. Mena Marugán, Hybrid Loop Quantum Cosmology: An overview, *Front. Astron. Space Sci.* **8**, 624824 (2021).
24. I. Agullo, A. Ashtekar, and W. Nelson, A quantum gravity extension of the inflationary scenario, *Phys. Rev. Lett.* **109**, 251301 (2012).
25. I. Agullo, A. Ashtekar, and W. Nelson, Extension of the quantum theory of cosmological perturbations to the Planck era, *Phys. Rev. D* **87**, 043507 (2013).
26. I. Agullo, A. Ashtekar, and W. Nelson, The pre-inflationary dynamics of Loop Quantum Cosmology: Confronting quantum gravity with observations, *Class. Quantum Grav.* **30**, 085014 (2013).

27. I. Agullo, Loop Quantum Cosmology, non-Gaussianity, and CMB power asymmetry, *Phys. Rev. D* **92**, 064038 (2015).
28. I. Agullo, A. Ashtekar, and B. Gupt, Phenomenology with fluctuating quantum geometries in Loop Quantum Cosmology, *Class. Quantum Grav.* **34**, 074003 (2017).
29. I. Agullo, B. Bolliet, and V. Sreenath, Non-Gaussianity in Loop Quantum Cosmology, *Phys. Rev. D* **97**, 066021 (2018).
30. B. Elizaga Navascués, R. Jiménez-Llamas, and G.A. Mena Marugán, Primordial perturbations in kinetically dominated regimes of general relativity and hybrid quantum cosmology, arXiv:2106.05628 (2021).
31. V. Mukhanov, Quantum theory of gauge-invariant cosmological perturbations, *Zh. Eksp. Teor. Fiz.* **94**, 1 (1998) [*Sov. Phys. JETP* **67**, 1297 (1988)].
32. M. Sasaki, Gauge invariant scalar perturbations in the new inflationary universe, *Prog. Theor. Phys.* **70**, 394 (1983).
33. H. Kodama and M. Sasaki, Cosmological perturbation theory, *Prog. Theor. Phys. Suppl.* **78**, 1 (1984).
34. A. Ashtekar, T. Pawłowski, and P. Singh, Quantum nature of the Big Bang: An analytical and numerical investigation, *Phys. Rev. D* **73**, 124038 (2006).
35. J.J. Halliwell, *Introductory lectures to quantum cosmology*, published in *Proceedings of the 1990 Jerusalem Winter School on Quantum Cosmology and Baby Universes*, eds. S. Coleman, J.B. Hartle, T. Piran, and S. Weinberg (World Scientific, Singapore, 1991).
36. T.S. Bunch and P. Davies, Quantum field theory in de Sitter space: Renormalization by point splitting, *Proc. R. Soc. Lond. A* **360**, 117 (1978).
37. B. Elizaga Navascués and G.A. Mena Marugán, Analytical investigation of pre-inflationary effects in the primordial power spectrum: From General Relativity to Hybrid Loop Quantum Cosmology, arXiv:2104.15002 (2021).
38. A. Ashtekar and B. Gupt, Initial conditions for cosmological perturbations, *Class. Quantum Grav.* **34**, 035004 (2017).
39. A. Ashtekar and B. Gupt, Quantum gravity in the sky: Interplay between fundamental theory and observations, *Class. Quantum Grav.* **34**, 014002 (2017).
40. B. Elizaga Navascués, G.A. Mena Marugán, and T. Thiemann, Hamiltonian diagonalization in Hybrid Quantum Cosmology, *Class. Quantum Grav.* **36**, 18 (2019).
41. B. Elizaga Navascués, G.A. Mena Marugán, and S. Prado, Non-oscillating power spectra in Loop Quantum Cosmology, *Class. Quantum Grav.* **38**, 035001 (2021).
42. A. Ashtekar, T. Pawłowski, and P. Singh, Quantum nature of the Big Bang: Improved dynamics, *Phys. Rev. D* **74**, 084003 (2006).
43. B. Elizaga Navascués and G. A. Mena Marugán, Perturbations in quantum cosmology: The continuum limit in Fourier space, *Phys. Rev. D* **98**, 103522 (2018).
44. A. Galindo and P. Pascual, *Quantum Mechanics II* (Springer, Berlin, 1991).

Revisiting the Hamiltonian formalism of the Ashtekar–Olmedo–Singh black hole model

Alejandro García-Quismondo

Instituto de Estructura de la Materia, IEM-CSIC, Serrano 121, 28006 Madrid, Spain
alejandro.garcia@iem.cfmac.csic.es

Guillermo A. Mena Marugán

Instituto de Estructura de la Materia, IEM-CSIC, Serrano 121, 28006 Madrid, Spain
E-mail: mena@iem.cfmac.csic.es

We reexamine the computation of the equations of motion of the Ashtekar–Olmedo–Singh black hole model in order to establish whether it is possible to construct a Hamiltonian formalism such that parameters that regulate the introduction of quantum geometry effects are suitably treated as true constants of motion. After suggesting that these parameters should capture contributions from two sectors of phase space that had been considered independent in the literature, we proceed to obtain the corresponding dynamical equations and investigate the repercussions of this more general choice. We restrict our discussion exclusively to these dynamical issues. We also analyze whether the proposed procedure can be reconciled with the results of Ashtekar, Olmedo, and Singh, at least in some limit.

Keywords: Loop Quantum Cosmology, Black Holes, AOS Model.

1. Introduction

Almost three years ago, Ashtekar, Olmedo, and Singh proposed a new model to describe black hole spacetimes within the framework of loop quantum cosmology[1–3] (from now on, referred to as the AOS model for short). This model is set apart from prior related investigations[4–39] for a number of reasons, including the fact that it is claimed that its physical predictions neither depend on fiducial structures nor display large quantum corrections in low curvature regions (which count among the problems that previous studies suffered from). By means of the inclusion of quantum geometry effects, which is regulated by two polymerization parameters,[a] the classical central singularity is found to be cured. In this model, it is replaced by a transition surface between a trapped region and an anti-trapped one and the metric, that we will call effective in the sense that it can be treated classically but incorporates quantum effects, is extended to encompass what can be regarded as a white horizon. This effective geometry is shown to be smooth and, in fact, the curvature invariants turn out to admit universal upper bounds that are independent of the mass of the black hole under consideration.[1–3] The authors of the model completed their

---
[a]Here, the term "polymerization" refers to the name "polymer quantization", which is often used for the quantization of symmetry reduced models with loop techniques.

investigation by formulating an analogous description of the exterior region that can be matched smoothly with that of the black hole interior, resulting in an effective extension of the whole Kruskal spacetime.

One of the defining features of the AOS model is their choice of polymerization parameters. In order to overcome the issues present in earlier works, they proposed a procedure in which the parameters are identified with certain Dirac observables (i.e., quantities that are constant along any given dynamical trajectory but not on the whole phase space), defined by minimal area conditions on the transition surface. Nonetheless, the parameters are treated as constants throughout the Hamiltonian derivation of the equations of motion and only once they have been obtained and solved does the aforementioned identification occur, whereby the parameters are fixed to the value of certain functions of the ADM mass, which is a Dirac observable itself.[b] This was already pointed out by Bodendorfer, Mele, and Münch. In Ref. 40, they showed that an extra phase space dependent factor would appear in the dynamical equations should the parameters be treated as genuine constants of motion from the very beginning. For this, they employed that, given a certain choice of lapse function, the Hamiltonian constraint of the system is essentially given by the difference of two Dirac observables, the on-shell values of which coincide and become proportional to the mass of the black hole. This simple structure was exploited to divide the phase space into two independent sectors (associated with the radial and angular degrees of freedom, respectively), where the dynamics is generated by the previously mentioned Dirac observables, which can be thought of as partial Hamiltonians. Additionally, these partial Hamiltonians were assumed to serve as polymerization parameters,[40] in the sense that each parameter was chosen to be a function of only its associated partial Hamiltonian. As a result, by evaluating the study on shell, one makes contact with the original proposal of Refs. 1–3 to the extent that the on-shell parameters are functions of the mass of the black hole.

Nevertheless, given the fact that the two partial Hamiltonians have coincident values on the constraint surface, there should be no way of telling apart their on-shell contributions. Consequently, one could argue that a more general choice of polymerization parameters would be such that each of them could depend on both partial Hamiltonians, a fact that would imply that the decoupling of phase space sectors that plays a central role in previous analyses would be broken both at the Hamiltonian and dynamical levels. In the following, we will focus on analyzing whether an alternative procedure to perform the Hamiltonian calculation can be constructed starting from this observation. We will ignore for the time being issues concerning the asymptotic behavior of the effective metric and its physical interpretation and quantum covariance, which lie beyond the scope of this work (see Refs. 41, 42, 43, and 44 for details on the criticisms that the model has received). The main objective

---

[b]The authors of Refs. 1 and 2 presented an argument supporting this procedure that involves an extension of phase space. See Appendix A of Ref. 2 for further details.

of our investigation is to explore the possibility that an alternative dynamical analysis where the polymerization parameters depend on both partial Hamiltonians can be developed and to ascertain whether such an analysis can reconcile the derivation of the solution in Refs. 1–3 with a genuine treatment of the parameters as dynamical constants.

The rest of this article[c] is organized as follows. In Sec. 2, after a brief introduction of the main elements of the AOS model, we discuss the selection of polymerization parameters, including our new proposal. In addition, we address the derivation of the dynamical equations that follow from our choice in Sec. 2.2. In Sec. 3, we delve into certain time redefinitions that lead our equations of motion to adopt a simpler form, paying the price of employing two different time variables instead of one. We also examine whether the existing freedom in the model may allow us to set both times equal. In Sec. 4, we extend this investigation to the asymptotic limit of large masses and study the relation between both time variables for finite values of the mass. Finally, in Sec. 5, we summarize the main ideas of this work and discuss our results. Throughout this paper, we set the speed of light and the reduced Planck constant equal to one.

2. The model

In this section, we briefly introduce the main ingredients of the effective model under consideration,[1–3] followed by a comment on the choice of polymerization parameters in Sec. 2.1 and the derivation of the equations that govern the dynamics of the system in Sec. 2.2. For further details, we refer the reader to the original works.

In this paper, we focus our attention on the interior region of a Schwarzschild black hole, which can be foliated by spatial Cauchy hypersurfaces (namely those characterized by $r = $ const, where r is the Schwarzschild radial coordinate). Furthermore, these spatial hypersurfaces are homogeneous, a property that permits a finite dimensional Hamiltonian description of the system. Indeed, the associated phase space is four dimensional and can be coordinatized by two connection variables b and c which encode the degrees of freedom of the Ashtekar connection, and two triad variables p_b and p_c which encode the degrees of freedom of the densitized triad. These form two canonical pairs with Poisson brackets[1,2]

$$\{b, p_b\} = G\gamma, \qquad \{c, p_c\} = 2G\gamma, \tag{1}$$

where G is the Newtonian gravitational constant and γ is the Immirzi parameter. Given that the first one contains the dynamical information about the radial direction and the second one the dynamical information about the angular directions, we will refer to these pairs and the sectors of phase space that they define as "radial" and "angular", respectively.

---

[c]The present manuscript is based on a previous publication of ours,[45] although we here provide a restructured and updated view on the subject.

By virtue of the symmetries inherited from general relativity, these variables are bound by a constraint, namely the Hamiltonian of the system, H. With the choice

$$N = \frac{\gamma \delta_b \sqrt{|p_c|}}{\sin \delta_b b}, \qquad (2)$$

the product of the lapse function and the Hamiltonian is given by[1,2]

$$NH = \frac{L_o}{G}(O_b - O_c), \qquad (3)$$

$$O_b = -\frac{1}{2\gamma}\left(\frac{\sin \delta_b b}{\delta_b} + \frac{\gamma^2 \delta_b}{\sin \delta_b b}\right)\frac{p_b}{L_o}, \qquad (4)$$

$$O_c = \frac{1}{\gamma}\frac{\sin \delta_c c}{\delta_c}\frac{p_c}{L_o}, \qquad (5)$$

where L_o is a fiducial length introduced to avoid divergences when integrating homogeneous quantities over space. In addition, δ_b and δ_c are the polymerization parameters that capture and introduce the effects of quantum geometry in the system. Should we take the limit where these parameters vanish, the classical Hamiltonian would be recovered. Notice that, if no cross-dependence is introduced through the δ-parameters, O_b and O_c only depend on the radial and angular sector, respectively. Therefore, up to multiplicative constants, these two objects would generate the dynamics in their respective sectors of phase space. As such, we refer to them as "partial Hamiltonians", although we emphasize that this interpretation is only valid when the polymerization parameters depend at most on the canonical variables of their respective sectors. In the following subsection, we discuss how to select these parameters.

2.1. Polymerization parameters as constants of motion

Let us briefly go over the main idea underlying the discussed identification and handling of the polymerization parameters suggested by the authors of the original model, mentioning an alternative related proposal that was put forward in a later work as well. Afterwards, we argue that, on the light of the dynamical properties of the system, a more general choice could be made, which we adopt for the subsequent analysis.

As already mentioned in the Introduction, one of the main features of the AOS model that set it apart from previous investigations is the way in which one deals with the polymerization parameters. Instead of taking the δ-parameters as constants on the whole phase space or as arbitrary functions of phase space, the authors of Refs. 1 and 2 proposed to tread an intermediate path: the model is based on selecting these parameters in such a way that they are eventually identified as Dirac observables, i.e. constant along any given dynamical trajectory. More concretely, they proposed a procedure where δ_b and δ_c are treated as constants throughout the Hamiltonian derivation of the dynamical equations and fixed to the value of certain Dirac observables only at the very end. These Dirac observables are given by functions of the mass of the black hole determined by minimal area conditions at the transition surface in the limit of large masses. For an argument supporting the validity of this procedure, we encourage the reader to consult Ref. 2 (and in particular its appendices).

In a later work,[40] this approach was criticized arguing that the attained dynamical equations are not the ones derived from their proposed Hamiltonian if the parameters were to be treated as constants of motion. Instead, an alternative proposal was put forward to use the partial Hamiltonians themselves as polymerization parameters in their respective sectors of phase space. In other words, the authors of Ref. 40 suggested to take each parameter as a function of its associated partial Hamiltonian. This idea is based on the fact that both partial Hamiltonians are Dirac observables in the AOS model. Furthermore, their values coincide on shell (that is, on the phase space surface on which the Hamiltonian constraint vanishes) and are proportional to the mass of the black hole

$$O_b|_{\text{on-shell}} = O_c|_{\text{on-shell}} = m. \tag{6}$$

With this choice, the nontrivial nature of the parameters as functions of phase space is taken into account in the Hamiltonian calculation from the very beginning, leading to contributions coming from the nonvanishing Poisson brackets of δ_b and δ_c which were absent in the original AOS dynamical equations.

Given the attention that the AOS model has drawn in the recent years and the interesting physical results derived from it, it seems to us that it is worth investigating whether these two approaches can be reconciled in some way (and if so, to which extent) in order to gain confidence on the meaningfulness of the physical picture that ensues from it. This is precisely the aim of our work and the intention behind the preliminary computation presented in the next sections. In order to address this question, we follow the ideas of Ref. 40, or rather an extension of them.

Our proposal is based on a simple observation. As we commented in the previous paragraphs, by virtue of the structure of the Hamiltonian constraint, both partial Hamiltonians have the exact same on-shell value. Therefore, we should in principle not be able to tell apart their contributions to the on-shell polymerization parameters. As such, we argue that the most general choice of this form should be

$$\delta_i = f_i(O_b, O_c), \tag{7}$$

where $i = b, c$ and f_i are functions of both O_b and O_c.[d] Moreover, we require that the on-shell value of our parameters coincide with those considered in Refs. 1–3,

---

[d]From now on, we will use this notation to refer to the radial and angular sectors indistinctly. Thus, letters from the middle of the Latin alphabet $(i, j, ...)$ take values on the set $\{b, c\}$; so that i, p_i, O_i, and δ_i denote the connection variable, the triad variable, the partial Hamiltonian, and the polymerization parameter associated with the radial or angular sector, depending on the value of the label i.

namely

$$\delta_b = \left(\frac{\sqrt{\Delta}}{\sqrt{2\pi}\gamma^2 m}\right)^{1/3} + o\left(m^{-1/3}\right), \quad \delta_c = \frac{1}{2L_o}\left(\frac{\gamma\Delta^2}{4\pi^2 m}\right)^{1/3} + o\left(m^{-1/3}\right), \quad (8)$$

where $o(\cdot)$ denotes the presence of terms that are subdominant with respect to the quantity in parenthesis. The inclusion of these subdominant terms has to do with the fact that the δ-parameters of the AOS model are derived in the limit of large black hole masses, where two relevant solutions to the minimal area conditions that define them in the first place coincide (see Appendix B of Ref. 2 for further details).

Notice that the proposed functional form of these parameters introduces a cross-dependence between the radial and angular sectors of phase space, which breaks the decoupling of these sectors that had been present in the literature until now. In the next subsection, we explore the immediate consequences of this decoupling as regards the derivation of the equations that govern the dynamics of the system.

2.2. Dynamical equations

Let us address the derivation of the equations of motion that follow from the effective Hamiltonian of the AOS model if the polymerization parameters δ_i are selected as discussed in Sec. 2.1. Since the time derivative of any phase space function can be obtained by means of its Poisson bracket with the Hamiltonian, it is immediate to see that

$$\partial_t i = s_i \frac{L_o}{G}\left(\{i, O_i\} - \{i, O_j\}\right), \quad (9)$$

where we recall that $i, j = b, c$. Besides, here $j \neq i$, t is the time variable associated with the lapse function N [see Eq. (2)], and s_i is a sign defined by

$$s_b = +1, \quad s_c = -1. \quad (10)$$

Let us now compute $\{i, O_i\}$ and $\{i, O_j\}$. The first of these brackets is given by

$$\{i, O_j\} = \{i, p_i\}\frac{\partial O_i}{\partial p_i} + \frac{\partial O_i}{\partial \delta_i}\left(\frac{\partial f_i}{\partial O_i}\{i, O_i\} + \frac{\partial f_i}{\partial O_j}\{i, O_j\}\right). \quad (11)$$

In a similar way,

$$\{i, O_j\} = \frac{\partial O_j}{\partial \delta_j}\left(\frac{\partial f_j}{\partial O_i}\{i, O_i\} + \frac{\partial f_j}{\partial O_j}\{i, O_j\}\right). \quad (12)$$

From the form of these two expressions, we realize that Eqs. (11) and (12) constitute a system of equations linear in $\{i, O_i\}$ and $\{i, O_j\}$. Recasting this system in an appropriate manner, we have

$$\begin{pmatrix} 1 - \Delta_{ii} & -\Delta_{ij} \\ -\Delta_{ji} & 1 - \Delta_{jj} \end{pmatrix} \begin{pmatrix} \{i, O_i\} \\ \{i, O_j\} \end{pmatrix} = \begin{pmatrix} \{i, p_i\}\frac{\partial O_i}{\partial p_i} \\ 0 \end{pmatrix}, \quad (13)$$

where we have defined

$$\Delta_{ij} = \frac{\partial O_i}{\partial \delta_i} \frac{\partial f_i}{\partial O_j}. \tag{14}$$

This system can be solved provided that the determinant of the first matrix does not vanish,

$$(1 - \Delta_{ii})(1 - \Delta_{jj}) - \Delta_{ij}\Delta_{ji} \neq 0. \tag{15}$$

From now on, we assume that this invertibility condition holds. Then, we find that the Poisson brackets that enter the equations of motion are given by

$$\begin{pmatrix} \{i, O_i\} \\ \{i, O_j\} \end{pmatrix} = \frac{\{i, p_i\} \frac{\partial O_i}{\partial p_i}}{(1 - \Delta_{ii})(1 - \Delta_{jj}) - \Delta_{ij}\Delta_{ji}} \begin{pmatrix} 1 - \Delta_{jj} \\ \Delta_{ji} \end{pmatrix}, \tag{16}$$

which results in

$$\partial_t i = \frac{1 - \Delta_{jj} - \Delta_{ji}}{(1 - \Delta_{ii})(1 - \Delta_{jj}) - \Delta_{ij}\Delta_{ji}} \left[s_i \frac{L_o}{G} \{i, p_i\} \frac{\partial O_i}{\partial p_i} \right], \tag{17}$$

with $j \neq i$. Following the same procedure with the triad variables, their corresponding dynamical equations turn out to be

$$\partial_t p_i = \frac{1 - \Delta_{jj} - \Delta_{ji}}{(1 - \Delta_{ii})(1 - \Delta_{jj}) - \Delta_{ij}\Delta_{ji}} \left[-s_i \frac{L_o}{G} \{i, p_i\} \frac{\partial O_i}{\partial i} \right], \tag{18}$$

where, again, $j \neq i$.

It is interesting to note that, in both cases, the expressions in square brackets are the equations of motion that are attained if the parameters are treated as constant numbers (and, thus, the ones considered in Refs. 1–3). These appear rescaled via a phase space dependent factor

$$C_{ij} = \frac{1 - \Delta_{jj} - \Delta_{ji}}{(1 - \Delta_{ii})(1 - \Delta_{jj}) - \Delta_{ij}\Delta_{ji}}, \tag{19}$$

which is *a priori* different in each sector. Therefore, we conclude that these C-factors that multiply the AOS dynamical equations contain all the information about the nontrivial functional form of the polymerization parameters. Indeed, if we ignore the brackets of δ_i, Δ_{ij} would vanish identically and C_{ij} would reduce to the identity, recovering the original AOS description. Likewise, if we consider that each parameter depends only on its corresponding partial Hamiltonian (reestablishing the radial-angular decoupling), Δ_{ij} vanish if $i \neq j$ and C_{ij} reduces to $(1 - \Delta_{ii})^{-1}$, which reproduces the result obtained in Ref. 40.

In Sec. 3 we discuss how to deal with these phase space dependent factors that result from the coupling of the radial and angular sectors in order to try and find solutions to the dynamics.

3. Local time redefinitions

As we saw in the previous section, the effect of considering polymerization parameters that are functions of both partial Hamiltonians is the appearance of two phase space dependent factors in the equations of motion. Interestingly, the obtained equations turn out to be a rescaling of the ones resulting from constant δ-parameters, and these rescalings, which are different in the radial and angular sectors, are given by the aforementioned factors C_{ij}. The fact that the nontrivial nature of the polymerization parameters affects the equations of motion precisely in this way implies that it can be absorbed through suitable time redefinitions. Indeed, taking these factors to the left-hand side of their respective dynamical equations, we realise that the definitions

$$dt_i = C_{ij} dt, \qquad j \neq i, \tag{20}$$

lead to equations that are identical to those considered by the authors of Refs. 1 and 2. From now on, we often refer to t_b and t_c as the "radial time" and the "angular time", respectively, for reasons that should be obvious. In terms of these newly defined time variables, the equations of motion adopt the same form as in the AOS model, which implies that the equations associated with the radial and angular sectors can be dealt with independently. Those corresponding to the c-sector can be solved in a straightforward manner, leading to[1,2]

$$\tan \frac{\delta_c c(t_c)}{2} = \frac{\gamma L_o \delta_c}{8m} e^{-2t_c}, \tag{21}$$

$$p_c(t_c) = 4m^2 \left(e^{2t_c} + \frac{\gamma^2 L_o^2 \delta_c^2}{64m^2} e^{-2t_c} \right), \tag{22}$$

where the integration constants have been fixed so that the effective metric coincides with the standard form of the interior Schwarzschild metric.

Similarly, the equation associated with b can be solved in a straightforward way. We obtain[1,2]

$$\cos \delta_b b(t_b) = b_o \tanh\left(\frac{b_o t_b}{2} + \tanh^{-1} \frac{1}{b_o} \right) = \frac{1 + b_o \tanh \frac{b_o t_b}{2}}{1 + b_o^{-1} \tanh \frac{b_o t_b}{2}}, \tag{23}$$

where $b_o = \sqrt{1 + \gamma^2 \delta_b^2}$ and the constant of integration has been fixed so that the horizon lies at $t_b = 0$ (which is equivalent to requiring that b vanishes there). Since the canonical variables are bound by the Hamiltonian constraint, there is no need to solve the fourth differential equation, which is more involved than the others. Indeed, it suffices to solve for p_b in $H = 0$. Since it is convenient not to mix the radial and angular times, we can employ the fact that O_b is a constant of motion. Actually, using Eqs. (21) and (22), we can determine that

$$O_c = \frac{1}{\gamma} \frac{\sin \delta_c c}{\delta_c} \frac{p_c}{L_o} = \frac{2}{\gamma L_o \delta_c} \frac{p_c \tan(\delta_c c/2)}{1 + \tan^2(\delta_c c/2)} = m. \tag{24}$$

Given that both partial Hamiltonians coincide on shell (as it follows immediately from $H = 0$), we then get $O_b = m$ as well. Therefore, solving for p_b in $O_b = m$, we obtain

$$p_b(t_b) = -2\gamma L_o m \frac{\sin \delta_b b(t_b)}{\delta_b} \frac{1}{\gamma^2 + \frac{\sin^2 \delta_b b(t_b)}{\delta_b^2}}, \quad (25)$$

where we can see that $p_b(0) = 0$, which is consistent with the requirement that the horizon correspond to $t_b = 0$.

So far, we have shown that suitable time redefinitions lead to dynamical equations that are identical to those obtained when δ_i are treated as constants, except for the fact that they are written in terms of two time variables. Hence, the solutions to the dynamics have the same form. Again, this is the case when expressed in two *a priori* different time variables, one per sector of the phase space. Since our objective is to determine whether it is possible to recover the results of the AOS model (at least in some sense), it seems natural to wonder whether we can use the off-shell freedom of our formalism to set both times equal. In the remainder of this section, we answer this question.

To begin with, we can find the relation between the radial and angular times by solving for dt in the definitions of both t_b and t_c and integrating the result of equating both expressions:

$$\int_{t_b}^0 dt'_b [1 - \Delta_{bb}(t'_b) - \Delta_{bc}(t'_b)] = \int_{t_c}^0 dt'_c [1 - \Delta_{cc}(t'_c) - \Delta_{cb}(t'_c)], \quad (26)$$

where we have canceled the denominators of C_{bc} and C_{cb}, which are identical [see Eq. (19) to realize that the denominator of these factors is symmetric under the exchange of i and j]. In this equation, $\Delta_{ij}(t_i)$ is obtained by plugging the solutions discussed above into the expression of Δ_{ij}. Moreover, the limits of integration have been chosen in accordance with the fact that the time variables are negative in the interior region of the black hole, as can be understood by examining the classical limit of the solutions to the effective dynamics.[1,2] Notice as well that we have used the existing freedom to make the origins of both time variables coincide.

Once we have fixed this freedom, asking whether t_b can be set equal to t_c is equivalent to asking whether C_{bc} can be chosen equal to C_{cb}. Therefore, the condition to be studied is

$$1 - \frac{\partial O_c}{\partial \delta_c} \frac{\partial f_c}{\partial \mu} = \alpha \left(1 - \frac{\partial O_b}{\partial \delta_b} \frac{\partial f_b}{\partial \mu}\right), \quad (27)$$

where we have called $\mu = (O_b + O_c)/2$, the on-shell value of which is simply given by m, and we have implicitly employed that the dependence of f_b and f_c on O_b and O_c can be equivalently described by their dependence on the difference and the sum of these quantities (divided by 2). In the previous expression, rather than demanding that t_b and t_c coincide, we have actually allowed for the more general case that these two times be proportional to each other, with proportionality factor α, hence reaching a strict equality in the limit $\alpha \to 1$. Evaluating this expression on shell and assuming that f_i are at least $\mathcal{C}^1$, so that the derivative and the on-shell limit commute, we obtain

$$1 - \frac{\partial f_c}{\partial m}\frac{\partial O_c}{\partial \delta_c} = \alpha\left[1 - \frac{\partial f_b}{\partial m}\frac{\partial O_b}{\partial \delta_b}\right], \tag{28}$$

where $\partial f_i/\partial m$ stands for the on-shell particularization of the partial derivative of f_i with respect to μ, and we have omitted the indication of the rest of on-shell evaluations for the sake of simplicity. In the remainder of this article, whether an expression is evaluated on shell or not will be clear from the context. At this point, the only remaining step is to compute the derivatives of the partial Hamiltonians with respect to the polymerization parameters and evaluate them on shell. A simple calculation shows that

$$\frac{\partial O_b}{\partial \delta_b} = -\frac{1}{2\gamma}\left(1 - \frac{\gamma^2 \delta_b^2}{\sin^2 \delta_b b}\right)\frac{\delta_b b \cos \delta_b b - \sin \delta_b b}{\delta_b^2}\frac{p_b}{L_o}, \tag{29}$$

$$\frac{\partial O_c}{\partial \delta_c} = \frac{1}{\gamma}\frac{\delta_c c \cos \delta_c c - \sin \delta_c c}{\delta_c^2}\frac{p_c}{L_o}. \tag{30}$$

The fact that these derivatives are functions on phase space appears to be in contrast with the requirement that the on-shell values of t_b and t_c be proportional (or equal), which one would ideally want to hold on the whole phase space. Therefore, we need to find a way to cancel the undesired phase space dependence. Given the fact that $\sin \delta_i i$ can be rewritten in terms of m and p_i on shell [see Eqs. (4) and (5)], every function of the connection variables i can be reexpressed in terms of the mass of the black hole and the triad variables. Hence, the above derivatives can be regarded as nontrivial functions of p_i from the point of view of their dependence on phase space. As a result, we have

$$1 - \frac{\partial f_c}{\partial m}\frac{\partial O_c}{\partial \delta_c}(p_c) = \alpha\left[1 - \frac{\partial f_b}{\partial m}\frac{\partial O_b}{\partial \delta_b}(p_b)\right], \tag{31}$$

where the form of $\partial O_i/\partial \delta_i(p_i)$ is irrelevant for the present argument, except for the fact that they are not trivial functions. Since the phase space contributions of the left-hand side cannot cancel those of the right-hand side, we conclude that the only possibility to achieve the required cancelation is by choosing $\partial f_i/\partial m$ to vanish identically. That is, we can set both time variables equal if and only if the on-shell values of the parameters are independent of the mass. However, this does not make any sense physically speaking. Indeed, we would expect the parameters to vanish in the limit of infinitely large black hole masses, so that the description of general relativity can then be recovered, but not to be constantly zero for any value of the mass.

As a result, we conclude that the answer to the question of whether we can set the radial and angular times equal on shell is in the negative as long as we want physically acceptable polymerization parameters in the sense that they have an appropriate large mass limit. Hence, we realize that the appearance of two distinct *time variables* is a defining feature of our formalism and cannot be avoided through an astute choice of parameters.

In the next section, we examine whether the proportionality condition (28) can hold in a suitable way in the limit of large black hole masses.

4. The large mass limit

Although we have shown that the radial and angular times cannot be set equal in general, this result does not imply that they may not coincide in some regime. From the point of view of the reconciliation with the results of Refs. 1 and 2, there is a particularly interesting situation, namely that of infinitely large masses. The reason behind this interest is twofold. On the one hand, it would seem especially desirable to achieve some sort of agreement in the large mass limit since the AOS model is adapted to describe very massive black holes to begin with. Indeed, as we commented in Sec. 2.1, their proposed parameters are only valid in that limit, given that they are extracted from the leading order of an asymptotic expansion of the area conditions that define them. On the other hand, astrophysical black holes, some of which may be susceptible of being probed by observations in the near future, are tremendously massive with respect to the Planck mass, which entails the importance of having a deep understanding of the similarities and differences between models in this regime. With these ideas in mind, let us perform an asymptotic expansion of the derivatives of the partial Hamiltonians with respect to the polymerization parameters, which are the functions of phase space that appear both in condition (28) and in the relation between the radial and angular time variables (26).

According to the discussed on-shell values of the polymerization parameters, it is immediate to realize that

$$\frac{\partial f_i}{\partial m} = -\frac{1}{3}\frac{\delta_i}{m} + o\left(\frac{\delta_i}{m}\right). \qquad (32)$$

This means that the dominant term goes as $m^{-4/3}$ in the asymptotic limit. Therefore, it is obvious that the proportionality condition (28) will hold for large masses provided that, in that limit,[e]

$$\frac{\partial O_i}{\partial \delta_i} \sim m^{n_i} \quad \text{with} \quad n_i \leq \frac{4}{3}. \qquad (33)$$

For simplicity, let us begin by computing the dominant term associated with the angular sector. Given the effective solutions discussed in Sec. 3, we see that the dominant term of the triad variable is given by

$$p_c = 4^{2t_c} m^2 + o(m^2). \qquad (34)$$

---

[e] If any of the two exponents n_i turned out to be equal to 4/3, then an additional condition on the coefficients of the dominant terms must be met for Eq. (28) to hold asymptotically.

An expansion of the trigonometric functions of the connection variable can be obtained in a similar manner. Since our effective solution involves the tangent of $\delta_c c/2$, it is convenient to write

$$\cos \delta_c c = \frac{1 - \tan^2(\delta_c c/2)}{1 + \tan^2(\delta_c c/2)} = 1 - \frac{\gamma^2 L_o^2}{32 e^{4t_c}} \frac{\delta_c^2}{m^2} + o\left(\frac{\delta_c^2}{m^2}\right). \tag{35}$$

From this expression, we can derive the asymptotic expansions of the remaining functions of the connection variable c. Nevertheless, it is important to bear in mind that, according to the conventions of Refs. 1–3, $b > 0$, $c > 0$, $p_b \leq 0$, and $p_c \geq 0$. Together with the fact that the polymerization parameters are infinitely small in this regime, this implies that every trigonometric function contained in $\partial O_c/\partial \delta_c$ is nonnegative. As a result, a simple calculation reveals that

$$\frac{\partial O_c}{\partial \delta_c} = -\frac{\gamma^2 L_o^2}{48 e^{4t_c}} \frac{\delta_c}{m} + o\left(\frac{\delta_c}{m}\right). \tag{36}$$

This result indicates that the left-hand side of Eq. (28) tends to one as the mass grows infinitely.

An analogous result can be obtained in the radial sector following the same reasoning. As a consequence of the form of the effective solution (23), we get

$$\cos \delta_b b = 1 + C_1 \delta_b^2 + o(\delta_b^2), \tag{37}$$

where

$$C_1 = \gamma^2 \frac{\tanh(t_b/2)}{1 + \tanh(t_b/2)}. \tag{38}$$

After a simple computation, we obtain that the relevant function of the connection variable b behaves as follows in the large mass regime:

$$\left(1 - \frac{\gamma^2 \delta_b^2}{\sin^2 \delta_b b}\right) \frac{\delta_b b \cos \delta_b b - \sin \delta_b b}{\delta_b^2} = -\frac{2}{3}(2C_1 + \gamma^2) \frac{C_1}{\sqrt{-2C_1}} \delta_b + o(\delta_b). \tag{39}$$

Lastly, the dominant term of the triad variable p_b can be found using Eq. (25) in conjunction with the expansion of $\sin \delta_b b$, which is easily found from that of $\cos \delta_b b$, written above. The outcome is

$$p_b = -2\gamma L_o \frac{\sqrt{-2C_1}}{\gamma^2 - 2C_1} m + o(m). \tag{40}$$

Thus, the derivative of the radial partial Hamiltonian with respect to δ_b exhibits the asymptotic behavior

$$\frac{\partial O_b}{\partial \delta_b} = -\frac{2}{3} C_1 \frac{\gamma^2 + 2C_1}{\gamma^2 - 2C_1} \delta_b m + o(\delta_b m). \tag{41}$$

This behavior indicates that $\Delta_{bb} + \Delta_{bc}$ vanishes asymptotically.

Taking into account these results, the proportionality condition reduces at leading asymptotic order to

$$\alpha = 1. \tag{42}$$

Hence, we conclude that, among all the possibilities that the two time variables become proportional in the limit of large black hole masses, the only one that is realized is that where the proportionality factor is the identity.

Using the asymptotic expansions that we have just derived, we can obtain the relation between the radial and angular times for finite masses up to the first subdominant order. Indeed, the implicit relation (26) evaluated on shell reduces to

$$t_b - t_c = \frac{\partial f_b}{\partial m} \int_0^{t_b} dt'_b \frac{\partial O_b}{\partial \delta_b}(t'_b) - \frac{\partial f_c}{\partial m} \int_0^{t_c} dt'_c \frac{\partial O_c}{\partial \delta_c}(t'_c). \tag{43}$$

Substituting the derivatives of the δ-parameters and inserting the asymptotic expansions of the derivatives of the partial Hamiltonians, we find that

$$t_b - t_c = \frac{2}{9}\delta_b^2 \int_0^{t_b} dt'_b C_1(t'_b) \frac{\gamma^2 + 2C_1(t'_b)}{\gamma^2 - 2C_1(t'_b)} + o(\delta_b^2), \tag{44}$$

where we have omitted the angular contribution because it is subdominant with respect to the radial term. Only the latter sector contributes to the difference between the two time variables at the lowest nontrivial order. A trivial integration reveals that

$$t_c = t_b - \frac{1}{9}\gamma^2(-3t_b + 3\sinh t_b + \cosh t_b - 1)\delta_b^2 + o(\delta_b^2). \tag{45}$$

This equation provides the relation between the radial and angular time variables up to first subdominant asymptotic order. The leading term reproduces the result commented before: the two time variables coincide in the limit of infinitely large masses, as made evident by the fact that their difference vanishes when $m \to \infty$. Additionally, the form of the next-to-leading order term allows us to draw yet another parallel with the results of Ref. 40: the difference $t_c - t_b$ vanishes close to the horizon, which is defined by $t_b \to 0$, at least at the considered truncation order.

To summarize, our analysis indicates that the AOS equations of motion are recovered in the limit of large masses, leading to a *partial* reconciliation with the Hamiltonian formalism presented in this work. Indeed, even though our dynamical equations reduce in the large mass limit to those that result from treating the parameters as constants and they can be written in a single time variable (the coincident limit of t_b and t_c), this time is fundamentally different from the one that appears in the AOS model as it was originally formulated. Therefore, the time component of the effective spacetime metric is altered with respect to their case. This constitutes a modification of the effective geometry that must be studied carefully, in order to fully understand the breadth of its effects. This might open the door to an alleviation of some of the criticisms that the model has received,[41–44] which lie beyond the scope of this article. We leave these issues for future studies.

5. Conclusions

In the present work, we have studied whether it is possible to formulate an effective Hamiltonian description of the interior region of a Schwarzschild black hole such that the polymerization parameters that mediate the inclusion of quantum geometry effects are appropriately treated as Dirac observables throughout the entire Hamiltonian calculation. The idea of identifying these parameters with constants of motion is one of the defining features of the effective solution proposed by Ashtekar, Olmedo, and Singh approximately three years ago.[1,2] In these works, this identification takes place at the very end, once the whole derivation of the Hamiltonian equations has been carried out dealing with these parameters as constant numbers. Only after this derivation, the parameters are fixed equal to the value of certain functions of the mass of the black hole. This procedure was criticized by the authors of a later work,[40] who insisted that the nontrivial nature of the parameters should be taken into account from the beginning, leading to extra terms in the equations that would fail to be accounted for otherwise. They remarked that, given the structure of the Hamiltonian constraint with a certain choice of the lapse function, there are two sectors of phase space (associated with the radial and angular directions, respectively) that are dynamically decoupled provided that the polymerization parameters do not introduce any cross-dependence on these sectors. Bearing this caveat in mind, their dynamics, which is generated by their associated partial Hamiltonians, can be studied independently. Then, they proposed to take each parameter to be a function of its respective partial Hamiltonian, both of which are constants of motion with a common on-shell value, essentially given by the mass of the black hole. This definition led to more complicated equations of motion where two brand new phase space dependent factors appeared. As shown in Ref. 40, these factors can be reabsorbed through time definitions, leading to simpler equations involving two time variables, one per sector of phase space.

We have extended the analysis carried out in Ref. 40 to encompass a more general choice of parameters with the objective of determining whether the two approaches described above can be reconciled in some sense. This reconciliation would give an extra degree of confidence on the very interesting qualitative results of Refs. 1–3. Our proposal is based on the fact that both partial Hamiltonians coincide on shell, which implies that their contributions should not be able to be told apart. Therefore, we have argued in Sec. 2.1 that the most general choice of parameters should capture the contributions from both the radial and angular partial Hamiltonians, breaking the decoupling that was present in previous works in the literature. As in the case of Ref. 40, our choice leads to equations of motion that are modified with respect to those considered in Refs. 1 and 2 by means of a pair of phase space dependent factors, one associated with the radial sector and the other with the angular sector (see Sec. 2.2). These factors are substantially more complicated than those found by the authors of Ref. 40, and can remain well defined in situations where the latter present pathologies. One can see that such previous results would be recovered in the limit where the decoupling is reestablished. On the other hand, as discussed in Sec. 3, appropriate local time redefinitions make the reabsorption of these factors possible, leading to the dynamical equations considered in Refs. 1 and 2, now written in terms of two different times. These equations can be solved analytically and the result is identical to the one obtained in Refs. 1 and 2 except for the fact that two time variables, namely the radial and angular times, now play a role instead of one. We have investigated whether the off-shell freedom of our Hamiltonian formalism can be exploited in order to set both time variables equal. Upon inspection of the mathematical condition that would guarantee this equality, we have demonstrated that this coincidence cannot be achieved with a physically reasonable choice of polymerization parameters. Therefore, we have proceeded to analyze whether this equality is possible at least in some regime. In the model under consideration, the large mass limit proves to be especially interesting. Indeed, the choice of parameters made by the authors of Refs. 1 and 2 is adapted for the description of very massive black holes in the first place. With this motivation in mind, we have analyzed in Sec. 4 the equality condition for masses much larger than the Planck mass. After performing an asymptotic expansion of the relevant functions of phase space, we have shown that this condition does hold in this regime: both time variables turn out to be equal for infinitely massive black holes. More precisely, using the exact implicit relation between both variables, we have seen that the leading contribution to the difference of both times goes as the square of the radial polymerization parameter, thus vanishing as $m^{-2/3}$ in the limit where the mass of the black hole grows infinitely. For finite masses that are sufficiently large, we find that the differences with respect to the description of Refs. 1 and 2 can be estimated by the size of this term, yielding a quantitative measure of the discrepancies between both formalisms.

Our conclusions imply that the results of Refs. 1–3 can be partially reconciled with a treatment where the polymerization parameters are regarded as proper dynamical constants for black holes with large masses, which are the focus of the analysis of those references. The wording "partially" is key here. Notably, it should not be forgotten that the spacetime geometry is modified by means of time redefinitions. Even if this apparently slight modification does not alter some of the conclusions of Refs. 1–3, it may affect e.g. the behavior of the exterior effective metric at spatial infinity, which has been claimed to be nonstandard (see Refs. 41 and 3 for further details). This issue will constitute the subject of future studies.

Acknowledgments

The authors are grateful to B. Elizaga Navascués for fruitful discussions. This work has been supported by Project. No. MICINN FIS2017-86497-C2-2-P and Project. No. MICINN PID2020-118159GB-C41 from Spain. The projects that gave rise to these results received the support of a fellowship from "la Caixa" Foundation (ID 100010434). The fellowship code is LCF/BQ/DR19/11740028.

References

1. A. Ashtekar, J. Olmedo, and P. Singh, Quantum transfiguration of Kruskal black holes, *Phys. Rev. Lett.* **121**, 241301 (2018).
2. A. Ashtekar, J. Olmedo, and P. Singh, Quantum extension of the Kruskal spacetime, *Phys. Rev. D* **98**, 126003 (2018).
3. A. Ashtekar and J. Olmedo, Properties of a recent quantum extension of the Kruskal geometry, *Int. J. Mod. Phys. D* **29**, 2050076 (2020).
4. A. Ashtekar and M. Bojowald, Black hole evaporation: A paradigm, *Class. Quantum Grav.* **22**, 3349 (2005).
5. A. Ashtekar and M. Bojowald, Quantum geometry and the Schwarzschild singularity, *Class. Quantum Grav.* **23**, 391 (2005).
6. D. Cartin and G. Khanna, Wave functions for the Schwarzschild black hole interior, *Phys. Rev. D* **73** 104009 (2006).
7. L. Modesto, Loop quantum black hole, *Class. Quantum Grav.* **23**, 5587 (2006).
8. M. Bojowald, D. Cartin, and G. Khanna, Lattice refining loop quantum cosmology, anisotropic models and stability, *Phys. Rev. D* **76**, 064018 (2007).
9. C. G. Boehmer and K. Vandersloot, Loop quantum dynamics of Schwarzschild interior, *Phys. Rev. D* **76**, 1004030 (2007).
10. M. Campiglia, R. Gambini, and J. Pullin, Loop quantization of a spherically symmetric midsuperspaces: The interior problem, *AIP Conf. Proc.* **977**, 52 (2008).
11. S. Sabharwal and G. Khanna, Numerical solutions to lattice-refined models in loop quantum cosmology, *Class. Quantum Grav.* **25**, 085009 (2008).
12. D. W. Chiou, Phenomenological loop quantum geometry of the Schwarzschild black hole, *Phys. Rev. D* **78**, 064040 (2008).
13. D. W. Chiou, Phenomenological dynamics of loop quantum cosmology in Kantowski-Sachs spacetime, *Phys. Rev. D* **78**, 044019 (2008).
14. J. Brannlund, S. Kloster, and A. DeBenedictis, The evolution of black holes in the mini-superspace approximation of loop quantum gravity, *Phys. Rev. D* **79**, 084023 (2009).
15. R. Gambini, J. Omedo, and J. Pullin, Quantum black holes in loop quantum gravity, *Class. Quantum Grav.* **31**, 095009 (2014).
16. R. Gambini and J. Pullin, Hawking radiation from a spherical loop quantum gravity black hole, *Class. Quantum Grav.* **31**, 115003 (2014).
17. N. Dadhich, A. Joe, and P. Singh, Emergence of the product of constant curvature spaces in loop quantum cosmology, *Class. Quantum Grav.* **32**, 185006 (2015).
18. H. M. Haggard and C. Rovelli, Quantum-gravity effects outside the horizon spark black to white hole tunneling, *Phys. Rev. D* **92**, 104020 (2015).
19. A. Joe and P. Singh, Kantowski-Sachs spacetime in loop quantum cosmology: Bounds on expansion and shear scalars and viability of quantization prescriptions, *Class. Quantum Grav.* **32**, 015009 (2015).
20. A. Corichi and P. Singh, Loop quantum dynamics of Schwarzschild interior revisited, *Class. Quantum Grav.* **33**, 055006 (2016).
21. M. Campiglia, R. Gambini, J. Olmedo, and J. Pullin, Quantum self-gravitating collapsing matter in a quantum geometry, *Class. Quantum Grav.* **33**, 18LT01 (2016).
22. S. Saini and P. Singh, Geodesic completeness and the lack of strong singularities in effective loop quantum Kantowski-Sachs spacetime, *Class. Quantum Grav.* **33**, 245019 (2016).
23. J. Cortez, W. Cuervo, H. A. Morales-Técotl, and J. C. Ruelas, On effective loop quantum geometry of Schwarzschild interior, *Phys. Rev. D* **95**, 064041 (2017).

24. J. Olmedo, S. Saini, and P. Singh, From black holes to white holes: A quantum gravitational symmetric bounce, *Class. Quantum Grav.* **34**, 225011 (2017).
25. A. Yonika, G. Khanna, and P. Singh, Von-Neumann stability and singularity resolution in loop quantized Schwarzschild black hole, *Class. Quantum Grav.* **35**, 045007 (2018).
26. E. Bianchi, M. Christodoulou, F. D'Ambrosio, H.M. Haggard, and C. Rovelli, White holes as remnants: A surprising scenario for the end of a black hole, *Class. Quantum Grav.* **35**, 225003 (2018).
27. N. Bodendorfer, F. M. Mele, and J. Münch, Effective quantum extended spacetime of polymer Schwarzschild black hole, *Class. Quantum Grav.* **36**, 195015 (2019).
28. E. Alesci, S. Bahrami, and D. Pranzetti, Quantum gravity predictions for black hole interior geometry, *Phys. Lett. B* **797**, 134908 (2019).
29. M. Bouhmadi-López, S. Brahma, C.-Y. Chen, P. Chen, and D.-h. Yeom, A consistent model of non-singular Schwarzschild black hole in loop quantum gravity and its quasinormal modes, *J. Cosmol. Astropart. Phys.* **07**, 066 (2020).
30. M. Bojowald, Black-hole models in loop quantum gravity, *Universe* **6**, 125 (2020).
31. J. Ben Achour, S. Brahma, S. Mukohyama, and J.-P. Uzan, Towards consistent black-to-white hole bounces from matter collapse, *J. Cosmol. Astropart. Phys.* **09**, 020 (2020).
32. R. Gambini, J. Olmedo, and J. Pullin, Spherically symmetric loop quantum gravity: Analysis of improved dynamics, *Class. Quantum Grav.* **37**, 205012 (2020).
33. J. G. Kelly, R. Santacruz, and E. Wilson-Ewing, Effective loop quantum gravity framework for vacuum spherically symmetric spacetimes, *Phys. Rev. D* **102**, 106024 (2020).
34. W.-C. Gan, N. O. Santos, F.-W. Shu, and A. Wang, Towards understanding of loop quantum black holes, *Phys. Rev. D* **102**, 124030 (2020).
35. J. G. Kelly, R. Santacruz, and E. Wilson-Ewing, Black hole collapse and bounce in effective loop quantum gravity, *Class. Quantum Grav.* **38**, 04LT01 (2021).
36. N. Bodendorfer, F. M. Mele, and J. Münch, Mass and horizon Dirac observables in effective models of quantum black-to-white hole transition, *Class. Quantum Grav.* **38**, 095002 (2021).
37. N. Bodendorfer, F. M. Mele, and J. Münch, (b,v)-type variables for black to white hole transitions in effective loop quantum gravity, *Phys. Lett. B* **819**, 136390 (2021).
38. R. G. Daghigh, M. D. Green, and G. Kunstatter, Scalar perturbations and stability of a loop quantum corrected Kruskal black hole, *Phys. Rev. D* **103**, 084031 (2021).
39. J. Münch, Causal structure of a recent loop quantum gravity black hole collapse model, *Phys. Rev. D* **104**, 046019 (2021).
40. N. Bodendorfer, F. M. Mele, and J. Münch, A note on the Hamiltonian as a polymerisation parameter, *Class. Quantum Grav.* **37**, 187001 (2019).
41. M. Bouhmadi-López, S. Brahma, C.-Y. Chen, P. Chen, and D.-h. Yeom, Asymptotic non-flatness of an effective black hole model based on loop quantum gravity, *Phys. Dark Univ.* **30**, 100701 (2020).
42. M. Bojowald, Comment (2) on "Quantum transfiguration of Kruskal black holes", `arXiv:1906.04650`.
43. M. Bojowald, No-go result for covariance in models of loop quantum gravity, *Phys. Rev. D* **102**, 046006 (2020).
44. D. Arruga, J. Ben Achour, and K. Noui, Deformed general relativity and quantum black holes interior, *Universe* **6**, 039 (2020).
45. A. García-Quismondo and G. A. Mena Marugán, *Front. Astron. Space Sci.* **8**, 701723 (2021).

A comparison of different choices of clocks in a reduced phase space quantization in loop quantum cosmology with an inflationary potential using effective techniques

Kristina Giesel[1], Bao-Fei Li[2] and Parampreet Singh[2]

[1] *Institute for Quantum Gravity, Department of Physics, Theoretical Physics III,*
FAU Erlangen-Nürnberg, Staudtstr. 7, 91058 Erlangen, Germany
kristina.giesel@gravity.fau.de

[2] *Department of Physics and Astronomy, Louisiana State University, Baton Rouge, LA 70803,*
USA
baofeili1@lsu.edu, psingh@lsu.edu

We review recent results that apply a reduced phase space quantization of loop quantum cosmology (LQC) for a spatially flat Friedmann-Lemaître-Robertson-Walker (FLRW) universe filled with reference fields and an inflaton field in a Starobinsky inflationary potential. All three models that we consider are two-fluid models and they differ by their choice of global clock which are chosen to be either Gaussian dust, Brown-Kuchař dust or a massless Klein-Gordon scalar field. Although two-fluid models are more complicated than models involving the inflaton only, it turns out that some of the technical hurdles in conventional quantum cosmological models can be bypassed in these models. Using the effective dynamics resulting from the reduced phase space quantization we discuss some phenomenological implications of these models including the resolution of the big bang singularity via a quantum bounce and in addition address the question whether different choices of clocks can leave an imprint on the inflationary dynamics.

Keywords: Loop quantum cosmology, reduced phase space quantization, effective techniques.

1. Introduction

Within the last decade in the framework of loop quantum gravity new models have been introduced that apply the technique of reduced phase space quantization to construct the physical Hilbert space and thus the physical sector of the theory.[1-9] This requires to construct Dirac observables at the classical level and derive their corresponding algebra. For this purpose all models have in common that they couple some kind of additional matter to gravity. In the context of the relational formalism, introduced in Refs. 10, 11 and further developed and applied in Refs. 12–17, these additional degrees of freedom are used as reference matter to construct Dirac observables and their corresponding dynamics. The latter is encoded in a so called physical Hamiltonian that becomes a non-vanishing Hamiltonian operator in the physical Hilbert space involved either in a Schrödinger-like or Heisenberg-like equations. For the reason that these reference fields are dynamically coupled to general relativity an interesting question in this context is how a given choice of reference fields influences the physical properties of the model. In full loop quantum gravity these dynamical equations have a complicated structure and an analysis for individual models as well as a comparison between different models is a non-trivial task. Therefore, the work in Ref. 18 focus on a simplified setting in the framework of loop quantum cosmology where techniques are already available to analyze such questions. The relational formalism has been applied in the context of loop quantum cosmology for instance in Refs. 18–33. The main difference to former models in loop quantum cosmology with reference matter, often also called clocks in cosmology, is that the work in Ref. 18 considers two-fluid models because the clock is coupled in addition to an inflaton. One of the main questions that one is interested in is how the inflationary scenario is affected by the presence of the additional clock degree of freedom and how the imprint of the clock compares for different models. Such questions will be investigated using effective techniques that in LQC have in former work mainly be applied to one-fluid models.

1.1. *Dust and scalar field clock models in loop quantum cosmology*

All three models in the analysis in Ref. 18 are based on models in general relativity coupled to an inflaton field and an additional coupling of 8 and 7 respectively additional dust and scalar fields respectively yielding to a system with second class constraints. After the reduction with respect to the second class constraints one ends up with first class systems with four additional reference fields, that can be used as reference matter for the Hamiltonian and spatial diffeomorphism constraint. The details about the Brown-Kuchař dust model can be found in Ref. 34 and its quantization using LQG techniques has been performed in Ref. 1. For the classical Gaussian dust model we refer the reader to Ref. 35 and its LQG implementation has been discussed in Ref. 36. The four scalar field model in Refs. 5, 6 can be understood as a modification of the model in Ref. 37, that, as shown in Ref. 5 cannot be quantized in the framework of LQG. For flat FLRW spacetimes where the spatial diffeomorphism constraint vanishes identically, the corresponding symmetry reduced models involve one temporal reference field, the clock, only. A reduced phase space quantization for all three symmetry reduced models has been derived in Ref. 18. There it is shown that in all three models the quantum dynamics is encoded in a Schrödinger-like equation in the physical Hilbert space. The explicit form of the physical Hamiltonian differs for the dust and scalar field models where the latter involves a square root. Although the model involve an inflaton with a generic potential due to the fact that clock is coupled additionally and one does not use the inflaton as the clock, as it has for instance be done in the APS-model in Ref. 21, all models possess physical Hamiltonians that are time-independent. This is of advantage for the construction of the physical inner product of the individual models. In this review we will focus on the effective dynamics of these models that were used in Ref. 18 to investigate the above mentioned questions. The quantum dynamics is formulated in the volume representation in Ref. 18 and thus the set of elementary variables in the dynamical equations are $\mathcal{O}_b, \mathcal{O}_V, \mathcal{O}_\varphi, \mathcal{O}_{\pi_\varphi}$, where $\mathcal{O}_f$

denotes the Dirac observable of quantity f. As shown in Ref. 18 the effective physical Hamiltonians of the dust and scalar field model take the form

$$\mathbf{H}_{\text{eff}}^{\text{FLRW, dust}} = -\frac{3\mathcal{O}_V}{8\pi G \lambda^2 \gamma^2} \sin^2(\lambda \mathcal{O}_b) + \frac{\mathcal{O}_{\pi_\varphi}^2}{2\mathcal{O}_V} + \mathcal{O}_V U(\mathcal{O}_\varphi) \tag{1}$$

$$\mathbf{H}_{\text{eff}}^{\text{FLRW, scalar}} = \sqrt{-2\mathcal{O}_V \left(-\frac{3\mathcal{O}_V}{8\pi G \lambda^2 \gamma^2} \sin^2(\lambda \mathcal{O}_b) + \frac{\mathcal{O}_{\pi_\varphi}^2}{2\mathcal{O}_V} + \mathcal{O}_V U(\mathcal{O}_\varphi) \right)}, \tag{2}$$

where $\lambda = \sqrt{\Delta} = \sqrt{4\sqrt{3}\pi\gamma \ell_p^2}$ denotes the polymerization parameter. Taking into account that the elementary Dirac observables satisfy the following standard Poisson brackets $\{\mathcal{O}_b, \mathcal{O}_V\} = 4\pi G\gamma$ and $\{\mathcal{O}_\varphi, \mathcal{O}_{\pi_\varphi}\} = 1$ with γ denoting the Immirzi parameter and where all remaining Poisson brackets vanish, the system of equations of motion for the Dirac observables in the individual models has been been derived in Ref. 18 and they provide the basis for the results discussed in the next section. Note that although in the case of flat FLRW spacetimes the physical Hamiltonian of the Brown-Kuchař model and the Gaussian dust model agree, these model are still not identical because within the Brown-Kuchař model the dust energy density can be chosen to be either positive or negative and the effect of these two different choices has also been analyzed in Ref. 18.

2. The effect of choosing different clocks on inflation

Similar to the one-fluid models that are obtained via Dirac quantization as for instance the APS-model in Ref. 21, the effective dynamics in the scalar field and dust models can be rewritten in terms of a modified Friedmann equations of the form

$$\mathcal{O}_H^2 = \frac{\dot{\mathcal{O}}_V^2}{9\mathcal{O}_V^2} = \frac{8\pi G}{3} \mathcal{O}_\rho \left(1 - \frac{\mathcal{O}_\rho}{\rho_{\max}}\right) \tag{3}$$

with $\rho_{\max} = \frac{3}{8\pi G \gamma^2 \lambda^2}$. The maximal density $\rho_{\max}$ is the same as in Refs. 21–23 but here $\mathcal{O}_\rho$ does not only depend on the inflaton but also on the clock energy density. Furthermore, the temporal coordinate with respect to which the Hubble parameter is determined is given by either the dust and scalar field clock respectively.

In order to analyze how a given choice of clock might affect inflation in Ref. 18 a Starobinsky potential

$$U = \frac{3m^2}{16\pi G} \left(1 - e^{-\sqrt{\frac{16\pi}{3}} \mathcal{O}_\varphi}\right)^2 \quad \text{with} \quad m = 2.44 \times 10^{-6} \tag{4}$$

was considered. The choice of initial conditions, set at the bounce, was guided by former results in LQC models[38] and chosen to be $\mathcal{O}_{b_i} = \pi/2\lambda$ and $\mathcal{O}_{V_i} = 10^3$ in Planck units. Fixing further values for $\mathcal{O}_{\varphi_i}, \mathcal{O}_{\pi_\varphi}$ determines $\mathbf{H}_{\text{eff}}^{\text{FLRW, dust}}$ from which one can obtain $\mathcal{O}_{\rho^{\text{clock}}}$. Therefore in Ref. 18 the initial values are parametrized by $(\mathcal{O}_\varphi, \mathcal{O}_{\rho^{\text{clock}}})$. In the case of the dust models a choice of initial conditions given by $\mathcal{O}_{\varphi_i} = -1.45$, $\mathcal{O}_{\rho^{\text{clock}}} = 10^{-8}$ yields to a quantum model with a pre-inflationary phase, often being present in LQC models after the bounce, and an inflationary phase where the number of inflationary e-foldings for the latter is 63.1. For a similar choice of initial conditions the one-fluid models without an additional clock degree of freedom yield 63.9 inflationary e-foldings, see Ref. 38. This shows that for these choice of initial conditions the dust clock plays only a subdominant role for inflation. This is exactly what one expects from a good clock because such a clock should not have a dominant imprint on the dynamics of the model. A similar analysis for the scalar field model leads to 63.8 inflationary e-foldings being closer to the value obtained in the one-fluid models and showing that the effect of the scalar field clock is weaker compared to the dust clock. However, this is also expected from the fact that the energy density of the scalar field comes with a higher inverse power of the scale factor than the dust contribution and thus decaying faster in the evolution. In a further investigation to better understand the influence of the clock energy density on inflation in Ref. 18 for the same set of initial conditions for the inflaton a varying dust energy density ranging from 10^{-8} up to 10^{-4} was considered. The results show that the number of inflationary e-foldings decrease with increasing dust energy density. The explanation given in Ref. 18 is that this results from the fact that $\mathcal{O}_{\varphi_{on}}$, the value of scalar field's Dirac observable at the onset of inflation, decreases due to a larger Hubble friction when the dust energy density is increased. For an initial dust energy of $\mathcal{O}_{\rho^{clock}} = 1.38 \times 10^{-4}$ in Planck units one reaches an upper bound for this set of initial conditions where inflation no longer occurs. The same analysis for the scalar field clock shows that also in this model the number of inflationary e-foldings decreases with higher clock energy density but the effect is less strong here. One sees a significant effect only if $\mathcal{O}_{\rho^{clock}} \geq 0.001$ in Planck units. As far as the number of pre-inflationary e-foldings is concerned the results from Ref. 18 demonstrate that the increase of the clock energy density has the opposite effect, namely that the number of pre-inflationary e-foldings increase.

3. Conclusions

As a first step towards an investigation how choices of different reference fields affect the physical properties of models the work in Ref. 18 considers different symmetry reduced reference matter models choosing either dust or a massless scalar field as the clock in addition to gravity and the inflaton leading to two-fluid LQC models. For the choice of a Starobinsky potential the fingerprint of the clock on the inflationary dynamics was analyzed in the framework of effective techniques. The analysis shows that initial conditions can be chosen such that the clock has no significant effect on the dynamics. Both models with dust and the scalar field clock respectively show a qualitatively similar behavior and can serve as good clocks. Some difference in the two models are found such as that the model with the scalar field clock has a larger number of inflationary e-foldings compared to the dust model. Furthermore, the scalar field model serves in larger parameter space as a good clock since it is less sensitive to the initial conditions of the clock energy density. Going beyond the first steps investigated in Ref. 18 and reviewed here requires a more detailed understanding on the physical solutions in these models at the level of the quantum theory. For this purpose the already existing numerical techniques[23,39] need to be generalized to the two-fluid case. Next to the question of singularity resolution at the level of the physical Hilbert space, such kind of generalization will be important because it will also allow to test the validity of effective techniques for two-fluid models.

References

1. K. Giesel and T. Thiemann, Algebraic quantum gravity (AQG). IV. Reduced phase space quantisation of loop quantum gravity, *Class. Quant. Grav.* **27**, p. 175009 (2010).
2. M. Domagala, K. Giesel, W. Kaminski and J. Lewandowski, Gravity quantized: Loop Quantum Gravity with a Scalar Field, *Phys. Rev.* **D82**, p. 104038 (2010).
3. V. Husain and T. Pawlowski, Dust reference frame in quantum cosmology, *Class. Quant. Grav.* **28**, p. 225014 (2011).
4. V. Husain and T. Pawlowski, Time and a physical Hamiltonian for quantum gravity, *Phys. Rev. Lett.* **108**, p. 141301 (2012).
5. K. Giesel and A. Vetter, Reduced loop quantization with four Klein–Gordon scalar fields as reference matter, *Class. Quant. Grav.* **36**, p. 145002 (2019).
6. K. Giesel and A. Oelmann, Comparison Between Dirac and Reduced Quantization in LQG-Models with Klein-Gordon Scalar Fields, *Acta Phys. Polon. Supp.* **10**, 339 (2017).
7. M. Ali, S. M. Hassan and V. Husain, Universe as an oscillator, *Phys. Rev.* **D98**, p. 086002 (2018).
8. M. Han and H. Liu, Effective Dynamics from Coherent State Path Integral of Full Loop Quantum Gravity, *Phys. Rev.* **D101**, p. 046003 (2020).
9. M. Han and H. Liu, Improved ($\bar{\mu}$-Scheme) Effective Dynamics of Full Loop Quantum Gravity (2019).
10. C. Rovelli, What Is Observable in Classical and Quantum Gravity?, *Class. Quant. Grav.* **8**, 297 (1991).
11. C. Rovelli, Partial observables, *Phys. Rev.* **D65**, p. 124013 (2002).
12. A. S. Vytheeswaran, Gauge unfixing in second class constrained systems, *Annals Phys.* **236**, 297 (1994).
13. B. Dittrich, Partial and complete observables for Hamiltonian constrained systems, *Gen. Rel. Grav.* **39**, 1891 (2007).
14. B. Dittrich, Partial and complete observables for canonical general relativity, *Class. Quant. Grav.* **23**, 6155 (2006).
15. T. Thiemann, Reduced phase space quantization and Dirac observables, *Class. Quant. Grav.* **23**, 1163 (2006).
16. J. Pons, D. Salisbury and K. Sundermeyer, Revisiting observables in generally covariant theories in the light of gauge fixing methods, *Phys. Rev. D* **80**, p. 084015 (2009).
17. J. Pons, D. Salisbury and K. Sundermeyer, Observables in classical canonical gravity: Folklore demystified, *J. Phys. Conf. Ser.* **222**, p. 012018 (2010).
18. K. Giesel, B.-F. Li and P. Singh, Towards a reduced phase space quantization in loop quantum cosmology with an inflationary potential, *Phys. Rev. D* **102**, p. 126024 (2020).

19. D. Kaup and A. Vitello, Solvable quantum cosmological model and the importance of quantizing in a special canonical frame, *Phys. Rev. D* **9**, 1648 (1974).
20. W. Blyth and C. Isham, Quantization of a Friedmann Universe Filled with a Scalar Field, *Phys. Rev. D* **11**, 768 (1975).
21. A. Ashtekar, T. Pawlowski and P. Singh, Quantum Nature of the Big Bang, *Phys. Rev. Lett.* **96**, p. 141301 (2006).
22. A. Ashtekar, T. Pawlowski and P. Singh, Quantum Nature of the Big Bang: An Analytical and Numerical Investigation. I., *Phys. Rev.* **D73**, p. 124038 (2006).
23. A. Ashtekar, T. Pawlowski and P. Singh, Quantum Nature of the Big Bang: Improved dynamics, *Phys. Rev.* **D74**, p. 084003 (2006).
24. A. Ashtekar, A. Corichi and P. Singh, Robustness of key features of loop quantum cosmology, *Phys. Rev.* **D77**, p. 024046 (2010).
25. A. Ashtekar, T. Pawlowski, P. Singh and K. Vandersloot, Loop quantum cosmology of k=1 FRW models, *Phys. Rev. D* **75**, p. 024035 (2007).
26. K. Vandersloot, Loop quantum cosmology and the k = - 1 RW model, *Phys. Rev. D* **75**, p. 023523 (2007).
27. E. Bentivegna and T. Pawlowski, Anti-deSitter universe dynamics in LQC, *Phys. Rev. D* **77**, p. 124025 (2008).
28. W. Kaminski and T. Pawlowski, The LQC evolution operator of FRW universe with positive cosmological constant, *Phys. Rev. D* **81**, p. 024014 (2010).
29. T. Pawlowski and A. Ashtekar, Positive cosmological constant in loop quantum cosmology, *Phys. Rev. D* **85**, p. 064001 (2012).
30. T. Pawlowski, R. Pierini and E. Wilson-Ewing, Loop quantum cosmology of a radiation-dominated flat FLRW universe, *Phys. Rev. D* **90**, p. 123538 (2014).
31. J. Mielczarek and W. Piechocki, Observables for FRW model with cosmological constant in the framework of loop cosmology, *Phys. Rev. D* **82**, p. 043529 (2010).
32. F. Amemiya and T. Koike, Gauge-invariant construction of quantum cosmology, *Phys. Rev. D* **80**, p. 103507 (2009).
33. S. Gryb and K. P. Thébault, Bouncing Unitary Cosmology I: Mini-Superspace General Solution, *Class. Quant. Grav.* **36**, p. 035009 (2019).
34. J. D. Brown and K. V. Kuchar, Dust as a standard of space and time in canonical quantum gravity, *Phys. Rev.* **D51**, 5600 (1995).
35. K. V. Kuchar and C. G. Torre, Gaussian reference fluid and interpretation of quantum geometrodynamics, *Phys. Rev.* **D43**, 419 (1991).
36. K. Giesel and T. Thiemann, Scalar Material Reference Systems and Loop Quantum Gravity, *Class. Quant. Grav.* **32**, p. 135015 (2015).
37. K. V. Kuchar and C. G. Torre, The Harmonic gauge in canonical gravity, *Phys. Rev. D* **44**, 3116 (1991).
38. B.-F. Li, P. Singh and A. Wang, Genericness of pre-inflationary dynamics and probability of the desired slow-roll inflation in modified loop quantum cosmologies, *Phys. Rev.* **D100**, p. 063513 (2019).
39. P. Diener, B. Gupt and P. Singh, Numerical simulations of a loop quantum cosmos: Robustness of the quantum bounce and the validity of effective dynamics, *Class. Quant. Grav.* **31**, p. 105015 (2014).

Initial conditions in LQC/mLQCs

Bao-Fei Li*, Parampreet Singh* and Anzhong Wang[†,‡]

*Department of Physics and Astronomy, Louisiana State University,
Baton Rouge, LA 70803, USA
†Institute for Theoretical Physics & Cosmology, Zhejiang University of Technology,
Hangzhou, 310032, China
‡GCAP-CASPER, Department of Physics, Baylor University,
Waco, TX 76798, USA

We compare the behavior of the effective masses in the Mukhanov-Sasaki equations of the linear scalar perturbations in the dressed metric and hybrid approaches in the standard loop quantum cosmology (LQC) and the modified LQC models (mLQCs). The effective mass of the Mukhanov-Sasaki equations depend on both the specific model and the approach we study. Analyzing the behavior of the effective masses plays an important role in the choice of the initial states for the scalar perturbations. Based on the properties of the effective masses in the contracting phase, we provide the initial states of the linear perturbations in LQC and mLQCs for the dressed metric and the hybrid approaches.

Keywords: Mukhanov-Sasaki equations; loop quantum cosmology.

1. Introduction

In loop quantum cosmology(LQC), the big bang singularity in the standard cosmology is resolved and replaced with a quantum bounce, and correspondingly the inflationary paradigm, which resolves several big bang puzzles and provides initial seeds for the formation of the large scale structure in the universe, can be extended to the Planck regime by using the effective dynamics.[1,2] Several approaches have been developed in LQC to compute the primordial power spectral produced by the quantum fluctuations which propagate on quantum geometries. However, such effects become negligible soon after the quantum bounce. In particular, at the beginning of inflation, where the energy density has decreased about 12 orders in comparing that at the bounce, $\rho_i/\rho_c \simeq 10^{-12}$, the quantum spacetime can be well approximated by a classical one, whereby the standard relativistic cosmology follows. Two of the most studied approaches are the dressed metric approach[3–5] and the hybrid approach.[6–9] Although these two approaches are formulated in different ways, the resulting equations of motion for the scalar modes in both approaches can be cast into the form

$$\nu_k'' + \left(k^2 + m_{\text{eff}}\right)\nu_k = 0, \qquad (1)$$

here m_{eff} denotes the effective mass which accounts for the differences between two approaches. Similar to the situation in the classical cosmology, the initial condition problem persists in LQC in the form that up to now there is no consensus on whether the initial states should be imposed in the Planck regime or in the contracting phase where the background dynamics becomes classical again. In this paper, we take the viewpoint to impose the initial states in the deep contracting phase. As a result, we focus on the behavior of the effective mass in the deep contracting phase. Besides, in addition to the standard LQC, we also investigate the behavior of the effective mass in two modified LQC models (mLQCs) in order to study the potential effects of the quantization ambiguities on the observables.

The said mLQCs originate from a separate treatment of the Lorentz term in the classical Hamiltonian constraint in the spatially flat FLRW universe.[10] Two of the mLQCs which attract attention recently are the so-called mLQC-I and mLQC-II. Both the background dynamics and the primordial power spectra of these two mLQCs have been extensively studied in the literature.[11–17] From these studies, we learn that the background dynamics in mLQC-II is qualitatively similar to that in LQC while the contracting phase of mLQC-I has distinctive feature which is characterized by an emergent cosmological constant and a rescaled Newton's constant. When applying the dressed metric and the hybrid approaches to the mLQCs, Planck scale magnitude of the power spectrum is observed in the infrared(IR) regime of mLQC-I with the dressed metric approach while in the hybrid approach, the magnitudes of the power spectra in mLQCs and LQC become comparable. As a result, the modified LQC models also provide good examples to compare the two approaches. In the following, we compare the effective masses in LQC, mLQC-I and mLQC-II, respectively, in the dressed metric and the hybrid approaches, and from the properties of the effective masses in the contracting phase, we seek the appropriate initial states to be imposed during this phase. For more details, we refer readers to Ref. 17.

2. The initial states in LQC/mLQCs in the dressed metric approach

In the dressed metric approach, the quantum fluctuations are described as propagating on a quantum background spacetime whose geometry can be well approximated by a manifold with a dressed metric for the sharply peaked states. Using the effective dynamics, it can be shown that the effective mass in (1) takes the same form as in the classical perturbation theory while the difference originates from two sources.[15] Firstly, the background quantities in m_{eff} should come from the effective dynamics governed by the effective Hamiltonian constraint in LQC. Secondly, the regularization of the conjugate momentum of the scale factor in m_{eff} should be also consistent with the effective Hamiltonian constraint for the background dynamics. With the above two points in mind, we impose the kinetic-energy-dominated initial conditions for the background evolution at the bounce and study the behavior of the effective mass for the chaotic and the Starobinsky potentials. In practice, one can define the comoving Hubble radius as,[17]

$$\lambda_H^2 = -\frac{1}{m_{\text{eff}}}. \qquad (2)$$

When the wavelength of the relevant modes is larger than λ_H^2, the mode function is oscillating. On the other hand, when the wavelength of the relevant modes are less than λ_H^2, the mode function is exponentially decaying or growing.

From our numerical results, we find the behavior of the comoving Hubble radius in mLQC-II is very similar to that in LQC. Its evolution is almost symmetric with respect to the bounce point. During the deflationary stage in the contracting phase, the comoving Hubble radius keeps increasing until it reaches positive infinity at some time $t = t_i < 0$ where a'' vanishes. After $t = t_i$, it is the intermediate regime where the comoving Hubble radius becomes negative and correspondingly all the modes are oscillating in this regime. Near the bounce, the comoving Hubble radius becomes positive and reaches its minimal right at the bounce, which corresponds to the characteristic wavelength in LQC/mLQC-II. As a result, we find the Bunch-Davies vacuum can be chosen in the intermediate regime of the contracting phase where $\lambda_H^2 < 0$ in LQC and mLQC-II. On the other hand, we find a different behavior of λ_H^2 in the contracting phase of mLQC-I. In particular, λ_H^2 is always positive in the contracting phase and it can be well approximated by $\eta^2/2$ with η denoting the conformal time in the quasi de Sitter regime of the contracting phase. As a result, we can choose the de Sitter state as the initial state in the contracting phase. The above analysis on the behavior of the comoving Hubble radius is robust with respect to the choice of the inflaton potentials and the regularization of the conjugate momentum of the scale factor in the effective mass as long as the bounce is dominated by the kinetic energy of the inflaton field.

3. The initial states in LQC/mLQCs in the hybrid approach

The application of the hybrid approach to the mLQCs is studied in detail in[16] where the equation of motion for the scalar perturbations are given explicitly. Using the effective mass given in the mode equation, we study its properties in the contracting phase when the initial conditions of the background dynamics are chosen the same as in the dressed metric approach. From our numerical results, we find the evolution of the comoving Hubble radius is generally not symmetric with respect to the bounce in any model and it also depends on the specific inflationary potential. Surprisingly, with the chaotic potential, the comoving Hubble radius behaves similarly in all three models. It increases monotonically from some negative value in the deep contracting phase and tends to positive infinity at time $t = \tilde t_i < 0$ where $a'' = 0$. Afterwards, it remains negative until the onset of inflation in the expanding phase. This implies the effective mass is always negative near the bounce. As a result, with the chaotic potential, one can choose the BD vacuum in the deep contracting regime or near the bounce in all three models. However, since the comoving Hubble radius becomes infinity at $t = \tilde t_i$, choosing BD vacuum at different times, either in the deep contracting regime or near the bounce is expected to give different power spectra in the IR regime due to particle creation effect.

On the other hand, with the Starobinsky potential, we find the comoving Hubble radius has similar behavior in LQC and mLQC-II. It remains negative throughout the contracting phase until the onset of inflation in the expanding phase. As a result, the choice of the BD vacuum can be made either in the deep contracting phase or near the bounce and the resulting power spectra are expected not to be significantly different from one to another. In contrast, in mLQC-I, although the comoving Hubble radius is still negative near the bounce, there exists a finite time interval in the contracting phase where it become positive. In the deep contracting phase, it becomes negative again. So similar to the case of the chaotic potential, imposing the BD vacuum at different times, either in the deep contracting phase or near the bounce is expected to yields different power spectra in the IR regime.

If we compare different approaches for the same model, the most striking difference lies in mLQC-I where the choice of the de Sitter state in the contracting phase in the dressed metric approach yields a Planck scale magnitude of the power spectra in the IR regime, while the choice of the BD vacuum in the deep contracting phase in the hybrid approach highly suppresses the magnitude of the resulting power spectrum in the IR regime. This serves as a concrete example where the different approaches can result in different qualitative behaviors in the power spectra.

4. Summary

We study the behavior of the effective masses in the equation of motion for the scalar mode in LQC and mLQCs in the dressed metric and the hybrid approaches. With the same kinetic-energy-dominated initial conditions for the background dynamics, we find the properties of the comoving Hubble radius in the contracting phase. In the dressed metric approach, the comoving Hubble radius has similar behavior for the chaotic and the Starobinsky potentials. One can choose the BD vacuum in the deep contracting phase of LQC and mLQC-II and the de Sitter state in the contracting phase of mLQC-I. On the other hand, the properties of the comoving Hubble radius in the hybrid approach depends on the specific inflationary potentials. One common feature of the comoving Hubble radius for all the models is that it is negative near the bounce and we find it appropriate to choose the BD vacuum in the hybrid approach for all three models in the deep contracting phase.

We are grateful to Robert Brandenberger and David Wands for valuable comments and helpful discussions. We thank Javier Olmedo and Tao Zhu for various discussions. This work is supported by NSF grant PHY-1454832.

References

1. A. Ashtekar and P. Singh, *Loop Quantum Cosmology: A Status Report*, Class. Quant. Grav. **28**, 213001 (2011).
2. I. Agullo and P. Singh, *Loop Quantum Cosmology*, in Loop Quantum Gravity: The First 30 Years, edited by A. Ashtekar and J. Pullin (World Scientific, Singapore, 2017).

3. I. Agullo, A. Ashtekar and W. Nelson, *Quantum gravity extension of the inflationary scenario*, Phys. Rev. Lett. **109**, 251301 (2012).
4. I. Agullo, A. Ashtekar and W. Nelson, *Extension of the quantum theory of cosmological perturbations to the Planck era*, Phys. Rev. D**87**, 043507 (2013).
5. I. Agullo, A. Ashtekar and W. Nelson, *The pre-inflationary dynamics of loop quantum cosmology: Confronting quantum gravity with observations*, Class. Quantum Grav. **30**, 085014 (2013).
6. L. Castelló Gomar, M. Fernández-Méndez, G. A. Mena Marugan and J. Olmedo, *Cosmological perturbations in hybrid loop quantum cosmology: Mukhanov-Sasaki variables*, Phys. Rev. D**90**, 064015 (2014).
7. M. Fernández-Méndez, G. A. Mena Marugán and J. Olmedo, *Hybrid quantization of an inflationary universe*, Phys. Rev. D**86**, 024003 (2012).
8. M. Fernández-Méndez, G. A. Mena Marugán and J. Olmedo, *Hybrid quantization of an inflationary model: The flat case*, Phys. Rev. D**88**, 044013 (2013).
9. L. Castelló Gomar, M. Martín-Benito, G. A. Mena Marugán, *Gauge-invariant perturbations in hybrid quantum cosmology*, JCAP 1506 (2015) 045.
10. J. Yang, Y. Ding and Y. Ma, *Alternative quantization of the Hamiltonian in loop quantum cosmology II: Including the Lorentz term*, Phys. Lett. B**682** (2009) 1.
11. B.-F. Li, P. Singh, A. Wang, *Towards cosmological dynamics from loop quantum gravity*, Phys. Rev. D**97**, 084029 (2018).
12. B.-F. Li, P. Singh, A. Wang, *Qualitative dynamics and inflationary attractors in loop cosmology*, Phys. Rev. D**98**, 066016 (2018).
13. I. Agullo, *Primordial power spectrum from the Dapor-Liegener model of loop quantum cosmology*, Gen. Relativ. Grav. **50** (2018) 91.
14. B.-F. Li, P. Singh, A. Wang, *Genericness of pre-inflationary dynamics and probability of the desired slow-roll inflation in modified loop quantum cosmologies*, Phys. Rev. D**100**, 063513 (2019).
15. B.-F. Li, P. Singh, A. Wang, *Primordial power spectrum from the dressed metric approach in loop cosmologies*, Phys. Rev. D**100**, 086004 (2020).
16. B.-F. Li, J. Olmedo, P. Singh, and A. Wang, *Primordial scalar power spectrum from the hybrid approach in loop cosmologies*, Phys. Rev. D**102**, 126025 (2020).
17. B.-F. Li, P. Singh, and A. Wang, *Phenomenological implications of modified loop cosmologies: An overview*, Front. Astron. Space Sci. 8 (2021) 701417.

Holonomy corrections in effective midisuperspace models

A. Alonso-Bardaji* and D. Brizuela[†]

Department of Physics, University of the Basque Country (UPV/EHU),
Leioa, 48940, Spain
* E-mail: asier.alonso@ehu.eus
† E-mail: david.brizuela@ehu.eus

We develop a systematic method to obtain spherically symmetric midisuperspace models with modifications inherited from loop quantum gravity. We obtain a family of effective constraints satisfying Dirac's deformation algebra and show that holonomy corrections can be consistently implemented in the presence of matter with local degrees of freedom.

Keywords: Polymerization; effective theories: loops quantum gravity.

1. Introduction

Holonomy-modified cosmological effective models capture the behavior of the dynamics predicted by loop quantum cosmology.[1,2] Such effective descriptions usually modify the Hamiltonian by hand to include the expected effects from loop quantum gravity. Holonomy corrections are directly related to the spacetime discreteness and replace the initial singularity by a quantum bounce.

We will work with spherically symmetric models of general relativity. The phase-space variables are the components of the symmetry-reduced triad and extrinsic curvature components,[3] with Poisson brackets given by

$$\{E^r(r_a), K_r(r_b)\} = \{E^\varphi(r_a), K_\varphi(r_b)\} = -\delta(r_a - r_b). \tag{1}$$

In addition, we will include the dynamics through a spherically symmetric scalar field:

$$\{\phi(r_a), P_\phi(r_b)\} = \delta(r_a - r_b). \tag{2}$$

In these effective midisuperspaces, the quantized notion of spacetime collides with the continuous diffeomorphism symmetry of general relativity. Hence, we will search for effective theories that explicitly satisfy covariance through Dirac's algebra,

$$\{D[N_1^r], D[N_2^r]\} = D[N_1^r N_2^{r\prime} - N_1^{r\prime} N_2^r], \tag{3a}$$

$$\{D[N^r], H[N]\} = H[N^r N'], \tag{3b}$$

$$\{H[N_1], H[N_2]\} = D[\beta E^r (E^\varphi)^{-2} (N_1 N_2' - N_1' N_2)], \tag{3c}$$

where $H[N] := \int dr\, N\mathcal{H}$ and $D[N^r] := \int dr\, N^r \mathcal{D}$ are, respectively, the infinitesimal generators of normal and tangential hypersurface deformations and β stands for possible quantum modifications.

In terms of the above variables, the classical constraints read,

$$\mathcal{D} = -E^{r\prime}K_r + E^{\varphi}K'_{\varphi} + \phi' P_\phi, \tag{4}$$

$$\mathcal{H} = -\frac{E^{\varphi}}{2\sqrt{E^r}}(1+K_\varphi^2) - 2\sqrt{E^r}K_rK_\varphi + \frac{(E^{r\prime})^2}{8\sqrt{E^r}E^{\varphi}} - \frac{\sqrt{E^r}}{2E^{\varphi 2}}E^{r\prime}E^{\varphi\prime} + \frac{\sqrt{E^r}}{2E^{\varphi}}E^{r\prime\prime}$$
$$+ \frac{P_\phi^2}{2\sqrt{E^r}E^{\varphi}} + \frac{(E^r)^{3/2}}{2E^{\varphi}}(\phi')^2 + \sqrt{E^r}E^{\varphi}V(\phi). \tag{5}$$

2. Deformed algebra

Previous studies acknowledge that holonomy corrections cannot be implemented in the presence of minimally coupled matter fields.[4] In fact, we extended that affirmation to the case when no coupling between the radial derivatives of the triads and curvature components are considered.[5]

For that reason, here we suggest a more ambitious approach in which we compute the algebraic relations (3) for the classical diffeomorphism constraint (4) along with a generic Hamiltonian constraint,

$$\mathcal{H} = a_0 + (E^{r\prime})^2 a_{rr} + (E^{\varphi\prime})^2 a_{\varphi\varphi} + (\phi')^2 a_{\phi\phi}$$
$$+ E^{r\prime}E^{\varphi\prime}a_{r\varphi} + E^{r\prime}\phi' a_{r\phi} + E^{\varphi\prime}\phi' a_{\varphi\phi} + E^{r\prime\prime}a_2, \tag{6}$$

that contains all quadratic combinations of the radial derivatives of E^r, E^{φ}, ϕ. The coefficients are given in terms of certain free functions $a_{ij} = a_{ij}(E^r, E^{\varphi}, \phi, K_r, K_\varphi, P_\phi)$, with $i,j = r, \varphi, \phi$, that depend on all the variables and momenta of the model. Concerning second-order radial derivatives, only $E^{r\prime\prime}$ has been considered, as it also appears in the classical Hamiltonian (5). Finally, $a_0 = a_0(E^r, E^{\varphi}, \phi, K_r, K_\varphi, P_\phi)$ encodes all the different terms that do not contain any radial derivative.

2.1. The $\{\mathcal{D}, \mathcal{H}\}$ bracket

First, we compute the Poisson brackets between the modified Hamiltonian constraint (6) and the classical diffeomorphism constraint (4). A number of anomalies appear, which can be easily solved. This procedure leads to the following most general form of the Hamiltonian constraint

$$\mathcal{H} = -\sqrt{E^r}\frac{g}{2}\Big(E^{\varphi}b_0 + E^{\varphi-1}(E^{r\prime})^2 b_{rr} - E^{\varphi-1}(\phi')^2 b_{\phi\phi} + E^{\varphi-1}E^{r\prime}\phi' b_{r\phi}$$
$$+ E^{\varphi-2}E^{r\prime}E^{\varphi\prime} - E^{\varphi-1}E^{r\prime\prime}\Big), \tag{7}$$

which provides a weakly vanishing bracket with the classical diffeomorphism constraint. In this expression, $b_0 = b_0(E^r, \phi, K_r/E^{\varphi}, K_\varphi, P_\phi/E^{\varphi})$ and $b_{ij} = b_{ij}(E^r, \phi, K_r/E^{\varphi}, K_\varphi, P_\phi/E^{\varphi})$, with $i,j = r, \phi$, are arbitrary functions of all possible scalar combinations of the model. In addition, a generic global factor g has been defined. The anomaly-free bracket between this constraint and the diffeomorphism constraint reads,

$$\{D[N^r], H[N]\} = H[N^r N'] + H[\mathcal{G}], \tag{8}$$

with the smearing $\mathcal{G}$ being a function of N, N^r, g and their derivatives. Nonetheless, for the Hamiltonian to be a density of weight $+1$, it is necessary that the global factor g is a scalar function. This means that all its arguments must be scalar quantities and thus the global factor takes the form $g = g(E^r, \phi, K_r/E^\varphi, K_\varphi, P_\phi/E^\varphi)$. Under this last condition, the function $\mathcal{G}$ vanishes. Hence, for any scalar global factor g, the bracket between the modified Hamiltonian constraint (7) and the diffeomorphism constraint (4) is given by its classical form (3b).

2.2. The $\{H, H\}$ bracket

The requirement of anomaly freedom in the bracket between the modified Hamiltonian constraint with itself, $\{H, H\}$, immediately fixes the form of the Hamiltonian with respect to all the densities (K_r, E^φ, P_ϕ), except as arguments of the global factor g. Hence, let us define the new modified constraint:

$$\mathcal{H} = -\sqrt{E^r}\frac{g}{2}\left(E^\varphi\left(f_0 + \frac{K_r}{E^\varphi}f_1 + \frac{P_\phi}{E^\varphi}h_0 + \frac{P_\phi^2}{E^{\varphi 2}}f_3\right)\right.$$
$$+ \frac{(E^{r\prime})^2}{E^\varphi}\left(f_2 + \frac{K_r}{E^\varphi}h + \frac{P_\phi}{E^\varphi}h_1 + \frac{P_\phi^2}{E^{\varphi 2}}h_2\right)$$
$$\left. + \frac{(\phi')^2}{E^\varphi}f_4 + \frac{E^{r\prime}\phi'}{E^\varphi}\left(h_3 + \frac{P_\phi}{E^\varphi}h_4\right) + \frac{E^{r\prime}E^{\varphi\prime}}{E^{\varphi 2}} - \frac{E^{r\prime\prime}}{E^\varphi}\right), \tag{9}$$

where $h = h(E^r, \phi, K_\varphi)$, $f_i = f_i(E^r, \phi, K_\varphi)$ and $h_i = h_i(E^r, \phi, K_\varphi)$, for $i = 0, 1, 2, 3, 4$, are free functions of the scalar variables (E^r, ϕ, K_φ). Note that the form of the classical Hamiltonian (5) is recovered for $f_0 \to (1 + K_\varphi^2)/E^r$, $f_1 \to 4K_\varphi$, $f_2 \to -1/(4E^r)$, $f_3 \to -1/E^r$, $f_4 \to -E^r$, $g \to 1$ and for a vanishing value of all the functions h_i and h. With this definition at hand, it is now possible to reduce the requirement of vanishing anomalies to the following system of differential equations:

$$\frac{\partial f_0}{\partial K_\varphi} = 2f_0 h - 2f_1 f_2 - h_0 h_3 + \frac{\partial f_1}{\partial E^r}, \tag{10a}$$

$$\frac{\partial f_1}{\partial K_\varphi} = f_1 h_4 + 4f_3 f_4, \tag{10b}$$

$$\frac{\partial f_2}{\partial K_\varphi} = -h_1 h_3 + \frac{\partial h}{\partial E^r}, \tag{10c}$$

$$\frac{\partial f_4}{\partial K_\varphi} = 2f_4(h - h_4), \tag{10d}$$

$$\frac{\partial f_3}{\partial K_\varphi} = -2f_1 h_2 + 2f_3(h - h_4), \tag{10e}$$

$$\frac{\partial f_1}{\partial \phi} = f_1 h_3 + 2h_0 f_4 \tag{10f}$$

$$\frac{\partial h_0}{\partial K_\varphi} = h_0(2h - h_4) - 2f_1 h_1 - 2f_3 h_3, \tag{10g}$$

$$\frac{\partial h_1}{\partial K_\varphi} = -h_1 h_4 - 2h_2 h_3, \tag{10h}$$

$$\frac{\partial h_2}{\partial K_\varphi} = -2h_2 h_4, \tag{10i}$$

$$\frac{\partial h_3}{\partial K_\varphi} = h_3(h - h_4) - 2h_1 f_4 + \frac{\partial h}{\partial \phi}, \tag{10j}$$

$$\frac{\partial h_4}{\partial K_\varphi} = h_4(h - h_4) - 4h_2 f_4 + \frac{\partial h}{\partial K_\varphi}. \tag{10k}$$

This is a system of eleven first-order partial differential equations for the eleven functions f_i, h_i, and h. The non-linearity of the system due to quadratic combinations of the functions makes the analytical resolution to be very complicated. But it is clear that the possible dependence of the Hamiltonian on the curvature component K_φ is severely restricted, since all the equations except one contain derivatives of the different functions with respect to K_φ.

In summary, whenever the above differential relations are satisfied, the constraint (9) will form a first-class algebra with the classical diffeomorphism constraint, and it will weakly commute with itself: $\{H[N_1], H[N_2]\} \approx 0$. Nonetheless, for H to be the generator of infinitesimal normal hypersurface deformations, one must impose an additional condition on the global factor, that is, $g = \exp(-2\int h\, dK_\varphi)$. In this way, the Poisson bracket of (9) with itself will be of the form (3c) with a deformation function,

$$\beta = \frac{g^2}{4}\left(\frac{\partial f_1}{\partial K_\varphi} + \left(\frac{E^{r\prime}}{E^\varphi}\right)^2 \frac{\partial h}{\partial K_\varphi}\right). \tag{11}$$

3. The vacuum reduction

Before trying a particular solution for the complete anomaly system (10), we proceed to solve the vacuum model. In the absence of matter, f_3, f_4, h_0, h_1, h_2, h_3 and h_4 vanish and we only need to worry about the reduced versions of (10a) and (10c) (Eq. (10b) is an additional restriction that appears only when matter is incorporated).

The general solution for the remaining functions f_0, f_1, f_2 and h can be written in terms of the global factor $g(E^r, K_\varphi)$ and two integration functions $f = f(E^r, K_\varphi)$ and $v = v(E^r)$. More precisely, the form of the modified vacuum Hamiltonian constraint reads,

$$\mathcal{H} = -\sqrt{E^r}\left[E^\varphi\left(\frac{1+f^2}{v}\frac{\partial v}{\partial E^r} + \frac{\partial f^2}{\partial E^r}\right) + K_r\frac{\partial f^2}{\partial K_\varphi} - g\frac{E^{r\prime\prime}}{2E^\varphi}\right.$$
$$\left. + g\frac{E^{r\prime}E^{\varphi\prime}}{2E^{\varphi 2}} - \left(\frac{E^{r\prime}}{2E^\varphi}\right)^2\left(\frac{E^\varphi}{v}\frac{\partial(gv)}{\partial E^r} + K_r\frac{\partial g}{\partial K_\varphi}\right)\right]. \tag{12}$$

In addition, we have been able to obtain a weak Dirac observable of the system,

$$m = \frac{v}{2}\left(1 + f^2 - g\left(\frac{E^{r\prime}}{2E^\varphi}\right)^2\right), \tag{13}$$

which commutes on-shell with the total Hamiltonian $\dot{m} = \{m, H[N] + D[N^r]\} \approx 0$, and represents the mass. In particular, the classical limit of the system is obtained for $g \to 1$, $f \to K_\varphi$ and $v \to \sqrt{E^r}$. In this limit, the above observable is just the usual expression of the Hawking (Schwarzschild) mass.

It is interesting to note that the expression of the effective mass (13) can be used to rewrite the deformation function as follows:

$$\beta = \frac{g^2}{2}\left(\frac{\partial}{\partial K_\varphi}\left[\frac{1}{g}\frac{\partial f^2}{\partial K_\varphi}\right] - \frac{1}{g}\frac{\partial^2 \ln g}{\partial K_\varphi^2}\left(1 + f^2 - \frac{2m}{v}\right)\right), \qquad (14)$$

which is free from radial derivatives.

4. An effective Hamiltonian with holonomy corrections

In effective models for cosmological scenarios, holonomy corrections are usually implemented through a polymerization of the connection components. In our current scenario, only K_φ might be subjected to modifications, since the dependence of the Hamiltonian on the other two momenta, K_r and P_ϕ, is completely fixed in (9).

Furthermore, we will search for the Hamiltonian that remains the most similar to the classical constraint. Hence, we fix the matter coefficients $f_3 = -1/E^r$ and $f_4 = -E^r$ (although further couplings with K_φ might be present through the global factor g). In addition, we consider that the scalar field ϕ only appears in a classical potential term $V(\phi)$.

Now, we can obtain a solution to the system (10) in terms of three integration functions $f = f(E^r, K_\varphi)$, $v = v(E^r)$ and $w = w(E^r)$:

$$f_1 = \frac{2}{g}\frac{\partial f^2}{\partial K_\varphi}, \qquad (15a)$$

$$f_2 = -\frac{1}{2}\frac{\partial \ln(gv)}{\partial E^r}, \qquad (15b)$$

$$h = h_4 = -\frac{1}{2}\frac{\partial \ln g}{\partial K_\varphi}, \qquad (15c)$$

$$g = \left(\frac{\partial f}{\partial K_\varphi}\right)^2 \left(1 + \frac{w}{f^2}\right)^{-1}, \qquad (15d)$$

$$f_0 = \frac{2}{g}\left(\frac{\partial f^2}{\partial E^r} + (1 + f^2)\frac{\partial \ln v}{\partial E^r} - V(\phi)\right), \qquad (15e)$$

$$h_0 = h_1 = h_2 = h_3 = 0. \qquad (15f)$$

Notice that when $V(\phi) = 0$, the solutions for f_0, f_1, f_2 and h take exactly the same form as that in the previous section. However, while in the vacuum model the global factor was completely free, when we couple matter g is determined by f and w through relation (15d). In essence, we lost one degree of freedom involving K_φ.

Classically, we have that $f(E^r, K_\varphi) = K_\varphi$. Therefore, in the classical limit $v \to \sqrt{E^r}$ and $w \to 0$. Indeed, we fix these two functions to their classical values in order to find the polymerized constraint that is closest to (5). In this way, we obtain

$$\mathcal{H} = -\frac{E^\varphi}{2\sqrt{E^r}}\left(1+f^2+4E^r f\frac{\partial f}{\partial E^r}\right) - 2\sqrt{E^r}K_r f\frac{\partial f}{\partial K_\varphi}$$
$$+ \left(\frac{(E^{r\prime})^2}{8\sqrt{E^r}E^\varphi} - \frac{\sqrt{E^r}}{2E^{\varphi 2}}E^{r\prime}E^{\varphi\prime} + \frac{\sqrt{E^r}E^{r\prime\prime}}{2E^\varphi}\right)\left(\frac{\partial f}{\partial K_\varphi}\right)^2$$
$$+ \left(\frac{P_\phi^2}{2\sqrt{E^r}E^\varphi} + \frac{E^{r3/2}(\phi')^2}{2E^\varphi}\right)\left(\frac{\partial f}{\partial K_\varphi}\right)^2 + \sqrt{E^r}E^\varphi V(\phi)$$
$$+ \frac{\sqrt{E^r}}{2E^{\varphi 2}}E^{r\prime}(E^{r\prime}K_r+\phi' P_\phi)\frac{\partial f}{\partial K_\varphi}\frac{\partial^2 f}{\partial K_\varphi{}^2} + \frac{\sqrt{E^r}}{2E^\varphi}(E^{r\prime})^2\frac{\partial f}{\partial K_\varphi}\frac{\partial^2 f}{\partial E^r \partial K_\varphi}, \quad (16)$$

which forms a first-class algebra along with the classical diffeomorphism constraint for any function $f=f(E^r,K_\varphi)$. This result allows us to consider holonomy corrections in the presence of a scalar field. In fact, these modifications can be made scale-dependent thanks to the free dependence on E^r. Nonetheless, in order to obtain a K_φ-periodic Hamiltonian constraint, we will restrict ourselves to a scale-invariant function. Setting $f=\sin(\lambda K_\varphi)/\lambda$,

$$\mathcal{H}^{(pol)} = -\frac{E^\varphi}{2\sqrt{E^r}}\left(1+\frac{\sin^2(\lambda K_\varphi)}{\lambda^2}\right) - \sqrt{E^r}K_r\frac{\sin(2\lambda K_\varphi)}{\lambda}\left(1+\left(\frac{\lambda E^{r\prime}}{2E^\varphi}\right)^2\right)$$
$$+ \left(\frac{(E^{r\prime})^2}{8\sqrt{E^r}E^\varphi} - \frac{\sqrt{E^r}}{2E^{\varphi 2}}E^{r\prime}E^{\varphi\prime} + \frac{\sqrt{E^r}}{2E^\varphi}E^{r\prime\prime}\right)$$
$$+ \left(\frac{P_\phi^2}{2\sqrt{E^r}E^\varphi} + \frac{E^{r3/2}(\phi')^2}{2E^\varphi}\right)\cos^2(\lambda K_\varphi)$$
$$+ \sqrt{E^r}E^\varphi V(\phi) - \frac{\sqrt{E^r}}{4E^{\varphi 2}}E^{r\prime}\phi' P_\phi \lambda \sin(2\lambda K_\varphi). \quad (17)$$

This constraint satisfies relation (3c) with the deformation function,

$$\beta = \cos^2(\lambda K_\varphi)\left(1+\left(\frac{\lambda E^{r\prime}}{2E^\varphi}\right)^2\right). \quad (18)$$

Following the results in the previous section, we can find the effective mass for this polymerized model:

$$m_{pol} = \frac{\sqrt{E^r}}{2}\left(1+\frac{\sin^2(\lambda K_\varphi)}{\lambda^2} - \left(\frac{E^{r\prime}}{2E^\varphi}\right)^2\cos^2(\lambda K_\varphi)\right). \quad (19)$$

While in vacuum it is a weak observable, the addition of matter makes its evolution non-trivial. Nevertheless, in either case, we can write the deformation as a function of this polymerized mass:

$$\beta = 1+\lambda^2\left(1-\frac{2m_{pol}}{\sqrt{E^r}}\right). \quad (20)$$

In this way, β is covariantly defined. The positiveness requirement for β that can be read from (18) means that the model has a lower bound for the radial component of the triad,

$$\sqrt{E^r} \geq \frac{2\lambda^2 m_{pol}}{1+\lambda^2}. \quad (21)$$

Its saturation corresponds to $\beta = 0$, i.e. the point where the curvature departs most from its classical behavior. In vacuum, m_{pol} should be positive (it is a generalized Schwarzschild mass), and the classical singularity at $E^r = 0$ is inside the forbidden region. In the dynamical case, in order to check whether the system might reach the singularity, one should study the behavior of m_{pol} as E^r approaches zero.

5. Discussion

We have systematically built modified spherically symmetric models coupled to a scalar matter field through a comprehensive study of Dirac's deformation algebra for a generic constraint with quadratic dependence on radial derivatives. The main result of our study is the modified Hamiltonian constraint (9), along with the consistency equations (10) that ensure that the theory remains covariant.

We have found the general vacuum solution in terms of two free functions, which provides the anomaly-free Hamiltonian (12). Moreover, the weak Dirac observable (13) can be interpreted as the mass of the modified system since its classical limit yields the Schwarzschild mass.

Then, we have obtained a particular solution for the full system of anomaly equations and found that a covariant polymerization of the system is possible even under the presence of a scalar field. This solution has led us to the constraint (16), which is parametrized by one free function of E^r and K_φ.

Finally, the polymeric constraint (17) shows a regular behavior for all values of K_φ and forms a first-class algebra with a deformation given by (20). The vanishing of this function corresponds to a minimum positive value of E^r and avoids the classical singularity.

Acknowledgments

AAB receives financial support from the FPI PRE2018-086516 fellowship. This work is funded by Project FIS2017-85076-P (MINECO/AEI/FEDER, UE) and Basque Government Grant No. IT956-16.

References

1. A. Ashtekar and P. Singh, "Loop Quantum Cosmology: A Status Report", *Class. Quant. Grav.* **28**, 213001 (2011).
2. I. Agullo and P. Singh, "Loop Quantum Cosmology" in *Loop quantum gravity: The first 30 years*, edited by A. Ashtekar and J. Pullin (WSP, 2017), pp. 183-240.

3. M. Bojowald and R. Swiderski, "Spherically symmetric quantum geometry: Hamiltonian constraint", *Class. Quant. Grav.* **23**, 2129-2154 (2006).
4. M. Bojowald, S. Brahma, and J. D. Reyes, "Covariance in models of loop quantum gravity: Spherical symmetry", *Phys. Rev. D* **92**, 045043 (2015).
5. A. Alonso-Bardaji and D. Brizuela, "Holonomy and inverse-triad corrections in spherical models coupled to matter", *Eur. Phys. J. C* **81**, 283 (2021).
6. A. Alonso-Bardaji and D. Brizuela, "Anomaly-free deformations of spherical general relativiy coupled to matter", *Phys. Rev. D* **104**, 084064 (2021).

Infrared signatures of quantum bounce in collapsing geometry

Harkirat Singh Sahota* and Kinjalk Lochan†

*Department of Physical Sciences, Indian Institute of Science Education & Research (IISER)
Mohali, Sector 81 SAS Nagar, Manauli PO 140306 Punjab, India*
E-mail: ph17078@iisermohali.ac.in
†*E-mail: kinjalk@iisermohali.ac.in*

We study the radiation profile of the unitarily evolving wave packet constructed for the quantum model of spherically symmetric dust shell collapsing in marginally bound Lemaître-Tolman-Bondi (LTB) model. In this analysis, we consider the quantum model of dust shell collapse in LTB spacetime,[1] where the dust shell collapse to black hole singularity is replaced by a bounce. We identify the observable natural to collapse/expansion character of dust shell, and study the mode decomposition in the quantum model. The incoming/outgoing modes are associated with the eigenfunctions of the Hermitian extension of the operator corresponding to this observable. For the wave packet representing the collapsing and expanding phase of the dust shell, we estimate the contributions of the incoming/outgoing modes. We find that the collapsing and expanding branches do not comprise entirely of incoming and outgoing radiation. The dust shell dynamics is insensitive to the large wavenumber modes as their contribution is negligible. Near the bounce point, the contribution of outgoing (incoming) modes in the collapsing (expanding) branch is substantial and it decreases as the dust shell moves away from the singularity. In the early (later) stage of the collapsing (expanding) phase, the incoming (outgoing) modes dominate. As the dynamics of the dust shell is sensitive to the near-infrared modes of the radiation, the information of the bounce is carried over to infrared modes much before it reaches the observer. In the infrared regime, a flip is observed from largely incoming to largely outgoing radiation as the evolution progresses from collapsing to expanding phase. The information of the short-scale physics is carried over to the longest wavelength in this quantum gravity model.

Keywords: Shell collapse; quantum bounce.

1. Introduction

Ever since the original analysis by Hawking and Unruh,[2,3] the study of particle content of the vacuum and the radiation profile in various geometries have been the frontier research topic in the quantum effects in curved spacetime. These effects are investigated in the context of quantum field theories in the curved spacetime.[4] The key result in this paradigm is that the particle content in the quantum states is not a generally covariant notion, which is the gist of the Hawking-Unruh effect.

The analysis of matter collapse in a consistent quantum gravity model has been addressed in the context of dust shell collapse,[5,6] LTB dust collapse model in canonical quantum gravity[7,8] and loop quantum gravity.[9–11] The radiation profile of dust collapse in the LTB model is studied in[12,13] under the midisuperpace quantization of this model. The Hawking radiation is recovered from the regularized solution of the Wheeler-DeWitt equation for this model and the non-thermal correction to the spectrum and entropy associated are also computed. In this approach, the Hawking radiation is thought of as the projection of wave functional along the outgoing modes defined in that approach.

There are some issues associated with the aforementioned quantum models. The incoming/outgoing modes defined in this approach are not orthogonal, thus, rendering the notion of incoming/outgoing modes mathematically ill-defined. This issue stems from the fact that the momentum operator in this model is not Hermitian. Apart from that the states in the Kernel of Hamiltonian constraint need not be orthonormal as they are degenerate states with zero eigenvalue.

In this work, we study the radiation profile for the unitarily evolving wave packet constructed for the quantum model for dust shell collapse in a marginally bound LTB geometry.[1] For the collapsing/expanding character of the dust shell, momentum conjugate to areal radius is a good indicator. In the quantum model, we study the mode decomposition viz-a-viz the eigenstates of momentum operator.

2. Minisuperspace Construction of Dust Collapse in Marginal LTB Model

LTB model is an inhomogeneous extension of the FRW model, which is spherically symmetric and sourced by a non-rotational dust of energy density ϵ.[14] The line element for the LTB model is,

$$ds^2 = -c^2 d\tau^2 + \frac{R'^2}{1+2f(\rho)} d\rho^2 + R^2 d\Omega^2, \tag{1}$$

here τ is the dust proper time and $R(\tau, \rho)$ is the areal radius of dust shell with coordinate label ρ at time τ, and $f(\rho)$ is called the energy function. Here, we will restrict ourselves with the marginally bound case of the LTB model for which $f(\rho) = 0$. Einstein's equation for this model is,

$$\frac{F'}{R^2 R'} = \frac{8\pi G \epsilon}{c^2} \quad \text{and} \quad \frac{R \dot{R}^2}{c^2} = F, \tag{2}$$

where $F(\rho)$ is first integral of Einstein's equation and is equal to twice of the Misner-Sharp(MS) mass[15] for LTB spacetime. This model has a curvature singularity when the cloud collapses to a point i.e., at $R = 0$.

Since the equation of motion which dictates the dynamics of the areal radius (2) depends only on R and F, and not on their spatial derivatives, it implies that the different dust shells are dynamically decoupled for a given mass function. We can write an on-shell action which dictates the dynamics of the outermost dust shell. The dynamics of the full dust cloud is then deduced from the action.[1]

$$S = -\frac{1}{2} \int d\tau R \dot{R}^2 \tag{3}$$

Here R is the areal radius of the outermost dust shell. The Hamiltonian for this model is,

$$H = -\frac{P^2}{2R} \qquad (4)$$

Using Brown-Kuchař dust[16,17] as the matter source, the Hamiltonian constraint for the model takes the form

$$\mathcal{H} \equiv p_\tau + H \approx 0. \qquad (5)$$

Since the momentum conjugate to scalar field τ appears linearly, the Wheeler-DeWitt equation takes a Schrödinger equation like form,

$$i\hbar \frac{\partial \Psi(R,\tau)}{\partial \tau} = \frac{1}{2} R^{-1+a+b} \frac{d}{dR} R^{-a} \frac{d}{dR} R^{-b} \Psi(R,\tau). \qquad (6)$$

The Hamiltonian is the product of areal radius and conjugate momentum, which implies that it does not have a unique quantum counterpart and that the model suffers from operator ordering ambiguity which is parameterized by a and b in equation (6). The eigenvalue of the Hamiltonian is interpreted as the ADM energy. The Hilbert space $L^2(\mathbb{R}^+, R^{1-a-2b} dR)$ is chosen, that makes this Hamiltonian Hermitian. The self adjoint extensions of the Hamiltonian (6) are discussed in.[1] A unitarily evolving wave packet is constructed from positive energy eigenstates,

$$\phi_E^1(R) = \frac{2}{\sqrt{3}} E^{\frac{1}{4}} J_{2|q|/3}\left(\frac{2}{3}\sqrt{2E} R^{\frac{3}{2}}\right). \qquad (7)$$

by choosing a Poisson-like distribution

$$A(\sqrt{E}) = \frac{\sqrt{2}\lambda^{\frac{1}{2}(\kappa+1)}}{\sqrt{\Gamma(\kappa+1)}} \sqrt{E}^{\kappa+\frac{1}{2}} e^{-\frac{\lambda}{2} E}, \qquad (8)$$

$$\psi(R,\tau) = \int_0^\infty d\sqrt{E} \phi_E(R) e^{iE\tau} A(\sqrt{E}), \qquad (9)$$

where the parameters of the distribution satisfy $\kappa \geq 0$ and $\lambda > 0$. The expectation value of the Hamiltonian operator with this choice of distribution is inversely proportional to λ. To simplify the expression, a prescription $\kappa = |1+a|/3$ is adopted[1] and the expression for the wave packet reduces to

$$\psi(R,\tau) = \sqrt{3} \frac{R^{\frac{1}{2}(1+a+|1+a|+2b)}}{\sqrt{\Gamma(\frac{1}{3}|1+a|+1)}} \left(\frac{\frac{\sqrt{2\lambda}}{3}}{\frac{\lambda}{2} - i\tau}\right)^{\frac{1}{3}|1+a|+1} e^{-\frac{2R^3}{9(\frac{\lambda}{2}-i\tau)}}. \qquad (10)$$

This choice comes at the cost that the distribution is now a function of operator ordering parameters. Since the dependence of observables on this parameter is contentious, one cannot be sure if it is a genuine signature of operator ordering or just a dependence on the shape of the distribution. In this analysis, we will focus on the radiation profile of the dust shell and address operator ordering ambiguity elsewhere.[18]

3. Mode Decomposition of Wave Packet

In the earlier midisuperspace models, various prescriptions are used to write incoming and outgoing modes. In,[12] the modes are associated with the asymptotic limit of the solutions of the WDW equation on $\mathcal{I}^+$ written in terms of the Killing time. While in,[13] the modes are associated with the positive/negative frequency solutions of the WDW equation after making transformation from the comoving time to the Killing time. In all these prescriptions, the modes are not orthonormal, making them ill-defined for the Bogoliubov analysis. The problem might lie with the fact that the states belong to the Kernel space of the operator and are degenerate and therefore, orthonormality is not guaranteed. Therefore, we need to identify another observable suitable for the mode decomposition.

Classically, the momentum conjugate to areal radius is given by $P = -R\dot{R}$ and we can associate positive momentum with the collapsing phase and negative momentum with the expanding phase of the dust shell. Thus, the momentum operator is a good choice for an observable that depicts the mode decomposition in the quantum model. The model[1] discussed in the previous section is robust enough for us to accommodate Hermitian Hamiltonian and momentum operator. Although the momentum operator on real half line is not self-adjoint, we will work with the Hermitian extension of the momentum operator. The detailed discussion on the self-adjointness and the Hermiticity of the momentum operator can be found in[18] and we have shown that the states are orthogonal in this case, making them suitable as incoming/outgoing modes.

Using the measure R^2 following the quantum scattering theory in spherical polar coordinates, we have a constraint $1+a+2b=0$ on operator ordering parameters. For this model, the expectation value of the general observable in a general wave packet is independent of the parameter b.[18] Therefore it appears as a free parameter in the model and the above constraint does not affect the physical content of the model. In this case, the Hermitian extension of the momentum operator is $\hat{P} = -iR^{-1}\partial_R R$. The eigenfunction of the momentum operator with eigenvalue k is given by e^{ikR}/R, where $k \in \mathbb{R}$. The wave packet can be expressed in the form,

$$\psi(R,\tau) = \int_0^\infty dE \int_0^\infty dk \left(\mathcal{A}(k,E) \frac{e^{ikR+i\tau E}}{R} + \mathcal{A}(-k,E) \frac{e^{-ikR+i\tau E}}{R} \right). \quad (11)$$

The contribution of incoming/outgoing radiation in the dust cloud is estimated by computing the projection of wave packet along incoming($u_{k,E} \equiv e^{ikR+iE\tau}/R$) and outgoing modes($u_{-k,E} \equiv e^{-ikR+iE\tau}/R$).

$$\tilde{\psi}_k(\tau) = \langle u_{k,E}(\tau)|\psi(R,\tau)\rangle = \int dR\, R^2\, \psi(R,\tau) \frac{e^{-ikR-iE\tau}}{R}, \quad (12)$$

$$= \frac{\sqrt{3}e^{-iE\tau}}{\sqrt{\Gamma(\frac{2}{3}|b|+1)}} \left(\frac{\frac{\sqrt{2\lambda}}{3}}{\frac{\lambda}{2}-i\tau}\right)^{\frac{2}{3}|b|+1} \int dR\, e^{-ikR} R^{1+|b|} e^{-\frac{2R^3}{9(\frac{\lambda}{2}-i\tau)}}, \quad (13)$$

$$= C(\tau) \int dR\, e^{-ikR} R^{1+|b|} e^{-\frac{2R^3}{9(\frac{\lambda}{2}-i\tau)}}. \quad (14)$$

The wavepacket in k space is normalized which implies $|\tilde{\psi}_k(\tau)|^2$ gives the contribution of modes with wavenumber k to the radiation profile at time τ. At $\tau = 0$, equation (14) can be written as

$$\tilde{\psi}_k(0) = C(0) \left(\int dR \, \cos(kR) \, R^{1+|b|} e^{-\frac{4R^3}{9\lambda}} - i \int dR \, \sin(kR) \, R^{1+|b|} e^{-\frac{4R^3}{9\lambda}} \right), \quad (15)$$

and we can see, $|\tilde{\psi}_k(0)|^2 = |\tilde{\psi}_{-k}(0)|^2$. Thus, at the point of classical singularity, the number of incoming modes is equal to the number of outgoing modes for all k. On the other hand, for finite τ, the equation (14) can be cast into the form,

$$|\tilde{\psi}_k(\tau)|^2 = |C(\tau)|^2 \int dR \int dS \, e^{-ik(R-S)} (RS)^{1+|b|} e^{-\frac{2R^3}{9\left(\frac{\lambda}{2}-i\tau\right)} - \frac{2S^3}{9\left(\frac{\lambda}{2}+i\tau\right)}}. \quad (16)$$

Here, $k \to -k$ is same as $\tau \to -\tau$. Thus, the ratio of incoming to outgoing modes $r_k(\tau) = |\tilde{\psi}_k(\tau)|^2/|\tilde{\psi}_{-k}(\tau)|^2$ flips after the bounce happens i.e. $r_k(\tau) = [r_k(-\tau)]^{-1}$, which can be seen in Fig. 1. The difference between the number of incoming and outgoing modes at an instant of time and at a fixed k can be written as,

$$\delta_k(\tau) = |\tilde{\psi}_k(\tau)|^2 - |\tilde{\psi}_{-k}(\tau)|^2, \quad (17)$$

$$= -2i |C(\tau)|^2 \int dR \int dS \, \sin(k(R-S)) (RS)^{1+|b|} e^{-\frac{2R^3}{9\left(\frac{\lambda}{2}-i\tau\right)} - \frac{2S^3}{9\left(\frac{\lambda}{2}+i\tau\right)}}. \quad (18)$$

$\delta_k(\tau)$ vanishes when $k \to \infty$, as $\lim_{k\to\infty} \sin(kx) = x\delta(x) = 0$. Thus, we expect the ratio to approach unity for large k, which can be seen in Fig. 1. On the other hand, for $k \to 0$ we have

$$\delta_k(\tau) = \frac{4k|C(\tau)|^2}{9^{(|b|+8)/3}} \Gamma\left[\frac{|b|}{3}+1\right] \Gamma\left[\frac{|b|+2}{3}\right] \left(\frac{\lambda^2}{4}+\tau^2\right)^{\frac{2|b|+5}{6}} \sin\left(\frac{1}{3}\tan^{-1}\left(\frac{-2\tau}{\lambda}\right)\right). \quad (19)$$

In the collapsing branch ($\tau < 0$), this function is positive and therefore, the incoming modes are dominating in this case. In the expanding branch ($\tau > 0$), this function is negative and the outgoing modes dominate in this case.

We have plotted the fraction of modes with wavenumber k and the ratio of the incoming to outgoing modes for fixed time in the Fig. 1 with the parameters specifying a narrow wave packet of unit energy. Early in the collapsing phase ($\tau = -10$), most of the contribution comes from the incoming modes and the outgoing modes contribute a small fraction only in the infrared (small k) regime. As we approach the classical singularity, the contribution of outgoing radiation in the collapsing phase keeps on increasing and becomes equals to the contribution of incoming radiation at the bounce point. After the bounce, initially in the expanding phase, there is significant contribution of incoming radiation. As the expansion progresses, this contribution keeps on decreasing to become negligible and contributes only in the infrared regime.

In the early stage of collapse, the ratio of incoming to outgoing modes starts from unity at $k = 0$ and comes back to one again at a finite wavenumber. In between,

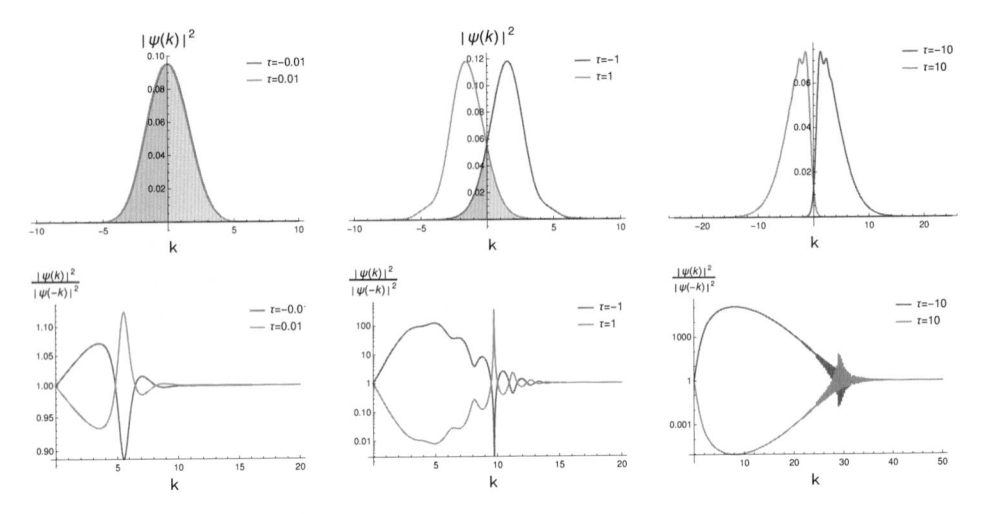

Fig. 1. Fraction of modes $|\tilde{\psi}_k(\tau)|^2$ and ratio of the incoming to outgoing modes vs k at different times. The blue shaded region gives the contribution of outgoing radiation in collapsing phase and the orange shaded region gives the contribution of incoming radiation in expanding phase.

the ratio attains a maximum and oscillates before settling at unity. Since for large wavenumbers, the contribution is minimal, these modes are insensitive to the dynamics of the dust shell. A ratio greater than one implies that the incoming modes are dominating. As we approach the bounce point, the magnitude of the maximum decreases and the ratio goes to unity at shorter wavenumber. At the bounce point, this ratio is one for all wavenumbers. Apart from this, there exists a crossover window of wavenumbers in which the fraction of outgoing modes is greater than incoming modes in the collapsing phase when the dust shell is closer to the classical singularity. This behavior is inverted for the expanding phase - the ratio attains a minimum before settling at unity.

Therefore, we see that the small wavenumber (infrared) modes are most sensitive to the dynamics of the dust cloud. If one observes in the infrared regime, there is an instantaneous flip from largely incoming to largely outgoing radiation when the dust shell goes from collapsing phase to expanding phase. Moreover, the contribution of the outgoing/incoming radiation in the collapsing/expanding regime is coming from the infrared part of the spectrum only. Thus, one should focus on the infrared regime of the dust shell for a signature of quantum bounce.

We have plotted the radiation profile for the wave packets which represents low energy dust shell broadly peaked ($\lambda = 10$) and high energy dust shells sharply peaked ($\lambda = 0.01$) on the classical trajectory in Fig. 2. We see that for the case of sharply peaked wave packet, the major contribution to radiation profile is coming from incoming (outgoing) modes in the collapsing (expanding) regime even near the classical singularity. Whereas, for low energy dust shells, the contribution of incoming (outgoing) modes in expanding (collapsing) branch is significant even far away from singularity.

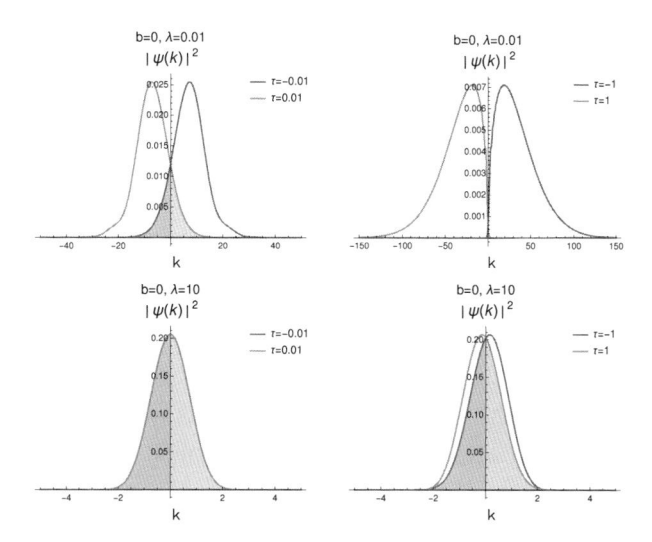

Fig. 2. Fraction of modes $|\tilde{\psi}_k(\tau)|^2$ and the ratio of incoming to outgoing modes for wave at different times. The parameters specify the high energy dust cloud ($\lambda = 0.01$) representing sharper wave packet, and low energy dust cloud($\lambda = 10$) representing broader wave packet.

At the classical singularity, the fraction of infrared modes is directly proportional to the minimal size of the dust shell i.e., the bounce radius.[18]

$$|\tilde{\psi}_{k\to 0}(0)|^2 = \frac{2^{(2|b|-5)/3} 3^{2/3} \Gamma\left(\frac{|b|+2}{3}\right)^2 \Gamma\left(\frac{2|b|+4}{3}\right)}{\sqrt{2\pi} \Gamma\left(\frac{2|b|+1}{3}\right) \Gamma\left(\frac{2|b|+3}{3}\right)} \bar{R}(0). \qquad (20)$$

Thus, the infrared regime of the radiation profile provides a direct estimation of the bounce radius.

4. Conclusions

In this work, we have studied the mode decomposition of wave packet constructed for the Quantum LTB model. We have considered the minisuperspace construction of the dust shell collapse in the LTB model.[1] The classical model of dust shell collapse exhibits black hole singularity which is replaced by bounce from the collapsing phase to expanding phase in the quantum model. We have identified the observable depicting mode decomposition, which is momentum conjugate to areal radius. After identifying the incoming and outgoing modes with the momentum's eigenstates with positive and negative eigenvalues, we have estimated the contribution of the incoming/outgoing modes in the contracting/expanding phase.

We choose the operator ordering parameters for which the Hamiltonian as well as the momentum operator are Hermitian. This is achieved by working with R^2 measure space and choosing the representation which is symmetric with this choice of inner product. This particular choice puts the constraint $a+2b+1 = 0$ on operator ordering parameters.

We find that at the point of classical singularity or bounce point $\tau = 0$, the number of incoming and outgoing modes is the same. In the contracting branch, apart from the incoming dust, we also have small contribution from the outgoing dust in the infrared regime. As the dust shell continues to move towards the singularity configuration, the contribution of outgoing modes in the infrared regime keeps increasing, culminating in an equal number of incoming and outgoing modes at the point of singularity. This behavior is inverted in the expanding branch. There exists a threshold wavenumber, above which the number of incoming modes is equal to the number of outgoing modes. For the contracting branch, the ratio of incoming to outgoing modes starts from one at $k = 0$, increases to attain a maximum, and then settles back to unity. After the bounce, outgoing modes start to dominate with a small fraction of incoming modes as well. As the dust shell expands, the fraction of the incoming modes keeps decreasing and while the contribution of the outgoing modes keeps increasing. At the later stage of dust shell expansion, most contribution comes from the outgoing modes. Thus, we can conclude that in quantum bounce, incoming radiation is always accompanied by outgoing radiation.

The infrared sector of the wave packet contains significant information about the dynamics of the dust cloud. The major contribution to the incoming/outgoing dust in collapsing/expanding branch comes from the modes with smaller wavenumber. There is a flip from largely incoming to largely outgoing radiation, observed in the infrared regime, as the evolution progresses from the contracting branch to the expanding branch. Therefore, the observer should look at small wavenumber or large wavelength modes to observe if the bounce has happened. Moreover, the fraction of infrared modes near classical singularity is proportional to the bounce radius. Thus, the infrared sector of the process apart from being highly sensitive to the dynamics of the dust cloud is also a direct estimator of the bounce radius, thereby, providing a unique infrared signature of the quantum gravity in the radiation profile of the dust cloud.

Acknowledgments

HSS would like to acknowledge the financial support from University Grants Commission, Government of India, in the form of Junior Research Fellowship (UGC-CSIR JRF/Dec- 2016/503905). Research of KL is partially supported by the Startup Research Grant of SERB, Government of India (SRG/2019/002202).

References

1. C. Kiefer and T. Schmitz, Singularity avoidance for collapsing quantum dust in the Lemaître-Tolman-Bondi model, *Physical Review D* **99**, p. 126010 (June 2019).
2. S. W. Hawking, Particle Creation by Black Holes, *Commun. Math. Phys.* **43**, 199 (1975), [Erratum: Commun. Math. Phys. 46, 206 (1976)].

3. W. G. Unruh, Notes on black-hole evaporation, *Phys. Rev. D* **14**, 870 (Aug 1976).
4. N. D. Birrell and P. C. W. Davies, *Quantum Fields in Curved Space*, Cambridge Monographs on Mathematical Physics (Cambridge Univ. Press, Cambridge, UK, 2 1984).
5. P. Hájíček and C. Kiefer, Singularity Avoidance by Collapsing Shells in Quantum Gravity, *International Journal of Modern Physics D* **10**, 775 (December 2001).
6. D. Malafarina, Classical Collapse to Black Holes and Quantum Bounces: A Review, *Universe* **3**, p. 48 (May 2017).
7. C. Vaz, L. Witten and T. P. Singh, Toward a midisuperspace quantization of LeMaître-Tolman-Bondi collapse models, *Physical Review D* **63**, p. 104020 (April 2001).
8. C. Vaz and L. Witten, Quantum black holes from quantum collapse, *Physical Review D* **64**, p. 084005 (September 2001).
9. M. Bojowald, T. Harada and R. Tibrewala, Lemaitre-Tolman-Bondi collapse from the perspective of loop quantum gravity, *Phys. Rev. D* **78**, p. 064057 (September 2008).
10. M. Bojowald, J. D. Reyes and R. Tibrewala, Nonmarginal Lemaitre-Tolman-Bondi-like models with inverse triad corrections from loop quantum gravity, *Phys. Rev. D* **80**, p. 084002 (October 2009).
11. K. Giesel, B.-F. Li and P. Singh, Non-singular quantum gravitational dynamics of an LTB dust shell model: The role of quantization prescriptions, *arXiv:2107.05797 [gr-qc]* (Aug 2021).
12. C. Vaz, C. Kiefer, T. P. Singh and L. Witten, Quantum general relativity and Hawking radiation, *Physical Review D* **67**, p. 024014 (January 2003).
13. C. Kiefer, J. Müller-Hill, T. P. Singh and C. Vaz, Hawking radiation from the quantum Lemaître-Tolman-Bondi model, *Physical Review D* **75**, p. 124010 (June 2007).
14. A. Krasinski, *Inhomogeneous cosmological models* (Cambridge Univ. Press, Cambridge, UK, 3 2011).
15. L. B. Szabados, Quasi-Local Energy-Momentum and Angular Momentum in General Relativity, *Living Reviews in Relativity* **12**, p. 4 (December 2009).
16. J. D. Brown and K. V. Kuchar, Dust as a Standard of Space and Time in Canonical Quantum Gravity, *Physical Review D* **51**, 5600 (May 1995).
17. H. Maeda, Unitary evolution of the quantum universe with a Brown-Kuchar dust, *Classical and Quantum Gravity* **32**, p. 235023 (December 2015).
18. H. S. Sahota and K. Lochan, Infrared signatures of quantum bounce in collapsing geometry, *arXiv:2110.06247 [gr-qc]* (Oct 2021).

Effective black hole interior and the Raychadhuri equation

Keagan Blanchette

Department of Physics and Astronomy, York University
4700 Keele Street, Toronto, Ontario M3J 1P3 Canada
E-mail: kblanch@yorku.ca

Saurya Das

Theoretical Physics Group and Quantum Alberta, Department of Physics and Astronomy,
University of Lethbridge, 4401 University Drive, Lethhbridge, Alberta T1K 3M4, Canada
E-mail: saurya.das@uleth.ca

Samantha Hergott

Department of Physics and Astronomy, York University
4700 Keele Street, Toronto, Ontario M3J 1P3 Canada
E-mail: sherrgs@yorku.ca

Saeed Rastgoo

Department of Physics and Astronomy, York University
4700 Keele Street, Toronto, Ontario M3J 1P3 Canada
E-mail: srastgoo@yorku.ca

We show that loop quantum gravity effects leads to the finiteness of expansion and its rate of change in the effective regime in the interior of the Schwarzschild black hole. As a consequence the singularity is resolved. We find this in line with previous results about curvature scalar and strong curvature singularities in Kantowski-Sachs model which is isometric to Schwarzschild interior.

Keywords: Black hole singularity, loop quantum gravity, expansion, Raychaudhuri equation

1. Introduction

Singularities are well-known predictions of General Relativity (GR). They are recognized as regions that geodesics can reach in finite proper time but cannot be extended beyond them. Such geodesics are called incomplete. This notion can be formulated in terms of the existence of conjugate points using the Raychaudhuri equation.[1] The celebrated Hawking-Penrose singularity theorems prove that under normal assumptions, all spacetime solutions of GR will have incomplete geodesics, and will therefore be singular.[1–3] These objects, however, are in fact predictions beyond the domain of applicability of GR. So there is a consensus among the gravitational physics community that they should be regularized in a full theory of quantum gravity. Although there is no such theory available yet, nevertheless there are a few candidates with rigorous mathematical structure with which we can investigate the question of singularity resolution. One such candidate is loop quantum gravity (LQG),[4] which is a connection-based canonical framework.

Within LQG, there have been numerous studies of both the interior and the full spacetime of black holes in four and lower dimensions.[5–18] These attempts were originally inspired by loop quantum cosmology (LQC), more precisely a certain quantization of the isotropic Friedmann-Lemaitre-Robertson-Walker (FLRW) model[19,20] which uses a certain type of quantization of the phase space variables called polymer quantization.[21–25] This quantiztion introduces a so called polymer parameter that sets the scale at which the quantum effects become important. There are various schemes of such quantization based on the form of the polymer parameter.

In this paper, we examine the issue of singularity resolution via the LQG-modified Raychaudhuri equation for the interior of the Schwarzschild black hole. By choosing adapted holonomies and fluxes, which are the conjugate variables in LQG, and using polymer quantization, we compute the corresponding expansion of geodesics and derive the effective Raychaudhuri equation. This way we show effective terms introduce a repulsive effect which prevents the formation of conjugate points. This implies that the classical singularity theorems are rendered invalid and the singularity is resolved, at least for the spacetime under consideration. The boundedness of expansion scalar and the resolution of strong curvature singularities have been studied and shown in the context of Kantowski-Sachs model in.[26,27]

This paper is organized as follows. In Sec. 2, we review the classical interior of the Schwarzschild black hole. In Sec. 3, we briefly discuss the classical Raychaudhuri equation and its importance. Then, in Sec. 4.1 we present the behavior of the Raychaudhuri equation in the classical regime. In Sec. 4.2, the effective Raychaudhuri equation for three different schemes of polymer quantization are derived and are compared with the classical behavior. Finally, in Sec. 5 we briefly discuss our results and conclude.

2. Interior of the Schwarzschild black hole

It is well known that the metric of the interior of the Schwarzschild black hole can be obtained by switching the the Schwarzschild coordinates t and r, due to the fact that spacelike and timelike curves switch their causal nature upon crossing the horizon. This yields the metric of the interior as

$$ds^2 = -\left(\frac{2GM}{t} - 1\right)^{-1} dt^2 + \left(\frac{2GM}{t} - 1\right) dr^2 + t^2\left(d\theta^2 + \sin^2\theta d\phi^2\right). \quad (1)$$

This metric is in fact a special case of a Kantowski-Sachs cosmological spacetime[28]

$$ds^2_{KS} = -N(T)^2 dT^2 + g_{xx}(T) dx^2 + g_{\theta\theta}(T) d\theta^2 + g_{\phi\phi}(T) d\phi^2 \quad (2)$$

One can obtain the Hamiltonian of the interior system in connection variables, one first considers the full Hamiltonian of gravity written in terms of (the curvature) of the $su(2)$ Ashtekar-Barbero connection A^i_a and its conjugate momentum, the densitized triad $\tilde{E}^i_a$. Using the Kantowski-Sachs symmetry, these variables can be written as[5]

$$A^i_a \tau_i dx^a = \frac{c}{L_0} \tau_3 dx + b\tau_2 d\theta - b\tau_1 \sin\theta d\phi + \tau_3 \cos\theta d\phi, \qquad (3)$$

$$\tilde{E}^a_i \tau_i \partial_a = p_c \tau_3 \sin\theta \partial_x + \frac{p_b}{L_0} \tau_2 \sin\theta \partial_\theta - \frac{p_b}{L_0} \tau_1 \partial_\phi, \qquad (4)$$

where b, c, p_b, and p_c are functions that only depend on time and $\tau_i = -i\sigma_i/2$ are a $su(2)$ basis satisfying $[\tau_i, \tau_j] = \epsilon_{ij}{}^k \tau_k$, with σ_i being the Pauli matrices. Here L_0 is a fiducial length of a fiducial volume, chosen to restrict the integration limits of the symplectic form so that the integral does not diverge. Substituting these into the full Hamiltonian of gravity written in Ashtekar connection variables, one obtains the symmetry reduced Hamiltonian constraint adapted to this model as[5–7,10,16]

$$H = -\frac{N}{2G\gamma^2} \left[(b^2 + \gamma^2) \frac{p_b}{\sqrt{p_c}} + 2bc\sqrt{p_c} \right]. \qquad (5)$$

while the diffeomorphism constraint vanishes identically due to the homogenous nature of the model. Here, γ is the Barbero-Immirzi parameter,[4] and $p_c \geq 0$. The corresponding Poisson brackets of the model become

$$\{c, p_c\} = 2G\gamma, \qquad \{b, p_b\} = G\gamma. \qquad (6)$$

The general form of the Kantowski-Sachs metric written in terms of the above variables becomes

$$ds^2 = -N(T)^2 dT^2 + \frac{p_b^2(T)}{L_0^2 p_c(T)} dx^2 + p_c(T)(d\theta^2 + \sin^2\theta d\phi^2). \qquad (7)$$

Comparing this with the standard Schwarzschild interior metric one obtains

$$p_b = 0, \qquad p_c = 4G^2 M^2, \qquad \text{on the horizon } t = 2GM, \qquad (8)$$
$$p_b \to 0, \qquad p_c \to 0, \qquad \text{at the singularity } t \to 0. \qquad (9)$$

3. The Raychaudhuri equation

The celebrated Raychaudhuri equation[1]

$$\frac{d\theta}{d\tau} = -\frac{1}{3}\theta^2 - \sigma_{ab}\sigma^{ab} + \omega_{ab}\omega^{ab} - R_{ab}U^a U^b \qquad (10)$$

describes the behavior of geodesics in spacetime purely geometrically and independent of the theory of gravity under consideration. Here, θ is the expansion term describing how geodesics focus or defocus; $\sigma_{ab}\sigma^{ab}$ is the shear which describes how, e.g., a circular configuration of geodesics changes shape into, say, an ellipse; $\omega_{ab}\omega^{ab}$ is the vorticity term; R_{ab} is the Ricci tensor; and U^a is the tangent vector to the geodesics. Note that, due the sign of the expansion, shear, and the Ricci term, they all contribute to focusing, while the vorticity terms leads to defocusing.

In our case, since we consider the model in vacuum, $R_{ab} = 0$. Also, in general in Kantowski-Sachs models, the vorticity term is only nonvanishing if one considers metric perturbations.[28] Hence, $\omega_{ab}\omega^{ab} = 0$ in our model, too. This reduces the Raychaudhuri equation for our analysis to

$$\frac{d\theta}{d\tau} = -\frac{1}{3}\theta^2 - \sigma_{ab}\sigma^{ab}. \tag{11}$$

To obtain the right hand side of the equation above, we need to consider a congruence of geodesics and derive their expansion and shear. By choosing such a congruence with 4-velocities $U^a = \left(\frac{1}{N}, 0, 0, 0\right)$ we obtain

$$\theta = \frac{\dot{p}_b}{Np_b} + \frac{\dot{p}_c}{2Np_c}, \tag{12}$$

$$\sigma^2 = \frac{2}{3}\left(-\frac{\dot{p}_b}{Np_b} + \frac{\dot{p}_c}{Np_c}\right)^2. \tag{13}$$

4. Classical vs effective Raychaudhuri equation

4.1. *Classical Raychaudhuri equation*

Having obtained the adapted form of the Raychaudhuri equation for our model, we set to find it explicitly. Looking at (11)-(13) we see that we need the solutions to the equations of motion to be able to compute them. In order to facilitate such a derivation, we choose a gauge where the lapse function is

$$N(T) = \frac{\gamma\sqrt{p_c(T)}}{b(T)}, \tag{14}$$

for which the Hamiltonian constraint becomes

$$H = -\frac{1}{2G\gamma}\left[(b^2 + \gamma^2)\frac{p_b}{b} + 2cp_c\right]. \tag{15}$$

The advantage of this lapse function is that the equations of motion of c, p_c decouple from those of b, p_b. These equations of motion should be solved together with enforcing the vanishing of the Hamiltonian constraint (15) on-shell (i.e., on the constraint surface). Replacing these solutions into (11) one obtains

$$\theta = \pm\frac{1}{2\sqrt{p_c}}\left(\frac{3b}{\gamma} - \frac{\gamma}{b}\right) = \pm\frac{-2t + 3GM}{t^{\frac{3}{2}}\sqrt{(2GM-t)}}, \tag{16}$$

$$\frac{d\theta}{d\tau} = -\frac{1}{2p_c}\left(1 + \frac{9b^2}{2\gamma^2} + \frac{\gamma^2}{2b^2}\right) = \frac{-2t^2 + 8GMt - 9G^2M^2}{(2GM-t)t^3}. \tag{17}$$

As expected, the right hand side of $\frac{d\theta}{d\tau}$ is negative (since $p_c > 0$) and both θ and $\frac{d\theta}{d\tau}$ diverge at the singularity in the classical regime. This can be seen from Fig. 1 which reaffirm the existence of a classical singularity at the center of the black hole.

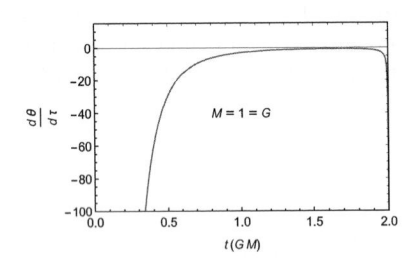

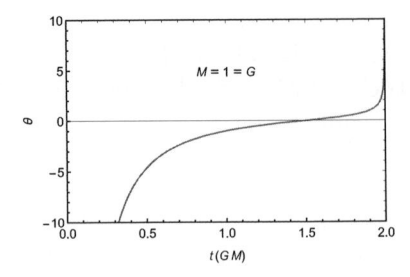

Fig. 1. Left: $\frac{d\theta}{d\tau}$ as a function of the Schwarzschild time t. Right: negative branch of θ as a function of t. Both θ and $\frac{d\theta}{d\tau}$ diverge as we approach $t \to 0$. Note that the divergence at the horizon is due to the choice of Schwarzschild coordinate system.

4.2. *Effective dynamics and Raychaudhuri equation*

The effective behavior of the interior of the Schwarzschild black hole can be deduced from its effective Hamiltonian (constraint). There are various equivalent ways to obtain such an effective Hamiltonian from the classical one.[5–7,10,16] It turns out that the easiest way is by replacing

$$b \to \frac{\sin(\mu_b b)}{\mu_b}, \tag{18}$$

$$c \to \frac{\sin(\mu_c c)}{\mu_c}, \tag{19}$$

in the classical Hamiltonian.

The free parameters μ_b, μ_c are the minimum scales associated with the radial and angular directions.[5,7,10,29] If these μ parameters are taken to be constant, the corresponding approach is called the μ_0 scheme. If, however, these parameters depend on the conjugate momenta, the approach is called improved dynamics which itself is divided into various subcategories. In case of the Schwarzschild interior and due to lack of matter content, it is not clear which scheme yields the correct semiclassical limit. Hence, for completeness, in this paper we will study the effective theory in the constant μ scheme, which here we call the $\mathring{\mu}$ scheme, as well as in two of the most common improved schemes, which we denote by $\bar{\mu}$ and $\bar{\mu}'$ schemes.

Replacing (18) and (19) into the classical Hamiltonian (5), one obtains an effective Hamiltonian constraint,

$$H_{\text{eff}}^{(N)} = -\frac{N}{2G\gamma^2} \left[\left(\frac{\sin^2(\mu_b b)}{\mu_b^2} + \gamma^2 \right) \frac{p_b}{\sqrt{p_c}} + 2 \frac{\sin(\mu_b b)}{\mu_b} \frac{\sin(\mu_c c)}{\mu_c} \sqrt{p_c} \right]. \tag{20}$$

In order to be able to compare the effective results with the classical case, we need to use the same lapse as we did in the classical part. Under (18), this lapse (14) becomes

$$N = \frac{\gamma \mu_b \sqrt{p_c}}{\sin(\mu_b b)}. \tag{21}$$

Using this in (20) we obtain

$$H_{\text{eff}} = -\frac{1}{2\gamma G}\left[p_b\left[\frac{\sin(\mu_b b)}{\mu_b} + \gamma^2 \frac{\mu_b}{\sin(\mu_b b)}\right] + 2p_c \frac{\sin(\mu_c c)}{\mu_c}\right]. \quad (22)$$

Note that both (20) and (22) reduce to their classical counterparts (5) and (15) respectively, as is expected.

To obtain the effective Raychadhuri equation, we consider three cases:

(1) $\mathring{\mu}$ scheme where $\mu_b = \mathring{\mu}_b$ and $\mu_c = \mathring{\mu}_c$ are constants,
(2) $\bar{\mu}$ scheme where we set

$$\mu_b = \bar{\mu}_b = \sqrt{\frac{\Delta}{p_b}}, \quad (23)$$

$$\mu_c = \bar{\mu}_c = \sqrt{\frac{\Delta}{p_c}}, \quad (24)$$

(3) $\bar{\mu}'$ scheme where we choose

$$\mu_b = \bar{\mu}'_b = \sqrt{\frac{\Delta}{p_c}}, \quad (25)$$

$$\mu_c = \bar{\mu}'_c = \frac{\sqrt{p_c \Delta}}{p_b}. \quad (26)$$

After replacing these (separately for each case) into the effective Hamiltonian constraint (22) and finding their corresponding equations of motion,[30] one replaces the solutions in the Raychadhuri equation (11) to obtain the form of $\frac{d\theta}{d\tau}$. It turns out that for all the three cases above we obtain

$$\frac{d\theta}{d\tau} = \frac{1}{\gamma^2 p_c} \frac{\sin^2(\mu_b b)}{\mu_b^2}\left[\cos(\mu_b b)\cos(\mu_c c) - \frac{\cos^2(\mu_b b)}{4} - 3\cos^2(\mu_c c)\right]$$
$$+ \frac{\cos(\mu_b b)}{p_c}\left[\frac{\cos(\mu_b b)}{2} - \cos(\mu_c c) - \frac{\gamma^2}{4}\cos(\mu_b b)\frac{\mu_b^2}{\sin^2(\mu_b b)}\right], \quad (27)$$

where it is understood that μ's should be substituted for from cases 1–3 suitably for each case.

4.2.1. $\mathring{\mu}$ scheme

Let us first consider this case perturbatively in an analytic manner. Replacing $\mu_b = \mathring{\mu}_b$ and $\mu_c = \mathring{\mu}_c$ as constants in (27) and then expanding for small values of μ's up to the second order we obtain

$$\frac{d\theta}{d\tau} \approx -\frac{1}{2p_c}\left(1 + \frac{9b^2}{2\gamma^2} + \frac{\gamma^2}{2b^2}\right) + \mathring{\mu}_b^2 \frac{1}{2p_c}\left(\frac{b^4}{\gamma^2} + \frac{\gamma^2}{3}\right) + \mathring{\mu}_c^2 \frac{c^2}{2p_c}\left(1 + \frac{5b^2}{\gamma^2}\right). \quad (28)$$

It is seen that the first term on the right-hand side above is the classical expression (17) which is always negative and leads to the divergence of classical expansion rate at the singularity, i.e., infinite focusing. However, Eq. (28) now involves two additional effective terms proportional to $\mathring{\mu}_b^2$ and $\mathring{\mu}_c^2$, both of which are positive. Furthermore, from the solutions to equations of motion,[30] one can infer that these two terms take over close to where the classical singularity used to be and stop θ and $\frac{d\theta}{d\tau}$ from diverging. This can, in fact, be confirmed by looking at the full nonperturbative behavior of $\frac{d\theta}{d\tau}$ plotted in Fig. 2. There, it is seen that the quantum gravity effects counter the attractive nature of classical terms and turn the curve around such that $\frac{d\theta}{d\tau}$ goes to zero for $t \to 0$.

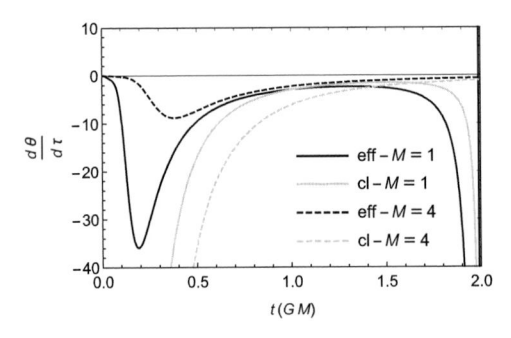

Fig. 2. Plot of $\frac{d\theta}{d\tau}$ as a function of the Schwarzschild time t, for two different masses in classical vs effective regimes. The figure is plotted using $\gamma = 0.5$, $G = 1$, $L_0 = 1$, and $\mathring{\mu}_b = 0.08 = \mathring{\mu}_c$.

4.2.2. $\bar{\mu}$ scheme

Similar to the $\mathring{\mu}$ scheme we start by analyzing the perturbative expansion of $\frac{d\theta}{d\tau}$ for this case by replacing (23) and (24) in (27) and expanding it for small $\bar{\mu}$'s up to the lowest correction terms which in this case is Δ (which can be considered as the second order in $\bar{\mu}$ scales). This way we get

$$\frac{d\theta}{d\tau} \approx -\frac{1}{2p_c}\left(1 + \frac{9b^2}{2\gamma^2} + \frac{\gamma^2}{2b^2}\right) + \frac{\Delta}{p_c}\left[\frac{1}{6p_b}\left(\frac{3b^4}{\gamma^2} + \gamma^2\right) + \frac{c^2}{2p_c}\left(1 + \frac{5b^2}{\gamma^2}\right)\right]. \quad (29)$$

Once again, the first term on the right-hand side is the classical expression of the Raychaudhuri equation (17), which contributes to infinite focusing at the singularity, but all the correction terms are positive and take over close to the position of the classical singularity. This stops $\frac{d\theta}{d\tau}$ from diverging similar to the $\mathring{\mu}$ scheme.

The full nonperturbative form of the modified Raychaudhuri equation in terms of t can also be plotted plotted by substituting the numerical solutions of the equations of motion for the $\bar{\mu}$ in (27). The result is plotted in Fig. 3. We see that, approaching from the horizon to where the classical singularity used to be, an initial bump or bounce in encountered, followed by a more pronounced bounce closer to where the singularity used to be. Once again, the quantum corrections become dominant close to the singularity and turn back the $\frac{d\theta}{d\tau}$ such that at $t \to 0$ no focusing happens at all. Furthermore, from the right plot in Fig. 3, we see that the first bounce in the

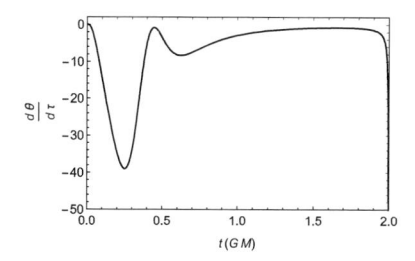

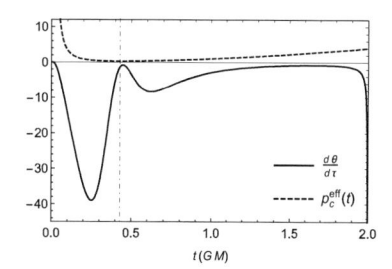

Fig. 3. Left: Raychaudhuri equation in the $\bar{\mu}$ scheme. Right: Raychaudhuri equation vs p_c. The vertical dot-dashed line at $t \approx 0.43GM$ is the position of the bounce of p_c where its minimum $p_c^{\min} = 0.29$ happens in this case. The figure is plotted using $\gamma = 0.5$, $M = 1$, $G = 1$, $L_0 = 1$, and $\Delta = 0.1$.

Raychaudhuri equation happens much earlier than the bounce in p_c for this batch of geodesics.

4.2.3. $\bar{\mu}'$ scheme

The perturbative analytical form of $\frac{d\theta}{d\tau}$ for this case, up to the first correction term turns out to be

$$\frac{d\theta}{d\tau} \approx -\frac{1}{2p_c}\left(1 + \frac{9b^2}{2\gamma^2} + \frac{\gamma^2}{2b^2}\right) + \frac{\Delta}{6\gamma^2}\left[\frac{1}{p_c^2}\left(3b^4 + \gamma^4\right) + \frac{3c^2}{p_b^2}\left(5b^2 + \gamma^2\right)\right]. \quad (30)$$

Although this perturbative form of the Raychaudhuri equation is a bit different from previous cases, nevertheless it exhibits the property that the quantum corrections are all positive and take over close to where the classical singularity used to be, and hence once again contribute to defocusing of the geodesics. This case is, however, rather different from the previous two cases since the behavior of some of the canonical variables as a function of the Schwarzschild time t deviates significantly from those cases. In particular, both b and p_c show a kind of damped oscillatory behavior close to the classical singularity,[30] which contributes to a more volatile behavior of the Raychaudhuri equation.

The full nonperturbative Raychaudhuri equation and its close-ups in this case are plotted in Fig. 4. It is seen that in this scheme, the Raychaudhuri equation exhibits a more oscillatory behavior and has various bumps particularly when we get closer to where the singularity used to be. Very close to the classical singularity, its form resembles those of b and p_c, behaving like a damped oscillation.[30]

Two particular features are worth noting in this scheme. First, as we also saw in previous schemes, quantum corrections kick in close to the singularity and dominate the evolution such that the infinite focusing is remedied, hence signaling the resolution of the singularity. Second, this scheme exhibits a nonvanishing value for $\frac{d\theta}{d\tau}$ at, or very close to, the singularity. In Fig. 4 with the particular choice of numerical values of γ, M, G, L_0 and Δ, the value of $\frac{d\theta}{d\tau}$ for $t \to 0$ is approximately -5.5. Hence, although a nonvanishing focusing is not achieved in this case at where

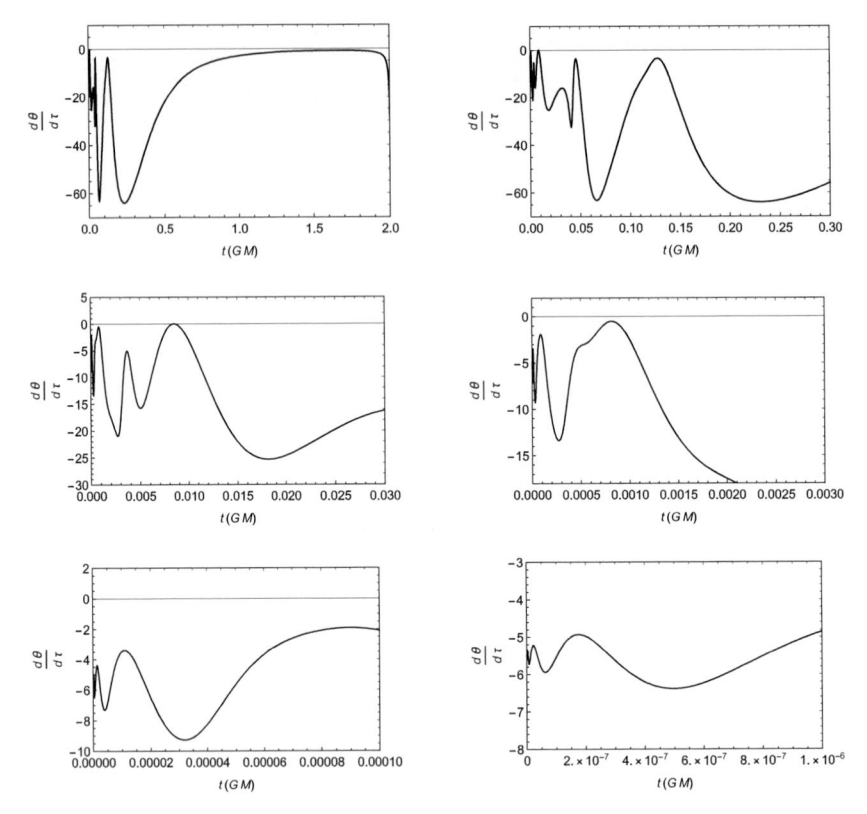

Fig. 4. Raychaudhuri equation in the $\bar{\mu}'$ scheme. The top left figure shows the behavior over the whole $0 \leq t \leq 2GM$ range. Other plots show various close-ups of that plot over smaller ranges of t. The figure is plotted using $\gamma = 0.5$, $M = 1$, $G = 1$, $L_0 = 1$, and $\Delta = 0.1$.

the singularity used to be, nevertheless, there exists a relatively small focusing and certainly $\frac{d\theta}{d\tau}$ remains finite.

5. Discussion and outlook

In this work, we probed the structure of the interior of the Schwarzschild black hole, particularly the region close to the classical singularity, using the effective Raychaudhuri equation. The effective terms in this equation result from considering the effective modifications to the Hamiltonian of the interior due to polymer quantization, which is equivalent to loop quantization of this model. We found out that while the classical rate of expansion $\frac{d\theta}{d\tau}$ diverges for $r \to 0$, the effective terms counter such a divergence close to the singularity and make $\frac{d\theta}{d\tau}$ finite at $r \to 0$. We considered three main schemes of polymer quantization and the results hold in all three. This is a strong indication that LQG points to the resolution of the singularity in the effective regime.

It is also worth noting that very similar behavior has been derived recently for several cases of Generalized Uncertainty Principle (GUP) models.[31,32] In particular, it seems that these cases bare a significant resemblance to $\hat{\mu}$ and $\bar{\mu}$. This can be taken as a cross-model affirmation that quantum gravity in general does resolve the singularity of the Schwarzschild black hole.

References

1. A. Raychaudhuri, Relativistic cosmology. 1., *Phys. Rev.* **98**, 1123 (1955).
2. R. Penrose, Gravitational collapse and space-time singularities, *Phys. Rev. Lett.* **14**, 57 (1965).
3. S. Hawking and R. Penrose, The Singularities of gravitational collapse and cosmology, *Proc. Roy. Soc. Lond. A* **314**, 529 (1970).
4. T. Thiemann, *Modern Canonical Quantum General Relativity*, Cambridge Monographs on Mathematical Physics (Cambridge University Press, 2007).
5. A. Ashtekar and M. Bojowald, Quantum geometry and the Schwarzschild singularity, *Class. Quant. Grav.* **23**, 391 (2006).
6. Böhmer, Christian G. and Vandersloot, Kevin, Loop Quantum Dynamics of the Schwarzschild Interior, *Phys. Rev. D* **76**, p. 104030 (2007).
7. A. Corichi and P. Singh, Loop quantization of the Schwarzschild interior revisited, *Class. Quant. Grav.* **33**, p. 055006 (2016).
8. A. Ashtekar, J. Olmedo and P. Singh, Quantum extension of the Kruskal spacetime, *Phys. Rev. D* **98**, p. 126003 (2018).
9. M. Bojowald and S. Brahma, Signature change in loop quantum gravity: Two-dimensional midisuperspace models and dilaton gravity, *Phys. Rev. D* **95**, p. 124014 (2017).
10. D.-W. Chiou, Phenomenological loop quantum geometry of the Schwarzschild black hole, *Phys. Rev. D* **78**, p. 064040 (2008).
11. A. Corichi, A. Karami, S. Rastgoo and T. Vukašinac, Constraint Lie algebra and local physical Hamiltonian for a generic 2D dilatonic model, *Class. Quant. Grav.* **33**, p. 035011 (2016).
12. R. Gambini, J. Olmedo and J. Pullin, Spherically symmetric loop quantum gravity: Analysis of improved dynamics, *Class. Quant. Grav.* **37**, p. 205012 (2020).
13. R. Gambini, J. Pullin and S. Rastgoo, New variables for 1+1 dimensional gravity, *Class. Quant. Grav.* **27**, p. 025002 (2010).
14. S. Rastgoo, A local true Hamiltonian for the CGHS model in new variables (4 2013).
15. A. Corichi, J. Olmedo and S. Rastgoo, Callan-Giddings-Harvey-Strominger vacuum in loop quantum gravity and singularity resolution, *Phys. Rev. D* **94**, p. 084050 (2016).
16. H. A. Morales-Técotl, S. Rastgoo and J. C. Ruelas, Effective dynamics of the Schwarzschild black hole interior with inverse triad corrections (6 2018).
17. J. Olmedo, S. Saini and P. Singh, From black holes to white holes: A quantum gravitational, symmetric bounce, *Class. Quant. Grav.* **34**, p. 225011 (2017).
18. L. Modesto, Black hole interior from loop quantum gravity, *Adv. High Energy Phys.* **2008**, p. 459290 (2008).
19. A. Ashtekar, T. Pawlowski and P. Singh, Quantum nature of the big bang, *Phys. Rev. Lett.* **96**, p. 141301 (2006).
20. A. Ashtekar, T. Pawlowski and P. Singh, Quantum Nature of the Big Bang: An Analytical and Numerical Investigation. I., *Phys. Rev. D* **73**, p. 124038 (2006).

21. A. Ashtekar, S. Fairhurst and J. L. Willis, Quantum gravity, shadow states, and quantum mechanics, *Class. Quant. Grav.* **20**, 1031 (2003).
22. A. Corichi, T. Vukasinac and J. A. Zapata, Polymer Quantum Mechanics and its Continuum Limit, *Phys. Rev. D* **76**, p. 044016 (2007).
23. H. A. Morales-Técotl, S. Rastgoo and J. C. Ruelas, Path integral polymer propagator of relativistic and nonrelativistic particles, *Phys. Rev. D* **95**, p. 065026 (2017).
24. H. A. Morales-Técotl, D. H. Orozco-Borunda and S. Rastgoo, Polymer quantization and the saddle point approximation of partition functions, *Phys. Rev. D* **92**, p. 104029 (2015).
25. E. Flores-González, H. A. Morales-Técotl and J. D. Reyes, Propagators in Polymer Quantum Mechanics, *Annals Phys.* **336**, 394 (2013).
26. A. Joe and P. Singh, Kantowski-Sachs spacetime in loop quantum cosmology: Bounds on expansion and shear scalars and the viability of quantization prescriptions, *Class. Quant. Grav.* **32**, p. 015009 (2015).
27. S. Saini and P. Singh, Geodesic completeness and the lack of strong singularities in effective loop quantum Kantowski–Sachs spacetime, *Class. Quant. Grav.* **33**, p. 245019 (2016).
28. C. Collins, Global structure of the Kantowski-Sachs cosmological models, *J. Math. Phys.* **18**, p. 2116 (1977).
29. D.-W. Chiou, Phenomenological dynamics of loop quantum cosmology in Kantowski-Sachs spacetime, *Phys. Rev. D* **78**, p. 044019 (2008).
30. K. Blanchette, S. Das, S. Hergott and S. Rastgoo, Black hole singularity resolution via the modified Raychaudhuri equation in loop quantum gravity, *Phys. Rev. D* **103**, p. 084038 (2021).
31. P. Bosso, O. Obregón, S. Rastgoo and W. Yupanqui, Deformed algebra and the effective dynamics of the interior of black holes, *Class. Quant. Grav.* **38**, p. 145006 (2021).
32. K. Blanchette, S. Das and S. Rastgoo, Effective GUP-modified Raychaudhuri equation and black hole singularity: Four models, *JHEP* **09**, p. 062 (2021).

Effect of loop quantization prescriptions on the physics of non-singular gravitational collapse

Kristina Giesel*, Bao-Fei Li† and Parampreet Singh†

*Institute for Quantum Gravity, Department of Physics, FAU Erlangen-Nürnberg,
Staudtstr. 7, 91058 Erlangen, Germany
†Department of Physics and Astronomy, Louisiana State University,
Baton Rouge, LA 70803, USA

We review recent developments in the physical implications of two loop quantization strategies for the interior of a homogeneous dust cloud. The first is the loop quantization with holonomies and the triads while the second is with holonomies and the gauge covariant fluxes. Although both of the quantization schemes resolve the classical central singularity regardless of the initial conditions, they also lead to a distinct phenomenology. For the first loop quantization, we find that when the dust mass is larger than a threshold value, both black hole and white hole would form and their evolution is symmetric with respect to the bounce point, leading to black hole-white hole twins. In contrast, in the second quantization, the evolution of the outermost dust shell is asymmetric with respect to the bounce point, and as a result the black hole-white hole twins can never form. Even in the situation when both black hole and white hole can form, the mass of the latter is only $2/\pi$ of the mass of the former.

Keywords: Homogeneous dust collapse; loop quantum cosmology.

1. Introduction

The singularity problem in the gravitational collapse results from the breakdown of the classical theory of general relativity (GR) and can thus be resolved by quantum gravity. Understanding the role of quantum gravity in determining the final state of the collapsing stars can help provide insights on the fundamental questions related with cosmic censorship conjecture and black hole evaporation. Because of the quantization ambiguities in quantum theories, it is important to understand if the physical predictions are robust against various quantization prescriptions. In the following, we address this question for a collapsing dust cloud whose interior spacetime is described by the Lemaître-Tolman-Bondi(LTB) metric and study two quantization prescriptions in a loop quantum gravity (LQG) scenario.

To make the problem of a collapsing dust cloud more manageable, we further assume a homogeneous evolution of the dust cloud in the marginally bound case. We then make use of the techniques from LQG to quantize the interior of the dust cloud. The loop quantization of the spacetimes with spherical symmetry dates back to quantization of the interior of the Schwarzschild black hole.[1–6] Later it was extended to include both interior and exterior of the black hole[7–13] as well as the dynamical collapsing spacetime which is filled with a massless scalar or the dust.[14–18] All these studies focussed on the resolution of the central singularity by incorporating quantum geometry effects via holonomies and/or inverse triad modification but not on comparaing the physics in different quantizations. Further, none of the forementioned models have been directly derived from LQG. Therefore, it is reasonable to ask whether the physical predictions in those models are robust when further modifications from LQG are included in the dynamics. To answer this question, we have studied two distinct quantization prescriptions for the interior of a collapsing dust cloud and compared their physical implications.[19] The first quantization employs holonomy and triads while in the second quantization, in addition to the holonomy corrections, we have also considered the contributions from the gauge-covariant fluxes[20] which have beenr ecently explored in the cosmological setting.[21-23] Our results have shown that although the resolution of the central singularity is robust against different quantization strategies, the resulting dynamics also exhibit distinctive features for each quantization ansatz. In particular, the first quantization results in black hole-white hole twins while the second quantization strategy generally leads to black hole-white hole asymmetry.

2. The classical dust shell model

The classical dust shell model describes the dynamics of the outermost shell of a collapsing dust cloud. It is based on the LTB model which is obtained from a spherically symmetric solution of Einstein's equations in GR with non-rotational dust as a matter source. The metric of LTB spacetime is given by

$$ds^2 = -d\tau^2 + \frac{(R')^2}{1+2f}dx^2 + R^2 d\Omega^2, \tag{1}$$

where R is the areal radius, $f(x)$ is the total energy of a unit mass at x and a prime denotes derivative with respect to the radial coordinate x. Depending on the sign of f, there are three distinct cases: the marginally bound case with $f=0$, the bound case with $f<0$ and the unbound case with $f>0$. In the following, we focus on the marginally bound case. The corresponding Hamiltonian constraint for the LTB dust model is explicitly given in terms of both canonical ADM variables and the Ashtekar variables for a general inhomogeneous dust cloud in.[24] The classical dust shell model can then be obtained from the LTB model by a homogeneous reduction where the energy density of the dust cloud is assumed to depend only on time.[25] Thanks to the spherical symmetry and the homogeneity of the dust cloud interior, one can integrate the classical Hamiltonian constraint of the LTB model along the radial direction as well as the angular part and arrive at the Hamiltonian constraint for the outermost dust shell which can be expressed in terms of a canonical pair consisting of the radial components of the extrinsic curvature and the densitized triad.[19] It turns out that for the homogeneous dust collapse, the interior spacetime is isometric to the spatially-flat Friedmann-Lemaître-Robertson-Walker (FLRW) spacetime. As a result, the classical Hamiltonian constraint of the outermost dust shell can be related with the one for the spatially-flat FLRW spacetime.[19]

For a complete description of thiS collapsing model, in addition to the dust interior, one still needs to specify the exterior spacetime which is glued to the dust interior at the boundary. We choose the exterior spacetime to be the generalized

Vaidya spacetime[26] so that it allows a non-vanishing effective dust pressure after quantum geometrical effects are taken into account.[14] The matching conditions are worked out under the requirements that the first and the second fundamental forms should be continuous across the boundary. In this way, it turns out that in the marginally bound case the Vaidya mass which is the mass of the dust cloud as seen by an outside observer differs from the mass function of the dust cloud by a factor of $1/2G$ with G denoting the Newton's constant.

3. Loop quantization of the dust shell model with holonomy and triad variables

The loop quantization of the dust shell model is based on the classical Hamiltonian constraint of the outermost dust shell which is expressed in terms of the Ashtekar variables.[19] Due to the quantization ambiguities, there are different quantization prescriptions which can result in distinct effective dynamics. Since the interior of a homogeneous dust cloud is isometric to a spatially-flat FLRW spacetime, one can apply techniques developed in loop quantum cosmology (LQC)[27] in a straightforward way. After quantizing the outermost dust shell by employing holonomies and the triads with the $\bar{\mu}$ scheme,[28] we find that the classical central singularity is resolved and replaced with a bounce which takes place at a fixed maximum energy density in the Planck regime. Meanwhile, the collapse of the dust cloud is succeeded by a re-expansion after the bounce point. The formation of the trapped surfaces during the contraction and the expansion of the dust cloud depends solely on the initial dust mass. There also exists a threshold dust mass M^* below which no black hole or white hole can form during the evolution of the dust cloud. On the other hand, when the initial dust mass is larger than M^*, a dynamical black hole can form during the collapse of the dust cloud and correspondingly a white hole can form during the re-expansion of the dust cloud. The evolution of the black hole and the white hole is always symmetric with respect to the bounce point and in particular the mass of the black hole is the same as the mass of the white hole. Moreover, right at the bounce, the trapped surfaces vanishes and the Vaidya mass becomes zero which implies that an asymptotic flat Minkowski spacetime emerges at the bounce point due to the quantum repulsive force. This repulsive force is also reflected by a negative effective pressure near the bounce point when the energy density is in the Planck regime.

4. Loop quantization of the dust shell model with holonomy and gauge covariant flux variables

Apart from the holonomy and triad quantization, we also study the physical consequences of using holonomy and the gauge covariant fluxes[20] which is motivated from the need to go beyond symmetry reduced triads in to obtain an effective Hamiltonian with loop quantum modifications from LQG using suitable coherent states. Its physical implications have been explored for the spatially-flat FLRW model recently.[21–23] This quantization strategy leads to distinct dynamical evolution of the outermost dust shell as compared with the one discussed in the last section.

In particular, although the classical central singularity is resolved and replaced with a quantum bounce which also takes place in the Planck regime, the formation/evolution of the black hole and the white hole is no longer symmetric with respect to the bounce point. Due to quantum gravity effects there exist two characteristic dust masses M_1 and M_2 ($M_1 < M_2$). When the initial dust mass is less than M_1, no trapped surfaces can form during the entire evolution of the dust cloud. On the other hand, when the initial dust mass lies between M_1 and M_2, only a black hole can form during the collapse of the dust cloud. Finally, when the initial dust mass is larger than M_2, both black hole and the white hole can form. In the last case, we find the evolution of the black hole and the white hole is not symmetric with respect to the bounce point and in particular the effective mass of the white hole is only $2/\pi$ of the one for the black hole and the black hole always outlives the white hole in the proper time. This asymmetry is due to the difference in the classical limits of the pre- and post-bounce regimes of the effective dynamics. As a result, black hole-white hole twins do not exist in this quantization strategy.

5. Summary

The gravitational collapse of a homogeneous dust cloud provides a platform to test different loop quantizations and investigate their resulting physical implications. We find even in this simple setting, quantization ambiguities can lead to very distinct phenomenological effects. In particular, we have studied two quantization strategies in this context, the one employing holonomies and triads and the other using holonomies and gauge covariant fluxes. Although in both cases, the central singularity is resolved and replaced with a quantum bounce, there are qualitative differences between two quantization prescriptions. In the former, when the dust mass is larger than the threshold mass, there are black hole-white hole twins. While in the latter, a black hole and white hole twin system is not possible and the the mass of the white hole is only $2/\pi$ of the mass of the black hole because of quantum gravity effects. Further, there can be situations in which only black hole forms during the collapse of the dust cloud.

We wish to thank Jahnvi Verma and Anzhong Wang for discussions. This work is supported by the DFG-NSF grants PHY-1912274 and 425333893, and PHY-1454832 and PHY-2110207.

References

1. A. Ashtekar and M. Bojowald, *Quantum geometry and the Schwarzschild singularity*, Class. Quant. Grav. **23**, 391 (2005).
2. C. G. Bohmer and K. Vandersloot, *Loop quantum dynamics of the Schwarzschild interior*, Phys. Rev. **76**, 104030 (2007).
3. A. Corichi and P. Singh, *Loop quantization of the Schwarzschild interior revisited*, Class. Quant. Grav. **33**, 055006 (2016).
4. J. Olmedo, S. Saini, and P. Singh, *From black holes to white holes: A quantum gravitational, symmetric bounce*, Class. Quant. Grav. **34**, 225011 (2017).

5. A. Ashtekar, J. Olmedo, and P. Singh, *Quantum transfiguration of Kruskal black holes*, Phys. Rev. Lett. **121**, 241301 (2018).
6. A. Ashtekar, J. Olmedo, and P. Singh, *Quantum extension of the Kruskal spacetime*, Phys. Rev. **D98**, 126003 (2018).
7. M. Bojowald and R. Swiderski, *Spherically symmetric quantum geometry: Hamiltonian constraint*, Class. Quant. Grav. **23**, 2129-2154 (2006).
8. R. Gambini and J. Pullin, *Black holes in Loop Quantum Gravity: The complete spacetime*, Phys. Rev. Lett. **101**, 161301 (2008).
9. D.-W. Chiou, W.-T. Ni, and A. Tang, *Loop quantization of spherically symmetric midisuperspaces and loop quantum geometry of the maximally extended Schwarzschild spacetime*, 2013, arXiv:1212.1265.
10. R. Gambini and J. Pullin, *Loop quantization of the Schwarzschild black hole*, Phys. Rev. Lett. **110**, 211301 (2013).
11. R. Gambini, J. Olmedo, and J. Pullin, *Quantum black holes in loop quantum gravity*, Class. Quant. Grav. **31**, 095009 (2014).
12. R. Gambini, J. Olmedo, and J. Pullin, *Spherically symmetric loop quantum gravity: Analysis of improved dynamics*, Class. Quant. Grav. **37**, 205012 (2020).
13. J. G. Kelly, R. Santacruz, and E. Wilson-Ewing, *Effective loop quantum gravity framework for vacuum spherically symmetric spacetimes*, Phys. Rev. **D102**, 106024 (2020).
14. M. Bojowald, R. Goswami, R. Maartens, and P. Singh, *Black hole mass threshold from nonsingular quantum gravitational collapse*, Phys. Rev. Lett. **95**, 091302 (2005).
15. R. Goswami, P. S. Joshi, and P. Singh, *Quantum evaporation of a naked singularity*, Phys. Rev. Lett. **96**, 031302 (2006).
16. R. Gambini, J. Pullin, and S. Rastgoo, *Quantum scalar field in quantum gravity: The vacuum in the spherically symmetric case*, Class. Quant. Grav. **26**, 215011 (2009).
17. C. Bambi, D. Malafarina, and L. Modesto, *Non-singular quantum-inspired gravitational collapse*, Phys. Rev. **D88**, 044009 (2013).
18. F. Benitez, R. Gambini, L. Lehner, S. Liebling, and J. Pullin, *Critical collapse of a scalar field in semiclassical Loop Quantum Gravity*, Phys. Rev. Lett. **124**, 071301 (2020).
19. K. Giesel, B.-F. Li, and P. Singh, *Non-singular quantum gravitational dynamics of an LTB dust shell model: The role of quantization prescriptions*, arXiv:2107.05797.
20. T. Thiemann, *Quantum spin dynamics (QSD): VII. Symplectic structures and continuum lattice formulations of gauge field theories*, Class. Quant. Grav. **18**, 3293-3338 (2001).
21. K. Liegener and P. Singh, *New loop quantum cosmology modifications from gauge-covariant fluxes*, Phys. Rev. **D100**, 124048 (2019).
22. K. Liegener and P. Singh, *Some physical implications of regularization ambiguities in SU(2) gauge-invariant loop quantum cosmology*, Phys. Rev. **D100**, 124049 (2019).
23. K. Liegener and P. Singh, *Gauge-invariant bounce from loop quantum gravity*, Class. Quant. Grav. **37**, 085015 (2020).
24. M. Bojowald, T. Harada, and R. Tibrewala, *Lemaître-Tolman-Bondi collapse from the perspective of loop quantum gravity*, Phys. Rev. **D78**, 064057 (2008).
25. C. Kiefer and T. Schmitz, *Singularity avoidance for collapsing quantum dust in the Lemaître-Tolman-Bondi model*, Phys. Rev. **D99**, 126010 (2019).
26. C. Barrabès and W. Israel, *Thin shells in general relativity and cosmology: The lightlike limit*, Phys. Rev. **D43**, 1129 (1991).
27. A. Ashtekar and P. Singh, *Loop Quantum Cosmology: A Status Report*, Class. Quant. Grav. **28**, 213001 (2011).
28. A. Ashtekar, T. Pawlowski, and P. Singh, *Quantum nature of the Big Bang: Improved dynamics*, Phys. Rev. **D74**, 084003 (2006).

Summary of the parallel session QG3

Jorge Pullin and Parampreet Singh

Department of Physics and Astronomy, Louisiana State University, Baton Rouge, LA 70803, USA

We summarize the main results of 19 talks presented at the QG3 session (loop quantum gravity: cosmology and black holes) of the 16th Marcel Grossmann Meeting held online from July 5th-10th, 2021.

Keywords: Loop quantum gravity; cosmology; black holes

The QG3 session was organized in two parts with a total of 19 talks. The first part of the session was held on July 5th (9 talks) focussing on loop quantum gravity effects in black hole spacetimes, and the second part was on July 8th (10 talks) focussing on cosmological implications. A summary of talks in a chronological order is as follows.

We-Cong Gan presented his joint work with Nilton O. Santos, Fu-Wen Shu, and Anzhong Wang on spherically symmetric polymer black holes.[1] Their work is based on a model by Bodendorfer, Mele and Münch and depend on three independent parameters. An exploration of the parameter space was made showing a wealth of physical possibilities including singularity resolution, wormholes and space-times with singularities.

Harkirat Singh Sahota discussed joint work with Kinjalk Lochan[2] about the quantization of the Lemaître–Tolman–Bondi model as a minisuperspace. It leads to a bounce eliminating the singularity and the talk explored how it manifests itself in the infrared regime to an observer looking at the collapse.

Aurélien Barrau discussed joint work with Léonard Ferdinand, Killian Martineau and Cyril Renevey.[3] There have been several proposals discussed in the literature in which after their evaporation black holes tunnel into metastable white holes. They have been considered a dark matter candidate. The talk showed that such models are severely constrained and suggested some possible detection paths.

Parampreet Singh presented his work with Kristina Giesel and Bao-Fei Li on a non-singular collapse of a dust shell model in Lemaître–Tolman–Bondi spacetime.[4] Two quantization prescriptions were studied. One using holonomies and triads, and another using holonomies and gauge-covariant fluxes. While both the prescriptions result in a bounce of the dust shell they lead to different mass gaps at which a trapped surface may form. Unlike in a quantization based on holonomies and triads, in presence of gauge-covariant fluxes, a formation of white hole in the expanding phase when a black hole forms in the contracting phase is not guaranteed.

Asier Alonso-Bardaji presented work with David Brizuela where they consider holonomy and inverse-triad corrections in spherically symmetric models of loop quantum gravity.[5] It constructs systematically anomaly-free constraints with such corrections. It concludes that holonomy corrections are consistent in the presence of matter fields. Contrary to earlier claims, authors demonstrate a model which provides a family of deformed Hamiltonian constraints with scale-dependent holonomy corrections in the presence of a scalar matter field.

Cong Zhang talked about joint work with Yongge Ma, Shupeng Song and Xiangdong Zhang on the loop quantum gravity quantization of the interior of the Schwarzschild black hole.[6] They study a Dirac observable corresponding to the ADM mass and note that zero is not in its spectrum, suggesting that a remnant is left after the evaporation of the black hole.

Alejandro García Quasimodo talked about work with Guillermo Mena Marugán about some modifications to the Ashtekar–Olmedo–Singh black hole model, in particular the use of polymerization parameters that are Dirac observables.[7] This may modify the asymptotic behavior of the model.

Saeed Rastgoo presented work with Keagan Blanchette, Saurya Das and Samantha Hergott on loop quantum gravity corrections to the Raychaudhuri equation.[8] These corrections imply defocusing of geodesics providing insights on the eliminiation of singularities in this context.

Patrick Fraser analyzed how classical are the Gaussian states in loop quantum cosmology.[9] He showed that contrary to common intuition, such states do not saturate their uncertainty relations and there exist Gaussian states for which the fluctuations are arbitrarily large. However, the usual volume regularization procedure allows to suppress those fluctuations as much as one wishes.

V. Sreenath talked about alleviating tensions in the cosmic microwave background using Planck scale physics in a joint work with Abhay Ashtekar, Brajesh Gupt and Donghui Jeong.[10] The idea is that there are several anomalies of low significance in the agreement of the predictions of the usual Λ-CDM model for the cosmic microwave background. Taken as a whole, however, they imply a tension between theory and data. The talk showed that considering loop quantum cosmology leads to a primordial power spectrum that is scale dependent at large scales. This can potentially alleviate the anomalies.

Sahil Saini discussed a matter-Ekpyrotic bounce model in loop quantum cosmology in a joint work with Bao-Fei Li and Parampreet Singh.[11] Unlike previous attempts in this direction in loop quantum cosmology, Ekpyrotic phase was sourced by a potential motivated from Ekpyrotic scenarios. It was shown that in contrast to previous results where a fixed ultra-stiff equation of state was assumed, the magnitude of power spectrum changes during evolution resulting from an Ekpyrotic potential. It was found that the bouncing regime only leaves imprints on the modes outside the scale-invariant regime. Further refinements in this direction are necessary since the spectral index shows inconsistency with the observational data.

Kristina Giesel presented a reduced phase space quantization for loop quantum cosmology in presence of inflationary potentials. This was a joint work with Bao-Fei Li and Parampreet Singh.[12] Unlike the case of a massless scalar field which has been addressed rigorously in loop quantum cosmology, singularity resolution at the quantum level in the presence of a potential has remained an open problem because of several conceptual and technical challenges. The idea is to introduce an additional clock degree of freedom to measure time evolution. It was shown that singularity resolution occurs in the presence of potentials at the level of quantum difference equation. Some properties of non-singular solutions were discussed using effective dynamics.

Guillermo Mena Marugán talked about his work with Beatriz Elizaga Navascués and Rafael Jiménez-Llamas on the way potential effects primordial perturbations in kinetic dominated regimes in classical and loop quantum cosmology.[13] Such a situation is of particular interest in loop quantum cosmology where so far kinetic dominated bounce has been studied. Authors found that the choice of Bunch-Davies vacuum may no longer be preferred in presence of such corrections. Further, there are changes in the effective mass in the Mukhanov-Sasaki equation.

Anzhong Wang discussed his joint work with Bao-Fei Li and Parampreet Singh on various subtleties in imposing initial conditions for cosmological perturbations in loop quantum cosmology and its modified versions (mLQC-I and mLQC-II).[14] The talk highlighted differences in choices which are forced by the assumptions in the dressed metric and hybrid approaches. Issues related to when to impose initial conditions – whether at bounce or in the contracting phase, and constraints on possible choices were discussed. It was shown that a consistent choice of the initial conditions depends not only on the choice of a potential but also on the two approaches used in loop quantum cosmology.

Javier Olmedo talked about effects on primordial perturbations in a bouncing model in loop quantum cosmology for a Bianchi-I spacetime in a joint work with Ivan Agullo and V. Sreenath.[15] They considered an evolution where anisotropies are non-vanishing at a bounce dominated by matter energy density. Though anisotropies were diminished in the pre-inflationary branch, effects were found in the scalar and tensor power spectrum. Modification to the angular correlation functions and the way EB and TB correlations may arise was discussed.

Bao-Fei Li discussed features of primordial power spectrum in modified versions of loop quantum cosmology in a joint work with Javier Olmedo, Parampreet Singh and Anzhong Wang.[16] They discussed the way dressed metric and hybrid approaches to perturbations result in different signatures in the primordial power spectrum, especially for mLQC-I model. Differences with loop quantum cosmology in the infra-red and intermediate regimes were also found which show that different loop quantum prescriptions potentially leave distinct signatures in CMB.

Dimitrios Kranas talked about his joint work with Ivan Agullo and V. Sreenath on understanding the origin of various anomalies in the CMB using a bouncing model.[17] They find that that non-Gaussian correlations between CMB modes and super-horizon wavelengths in the power spectrum can potentially explain a power suppression, a dipolar asymmetry, and existence of odd-parity correlations in the power spectrum.

Adriá Delhom i Latorre discussed hos joint work with Gonzalo Olmo and Parampreet Singh.[18] They investigate the existence of a covariant action in $f(R)$ Palatini theories which can reproduce effective equations for modified versions of loop quantum cosmology. It was found that the Lagrangians which result in effective dynamics of LQC, mLQC-I and mLQC-II are part of a three-parameter family of f(R) theories, where two parameters are fixed by initial conditions at the bounce.

Hongguang Liu talked about his work with Muxin Han on a path integral approach based on reduced phase space loop quantum gravity to derive effective dynamical equations in which the graph changes dynamically in the physical time evolution.[19] They were able to derive the so-called improved dynamics from this method found earlier in loop quantum cosmology by Ashtekar, Pawlowski and Singh which results in a singularity resolution. The method also generalizes the path integral formulation used in full LQG to take into account an additional real scalar field.

Acknowledgments

This work was supported in part by grant NSF-PHY-1454832, NSF-PHY-1903799, DFG-NSF-PHY-1912274, NSF-PHY-2110207 and funds of CCT-LSU and the Horace Hearne Institute for Theoretical Physics.

References

1. W. C. Gan, N. O. Santos, F. W. Shu and A. Wang, "Properties of the spherically symmetric polymer black holes," Phys. Rev. D **102**, 124030 (2020).
2. H. S. Sahota, K. Lochan, *To appear*.
3. A. Barrau, L. Ferdinand, K. Martineau and C. Renevey, "Closer look at white hole remnants," Phys. Rev. D **103**, no. 4, 043532 (2021).
4. K. Giesel, B. F. Li and P. Singh, "Non-singular quantum gravitational dynamics of an LTB dust shell model: The role of quantization prescriptions," [arXiv:2107.05797 [gr-qc]].
5. A. Alonso-Bardaji and D. Brizuela, "Anomaly-free deformations of spherical general relativity coupled to matter," [arXiv:2106.07595 [gr-qc]].
6. C. Zhang, Y. Ma, S. Song and X. Zhang, "Loop quantum deparametrized Schwarzschild interior and discrete black hole mass," [arXiv:2107.10579 [gr-qc]].
7. A. García-Quismondo and G. A. Mena Marugán, "Exploring alternatives to the Hamiltonian calculation of the Ashtekar-Olmedo-Singh black hole solution," Front. Astron. Space Sci. **8**, 701723 (2021).

8. K. Blanchette, S. Das, S. Hergott and S. Rastgoo, "Black hole singularity resolution via the modified Raychaudhuri equation in loop quantum gravity," Phys. Rev. D **103**, no. 8, 084038 (2021).
9. P. Fraser, "Taming Fluctuations for Gaussian States in Loop Quantum Cosmology," Phys. Rev. D **103**, no. 8, 086014 (2021).
10. A. Ashtekar, B. Gupt, D. Jeong and V. Sreenath, "Alleviating the Tension in the Cosmic Microwave Background using Planck-Scale Physics," Phys. Rev. Lett. **125**, no. 5, 051302 (2020); A. Ashtekar, B. Gupt and V. Sreenath, "Cosmic Tango Between the Very Small and the Very Large: Addressing CMB Anomalies Through Loop Quantum Cosmology," Front. Astron. Space Sci. **8**, 76 (2021).
11. B. F. Li, S. Saini and P. Singh, "Primordial power spectrum from a matter-Ekpyrotic bounce scenario in loop quantum cosmology," Phys. Rev. D **103**, no. 6, 066020 (2021).
12. K. Giesel, B. F. Li and P. Singh, "Towards a reduced phase space quantization in loop quantum cosmology with an inflationary potential," Phys. Rev. D **102**, no. 12, 126024 (2020).
13. B. Elizaga Navascués, R. Jiménez-Llamas and G. A. Mena Marugán, "Primordial perturbations in kinetically dominated regimes of general relativity and hybrid quantum cosmology," [arXiv:2106.05628 [gr-qc]].
14. B. F. Li, P. Singh and A. Wang, "Phenomenological implications of modified loop cosmologies: An overview," Front. Astron. Space Sci. **8**, 701417 (2021).
15. I. Agullo, J. Olmedo and V. Sreenath, "Predictions for the Cosmic Microwave Background from an Anisotropic Quantum Bounce," Phys. Rev. Lett. **124**, no. 25, 251301 (2020).
16. B. F. Li, P. Singh and A. Wang, "Primordial power spectrum from the dressed metric approach in loop cosmologies," Phys. Rev. D **101**, no. 8, 086004 (2020); B. F. Li, J. Olmedo, P. Singh and A. Wang, "Primordial scalar power spectrum from the hybrid approach in loop cosmologies," Phys. Rev. D **102**, 126025 (2020).
17. I. Agullo, D. Kranas and V. Sreenath, "Anomalies in the CMB from a cosmic bounce," Gen. Rel. Grav. **53**, no. 2, 17 (2021).
18. A. D. i Latorre, G. J. Olmo, P. Singh, *To appear*.
19. M. Han and H. Liu, "Loop quantum gravity on dynamical lattice and improved cosmological effective dynamics with inflaton," Phys. Rev. D **104**, no. 2, 024011 (2021).

Reliable equations of state of viscous strong and electroweak matter

A. Tawfik

Egyptian Center for Theoretical Physics (ECTP), Cairo, Egypt
World Laboratory for Cosmology And Particle Physics (WLCAPP), Cairo, Egypt
E-mail: a.tawfik@cern.ch

For the first time, a reliable estimation for the equations of state (EoS), bulk viscosity, and relaxation time, at temperatures ranging from a few MeV up to TeV or energy density up to 10^{16} GeV/fm^3. This genuine study covers both strong and electroweak epochs of the early Universe. Non–perturbation (up, down, strange, charm, and bottom quark flavor) and perturbative calculations (up, down, strange, charm, bottom, and top quark flavors), are phenomenologically combined, at vanishing baryon–chemical potential. In these results, calculations from Polyakov linear–sigma model (PLSM) of the vacuum and thermal condensations of the gluons and the quarks (up, down, strange, and charm flavors) are also integrated. Furthermore, additional degrees of freedom (photons, neutrinos, charged leptons, electroweak particles, and scalar Higgs boson) are found significant along the entire range of temperatures. As never done before, the present study brings the standard model of elementary particles closer to the standard model for cosmology.

Keywords: Strong and electroweak epochs, Perturbative and non–perturbative calculations, Equations of state, Bulk viscosity, Relaxation time

1. Introduction

Understanding the strong and electroweak epochs of the early Universe, at least, through determining their equations of state (EoS) is impactful for various cosmological studies, such as the nucleosynthesis and the cosmological large–scale structure. Until present date, cosmology is dictated by the standard model of cosmology (SMC). SMC assumes that the cosmic background is isotropically and homogeneously characterized by an ideal fluid. With this regard, we recall that a first proposal that the viscous coefficients are also connected with particle physics was presented Ref.[1,2]. It was also assumed that the influence of viscous coefficients becomes significant first at the end of the lepton era,[3] i.e., during neutrino decoupling epoch or temperature $T \simeq 10^{10}$ K ($\simeq 1$ MeV) which takes place not long after the end of the QCD phase transition from colored quark–gluon plasma (QGP) to colorless hadrons. The QCD phase transition[4–7] takes place at $T \simeq 160$ MeV. Recent studies concluded that the viscous coefficients likely impact early epoches of the Universe.[8]

Taking advantage of recent developments in ultra–relativistic nuclear experiments and non–perturbative lattice QCD simulations, and perturbative calculations, various thermodynamic quantities including pressure p, energy density ρ, bulk viscosity ζ, and relaxation time τ are calculated up to the TeV-scale and a reliable evolution of the early Universe could be achieved. The present study offers an access to deep epochs of the early Universe with T up to TeV-scale and ρ up to 10^{16} GeV/fm^3.

For Friedmann–Lemaitre–Robertson–Walker (FLRW) metric

$$ds^2 = dt^2 - a(t)^2 \left[\frac{dr^2}{1-kr^2} + r^2 \left(d\theta^2 + \sin^2\theta d\phi^2 \right) \right], \quad (1)$$

where $a(t)$ is the dimensionless scale factor, $k = \{-1, 0, +1\}$ represents elliptical, flat (Euclidean), and hyperbolic cosmic space, or negative, flat, and positive curvature, respectively. The theory of general relativity (GR) inters the play, when temporal evolution of the line element $s(t)$ can be determined. To this end, GR has to be combined with the matter–energy content of the cosmic geometry,

$$R_{\mu\nu} - \frac{1}{2} g_{\mu\nu} R + \Lambda_{\mu\nu} = \frac{8\pi}{3} T_{\mu\nu}, \quad (2)$$

where μ, ν run over 0, 1, 2, and 3.

Then, the Einstein field equations in natural units read

$$H(t)^2 = \frac{8\pi}{3} \rho(t) - \frac{k}{a(t)^2} + \frac{\Lambda}{3}, \quad (3)$$

$$\dot{H}(t) + H(t)^2 = -\frac{4\pi}{3} \left[\rho(t) + 3p_{\text{eff}}(t) \right] + \frac{\Lambda}{3}, \quad (4)$$

where $H(t) = \dot{a}(t)/a(t)$ is the Hubble parameter. From (3) and (4), the time evolution of the Hubble parameter can be deduced

$$\dot{H}(t) = -4\pi \left[\rho(t) + p_{\text{eff}}(t) \right] + \frac{k}{a(t)^2}. \quad (5)$$

An EoS relating p with ρ is needed to have a closed system of equations.

The present script is organized as follows. The most reliable non-perturbative and perturbative calculations are reviewed in section 2. Our results on EoS, bulk viscosity and relaxation time for almost the entire SM dof are presented in section 3. The conclusions are outlined in section 4.

2. Most reliable non-perturbative and perturbative calculations

For relaible EoS, various general considerations have been assumed in the recent non-perturbative lattice QCD simulations.[9] The first one is the quark masses. For a dynamical dependence of the quark masse m_q and the lattice spacing a on the guage coupling β, four flavor staggered action with 4 levels of stout smearing has been utilized, where $u, d, s,$ and c quarks are realized as 2+1+1 and 3+1,[9] i.e., except for strange and charm quark masses, $m_{ud} = R \times m_s^{st}(\beta)$, with $m_s^{st}(\beta)$, $1/R = 27.63$ and β is the guage coupling. The c quark mass is given as a function of the gauge coupling; $m_c = C \times m_s^{st}(\beta)$, with $C = 11.85$. Although the degenerate masses of the light quarks, a small isospin asymmetry could also be included, analytically.[9]

The second general consideration is the temperature T, which can primarily be determined as a function of the temporal lattice dimension; $T = (aN_\tau)^{-1}$. Alternatively, varying the gauge coupling β leads to changing T, as well, even if the spacial and temporal lattice dimensions might not be varied. The gauge coupling can not only allow for varying T, but also it measures the pseudoscalar pion mass m_π and the Wilson–flow based scale ω_0, where $\omega_0 = 0.153 \pm 0.001$ fm and $m_\pi = 712 \pm 5$ MeV. At $T = 0$, ω_0 gives the inverse flow time.[10]

The third general consideration is the lattice QCD computational procedure. After applying a Wilson–flow equation, the clover definition of the topological charge was made in $2+1+1$ and $3+1$ ensembles. To make the computational process more economic, an adaptive step size integration scheme was utilized. The time flow $(8T^2)^{-1}$ was introduced to estimate the finite T of both ensembles, where a variation in the time flow is also allowed. This procedure has greatly contributed to reducing the systematic errors. To control their simulations, it should be checked whether these configurations lead to saturated susceptibility, at large flow times.[9] To determine the topological susceptibility, topological charge was utilized with and without rounding.

The fourth general consideration is the acceptance accuracy. As already outlined for the $2+1+1$ simulations, same configurations have been used also for $3+1$ simulations. Here, the mass ratio of the charm quark and the degenerate lighter quarks (u, d, and s) was taken to be 11.85. As mentioned, for the masses of up– and down–quarks, the physical values are used, while the mass of the strange quark is a function of the guage coupling, $m_s^{\text{st}}(\beta)$. At $T = 0$, simulations were done on 64×32^3 lattice with seven values of the lattice spacing descendingly ranging from 0.15 to 0.06 fm. But at finite T, the same parameters as in $2+1+1$ case were used. The topological charge is measured for every Hybrid Monte–Carlo trajectory. The configurations leading to a topology change are rejected. In other words, configurations are generated, at fixed topology. Quantitatively, this leads to an acceptance probability of about 40% for the coarsest lattice, but higher probabilities for the finest ones.

In the following section we review how various thermodynamic quantities have been determined.

2.1. *Lattice QCD Equation of State in Non-Perturbative Regime*

The inclusion of up–, down–, strange–, and charm–quark in non–perturbative lattice QCD simulations[11, 12] assumes that the masses of some quarks are very heavy (partially quenched). Other lattice QCD simulations assume that the four quarks are non–degenerate with unphysical masses.[13, 14] The ultimate goal is to carry out non–perturbative simulations with dynamical quarks and physical masses.[15] To this end, $2+1+1$ simulations with staggered action, and 4 levels of stout smearing have been carried out in Ref.[16].

One restriction in the lattice QCD simulations is the universal assumption of thermal equilibrium. This might not fully true, especially because the hadron and parton matter is undergoing phase transition, whether prompt of slows crossover, at critical temperatures, i.e., non–equilibrium due to changes in the underlying dynamics, symmetry, and degrees of freedom. Another restriction is that the temperature dependence of pressure p, energy density ρ, and entropy s can be deduced from the trace anomaly, at vanishing chemical potential,

$$\frac{I(T)}{T^4} = \frac{\rho - 3p}{T^4}, \tag{6}$$

$$\frac{\rho + p}{T^4} = \frac{s}{T^3}. \tag{7}$$

A third restriction is the common practice to get rid of the temperature independent divergence of the trace anomaly so that its physical value can be evaluated, accurately. A vanishing-T ensemble is subtracted from each finite-T ensemble. As this method doesn't work well at high temperatures, where short lattice spacing and increasing autocorrelation times and computational costs are likely, a renormalization ensemble is generated for each finite-T ensemble, at exactly half of its temperature.[9] The physical trace anomaly in a wide range of temperatures including low T, can be obtained from the subtraction of each half-T from its finite-T ensemble, $[I(T) - I(T/2)]/T^4$. The resulting ρ and s can straightforwardly be estimated from Eqs. (6) and (7).

Up to four quark flavors were included in the non–perturbative lattice QCD simulations. This was achieved by several steps of tree–level corrections.

2.2. Inclusion of c-Quark in Non–Perturbative Lattice QCD Simulations

It was concluded[17] that the free energy calculated in next–to–next–to–leading order (NNLO) Hard Thermal Loop (HTL) perturbation theory is in good agreement with $2 + 1$ and $2 + 1 + 1$ non–perturbative lattice QCD simulations, where c–quark is taken massless in the perturbative calculations but assigned the physical mass in the non–perturbative simulations. The mass of c–quark was perturbatively[18] and non–perturbatively[9] estimated. In the perturbative calculations, the effect of heavy quarks is determined to a lower leading order, and accordingly, it was concluded that this refers to $(3 + 1)$ quark flavors pressure normalized to (3) quark flavors pressure p. On the other hand, when comparing p with and without c–quark in both non–perturbative and perturbative calculations, an excellent agreement ($< 3\%$) was obtained.[9] The tree–level correction due to c–quark reads

$$\frac{p^{(2+1+1)}(T)}{p^{(2+1)}(T)} = \frac{SB^{(3)}(T) + F_Q(m_c/T)}{SB^{(3)}(T)}, \tag{8}$$

where SB stand for Stefan–Boltzmann approximation and $F_Q(m_c/T)$ is the free energy density of a free quark with mass $m_c = 1.29$ GeV.

The following section elaborates how the b–quark flavor is included non–perturbative lattice QCD simulations. This was achieved by several steps of tree–level corrections.

2.3. Inclusion of b–Quark in Non–Perturbative Lattice QCD Simulations

The success with the inclusion of the c–quark encouraged a recent attempt with the bottom quark, especially that the $2+1+1$ non–perturbative simulations up to $T \lesssim 1$ GeV control the accuracy of the proposed procedure and the perturbative contributions likely dominate, at $T \gtrsim 500$ MeV.[19,20] Recent perturbative calculations were performed up to $\mathcal{O}(g^6 \log g)$.[9] Thus, the inclusion of b–quark and a continuation to higher T look straightforward. A tree–level correction for the b–quark similar to that for the c–quark, Eq. (8), was suggested.

It was concluded that tree–level correction for b–quark works well. When comparing the ratio of the massless $2+1+1$ to $2+1+1+1$ perturbative pressure with the pressure ratio in the SB limit, an excellently agreement ($< 0.3\%$) is obtained. With a phenomenological approach similar to Eq. (8), reliable non–perturbative lattice QCD simulations become feasible, at 500 MeV $< T <$ 10 GeV. This T–range apparently covers various epochs in the early Universe, where different phase transitions and accordingly different dynamics and degrees of freedom become dominant.

In the following section, we review features of the perturbative calculations up to TeV temperatures.

2.4. Perturbative Calculations up to TeV Temperature–Scales

In the previous sections, we have discussed on the various restrictions of the non–perturbative lattice QCD simulations and their possible extensions to a large number of quark flavors and to higher temperatures. The perturbative calculations, on the other hand, allow to cover much higher temperatures and to include more quark flavors. By combining recent perturbation calculations up to a largest leading order with the non–perturbative lattice QCD simulations, reliable EoS for strong and electroweak matter can be deduced.[21,22] It is conjectured that this covers temperatures up to ~ 200 TeV.

2.4.1. QCD Domain

In this domain, $0.2 \lesssim T \lesssim 1$ GeV, the gluons and the lightest four quark flavors and the gluons are partonic dof of the strongly interacting matter.[21] The perturbative corrections to the ideal (masslss, noninteracting) Stefan-Boltzmana (SB) EoS can be determined up to different orders of strong coupling constant $\mathcal{O}(g)$. Although, the perturbative contributions up to $\mathcal{O}(g^6 \log g)$ are well known,[19,23,24] where g is expressed as function of N_c the colors dof, N_f the massless quark flavors dof, and μ_f the quark chemical potential, only $\mathcal{O}(g^2)$ terms, at $T = 0$ but $\mu_f \neq 0$, have been precisely, analyzed.

Besides the contributions of gluons up to $\mathcal{O}(g^6 \log g)$ and that of NLO $\mathcal{O}(g^2)$, it was found that these are similar to that of LO $\mathcal{O}(g^0)$, where no $\mathcal{O}(g^6 \log g)$ calculations for finite quark masses are available so far.[18] An alternative procedure was suggested. This starts with $N_f = 0$ and $N_c = 3$ corresponding to very heavy quark flavors. Then, it calculates the change in the pressure by lowering the quark masses down to their physical values[a]. This procedure suggests that the perturbative calculations are based on the grand–canonical pressure (or free energy).[9] As discussed earlier, the non–perturbative lattice QCD simulations starts with the trace anomaly (also known as the interaction measure) $I(T, \mu_f, \cdots)$, Eq. (6), from which the various thermodynamic quantities can be determined. Based on this renormalization procedure, the ultraviolet divergences are likely removed.

In order to extend the perturbative calculations to the electroweak domain, the so–called *hard modes* should first be removed through either integration with respect to momenta or summation over the Matsubara frequencies, $2\pi T$, gT, $g^2 T$, $\cdots$. Second, the effective mass parameters and the gauge couplings have to be specified and normalized in $\overline{\text{MS}}$–scheme. Third, the connection factors should then be estimated, at changing T and fixed $\Lambda_{\overline{\text{MS}}}$. These can be achieved, when multiplying the non–perturbative lattice results for $N_f = 0$, $N_c = 3$, finite quark masses by the corresponding ones obtained in the SB limit, Eq. (8). The connection factors facilitate the inclusion of heavier quarks, at temperatures greater that strong QCD scale parameter $\Lambda_{QCD} \sim 200$ MeV.

2.4.2. *Electroweak Domain*

As discussed, the perturbative calculations are initiated from the free energy (or thermodynamic pressure), the Higgs potential parameters $v^2(\bar{\mu})$ and $\lambda(\bar{\mu})$ are given as functions of the normalization scale $\bar{\mu}$. Assuming that the bottom and top quarks weakly interact, the free energy, at finite T and $\boldsymbol{\mu}$, reads[18]

$$f(v, T, \boldsymbol{\mu}) = -\frac{1}{2} v^2(\bar{\mu}) v^2 + \frac{1}{4} \lambda(\bar{\mu}) v^4 + \sum_{i}^{n_q+n_g} \pm J_i(m_i(v), T, \mu_i), \quad (9)$$

where n_q (n_g) are the number of quarks (gluons), v is the Higgs expectation value, $m_i(v)$ is the tree–level mass of i–th particle, $\pm$ stand for bosons and fermions, respectively, and $J_i(m_i(v), T, \mu_i)$ counts for the contributions of the physical dof (scalars, vectors, and fermions). The normalization scale $\bar{\mu}$ could be fixed to 100 GeV[b]. Nevertheless, the electroweak free energy, Eq. (9), can be determined, at temperatures far beyond the electroweak scale $\bar{\mu} \sim 100$ GeV.

As the proposed EoS characterizes electroweak matter, a few remarks on the nature of the phase transitions is now in order. In some perturbative calculations, it was concluded that the electroweak EoS seems approaching that of an ideal gas,[18] while in others significant deviations have been obtained.[25] With this regard, it should be considered that the strength of electroweak phase transition is

---

[a] Decreasing the quark masses increases the thermodynamic pressure.
[b] This is a model–depending assumption. Originally, the electroweak theory has different scales along its wide range of temperatures and chemical potentials.

determined by different SM Lagrangian parameters, which so far aren't determined. The recently estimation of the Higgs mass allowed for a smooth crossover and electroweak baryogenesis.[26,27]

2.5. *Combining Non-Perturbative and Perturbative EoS*

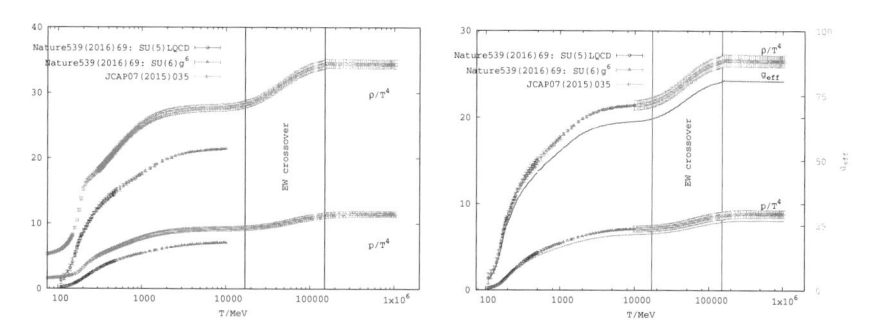

Fig. 1. Left panel: A comparison between non–perturbative lattice QCD simulations[9] and the perturbative calculations[18] for normalized pressure and energy density as functions of temperatures. Right panel: The same as in the left panel but here the perturbative calculation are rescaled (see main text). The vertical lines approximately determine the temperatures, where the electroweak crossover takes place. The curves in right panel present the effective dof $g_{\text{eff}}(T)$ related to pressure and energy density.

As discussed, the proposal to combine reliable non–perturbative with perturbative calculations was already applied in various studies. In the present study, we combine the non–perturbative[9] with the perturbative calculations[18] for different thermodynamic quantities.

The temperature dependence of the normalized pressure and energy density calculated non–perturbatively and perturbatively is illustrated in the left panel of Fig. 1. Here, the temperature covers up to ~ 10 GeV and ~ 1 TeV in non–perturbative and perturbative simulations, respectively. It is obvious that although both types of simulations look quantitatively different, they are qualitatively similar. We find that the perturbative results are significantly larger than the non–perturbative ones.

There are many reasons supporting the assumption that the non–perturbative lattice QCD simulations are more reliable than the perturbative ones, especially at low temperatures. In this range of temperatures, even the vacuum energy change is best evaluated by non–perturbative simulations. On one hand, the non–perturbative lattice QCD simulations are most reliable, at low temperatures, the so–far perturbative calculations are not as accurate even at high temperatures. Thus, we concretely propose that the non–perturbative lattice QCD simulations are most reliable, at $T \gtrsim \Lambda_{\text{QCD}} \approx 200$ MeV up to a few GeV,[28] while the perturbative calculations are the only approach possible, at temperatures up to the TeV–scale. From Fig. 1, a temperature–indenedent systematic difference of ∼ 20% between both sets of calculations[c] is obtained. Also, we assumed that the systematic difference of ∼ 20% ins the same for both pressure and energy density.

For a contineous temperature–dependence of pressure and energy density, we propose to rescale the perturbative calcuations, at high temperatures.[18] The rescaling factor is phenomenologically adjusted to match the perturbative calculations, at high temperatures, with the non–perturbative lattice QCD simulations, at low temperatures. We assume that a rescaling factor of 0.77 remains constant, at the entire range of temperatures, right panel of Fig. 1. The non–perturbative lattice QCD simulations aren't rescaled, at all. In both thermodynamic quantities, both non–perturbative (T up to ~ 10 GeV) and perturbative ($10 \text{ GeV} \lesssim T \lesssim 1$ TeV) calculations are phenomenologically combined. The effective dof $g_{\text{eff}}(T)$ corresponding to pressure, $g_{\text{eff}}(T) = p(T)/p_0$, and to energy density, $g_{\text{eff}}(T) = \rho(T)/\rho_0$, are also depicted in the right panel of Fig. 1, where $\rho_0 = (\pi^2/30)T^4$ is the energy density and p_0 is the pressure for an ideal gas of scalar massless bosons $p_0 = (\pi^2/90)T^4$. The perfect matching of $g_{\text{eff}}(T)$, at low and high temperatures, supports the conclusion that the temperature–independent proposed rescaling, 0.77, seems precise.

3. EoS, bulk viscosity and relaxation time for almost entire SM dof

3.1. *EoS for Strong and Electroweak Matter*

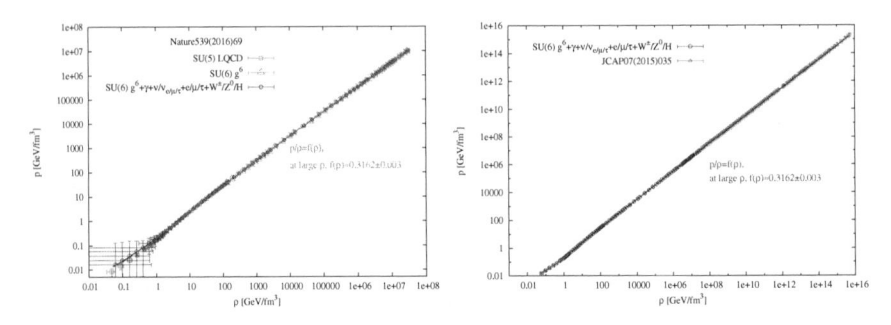

Fig. 2. Left panel: The thermodynamic pressure calculated in SU(5) non–perturbative and perturbative lattice QCD in dependence on the corresponding energy density (red and green symbols)[9] is confronted to the same calculations extended to other dof; γ, neutrinos, leptons, EW, and Higgs bosons (blue symbols). Right panel: The extended SU(5) lattice QCD calculations are combined with SU(6)g^6 non–perturnative calculations.[21,29]

Left panel of Fig. 2 shows the EoS deduced from SU(5) non–perturbative and perturbative lattice QCD simulations (red and green symbols).[9] The thermodynamic contributions from γ, ν, e, μ, τ, ν_e, ν_μ, ν_τ, $W^\pm$, and the Higgs boson H are summed

---

[c]It was reported in Ref.[9] that this difference reads $7 - 17\%$ and is temperature dependent!

up with the SU(5) results (blue symbols). For each type of the additional particles, a partition function is constructed, from which the temperature dependence of the different thermodynamic quantities, such as the thermodynamic pressure and the energy density, can straightforwardly be derived. It is obvious that the additional dof considerably contribute to both thermodynamic quantities. The quantitative contributions are considrable, for example, within the hadronic phase, the proportionality constant in $p \propto \rho$ increases with the additive dof, i.e., increasing speed of sound squared.[30] In quark–gluon plasma and electroweak phases, more structures are added to the one corresponding EoS based on SU(5) lattice QCD simulations.

The fitting functions illustrated in the bottom panel of Fig. 2 are

$$\text{HP}: \quad p = \alpha_1 + \alpha_2 \rho, \tag{10}$$

$$\text{QGP/EW}: \quad p = \beta_1 + \beta_2 \rho + \beta_3 \rho^{d_2}, \tag{11}$$

$$\text{Asymp.}: \quad p = \gamma \rho, \tag{12}$$

where $\alpha_1 = 0.0034 \pm 0.0023$, $\alpha_2 = 0.1991 \pm 0.0022$, $\beta_1 = 0.0484 \pm 0.0164$, $\beta_2 = 0.3162 \pm 0.0031$, $\beta_3 = -0.21 \pm 0.014$, and $\gamma = 0.3162 \pm 0.003$.

3.2. Bulk Viscosity for Strong and Electroweak Matter

It was concluded that the shear viscosity normalized to the entropy density for perturbative gauge QCD likely approaches the lower bound of Anti–de Sitter/Conformal Field Theory (AdS/CFT).[31] A non–perturbative estimation for viscous coefficients, at temperatures several times the QCD scale, has been reported in Ref.[32, 33]. This was possible through accumulating a large amount of configurations for the Green function expressed in the Matsubara frequencies and implemented on isotropic $24^2 \times 8$ and $16^2 \times 8$ lattices. The viscous coefficients are determined as slopes of the spectral functions, at vanishing Matsubara frequency. A recent estimation for the temperature dependence of the bulk viscosity of SU(3) gluodynamics was possible with $48^3 \times 16$ lattice QCD simulations.[33] Another estimation is based the retarded Green function defined by the Kramers–Kronkig relation in terms of different thermodynamic quantities.[34, 35] In Ref.[35], it was taken into consideration that the bulk viscosity measures the violation of the conformal invariance. This allowed to conclude that QCD at classical level is conformally invariant.

$$\zeta = \frac{1}{9\omega_0} \Big[Ts \left(\frac{\partial \rho}{\partial p} - 3 \right) - 4(\rho - 3p) \quad \text{thermal parts}$$

$$+ \left(T \frac{\partial}{\partial T} - 2 \right) \langle \bar{q}q \rangle(T) + g_g\, G^2(T) \quad \text{thermal q \& g condensates}$$

$$+ g_f \left(m_\pi^2 f_\pi^2 + m_K^2 f_K^2 + m_D^2 f_D^2 + \cdots \right) \Big]. \quad \text{vacuum q \& g condensates} \tag{13}$$

where g_g (g_f) are the degeneracy factors for gluons (quarks). The spin polarization multiplied is $g_g = 16$. The color degrees of freedom reads $N_c^2 - 1$, with N_c is the color quantum number. $g_f = 12\, n_f$ with n_f are the degrees of freedom of the quark flavors. m_D (f_D) are mass (decay constant of D-meson). The scale parameter ω_0 determines the applicability of the parturbation theory. ζ is obtained by using the frequency limit of the spectral density, at vanishing spatial momentum[35,36] and by implementing the various thermodynamic quantities are detailed in Eq. (13).

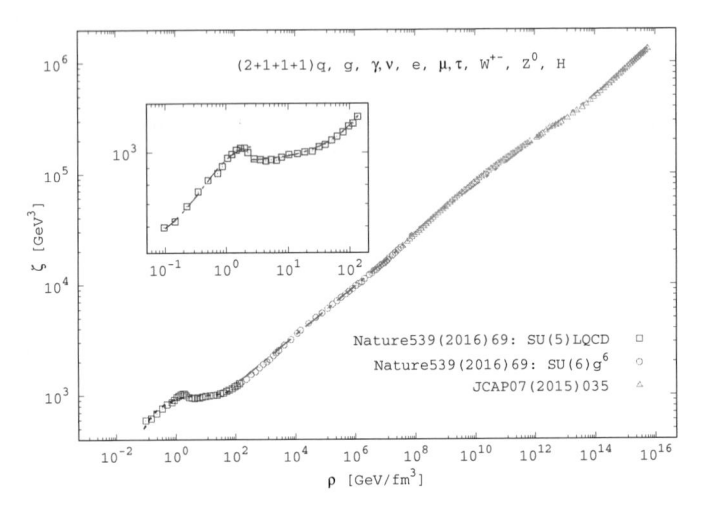

Fig. 3. The bulk viscosity ζ in dependence of the energy density ρ. Both quantities are calculated, at vanishing baryon–chemical potential and given in physical units. The inside box magnifies the region, at low temperature, where $\zeta(\rho)$ is non–monotonic.

By combining the gluons and $(2+1+1+1)$ quark contributions and that of the gauge bosons; the photons, $W^\pm$, and Z^0, of the charged leptons; neutrino, electron, muon, and tau, and of the Higgs bosons; scalar Higgs particle,[8] the bulk viscosity is shown in Fig. 3. We conclude that the almost entire SM contributions are very significant. The missing SM–contributions are vacuum and thermal bottom quark condensate, the entire gravitational sector, neutral leptons, and top quark. ζ almost linearly increases with increasing energy–density, so that following three regions of parameterizations (curves) can be distinguished

$$\text{Hadron} - \text{QGP}: \zeta = a_1 + a_2\rho + a_3\rho^{a_4}, \qquad (14)$$

$$\text{QCD}: \zeta = b_1 + b_2\rho^{b_3}, \qquad (15)$$

$$\text{EW}: \zeta = c_1 + c_2\rho^{c_3}. \qquad (16)$$

For Hadron–QCD: $a_1 = -9.336 \pm 4.152$, $a_2 = 0.232 \pm 0.003$, $a_3 = 11.962 \pm 4.172$, and $a_4 = 0.087 \pm 0.029$. For QCD: $b_1 = 8.042 \pm 0.056$, $b_2 = 0.301 \pm 0.002$, and $b_3 = 0.945 \pm 0.0001$. For EW: $c_1 = 0.350 \pm 0.065$, $c_2 = 10.019 \pm 0.934$, and $c_3 = 0.929 \pm 8.898 \times 10^{-5}$.

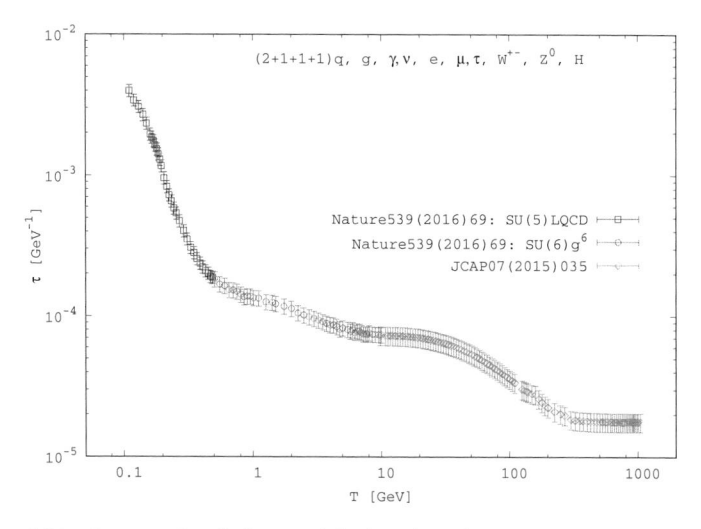

Fig. 4. At vanishing baryon–chemical potential, the relaxation time τ is presented in dependence on the temperature T. The results are based on non–perturbative and perturbative lattice QCD simulations, in which contributions from the quark and gluon condensates and the thermodynamic quantities of gauge bosons, charged leptons, and Higgs bosons (left symbols) are integrated.

3.3. *Relaxation Time for Strong and Electroweak Matter*

The relaxation time τ_f, which involves complicated collision integrals, can be determined as the mean collision time and averages of thermodynamic quantities[37–39]

$$\tau_f(T) = \frac{1}{n_f(T) \langle v(T) \rangle \sigma(T)}, \qquad (17)$$

where σ is cross section, $\langle v(T) \rangle$ stands for mean relative velocity, and $n_f(T)$ represents the number density. Approaches for $\langle v(T) \rangle$ and σ have been discussed in Ref.[39]. The temperature dependence of the relaxation time $\tau_f(T)$ plays an essential role in bulk viscosity $\zeta(T)$.

Figure 4 presents $\tau(T)$ deduced from the non–perturbative and perturbative QCD simulations[8,9,21,29] (bottom symbols). Contributions from the quark and gluon condensates and the thermodynamic quantities of the gauge bosons, charged leptons, and Higgs bosons are added (left symbols). We notice that τ steadily decreases with increasing T. In the different phases, there are different rates of decreasing τ.

4. Conclusions

Most reliable non–perturbative lattice QCD simulations and perturbative calculations with as much as possible quark flavors with physical masses are phenomenologically combined. The thermodynamic contributions of photons, charged neutrinos, leptons, electroweak particles ($W^\pm$ and Z^0 bosons), and the scalar Higgs bosons are also integrated in. This makes the present study pioneering in a) simultaneous accessing hadron, quark–gluon plasma and electroweak epochs of the early Universe and b) including almost all degrees of freedom of the standard model. With this regard, we emphasize that the only missing SM dof are vacuum and thermal bottom quark condensate, the entire gravitational sector, neutral leptons, and top quark flavor.

We have introduced various thermodynamic quantities, including pressure, energy density, bulk viscosity, and relaxation time, at vanishing net–baryon cosmic matter and temperatures up to the TeV–scale. The main result is that recent non–perturbative lattice QCD simulations and perturbative calculations jointly lead to EoS covering a wide range of temperatures. As never done before, this study makes introduces a framework to combine the standard model of the elementary particles and the standard model for cosmology.

References

1. C. W. Misner, The isotropy of the universe, *The Astrophysical Journal* **151**, p. 431 (1968).
2. Ya. B. Zeldovich and I. D. Novikov, *Relativistic Astrophysics. Vol. 2. The Structure and Evolution of the Universe* 1983.
3. L. Husdal, Viscosity in a lepton-photon universe, *Astrophysics and Space Science* **361**, 1 (2016).
4. A. Tawfik, QCD phase diagram: A Comparison of lattice and hadron resonance gas model calculations, *Phys. Rev. D* **71**, p. 054502 (2005).
5. A. Tawfik, M. Wahba, H. Mansour and T. Harko, Hubble Parameter in QCD Universe for finite Bulk Viscosity, *Annalen Phys.* **522**, 912 (2010).
6. L. Adamczyk et al., Probing parton dynamics of QCD matter with Ω and ϕ production, *Phys. Rev. C* **93**, p. 021903 (2016).
7. E. A. Hakk, A. N. Tawfik, A. Nada and H. Yassin, Cosmic Evolution of Viscous QCD Epoch in Causal Eckart Frame, *Universe* **7**, p. 112 (2021).
8. A. N. Tawfik and I. Mishustin, Equation of State for Cosmological Matter at and beyond QCD and Electroweak Eras, *J. Phys. G* **46**, p. 125201 (2019).
9. S. Borsanyi et al., Calculation of the axion mass based on high-temperature lattice quantum chromodynamics, *Nature* **539**, 69 (2016).
10. S. Borsanyi et al., High-precision scale setting in lattice QCD, *JHEP* **09**, p. 010 (2012).
11. M. Cheng, Charm Quarks and the QCD Equation of State, *PoS* **LATTICE2007**, p. 173 (2007).
12. L. Levkova, Effects of the charm quark on the QCD equation of state, *PoS* **LAT2009**, p. 170 (2009).
13. F. Burger, G. Hotzel, M. Müller-Preussker, E.-M. Ilgenfritz and M. P. Lombardo, Towards thermodynamics with $N_f = 2+1+1$ twisted mass quarks, *PoS* **Lattice2013**, p. 153 (2013).
14. A. Bazavov et al., Update on the 2+1+1 Flavor QCD Equation of State with HISQ, *PoS* **LATTICE2013**, p. 154 (2014).
15. S. Borsanyi, G. Endrodi, Z. Fodor, S. D. Katz, S. Krieg, C. Ratti, C. Schroeder and K. K. Szabo, The QCD equation of state and the effects of the charm, *PoS* **LATTICE2011**, p. 201 (2011).
16. R. Bellwied, S. Borsanyi, Z. Fodor, S. D. Katz, A. Pasztor, C. Ratti and K. K. Szabo, Fluctuations and correlations in high temperature QCD, *Phys. Rev. D* **92**, p. 114505 (2015).

17. J. O. Andersen, L. E. Leganger, M. Strickland and N. Su, NNLO hard-thermal-loop thermodynamics for QCD, *Phys. Lett. B* **696**, 468 (2011).
18. M. Laine and Y. Schroder, Quark mass thresholds in QCD thermodynamics, *Phys. Rev. D* **73**, p. 085009 (2006).
19. K. Kajantie, M. Laine, K. Rummukainen and Y. Schroder, The Pressure of hot QCD up to g6 ln(1/g), *Phys. Rev. D* **67**, p. 105008 (2003).
20. N. Brambilla, X. Garcia i Tormo, J. Soto and A. Vairo, The Logarithmic contribution to the QCD static energy at N**4 LO, *Phys. Lett. B* **647**, 185 (2007).
21. M. Laine and M. Meyer, Standard Model thermodynamics across the electroweak crossover, *JCAP* **07**, p. 035 (2015).
22. M. Laine, G. Nardini and K. Rummukainen, First order thermal phase transition with 126 GeV Higgs mass, *PoS* **LATTICE2013**, p. 104 (2014).
23. A. D. Linde, Infrared Problem in Thermodynamics of the Yang-Mills Gas, *Phys. Lett. B* **96**, 289 (1980).
24. D. J. Gross, R. D. Pisarski and L. G. Yaffe, QCD and Instantons at Finite Temperature, *Rev. Mod. Phys.* **53**, p. 43 (1981).
25. A. Gynther and M. Vepsalainen, Pressure of the standard model at high temperatures, *JHEP* **01**, p. 060 (2006).
26. K. Kajantie, M. Laine, K. Rummukainen and M. E. Shaposhnikov, Is there a hot electroweak phase transition at $m_H \gtrsim m_W$?, *Phys. Rev. Lett.* **77**, 2887 (1996).
27. Y. Aoki, F. Csikor, Z. Fodor and A. Ukawa, The Endpoint of the first order phase transition of the SU(2) gauge Higgs model on a four-dimensional isotropic lattice, *Phys. Rev. D* **60**, p. 013001 (1999).
28. S. J. Brodsky, S. Menke, C. Merino and J. Rathsman, On the behavior of the effective QCD coupling alpha(tau)(s) at low scales, *Phys. Rev. D* **67**, p. 055008 (2003).
29. M. D'Onofrio and K. Rummukainen, Standard model cross-over on the lattice, *Phys. Rev. D* **93**, p. 025003 (2016).
30. A. Nasser Tawfik and H. Magdy, Hadronic Equation of State and Speed of Sound in Thermal and Dense Medium, *Int. J. Mod. Phys. A* **29**, p. 1450152 (2014).
31. P. Kovtun, D. T. Son and A. O. Starinets, Viscosity in strongly interacting quantum field theories from black hole physics, *Phys. Rev. Lett.* **94**, p. 111601 (2005).
32. S. Sakai and A. Nakamura, Lattice calculation of the QGP viscosities: Present results and next project, *PoS* **LATTICE2007**, p. 221 (2007).
33. N. Y. Astrakhantsev, V. V. Braguta and A. Y. Kotov, Temperature dependence of the bulk viscosity within lattice simulation of $su(3)$ gluodynamics, *Phys. Rev. D* **98**, p. 054515 (Sep 2018).
34. D. Kharzeev and K. Tuchin, Bulk viscosity of QCD matter near the critical temperature, *JHEP* **09**, p. 093 (2008).
35. F. Karsch, D. Kharzeev and K. Tuchin, Universal properties of bulk viscosity near the QCD phase transition, *Phys. Lett.* **B663**, 217 (2008).
36. J. Noronha-Hostler, J. Noronha and C. Greiner, Transport Coefficients of Hadronic Matter near T(c), *Phys. Rev. Lett.* **103**, p. 172302 (2009).
37. A. N. Tawfik, A. M. Diab and M. T. Hussein, SU(3) Polyakov linear-sigma model: Conductivity and viscous properties of QCD matter in thermal medium, *Int. J. Mod. Phys.* **A31**, p. 1650175 (2016).
38. A. Tawfik and T. Harko, Quark-Hadron Phase Transitions in Viscous Early Universe, *Phys. Rev.* **D85**, p. 084032 (2012).
39. A. Tawfik, M. Wahba, H. Mansour and T. Harko, Viscous Quark-Gluon Plasma in the Early Universe, *Annalen Phys.* **523**, 194 (2011).

Neutral fermion pair production by Sauter-like magnetic step

T. C. Adorno

Department of Physics, College of Physical Sciences and Technology, Hebei University, Wusidong Road 180, 071002, Baoding, China;
Key Laboratory of High-precision Computation and Application of Quantum Field Theory of Hebei Province, Hebei University, Wusidong Road 180, 071002, Baoding, China;
Department of Physics, Tomsk State University, Lenin Prospekt 36, 634050, Tomsk, Russia
E-mail: adorno@hbu.edu.cn

Zi-Wang He

Department of Physics, College of Physical Sciences and Technology, Hebei University, Wusidong Road 180, 071002, Baoding, China;
Key Laboratory of High-precision Computation and Application of Quantum Field Theory of Hebei Province, Hebei University, Wusidong Road 180, 071002, Baoding, China
E-mail: 1248049347@qq.com

S. P. Gavrilov

Department of Physics, Tomsk State University, Lenin Prospekt 36, 634050, Tomsk, Russia;
Department of General and Experimental Physics, Herzen State Pedagogical University of Russia, Moyka embankment 48, 191186, St. Petersburg, Russia
E-mail: gavrilovsp@herzen.spb.ru

D. M. Gitman

Department of Physics, Tomsk State University, Lenin Prospekt 36, 634050, Tomsk, Russia;
P. N. Lebedev Physical Institute, 53 Leninskiy prospekt, 119991, Moscow, Russia;
Instituto de Física, Universidade de São Paulo, Caixa Postal 66318, CEP 05508-090, São Paulo, S.P., Brazil
E-mail: gitman@if.usp.br

We review our recent results on the creation from the vacuum of neutral fermions with anomalous magnetic moments by a Sauter-like magnetic field. We construct in- and out solutions of the Dirac-Pauli equation with this field and calculate with their help pertinent quantities characterizing the vacuum instability, such as differential mean numbers and flux density of created pairs and and vacuum-to-vacuum transition amplitudes. Special attention is paid to situations where the external field lies in two particular configurations, varying either "gradually" or "sharply" along the inhomogeneity direction. We also estimate critical magnetic field intensities, near which the phenomenon could be observed.

Keywords: Dirac-Pauli equation; quantum electrodynamics; pair production; neutral fermions with anomalous magnetic moment

1. Introduction

The violation of the vacuum stability stimulated by external electromagnetic fields is commonly associated with the possibility of such backgrounds producing work on virtual pairs of particles and antiparticles. The most well-known examples are electric-like fields, as they produce work on charged particles and are able to tear apart electron/positron pairs from the vacuum if the field amplitudes approach the so-called Schwinger critical value $E_c = m^2c^3/e\hbar \approx 1.3 \times 10^{16}$ V/cm.[1] The phenomenon has been a subject of intense investigation since the seminal works of Klein,[2] Sauter,[3,4] Heisenberg and Euler,[5] and Schwinger.[1] An extensive discussion about the origin of the effect, theoretical foundations, and experimental aspects can be found in some reviews and monographs; see e.g.[6–15] and references therein.

Following the above interpretation, one may ask oneself about the possibility that inhomogeneous macroscopic magnetic fields which produce a work on particles with a magnetic moment, may create pairs from the vacuum. The answer to this question is affirmative, provided the particles are neutral and have an anomalous magnetic moment. Bearing in mind, first of all, very strong magnetic fields observed in astrophysics, we can assume that this type of field is practically time-independent and steplike, that is, their gradient has a well-defined sign. At present, there exist two types of particles enjoying the properties mentioned above: the neutron and the neutrino. According to experimental data, neutrons have a magnetic moment $\mu_N \approx -1.04187563(25) \times 10^{-3} \mu_B$,[16] where μ_B is the Bohr magneton. As for neutrinos, there is not a general consensus because of the different types of neutrinos, mechanism under which neutrinos acquires magnetic moment, specific models, etc. Presently, experimental constraints range from $\mu_{\nu_\tau} < 3.9 \times 10^{-7} \mu_B$ (for the tau neutrino)[17] until $\mu_{\nu_e} < 2.9 \times 10^{-11} \mu_B$ (for the electron neutrino).[18] Moreover, stringent constraints obtained from astrophysical observations[19–24] indicate that $\mu_\nu < (2.6 - 4.5) \times 10^{-12} \mu_B$ while lower upper bounds, predicted by effective theories above the electroweak scale, suggest that $\mu_\nu < 10^{-14} \mu_B$.[25] It is important to point out that for some theories beyond the Standard Model (SM),[26] it was reported that the magnetic moment for the neutrinos lie within the range $(10^{-12} - 10^{-14}) \mu_B$. For a more extensive discussion concerning experimental aspects and theoretical predictions for neutrinos' electromagnetic properties, see e.g. the reviews[27–31] and references therein.

In this work, we review our recent results on the creation of neutral fermions with anomalous magnetic moments from the vacuum by Sauter-like magnetic field.[32] We follow the general formulation developed to describe the effect nonperturbatively, which is based on the canonical quantization of fermion fields with time-independent inhomogeneous external fields.[33–35] The system under consideration is placed in the four-dimensional Minkowski spacetime, parameterized by coordinates $X = (X^\mu, \mu = 0, i) = (t, \mathbf{r})$, $X^0 = t$, $X^i = \mathbf{r} = (x, y, z)$, $i = 1, 2, 3$, with the metric tensor $\eta_{\mu\nu} = \mathrm{diag}(+1, -1, -1, -1)$. We also employ natural units, in which $\hbar = 1 = c$.

2. Solutions of Dirac-Pauli equation with Sauter-like magnetic step

The Dirac-Pauli (DP) equation[36] for a neutral spin 1/2 particle with the anomalous magnetic moment μ, the mass m interacting with external electromagnetic backgrounds $A^\mu = (A^0, \mathbf{A})$ has the form:

$$\left(i\gamma^\mu \partial_\mu - m - \frac{1}{2}\mu\sigma^{\mu\nu} F_{\mu\nu}\right)\psi(X) = 0,$$

$$\sigma^{\mu\nu} = \frac{i}{2}[\gamma^\mu, \gamma^\nu]_-, \quad F_{\mu\nu} = \partial_\mu A_\nu - \partial_\nu A_\mu. \tag{1}$$

Here $\psi(X)$ is a bispinor, $\gamma^\mu = (\gamma^0, \boldsymbol{\gamma})$ are Dirac matrices, and μ is the algebraic value of the anomalous magnetic moment (e.g., $\mu = -|\mu_N|$ for a neutron). In what follows we consider external electromagnetic fields of a specific type, corresponding to a time-independent magnetic field oriented along the positive direction of the z-axis, inhomogeneous along the y-direction, $\mathbf{B}(\mathbf{r}) = (0, 0, B_z(y))$, and homogeneous at remote distances, $B_z(\pm\infty) = \mathrm{const}$. Moreover, it is assumed that its gradient is always positive $\partial_y B(y) \geq 0$, $\forall y \in (-\infty, +\infty)$, meaning that $B_z(+\infty) > B_z(-\infty)$ and that the field is genuinely a step (or steplike, in short). To study neutral fermion pair production by steplike magnetic fields, we consider that the magnetic field inhomogeneity is given by the analytic function

$$B_z(y) = \varrho B' \tanh(y/\varrho), \quad B' > 0, \quad \varrho > 0, \tag{2}$$

which meets the conditions discussed above and allows solving the DP equation exactly. The amplitude B' and the length scale ϱ describe, respectively, the "slope" of the field with respect to the y-axis and how "rectilinear" it is in the neighborhood of the z-axis. Thus, the larger B' and ϱ, the more "steep" and the more "rectilinear" the pattern of (2) near the z-axis. Because the field (2) resembles a step-like "potential" for charged particles and its gradient has a Sauter profile,[4] we call the field (2) Sauter-like magnetic step. For illustrative purposes, we present the field (2) and its gradient for some values of ϱ and B' in Fig. 1.

In the Schrödinger form, the DP equation (1) reads[32,33,37]

$$i\partial_t \psi(X) = \hat{H}\psi(X), \quad \hat{H} = \gamma^0\left(\gamma^3 \hat{p}_z + \Sigma_z \hat{\Pi}_z\right). \tag{3}$$

Here $\Sigma_z = i\gamma^1\gamma^2$ and

$$\hat{\Pi}_z = \hat{\pi}_z - \mathbb{I}\mu B_z(y), \quad \hat{\pi}_z = \Sigma_z(\boldsymbol{\gamma}\hat{\mathbf{p}}_\perp + m), \tag{4}$$

is an integral-of-motion spin operator, $\left[\hat{\Pi}_z, \hat{H}\right]_- = 0$. The subscript "$\perp$" labels quantities perpendicular to the field, e.g. $\hat{\mathbf{p}}_\perp = (\hat{p}_x, \hat{p}_y)$ and $\mathbb{I}$ denotes the 4×4 identity matrix. Since the operators $\hat{p}_0$, $\hat{p}_x$, and $\hat{p}_z$ are compatible with the Hamiltonian (and also with $\hat{\Pi}_z$), the DP spinor admits the general form $\psi_n(X) = \exp(-ip_0 t + ip_x x + ip_z z)\psi_n(y)$, where $\psi_n(y)$ depends exclusively on y

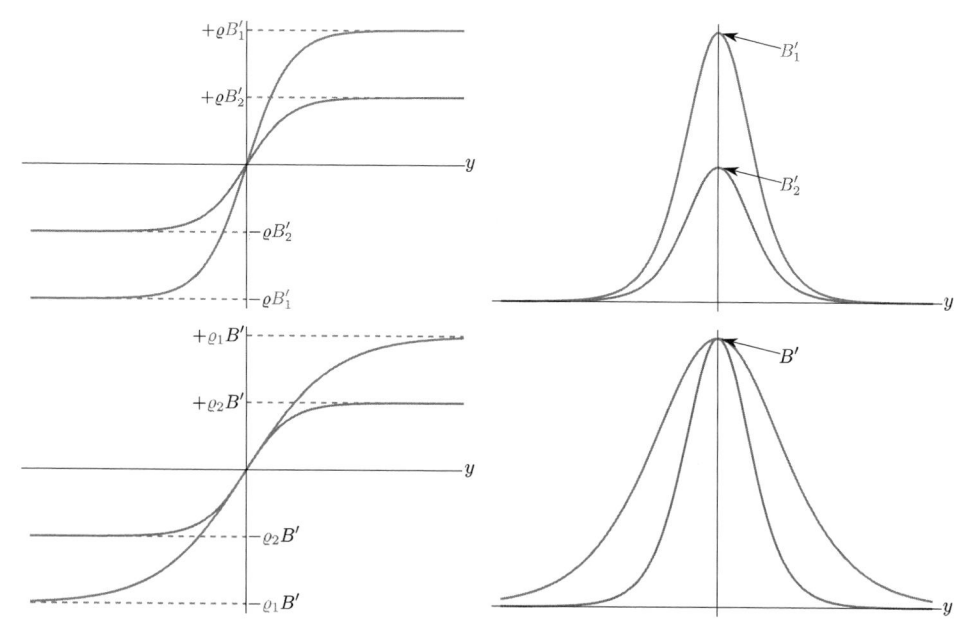

Fig. 1. Sauter-like magnetic steps (2) (pictures on the left) and its gradient (pictures on the right). In the upper panel, $B'_1 = 2 \times B'_2$ while in the lower panel, $\varrho_1 = 2 \times \varrho_2$.

and is solution of the eigenvalue equation:

$$\hat{\Pi}_z \psi_n(X) = e^{-ip_0 t + ip_x x + ip_z z} \Pi_z \psi_n(y) , \quad \Pi_z \psi_n(y) = s\omega \psi_n(y) , \quad s = \pm 1,$$
$$\Pi_z = \hat{\pi}_z - \mathbb{I}\mu B_z(y) , \quad \hat{\pi}_z = \Sigma_z \left(\gamma^1 p_x + \gamma^2 \hat{p}_y + m\right), \quad p_0^2 = \omega^2 + p_z^2. \quad (5)$$

Due to the structure of the external field (2), there is an additional integral-of-motion spin operator

$$\hat{R} = \hat{H}\hat{\Pi}_z^{-1} \left[\mathbb{I} + \left(\hat{p}_z \hat{\Pi}_z^{-1}\right)^2\right]^{-1/2} , \quad (6)$$

which is compatible with the Hamiltonian $\left[\hat{R}, \hat{H}\right]_- = 0$ and with all previous operators, $\left[\hat{R}, \hat{\Pi}_z\right]_- = \left[\hat{R}, \hat{p}_0\right]_- = \left[\hat{R}, \hat{p}_x\right]_- = \left[\hat{R}, \hat{p}_z\right]_- = 0$. In particular, the operator (6) implies that $\psi_n(y)$ is a solution of the eigenvalue equation

$$\hat{R}\psi_n(X) = e^{-ip_0 t + ip_x x + ip_z z} R\psi_n(y) , \quad R\psi_n(y) = s\psi_n(y) ,$$
$$R = \Upsilon\gamma^0 \left(\Sigma_z + \frac{sp_z}{\omega}\gamma^3\right), \quad \Upsilon = \frac{1}{\sqrt{1 + p_z^2/\omega^2}}. \quad (7)$$

As a result, the complete set of commuting operators is $\hat{p}_x$, $\hat{p}_z$, $\hat{\Pi}_z$, $\hat{R}$ and the corresponding quantum numbers are $n = (p_x, p_z, \omega, s)$.

The set of equations (5) and (7) are simultaneously satisfied choosing $\psi_n(y)$ in the form

$$\psi_n(y) = (\mathbb{I} + sR)\left[\hat{\pi}_z + \mathbb{I}(\mu B_z(y) + s\omega)\right]\varphi_{n,\chi}(y) v_\kappa^{(\chi)}, \quad (8)$$

where $v_\kappa^{(\chi)}$ belongs to a set of four constant spinors, satisfying the eigenvalue equations

$$i\gamma^1 v_\kappa^{(\chi)} = \chi v_\kappa^{(\chi)}, \quad \gamma^0 \gamma^2 v_\kappa^{(\chi)} = \kappa v_\kappa^{(\chi)}, \quad \chi = \pm 1, \quad \kappa = \pm 1, \quad (9)$$

and the orthonormality conditions $v_{\kappa'}^{(\chi')\dagger} v_\kappa^{(\chi)} = \delta_{\chi'\chi}\delta_{\kappa'\kappa}$. As for the scalar functions $\varphi_{n,\chi}(y)$, they are solutions of the second-order ordinary differential equation:

$$\left\{-\frac{d^2}{dy^2} - [s\omega + \mu B_z(y)]^2 + \pi_x^2 + i\mu\chi B_z'(y)\right\}\varphi_{n,\chi}(y) = 0, \quad \pi_x^2 = m^2 + p_x^2. \quad (10)$$

The potential energy of a neutral fermion interacting with the field is $U_s(y) = sU(y)$, where $U(y) = -\mu B_z(y)$. To facilitate subsequent discussions, it is convenient to select a fixed sign for particle magnetic moment. From now on, we choose a fermion with a negative magnetic moment as the main particle, $\mu = -|\mu|$. Because the field (2) increases monotonically with y, the maximum potential energy that may be experienced by the fermion is determined by the magnitude of the "step" $\mathbb{U}$

$$\mathbb{U} \equiv U_R - U_L = 2\varrho|\mu|B' > 0, \quad (11)$$

which is the difference between the asymptotic values $U_R = U(+\infty) = |\mu|\varrho B'$, $U_L = U(-\infty) = -|\mu|\varrho B'$ and is positive, by definition[a]. At remote distances–where the field can be considered homogeneous and no longer accelerates particles–the term proportional to χ in Eq. (10) is absent. Therefore, solutions of Eq. (10) have well-defined "left" $_\zeta\varphi_{n,\chi}(y)$ and "right" $^\zeta\varphi_{n,\chi}(y)$ asymptotic forms:

$$_\zeta\varphi_{n,\chi}(y) = {_\zeta\mathcal{N}}\exp\left(i\zeta\left|p^L\right|y\right), \quad \zeta = \text{sgn}(p^L), \quad y \to -\infty,$$
$$^\zeta\varphi_{n,\chi}(y) = {^\zeta\mathcal{N}}\exp\left(i\zeta\left|p^R\right|y\right), \quad \zeta = \text{sgn}(p^R), \quad y \to +\infty. \quad (12)$$

Here, $_\zeta\mathcal{N}$, $^\zeta\mathcal{N}$ are normalization constants, $\left|p^{L/R}\right|$ are y-components of fermions momenta at remote regions

$$\left|p^{L/R}\right| = \sqrt{[s\pi_s(L/R)]^2 - \pi_x^2}, \quad \pi_s(L/R) = \omega - sU_{L/R}, \quad (13)$$

and $\pi_s(L/R)$ are their transverse kinetic energies at remote areas. Correspondingly, asymptotically-"left" $_\zeta\psi_n(X) = \exp(-ip_0t + ip_xx + ip_zz)\,_\zeta\psi_n(y)$ and asymptotically-"right" $^\zeta\psi_n(X) = \exp(-ip_0t + ip_xx + ip_zz)\,^\zeta\psi_n(y)$ sets of DP spinors are solutions of the eigenvalue equations

$$\hat{p}_y\,_\zeta\psi_n(X) = \zeta\left|p^L\right|\,_\zeta\psi_n(X), \quad \hat{h}_\perp^{\text{kin}}\,_\zeta\psi_n(X) = s\pi_s(L)\,_\zeta\psi_n(X), \quad y \to -\infty,$$
$$\hat{p}_y\,^\zeta\psi_n(X) = \zeta\left|p^R\right|\,^\zeta\psi_n(X), \quad \hat{h}_\perp^{\text{kin}}\,^\zeta\psi_n(X) = s\pi_s(R)\,^\zeta\psi_n(X), \quad y \to +\infty, \quad (14)$$

---

[a] The labels "L" and "R" mean "asymptotic left region $y \to -\infty$" and "asymptotic right region $y \to +\infty$", respectively.

where $\hat{h}_\perp^{\text{kin}} = \hat{\Pi}_z - \mathbb{I}|\mu| B_z(y)$ is the one-particle transverse kinetic energy operator.

Substituting the field (2) into Eq. (10) and performing a simultaneous change of variables

$$\varphi_{n,\chi}(y) = \xi^\rho (1-\xi)^\sigma f(\xi), \quad \xi(y) = \frac{1}{2}[1 + \tanh(y/\varrho)], \tag{15}$$

we may convert Eq. (10) to the form of the differential equation for the Gauss Hypergeometric Function[38]

$$\xi(1-\xi) f'' + [c - (a+b+1)\xi] f' - abf = 0, \tag{16}$$

provided the parameters ρ, σ, a, b, and c are:

$$a = \frac{1}{2}(1-\chi) - \frac{i\varrho}{2}\left(\mathbb{U} + |p^L| - |p^R|\right),$$

$$b = \frac{1}{2}(1+\chi) + \frac{i\varrho}{2}\left(\mathbb{U} + |p^R| - |p^L|\right),$$

$$c = 1 - i\varrho\left|p^L\right|, \quad \rho = -\frac{i}{2}\varrho\left|p^L\right|, \quad \sigma = \frac{i}{2}\varrho\left|p^R\right|. \tag{17}$$

Among the 24 Hypergeometric functions satisfying Eq. (16),[38] we select those that tend to unity when $y \to \mp\infty$. Solutions meeting this property are proportional to Hypergeometric functions of type $F(a', b'; c'; \xi)$ and $F(a'', b''; c''; 1-\xi)$. For example, a possible set of exact solutions to Eq. (10) behaving asymptotically like Eqs. (12) is

$$_\varsigma\varphi_{n,\chi}(y) = {}_\varsigma\mathcal{N} \exp\left(i\varsigma\left|p^L\right|y\right) [1 + \exp(2y/\varrho)]^{-i\varrho(\varsigma|p^L|+|p^R|)/2} {}_\varsigma u(\xi),$$

$$^\varsigma\varphi_{n,\chi}(y) = {}^\varsigma\mathcal{N} \exp\left(i\varsigma\left|p^R\right|y\right) [1 + \exp(-2y/\varrho)]^{i\varrho(|p^L|+\varsigma|p^R|)/2} {}^\varsigma u(\xi), \tag{18}$$

where

$$_-u(\xi) = F(a,b;c;\xi), \quad _+u(\xi) = F(a+1-c, b+1-c; 2-c; \xi),$$
$$^-u(\xi) = F(a,b; a+b+1-c; 1-\xi), \quad ^+u(\xi) = F(c-a, c-b; c+1-a-b; 1-\xi). \tag{19}$$

With the aid of these solutions, we may finally introduce the sets of DP spinors

$$_\varsigma\psi_n(X) = e^{-i(p_0 t - p_x x - p_z z)}(\mathbb{I} + sR)\{\hat{\pi}_z + \mathbb{I}[s\omega - |\mu| B_z(y)]\} {}_\varsigma\varphi_{n,\chi}(y) v_\kappa^{(\chi)},$$
$$^\varsigma\psi_n(X) = e^{-i(p_0 t - p_x x - p_z z)}(\mathbb{I} + sR)\{\hat{\pi}_z + \mathbb{I}[s\omega - |\mu| B_z(y)]\} {}^\varsigma\varphi_{n,\chi}(y) v_\kappa^{(\chi)}, \tag{20}$$

provided the quantum numbers n obey the conditions

$$[s\pi_s(\text{L/R})]^2 > \pi_x^2. \tag{21}$$

These inequalities ensure the nontriviality of DP spinors with real asymptotic momenta p^L and p^R in remote areas, fulfilling Eqs. (14).

To calculate the normalization constants $_\varsigma\mathcal{N}$, $^\varsigma\mathcal{N}$, we use the inner product on the timelike surface $y = \text{const.}$,

$$(\psi, \psi')_y = \int dt dx dz \psi^\dagger(X) \gamma^0 \gamma^2 \psi'(X), \tag{22}$$

after imposing specific normalization conditions[b]. We assume that all processes take place within a macroscopically large space-time box, of volume TV_y, $V_y = L_x L_z$, and impose periodic boundary conditions upon DP spinors in the variables t, x, z at the boundaries. Thus, the integrals in (22) are calculated from $(-T/2, -L_x/2, -L_z/2)$ to $(+T/2, +L_x/2, +L_z/2)$ and the limits $(T, L_x, L_z) \to \infty$ are taken at the end of calculations. Under these conditions, the inner product is y-independent and we may impose the following normalization conditions:

$$\left(_{\varsigma'}\psi_{n'}, {}_\varsigma\psi_n\right)_y = \varsigma\eta_L \delta_{n'n}\delta_{\varsigma'\varsigma}, \quad \left({}^{\varsigma'}\psi_{n'}, {}^\varsigma\psi_n\right)_y = \varsigma\eta_R \delta_{n'n}\delta_{\varsigma'\varsigma}, \qquad (23)$$

where $\eta_{L/R} = \mathrm{sgn}\,[\pi_s\,(L/R)]$. It should be noted that the time independence of the magnetic field under consideration is an idealization. Physically, it is meaningful to believe that the field inhomogeneity was switched on sufficiently fast before instant t_{in}. By this time, it had time to spread to the whole area under consideration and then acted as a constant field during a large time T. It is supposed that one can ignore effects of its switching on and off. This is a kind of regularization, which could, under certain conditions, be replaced by periodic boundary conditions in t, see Refs.[34,35] for details. Evaluating the inner product (22) for each DP spinor (20) and imposing the normalization conditions (23), we obtain

$$|_\varsigma\mathcal{N}| = \frac{[TV_y \Upsilon\,(1-s\kappa\chi\Upsilon)]^{-1/2}}{2\sqrt{|p^L|\,|\pi_s\,(L)-s\chi\varsigma\,|p^L|\,|}}, \quad |{}^\varsigma\mathcal{N}| = \frac{[TV_y \Upsilon\,(1-s\kappa\chi\Upsilon)]^{-1/2}}{2\sqrt{|p^R|\,|\pi_s\,(R)-s\chi\varsigma\,|p^R|\,|}}. \qquad (24)$$

Considering that the "left" and "right" sets of DP spinors (20) are orthonormal and complete (with respect to the inner product (22)), we may decompose one set into another with the help of some g-coefficients

$$\eta_L\,{}^\varsigma\psi_n(X) = g\left(+|^\varsigma\right)\,{}_+\psi_n(X) - g\left(-|^\varsigma\right)\,{}_-\psi_n(X),$$
$$\eta_R\,{}_\varsigma\psi_n(X) = g\left({}^+|_\varsigma\right)\,{}^+\psi_n(X) - g\left({}^-|_\varsigma\right)\,{}^-\psi_n(X), \qquad (25)$$

which, by definition, are inner products between different sets of DP spinors

$$\left({}_\varsigma\psi_n, {}^{\varsigma'}\psi_{n'}\right)_y = \delta_{nn'} g\left(_\varsigma|^{\varsigma'}\right) = \delta_{nn'} g\left({}^{\varsigma'}|_\varsigma\right)^*, \qquad (26)$$

and play an important role in the quantization of DP spinors with steplike magnetic fields. These coefficients link different sets of creation and annihilation operators and contains all the necessary information about vacuum instability, as shall be seen below. Substituting the identities (25) into normalization conditions (23) supply us with two important identities

$$\sum_{\varsigma''=\pm} \varsigma'' g\left({}^{\varsigma'}|_{\varsigma''}\right) g\left(_{\varsigma''}|^\varsigma\right) = \varsigma \eta_L \eta_R \delta_{\varsigma'\varsigma} = \sum_{\varsigma''=\pm} \varsigma'' g\left(_{\varsigma'}|^{\varsigma''}\right) g\left({}^{\varsigma''}|_\varsigma\right), \qquad (27)$$

from which we may derive a number of identities, for example $|g\,(_+|^-)|^2 = |g\,(_-|^+)|^2$, $|g\,(_+|^+)|^2 = |g\,(_-|^-)|^2$, and $|g\,(_+|^+)|^2 - |g\,(_+|^-)|^2 = \eta_L \eta_R$.

---

[b]Note that for $\psi' = \psi$, the inner product (22) divided by T coincides with the definition of the current density accross the y-const. hyperplane.

3. Pair production

Besides providing conditions for the existence of solutions (20), the inequalities (21) imposes certain limitations on the quantum numbers. For critical Sauter-like magnetic steps, whose step magnitudes (11) meet the condition

$$\mathbb{U} > \mathbb{U}_c = 2m, \tag{28}$$

the whole manifold of quantum numbers divides into five sub-ranges, Ω_k, $k = 1, ..., 5$. Neutral fermion pair production takes place only in a well-defined bounded set of quantum numbers[32–34]

$$\Omega_3 = \{n : U_L + \pi_x \leq s\omega \leq U_R - \pi_x, \ \pi_{xz} \leq \mathbb{U}/2\}, \ \pi_{xz} = \sqrt{\pi_x^2 + p_z^2}, \tag{29}$$

which is conventionally called *Klein zone*, Ω_3. In this subrange, $s\pi_s(L) \geq \pi_x$ and $s\pi_s(R) \leq -\pi_x$, which means that $s\eta_L = +1$ and $s\eta_R = -1$. As a result, there exist two linearly-independent "left" $_\varsigma\psi_{n_3}(X)$ and "right" $^\varsigma\psi_{n_3}(X)$ sets of DP spinors with quantum numbers within the Klein zone $n_3 = n \in \Omega_3$.

To quantize the DP field operators using sets of solutions in this subrange, we need to classify them as particle or antiparticle states and as incoming waves (waves traveling toward the "step") or outgoing waves (waves traveling outward the "step") in remote areas. The correct classification demands a careful study of the inner product on y- and t-constant hyperplanes because important quantities to the scattering problem are expressed as surface integrals on such hyperplanes. After a detailed study of these quantities, which was presented in Refs.[34,35] for charged particles and in[33] for neutral fermions, "in"-solutions (incoming waves) and "out"-solutions (outgoing waves) are

in-solutions: $_{-}\psi_{n_3}(X)$, $^{-}\psi_{n_3}(X)$, out-solutions: $_{+}\psi_{n_3}(X)$, $^{+}\psi_{n_3}(X)$. (30)

The above sets of solutions are complete and orthogonal with respect to the inner product on t-constant hyperplane

$$(\psi_n, \psi'_{n'}) = \int_{V_y} dxdz \int_{-K^{(L)}}^{K^{(R)}} dy \psi_n^\dagger(X) \psi'_{n'}(X), \tag{31}$$

in which the lower/upper cutoffs $K^{(L/R)}$ are macroscopic but finite parameters of the volume regularization that are situated far beyond the region of a large gradient $\partial_y B_z(y)$; see Ref.[34,35] for details. In particular, the inner product (31) between "in" and "out" sets of DP spinors have the form

$$(_\varsigma\psi_n, _\varsigma\psi_{n'}) = (^\varsigma\psi_n, ^\varsigma\psi_{n'}) = \mathcal{M}_n \delta_{nn'}, \ (_\varsigma\psi_n, ^\varsigma\psi_{n'}) = 0, \ n, n' \in \Omega_3. \tag{32}$$

where $\mathcal{M}_n = 2|g(_+|^-)|^2 t^{(L/R)}/T$, $t^{(L/R)} = K^{(L/R)} |\pi_s(L/R)/p^{L/R}|$. Because there are two linearly independent sets of spinors (30), the quantization is performed using two distinct "in" and "out" sets of annihilation & creation operators

$$\text{in-set: } _{-}b_{n_3}(\text{in}), \ _{-}b^\dagger_{n_3}(\text{in}), \ ^{-}a_{n_3}(\text{in}), \ ^{-}a^\dagger_{n_3}(\text{in}),$$
$$\text{out-set: } _{+}b_{n_3}(\text{out}), \ _{+}b^\dagger_{n_3}(\text{out}), \ ^{+}a_{n_3}(\text{out}), \ ^{+}a^\dagger_{n_3}(\text{out}), \tag{33}$$

which, in turn, obey the following anticommutation relations

$$\left[\,^-a_{n_3'}(\text{in}),\,^-a_{n_3}^\dagger(\text{in})\right]_+ = \left[\,_-b_{n_3'}(\text{in}),\,_-b_{n_3}^\dagger(\text{in})\right]_+ = \delta_{n_3'n_3},$$
$$\left[\,^+a_{n_3'}(\text{out}),\,^+a_{n_3}^\dagger(\text{out})\right]_+ = \left[\,_+b_{n_3'}(\text{out}),\,_+b_{n_3}^\dagger(\text{out})\right]_+ = \delta_{n_3'n_3}, \quad (34)$$

and whose annihilation operators (33) annihilate the corresponding vacuum states

$$_-b_{n_3}(\text{in})\,|0,\text{in}\rangle = \,^-a_{n_3}(\text{in})\,|0,\text{in}\rangle = 0,\; _+b_{n_3}(\text{out})\,|0,\text{out}\rangle = \,^+a_{n_3}(\text{out})\,|0,\text{out}\rangle = 0. \quad (35)$$

Finally, the quantized DP field operator in the Klein zone reads

$$\hat{\Psi}(X) = \sum_{n\in\Omega_3} \mathcal{M}_n^{-1/2}\left[\,^-a_n(\text{in})\,^-\psi_n(X) + \,_-b_n^\dagger(\text{in})\,_-\psi_n(X)\right],$$
$$= \sum_{n\in\Omega_3} \mathcal{M}_n^{-1/2}\left[\,^+a_n(\text{out})\,^+\psi_n(X) + \,_+b_n^\dagger(\text{out})\,_+\psi_n(X)\right]. \quad (36)$$

Using orthogonality relations between DP spinors (23), (32) and the relations given by Eqs. (25), one may establish a linear relation between the "in"-set of creation/annihilation operators in terms of the "out"-set and *vice-versa*. For example, two (out of four) canonical transformations have the following form

$$_-b_n^\dagger(\text{in}) = -g\left(^+|_-\right)^{-1}\,^+a_n(\text{out}) + g\left(_+|^-\right)^{-1} g\left(_-|^-\right)\,_+b_n^\dagger(\text{out}),$$
$$^+a_n(\text{out}) = -g\left(_-|^+\right)^{-1}\,_-b_n^\dagger(\text{in}) + g\left(^-|_+\right)^{-1} g\left(^+|_+\right)\,^-a_n(\text{in}). \quad (37)$$

With the aid of the canonical transformations (37), we may finally define vacuum instability quantities, such as the differential mean numbers of "out" particles created from the "in" vacuum,

$$N_n^{\text{cr}} = \langle 0,\text{in}|\,^+a_n^\dagger(\text{out})\,^+a_n(\text{out})|\text{in},0\rangle = \left|g\left(_-|^+\right)\right|^{-2}, \quad n\in\Omega_3, \quad (38)$$

and the flux density of particles created with a given s,

$$n_s^{\text{cr}} = \frac{1}{V_y T}\sum_{n\in\Omega_3} N_n^{\text{cr}} = \frac{1}{(2\pi)^3}\int dp_z \int dp_x \int dp_0\, N_n^{\text{cr}}. \quad (39)$$

The total flux density of particles created with both spin polarizations is $n^{\text{cr}} = n_{+1}^{\text{cr}} + n_{-1}^{\text{cr}}$ and the vacuum-vacuum transition probability reads:

$$P_v = |\langle 0,\text{out}|0,\text{in}\rangle|^2 = \exp\left[\sum_{s=\pm 1}\sum_{n\in\Omega_3}\ln\left(1-N_n^{\text{cr}}\right)\right]. \quad (40)$$

It should be noted that if the total number of created particles $N^{\text{cr}} = V_y T n^{\text{cr}}$ is small, one may neglect higher-order terms in Eq. (40) to conclude that $P_v \approx 1 - N^{\text{cr}}$. With the aid of this relation, we may link the total number of neutral fermions created from the vacuum with the imaginary part of an effective action S_{eff} provided it satisfies the Schwinger relation $P_v = \exp(-2\text{Im}S_{\text{eff}})$, and it is small, so that $P_v \approx 1 - 2\text{Im}S_{\text{eff}}$. Therefore,

$$\text{Im}S_{\text{eff}} \approx V_y T n^{\text{cr}}/2. \quad (41)$$

From these equations, we observe that all the information about pair creation by the external field is enclosed in $g\left(_-|^+\right)$. To obtain this coefficient, we may use an appropriate Kummer relation[38] that connects three Gauss Hypergeometric functions appearing in one of the relations given by Eq. (25). After obtaining this coefficient and calculating its absolute square $|g\left(_-|^+\right)|^{-2}$, we finally obtain the differential mean numbers of pairs created from the vacuum:

$$N_n^{\text{cr}} = \frac{\sinh\left(\pi\varrho\left|p^{\text{R}}\right|\right)\sinh\left(\pi\varrho\left|p^{\text{L}}\right|\right)}{\sinh\left[\pi\varrho\left(\mathbb{U}+\left|p^{\text{L}}\right|-\left|p^{\text{R}}\right|\right)/2\right]\sinh\left[\pi\varrho\left(\mathbb{U}+\left|p^{\text{R}}\right|-\left|p^{\text{L}}\right|\right)/2\right]}. \quad (42)$$

Note that N_n^{cr} are positive-definite because the difference $\left||p^{\text{L}}|-|p^{\text{R}}|\right|$ bounded in this subrange; $0 \leq \left||p^{\text{L}}|-|p^{\text{R}}|\right| \leq \sqrt{\mathbb{U}\left(\mathbb{U}-2\pi_x\right)}$. The above expression gives the exact distribution of neutral fermions created from the vacuum by the field (2). When summed over the quantum numbers, it provides exact expressions for the flux density of the created particles (39) and the vacuum-vacuum transition probability (40). Lastly, it is noteworthy to discuss some peculiarities associated with the choice of the quantum number s and its impact on the quantization (36). As pointed out in Sec. 2, there are two species of neutral fermions, one with $s = +1$ and another with $s = -1$. In the latter case, the classification differs from the one given by Eq (30), namely $_+\psi_{n_3}(X)$, $^+\psi_{n_3}(X)$ are "in"-solutions while $_-\psi_{n_3}(X)$, $^-\psi_{n_3}(X)$ are "out"-solutions. Although this classification changes the quantization (36), it does not change the mean numbers (38). This means that the flux density of particles created with $s = -1$ equals the one with $s = +1$, $n_{+1}^{\text{cr}} = n_{-1}^{\text{cr}}$. Therefore, summations over s in Eqs. (39), (40) just produce an extra factor of 2 in final expressions and that is why it is enough selecting s fixed to perform specific calculations; hereafter, we select $s = +1$ for convenience. In what follows, we analyze vacuum instability quantities when the field lies in two special configurations, varying either "gradually" or "sharply" along the inhomogeneity direction.

3.1. "Gradually"-varying field configuration

This field configuration corresponds to the case where the amplitude B' is sufficiently large and the field inhomogeneity stretches over a relatively wide region of the space, such that the condition

$$\sqrt{\varrho\mathbb{U}/2} \gg \max\left(1, \frac{m}{\sqrt{|\mu|\,B'}}\right), \quad (43)$$

is satisfied. Accordingly, the arguments of the hyperbolic functions in (42) are large, meaning that the mean numbers of pairs created acquires the following approximate form,

$$N_n^{\text{cr}} \approx e^{-\pi\tau}, \quad \tau = \varrho\left(\mathbb{U}-\left|p^{\text{R}}\right|-\left|p^{\text{L}}\right|\right). \quad (44)$$

The above distribution is exponentially small for large values of ω and p_x. Its most significant contribution comes from a finite range of values of quantum numbers such that the conditions $\min\left(\pi_{+1}^{2}\left(\mathrm{L}\right),\pi_{+1}^{2}\left(\mathrm{R}\right)\right)\gg\pi_{x}^{2}$ remains valid. In this case, τ admits the following approximation

$$\tau=\frac{\left(\mathrm{U}/2\right)^{2}}{\left(\mathrm{U}/2\right)^{2}-\omega^{2}}\lambda+O\left(\pi_{x}^{4}/\left|\pi_{+1}\left(\mathrm{R}\right)\right|^{3}\right)+O\left(\pi_{x}^{4}/\left|\pi_{+1}\left(\mathrm{L}\right)\right|^{3}\right). \quad (45)$$

Now, we can estimate the flux density of pairs created n^{cr} for a magnetic step evolving gradually along the y-direction according to (43). To this end, it is convenient to transform the original integral over p_0 into an integral over ω through the relation between p_0, ω, and p_z discussed before, $p_0^2 = \omega^2 + p_z^2$. Performing such a change of variables, the flux density of the particles created by the external field in the configuration (43) has the form

$$n^{\mathrm{cr}} \approx \frac{4}{(2\pi)^3} \int_0^{p_z^{\max}} dp_z \int_{-p_x^{\max}}^{p_x^{\max}} dp_x \int_0^{\omega_{\max}^2} d\omega^2 \frac{e^{-\pi\tau}}{\sqrt{\omega^2+p_z^2}},$$

$$p_z^{\max} = \sqrt{(\mathrm{U}/2)^2 - m^2}, \quad p_x^{\max} = \sqrt{(\mathrm{U}/2)^2 - m^2 - p_z^2}, \quad \omega_{\max} = \mathrm{U}/2 - \pi_x. \quad (46)$$

The multiplicative factor 4 comes from the summation over s and from the fact that the integrand is symmetric in p_z. To obtain an analytical expression to N^{cr}, we formally extend the integration limits of the last two integrals to infinity. This procedure amounts to incorporating exponentially small contributions to n^{cr} since the differential mean numbers are exponentially small at large p_x and ω. In this case, we may technically interchange the order of the last two integrals in (46) and use the approximation given by Eq. (45) to discover that the flux density of the created particles is approximately given by

$$n^{\mathrm{cr}} \approx \frac{m}{(2\pi)^3} \mathrm{U}^2 \sqrt{b'} e^{-\pi b'} I_{b'}, \quad I_{b'} = \int_0^\infty \frac{du}{(u+1)^{5/2}} \ln\left(\frac{\sqrt{1+u}+\sqrt{1+2u}}{\sqrt{u}}\right) e^{-\pi b' u}, \quad (47)$$

where $b' = m^2/|\mu| B'$ and $\mathrm{U} = 2\varrho|\mu| B'$. At last, one may use the identity $\ln(1-N_n^{\mathrm{cr}}) = -\sum_{l=1}^{\infty} (N_n^{\mathrm{cr}})^l/l$ and perform integrations similar to the ones discussed before to discover that the vacuum-vacuum transition probability admits the final form

$$P_v = \exp\left(-\beta V_y T n^{\mathrm{cr}}\right), \quad \beta = \sum_{l=0}^{\infty} \frac{\epsilon_{l+1}}{(l+1)^{3/2}} \exp\left(-l\pi b'\right), \quad \epsilon_l = \frac{I_{b'l}}{I_{b'}}, \quad (48)$$

with n^{cr} given by Eq. (47).

It is noteworthy mentioning that relation (40)–which is well-known for strong-field QED with external electromagnetic fields–holds for the case under consideration as well. However, a direct similarity of total quantities for both cases is absent. We see that the flux density of created neutral fermion pairs and the quantity $\ln P_v^{-1}$ are quadratic in the magnitude of the step. This is a consequence of the fact that the number of states with all possible ω and p_z excited by the magnetic-field inhomogeneity is quadratic in the increment of the kinetic momentum. This is also the reason why the flux density of created pairs and $\ln P_v^{-1}$ per unit of the length are not uniform.

3.2. "Sharply"-varying field configuration

A second configuration of interest is when the field (2) "sharply" steeps near the origin. Such a configuration is specified by the conditions:

$$1 \gg \sqrt{\varrho \mathbb{U}/2} \gtrsim \frac{m}{\sqrt{|\mu| B'}}. \tag{49}$$

The first inequality indicates that the gradient $\partial_y B_z(y)$ sharply peaks about the origin, while the second implicates that the Klein zone is relatively small. This configuration is particularly important due to a close analogy to charged pair production by the Klein step, see Ref.[39] for the review. For electric fields whose spatial inhomogeneity meets conditions equivalent to (49), it was demonstrated that the imaginary part of the QED effective action features properties similar to those of continuous phase transitions.[40,41] Recently,[42] we have demonstrated for the inverse-square electric field that this peculiarity also follows from the behavior of total quantities when the Klein zone is relatively small. Because of the condition (49), not only the parameter $\varrho \mathbb{U}/2$ is small but all parameters involving the quantum numbers p_x, p_z, and ω are small as well on account of the inequalities (29). As a result, the arguments of the hyperbolic functions in (42) are small, which means that we may expand the hyperbolic functions in ascending powers and truncate the corresponding series to first-order to demonstrate that the mean numbers admit the approximate form:

$$N_n^{\mathrm{cr}} \approx \frac{4 |p^\mathrm{R}| |p^\mathrm{L}|}{\mathbb{U}^2 - (|p^\mathrm{L}| - |p^\mathrm{R}|)^2}. \tag{50}$$

To implement the conditions (49), we conveniently introduce the Keldysh parameter $\gamma = 2m/\mathbb{U}$ and observe that it obeys the condition $1 - \gamma^2 \ll 1$ on account of (49). Next, we perform the change of variables

$$\frac{\omega}{m} = \frac{1}{2}(1 - \gamma^2)(1 - v), \quad \frac{p_x^2}{m^2} = (1 - \gamma^2) r, \tag{51}$$

and expand the asymptotic momenta $|p^{\mathrm{L/R}}|$ in ascending powers of $1 - \gamma^2$ to learn that $|p^\mathrm{R}|/m = (1 - \gamma^2)^{1/2} \sqrt{v - r} + O\left((1 - \gamma^2)^{3/2}\right)$, $|p^\mathrm{L}|/m = (1 - \gamma^2)^{1/2} \sqrt{2 - v - r} + O\left((1 - \gamma^2)^{3/2}\right)$. Substituting these approximations into (50) we obtain

$$N_n^{\mathrm{cr}} = (1 - \gamma^2) \sqrt{(1 - r)^2 - (1 - v)^2} + O\left((1 - \gamma^2)^2\right). \tag{52}$$

We now wish to estimate the total number of pairs created from the vacuum by a sharply varying external field. In this case, it is convenient to first integrate over p_z, which is allowed as long as we swap the integration limits indicated in (46), i.e.

$p_z^{\max} = \sqrt{(\mathbb{U}/2)^2 - m^2 - p_x^2}$ and $p_x^{\max} = \sqrt{(\mathbb{U}/2)^2 - m^2}$. Calculating the integral and performing the change of variables proposed in (51), we expand the result in power series of $1 - \gamma^2$ to find

$$\int_0^{p_z^{\max}} \frac{dp_z}{\sqrt{\omega^2 + p_z^2}} = -\frac{1}{2}\ln\left(1 - \gamma^2\right) + 2\ln 2 + \ln\sqrt{1 - r} - \ln\sqrt{(1 - v)^2} + O\left(1 - \gamma^2\right). \tag{53}$$

The most significant contribution to total quantities in this regime comes from the logarithm $\ln\left(1 - \gamma^2\right)$, as $1 - \gamma^2 \ll 1$. Neglecting higher-order terms in $1 - \gamma^2$, the flux density of the particles created is approximately given by

$$n^{\mathrm{cr}} \approx \frac{\left(1 - \gamma^2\right)^{7/2}\left|\ln\left(1 - \gamma^2\right)\right| m^3}{(2\pi)^3} \int_0^{r_{\max}} \frac{dr}{\sqrt{r}} \int_{v_{\min}}^{v_{\max}} dv\, (1 - v)\sqrt{(1 - r)^2 - (1 - v)^2}, \tag{54}$$

where $v_{\min} \approx r$ and $v_{\max} \approx r_{\max} \approx 1$. After straightforward integrations, the flux density of the particles created from the vacuum by a sharply varying Sauter-like magnetic step takes the approximate form

$$n^{\mathrm{cr}} \approx \frac{4}{105\pi^3} m^3 \left(1 - \gamma^2\right)^{7/2}\left|\ln\left(1 - \gamma^2\right)\right|. \tag{55}$$

Due to the smallness of the coefficient $\left(1 - \gamma^2\right)^{7/2}$, the total number of neutral fermions pairs created from the vacuum is also small $N^{\mathrm{cr}} = V_y T n^{\mathrm{cr}}$, which means that the vacuum-vacuum transition probability is approximately given by $P_v \approx 1 - N^{\mathrm{cr}}$. We may use this result to link the flux density of pairs created (55) with the imaginary part of the effective action, given by the approximation (41).

4. Concluding remarks

Here we review our recent results on the creation of neutral fermion pairs with anomalous magnetic moments from the vacuum by Sauter-like magnetic field.[32] We show that the problem is technically analogous to the problem of charged-particle creation by an electric step, for which the nonperturbative formulation of strong-field QED exists.[34,35] To employ this formulation, we first find exact solutions of the DP equation with Sauter-like magnetic field with well-defined spin polarization and calculated all quantities characterizing the effect, in particular when the field lies in two specific configurations. When the field varies "gradually" along the inhomogeneity direction, we found that the flux density of created neutral fermion pairs is quadratic in the magnitude of the step $\mathbb{U}$. This feature is particularly different from the case of charged pair production by electric steps, in which the the flux density features a linear dependence on the magnitude of the electric step. The quadratic dependence for neutral fermions derives from the non-cartesian geometry of the parameter space formed by the quantum numbers, and it is inherent to the dynamics of neutral fermions with anomalous magnetic moments in inhomogeneous magnetic fields. This also explains why the flux density of created pairs per unit of the length are not uniform. In particular, it means that the Schwinger method of the effective action works for the case under consideration only after a suitable parameterization. The second feature worth discussing is the behavior of total quantities when the field "sharply" varies. It is exactly the form of the Klein effect.[39] If we compare the flux density of neutral fermion pairs created with the total number of electron-positron pairs created from the vacuum by inhomogeneous electric fields (given, for example, by Eq. (88) with $d = 4$ in[42]), we observe two major differences: the first is the presence of a logarithmic coefficient $\left|\ln\left(1-\gamma^2\right)\right|$, that can be traced back to the integration over p_z (53) and therefore does not depend on the external field. To our knowledge, this term has no precedents in QED (although a logarithmic coefficient of this type may appear in scalar QED). The second, and more important, is the value of the scaling (or critical) exponent seen in (55). In contrast to QED in $3+1$ dimensions, in which $N^{\mathrm{cr}} \sim \left(1-\gamma^2\right)^3$,[40–42] the total number of neutral fermions pairs created from the vacuum features a larger exponent, $7/2$. Aside from minor numerical differences, this means that the total number (55) has an extra term $\sqrt{1-\gamma^2}\left|\ln\left(1-\gamma^2\right)\right|$, which is always less than unity in the range of values to γ within the interval $0 \leq \gamma < 1$. Formally, this indicates that backreaction effects caused by neutral fermions produced by sharply-evolving inhomogeneous magnetic fields may be significantly smaller compared to QED under equivalent conditions.

The mechanism here described raises the question about the critical magnetic field intensity, near which the phenomenon could be observed. It is possible to estimate such a value based on fermion's mass and its magnetic moment. Since $\max B_z(y) = B_z(+\infty) = \varrho B' \equiv B_{\max}$, the nontriviality of the Klein zone (29) yields the following condition

$$\mathbb{U} = 2\left|\mu\right|\varrho B' > 2m \Rightarrow B_{\max} > B_{\mathrm{cr}}, \quad B_{\mathrm{cr}} \equiv \frac{m}{|\mu|} \approx 1.73 \times 10^8 \times \left(\frac{m}{1\,\mathrm{eV}}\right)\left(\frac{\mu_{\mathrm{B}}}{|\mu|}\right)\mathrm{G}, \tag{56}$$

where $\mu_{\mathrm{B}} = e/2m_e \approx 5.8 \times 10^{-9}$ eV/G is the Bohr magneton.[16] For neutrons, whose mass and magnetic moment are $m_N \approx 939.6 \times 10^6$ eV, $\mu_N \approx -1.042 \times 10^{-3}\mu_{\mathrm{B}}$, the critical magnetic field (56) is $B_{\mathrm{cr}} \approx 1.56 \times 10^{20}$ G. More optimistic values can be estimated for neutrinos because of their light masses and small magnetic moments. For example, considering recent constraints for neutrinos effective magnetic moment $\mu_\nu \approx 2.9 \times 10^{-11}\mu_{\mathrm{B}}$,[18] and mass $m_\nu \approx 10^{-1}$ eV,[30] we find $B_{\mathrm{cr}} \approx 5.97 \times 10^{17}$ G. Evidently, this value changes considering different values to neutrinos' magnetic moment and mass. Taking, for instance, the experimental estimate to the tau-neutrino magnetic moment $\mu_\tau \approx 3.9 \times 10^{-7}\mu_{\mathrm{B}}$,[17] and assuming its mass $m_{\nu_\tau} \approx 10^{-1}$ eV we obtain a value to B_{cr} near QED critical field $B_{\mathrm{QED}} = m^2/e \approx 4.4 \times 10^{13}$ G, namely $B_{\mathrm{cr}} \approx 4.44 \times 10^{13}$ G. On the other hand, assuming the lower bound found in Ref.[25] $\mu_\nu \approx 10^{-14}\mu_{\mathrm{B}}$ and the same mass $m_\nu \approx 10^{-1}$ eV we obtain a value to B_{cr} orders of magnitude larger than B_{QED}, $B_{\mathrm{cr}} \approx 1.73 \times 10^{21}$ G. The critical magnetic field surprisingly increases if one considers the magnetic moment predicted by the SM,

$\mu_\nu \approx 3.2 \times 10^{-19} \mu_B \times (m_\nu/1\,\text{eV})$.[27,30] Substituting this value into (56) and considering $m_\nu \approx 1\,\text{eV}$ we find $B_{\text{cr}} \approx 5.41 \times 10^{26}\,\text{G}$. Based on these estimates, we believe that neutral fermion pair production may occur in astrophysical enviroments, in particular during a supernova explosion or in the vicinity of magnetars, whose typical order of magnetic field intensities range from $10^{16} - 10^{18}\,\text{G}$ (or up to $10^{20}\,\text{G}$), as reported in Refs.[43–46].

Acknowledgments

T.C.A. was supported by the Advanced Talents Development Program of the Hebei University, grant no. 801260201271. Z.-W.H. was supported by the Post-graduate's Innovation Fund Project of Hebei Province, grant No. CXZZSS2021016. The work of S.P. Gavrilov and D.M. Gitman was supported by Russian Science Foundation, grant no. 19-12-00042.

References

1. J. Schwinger, Phys. Rev. **82**, 664 (1951).
2. O. Klein, Z. Phys. **53**, 157 (1929).
3. F. Sauter, Z. Phys. **69**, 742 (1931).
4. F. Sauter, Z. Phys. **73**, 547 (1932).
5. W. Heisenberg and H. Euler, Z. Phys. **98**, 714 (1936).
6. W. Greiner, B. Müller, and J. Rafelski, *Quantum Electrodynamics of Strong Fields* (Springer-Verlag, Berlin, 1985).
7. A. A. Grib, S. G. Mamaev and V. M. Mostepanenko, *Vacuum Quantum Effects in Strong Fields* (Friedmann Laboratory, St. Petersburg, 1994).
8. E. S. Fradkin, D. M. Gitman, and S. M. Shvartsman, *Quantum Electrodynamics with Unstable Vacuum* (Springer-Verlag, Berlin, 1991).
9. G. V. Dunne, *Heisenberg-Euler Effective Lagrangians: Basics and Extensions*, in I. Kogan Memorial Volume, From Fields to Strings: Circumnavigating Theoretical Physics, pp. 445-522, edited by M Shifman, A. Vainshtein, and J. Wheater (World Scientific, Singapore, 2005).
10. R. Ruffini, G. Vereshchagin, and S. Xue, Phys. Rep. **487**, 1 (2010).
11. G. Dunne, Eur. Phys. J. D **55**, 327 (2009).
12. F. Gelis and N. Tanji, Prog. Part. Nucl. Phys. **87**, 1 (2016).
13. A. Di Piazza, C. Müller, K. Z. Hatsagortsyan, and C. H. Keitel, Rev. Mod. Phys. **84**, 1177 (2012).
14. B. M. Hegelich, G. Mourou, and J. Rafelski, Eur. Phys. J. Spec. Top. **223**, 1093 (2014).
15. T. C. Adorno, S. P. Gavrilov, and D. M. Gitman, Int. J. Mod. Phys. **32**, 1750105 (2017).
16. The Nist Reference on Constants, Units, and Uncertainty https://physics.nist.gov/cuu/Constants/index.html
17. Schwienhorst, R., et al. (DONUT Collaboration), Phys. Lett. B **513**, 23 (2001).
18. A. Beda et al., Adv. High Energy Phys. **2012**, 350150 (2012).
19. G. G. Raffelt, Phys. Rev. Lett. **64**, 2856 (1990).
20. G. G. Raffelt, Astrophys. J. **365**, 559 (1990).
21. G. G. Raffelt and A. Weiss, Astron. Astrophys. **264**, 536 (1992).
22. V. Castellani and S. Degl'Innocenti, Astrophys. J. **402**, 574 (1993).

23. M. Catelan, J. F. Pacheco, and J. Horvath, Astrophys. J. **461**, 231 (1996).
24. N. Viaux, M. Catelan, P. B. Stetson, G. G. Raffelt, J. Redondo, A. A. R. Valcarce, and A.Weiss, Astron. Astrophys. **558**, A12 (2013).
25. N. F. Bell, V. Cirigliano, M. J. Ramsey-Musolf, P. Vogel, and M. B. Wise, Phys. Rev. Lett. **95**, 151802 (2005).
26. A. Aboubrahim, T. Ibrahim, A. Itani, and P. Nath, Phys. Rev. D **89**, 055009 (2014).
27. C. Giunti and A. Studenikin, Phys. Atom. Nucl. **72**, 2089 (2009).
28. M. Dvornikov, in *Neutrinos: Properties, Sources and Detection*, edited by J. P. Greene (Nova Science Publishers, New York, 2011), p. 23.
29. C. Broggini, C. Giunti, and A. Studenikin, Adv. High Energy Phys. **2012**, 459526 (2012).
30. C. Giunti and A. Studenikin, Rev. Mod. Phys. **87**, 531 (2015).
31. C. Giunti, K. A. Kouzakov, Y-F. Li, A. V. Lokhov, A. I. Studenikin, and S. Zhou, Ann. Phys. **528**, 198 (2016).
32. T. C. Adorno, Z.-W. He, S. P. Gavrilov and D. M. Gitman, arXiv:2109.06053.
33. S. P. Gavrilov and D. M. Gitman, Phys. Rev. D **87**, 125025 (2013).
34. S. P. Gavrilov and D. M. Gitman, Phys. Rev. D **93**, 045002 (2016).
35. S. P. Gavrilov and D. M. Gitman, Eur. Phys. J. C **80**, 820 (2020).
36. W. Pauli, Rev. Mod. Phys. **13**, 203 (1941).
37. V. G. Bagrov and D. M. Gitman, *The Dirac Equation and Its Solutions* (De Gruyter, Berlin, 2014).
38. A. Erdelyi *et al.* (Ed.), *Higher Transcendental Functions* (*Bateman Manuscript Project*), Vol. 1 (McGraw-Hill, New York, 1953).
39. N. Dombey and A. Calogeracos, Phys. Rep. **315**, 41 (1999).
40. H. Gies, G. Torgrimsson, Phys. Rev. Lett. **116**, 090406 (2016).
41. H. Gies, G. Torgrimsson, Phys. Rev. D **95**, 016001 (2017).
42. T. C. Adorno, S. P. Gavrilov and D. M. Gitman, Eur. Phys. J. C **80**, 88 (2020).
43. D. Lai, Rev. Mod. Phys. **73**, 629 (2001).
44. S. Akiyama, J. C. Wheeler, D. L. Meier, and I. Lichtenstadt, Astrophys. J. **584**, 954 (2003).
45. S. Mereghetti, Astron. Astrophys. Rev. **15**, 225 (2008).
46. E. J. Ferrer, V. de la Incera, J. P. Keith, I. Portillo, and P. Springsteen, Phys. Rev. C **82**, 065802 (2010); L. Paulucci, E. J. Ferrer, V. de la Incera, and J. E. Horvath, Phys. Rev. D **83**, 043009 (2011).

On the magnetic field screening in strong crossed electromagnetic field

S. Campion

ICRA, Dipartimento di Fisica, Sapienza Università di Roma, P.le Aldo Moro 5, Rome, 00185, Italy
E-mail: stefano.campion@icranet.org
www.phys.uniroma1.it/fisica

International Center for Relativistic Astrophysics Network, Piazza della Repubblica 10, Pescara, 65122, Italy

Dipartimento di Fisica, Sapienza Università di Roma, P.le Aldo Moro 5, Rome, 00185, Italy

J. A. Rueda Hernandez

International Center for Relativistic Astrophysics Network, Piazza della Repubblica 10, Pescara, 65122, Italy,
E-mail: jorge.rueda@icra.it

ICRA, Dipartimento di Fisica, Università di Roma "La Sapienza", Piazzale Aldo Moro 5, Roma, 00185, Italy

ICRANet-Ferrara, Dipartimento di Fisica e Scienze della Terra, Università degli Studi di Ferrara, Via Saragat 1, Ferrara, 44122, Italy

Dipartimento di Fisica e Scienze della Terra, Università degli Studi di Ferrara, Via Saragat 1, Ferrara, 44122, Italy

INAF, Istituto de Astrofisica e Planetologia Spaziali, Via Fosso del Cavaliere 100, Rome, 00133, Italy

S.-S. Xue

International Center for Relativistic Astrophysics Network, Piazza della Repubblica 10, Pescara, 65122, Italy,
E-mail: xue@icra.it

ICRA, Dipartimento di Fisica, Università di Roma "La Sapienza", Piazzale Aldo Moro 5, Roma, 00185, Italy

R. Ruffini

International Center for Relativistic Astrophysics Network, Piazza della Repubblica 10, Pescara, 65122, Italy
E-mail: ruffini@icra.it

ICRA, Dipartimento di Fisica, Sapienza Università di Roma, P.le Aldo Moro 5, Rome, 00185, Italy

Université de Nice Sophia Antipolis, CEDEX 2, Grand Château Parc Valrose,
Nice, France

ICRANet-Rio, Centro Brasileiro de Pesquisas Físicas, Rua Dr. Xavier Sigaud 150,
Rio de Janeiro, 22290-180, Brazil

INAF, Viale del Parco Mellini 84,
Rome, 00136, Italy

We study the screening of a strong magnetic field operated by an initial huge number of $e^{\pm}$ pairs (we do not discuss here their production mechanism). The background fields configuration is of crossed fields, $(\vec{B} = B\hat{z}, \vec{E} = E\hat{y})$, with $E/B < 1$. In this system the following series of processes occur: 1) the electric field accelerates the pairs, which radiate high-energy synchrotron photons; 2) these synchrotron photons interact with the background magnetic field via the magnetic pair production process (MPP hereafter), i.e. $\gamma + B \to e^+ + e^-$, producing additional pairs; 3) the dynamic of all the pairs around the magnetic field lines generates a current that induces a magnetic field oriented in the opposite direction to the background one and then shielding it. We get that, for instance, for an initial number of pairs $N_{\pm,0} = 10^{10}$, an initial magnetic field of 10^{12} G can be reduced by a few percent. The whole screening process described by the steps above, occurs in the short timescales $10^{-21} \leq t \leq 10^{-15}$ s, i.e. the time necessary before the particles acceleration timescale equals the synchrotron cooling timescale. Further developments (as the study of this mechanism in different geometries of the $\vec{E}$ and $\vec{B}$ fields, quantum effects in overcritical fields, other mechanisms for the production, distribution and multiplicity of the $e^{\pm}$ pairs) are necessary in order to apply this model to specific and extreme astrophysical systems (as Black Hole or Neutron Star).

Keywords: Magnetic Pair Production; Magnetic field screening; Shower processes

1. Introduction

For many years the screening of a strong electric field, operated by $e^{\pm}$ pairs created by QED processes, has been studied (e.g. see recently Ref. 1[a]). No analogous work and conclusions have been reached for a magnetic field. The main topic of this paper is to build a simple model to analyze the magnetic field screening (MFS hereafter) process owing to the motion of $e^{\pm}$ pairs in a region filled by magnetic $\vec{B}$ and electric $\vec{E}$ fields, oriented in a crossed configuration.

The basic idea of the screening process is described by the following series steps:

(1) An initial number of $e^{\pm}$ is placed in a region filled by $\vec{E}$ and $\vec{B}$, with $E/B < 1$, $B \leq B_{cr} = m_e^2 c^3/(e\hbar) \approx 4.4 \times 10^{13}$ G and then $E < E_{cr}$. We do not discuss here the creation process of these initial pairs (that could be, for example, the vacuum breakdown).

---

[a]In this paper it is shown that an electric field as high as $E \sim \alpha_f E_{cr}$, with α_f the fine structure constant and $E_{cr} = m_e^2 c^3/(e\hbar) \approx 1.32 \times 10^{16}$ V/cm the critical field for vacuum polarization, cannot be maintained since the creation of particle showers depletes the field

(2) The initial pairs are accelerated by $\vec{E}$ and emit radiation via the curvature/synchrotron mechanism (or their combination), due to the $\vec{B}$ field. We assume that the electric and magnetic field strength are related by the following relation

$$E(t) = \Upsilon\, B(t), \qquad (1)$$

with $0 < \Upsilon \leq 1$, since we are interested in conditions of magnetic dominance.

(3) The photons create a new $e^{\pm}$ pairs via the magnetic pair production process (MPP), $\gamma + B \to e^- + e^+$.

(4) Also these new pairs are accelerated and radiate synchrotron photons. All the pairs, initial + created by the MPP process, circularize around the magnetic field lines generating a current that gives rise to an induced magnetic field, $\vec{B}_{\text{ind}}$, oriented in the opposite direction with respect to the original one, thereby screening it. Because of the creation of these new charged particles and the proportionality between the strength of the fields, also the electric field is screened.

(5) This series of the processes occurs at every time t leading to the development of a particles shower.

This model can find useful application in extreme astrophysical systems, as GRBs. Indeed, following the "*inner engine*" model for GRBs[2,3] within the binary-driven hypernova (BdHN) framework (see, e.g., Refs. 4–6), these type of systems are composed by a rotating back hole, surrounded by the magnetic field and low-density ionized matter. The gravitomagnetic interaction of the rotating BH and the magnetic field induces an electric field which accelerates e^- which emit GeV photons by synchrotron radiation.[2] Then a decrease of the magnetic field leads to the decrease of the optical depth for synchrotron photons, which can reach the threshold to freely escape from the region near the BH and become observable. Therefore, from this brief introduction of the model it is easy to understand that the physical process that we present here could be necessary for the explanation of some emission in extreme astrophysical systems.

2. Model equations

Here we analyze the whole screening process for the specific configuration of perpendicular fields: $\vec{E} = E\,\hat{y}$ for the electric field and $\vec{B} = B\,\hat{z}$ for the magnetic field. In this section we just summarize the fundamental equations that describe the system. The entire set of equations and their derivation can be found in Refs. 7, 8.

In order to follow the entire screening process we have built a set of ordinary differential equations which describe, at the same time: 1) the motion of the particles; 2) the creation of new particles via the energy loss and the MPP processes; 3) the decrease of the magnetic field due to the generation of an induced magnetic field by the particles currents.

The equations of motion of a particle immersed in an EM field [b] read (see, e.g., Refs. 9, 10)

$$\frac{dp^\alpha}{d\tau} = m\frac{du^\alpha}{d\tau} = \frac{e}{c}\mathcal{F}^{\alpha\beta}u_\beta. \tag{2}$$

and for the radiation emitted we use the energy loss formula in quantum regime, $I = |-dE/dt|$, given in Ref. 11.

In this paper they use the parameter $\chi \equiv \varepsilon_*/2\varepsilon_e$ to distinguish between emission in quantum ($\chi \gtrsim 1$) and classical ($\chi < 1$) regimes, where $\varepsilon_e = \gamma m_e c^2$ is the electron energy and $\varepsilon_* = \hbar\omega^* = (3e\gamma^2/2m_e c)\sqrt{(\vec{E}+\vec{\beta}\times\vec{B})^2 - (\vec{\beta}\cdot\vec{E})^2}$ the critical photons energy.

The photons production rate, $\dot{N}_\gamma(t,\phi)$ (with ϕ the angle between the particle/photon direction and the magnetic field) can be calculated as the product between the number of pairs present at the specific time t, $N_\pm(t,\phi)$ and the rate of photons production via synchrotron emission, I/ε_γ^e (with ε_γ^e the energy of synchrotron photons emitted by the $e^\pm$). The equation for the evolution of the number of pairs is strictly related to the one for the number of photons. Indeed, the rate of pair production $\dot{N}_\pm(t,\phi)$ is given by the product of the photon number N_γ, the attenuation coefficient for the MPP process $R_A^e(t,\phi)$ times the velocity of light c.

The motion of a particle inside an electromagnetic field can be considered as the combination of an acceleration along the z-direction, and of a circular motion in the $x-y$ plane, around the magnetic field lines. This circular motion of the pairs produces coils traversed by the electric current. This current creates an induced magnetic field, from the Biot–Savart law, whose evolution with time is described by the following formula (calculated at the center of the coil):

$$\frac{dB_{z,\,\text{ind}}}{dt} = e\frac{\beta_\perp(t)}{R_c(t)^2}\frac{dN_\pm}{dt}. \tag{3}$$

with $\beta_\perp = (\beta_x^2 + \beta_y^2)^{1/2}$ the perpendicular component of the particle velocity and $R_c^{-1} = |d\vec{\beta}/cdt| = (e/\gamma mc^2)\sqrt{(\vec{E}_{\text{tot}}+\vec{\beta}\times\vec{B}_{\text{tot}})^2 - (\vec{\beta}\cdot\vec{E}_{\text{tot}})^2}$ the curvature radius for the particle trajectory.

We have introduced the attenuation coefficient for the magnetic pair production and we have called it R_A^e. From now on, we refer to as $\zeta \equiv R_A^e c$ the MPP rate. In Ref. 12, the expression for the pair production rate has been derived in the observer frame at rest, for strong perpendicular electric and magnetic fields ($\vec{E}\cdot\vec{B} = 0$). In order to get the expression of the MPP rate in our frame we have: 1) moved to a new K' frame, where no electric field is present, through a Lorentz transformation; 2) calculated all the necessary quantities (energy, momentum and director cosines of the photons, the component of the magnetic field perpendicular to the propagation direction of the photons, the MPP rate); 3) transforming back the rate to the

---

[b] We use throughout cgs-Gaussian units, in which the magnetic and electric fields share the same dimensions ($g^{1/2}$ cm$^{-1/2}$ s^{-1}) and a -2 signature so the spacetime metric is $\eta_{\mu\nu} = (1,-1,-1,-1)$.

original frame. The expression for the MPP rate in the laboratory frame (observer at infinity, the frame where we work) assumes the following form (further details on this procedure can be found in Refs. 7, 8):

$$\zeta = 0.23 \frac{\alpha_f c}{\lambda_c} \frac{B_z}{B_{cr}} \left(1 - \frac{E_y^2}{B_z^2}\right) \frac{\sqrt{\eta_y^2 \left(1 - \frac{E_y^2}{B_z^2}\right) + \left(\eta_x - \frac{E_y}{B_z}\right)^2}}{1 - \frac{E_y}{B_z}\eta_x}$$

$$\times \exp\left\{-\frac{8}{3}\frac{mc^2}{\varepsilon_\gamma}\frac{B_{cr}}{B_z}\left[\eta_y^2\left(1 - \frac{E_y^2}{B_z^2}\right) + \left(\eta_x - \frac{E_y}{B_z}\right)^2\right]^{-1/2}\right\}, \qquad (4)$$

which is valid until the following condition is satisfied

$$\Psi = \frac{3}{4}\frac{e\hbar}{mc}\frac{B^2}{B_{cr}}\gamma^2 \sqrt{\beta_y^2\left(1 - \frac{E^2}{B^2}\right) + \left(\frac{E}{B} - \beta_x\right)^2}\sqrt{\eta_y^2\left(1 - \frac{E^2}{B^2}\right) + \left(\eta_x - \frac{E}{B}\right)^2} \ll 1. \qquad (5)$$

In Eq. (4) and Eq. (5) the quantities $\vec{\eta}$ are the photon director cosines, whose expression as a function of the electron velocity, polar and azimuthal angle of their emission in the comoving frame can be found in Ref. 7.

3. Results

We now present the results of the numerical integration of the set of equations described in the previous section. We have selected three values for the parameter $\Upsilon = (1/2, 1/10, 1/100)$. Since the proportionality between the fields is requested at any time, when $B(t)$ changes even $E(t)$ changes accordingly to keep Υ constant. These combination of these effects affect the motion of particles and, consequently, all the related processes that give rise to the screening.

The condition on Ψ in Eq. (5) brings with it three initials conditions for the background magnetic field, the electron Lorentz factor and for the emission direction of the pairs $(B_0, \gamma_0, \vec{\beta}_0)$. A further condition is necessary for the director cosines of the photons $\vec{\eta}$. Then, we need to choose the right values for these variables and parameters in order to apply the equation for the rate

We select three emission directions of the particles: 1) along the $\hat{y}$–axis; 2) along the $\hat{z}$–axis; 3) along a direction characterized by polar and azimuth angles, respectively, $\theta = 75°$ and $\phi = 30°$ (hereafter we refer to this direction as "*generic*" or "*G*"). For each direction, we have chosen the initial value of the magnetic field B_0 and, consequently, the maximum value of particles Lorentz factor γ_0, which satisfy Eq. (5). After we have integrated the set of equations that describe the entire screening process considering different number of emitted particles $N_{\pm,0} = 1, 10^3, 10^6, 10^{10}$ and photons $N_{\gamma,0} = 0$; $N_{\gamma,0} = 10^3$, with $N_{\pm,0} = 1$. Each numerical integration starts at $t_0 = 10^{-21}$ s and stops when the Lorentz factor of the pairs becomes 1, i.e. when the particle has lost all of its energy, at $t_f \sim 10^{-17} - 10^{-15}$ s.

In Table 1, Table 2, Table 3 we show the results we have obtained from the integrations of our set of equations describing, for all the considered initial conditions

Table 1. Results for the integrations of the set of equations for the different initial conditions, with $\Upsilon = 1/2$. **Column (1)**: initial emission direction for particles; **Column (2)**: initial value of the magnetic field strength; **Column (3)**: initial value of the Lorentz factor; **Column (4)**: percentage variation of the magnetic field (calculated as $\left[(B(t_0) - B(t_f))/B(t_0)\right] \times 100$); **Column (5)**: initial number of emitted particles; **Column (6)**: final number of created particles; **Column (7)**: initial number of emitted photons; **Column (8)**: final number of emitted photons.

Direction	$B_0(B_{cr})$	γ_0	$\Delta B(\%)$	$N_{\pm,0}$	$N_{\pm,f}$	$N_{\gamma,0}$	$N_{\gamma,f}$
Generic	0.1	6.48	$-4.7 \times 10^{-12}\%$	1	1	0	3.5
			$-4.7 \times 10^{-9}\%$	10^3	10^3	0	3500
			$-4.7 \times 10^{-6}\%$	10^6	$\gtrsim 10^6$	0	3.5×10^6
			$-4.66 \times 10^{-2}\%$	10^{10}	$\gtrsim 10^{10}$	0	3.5×10^{10}
			$-6.3 \times 10^{-8}\%$	1	1	10^3	1003
	0.3	2.27	$-1.34 \times 10^{-10}\%$	1	1	0	0.45
			$-1.34 \times 10^{-7}\%$	10^3	10^3	0	447
			$-1.34 \times 10^{-4}\%$	10^6	10^6	0	4.48×10^5
			-1.09%	10^{10}	$\gtrsim 10^{10}$	0	4.46×10^9
			$-1.46 \times 10^{-6}\%$	1	1	10^3	1000.4
Along y	0.1	3.66	$-2.25 \times 10^{-10}\%$	1	1	0	2.79
			$-2.25 \times 10^{-7}\%$	10^3	10^3	0	2798
			$-2.2 \times 10^{-4}\%$	10^6	10^6	0	2.8×10^6
			-1.72%	10^{10}	$\gtrsim 10^{10}$	0	2.84×10^{10}
			$-1.7 \times 10^{-6}\%$	1	1	10^{-3}	1002
Along z	0.1	7.098	$-1 \times 10^{-12}\%$	1	1	0	11.3
			$-1 \times 10^{-9}\%$	10^3	10^3	0	1.13×10^4
			$-1 \times 10^{-6}\%$	10^6	10^6	0	1.13×10^7
			-0.01%	10^{10}	$\gtrsim 10^{10}$	0	1.13×10^{11}
			$-1.5 \times 10^{-8}\%$	1	1	10^3	1011
	0.3	2.14	$-1.06 \times 10^{-10}\%$	1	1	0	2.33
			$-1.6 \times 10^{-7}\%$	10^3	10^3	0	2333
			$-1.6 \times 10^{-4}\%$	10^6	10^6	0	2.3×10^6
			-1.27%	10^{10}	$\gtrsim 10^{10}$	0	2.4×10^{10}
			$-1.5 \times 10^{-6}\%$	1	1	10^3	1002

(emission direction, B_0, γ_0, $N_{\pm,0}$, $N_{\gamma,0}$). We report the percentage variation of the magnetic field $\Delta B(\%)$, the final number of created pairs $N_{\pm,f}$ and photons $N_{\gamma,f}$. In Table 1 the results are for $\Upsilon = 1/2$, Table 2 is for $\Upsilon = 1/10$ and Table 3 for $\Upsilon = 1/100$. From Table 1, Table 2 and Table 3, we can get some interesting results. Indeed, we can see that the model (namely the system of equations we have built) is strictly correlated to the initial conditions and, in particular, to the particles emission direction and to the strength of the background magnetic field. A sufficient decrease of $\vec{B}$ is obtained when a huge initial number of particles $N_{\pm,0} \gtrsim 10^{10}$ is injected. For particles emitted along the $\hat{z}$-axis and along the *generic* direction, the stronger the background field, the higher the reduction of the field itself is. Even when they are emitted along the $\hat{y}$-axis, there is a significant reduction of $\vec{B}$, but this

Table 2. Same results of Table 1, but for $\Upsilon = 1/10$.

Direction	$B_0(B_{cr})$	γ_0	$\Delta B(\%)$	$N_{\pm,0}$	$N_{\pm,f}$	$N_{\gamma,0}$	$N_{\gamma,f}$
Generic	0.1	4.18	$-3.2 \times 10^{-11}\%$	1	1	0	4.63
			$-3.2 \times 10^{-8}\%$	1000	10^3	0	4633
			$-3.2 \times 10^{-5}\%$	10^6	10^6	0	4.63×10^6
			-0.308%	10^{10}	$\gtrsim 10^{10}$	0	4.62×10^{10}
			$-4.35 \times 10^{-7}\%$	1	1	10^3	1004
Along y	0.1	3.71	$-9.14 \times 10^{-11}\%$	1	1	0	4.45
			$-9.14 \times 10^{-8}\%$	10^3	10^3	0	4457
			$-9.14 \times 10^{-5}\%$	10^6	10^6	0	4.46×10^6
			-0.798%	10^{10}	$\gtrsim 10^{10}$	0	4.42×10^{10}
			$-9.49 \times 10^{-7}\%$	1	1	10^{-3}	1004
Along z	0.1	22.66	0%	1	1	0	64
			0%	10^3	10^3	0	6.4×10^4
			$-2.2 \times 10^{-14}\%$	10^6	10^6	0	6.4×10^7
			$-4.2 \times 10^{-11}\%$	10^{10}	10^{10}	0	6.4×10^{11}
			0%	1	1	10^3	1063
	0.3	10.04	$-1.13 \times 10^{-12}\%$	1	1	0	19.6
			$-1.15 \times 10^{-9}\%$	10^3	10^3	0	1.96×10^4
			$-1.15 \times 10^{-6}\%$	10^6	10^6	0	1.96×10^7
			$-1.15 \times 10^{-2}\%$	10^{10}	$> 10^{10}$	0	1.96×10^{11}
			$-8 \times 10^{-9}\%$	1	1.0025	10^3	1019
	0.5	4.8	$-1.75 \times 10^{-11}\%$	1	1	0	10.6
			$-1.75 \times 10^{-8}\%$	10^3	10^3	0	1.05×10^4
			$-1.75 \times 10^{-5}\%$	10^6	10^6	0	1.05×10^7
			-0.171%	10^{10}	$> 10^{10}$	0	1.05×10^{11}
			$-8.3 \times 10^{-8}\%$	1	1.0036	10^3	1010
	0.7	2.63	$-8.3 \times 10^{-11}\%$	1	1	0	5.8
			$-8.3 \times 10^{-8}\%$	10^3	10^3	0	5811
			$-8.3 \times 10^{-5}\%$	10^6	10^6	0	5.81×10^6
			-0.734%	10^{10}	$> 10^{10}$	0	5.93×10^{10}
			$-2.87 \times 10^{-7}\%$	1	1.0027	10^3	1005

occurs with a lower strength of the field. These characteristics can be understood by looking on how the fundamental ingredients of the model $\left(\vec{B}, \vec{\beta}, \vec{\eta}, N_{\pm}\right)$ enter in the equations and, in particular, looking at the dependence of the rate $\zeta(t)$ in Eq. (4) on $B(t)$ and $\vec{\eta}$.

In Fig. 1 is shown the variation of the parameter Ψ in Eq. (5), for three considered values of Υ and for the three directions of emission (**generic**, **ŷ-axis** and **ẑ-axis**), with $B_0 = 0.1\ B_{cr}$ and $N_{\pm,\,0} = 10^6$. It is evident that the condition in Eq. (5) is well satisfied for all the analyzed cases and for all the integration time. In Fig. 2 we present the result for the screening of the magnetic field when an initial number of particles $N_{\pm,0} = 10^{10}$ is emitted along the: 1) *generic* direction with $\gamma_0 = 2.27$; 2) ẑ-axis with $\gamma_0 = 2.14$, with initial strength of the background magnetic field $B_0 = 0.3\ B_{cr}$ and $\Upsilon = 1/2$.

Table 3. Same results of Table 1, but for $\Upsilon = 1/100$.

Direction	$B_0(B_{cr})$	γ_0	$\Delta B(\%)$	$N_{\pm,0}$	$N_{\pm,f}$	$N_{\gamma,0}$	$N_{\gamma,f}$
Generic	0.1	3.81	$-2.5 \times 10^{-11}\%$	1	1	0	5.15
			$-2.5 \times 10^{-8}\%$	10^3	10^3	0	5153
			$-2.5 \times 10^{-5}\%$	10^6	10^6	0	5.15×10^6
			-0.237%	10^{10}	$\geq 10^{10}$	0	5.14×10^{10}
			$-3.4 \times 10^{-7}\%$	1	1	10^3	1005
Along y	0.1	3.71	$-8 \times 10^{-11}\%$	1	1	0	4.91
			$-8 \times 10^{-8}\%$	10^3	10^3	0	4912
			$-8 \times 10^{-5}\%$	10^6	10^6	0	4.91×10^6
			-0.711%	10^{10}	$\geq 10^{10}$	0	5.02×10^{10}
			$-8.8 \times 10^{-7}\%$	1	1	10^{-3}	1004
Along z	0.1	22.66	0%	1	1	0	22.23
			0%	10^3	10^3	0	2.22×10^4
			0%	10^6	10^6	0	2.22×10^7
			0%	10^{10}	10^{10}	0	2.22×10^{11}
			0%	1	1	10^3	1022
	1.1	10.04	$-1.6 \times 10^{-14}\%$	1	1	0	26.8
			$-7.8 \times 10^{-12}\%$	10^3	10^3	0	1.49×10^4
			$-7.8 \times 10^{-9}\%$	10^6	10^6	0	1.77×10^7
			$-7.5 \times 10^{-5}\%$	10^{10}	$\geq 10^{10}$	0	1.75×10^{11}
			$-2.7 \times 10^{-11}\%$	1	1.0022	10^3	1026
	2.5	2.13	$-5.7 \times 10^{-12}\%$	1	1	0	35.3
			$-5.4 \times 10^{-9}\%$	10^3	10^3	0	3.53×10^4
			$-5.6 \times 10^{-6}\%$	10^6	$\geq 10^6$	0	3.53×10^7
			$-5.5 \times 10^{-2}\%$	10^{10}	$> 10^{10}$	0	3.52×10^{11}
			$-1.3 \times 10^{-8}\%$	1	1.025	10^3	1036

Figure 3, instead, shows the emitted photons energy for $N_{\pm,0} = 10^{10}$ particles emitted along the *generic* direction, for the three considered values of $\Upsilon = 1/2, 1/10, 1/100$ and for $B_0 = 0.1\ B_{cr}$.

4. Conclusions

In this work, we have built a simplified model to study the magnetic field screening process operated by a huge number of $e^\pm$ pairs in presence of a strong crossed electromagnetic field. The model we have built is based on two principal assumptions:

(1) We have constructed one-particle equations to describe the particles motion as a fluid. This assumption is justified considering the dynamics of the entire process and the initial conditions (the particles obey to the continuity equation and are forced to follow the same trajectory due to the high strength of the fields).
(2) Due to the proportionality between the magnetic and electric field, also the electric field is screened. This effect can be justified considering that the creation of new charged particles, via the MPP and synchrotron processes, leads to the

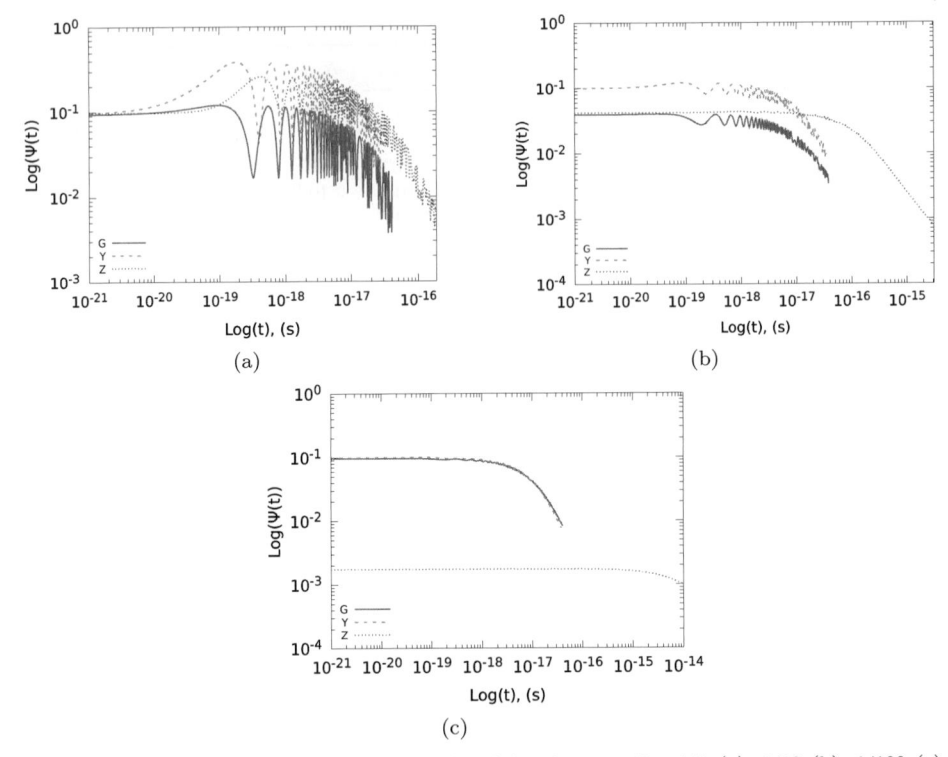

Fig. 1. Variation of the Ψ parameter, calculated for the case $\Upsilon = 1/2$ (a), $1/10$ (b), $1/100$ (c), for the three directions of emission (**generic**, **ŷ-axis** and **ẑ-axis**) and for an initial magnetic field strength of $B_0 = 0.1\, B_{cr}$.

formation of a current which screens the electric field too. We address to future work a more detailed treatment of this process.

We briefly summarized here the results that we got from our research. Further and more complete details can be found in Refs. 7, 8. We have obtained that the screening process occurs and the significance of the process (and, then, of the reduction of the field) depends by

(I) the number of initial pairs injected in the system: the screening is more efficient if one increases $N_{\pm,0}$ from 10^6 to 10^{10}–10^{15};
(II) the initial particles emission direction: the major effect is obtained when the particles are emitted with a higher perpendicular component of their velocity $\beta_\perp$ (namely along the *generic* and *ŷ*-axis directions);
(III) the parameter Υ. For particle with lower $\beta_\perp$ (*generic* direction) a decrease of Υ leads to a stronger screening effect. Instead, for particles with a higher $\beta_\perp$ (namely emitted along the *ŷ*-axis), the screening increases if Υ decreases.

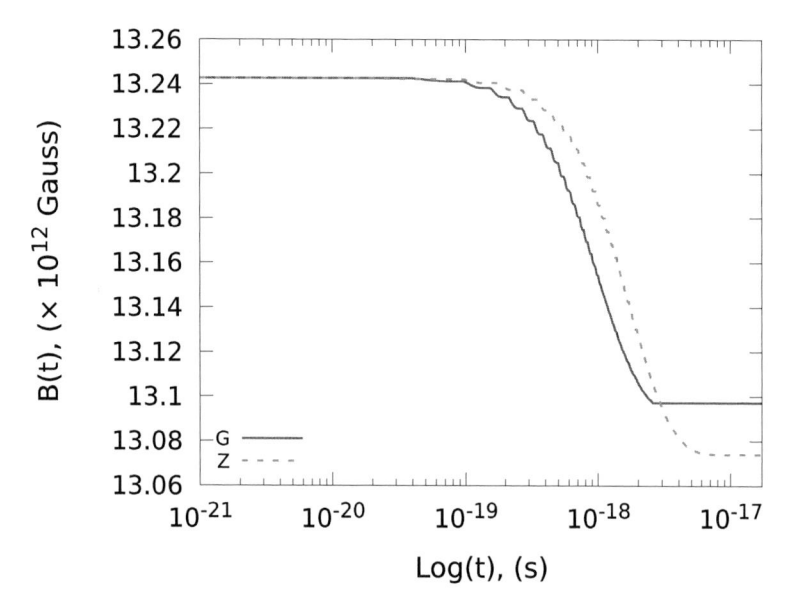

Fig. 2. Magnetic field decrease due to an initial number of particles, $N_{\pm,0} = 10^{10}$, emitted initially along the *generic* direction (with $\gamma_0 = 2.27$) and along the $\hat{z}$-axis (with $\gamma_0 = 2.14$). Here $\Upsilon = 1/2$ and $B_0 = 0.3\, B_{\mathrm{cr}}$.

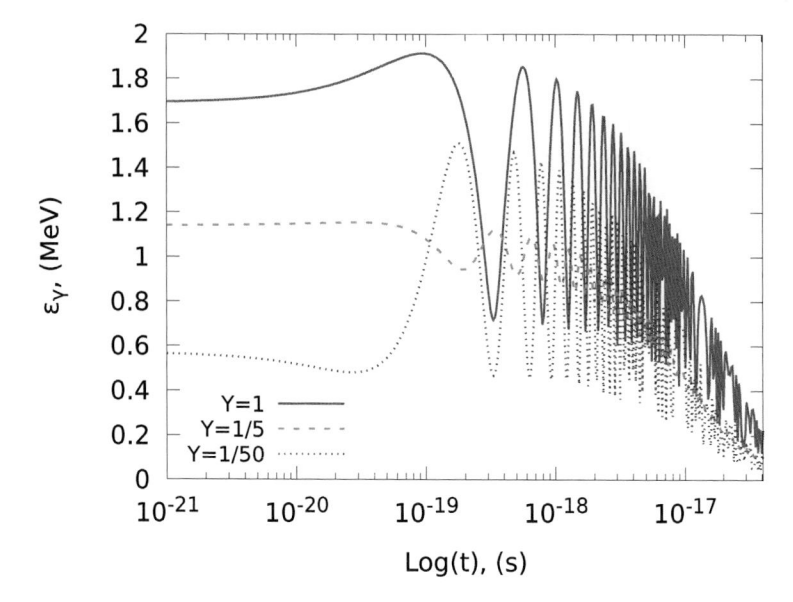

Fig. 3. Emitted photons energy, as a function of time, for $N_{\pm,0} = 10^{10}$ emitted along the *generic* direction, with $B_0 = 0.1\, B_{\mathrm{cr}}$, for $\Upsilon = 1/2,\ 1/10,\ 1/100$.

We conclude that, under the studied physical conditions, the screening effect occurs and leads to a reduction of the field up to a few percent (for the specific initial conditions considered in this work). This implies that this process needs to be taken into account in the treatment of particles dynamics in extreme astrophysical systems, as pulsars and gamma-ray bursts. This study has been the first one on this subject and, in order to apply it to real physical systems, some improvements are necessary. Future development of this work concern its extension to different configurations between the electric and magnetic fields, the extension of the treatment to the case of overcritical fields (where the entire process can be no longer treated classically). However, the present approach have helped us to clarify the main physical ingredients and the necessary conditions for the occurrence of this effect.

References

1. A. Fedotov, N. Narozhny, G. Mourou and G. Korn, Limitations on the attainable intensity of high power lasers, *Physical review letters* **105**, p. 080402 (2010).
2. R. Ruffini, R. Moradi, J. A. Rueda, L. Becerra, C. L. Bianco, C. Cherubini, S. Filippi, Y. C. Chen, M. Karlica, N. Sahakyan, Y. Wang and S. S. Xue, On the GeV Emission of the Type I BdHN GRB 130427A, *APJ* **886**, p. 82 (Dec 2019).
3. J. A. Rueda and R. Ruffini, The blackholic quantum, *European Physical Journal C* **80**, p. 300 (April 2020).
4. L. Becerra, C. L. Ellinger, C. L. Fryer, J. A. Rueda and R. Ruffini, SPH Simulations of the Induced Gravitational Collapse Scenario of Long Gamma-Ray Bursts Associated with Supernovae, *APJ* **871**, p. 14 (January 2019).
5. Y. Wang, J. A. Rueda, R. Ruffini, L. Becerra, C. Bianco, L. Becerra, L. Li and M. Karlica, Two Predictions of Supernova: GRB 130427A/SN 2013cq and GRB 180728A/SN 2018fip, *APJ* **874**, p. 39 (March 2019).
6. J. A. Rueda, R. Ruffini, M. Karlica, R. Moradi and Y. Wang, Magnetic Fields and Afterglows of BdHNe: Inferences from GRB 130427A, GRB 160509A, GRB 160625B, GRB 180728A, and GRB 190114C, *APJ* **893**, p. 148 (April 2020).
7. S. Campion, J. Rueda, R. Ruffini and S. Xue, Magnetic field screening in strong crossed electromagnetic fields, *Physics Letters B* **820**, p. 136562 (2021).
8. S. Campion, Neutrino emission via proton-proton interaction and magnetic field screening in GRBs, PhD thesis, ICRANeT & Sapienza University of Rome (Rome, Italy, 2021), p. 191.
9. L. D. Landau and E. M. Lifshitz, *The classical theory of fields* (Pergamon, 1971).
10. J. D. Jackson, *Classical electrodynamics* (American Association of Physics Teachers, 1999).
11. S. R. Kelner, A. Y. Prosekin and F. A. Aharonian, Synchro-curvature radiation of charged particles in the strong curved magnetic fields, *The Astronomical Journal* **149**, p. 33 (2015).
12. J. Daugherty and I. Lerche, On pair production in intense electromagnetic fields occurring in astrophysical situations, *Astrophysics and Space Science* **38**, 437 (1975).

Particle creation by strong fields and quantum anomalies[*]

José Navarro-Salas

Departamento de Física Teórica and IFIC, Centro Mixto Universidad de Valencia-CSIC, Facultad de Física, Universidad de Valencia, Burjassot-46100, Valencia, Spain
E-mail: jnavarro@ific.uv.es

Particle creation by strong and time-varying backgrounds is a robust prediction of quantum field theory. Another well-established feature of field theory is that classical symmetries do not always extend to the quantized theory. When this occurs, we speak of quantum anomalies. In this contribution we discuss the entwining relationship between both predictions, relating chiral anomalies with an underlying process of particle creation. Within this context, we will also argue that the symmetry under electric-magnetic duality rotations of the source-free Maxwell theory is anomalous. This is a quantum effect, and it can be understood as the generalization of the fermion chiral anomaly to fields of spin one. This implies that the net polarization of photons propagating in a gravitational field could change in time.

Keywords: Chiral anomalies, gravitational particle creation, electromagnetic duality rotations, photon helicity

1. Introduction

Two fundamental predictions of quantum field theory in presence of strong field backgrounds were established in the sixties:

i) The spontaneous creation of particles out of the vacuum by time-varying gravitational fields. This was first discovered in the analysis of quantized fields in an expanding universe[1] and some years later applied to black holes[2] (for reviews see,[3–8] and for a historical perspective see[9,10]). It also offered a better understanding of the pair creation phenomena induced by electric fields, as explored by Heisenberg and Euler[11,12] and also Schwinger.[13]

ii) The breaking of the axial symmetry of Dirac fermions by quantum effects.[14,15] Classical symmetries of field theories may fail to survive quantization, leading to what is known in the literature as quantum anomalies (for a review see[16]). The origin of the anomalies is rooted in the renormalization mechanism need to tame the ultraviolet divergences that affect most models of quantum field theory. Renormalization in presence of an electromagnetic background can spoil the classical conservation law of the axial Noether current J_5^μ of massless charged fermions. It is codified by the Adler-Bell-Jackiw anomaly[14,15] ($\alpha = e^2/(4\pi\hbar)$ is the fine-structure

---

[*]Invited talk given at the Sixteenth Marcel Grossmann Meeting (2021), Session: Strong Electromagnetic and Gravitational Field Physics.

constant; we take $c=1$)

$$\partial_\mu \langle 0|J_5^\mu|0\rangle = \frac{\alpha}{2\pi} F_{\mu\nu}{}^* F^{\mu\nu} . \tag{1}$$

The axial anomaly can also be interpreted as a low-energy phenomena in terms of particle production. A time-varying electric field creates both left-handed and right-handed fermions. The net amount of created chirality ΔQ_5 (i.e., the number of right-handed fermions N_R minus the number of left-handed fermions N_L created between t_1 and t_2)) is evaluated according to[a]

$$\Delta Q_5 = \hbar(N_R - N_L) = \int_{t_1}^{t_2} dt \int_{\Sigma_t} d\Sigma_\mu \langle 0|J_5^\mu|0\rangle = \frac{\alpha}{2\pi} \int_{t_1}^{t_2} \int_{\Sigma_t} d^4x F_{\mu\nu}{}^* F^{\mu\nu} . \tag{2}$$

It is important to stress that the minimum amount of created (massless) fermions is obtained in the adiabatic limit,[17] and it is just encapsulated in the creation of the chirality accounted by the anomaly. This might be somewhat surprising since the particle number is naively expected to be an adiabatic invariant[b]. The breaking of the adiabatic invariance of the particle number can then be understood as a signal of the chiral anomaly. Furthermore, the existence of the axial anomaly implies that there is necessarily a minimum amount of particle creation, even for an adiabatic process, to account for the creation of chirality. In more pedestrian words, the creation of chirality can be regarded as the "smoking gun" of the full particle creation process. We can summarize these features schematically:

$$\boxed{Quiral\ Anomaly \to Particle\ creation}$$

$$\boxed{Adiabatic\ Particle\ creation \to Quiral\ Anomaly}$$

The above results on the chiral anomaly can be extended to curved spacetime.[19] Expression (1) generalize to

$$\nabla_\mu \langle 0|J_5^\mu|0\rangle = \frac{\alpha}{2\pi} F_{\mu\nu}{}^* F^{\mu\nu} + \frac{\hbar}{192\pi^2} R_{\mu\nu\alpha\beta}{}^* R^{\mu\nu\alpha\beta} , \tag{3}$$

where $R_{\mu\nu\alpha\beta}$ is the Riemann tensor and $^*R^{\mu\nu\alpha\beta}$ its dual, and ∇_μ is the covariant derivative. We note that the gravitational part of the chiral anomaly persists for all type of fermions, either charged or neutral. Therefore, the chirality of (neutral) fermions fails also to be conserved in curved spacetimes for which

$$\Delta Q_5 = \frac{\hbar}{192\pi^2} \int_{t_1}^{t_2} \int_\Sigma d^4x \sqrt{-g}\, R_{\mu\nu\alpha\beta}{}^* R^{\mu\nu\alpha\beta} \tag{4}$$

is non-vanishing. This can be heuristically understood as a consequence of the universal character of gravity, as prescribed by Einstein's equivalence principle. If (4) is valid for a type of massless spin-1/2 field it must also be valid for any other type.

---

[a]We assume that a consistent particle interpretation is available at early and late times.
[b]It can be proved rigorously for a scalar field in an expanding universe.[1,18]

On physical grounds one can also argue that the universality of gravity suggests that these anomalies are not specific of spin 1/2 fermions. Therefore, one could also expect that a somewhat similar anomaly (also associated to an underlying particle production process) will arise for other fields admitting axial-type symmetries.

In this work we will further discuss the entwining relationship between particle creation and quantum anomalies. In particular, we are especially interested in exploring a new scenario in which (spontaneous and stimulated) particle creation can be relevant. The proposed scenario will be suggested by its link with quantum anomalies, as first explored in.[20] Our heuristic and intuitive argument is based on the universality of gravity, which suggest that the chiral anomaly for spin 1/2 fields should also be extended to the electromagnetic field. In the language of particle creation, one would also expect that a chiral gravitational configuration will create photons with different helicities in unequal amounts, in the same way as it happens, according to (4), for spin 1/2 fermions.

2. Trace and Axial anomalies for massless fermions

Free massless Dirac spinors are highly symmetric. In addition to their Poincaré invariance in Minkowski spacetime, they exhibit two extra symmetries: conformal and axial invariance. The conformal (or Weyl symmetry) implies the tracelessness of the stress-energy tensor $T_{\mu\nu}$, while the axial symmetry ($\psi \to e^{i\theta\gamma^5}\psi$) implies the conservation of the axial current $J_5^\mu = \bar\psi\gamma^\mu\gamma^5\psi$. Both symmetries cannot be extended to the quantum theory when the Dirac field is coupled to an electromagnetic background. The conservation of the axial current is broken according to (1). Furthermore, the trace of the stress-energy tensor also acquires a non-vanishing vacuum expectation value[16,21,22] (for a more recent derivation, see[23])

$$\langle T^\mu_\mu \rangle = \frac{\alpha}{6\pi} F_{\mu\nu}F^{\mu\nu} , \qquad (5)$$

which is usually interpreted in terms of the running of the coupling constant in quantum electrodynamics.[24] In the same way, neither of the two symmetries is preserved when the Dirac field is coupled to a gravitational background. One also finds a trace anomaly

$$\langle T^\mu_\mu \rangle = \frac{\hbar}{2880\pi^2} [aC_{\mu\nu\rho\sigma}C^{\mu\nu\rho\sigma} + bG + c\Box R] , \qquad (6)$$

where $C_{\mu\nu\rho\sigma}$ is the Weyl tensor and G is the integrand of the Gauss-Bonnet topological invariant. The numerical coefficients are given by $a = -9$, $b = 11/2$, $c = 6$, and they can be obtained by different methods.[22,25] It is interesting to point out that the specific form of the trace anomaly implies that there are no massless fermions created in Friedman-Lemaître-Robertson-Walker (FLRW) universes (in this case the trace anomaly is proportional to G, up to total derivatives, and no further term proportional to R^2 appears[26]). This is fully consistent with earlier results[1] showing the absence of particle creation for fields obeying conformally invariant equations.

As remarked in the introduction one also finds an axial anomaly of the form

$$\nabla_\mu \langle J_5^\mu \rangle = \frac{\hbar}{192\pi^2} R_{\mu\nu\alpha\beta}{}^* R^{\mu\nu\alpha\beta} \ . \tag{7}$$

This anomaly can be interpreted in terms of particle creation induced by a chiral gravitational configuration (see[27] for a cosmological setting). Here we want to remark that (7) is consistent with late-time black hole emission.[2] Stationary Kerr black holes emit fermions with a helicity-dependent angular distribution,[28–30] as one could heuristically expect from the local form of the anomaly (7). Fermions with positive helicity are emitted preferentially along the direction of rotation, while fermions with negative helicity in the opposite direction.[For instance, neutrinos are preferentially emitted in the direction opposite to hole's rotation, while antineutrinos in the direction of rotation]. However, the net contribution when integrated over all angles is zero, in agreement with the vanishing of (4) for the Kerr metric. Nevertheless, in the transient process through the formation of a single Kerr black hole, as for instance the merger of two black holes (as the ones currently observed by LIGO-Virgo), the net contribution is not zero, as it has been evaluated using numerical relativity.[31] [For neutrinos/antineutrinos this means creation of matter-antimatter asymmetry]. Although the net creation of helicity is still small, due to the short duration of the process, it could be more significant in scenarios displaying an accumulative process over long periods of time. In any case, one should always take into account that the net creation of helicity represents only a lower bound of the full particle creation process. More particles could be produced without contributing to the creation of helicity.

The above discussion applies equally to the emission of photons. Right-handed photons are radiated more abundantly in the direction parallel to the axis of rotation of a Kerr black hole, and left-handed photons are emitted more abundantly in the opposite direction. This suggests the existence of an "axial anomaly" for spin-1 fields.

3. Electro-magnetic duality as an axial anomalous symmetry

Can we extend the above considerations to the electromagnetic field? Concerning the conformal symmetry, it is well-known that it is broken by quantum effects induced by the gravitational background. The trace of the renormalized stress-energy tensor can be expressed as

$$\langle T^\mu_\mu \rangle = \frac{-62\hbar}{2880\pi^2}\left(R^{\mu\nu}R_{\mu\nu} - \frac{1}{3}R^2\right) + \frac{\hbar}{16\pi^2} c\Box R \ , \tag{8}$$

where c is an ambiguous coefficient, which depend on the particular regularization method ($c = -1/10$ for point-plitting and zeta-function regularization, and $c = 1/15$ for dimensional regularization[22]). We note again[26] that, for a FLRW universe, the trace anomaly turns out to be proportional to the integrand of the Gauss-Bonnet invariant G, up to the ambiguous and total derivative term $\Box R$. The absence of an extra term proportional R^2 is crucial to predict the absence of massless, spin-1 particle creation in an isotropically expanding universe.

The point now is: what is the analog of axial symmetry for the free electromagnetic field? A natural candidate are the well-known electric-magnetic duality transformations, defined by

$$F^{\mu\nu} \to F'^{\mu\nu} = \sin\theta \, {}^*F^{\mu\nu} + \cos\theta \, F^{\mu\nu} \, . \tag{9}$$

The above transformations leave the action

$$S_{Maxwell} = -\frac{1}{4}\int d^4x \sqrt{-g}(\nabla_\mu A_\nu - \nabla_\nu A_\mu)(\nabla^\mu A^\nu - \nabla^\nu A^\mu) \tag{10}$$

invariant, as first proved in Refs.[32,33] in Minkowski space and in Refs.[34,35] in curved space. The associated Noether current can be expressed as

$$j_D^\mu = \frac{1}{2}[A_\nu \, {}^*F^{\mu\nu} - Z_\nu \, F^{\mu\nu}] \, , \tag{11}$$

where the auxiliary field Z_μ is defined as $\nabla_\mu Z_\nu - \nabla_\nu Z_\mu = {}^*F_{\mu\nu}$. j_D^μ is gauge invariant, but it cannot be expressed locally in terms of the field strength, in sharp contrast with the stress-energy tensor. The conserved charge[c]

$$Q_D = \int_{\Sigma_t} d\Sigma_\mu j_D^\mu \tag{12}$$

evaluates the electromagnetic helicity of a classical electromagnetic configuration.[33]

We note that Q_D can be decomposed in two contributions[37]

$$Q_D = Q_m + Q_e \, , \tag{13}$$

where

$$Q_m = \frac{1}{2}\int_{\Sigma_t} d\Sigma_\mu A_\nu \, {}^*F^{\mu\nu}$$
$$Q_e = -\frac{1}{2}\int_{\Sigma_t} d\Sigma_\mu Z_\nu \, F^{\mu\nu} \, . \tag{14}$$

Q_m is the magnetic helicity and Q_e the electric helicity. Neither Q_m or Q_e are conserved quantities, in general.

At the quantum level Q_D is proportional to the difference between the number of right-handed and left-handed photons[33,38]

$$Q_D = \hbar(N_R - N_L) \, . \tag{15}$$

Therefore, this quantity is no longer conserved if the symmetry is afflicted by an anomaly. This issue was worked out in Refs.[20,39–41] from different methods and viewpoints, arguing that the symmetry under electric-magnetic duality rotations

---

[c]Q_D can be written in terms of a non-local integral involving only electric and magnetic fields.[36]

becomes anomalous in curved spacetime. The result is somewhat parallel to that found for spin-1/2 fields

$$\nabla_\mu \langle j_D^\mu \rangle \propto \hbar R_{\mu\nu\alpha\beta}{}^* R^{\mu\nu\alpha\beta} . \tag{16}$$

We want to remark here that previous works in the eighties[42–44] computed the divergence of the Pauli-Lubansky vector $K^\mu \propto A_\nu {}^* F^{\mu\nu}$ in curved space

$$\nabla_\mu \langle A_\nu {}^* F^{\mu\nu} \rangle = \frac{1}{2} \langle F_{\mu\nu} {}^* F^{\mu\nu} \rangle = \frac{\hbar}{96\pi^2} R_{\mu\nu\alpha\beta} {}^* R^{\mu\nu\alpha\beta} . \tag{17}$$

This result is indeed related to the (classically non-conserved) magnetic helicity, instead of the electromagnetic helicity. We can easily realize this from the fact that the Pauli-Lubansky vector is proportional to the current

$$j_m^\mu \equiv \frac{1}{2} A_\nu {}^* F^{\mu\nu} . \tag{18}$$

This current gives the magnetic helicity as the integral

$$Q_m(t) = \int_{\Sigma_t} d\Sigma_\mu j_m^\mu . \tag{19}$$

j_m^μ is not a Noether current, hence Q_m is not time-independent. The proper Noether current associated to the electro-magnetic duality symmetry involves an extra contribution $j_e^\mu \equiv -\frac{1}{2} Z_\nu F^{\mu\nu}$. This additional term is crucial to produce a classical conserved current

$$j_D^\mu = j_m^\mu + j_e^\mu , \tag{20}$$

which can be physically interpreted in terms of the spin-1 axial anomaly if $\nabla_\mu \langle j_D^\mu \rangle$ is different from zero. Since $\nabla_\mu \langle j_e^\mu \rangle = -\langle F_{\mu\nu}^* F^{\mu\nu} \rangle - \frac{1}{2} \langle Z_\nu \nabla_\mu F^{\mu\nu} \rangle$, one gets

$$\nabla_\mu \langle j_D^\mu \rangle = -\frac{1}{2} \langle Z_\nu \nabla_\mu F^{\mu\nu} \rangle . \tag{21}$$

It has been argued in[39–41] that the above vacuum expectation value is nonvanishing and that it is proportional, as expected, to $R_{\mu\nu\alpha\beta}{}^* R^{\mu\nu\alpha\beta}$, in parallel with the fermionic case. As stressed above, and in the language of particles, this would imply that the difference in the number of photons with positive and negative helicities, $N_R - N_L$, is not necessarily conserved in curved spacetimes.

Nevertheless, we want to remark that the result (17) contains an indirect signal of the electromagnetic axial anomaly found in.[39–41] If the invariance of the electromagnetic field equations under the duality transformation $F^{\mu\nu} \to F'^{\mu\nu} = \sin\theta \; {}^* F^{\mu\nu} + \cos\theta \; F^{\mu\nu}$ is strictly translated to composite quantum operators one would get

$$\langle F_{\mu\nu}{}^* F^{\mu\nu} \rangle = (\cos^2\theta - \sin^2\theta) \langle F_{\mu\nu}{}^* F^{\mu\nu} \rangle - \sin\theta \cos\theta (\langle F_{\mu\nu} F^{\mu\nu} \rangle - \langle {}^* F_{\mu\nu}{}^* F^{\mu\nu} \rangle) . \tag{22}$$

This would force $\langle F_{\mu\nu}{}^* F^{\mu\nu} \rangle = 0 = \langle F_{\mu\nu} F^{\mu\nu} \rangle - \langle {}^* F_{\mu\nu}{}^* F^{\mu\nu} \rangle$. Since neither $\langle F_{\mu\nu}{}^* F^{\mu\nu} \rangle$ or $(\langle F_{\mu\nu} F^{\mu\nu} \rangle - \langle {}^* F_{\mu\nu}{}^* F^{\mu\nu} \rangle)$ are zero (see[45] for a detailed discussion on this), we should conclude that electro-magnetic duality fails for non-linear vacuum expectation values. This is the underlying reason permitting the result

$$\nabla_\mu \langle j_m^\mu \rangle + \nabla_\mu \langle j_e^\mu \rangle \neq 0 \ . \tag{23}$$

3.1. *Chiral anomalies and gravitational radiation*

We end this section by outlining an very interesting connection between chiral anomalies and gravitation radiation.[31,46] It is well-know that the right-hand side of (16), as for anomalies in gauge theories, is a total divergence. This simple fact suggests to reinterpret the result (16), or the analogous one for massless fermions, in a physically appealing manner. To evaluate the produced quirality induced by particle creation one should evaluate four-dimensional integrals of the form (4). In doing this one gets crucial contributions from the boundary of the spacetime (i.e., null infinity) involving the outgoing flux of gravitational waves. The contribution of the chiral anomaly can then be exactly related to the amount of circular polarization of the outoging gravitation radiation. Following[31,46] one gets the intriguing relation (see[46] for details)

$$\int d^4 x R_{\mu\nu\lambda\sigma}{}^\star R^{\mu\nu\lambda\sigma} \propto \int_0^\infty \frac{d\omega \omega^3}{24\pi^3} \sum_{\ell m}[|h_+^{\ell m}(\omega)+ih_\times^{\ell m}(\omega)|^2 - |h_+^{\ell m}(\omega)-ih_\times^{\ell m}(\omega)|^2] \ , \tag{24}$$

where h_+, $h_\times$ are the standard gravitational waves polarization modes. The right-hand-side is related to the difference in the intensity between right and left circularly-polarized gravitational waves reaching future null infinity. This shows that a flux of circularly polarized gravitational waves triggers the spontaneous creation of quanta with net helicity. Note the similarity with the Hawking emission by rotating black holes. The angular momentum of the Kerr black hole triggers the spontaneous creation of quanta with net angular momentum.

4. Final remarks

It is well-known that spontaneous emission induces stimulated emission in presence of bosons. This is also true for gravitational particle creation.[1] One can write the simple and basic result

$$\langle N_i(t) \rangle \equiv \langle \Psi | a_i^\dagger(t) a_i(t) | \Psi \rangle = \langle N_i^0 \rangle + (1+2\langle N_i^0 \rangle)|\beta_i(t)|^2 \tag{25}$$

where N_i^0 is the initial number of quanta in mode i contained in the quantum state $|\Psi\rangle$ (the effect is reversed for fermions). This was also considered for black hole radiation in,[47,48] and more recently in[49,50] for non-gaussianities during inflation.

The stimulated counterpart effect is the main difference in the consequences of the axial anomaly for spin-1/2 fermions and photons. In the latter case, the presence of photons in a given mode will trigger the creation of photons of the same mode. It is not easy to evaluate quantitatively the consequences of this effect on a macroscopic pulse of radiation. But it not difficult to guess that it will change the circular polarization of light-rays, with trajectory $x^\mu = x^\mu(\tau)$, propagating through a gravitational field with non-trivial $R_{\mu\nu\lambda\sigma}{}^\star R^{\mu\nu\lambda\sigma}(x(\tau))$. This is a quantum effect, probably very tiny, to be added to the classical gravitational redshift and the deflection of light rays by massive bodies.[51]

Acknowledgements

This work was supported in part by Spanish Ministerio de Economia, Industria y Competitividad Grants No. FIS2017-84440-C2-1-P(MINECO/FEDER, EU), No. FIS2017-91161-EXP and the project PROMETEO/2020/079 (Generalitat Valenciana).

References

1. L. Parker, *The creation of particles in an expanding universe*, Ph.D. thesis, Harvard University (1966). Dissexpress.umi.com, Publication Number 7331244; Phys. Rev. Lett. **21**, 562 (1968); Phys. Rev. D **183**, 1057 (1969); Phys. Rev. D **3**, 346 (1971).
2. S. W. Hawking, Commun. Math. Phys. **43**, 199 (1975).
3. N. D. Birrell and P. C. W. Davies, *Quantum fields in curved space*, Cambridge University Press, Cambridge, UK (1982).
4. S. A. Fulling, *Aspects of quantum field theory in curved space-time*, Cambridge University Press, Cambridge, UK (1989).
5. R. M. Wald, *Quantum field theory in curved spacetime and black hole thermodynamics*, Chicago University Press, Chicago, USA (1994).
6. L. Parker and D. J. Toms, *Quantum field theory in curved spacetime: Quantized fields and gravity*, Cambridge University Press, Cambridge, UK (2009).
7. V. P. Frolov and I. D. Novikov, *Black hole physics*, Kluwer Academic Publishers, Dordrecht, The Netherlands (1998).
8. A. Fabbri and J. Navarro-Salas, *Modeling black hole evaporation*, ICP-World Scientific, London, UK (2005).
9. L. Parker, J. Phys. Conf. Ser. **600**, 1, 012001 (2015); arXiv: 1503.00359.
10. L. Parker and J. Navarro-Salas, *Fifty years of cosmological particle creation*, arXiv:1702.07132.
11. W. Heisenberg and H. Euler, Z. Phys. **98**, 714 (1936). English translation: arXiv:physics/0605038.
12. G. V. Dunne, Int. J. Mod. Phys. A **27**, 1260004 (2012); F. Karbstein, *Particles* **3**, 39 (2020).
13. J. Schwinger, Phys. Rev. **82**, 664 (1951).
14. S. L. Adler, Phys. Rev. **82**, 2426 (1969).
15. J. S. Bell and R. Jackiw, Nuovo Cimento A **51**, 47 (1969).
16. R. A. Bertlmann, *Anomalies in quantum field theory*, Oxford University Press, Oxford.
17. P. Beltran-Palau, A. Ferreiro, J. Navarro-Salas and S. Pla, Phys. Rev. D **100**, 085014 (2019).
18. L. Parker, J. Phys. A **45**, 374023 (2012).
19. T. Kimura, Progress. Theor. Phys. **42**, 1191 (1969).
20. I. Agullo, A. del Rio and J. Navarro-Salas, Int. J. Mod. Phys. D **26**, 1742001 (2017).

21. R. J. Crewther, Phys. Rev. Lett. **28**, 1421 (1972).
22. M. J. Duff, Class. Quantum Grav. **11** 1397 (1994).
23. P. Beltran-Palau, A. Ferreiro, J. Navarro-Salas and S. Pla, Phys. Rev. D **101**, 105014 (2020).
24. S. L. Adler, J. C. Collins and A. Duncan, Phys. Rev. D **15**, 1712 (1977).
25. A. Landete, J. Navarro-Salas and F. Torrenti, Phys. Rev. D **88** (2013) 061501; Phys. Rev. D **89** 044030 (2014). J. F. Barbero G., A. Ferreiro, J. Navarro-Salas and E. J. S. Villaseñor, Phys. Rev. D **98**, 025016 (2018).
26. L. Parker, *Aspects of quantum field theory in curved spacetime: Effective action and energy-momentum tensor*, in Recent Developments in Gravitation, Cargese 1978, ed. M. Lévy and S. Deser (Plenum Press, New York), 219-273.
27. G. W. Gibbons, Phys. Lett. B **84**, 431 (1979).
28. Don N. Page, Phys. Rev. D **14**, 3260 (1976).
29. A. Vilenkin, Phys. Rev. D **20**, 1807 (1979).
30. D. A. Leahy and W. G. Unruh, Phys. Rev. D **19**, 3509 (1979).
31. A. del Rio et al., Phys. Rev. Lett. **124**, 211301 (2020).
32. D. M. Lipkin, J. of Math. Phys. **5**, 696 (1964).
33. M. G. Calkin, Am. J. Phys. **33**, 958 (1965)
34. S. Deser, and C. Teitelboim, Phys. Rev. D **13**, 1592 (1976).
35. S. Deser, J. Phys. A **15**, 1053 (1982).
36. J. Bernabeu and J. Navarro-Salas, Symmetry **11** (10), 1191 (2019); arXiv:1910.05041.
37. M. Galaverni and G. S. J. Gabriele, Gen. Relativ. Gravit. **53**, 46 (2021).
38. J. L. Trueba and A. F. Rañada, European Journal of Physics **17**, 141 (1996).
39. I. Agullo, A. del Rio and J. Navarro-Salas, Phys. Rev. Lett. **118**, 111301 (2017).
40. I. Agullo, A. del Rio and J. Navarro-Salas, Phys. Rev. D **98**, 125001 (2018).
41. I. Agullo, A. del Rio and J. Navarro-Salas, Symmetry **10**, 763 (2018).
42. A. D. Dolgov, I. B. Khriplovich and V. I. Zakharov, JETP Lett. **45**, 651 (1987).
43. A. D. Dolgov, I. B. Khriplovich, A. I. Vainshtein and V. I. Zakharov, Nucl. Phys. B **315**, 138 (1989).
44. M. Reuter, Phys. Rev. D **37**, 1456 (1988).
45. I. Agullo, A. Landete and J. Navarro-Salas, Phys. Rev. D **90**, 124067 (2014).
46. A. del Rio, Phys. Rev. D **104**, 065012 (2021).
47. R. M. Wald, Phys. Rev. D **13**, 3176 (1976).
48. J. D. Bekenstein and A. Meisels, Phys. Rev. D **15**, 2775 (1977).
49. I. Agullo and L. Parker, Phys. Rev. D **83**, 063526 (2011); Gen. Rel. Grav. **43**, 2541 (2011).
50. I. Agullo, J. Navarro-Salas and L. Parker, J. Cosmol. Astropart. Phys. **05**, 019 (2012).
51. C. W. Misner, K. S. Thorne, and J. A. Wheeler, *Gravitation*, W. H. Freeman, San Francisco, USA (1973).

Constraints on the non-minimal coupling of electromagnetic fields from astrophysical observations

Susmita Jana and S. Shankaranarayanan

Department of Physics, Indian Institute of Technology Bombay,
Mumbai, 400076, India
E-mail: susmitajana@iitb.ac.in, shanki@phy.iitb.ac.in

Strong gravity regions, like the neighborhood of black holes or neutron stars, can induce non-minimal couplings between electromagnetic fields(EM) and gravity. In these regions, gravitational fields behave as a non-linear medium in which the electromagnetic fields propagate. For a system of mass M and size R, the surface potential scales as M/R. Pulsar timing array, Double pulsar Shapiro delay, and Event horizon telescope probe that largest surface potentials $[10^{-4} - 10^{-2}]$. With many future experiments, it is possible to constrain the non-minimal coupling between electromagnetic fields and gravity. As a step in this direction, we consider the non-minimal coupling of EM field tensor through Riemann tensor for a dynamical black-hole, described by Sultana-Dyer(SD) metric. The non-minimal coupling leads to modified dispersion relations of photons, which get simplified at $\tilde{E}/\tilde{L} \gg 1$ regime, where $\tilde{E}$ and $\tilde{L}$ are two conserved quantities obtained by taking into account the symmetries of the metric. We calculate polarization-dependent photon deflection angle and arrival time from these dispersion relations, which we evaluate considering different astrophysical sources of photons. We compare the analytical results with the current astrophysical observations to constraint the non-minimal coupling parameters to Riemann tensor more stringently.

Keywords: Non-minimal coupling, time-dependent black hole, strong fields; Based on.[1]

1. Introduction

The general theory of relativity has been tested in the weak-field regime with great accuracy from astrophysical observations — gravitational redshift, light deflection, and perihelion precession of planetary orbits.[2] However, it has not been verified well in strong-field regions such as near a black hole or a neutron star and many have proposed higher-order curvature corrections to GR.[3-7] Testing theories of gravity both in the strong and weak sector requires astrophysical observations, electromagnetic wave is an important source of such observations.

While testing GR through properties associated with photons we consider the minimal coupling of EM fields with gravity —Maxwell's action in curved space-time. Theories with minimal coupling are well tested in weak, but not in strong gravity regions.[8,9] Hence, the accuracy of the theories of gravity including the minimal coupling of the electromagnetic field requires investigation. To test GR in the strong-field limit it is essential to understand how does gravity interact with electromagnetic fields in such regions. One possibility is to consider coupling of the electromagnetic field tensor with the curvature of the space-time through Riemann and Ricci tensors, known as non-minimal coupling of electromagnetic fields.[3]

A model describing non-minimal coupling of electromagnetic fields with curved space-time, violating Einstein's equivalence principle, was first introduced in Ref.[3]. After that different models with more generalized actions were proposed in Refs.[4-7]. As a result, they obtained polarization-dependent photon propagation obeying distinct dispersion relations for the individual polarization modes. Whereas, minimally coupled photons follow dispersion relation $p^\mu p_\mu = 0$ irrespective of their polarization mode.

Even though non-minimal coupling in the space-time of static black hole reveals new behavior of EM waves, it is essential to study the same for a time-dependent black hole as well. One example of a time-dependent black hole is the Sultana-Dyer[10] black hole which describes a Schwarzschild black hole immersed in background FLRW space-time. In this talk we have discussed the properties of photons, non-minimally coupled to the curvature produced by a Sultana-Dyer black-hole. We expect separate dispersion relations of photons for each polarization mode, different than what was obtained for a time-independent black hole.

We also inspect the trajectory of non-minimally coupled photon for an individual mode of polarizations in the vicinity of a time-dependent black hole. In order to do so, we calculate the polarization-dependent deflection angle of a photon in Sultana Dyer space-time. We include coupling of EM field tensor with Riemann tensor only in our analysis as mentioned in.[3] From the expression of the polarization-dependent deflection angles, we constraint the value of the coupling-constant present in action. Inclusion of the dynamical black hole instead of a static one improves the bound on the coupling constant up to $\mathcal{O}(10^{10})$ for a solar-mass black hole.

2. General model

Action describing the most general model of non-minimal coupling that consists coupling of electromagnetic field tensor with Riemann, Ricci tensors and Ricci scalar is[7]:

$$S_{NC} = \int d^4x \sqrt{-g} \left[\frac{R}{\kappa} - \frac{1}{4} F_{\mu\nu} F^{\mu\nu} + \chi^{\mu\nu\alpha\beta} F_{\mu\nu} F_{\alpha\beta} \right], \quad (1)$$

where,

$$\chi^{\mu\nu\alpha\beta} = \frac{q_1 R}{2} \left(g^{\mu\alpha} g^{\nu\beta} - g^{\mu\beta} g^{\nu\alpha} \right) + \frac{q_2}{2} \left(R^{\mu\alpha} g^{\nu\beta} - R^{\mu\beta} g^{\nu\alpha} + R^{\nu\beta} g^{\mu\alpha} - R^{\nu\alpha} g^{\mu\beta} \right)$$
$$+ \frac{\lambda}{2} R^{\mu\nu\alpha\beta}. \quad (2)$$

As mentioned earlier, the models of non-minimal coupling violate the Einstein equivalence principle(EEP), hence this model also violates EEP while being invariant under CPT and general coordinate transformation. A simpler model from the above action can be obtained by choosing $q_1 = q_2 = 0$.[11]

$$S = \int d^4x \sqrt{-g} \left(-\frac{1}{4} F_{\mu\nu} F^{\mu\nu} + \frac{\lambda}{2} R^{\mu\nu\alpha\beta} F_{\mu\nu} F_{\alpha\beta} \right). \quad (3)$$

Authors in Ref.[11] have studied properties of non-minimally coupled photon obeying this action for a spherically symmetric static black hole described by Schwarzschild metric. They have obtained non-identical modified dispersion relation for each mode of polarization followed by two polarization-dependent photon arrival times. Calculating the difference between arrival time for individual polarization they obtained constraints on the coupling coefficient λ to be $\mathcal{O}(10^{20})$ cm^2 for a Solar mass black hole.

However, in reality, the black holes are non-static — embedded in the background expanding universe. That is why in search of the imprints of a dynamical black hole we have done a similar analysis for a time-dependent black hole with mass $[M_\odot 10^{-10}, M_\odot]$.

Electromagnetic fields non minimally coupled to the curvature of space-time obey the following equation of motion,

$$\nabla_\nu F^{\mu\nu} = 2\lambda \left[R^{\mu\nu\alpha\beta} \left(\nabla_\nu F_{\alpha\beta}\right) + \left(\nabla_\alpha R^\mu_{\ \beta}\right) F^{\alpha\beta} \right]. \tag{4}$$

The LHS of the above equation contains dynamical properties of the EM field, whereas the RHS of the EoM depends on the geometry of the space-time. The first term in RHS acts as a metric-dependent momentum term which varies with the component of the electromagnetic field tensor. The second term in RHS is similar to a mass term, in this case, it differs for each value of μ. For a static black hole described by Schwarzschild or Kerr metric the term with $\nabla_\alpha R^\mu_{\ \beta}$ is zero in Eq. (4) as $R_{\mu\nu} = 0$ for such metrics.

Our goal is to get dispersion relation of photon that depends on photon momentum, hence it is reasonable to define a local inertial frame attached to the non-inertial one and define the photon momentum in the local inertial frame by $p_{(\mu)}$. Momentum in local frame is related to momentum in non-inertial frame (p_ν) by the relation: $p_\nu = e_\nu^{\ (\mu)} p_{(\mu)}$, where, $e_\nu^{\ (\mu)}$ is the tetrad connecting the two — inertial and non-inertial frames.

In the case of black-hole space-times we consider, the variations of the curvature along the spatial coordinate $(\mathcal{L})$ and the time $(\mathcal{T})$ are large compared to the wavelength and period of electromagnetic waves, i.e.

$$\mathcal{L} \gg \bar{\lambda} = 1/\bar{k}, \quad \mathcal{T} \gg 1/\omega \tag{5}$$

Under the Eikonal approximation, locally we can treat the EM waves as planar and monochromatic[11]:

$$\nabla_{(\mu)} F^{(\mu)(\nu)} = p_{(\mu)} F^{(\mu)(\nu)} \tag{6}$$

Using this relation into Eq. (4) we get the equation that describes the dynamics of the electromagnetic field in the local inertial frame,

$$p_{(\nu)} F^{(\mu)(\nu)} = 2\lambda \left[R^{(\mu)(\nu)(\alpha)(\beta)} p_{(\nu)} F_{(\alpha)(\beta)} + \left(\nabla_{(\alpha)} R^{(\mu)}_{\ (\beta)}\right) F^{(\alpha)(\beta)} \right]. \tag{7}$$

Setting the space-time index μ to the 3-space index j followed by incorporation of the Bianchi identity in local inertial frame into the above equation leads us to the equation below.

$$[\, p^{(\mu)} p_{(\mu)} \delta^{(j)}_{(k)} - p_{(k)} p^{(j)} + 4\lambda\, R^{(j)(\mu)(\nu)}{}_{(k)}\, p_{(\mu)} p_{(\nu)}$$
$$+ 2\lambda \left(\nabla_{(\alpha)} R^{(j)}{}_{(k)}\, p^{(\alpha)} - \nabla_{(k)} R^{(j)}{}_{(\alpha)} p^{(\alpha)} \right)]\, F^{(0)(k)} = 0 \tag{8}$$

Using Eq. (7) into the above equation, the equation of motion of the EM field in the Eikonal approximation is:

$$\left[p^{(\mu)} p_{(\mu)} \delta^{(j)}_{(k)} + 4\lambda \left(\frac{p^{(j)}}{p_{(0)}} \epsilon^{(0)}{}_{(k)} + \epsilon^{(j)}{}_{(k)} \right) \right.$$
$$+ 2\lambda \left(\frac{p^{(j)}}{p_{(0)}} \nabla_{(\alpha)} R^{(0)}{}_{(k)}\, p^{(\alpha)} + \nabla_{(\alpha)} R^{(j)}{}_{(k)} p^{(\alpha)} \right)$$
$$\left. - 2\lambda \left(\frac{p^{(j)}}{p_{(0)}} \nabla_{(k)} R^{(0)}{}_{(\alpha)}\, p^{(\alpha)} + \nabla_{(k)} R^{(j)}{}_{(\alpha)} p^{(\alpha)} \right) \right] F^{(0)(k)} = 0, \tag{9}$$

where, $\epsilon^{(\alpha)}{}_{(\beta)} \equiv R^{(\alpha)(\mu)(\nu)}{}_{(\beta)}\, p_{(\mu)} p_{(\nu)}$ acts as a polarization tensor that generates correction to EoM according to the component of electric field.

From the above equation, one can study the trajectory of non-minimally coupled photons considering different space-time metrics. As mentioned earlier for photons in Schwarzschild and Kerr black hole terms with Ricci tensor in Eq. (9) will vanish and the EoM reduces to,

$$\left[p^{(\mu)} p_{(\mu)} \delta^{(j)}_{(k)} + 4\lambda \left(\frac{p^{(j)}}{p_{(0)}} \epsilon^{(0)}{}_{(k)} + \epsilon^{(j)}{}_{(k)} \right) \right] F^{(0)(k)} = 0, \tag{10}$$

Our goal is to study the effects of the curvature coupling on photon trajectory near a time-dependent black-hole and identify the differences with the same due to a static black hole. In literature the analysis has been done only for static black holes and as a result constraint on λ has also been obtained. As a step ahead, We do this analysis for a cosmological black hole described by Sultana Dyer metric.[10]

3. Sultana Dyer metric

In reality, black holes are non-static and the Sultana Dyer metric describes such a time-dependent black hole.[10] Sultana Dyer black hole metric can be interpreted as a Schwarzchild black hole immersed in the background FLRW metric:

$$ds^2 = \left(\frac{\eta}{\eta_0} \right)^4 \left[-\left(1 - \frac{2GM}{r} \right) d\eta^2 + \frac{4GM}{r} d\eta dr + \left(1 + \frac{2GM}{r} \right) dr^2 + r^2\, d\Omega^2 \right] \tag{11}$$

where η is the conformal time—related to comoving time t as, $dt = a(\eta)d\eta$; $\eta = \eta_0$ at $t = t_0$, where t_0 is current cosmic time. M is mass of the black hole.

Sultana Dyer metric has been obtained by performing conformal transformation $a(t) \propto t^{2/3}$ to the Schwarzschild metric. Thus it corresponds to black-holes in the matter-dominated epoch. The conformal transformation preserves the casual structure also, as a result, the black hole has the horizon at $r_H = 2GM/c^2$. Sultana-Dyer space-time is sourced by two non-interacting perfect fluids — null dust and massive dust. At the horizon, $r = r_H$ the dust particles become superluminal for time $\eta > 2r_H$.[10]

Writing the above equation in non-geometrised unit—$\eta \to c\eta$, $r_H \to \frac{r_H}{c^2}$ and substituting the following dimensionless variables:

$$\tilde{r} = \frac{c^2 r}{r_H}; \quad \tilde{\eta} \equiv H_0 \eta; \quad \tilde{\eta}_0 \equiv H_0 \eta_0, \qquad (12)$$

in the metric we have

$$ds^2 = \alpha_0^2 \, \tilde{\eta}^4 \left[-\left(1 - \frac{1}{\tilde{r}}\right) \beta_0^2 d\tilde{\eta}^2 + \frac{2}{\tilde{r}} \beta_0 \, d\tilde{\eta} d\tilde{r} + \left(1 + \frac{1}{\tilde{r}}\right) d\tilde{r}^2 + \tilde{r}^2 \, d\Omega^2 \right] = \alpha_0^2 \, d\tilde{s}^2 \qquad (13)$$

where H_0 is Hubble constant,

$$d\tilde{s}^2 = \tilde{\eta}^4 \left[-\left(1 - \frac{1}{\tilde{r}}\right) \beta_0^2 d\tilde{\eta}^2 + \frac{2}{\tilde{r}} \beta_0 \, d\tilde{\eta} d\tilde{r} + \left(1 + \frac{1}{\tilde{r}}\right) d\tilde{r}^2 + \tilde{r}^2 \, d\Omega^2 \right] \qquad (14)$$

$$\alpha_0 = \frac{r_H}{c^2 \tilde{\eta}_0^2} \quad \beta_0 = \frac{c^3}{r_H \, H_0} \qquad (15)$$

From here we will be using the dimensionless line-element $d\tilde{s}$ defined in Eq. (14). This choice is suitable because the affine parameter (τ) and all the physical quantities in this space-time depend on τ.

3.1. *Conserved quantities from symmetries of the metric*

The trajectory of a null object such as a photon is being fixed by its momentum p^μ. In this work, we focus on photons moving in the orbital plane of the black hole. For the metric (13), we define the contravariant photon momentum as,

$$p^0 = \frac{d\tilde{\eta}}{d\tau}, \quad p^1 = \frac{d\tilde{r}}{d\tau}, \quad p^2 = 0, \quad p^3 = \frac{d\phi}{d\tau} \qquad (16)$$

Using the metric and the relation $p_\nu = g_{\mu\nu} p^\mu$ we get the covariant form:

$$p_0 = \tilde{\eta}^4 \left(-\beta_0^2 \, A \frac{d\tilde{\eta}}{d\tau} + C_1 \frac{d\tilde{r}}{d\tau} \right) := \tilde{E}; \quad p_1 = -\frac{C_1}{A} \tilde{E} + \tilde{\eta}^4 \left(\frac{C_1^2}{A} + B \right) \frac{d\tilde{r}}{d\tau} \qquad (17)$$

$$p_3 = \tilde{\eta}^4 C_2 \frac{d\phi}{d\tau} := \tilde{L} \qquad (18)$$

Though the metric is time-dependent it is —conformally invariant w.r.t η or $\tilde{\eta}$ and spherically symmetric. Taking into account these two symmetries it can be shown that $\tilde{E}$ and $\tilde{L}$ defined in Eq. (17) are conserved w.r.t the affine parameter τ. where, $A = (1 - \frac{1}{\tilde{r}})$, $B = (1 + \frac{1}{\tilde{r}})$, $C_1 = \frac{\beta_0}{\tilde{r}}$, $C_2 = \tilde{r}^2$.

Our goal is to see effects on the non-minimally coupled photon close to the black hole, and later it will be clear that the effects depend on $\tilde{E}/\tilde{L}$, which is:

$$\frac{\tilde{E}}{\tilde{L}} = \left(\frac{r_H}{c^2 r}\right)^2 \left(-\left(1 - \frac{r_H}{c^2 r}\right) \beta_0^2 H_0 \frac{d\eta}{d\phi} + \frac{\beta_0}{r} \frac{dr}{d\phi}\right) \tag{19}$$

Close to the black hole at radius of photon sphere, $r = 3r_H/(2c^2)$, it can be shown that for M in the range $[M_\odot 10^{-10}, M_\odot]$ the ratio $\tilde{E}/\tilde{L} \gg 1$.

4. Modified dispersion relation

As a result of the non-minimal coupling dispersion relation for photon near Schwarzschild and Sultana Dyer black hole can be obtained from Eq. (10) as[11]:

$$p^2 = \pm \frac{6\lambda}{r_H^2 \tilde{r}^3} p_{(3)}^2. \tag{20}$$

From the above expression, we infer that the photon dispersion relation remains quadratic also as similar to the relation $p^\mu p_\mu = 0$ with r-dependent corrections. There ($\pm$) sign refers to dispersion relation for ($\pm$) polarization mode. We have verified that for the Kerr metric, describing a time-independent rotating black hole the dispersion relation remains quadratic — even in the inertial frame of reference it gives the same dispersion relation (20).

The dispersion relations for the Sultana Dyer metric will be obtained from Eq. (9). Unlike Schwarzschild and Kerr black holes, the Ricci tensor is non-zero for Sultana-Dyer black hole. Hence, the terms with the Ricci tensor and its derivative will contribute to the dispersion relation. However, it is possible to check that the contribution arising from the Ricci tensor containing terms is much smaller than the other terms in the dispersion relation. Finally, keeping only the relevant terms we obtain the dispersion relations for the local inertial frame in the Sultana-Dyer metric as:

$$-f_1 p_{(0)}^2 + f_1 p_{(1)}^2 + f_2 p_{(3)}^2 + f_3 \frac{p_{(1)} p_{(3)}^2}{p_{(0)}} = 0 \tag{21}$$

$$-f_4 p_{(0)}^2 + f_2 p_{(1)}^2 + f_5 p_{(3)}^2 + 2 f_3 p_{(1)} p_{(0)} = 0. \tag{22}$$

where, $f_n(\tilde{r}, \tilde{\eta})$ depends on the coupling constant $\tilde{\lambda} \equiv \lambda/\alpha_0^2$ and the components of Riemann tensor in local inertial frame for Sulatana-Dyer metric — $R_{(\alpha)(\beta)(\mu)(\nu)}$. These two dispersion relations in the local frame lead to the following relations in the non-inertial frame:

$$\frac{(C_1^3 - C_1)}{B} p_1^3 + (1 - 3C_1^2) p_0 p_1^2 + \left(3C_1 B p_0^2 + \frac{(f_3 - f_2 C_1)}{f_1 C_2} p_3^2\right) p_1 - B^2 p_0^3 + \frac{f_2 B}{f_1 C_2} p_0 p_3^2 = 0 \tag{23}$$

$$(-f_4 C_1^2 - 2 f_3 C_1 + f_2) p_1^2 + 2(f_3 + f_4 C_1) B p_0 p_1 - f_4 B^2 p_0^2 + f_5 \frac{B}{C_2} p_3^2 = 0 \tag{24}$$

It is important to note here that the above-mentioned dispersion relations for the Sultana Dyer metric are very different than the dispersion relations obtained for the Schwarzschild metric. For Schwarzschild case the dispersion relations do not contain terms with $p_0 p_1$ or $p_1 p_3^2$. Secondly, in the dispersion relations for Sultana Dyer metric terms with every component of momentum get modified whereas for Schwarzschild metric only the term with p_3 gets modified. Last point, Eq. (23) is cubic and it occurs due to the last term in Eq. (21), while for the Schwarzschild case both the dispersion relations are quadratic.

5. Results

Till now we have discussed how photon dispersion relations get modified due to the presence of non-minimal coupling in Sultana Dyer space-time as compared to Schwarzschild metric. In this part we discuss the effects of these modified dispersion relations on photon trajectory. To see the effects one needs to study the modification to the trajectory of the photon, which can be done through these astrophysical observables — 1) Photon arrival-time at the detector, 2) Photon deflection-angle at the detector. Since we are working with Sultana Dyer black hole — a time-dependent and non-diagonal metric, we prefer deflection-angle over photon arrival-time.

For verifying the existence of non-minimal coupling we have primarily two goals — 1) Put constraint on the non-minimal coupling coefficient, 2) Compare the effects on non-minimally coupled photon trajectory caused by time-independent and time-dependent black hole.

Reaching the above-mentioned goals requires derivation of the the deflection angle of photon for each polarization mode, and then their difference considering time-independent(Schwarzschild) and time-dependent(Sultana Dyer) black hole. For simplicity, we derive the difference in the deflection angle comparison at a radius of photon sphere — $\tilde{r} = 3/2$ as we are interested in the behavior of photons near the black hole.

For Schwarzschild metric at $r = (3/2)r_H$ and $\tilde{\eta}_0$ the difference between the deflection angle for (+) and (−) polarization is,

$$\left.\frac{d\phi}{dr}\right|^+_{\text{Sch}} - \left.\frac{d\phi}{dr}\right|^+_{\text{Sch}} = \frac{4\beta_0 b}{9 r_H} \left[\left[1 - \frac{4\beta_0^2 b^2}{27}\left(1 - \frac{16\tilde{\lambda}}{729}\right)\right]^{-\frac{1}{2}} \right.$$
$$\left. - \left[1 - \frac{4\beta_0^2 b^2}{27}\left(1 + \frac{16\tilde{\lambda}}{729}\right)\right]^{-\frac{1}{2}} \right]. \quad (25)$$

where, $b = \tilde{L}/\tilde{E}$ at fixed $\tilde{r}$ and $\tilde{\eta} = \tilde{\eta}_0$. The LHS of the above equation will be real if and only if,

$$1 - \frac{4\beta_0^2 b^2}{27}\left(1 \mp \frac{16\tilde{\lambda}}{729}\right) > 0. \quad (26)$$

From this condition, we determine the value of b, provided the values of β_0 and $\tilde{\lambda}$ are known.

Now for Sultana Dyer space-time, the difference between the polarization-dependent deflection angles can be obtained from the cubic (23) and the quadratic dispersion relation (24) separately. For the limit, $\beta_0 \gg 1$ and $\tilde{E}/\tilde{L} \gg 1$ both Eqs. (23) and (24) get simplified and the cubic dispersion relation becomes entirely independent of the coupling coefficient $\tilde{\lambda}$. This implies the simplified cubic dispersion relation does not hold any imprint of non-minimal coupling. Hence we stress our analysis into the quadratic dispersion relation only. From the simplified quadratic dispersion relation we get the deflection angle:

$$\frac{d\phi}{d\tilde{r}} = \frac{\tilde{L}\left(\frac{C_1^2}{A} + B\right)}{C_2 \left(\frac{-(2f_4 C_1 B\tilde{E}) \pm \sqrt{(2f_4 C_1 B\tilde{E})^2 - 4(-f_4 C_1^2)B\tilde{L}^2\left(-f_4 B\frac{\tilde{E}^2}{\tilde{L}^2} + \frac{f_5}{C_2}\right)}}{2(-f_4 C_1^2)} + \frac{C_1}{A}\tilde{E}\right)}. \qquad (27)$$

The difference between the deflection angle for $(\pm)$ polarizations at fixed $r = (3/2)r_H$ and current comoving time $\tilde{\eta}_0 = 3$ becomes,

$$\left.\frac{d\phi}{dr}\right|_{SD}^{+} - \left.\frac{d\phi}{dr}\right|_{SD}^{-} \sim \frac{162\, b^2 \sqrt{\left(3^6 - 16\tilde{\lambda}\right)\left(8\tilde{\lambda} + 3^6\right)}}{16\, k^3 r_H^4 \left(8\tilde{\lambda} + 3^6\right)} \frac{1}{\beta_0^2}. \qquad (28)$$

where, $k = H_0/c$. Eqs. (25) and (28) depend on r_H, β_0, b and $\tilde{\lambda}$. But it is crucial to note that in Schwarzschild space-time the difference between two deflection angles (25) depends on $b\beta_0$, whereas in Sultana Dyer space time (28) is proportional to b/β_0. Hence, at this point we stress that photon trajectory gets modified in different manner while travelling near a Schwarzschild or Sultana Dyer black hole. Understanding this fact better requires the value of b and $\tilde{\lambda}$.

From the condition that Eq. (28) will be real if and only if the constraint $\tilde{\lambda} < \frac{729}{16}$ is followed. As $\tilde{\lambda} = \lambda/\alpha_0^2$ we get the constraint of the coupling coefficient λ as: $\lambda < (9/16)r_H^2$. This is another important result regarding which we like to stress the following points: First, the coupling constant λ is an intrinsic property of the field and should be independent of the parameters of the model. However, from the above expression, we see that the constraint on λ depends on the mass of the black hole. On the face of it, this might look unphysical. However, it can be pointed that the energy density of the mull dust in Sultana Dyer space-time does not remain positive for all values of η. The condition that the energy density remains positive at the photon radius translates to $\eta < 15 r_H/4$. Since, we have fixed $\eta = \eta_0$, this leads to the condition on λ. Thus, the above constraint on the coupling parameter λ ensures that the energy density of the electromagnetic field is non-negative. The table below gives the upper limit on λ for black holes with different mass ranges. Finally, it is interesting to compare the bounds on λ compared to obtained in the literature. In Ref.[11], the authors obtained constraints on λ considering photons in Schwarzschild space-time. Considering signals from radar ranging past the Sun, the authors found $\lambda \sim 1.1 \times 10^{20}$ cm^2, which is about three orders of magnitude more stringent than the one obtained in Ref.[12]. Our analysis shows that $\lambda < 0.563 \times 10^{10}$cm^2 for the Sultana-Dyer black hole of solar-mass. Note that, in the case of signals coming from binary pulsar PSR B1534+12, the bound on $\lambda \sim 0.6 \times 10^{11}$ cm^2.[13]

Black hole mass	r_H (cm)	λ (cm^2)
Solar-mass	10^5	0.563×10^{10}
$10^{-3} M_\odot$	10^2	0.563×10^4
$10^{-5} M_\odot$	1	0.563
$10^{-10} M_\odot$	10^{-5}	0.563×10^{-10}

Now using the value of $\tilde{\lambda}$ ranging between $[0, 729/16]$ into condition (26) with the (-) sign we get the constraint $b\beta_0 < 1.8$. Similarly for the (+) sign we get the constraint as $b\beta_0 < 2.598$. However, for the constraint $b\beta_0 < 1.8$ Eq. (26) is valid for both ($\pm$) sign. From this constraint, we have fixed the value of b for a particular value of β_0, where the value of β_0 varies with the mass of the black hole.

Since we have fixed the variables $\tilde{\lambda}$, r_H, β_0 and b, now we compare Eqs. (25) and (28) by evaluating their values for black holes with mass — $M_\odot$ and $10^{-5} M_\odot$. We evaluate the difference between two deflection angles in Schwarzschild and Sultana Dyer space-time considering two separate cases, 1) $b\beta_0 \sim 1$ and 2) $b\beta_0 \sim 10^{-3}$. Both these cases satisfies the condition $b\beta_0 < 1.8$. All the values has been mentioned in the table below.

Black hole mass	$b\beta_0$	$\Delta\left(\frac{d\phi}{dr}\right)_{Sch}$	$\Delta\left(\frac{d\phi}{dr}\right)_{SD}$
$M_\odot$	1	-1.322×10^{-5}	7.893×10^{-7}
	10^{-3}	-1.032×10^{-14}	7.893×10^{-13}
$10^{-5} M_\odot$	1	-1.322	0.079
	10^{-3}	-1.032^{-9}	7.893×10^{-8}

Inspecting the numbers in the above table we infer one more important key feature: for $b\beta_0 \sim 1$ the modulus of the difference between the deflection angles for Schwarzschild is greater than the same in Sultana Dyer space-time. However, for, $b\beta_0 \sim 10^{-3}$ the difference between the deflection angles for Sultana Dyer black hole is greater. The reason behind this behavior is that the difference between the deflection angle (28) for the Sultana Dyer black hole is proportional to b^2/β_0^2 and the same quantity (25) for the Schwarzschild black hole depends on b and β_0 differently.

As a result, we see the larger the value of b larger the effects due to Schwarzschild, and smaller the value of b the effects are larger for Sultana Dyer black hole. Another crucialfeature is that, the difference between the photon deflection angles for Schwarzschild metric is negative, while for Sultana Dyer it is always positive — that manifests two distinct signatures of two black holes. Similar behavior in the difference of deflection angles has been observed for a black hole of mass $10^{-5} M_\odot$ as well.

6. Conclusions and discussions

In this work, we have studied the effects of non-minimal coupling of electromagnetic fields with gravitational field near a cosmological black hole, described by Sultana Dyer metric, and compared them with the effects obtained for a Schwarzschild black hole. To our knowledge, the analysis for non-minimal coupling near a time-dependent black hole has not been explored in literature. For doing the analysis we have applied Eikonal approximation in a local inertial frame assuming that the wavelength and time period of the propagating electromagnetic wave is lesser than the variation of curvature with respect to the space-time. Our study for the Sultana Dyer metric produced a pair of modified dispersion relations which consist of corrections in all components of momentum, while for the Schwarzschild case the modification occurs only in the p_3 component. Besides that, one of the modified dispersion relations for the Sultana Dyer metric is cubic, while for the Schwarzschild metric both the dispersion relations remain quadratic. By calculating photon deflection angle for individual polarization mode in Sultana Dyer space-time we get a bound on λ for a solar mass black hole which is more stringent of order 10^{10} than the bound obtained in Ref.[11]. Through the evaluation of the difference between deflection angles for two polarizations we have found distinct signatures of two black holes — Schwarzschild and Sultana Dyer.

We hope that through observing electromagnetic emission in broad wave-band from different astrophysical events it is plausible to measure the deflection angle of electromagnetic wave and confirm the existence or non-existence of the non-minimal coupling.

For the entire work, we have assumed the time-dependent black hole to be spherically symmetric and non-rotating. To observe the signatures mentioned in this work from astrophysical observation might involve axially symmetric (like Kerr) black hole. Hence, we are investigating the possibilities to extend the analysis for a rotating black-hole space-time.

Acknowledgements

This work is supported by MATRICS-SERB grant. The authors thank the service personnel in India whose untiring work allowed the authors to continue this work during the COVID-19 outbreak.

References

1. S. Jana and S. Shankaranarayanan, Constraints on the non-minimal coupling of electromagnetic field from astrophysical observations (Oct 2021).
2. T. A. Wagner, S. Schlamminger, J. H. Gundlach and E. G. Adelberger, Torsion-balance tests of the weak equivalence principle, *Class. Quant. Grav.* **29**, p. 184002 (2012).
3. A. Prasanna, A new invariant for electromagnetic fields in curved space-time, *Physics Letters A* **37**, 331 (1971).
4. G. W. Horndeski, Conservation of Charge and the Einstein-Maxwell Field Equations, *J. Math. Phys.* **17**, 1980 (1976).
5. H. A. Buchdahl, Theories of gravitation with nonminimal coupling of matter and the gravitational field, *J. Phys. A* **12**, 1037 (1979).
6. G. M. Shore, A Local effective action for photon gravity interactions, *Nucl. Phys. B* **646**, 281 (2002).
7. A. B. Balakin and J. P. S. Lemos, Non-minimal coupling for the gravitational and electromagnetic fields: A General system of equations, *Class. Quant. Grav.* **22**, 1867 (2005).
8. E. Berti et al., Testing General Relativity with Present and Future Astrophysical Observations, *Class. Quant. Grav.* **32**, p. 243001 (2015).
9. D. Psaltis, Probes and Tests of Strong-Field Gravity with Observations in the Electromagnetic Spectrum, *Living Rev. Rel.* **11**, p. 9 (2008).
10. J. Sultana and C. C. Dyer, Cosmological black holes: A black hole in the Einstein- de Sitter universe, *Gen. Rel. Grav.* **37**, 1347 (2005).
11. A. R. Prasanna and S. Mohanty, Constraints on nonminimally coupled curved space electrodynamics from astrophysical observations, *Class. Quant. Grav.* **20**, 3023 (2003).
12. M. L. Bedran and B. Lesche, An example of affine collineation in the Robertson–Walker metric, *Journal of Mathematical Physics* **27**, 2360 (1986).
13. I. H. Stairs, S. E. Thorsett, J. H. Taylor and A. Wolszczan, Studies of the relativistic binary pulsar psr b1534+12: I. Timing analysis, *Astrophys. J.* **581**, 501 (2002).

New partial resummation of the QED effective action

Silvia Pla[*] and José Navarro-Salas[†]

Departamento de Fisica Teorica and IFIC, Centro Mixto Universidad de Valencia-CSIC, Facultad de Fisica, Universidad de Valencia, Burjassot-46100, Valencia, Spain
[*] *E-mail: silvia.pla@uv.es*
[†] *E-mail: jnavarro@ific.uv.es*

We explain a conjecture which states that the proper-time series expansion of the one-loop effective Lagrangian of quantum electrodynamics can be partially summed in all terms containing the field-strength invariants $\mathcal{F} = \frac{1}{4}F_{\mu\nu}F^{\mu\nu}(x)$, $\mathcal{G} = \frac{1}{4}\tilde{F}_{\mu\nu}F^{\mu\nu}(x)$. This summation is encapsulated in a factor with the same form as the (spacetime-dependent) Heisenberg-Euler Lagrangian density. We also discuss some implications and a possible extension in presence of gravity. We will focus on the scalar field case.

Keywords: One-loop effective Lagrangian; Partial resummation; Heisenberg-Euler Lagrangian; asymptotic expansion.

1. Introduction

In this contribution[a], we give more details on a conjecture proposed in Ref.[2], that claims that it is possible to make a factorization in the proper-time series of the one-loop effective Lagrangian of quantum electrodynamics (QED) that captures all explicit dependence on the field-strength invariants $\mathcal{F}$ and $\mathcal{G}$. The text is organized as follows. First, in Sections 1.1 and 1.2 we review some basics about the one-loop effective Lagrangian and its proper-time series expansion. We focus on the scalar QED effective Lagrangian and also on the corresponding effective Lagrangian in presence of gravity. We emphasize the existence of a modified, asymptotic expansion (also called R-summed expansion) in the gravitational scenario. In Section 2 we explain our conjecture for scalar QED (a sketch for spinor QED is given in Ref.[2]). We also check it up to order $n = 6$ (the last available coefficient in the literature). In Section 3 we explain some physical consequences that can be easily obtained using our results. Finally, in Section 4 we give a brief summary of this contribution. For simplicity, we will focus on the scalar QED case. In Appendices A and B we give the coefficients of the usual and the resummed proper-time series expansions for scalar QED.

1.1. *Heisenberg-Euler Lagrangian and the proper-time series expansion*

The Heisenberg-Euler Lagrangian captures the one-loop quantum corrections to the classical electromagnetic Lagrangian for quantum electrodynamics. It is obtained

---
[a]Expanded version of the talk given by S.P. in the Sixteenth Marcel Grossmann Meeting (2021).

by integrating out the matter degrees of freedom, keeping the strength of the electromagnetic background constant.[3,4] The intrinsic nonlinearities of the quantum corrections have important implications, such as pair creation from vacuum and vacuum polarization,[5] or light by light scattering or vacuum polarization (see, for example, Ref.[6] and references therein). It was originally derived by Heisenberg and Euler[7] for spinor QED in 1936. A few months later, it was obtained by Weisskopf[8] for scalar QED (see Ref.[9] for a charged spin 1 field). These two theories are regarded as the paradigm of the modern effective theories in Quantum Field Theory. From now on, we will focus on the scalar QED Heisenberg-Euler Lagrangian. It is usually written in terms of the proper time parameter s, but, apart from this, it be written in several ways. By convenience, here we use the following form borrowed from Ref.[10]:

$$\mathcal{L}_{scalar}^{(1)} = -\frac{1}{(4\pi)^2} \int_0^\infty \frac{ds}{s^3} e^{-im^2 s} \left[\det\left(\frac{esF}{\sinh(esF)}\right)\right]^{1/2}, \quad (1)$$

where $F \equiv F^\mu_\nu$. As we have stressed before, this result was obtained for constant electromagnetic backgrounds, but for arbitrary background configurations the form of the effective action is, in general, *unknown*.

However, it is possible to build a general, asymptotic expansion for the one-loop effective Lagrangian in terms of the proper-time parameter. Here we use the expansion given in Ref.[11], obtained via the string-inspired method in the world-line formalism (see Refs.[11–14] and also Refs.[15,16]), namely

$$\mathcal{L}_{scalar}^{(1)} = \int_0^\infty \frac{ds}{s} e^{-im^2 s} g(x; is) , \quad (2)$$

with

$$g(x; is) = \frac{1}{(4\pi is)^2} \sum_{n=0}^\infty \frac{(-is)^n}{n!} O_n(x) \rightarrow \begin{cases} O_0 = 1, \quad O_1 = 0, \\ O_2 = -\frac{e^2}{6} F_{\kappa\lambda} F^{\kappa\lambda} \\ O_3 = -\frac{e^2}{20} \partial_\mu F_{\kappa\lambda} \partial^\mu F^{\kappa\lambda} \\ (\cdots) \end{cases} \quad (3)$$

The expression above consist of an expansion in the number of external fields and the number of derivatives, and captures some general behaviour of the unknown formal one-loop effective Lagrangian for arbitrary backgrounds. The coefficients O_n are gauge-invariant and have mass dimension $2n$. They have been obtained up to 12th adiabatic order ($n = 6$), and their length grows substantially with n. In Appendix A can be found the complete list of coefficients. We would like to stress that this expansion presents some clear advantages with respect to other proposals. In particular, it is written in the most compact form possible. Using the Bianchi identity, the antisymmetry of $F_{\mu\nu}$ and also integration by parts, the gauge-invariant coefficients O_n have been simplified to the so-called minimal basis.[17]

1.2. *One loop effective Lagrangian in presence of gravity*

The role of the classical electromagnetic background can be replaced by a gravitational field, which is naturally coupled to quantized matter fields. In other words, it is possible to obtain quantum corrections to the Einstein-Hilbert Lagrangian induced by a quantum scalar field. In general, the form of the effective action is not known, but it is also possible to make an asymptotic expansion of it,[18] as in the previous case.

In this context, the expansion of the one-loop effective Lagrangian is usually obtained in terms of the Schwinger proper-time expansion of the Feynman propagator,[5] closely connected to the heat-kernel expansion and related techniques.[19] Specifically, the one loop effective Lagrangian in terms of the heat-kernel reads

$$\mathcal{L}^{(1)}_{scalar} = \int_0^\infty \frac{ds}{s} e^{-im^2 s} \langle x, s|x, 0\rangle \,. \tag{4}$$

In this expression, $\langle x', s|x, 0\rangle$ is the kernel or "transition amplitude" associated to the Feynman propagator, which obeys a Schrodinger-type equation in terms of the proper time parameter with appropriated boundary conditions, and $\langle x, s|x, 0\rangle$ represents the coincident limit $x' \to x$. In general, the kernel admits a general asymptotic expansion in terms of the proper time parameter, i.e.,

$$\langle x, s|x, 0\rangle = \frac{1}{(4\pi i s)^2} \sum_{n=0}^{\infty} (is)^n a_n(x). \tag{5}$$

The coefficients $a_n(x)$ are called DeWitt coefficients. These quantities of mass dimension $2n$ are local, covariant and gauge invariant.[18,20] We recall here that for QED, the expansion $g(x; is)$ [see Eq. (5)] coincides with the heat kernel expansion, up to total derivatives

$$g(x; is) = \langle x, s|x, 0\rangle + total\ derivatives. \tag{6}$$

Although the general form of the gravitational one-loop effective Lagrangian is not known, there is one special case where it can be evaluated exactly[21]: the Static Einstein Universe. In this case, the kernel $\langle x, s|x, 0\rangle$ reads

$$\langle x, s|x, 0\rangle = \frac{e^{-i(\xi - \frac{1}{6})Rs}}{(4\pi i s)^2}. \tag{7}$$

where R is the Ricci scalar and ξ is the coupling constant to the scalar field. This is a non-perturbative result, that involves all powers of the proper time parameter s. From this result, Parker and Toms proposed in 1985 a new asymptotic expansion for the kernel,[22] defined as

$$\langle x, s|x, 0\rangle = \frac{e^{-i(\xi - \frac{1}{6})R(x)s}}{(4\pi i s)^2} \sum_{n=0}^{\infty} (is)^n \bar{a}_n(x). \tag{8}$$

The new adiabatic expansion in terms of the coefficients $\bar{a}_n(x)$ has an important advantage with respect to the previous one: it does not contain any term that vanishes when $R(x)$ is replaced by zero (see Ref.[23] for detailed proof). In other words, the non-perturbative exponential factor captures the exact dependence on the Ricci scalar in the generic Schwinger-DeWitt asymptotic expansion. This factorization has some important physical consequences, related, for example, to the effective dynamics of the Universe[24] or to the curvature dependence in the running of the gauge coupling constants.[25]

The key idea is that, from a solvable case, it is possible to extract a non-perturbative factor in the general asymptotic expansion of the one-loop effective Lagrangian that completely captures its dependence with the curvature scalar $R(x)$. In this context, a natural question arises: is it possible to find a similar factorization for the QED Lagrangian?

2. The conjecture

Based on the gravitational case, we propose the following conjecture for the electromagnetic case[2]: *The proper-time asymptotic expansion of the QED effective Lagrangian admits an exact resummation in all terms involving the field-strength invariants $\mathcal{F} = \frac{1}{4}F_{\mu\nu}F^{\mu\nu}$ and $\mathcal{G} = \frac{1}{4}\tilde{F}_{\mu\nu}F^{\mu\nu}$. The form of the factor is just the Heisenberg-Euler Lagrangian for QED, where the electric and magnetic fields depend arbitrarily on space-time coordinates*, namely

$$\mathcal{L}^{(1)}_{scalar} = \int_0^\infty \frac{ds}{s} e^{-im^2 s} \left[\det\left(\frac{esF(x)}{\sinh(esF(x))}\right)\right]^{1/2} \bar{g}(x;is) \qquad (9)$$

[to compare with (5)], where the new asymptotic expansion $\bar{g}(x;is)$ reads

$$\bar{g}(x;is) = \frac{1}{(4\pi is)^2} \sum_{n=0}^\infty \frac{(-is)^n}{n!} \bar{O}_n(x), \qquad (10)$$

and where the coefficients $O_n(x)$ do not have terms that vanish when the electromagnetic invariants $\mathcal{F}(x)$ and $\mathcal{G}(x)$ are replaced by zero. The asymptotic expansions $g(x;is)$ and $\bar{g}(x;is)$ are related by

$$g(x;is) = \left[\det\left(\frac{esF(x)}{\sinh(esF(x))}\right)\right]^{1/2} \bar{g}(x;is). \qquad (11)$$

In summary, we have proposed a new adiabatic expansion $\bar{g}(x;is)$ that can be built from the previous one via Eq. (11), and we have conjectured that, if the pre-factor is just the Euler Heisenberg Lagrangian, the new coefficients $\bar{O}_n$ associated with the new expansion will not have terms that vanish when the electromagnetic invariants are replaced by zero.

In the last part of the section, we are going to compute the new coefficients and check that, effectively, our conjecture is satisfied. First, we should expand the

Heisenberg-Euler determinant in terms of the proper time,

$$\left[\det\left(\frac{esF(x)}{\sinh(esF(x))}\right)\right]^{1/2} \sim 1 + U_2(x)(-is)^2 + U_4(x)(-is)^4 + U_6(x)(-is)^6 + \cdots, \quad (12)$$

where

$$U_2(x) = \frac{e^2}{12}\operatorname{Tr}(F^2), \quad (13)$$

$$U_4(x) = \frac{e^4}{288}\operatorname{Tr}(F^2)^2 + \frac{e^4}{360}\operatorname{Tr}(F^4), \quad (14)$$

$$U_6(x) = \frac{e^6}{10368}\operatorname{Tr}(F^2)^3 + \frac{e^6}{4320}\operatorname{Tr}(F^2)\operatorname{Tr}(F^4) + \frac{e^6}{5670}\operatorname{Tr}(F^6). \quad (15)$$

we note here that the trace $\operatorname{Tr}(F^{2n})$ can be always written in terms of powers of the electromagnetic invariants $\mathcal{F}$ and $\mathcal{G}$. For example, $\operatorname{Tr}(F^2) = -F_{\mu\nu}F^{\mu\nu} = -4\mathcal{F}$. Now, inserting expansions (12), (3) and (10) in Eq. (11) we find

$$O_0 + O_1 + (-is) + \frac{O_2}{2}(-is)^2 \ldots = (1 + U_2(-is)^2 + \ldots) \cdot (\bar{O}_0 + \bar{O}_1(-is) + \frac{\bar{O}_2}{2}(-is)^2 + \ldots) \quad (16)$$

and equating order by order we arrive to $\bar{O}_0 = 1$, $\bar{O}_1 = 0$,

$$\bar{O}_2 = O_2 - 2U_2 = 0, \quad (17)$$
$$\bar{O}_3 = O_3, \quad (18)$$
$$\bar{O}_4 = O_4 - 4!\,U_4, \quad (19)$$
$$\bar{O}_5 = O_4 - 20\,U_2 O_3, \quad (20)$$
$$\bar{O}_6 = O_6 - 6!\,U_6 - 30\,U_2\bar{O}_4. \quad (21)$$

Finally, substituting the values of the coefficients U_n and O_n in the previous equations we arrive at the explicit values of $\bar{O}_n$, which can be found in Appendix B. It is easy to see that our conjecture is satisfied. Comparing the coefficients O_n (Appendix A) with $\bar{O}_n$, one sees that all terms going with $\operatorname{Tr}(F^{2n})$ [or, equivalently, with $\mathcal{F}$ or $\mathcal{G}$] have disappeared.

2.1. *Some comments about the proper-time series expansion*

The asymptotic expansion (proper-time series expansion) that we are using here [see Eqs. (3) and (5)] is an expansion that group terms with the same mass dimension (remember that the coefficients O_n and a_n have mass dimension $2n$). This expansion is closely related with the adiabatic expansion of the scalar field modes, widely used in cosmology [see Ref.[26] for the equivalence in curved spacetime, and[27] for the adiabatic counterpart of the R-summed expansion given in (8)]. In its normal form, it is commonly used to renormalize physical quantities. It is important to recall that this expansion is not a derivative expansion (i.e., an expansion that groups terms with the same number of derivatives; see, for example, Ref.[28]). For a detailed explanation of the differences between both expansions see Ref.[3].

3. Main consequences

Our factorization, allow us to predict or reproduce some interesting physical consequences. First, it is possible to find some exactly solvable electromagnetic backgrounds. For electric and magnetic fields pointing in the $\hat{z}$ direction that depend arbitrarily on the light-cone coordinate $x^+ = (t+z)$, we find that $\bar{O}_0 = 1$ and $\bar{O}_{n>0} = 0$. Therefore, the exact form of the unrenormalized effective Lagrangian should be (in agreement with Refs.[29–31])

$$\mathcal{L}^{(1)}_{scalar} = -\frac{1}{16\pi^2} \int_0^\infty \frac{ds}{s^3} e^{-im^2 s} \frac{e^2 s^2 E(x^+) B(x^+)}{\sinh es E(x^+) \sin es B(x^+)}. \qquad (22)$$

For a single electromagnetic plane wave, $\mathcal{F}(x) = 0$ and $\mathcal{G}(x) = 0$, therefore, according to our conjecture, the one-loop effective action trivially vanishes, in agreement with the result obtained in Ref.[5] by other methods. Second, our results seem to be consistent in presence of gravity. [b]. In this case, it is possible to perform a double factorization (the exponential $R(x)$ factorization is ensured[23]),

$$g(x,is) = e^{-is(\xi - \frac{1}{6})R(x)} \left[\det \left(\frac{esF(x)}{\sinh(esF(x))} \right) \right]^{1/2} \tilde{g}(x;is). \qquad (23)$$

Finally, the conjecture allows us to make some general predictions regarding the Schwinger's formula for the pair production rate. The factorization suggests that the poles of the imaginary part of the one-loop effective Lagrangian are located at the same points as in the constant electric field case $\tau_n = n\pi/|eE(x)|$.

4. Summary and conclusions

The one-loop (scalar) QED effective-Lagrangian is, in general, unknown. However, it is possible to obtain an adiabatic expansion of it in terms of the functions $g(x;is)$ defined in (2). We have proposed an alternative adiabatic expansion $\bar{g}(x;is)$, which encapsulates in a global pre-factor all its dependence on the electromagnetic invariants $\mathcal{F}(x)$ and $\mathcal{G}(x)$. The form of the non-perturbative factor involved in this partial resummation is just the Heisenberg-Euler Lagrangian for QED, but with the electric and magnetic fields depending arbitrarily on spacetime coordinates. The new expansion does not contain terms that vanish when $\mathcal{F}(x)$ and $\mathcal{G}(x)$ are replaced by zero. This factorization allows us to obtain some exact solutions and seems to be consistent in presence of gravity. In this contribution, we have focused on the scalar case, but our conjecture is also valid for the spin-$\frac{1}{2}$ case. We expect our results to be consistent for non-abelian gauge backgrounds. Most of the computations in this paper have been done with the help of the xAct package of the *Mathematica Software*.[34] This work was supported in part by Spanish Ministerio de Economia, Industria y Competitividad Grants No. FIS2017-84440-C2-1-P(MINECO/FEDER, EU), No. FIS2017-91161-EXP and the project PROMETEO/2020/079 (Generalitat Valenciana). S. P. is supported by a Ph.D. fellowship, Grant No. FPU16/05287.

---

[b]For $\nabla_\rho F^{\mu\nu} = 0$ the factorization of the Euler-Heisenberg Lagrangian was found in Refs.[32,33].

Appendix A

Here we give the coefficients O_n of the original expansion $g(x;is)$. $O_0 = 1$,

$$O_1 = 0, \quad O_2 = -\frac{\mathbf{e^2}}{\mathbf{6}}\mathbf{F}_{\kappa\lambda}\mathbf{F}^{\kappa\lambda}, \quad O_3 = -\frac{e^2}{20}\partial_\mu F_{\kappa\lambda}\partial^\mu F^{\kappa\lambda}, \tag{A.1}$$

$$O_4 = \frac{\mathbf{e^4}}{\mathbf{15}}\mathbf{F}_\kappa{}^\mu \mathbf{F}^{\kappa\lambda}\mathbf{F}_\lambda{}^\nu\mathbf{F}_{\mu\nu} + \frac{\mathbf{e^4}}{\mathbf{12}}\mathbf{F}_{\kappa\lambda}\mathbf{F}^{\kappa\lambda}\mathbf{F}_{\mu\nu}\mathbf{F}^{\mu\nu}$$
$$-\frac{e^2}{70}\partial_\nu\partial_\mu F_{\kappa\lambda}\partial^\nu\partial^\mu F^{\kappa\lambda}, \tag{A.2}$$

$$O_5 = \frac{2e^4}{7}F^{\kappa\lambda}F^{\mu\nu}\partial_\lambda F_{\nu\rho}\partial_\mu F_\kappa{}^\rho - \frac{4e^4}{63}F_\kappa{}^\mu F^{\kappa\lambda}\partial_\lambda F^{\nu\rho}\partial_\mu F_{\nu\rho}$$
$$-\frac{e^4}{9}F_\kappa{}^\mu F^{\kappa\lambda}F^{\nu\rho}\partial_\mu\partial_\lambda F_{\nu\rho} - \frac{16e^4}{63}F^{\kappa\lambda}F^{\mu\nu}\partial_\mu F_\kappa{}^\rho\partial_\nu F_{\lambda\rho}$$
$$+\frac{5e^4}{18}F^{\kappa\lambda}F^{\mu\nu}\partial_\rho F_{\mu\nu}\partial^\rho F_{\kappa\lambda} + \frac{34e^4}{189}F^{\kappa\lambda}F^{\mu\nu}\partial_\nu F_{\lambda\rho}\partial^\rho F_{\kappa\mu}$$
$$+\frac{25e^4}{189}F^{\kappa\lambda}F^{\mu\nu}\partial_\rho F_{\lambda\nu}\partial^\rho F_{\kappa\mu} + \frac{4e^4}{21}F_\kappa{}^\mu F^{\kappa\lambda}\partial_\rho F_{\mu\nu}\partial^\rho F_\lambda{}^\nu$$
$$+\frac{\mathbf{e^4}}{\mathbf{12}}\mathbf{F}_{\kappa\lambda}\mathbf{F}^{\kappa\lambda}\partial_\rho\mathbf{F}_{\mu\nu}\partial^\rho \mathbf{F}^{\mu\nu} - \frac{e^2}{252}\partial_\rho\partial_\nu\partial_\mu F_{\kappa\lambda}\partial^\rho\partial^\nu\partial^\mu F^{\kappa\lambda}, \tag{A.3}$$

$$O_6 = -\frac{\mathbf{8}}{\mathbf{63}}\mathbf{F}_\kappa{}^\mu \mathbf{F}^{\kappa\lambda}\mathbf{F}_\lambda{}^\nu\mathbf{F}_\mu{}^\rho\mathbf{F}_\nu{}^\sigma\mathbf{F}_{\rho\sigma} - \frac{\mathbf{1}}{\mathbf{6}}\mathbf{F}_{\kappa\lambda}\mathbf{F}^{\kappa\lambda}\mathbf{F}_\mu{}^\rho\mathbf{F}^{\mu\nu}\mathbf{F}_\nu{}^\sigma\mathbf{F}_{\rho\sigma}$$
$$-\frac{\mathbf{5}}{\mathbf{72}}\mathbf{F}_{\kappa\lambda}\mathbf{F}^{\kappa\lambda}\mathbf{F}_{\mu\nu}\mathbf{F}^{\mu\nu}\mathbf{F}_{\rho\sigma}\mathbf{F}^{\rho\sigma} + \frac{397}{3465}F^{\kappa\lambda}\partial_\kappa F^{\mu\nu}\partial_\mu F^{\rho\sigma}\partial_\nu\partial_\lambda F_{\rho\sigma}$$
$$+\frac{1}{63}F^{\kappa\lambda}F^{\mu\nu}\partial_\mu\partial_\kappa F^{\rho\sigma}\partial_\nu\partial_\lambda F_{\rho\sigma} + \frac{187}{1260}\partial_\mu F^{\rho\sigma}\partial^\mu F^{\kappa\lambda}\partial_\nu F_{\rho\sigma}\partial^\nu F_{\kappa\lambda}$$
$$-\frac{1079}{3465}F^{\kappa\lambda}\partial_\mu\partial_\lambda F_{\rho\sigma}\partial_\nu F^{\rho\sigma}\partial^\nu F_\kappa{}^\mu - \frac{43}{3465}F^{\kappa\lambda}\partial_\mu F^{\rho\sigma}\partial_\nu\partial_\lambda F_{\rho\sigma}\partial^\nu F_\kappa{}^\mu$$
$$-\frac{4}{35}F^{\kappa\lambda}\partial_\lambda F^{\rho\sigma}\partial_\nu\partial_\mu F_{\rho\sigma}\partial^\nu F_\kappa{}^\mu - \frac{101}{3465}\partial_\lambda F_{\rho\sigma}\partial^\mu F^{\kappa\lambda}\partial_\nu F_\mu{}^\sigma\partial^\rho F_\kappa{}^\nu$$
$$+\frac{43}{3465}\partial_\mu F_{\nu\sigma}\partial^\mu F^{\kappa\lambda}\partial_\rho F_\lambda{}^\sigma\partial^\rho F_\kappa{}^\nu - \frac{2}{21}F^{\kappa\lambda}\partial_\rho F_\mu{}^\sigma\partial^\rho F^{\mu\nu}\partial_\sigma\partial_\nu F_{\kappa\lambda}$$
$$-\frac{4}{21}F^{\kappa\lambda}F^{\mu\nu}\partial_\sigma\partial_\rho\partial_\lambda F_{\mu\nu}\partial^\sigma F_\kappa{}^\rho + \frac{1486}{3465}\partial_\mu F_{\nu\sigma}\partial^\mu F^{\kappa\lambda}\partial^\rho F_\kappa{}^\nu\partial^\sigma F_{\lambda\rho}$$
$$+\frac{428}{1155}\partial^\mu F^{\kappa\lambda}\partial^\rho F_\kappa{}^\nu\partial_\sigma F_{\mu\nu}\partial^\sigma F_{\lambda\rho} + \frac{3}{35}\partial_\mu F_\kappa{}^\nu\partial^\mu F^{\kappa\lambda}\partial_\sigma F_{\nu\rho}\partial^\sigma F_\lambda{}^\rho$$
$$+\frac{6}{35}F^{\kappa\lambda}\partial^\nu F_\kappa{}^\mu\partial_\sigma\partial_\nu F_{\mu\rho}\partial^\sigma F_\lambda{}^\rho + \frac{13}{42}F^{\kappa\lambda}\partial^\rho F^{\mu\nu}\partial_\sigma\partial_\rho F_{\kappa\lambda}\partial^\sigma F_{\mu\nu}$$
$$-\frac{2}{35}\partial^\mu F^{\kappa\lambda}\partial^\nu F_{\kappa\lambda}\partial_\sigma F_{\nu\rho}\partial^\sigma F_\mu{}^\rho + \frac{64}{231}F^{\kappa\lambda}\partial_\kappa F^{\mu\nu}\partial_\sigma\partial_\lambda F_{\nu\rho}\partial^\sigma F_\mu{}^\rho$$
$$+\frac{118}{693}F^{\kappa\lambda}\partial^\nu F_\kappa{}^\mu\partial_\sigma\partial_\lambda F_{\nu\rho}\partial^\sigma F_\mu{}^\rho - \frac{302}{3465}F^{\kappa\lambda}\partial_\kappa F^{\mu\nu}\partial_\sigma\partial_\nu F_{\lambda\rho}\partial^\sigma F_\mu{}^\rho$$
$$+\frac{1388}{3465}F^{\kappa\lambda}\partial^\nu F_\kappa{}^\mu\partial_\sigma\partial_\nu F_{\lambda\rho}\partial^\sigma F_\mu{}^\rho + \frac{344}{1155}F^{\kappa\lambda}\partial_\kappa F^{\mu\nu}\partial_\sigma\partial_\rho F_{\lambda\nu}\partial^\sigma F_\mu{}^\rho$$
$$+\frac{398}{3465}F^{\kappa\lambda}\partial^\nu F_\kappa{}^\mu\partial_\sigma\partial_\rho F_{\lambda\nu}\partial^\sigma F_\mu{}^\rho - \frac{62}{165}F^{\kappa\lambda}\partial^\nu F_\kappa{}^\mu\partial_\sigma\partial_\lambda F_{\mu\rho}\partial^\sigma F_\nu{}^\rho$$
$$+\frac{76}{693}F^{\kappa\lambda}\partial^\nu F_\kappa{}^\mu\partial_\sigma\partial_\mu F_{\lambda\rho}\partial^\sigma F_\nu{}^\rho - \frac{326}{1155}F^{\kappa\lambda}\partial^\nu F_\kappa{}^\mu\partial_\sigma\partial_\rho F_{\lambda\mu}\partial^\sigma F_\nu{}^\rho$$
$$+\frac{1}{40}\partial_\mu F_{\kappa\lambda}\partial^\mu F^{\kappa\lambda}\partial_\sigma F_{\nu\rho}\partial^\sigma F^{\nu\rho} + \frac{1}{3}F^{\kappa\lambda}\partial^\mu F_{\kappa\lambda}\partial_\sigma\partial_\mu F_{\nu\rho}\partial^\sigma F^{\nu\rho}$$
$$-\frac{1}{15}F_\kappa{}^\mu F^{\kappa\lambda}\partial_\sigma\partial_\mu\partial_\lambda F_{\nu\rho}\partial^\sigma F^{\nu\rho} - \frac{2}{105}F_\kappa{}^\mu F^{\kappa\lambda}\partial_\sigma\partial_\mu F_{\nu\rho}\partial^\sigma\partial_\lambda F^{\nu\rho}$$
$$+\frac{43}{231}F^{\kappa\lambda}F^{\mu\nu}\partial_\sigma\partial_\lambda F_{\nu\rho}\partial^\sigma\partial_\mu F_\kappa{}^\rho - \frac{43}{231}F^{\kappa\lambda}F^{\mu\nu}\partial_\sigma\partial_\nu F_{\lambda\rho}\partial^\sigma\partial_\mu F_\kappa{}^\rho$$
$$+\frac{1}{6}F^{\kappa\lambda}F^{\mu\nu}\partial_\sigma\partial_\rho F_{\mu\nu}\partial^\sigma\partial^\rho F_{\kappa\lambda} + \frac{103}{693}F^{\kappa\lambda}F^{\mu\nu}\partial_\sigma\partial_\nu F_{\lambda\rho}\partial^\sigma\partial^\rho F_{\kappa\mu}$$
$$+\frac{46}{693}F^{\kappa\lambda}F^{\mu\nu}\partial_\sigma\partial_\rho F_{\lambda\nu}\partial^\sigma\partial^\rho F_{\kappa\mu} + \frac{2}{21}F_\kappa{}^\mu F^{\kappa\lambda}\partial_\sigma\partial_\rho F_{\mu\nu}\partial^\sigma\partial^\rho F_\lambda{}^\nu$$
$$+\frac{\mathbf{1}}{\mathbf{28}}\mathbf{F}_{\kappa\lambda}\mathbf{F}^{\kappa\lambda}\partial_\sigma\partial_\rho\mathbf{F}_{\mu\nu}\partial^\sigma\partial^\rho\mathbf{F}^{\mu\nu} - \frac{1}{924}\partial_\sigma\partial_\rho\partial_\nu\partial_\mu F_{\kappa\lambda}\partial^\sigma\partial^\rho\partial^\nu\partial^\mu F^{\kappa\lambda}. \tag{A.4}$$

The terms that have to disappear when computing the modified expansion $\bar{g}(x;is)$ for our conjecture to be satisfied appeared highlighted.

Appendix B

Here we give the coefficients $\bar{O}_n$ of the $(\mathcal{F}, \mathcal{G})$–summed expansion $\bar{g}(x; is)$, $\bar{O}_0 = 1$,

$$\bar{O}_1 = 0, \quad \bar{O}_2 = 0, \quad \bar{O}_3 = -\tfrac{e^2}{20} \partial_\mu F_{\kappa\lambda} \partial^\mu F^{\kappa\lambda}, \tag{B.1}$$

$$\bar{O}_4 = -\tfrac{e^2}{70} \partial_\nu \partial_\mu F_{\kappa\lambda} \partial^\nu \partial^\mu F^{\kappa\lambda}, \tag{B.2}$$

$$\begin{aligned}
\bar{O}_5 =\ & \tfrac{2e^4}{7} F^{\kappa\lambda} F^{\mu\nu} \partial_\lambda F_{\nu\rho} \partial_\mu F_\kappa{}^\rho - \tfrac{4e^4}{63} F_\kappa{}^\mu F^{\kappa\lambda} \partial_\lambda F^{\nu\rho} \partial_\mu F_{\nu\rho} \\
& -\tfrac{e^4}{9} F_\kappa{}^\mu F^{\kappa\lambda} F^{\nu\rho} \partial_\mu \partial_\lambda F_{\nu\rho} - \tfrac{16e^4}{63} F^{\kappa\lambda} F^{\mu\nu} \partial_\mu F_\kappa{}^\rho \partial_\nu F_{\lambda\rho} \\
& +\tfrac{5e^4}{18} F^{\kappa\lambda} F^{\mu\nu} \partial_\rho F_{\mu\nu} \partial^\rho F_{\kappa\lambda} + \tfrac{34e^4}{189} F^{\kappa\lambda} F^{\mu\nu} \partial_\nu F_{\lambda\rho} \partial^\rho F_{\kappa\mu} \\
& +\tfrac{25e^4}{189} F^{\kappa\lambda} F^{\mu\nu} \partial_\rho F_{\lambda\nu} \partial^\rho F_{\kappa\mu} + \tfrac{4e^4}{21} F_\kappa{}^\mu F^{\kappa\lambda} \partial_\rho F_{\mu\nu} \partial^\rho F_\lambda{}^\nu \\
& -\tfrac{e^2}{252} \partial_\rho \partial_\nu \partial_\mu F_{\kappa\lambda} \partial^\rho \partial^\nu \partial^\mu F^{\kappa\lambda},
\end{aligned} \tag{B.3}$$

$$\begin{aligned}
\bar{O}_6 =\ & +\tfrac{397}{3465} F^{\kappa\lambda} \partial_\kappa F^{\mu\nu} \partial_\mu F^{\rho\sigma} \partial_\nu \partial_\lambda F_{\rho\sigma} + \tfrac{1}{63} F^{\kappa\lambda} F^{\mu\nu} \partial_\mu \partial_\kappa F^{\rho\sigma} \partial_\nu \partial_\lambda F_{\rho\sigma} \\
& +\tfrac{187}{1260} \partial_\mu F^{\rho\sigma} \partial^\mu F^{\kappa\lambda} \partial_\nu F_{\rho\sigma} \partial^\nu F_{\kappa\lambda} - \tfrac{1079}{3465} F^{\kappa\lambda} \partial_\mu \partial_\lambda F_{\rho\sigma} \partial_\nu F^{\rho\sigma} \partial^\nu F_\kappa{}^\mu \\
& -\tfrac{43}{3465} F^{\kappa\lambda} \partial_\mu F^{\rho\sigma} \partial_\nu \partial_\lambda F_{\rho\sigma} \partial^\nu F_\kappa{}^\mu - \tfrac{4}{35} F^{\kappa\lambda} \partial_\lambda F^{\rho\sigma} \partial_\nu \partial_\mu F_{\rho\sigma} \partial^\nu F_\kappa{}^\mu \\
& -\tfrac{101}{3465} \partial_\lambda F_{\rho\sigma} \partial^\mu F^{\kappa\lambda} \partial_\nu F_\mu{}^\sigma \partial^\rho F_\kappa{}^\nu + \tfrac{43}{3465} \partial_\mu F_{\nu\sigma} \partial^\mu F^{\kappa\lambda} \partial_\rho F_\lambda{}^\sigma \partial^\rho F_\kappa{}^\nu \\
& -\tfrac{2}{21} F^{\kappa\lambda} \partial_\rho F_\mu{}^\sigma \partial^\rho F^{\mu\nu} \partial_\sigma \partial_\nu F_{\kappa\lambda} \tfrac{4}{21} F^{\kappa\lambda} F^{\mu\nu} \partial_\sigma \partial_\rho \partial_\lambda F_{\mu\nu} \partial^\sigma F_\kappa{}^\rho \\
& +\tfrac{1486}{3465} \partial_\mu F_{\nu\sigma} \partial^\mu F^{\kappa\lambda} \partial^\rho F_\kappa{}^\nu \partial^\sigma F_{\lambda\rho} + \tfrac{428}{1155} \partial^\mu F^{\kappa\lambda} \partial^\rho F_\kappa{}^\nu \partial_\sigma F_{\mu\nu} \partial^\sigma F_{\lambda\rho} \\
& +\tfrac{3}{35} \partial_\mu F_\kappa{}^\nu \partial^\mu F^{\kappa\lambda} \partial_\sigma F_{\nu\rho} \partial^\sigma F_\lambda{}^\rho + \tfrac{6}{35} F^{\kappa\lambda} \partial^\nu F_\kappa{}^\mu \partial_\sigma \partial_\nu F_{\mu\rho} \partial^\sigma F_\lambda{}^\rho \\
& +\tfrac{13}{42} F^{\kappa\lambda} \partial^\rho F^{\mu\nu} \partial_\sigma \partial_\rho F_{\kappa\lambda} \partial^\sigma F_{\mu\nu} - \tfrac{2}{35} \partial^\mu F^{\kappa\lambda} \partial^\nu F_{\kappa\lambda} \partial_\sigma F_{\nu\rho} \partial^\sigma F_\mu{}^\rho \\
& +\tfrac{64}{231} F^{\kappa\lambda} \partial_\kappa F^{\mu\nu} \partial_\sigma \partial_\lambda F_{\nu\rho} \partial^\sigma F_\mu{}^\rho + \tfrac{118}{693} F^{\kappa\lambda} \partial^\nu F_\kappa{}^\mu \partial_\sigma \partial_\lambda F_{\nu\rho} \partial^\sigma F_\mu{}^\rho \\
& -\tfrac{302}{3465} F^{\kappa\lambda} \partial_\kappa F^{\mu\nu} \partial_\sigma \partial_\nu F_{\lambda\rho} \partial^\sigma F_\mu{}^\rho + \tfrac{1388}{3465} F^{\kappa\lambda} \partial^\nu F_\kappa{}^\mu \partial_\sigma \partial_\nu F_{\lambda\rho} \partial^\sigma F_\mu{}^\rho \\
& +\tfrac{344}{1155} F^{\kappa\lambda} \partial_\kappa F^{\mu\nu} \partial_\sigma \partial_\rho F_{\lambda\nu} \partial^\sigma F_\mu{}^\rho + \tfrac{398}{3465} F^{\kappa\lambda} \partial^\nu F_\kappa{}^\mu \partial_\sigma \partial_\rho F_{\lambda\nu} \partial^\sigma F_\mu{}^\rho \\
& -\tfrac{62}{165} F^{\kappa\lambda} \partial^\nu F_\kappa{}^\mu \partial_\sigma \partial_\lambda F_{\mu\rho} \partial^\sigma F_\nu{}^\rho + \tfrac{76}{693} F^{\kappa\lambda} \partial^\nu F_\kappa{}^\mu \partial_\sigma \partial_\mu F_{\lambda\rho} \partial^\sigma F_\nu{}^\rho \\
& -\tfrac{326}{1155} F^{\kappa\lambda} \partial^\nu F_\kappa{}^\mu \partial_\sigma \partial_\rho F_{\lambda\mu} \partial^\sigma F_\nu{}^\rho + \tfrac{1}{40} \partial_\mu F_{\kappa\lambda} \partial^\mu F^{\kappa\lambda} \partial_\sigma F_{\nu\rho} \partial^\sigma F^{\nu\rho} \\
& +\tfrac{1}{3} F^{\kappa\lambda} \partial^\mu F_{\kappa\lambda} \partial_\sigma \partial_\mu F_{\nu\rho} \partial^\sigma F^{\nu\rho} - \tfrac{1}{15} F_\kappa{}^\mu F^{\kappa\lambda} \partial_\sigma \partial_\mu \partial_\lambda F_{\nu\rho} \partial^\sigma F^{\nu\rho} \\
& -\tfrac{2}{105} F_\kappa{}^\mu F^{\kappa\lambda} \partial_\sigma \partial_\mu F_{\nu\rho} \partial^\sigma \partial_\lambda F^{\nu\rho} + \tfrac{43}{231} F^{\kappa\lambda} F^{\mu\nu} \partial_\sigma \partial_\lambda F_{\nu\rho} \partial^\sigma \partial_\mu F_\kappa{}^\rho \\
& -\tfrac{43}{231} F^{\kappa\lambda} F^{\mu\nu} \partial_\sigma \partial_\nu F_{\lambda\rho} \partial^\sigma \partial_\mu F_\kappa{}^\rho + \tfrac{1}{6} F^{\kappa\lambda} F^{\mu\nu} \partial_\sigma \partial_\rho F_{\mu\nu} \partial^\sigma \partial^\rho F_{\kappa\lambda} \\
& +\tfrac{103}{693} F^{\kappa\lambda} F^{\mu\nu} \partial_\sigma \partial_\nu F_{\lambda\rho} \partial^\sigma \partial^\rho F_{\kappa\mu} + \tfrac{46}{693} F^{\kappa\lambda} F^{\mu\nu} \partial_\sigma \partial_\rho F_{\lambda\nu} \partial^\sigma \partial^\rho F_{\kappa\mu} \\
& +\tfrac{2}{21} F_\kappa{}^\mu F^{\kappa\lambda} \partial_\sigma \partial_\rho F_{\mu\nu} \partial^\sigma \partial^\rho F_\lambda{}^\nu - \tfrac{1}{924} \partial_\sigma \partial_\rho \partial_\nu \partial_\mu F_{\kappa\lambda} \partial^\sigma \partial^\rho \partial^\nu \partial^\mu F^{\kappa\lambda}.
\end{aligned} \tag{B.4}$$

References

1. S. Pla, *New partial resummation of the QED effective action*, contribution to the Marcel Grossman Meeting (MG16), https://indico.icranet.org/event/1/contributions/979/
2. J. Navarro-Salas and S. Pla, Phys. Rev. D **103**, L081702 (2021).
3. G. D. Dunne, in *From Fields to Strings: Circumnavigating Theoretical Physics*, edited by M. Shifman, A. Vainshtein and J. Wheater (World Scientific, 2005), pp. 445-522; arXiv:hep-th/0406216.
4. M. D. Schwartz, *Quantum Field Theory and the Standard Model* (Cambridge University Press, Cambridge, England, 2014).
5. J. Schwinger, Phys. Rev. **82**, 664 (1951).
6. G. V. Dunne, Int. J. Mod. Phys. A **27**, 1260004 (2012); F. Karbstein, *Particles* **3**, 39 (2020).
7. W. Heisenberg and H. Euler, Z. Phys. **98**, 714 (1936). English translation: arXiv:physics/0605038.
8. V. Weisskopf, The electrodynamics of the vacuum based on the quantum theory of the electron, Kong. Dans. Vid. Selsk. Math-fys. Medd. **14N6** (1936).
9. V. S. Vanyashin and M. V. Terent'ev, Sov. Phys. JETP **21**, 375 (1965).
10. L. Parker and D. J. Toms, *Quantum Field Theory in Curved Spacetime: Quantized Fields and Gravity* (Cambridge University Press, Cambridge, England, 2009).
11. D. Fliegner, P. Haberl, M. G. Schmidt and C. Schubert, Ann. Phys. (N.Y.) **264**, 51 (1998).
12. D. Fliegner, M. G. Schmidt and C. Schubert, Nucl. Instrum. Methods Phys. Res., Sect. A **389**, 374 (1997).
13. D. Fliegner, M. G. Schmidt and C. Schubert, Z. Phys. C **64**, 111 (1994).
14. M. Reuter, M. G. Schmidt, C. Schubert, Ann. Phys. (N.Y.) **259**, 313 (1997).
15. M. G. Schmidt and C. Schubert, Phys. Lett. B **318**, 438 (1993).
16. Z. Bern and D. A. Kosower, Phys. Rev. Lett. **66**, 1669 (1991).
17. U. Müller, *New Computing Techniques in Physics Research IV* (World Scientific, Singapore, 1996), p. 193; DESY-96-154, arXiv:hep-th/9701124.
18. B. S. DeWitt, *Dynamical Theory of Groups and Fields* (Gordon and Breach, New York, 1965).
19. D. V. Vassilevich, Phys. Rep. **388**, 279 (2003).
20. P. B. Gilkey, J. Differ. Geom. **10**, 601 (1975).
21. J.D. Bekenstein and L. Parker, Phys. Rev. D **23**, 2850 (1981).
22. L. Parker and D. J. Toms, Phys. Rev. D **31**, 953 (1985).
23. I. Jack and L. Parker, Phys. Rev. D **31**, 2439 (1985).
24. L. Parker and A. Raval, Phys. Rev. D **60**, 063512 (1999); Phys. Rev. D **62**, 083503 (2000); L. Parker and D. A. T. Vanzella, Phys. Rev. D **69**, 104009 (2004); R.R. Caldwell, W. Komp, L. Parker, and D.A.T. Wanzella, Phys. Rev. D **73**, 023513 (2006); E. Di Valentino, E. V. Linder, and A. Melchiorri, Phys. Rev. D **97**, 043528 (2018); T. Markkanen, S. Nurmi, A. Rajantie, and S. Stopyr, J. High Energy Phys. 06 (2018) 040; E. V. Castro, A. Flachi, P. Ribeiro, and V. Vitagliano, Phys. Rev. Lett. **121**, 221601 (2018); O. Czerwinska, Z. Lalak, and L. Nakonieczny, J. High Energy Phys. 11 (2015) 207.
25. E. Calzetta, I. Jack, and L. Parker, Phys. Rev. Lett. **55**, 1241 (1985).
26. A. del Rio and J. Navarro-Salas, Phys. Rev. D **91**, 064031 (2015); P. Beltrán-Palau, A. del Río, S. Nadal-Gisbert and J. Navarro-Salas, Phys. Rev. D **103**, 105002 (2021).
27. A. Ferreiro, J. Navarro-Salas and S. Pla, Phys. Rev. D **101** 105011 (2020).

28. V. P. Gusynin and I. A. Shovkovy, J. Math. Phys. (N.Y.) **40**, 5406 (1999).
29. H. M. Fried and R. P. Woodard, Phys. Lett. B **524**, 233 (2002).
30. T. N. Tomaras, N. C. Tsamis, and R. P. Woodard, Phys. Rev. D **62**, 125005 (2000).
31. A. Ilderton, J. High Energy Phys. 09 (2014) 166.
32. I.G. Avramidi and G. Fucci, Commun. Math. Phys. **291**, 543 (2009).
33. G. Fucci and I.G. Avramidi, On the Gravitationally Induced Schwinger Mechanism, in *9th Conference on Quantum Field Theory under the Influence of External Conditions (QFEXT 09)*, pp. 485-491 [arXiv:0911.1099].
34. J. M. Martín-García, xAct: Efficient tensor computer algebra for the Wolfram language, https://www.xAct.es.

Can a detector detect soft photons

Sanved Kolekar

Indian Institute of Astrophysics,
2nd Block, Koramangala, Bangalore 560034, India
E-mail: sanved.kolekar@iiap.res.in
www.iiap.res.in

Jorma Louko

School of Mathematical Sciences, University of Nottingham,
Nottingham NG7 2RD, UK
E-mail: jorma.louko@nottingham.ac.uk

We explore the question whether the presence of soft photons in a system can have direct or indirect consequences in the outcome of suitably defined quantum processes involving the system. We consider an local quantum detector with dual energy levels and coupled to the background gauge invariant charged scalar field in a flat spacetime. The de-excitation rate for downward transitions for such a system on an inertial trajectory is found to depend on the soft charges corresponding to the radial component of the electric field dressing chosen at the asymptotic boundary. While the excitation rate for upward transitions still vanishes as expected. The implications are discussed.

Keywords: Soft photon, gauge invariance, detector

1. Introduction

The BMS symmetries[1] of asymptotically flat spacetimes found by Bondi, Metzner and Sachs in 1962; the gravitational memory effect[2] first proposed by Zeldovich and Polnarev in 1974 and the Weinberg's soft theorems are related to each other through the so called Universal triad relations.[5–9] When acted upon by a BMS transformation corresponding to a BMS diffeomorphism vector at the asymptotic flat boundary or equivalently due to the passage of a gravitational wave at the asymptotic flat boundary, the vacuum state at the boundary - although classically same before and after the transformation, differs quantum mechanically in the content of soft particles and hence the soft charges defined at the boundary. Analogous to the gravitational case, there is a universal triad for the electromagnetic case as well. The electromagnetic memory effect, the $U(1)$ large gauge transformations and the Weinberg's soft photon theorem are also related to one other through analogous type connections. The significance of these universal triad relations were realised by Hawking, Perry and Strominger[3,4] to conjecture soft hair for black holes. In a recent work, a quantum version of the gravitational memory effect was shown to arise due to the BMS symmetries in a Schwarzschild spacetime.[10,11]

In the related context. we explore the question whether the presence of soft photons in a system can have direct or indirect consequences in the outcome of suitably defined quantum processes involving the system.[12] We consider a local quantum system moving on an inertial trajectory in a flat spacetime and linearly couples to a gauge invariant charged scalar field. The gauge invariant form of the field is as defined by Dirac[13] in 1955 to account for the fact that an electric charge is always accompanied by it electric field. We compute the transition rates for such a system when the system is at rest in an inertial frame and the electric field is given a soft photon dressing. Interestingly, we find that the transition rate of the local quantum system shows a de-excitation for downward transitions which depends on the soft charges corresponding to the dressed electric field. This holds true for a wide class of functions that can be chosen for the soft photon dressing of the electric field. We find that the excitation rate for upward transitions of the system vanishes as expected.

2. The local quantum system and the dressing field

We consider a flat spacetime with background electromagnetic and charged scalar fields. We then use the gauge invariant construction of a charged scalar field as defined by Dirac.[13] The 'dressed' field gauge invariant operator is defined by

$$\Phi(x) = e^{iC(x)} \phi(x), \tag{1}$$

where

$$C(x) = \int d^4x'\, f^a(x, x') A_a(x'), \tag{2}$$

Here $A_a(x')$ is the electromagnetic four vector potential and the two-point function $f^a(x, x')$ that specifies the dressing satisfies the four-dimensional Poisson's equation

$$\partial'_a f^a(x, x') = q\, \delta^4(x - x'). \tag{3}$$

Under the gauge transformation, the phase factor $e^{iC(x)}$ transforms as

$$e^{iC(x)} \to e^{iC(x)}\, e^{-iq\Omega(x)}, \tag{4}$$

Thus rendering the $\Phi(x)$ operator to be gauge invariant. The physical significance of the construction in Eq. (1) is that a charge can never be completely described without its electric field and the exponential phase factor in front of $\phi(x)$ precisely does that. The two-point function $f^a(x, x')$ contains the information about the electric field of the charge which can include soft dressing contributions in addition to the usual Coulombic electric field in the rest frame of the charge. We quantize the system by the usual standard procedures and assume the fields $A_a(x)$ and $\phi(x)$ to be free fields at the lowest order in perturbation theory.

The local quantum system is defined to be a pointlike charged two-level system moving on an pointlike trajectory $x^a(\tau)$ and parametrised by the proper time τ.

The monopole moment $m(\tau)$ of the system couples linearly to the gauge invariant scalar field operator Φ with the interaction Hamiltonian being defined as

$$\mathcal{H}_{int} = \lambda \chi(\tau) \left(m(\tau)\Phi(\tau) + m^\dagger(\tau)\Phi^\dagger(\tau) \right), \tag{5}$$

where λ is a real-valued coupling constant, $\Phi(\tau)$ is the pull-back of $\Phi(x)$ to the detector's worldline, and the real-valued switching function χ specifies how the interaction is switched on and off. One can check that the $\mathcal{H}_{int}$ is gauge invariant by construction as well as Hermitian as required for the conservation of total charge.

The time independent response function for the local quantum system on an inertial trajectory $t(\tau) = \tau$ and $\mathbf{x} = 0$ coupled to the Minkowski vacuum state in linear order of perturbation theory is determined to be

$$F(E) = \int_{-\infty}^{\infty} ds \, e^{-iEs} \, W_\phi(s) \, W_A(s), \tag{6}$$

where E is the difference between the energies of excited state and the ground state of the local quantum system. Hence $E > 0$ determines upward transitions, that is excitations, while $E < 0$ determines downward transitions, that is de-excitations. $W_\phi(s)$ is the pull-back of the usual charged scalar field Wightman function

$$W_\phi(x'', x') = \langle 0_\phi | \phi^\dagger(x'') \phi(x') | 0_\phi \rangle = \langle 0_\phi | \phi(x'') \phi^\dagger(x') | 0_\phi \rangle$$
$$= \int \frac{d^3\mathbf{k}}{(2\pi)^3} \frac{1}{2\omega_\mathbf{k}} e^{-i\omega_\mathbf{k}(t''-t')} e^{i\mathbf{k}\cdot(\mathbf{x''}-\mathbf{x'})}, \tag{7}$$

on the detector's worldline and $W_A(s)$ is the pull-back of the electromagnetic dressing two-point function,

$$W_A(x'', x') = \frac{1}{|\alpha|^2 + |\beta|^2} \Big(|\alpha|^2 \langle 0_A | e^{-iC(x'')} e^{iC(x')} | 0_A \rangle$$
$$+ |\beta|^2 \langle 0_A | e^{iC(x'')} e^{-iC(x')} | 0_A \rangle \Big). \tag{8}$$

where α and β are fixed constants pertaining to the excited energy state of the detector more precisely defined in.[12] From the form of response function in Eq. (6), one can note that for the local quantum system considered here with the gauge invariant operator, there is an extra dependence through the $W_A(s)$ factor than in the corresponding expression of the standard detector[15] without the gauge invariance. It is this extra factor which brings the dependence of the soft photons in the de-excitation rate of the system.

3. The result

We choose the electric field dressing to have a $1/r^2$ radial dependence but allow the magnitude to have arbitrary angular dependence as well, which provides the soft photon dressing to the standard Coulombic field. The following form is chosen[14]

$$\tilde{\mathbf{f}}(\mathbf{x}, \mathbf{x'}) = \frac{q}{4\pi\epsilon_0} \frac{g(\theta^{A'})}{|\mathbf{x} - \mathbf{x'}|^3} (\mathbf{x} - \mathbf{x'}), \tag{9}$$

where the function $g(\theta^{A'})$ depends only on the angular coordinates and it satisfies the normalisation condition $\int_0^\pi \int_0^{2\pi} g(\theta^A) \sin\theta \, d\theta \, d\phi = 4\pi$. The soft charge for the dressed electric field in Eq. (9) can be found to be

$$Q_\epsilon = \int d\Omega \, \epsilon(\theta^A) \lim_{r \to \infty} \left(r^2 E^r \right)$$
$$= \int d\Omega \, \epsilon(\theta^A) \, g(\theta^A), \tag{10}$$

where the integral over $d\Omega$ runs over the transverse angular coordinates, $\epsilon(\theta^A)$ is a weight function and E^r is the radial component of the electric field.

The response function for the dressed field in Eq. (9) is found through the expression in Eq. (6) to be[12]

$$F(E) = \frac{(-E)\,\Theta(-E)}{2\pi} \times \frac{e^{-\tilde{Q}\gamma}(-E/\Lambda)^{\tilde{Q}}}{\Gamma(2+\tilde{Q})}. \tag{11}$$

where γ is the Euler-Mascheroni constant, Λ is the ultraviolet cut-off and $\tilde{Q}$ depends on the averaged squares of soft charges through

$$\tilde{Q} := \frac{q^2}{64\pi^4 \epsilon_0^2} \left\{ \langle Q_{\epsilon_1}^2 \rangle + \langle Q_{\epsilon_2}^2 \rangle + \langle Q_{\epsilon_3}^2 \rangle + \langle Q_{\epsilon_4}^2 \rangle \right\}. \tag{12}$$

In the limit of no soft charges, $\tilde{Q} \to 0$, the response function $F(E)$ reduces to the standard expression of the response of a detector without a gauge field coupling.[15]

$$F_{\text{Mink}}(E) = \frac{(-E)\,\Theta(-E)}{2\pi}, \tag{13}$$

In the presence of the soft charges, $\tilde{Q} > 0$, the excitation rate in Eq. (11) vanishes as expected, but the dependence of the de-excitation rate on the energy gap E gets modified through a different power dependence. We conclude that the soft charges, and hence the soft photon dressing to the electric field, do not induce spontaneous excitations in our local quantum system, but they do affect the detector's de-excitation rate. The general features of these results, in particular the vanishing of excitation rate and the dependence of the de-excitation rate on soft charges, were shown to hold for our local quantum system for a wide class of soft photon dressed electric fields defined only by their asymptotic properties.[12]

References

1. H. Bondi, M. G. J. van der Burg and A. Metzner, Proc. Roy. Soc. Lond. **A269**, 21-52 (1962); R. Sachs, Proc. Roy. Soc. Lond. **A270**, 103-126 (1962); R. Sachs, Phys. Rev. **128**, 2851-2864 (1962).
2. B. Zeldovich and A. G. Polnarev, Sov. Astron. Lett. **18**, 17-23 (1974).
3. S. W. Hawking, M. J. Perry and A. Strominger, Phys. Rev. Lett. **116**, 231301 (2016) [arXiv:1601.00921 [hep-th]].
4. S. W. Hawking, M. J. Perry and A. Strominger, JHEP **1705**, 161 (2017) [arXiv:1611.09175 [hep-th]].

5. A. Strominger, JHEP **1407**, 152 (2014) [arXiv:1312.2229].
6. T. He, V. Lysov, P. Mitra and A. Strominger, [arXiv:1401.7026 hep-th].
7. J. Winicour, Class. Quant. Grav. **31**, 205003 (2014) [arXiv:1407.0259].
8. A. Ashtekar, Surveys in Differential Geometry **20**, 99 (2015) [arXiv:1409.1800].
9. A. Strominger and A. Zhiboedov, JHEP **1601**, 086 (2016) [arXiv:1411.5745].
10. S. Kolekar and J. Louko, Phys. Rev. D **96**, 024054 (2017) [arXiv:1703.10619 [hep-th]].
11. S. Kolekar and J. Louko, Phys. Rev. D **97**, 085012 (2018) [arXiv:1709.07355 [hep-th]].
12. S. Kolekar and J. Louko, "Can a local quantum system see soft photons," [arXiv: 2108.04278 [hep-th]].
13. P. A. M. Dirac, Can. J. Phys. **33**, 650 (1955).
14. S. Giddings, Phys. Rev. D **100**, 126001 (2019).
15. N. D. Birrell and P. C. W. Davies, *Quantum Fields in Curved Space* (Cambridge University Press 1982).

Breaking of the adiabatic invariance in the production of particles by strong fields*

P. Beltrán-Palau[†], A. Ferreiro, J. Navarro-Salas and S. Pla

Departamento de Fisica Teorica and IFIC, Centro Mixto Universidad de Valencia-CSIC.
Facultad de Fisica, Universidad de Valencia,
Burjassot-46100, Valencia, Spain
[†]*E-mail: pau.beltran@uv.es*

Particles are spontaneously created from the vacuum by time-varying gravitational or electromagnetic backgrounds. It has been proven that the particle number operator in an isotropically expanding universe is an adiabatic invariant. In this work we show that, in some special cases the expected adiabatic invariance of the particle number breaks down in presence of electromagnetic backgrounds. We also show a close relation between this breaking of the adiabatic invariance and the emergence of the axial anomaly.

Keywords: Particle creation, Schwinger effect, adiabatic invariance, axial anomaly.

1. Introduction

The proper understanding of the particle creation phenomena, via Bogoliubov transformations, was pioneered in the analysis of quantized fields in an isotropically expanding universe.[1–3] A fundamental issue in the study of particle creation in an expanding universe was the adiabatic invariance of the number of created particles. The particle number of a quantized field, in the limit of an infinitely slow and smooth expansion of the universe, does not change with time,[4] even if the quantized field is massless. In other words, the density of created particles by the expanding universe approach zero when the Hubble rate $\dot{a}/a$ is each time negligible even if the final amount of expansion $a(t_{final})/a(t_{initial})$ is large. Moreover, pair production can also take place in time-varying electric backgrounds,[5] and it can be regarded as a very important non-perturbative process in quantum field theory.[6]

The main purpose of this work is to generalize the analysis of the adiabatic invariance of the particle number observable in presence of an electromagnetic background. We find that, for massive fields, adiabatic invariance is, as expected, preserved (for more details see[7]). For slowly varying electromagnetic potentials no quanta is being produced, even if the change in A_μ over a long period is very large. However, in some cases and only for massless fields, the particle number is not an adiabatic invariant. We analyze the problem in detail in a two-dimensional scenario, for both scalar and Dirac fields. The main results can be easily translated to four dimensions. As a by-product of our analysis, we point out a connection between the

---

*Talk given by P. Beltran-Palau at the Sixteenth Marcel Grossmann Meeting (2021).

(anomalous) breaking of the adiabatic invariance of the particle number operator and the emergence of a quantum anomaly in the chiral symmetry. The requirements for the non-conservation of chirality seems to be directly related to those found for the breaking of the adiabaticity in the particle number observable. Concerning the renormalization, it is convenient in this context to use the adiabatic renormalization method[1–3] for a scalar field in a gravitational background, and recently extended for a Dirac field[8,9] and for an electric background.[10–13]

2. Brief introduction to particle creation in an expanding universe

First of all, we will introduce the phenomenon of the spontaneous particle creation in the gravitational context. It was firstly introduced by L. Parker[1,2] in the context of cosmology, and he developed the analysis for a real scalar field in an expanding universe, given by the Friedmann-Lemaitre-Robertson-Walker (FLRW) metric $ds^2 = dt^2 - a^2(t)d\vec{x}^2$. Following the prescription of the Quantum Field Theory in curved spacetimes, the gravitational field can be considered as a classical background and scalar the quantum field is described by the Klein-Gordon equation in curved space-times

$$(g^{\mu\nu}\nabla_\mu\nabla_\nu + m^2 + \xi R)\phi = 0, \tag{1}$$

where ξ is the coupling constant of the field with the gravitational background. We expand the quantum field as

$$\phi(t,\vec{x}) = \int \frac{d^3k}{\sqrt{2(2\pi)^3 a(t)^3}} \left(A_{\vec{k}} h_k(t) e^{i\vec{k}\vec{x}} + A^\dagger_{\vec{k}} h^*_k(t) e^{-i\vec{k}\vec{x}}\right), \tag{2}$$

where $\omega_k = \sqrt{m^2 + (k/a)^2}$ and $A^\dagger_{\vec{k}}$ and $A_{\vec{k}}$ are the usual creation and annihilation operators. Introducing it into the Klein-Gordon equation we obtain the following differential equation for the modes

$$\frac{d^2 h_k}{dt^2} + \Omega_k(t)^2 h_k = 0, \tag{3}$$

where

$$\Omega_k(t)^2 = \omega_k^2 + \left(6\xi - \frac{3}{4}\right)\left(\frac{\dot{a}}{a}\right)^2 + \left(6\xi - \frac{3}{2}\right)\frac{\ddot{a}}{a}. \tag{4}$$

This is the equation of a harmonic oscillator with a time-varying frequency, which depends on the derivatives of the metric. this idea will be usefull to understand the concept of adiabatic invariance.

It is well-known that the notion of particle is not well defined when the universe is in expansion, therefore a useful strategy to analyze the phenomenon is to choose a configuration where the expansion is bounded at early and late times, as shown in Fig. 1. In this case the number of particles is well defined at early and late times, and then we can compare the difference between them.

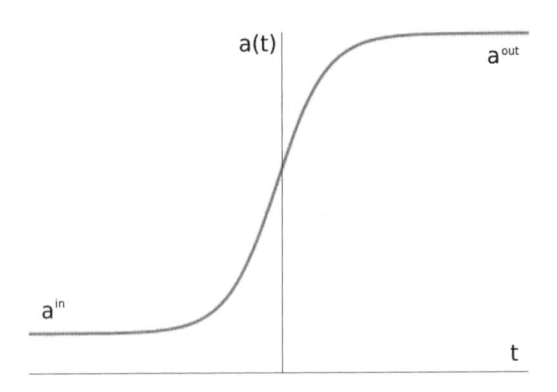

Fig. 1. Scale factor of a bounded expanding universe

We consider that at $t \to -\infty$ the vacuum expectation value of the particle number is zero, i.e., we choose the vacuum state at early times. This is analogous to choose the (normalized) positive frequency solution at early times

$$h_k^{in}(t) = \frac{1}{\sqrt{\omega_{in}}} e^{-i\omega_k^{in} t}, \quad (5)$$

where $\omega_k^{in} = \sqrt{m^2 + (k/a^{in})^2}$. However, the expansion of the universe induces a final state which is a combination of positive and negative frequency solutions

$$h_k^{out}(t) = \frac{1}{\sqrt{\omega_{out}}} \left(\alpha_k e^{-i\omega_k^{out} t} + \beta_k e^{i\omega_k^{out} t} \right), \quad (6)$$

where $\omega_k^{in} = \sqrt{m^2 + (k/a^{out})^2}$ and α_k and β_k are the well-known Bogoliubov coefficients. It can be proven that the vacuum expectation value of the particle density at late times is not null, as a consequence of the presence of the negative frequency solution at late times. It is given by

$$\langle N^{out} \rangle = \frac{1}{(2\pi a^{out})^3} \int d^3k |\beta_k|^2. \quad (7)$$

Therefore, the beta coefficient gives the spectrum of momenta of the spontaneously created particles.

2.1. Adiabatic invariance of the particle number

Let us now introduce the concept of adiabatic invariance. As we have seen above the modes of the field follow an equation of a harmonic oscillator with time-varying frequency. In the model we are considering it would be an oscillator that starts oscillating with an specific frequency ω_k^{in} and decreases slowly its frequency tending asymptotically to ω_k^{out}. The energy of an oscillator of this kind changes in time, and is be given by the expression

$$E_k(t) = \frac{1}{2} \left(|\dot{h}_k(t)|^2 + \Omega_k(t)^2 |h_k(t)|^2 \right). \quad (8)$$

A main property of this kind of oscillators is that the quantity $E_k(t)/\Omega_k(t)$ is an adiabatic invariant, which means that it remains constant in the limit of an infinitely slow variation of the frequency. This limit is known as adiabatic limit. A straightforward calculation gives us the expressions of the initial and final energy in our particular case of the bounded expansion

$$E_k^{in} = \omega_k^{in} \tag{9}$$

$$E_k^{out} = \omega_k^{out}(1 + 2|\beta_k|^2). \tag{10}$$

By the property mentioned above, the difference of quotients $(E^{in}/\omega_k^{in}) - (E^{out}/\omega_k^{out})$ should tend to 0 in the adiabatic limit. One can see easily that this implies necessarily that $|\beta_k|^2 \to 0$ in the adiabatic limit. This means that in the limit of an infinitely slow expansion of the universe no particles would be created by the effect of the gravity, and that's why we say that the particle number is an adiabatic invariant in this context (for more details on this concept see[4]). But there are other scenarios of particle creation in which this adiabatic invariance of the particle number can be broken, as we will see in the following sections.

3. Breaking of the adiabatic invariance by the electric field in 2D

We know that the phenomenon of particle creation is not a particular property of the gravitational field. For instance, a strong electric background can also produce spontaneously pairs particle-antiparticle from the vacuum. This phenomenon is known as the Schwinger effect.[6] A logical question we can formulate is, does the adiabatic invariance of the particle number remains when the particle production is induced by an electric field? To answer this question, we will firstly analyze the 2-dimensional case and then we will extend it to 4 dimensions. Let us consider a spatially homogeneous and time dependent classical electric field $E(t)$ acting in the unique spatial direction. For convencience we choose a particular form of this background, which is a Sauter-type[14] electric pulse given by

$$E(t) = -\frac{\rho A_0}{2} \cosh^{-2}(\rho t), \tag{11}$$

shown in Fig. 2(a). It can also be described by the potential $A_\mu = (0, -A(t))$, with $E(t) = -\dot{A}(t)$, i.e.

$$A(t) = \frac{1}{2} A_0 (\tanh(\rho t) + 1). \tag{12}$$

This potential, analogously to the scale factor in the gravitational case, is bounded at early and late times, as shown explicitly in Fig. 2(b), starting in 0 and tending to a constant value that we denote as A_0. Note that ρ plays the role of a slowness parameter. The variation of the potential vector is slower when ρ decreases, then the adiabatic limit is equivalent to the limit $\rho \to 0$. As a first approach we will consider the 2-dimensional case for simplicity, and in the next section we will extend the results to the 4-dimensional case.

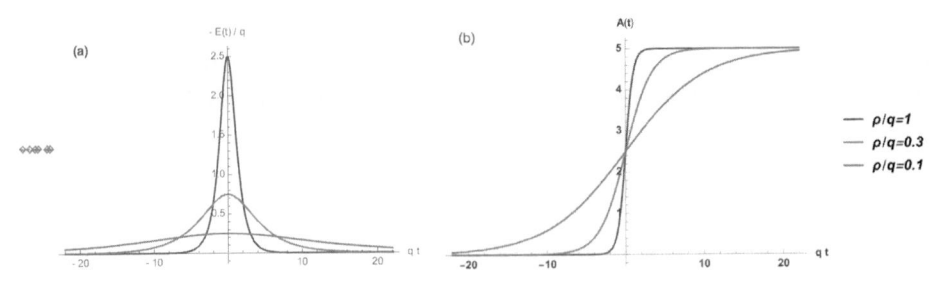

Fig. 2. (a) Sauter-type electric pulse for $A_0 = 5$ and for different values of the slowness parameter ρ. (b) Electric potential associated to the pulse for the same values of ρ. The adiabatic limit corresponds to $\rho \to 0$. The variables have been scaled with q to obtain dimensionless variables.

3.1. Scalar field

We will firstly analyze the case of the creation of scalar particles by an electric field. The Klein-Gordon equation for an electric background is given by

$$(D_\mu D^\mu + m^2)\phi = 0, \tag{13}$$

where $D_\mu \phi = (\partial_\mu + iqA_\mu)\phi$. We expand the field in terms of the usual annihilation and creation operators as

$$\phi(t,x) = \int_{-\infty}^{\infty} \frac{dk}{\sqrt{2(2\pi)}} [A_k e^{ikx} h_k(t) + B_k^\dagger e^{-ikx} h_{-k}^*(t)]. \tag{14}$$

Therefore the differential equation for the modes is given by

$$\ddot{h}_k(t) + \left(m^2 + (k - qA(t))^2\right) h_k(t) = 0. \tag{15}$$

Analogously to the gravitational case we locate the vacuum at early times, which is analogous to choose the positive frequency solution, and solving the equation we obtain at late times a combination of positive and negative frequency solutions, in terms of Bogoliubov coefficients. Finally we obtain the expression for the β_k coefficient which gives the spectrum of momenta of the created scalar particles

$$|\beta_k|^2 = \frac{\cosh\left(\pi \frac{\omega_{out} - \omega_{in}}{\rho}\right) + \cosh\left(\pi \sqrt{(\frac{qA_0}{\rho})^2 - 1}\right)}{2 \sinh\left(\pi \frac{\omega_{in}}{\rho}\right) \sinh\left(\pi \frac{\omega_{out}}{\rho}\right)}, \tag{16}$$

where $\omega_{in} = \sqrt{k^2 + m^2}$ and $\omega_{out} = \sqrt{(k - qA_0)^2 + m^2}$. For conservation of the charge, the same amount of anti-particles will also be created with the same spectrum, but in the opposite direction, i.e., $|\beta_{-k}|^2$.

From this expression one can prove[7] that in the adiabatic limit, $\rho \to 0$, $|\beta_k|^2$ tends to 0 for massive particles, but in the massless case it tends to 1 inside the interval of momenta $k \in (0, qA_0)$, and it is 0 elsewhere. In other words, in the limit of an infinitely slow electric pulse only massless particles would be spontaneously created. Therefore, in the case of massless particles the adiabatic invariance of the particle number is broken.

The density of created particles can be obtained by integrating $|\beta_k|^2$ in all momenta. In Fig. 3 we represent the density of particles for different values of the mass in terms of the slowness parameter ρ. Note that in all the massive cases the production of particles is reduced when the process is more adiabatic, and in the limit when it is infinitely adiabatic ($\rho \to 0$) the number of particles is 0. However, in the massless case the particle density tends to a non-null value, which is given by $\langle N \rangle = \frac{|qA_0|}{\pi}$.

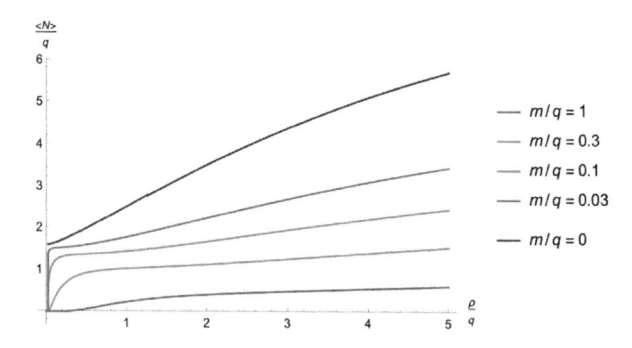

Fig. 3. Density of late-time created scalar particles as a function of the adiabaticity parameter ρ, for $A_0 = 5$ and for different values of the mass.

3.2. Dirac field

A Dirac field coupled to an electric background in 2 dimensions is described by the following Dirac equation

$$(i\gamma^\mu D_\mu - m)\psi = 0, \tag{17}$$

where γ^μ are the Dirac matrices and $D_\mu \equiv \partial_\mu - iqA_\mu$. We expand the field in terms of the creation and annihilation operators and normalized spinors as follows

$$\psi(t,x) = \int_{-\infty}^{\infty} \frac{dk}{\sqrt{2\pi}} \left[B_k e^{ikx} \begin{pmatrix} h_k^I(t) \\ -h_k^{II}(t) \end{pmatrix} + D_k^\dagger e^{-ikx} \begin{pmatrix} h_{-k}^{II*}(t) \\ h_{-k}^{I*}(t) \end{pmatrix} \right]. \tag{18}$$

The field equation is converted into the system of differential equations

$$\dot{h}_k^I - i(k+qA)h_k^I - imh_k^{II} = 0 \tag{19}$$

$$\dot{h}_k^{II} + i(k+qA)h_k^{II} - imh_k^I = 0. \tag{20}$$

Following a similar procedure as in the scalar case, we impose a positive frequency solution at early times and solve the equation, obtaining at late times also a negative frequency term.[7] From that expression we can obtain the Bogoloiubov coefficient that describes the spectrum of momenta of the created particles

$$|\beta_k|^2 = \frac{\cosh\left(\pi \frac{\omega_{out} - \omega_{in}}{\rho}\right) - \cosh\left(\pi \frac{qA_0}{\rho}\right)}{2\sinh\left(\pi \frac{\omega_{in}}{\rho}\right)\sinh\left(\pi \frac{\omega_{out}}{\rho}\right)}. \tag{21}$$

Note that $|\beta_k|^2 \leq 1$ in accordance with the the Pauli's exclusion principle. As for the scalar field, in the adiabatic limit $\rho \to 0$ this expression tends to 0 in the massive case, but in the massless case instead $|\beta_k|^2 = 1$ inside the interval $k \in (0, qA_0)$. Therefore, the adiabatic invariance is also broken for massless Dirac fermions. To clarify this idea, in Fig. 4 we show the density of particles, after integrating in all momenta, in terms of ρ for different masses. Note that, unlike the scalar case, the density of particles in the massless case is the same ($\langle N \rangle = |qA_0|/\pi$) for any value of ρ, i.e., it only depends on the final value of the electric potential, not on its form.

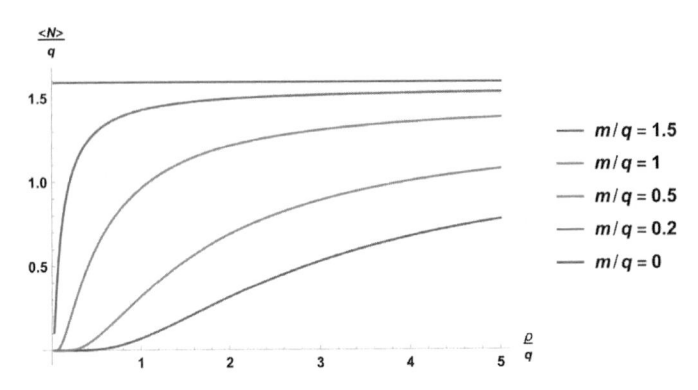

Fig. 4. Density of late-time created Dirac fermions as a function of the adiabaticity parameter ρ, for $A_0 = 5$ and for different values of the mass.

3.3. Relation with the axial anomaly

This breaking of the adiabatic invariance is closely related with the axial anomaly, which is also manifested in the creation of massless particles. Let us analyze this relation. It is well-known that the classical axial symmetry of the massless Dirac field is broken when considering it as a quantum field, which is known as axial anomaly. In 2 dimensions this anomaly can be expressed by[15]

$$\partial_\mu \langle j_A^\mu \rangle_{ren} = -\frac{q}{2\pi} \epsilon^{\mu\nu} F_{\mu\nu} = \frac{q\dot{A}}{\pi}, \tag{22}$$

where $\langle j_A^\mu \rangle$ is the 4-vector that contains the axial charge and current. Note that its divergence gives a non-vanishing value, unlike in the classical case.

In 2 dimensions it is easy to see the relation of this phenomenon with the creation of particles, since the chirality of a particle is linked to its electric charge and the direction of its movement. For instance, a positive charged particle moving in the positive direction of movement would have right-handed chirality. The created particles by the electric field are produced in pairs with opposite charge and opposite direction of movement, therefore both particles of every pair will have the same chirality, creating a net chiral charge. In fact, the created pairs generate a electric current, which in 2 dimensions is directly proportional to the chiral charge. This observable can be calculated by using adiabatic renormalization, and the result of the total chiral charge of the created massless Dirac fermions is

$$\langle j_A^0 \rangle_{ren} = \frac{qA(t)}{\pi}. \tag{23}$$

(for more details on the adiabatic renormalization method for Dirac fields see[10, 12, 13]) Note that this expression coincides with the one obtained by integrating (22), i.e., the chiral charge created by the massless fermions is the one predicted by the axial anomaly. This anomaly remains even if the background changes infinitely slow, just like the creation of massless particles as we have seen in the previous section. Then we can see the close relation between the axial anomaly and the breaking of the adibatic invariance. It is also interesting to remark that for massless scalar fields in 2 dimensions one can define an analogue axial anomaly, and it can be proven to be also compatible with the particle production effect.

4. Generalization to 4 dimensions

In this section we will generalize the previous results to the 4-dimensional case, and will analyze the influence of the introduction of a magnetic background apart from the electric one. We will choose the electric field acting in the direction z. We will not give the explicit details of the calculation but a summary of it, since it is analogue to the one in 2D. In fact one can see that the differential equations for the modes (and therefore the expression of β_k) can be related with the 2D ones by changing k by k_3 and the mass by an effective mass, which depends on the case. This simplifies a lot the analysis, since we know for the previous analysis that the breaking of the adiabatic invariance (i.e. $|\beta_{\vec{k}}| \neq 0$ when $\rho \to 0$) is given when this effective mass (m_{eff}) is 0.

If we consider only an electric background, the effective mass is $m_{eff}^2 = m^2 + k_1^2 + k_2^2$, and then for $m = k_1 = k_2 = 0$ the Bogoliubov coefficient would tend to a non-null value when $\rho \to 0$. But since the momentum is a continuous quantum number and the density of particles is obtained by the integration in all momenta, the amount of created particles with this specific momentum is diluted in the infinite space, and the total particle density vanishes in the adiabatic limit. And then the adiabatic invariance is preserved in this case.

But the situation changes when adding a classical magnetic background. We choose for simplicity a constant magnetic field in the same direction as the electric one. In this case the perpendicular momentum $k_\perp$ is quantized in the well known Landau levels. For the scalar field the effective mass is $m_{eff}^2 = m^2 + (2n+1)|qB|$, where n denote the Landau levels. This quantity never vanishes, and then the adiabatic invariance is preserved. On the other hand, for the Dirac field the effective mass is $m_{eff}^2 = m^2 + 2n|qB|$, which vanishes for $m = 0$ and in the ground level

$n = 0$. In this case the particle number is obtained by the summation of all levels, and then the contribution of $n = 0$ is not diluted. Therefore in this case the particle density does not vanish in the adiabatic limit, which means that there is a breaking of the adiabatic invariance.

We can also see in this cases the close relation between this phenomenon and the axial anomaly. On one hand, in 4 dimensions this anomaly appears in the same conditions as the breaking of the adiabatic invariance, which are massless fermions in presence of not perpendicular electric and magnetic background fields. On the other hand, the chiral charge of the created massles fermions is given by

$$\langle j_A^0 \rangle_{ren} = -\frac{q^2}{2\pi^2} \int_{-\infty}^t dt' \vec{E}(t')\vec{B}, \qquad (24)$$

which has been obtained by using adiabatic renormalization. This expression coincides with the axial anomaly in 4 dimensions. And finally, the only mode that contributes to the chiral charge created by the axial anomaly is the lower one, $n = 0$, which is also the one that produces the breaking of the adiabatic invariance, as seen before.

5. Summary and conclusions

We have analyzed the adiabatic invariance of the particle density spontaneously created by an electromagnetic background. This property, which is verified in the case of a gravitational background, is broken in some cases when the background is an electromagnetic field. Specifically for massless scalar and Dirac fields in 2 dimensions in presence of an electric background, and for massless Dirac fields in 4 dimensions in presence of non perpendicular electric and magnetic background fields. We have also seen that there is a close relation between the breaking of the adiabatic invariance and the axial anomaly since both phenomena emerge in the same cases. Morover the amount of chiral charge produced by the creation of massless particles that remains in the adiabatic limit coincides with the expected one by the axial anomaly.

Acknowledgements

We thank I.Agullo and A. del Rio for useful comments and discussions. This work was supported by Spanish Ministerio de Economia, Industria y Competitividad Grants No. FIS2017-84440-C2-1-P (MINECO/FEDER, EU), No. FIS2017-91161-EXP and by the project PROMETEO/2020/079 (Generalitat Valenciana). P. B. is supported by the Ministerio de Ciencia, Innovación y Universidades, Ph.D. fellowship, Grant No. FPU17/03712. S. P. is supported by the Ministerio de Ciencia, Innovación y Universidades, Ph.D. fellowship, Grant No. FPU16/05287. A. F. is supported by the Severo Ochoa Ph.D. fellowship, Grant No. SEV-2014-0398-16-1, and the European Social Fund.

References

1. L. Parker, *The creation of particles in an expanding universe*, Ph.D. thesis, Harvard University (1966). Dissexpress.umi.com, Publication Number 7331244; *Phys. Rev. Lett.* **21**, 562 (1968); *Phys. Rev. D* **183**, 1057 (1969); *Phys. Rev. D* **3**, 346 (1971).
2. L. Parker and D. J. Toms, *Quantum Field Theory in Curved Spacetime: Quantized Fields and Gravity*, Cambridge University Press, Cambridge, England (2009).
3. N. D. Birrell and P. C. W. Davies, *Quantum Fields in Curved Space*, Cambridge University Press, Cambridge, England (1982).
4. L. Parker, *J. Phys. A* **45**, 374023 (2012).
5. W. Pittrich and H. Gies, *Probing the Quantum Vacuum*, Springer, Heidelberg (2000).
6. J. Schwinger, *Phys. Rev.* **82**, 664 (1951).
7. P. Beltrán, A. Ferreiro, J. Navarro-Salas and S. Pla *Phys. Rev. D* **100**, 085014 (2019).
8. A. Landete, J. Navarro-Salas and F. Torrenti, *Phys. Rev. D* **88**, 061501 (2013).
9. A. del Rio, J. Navarro-Salas and F. Torrenti, *Phys. Rev. D* **90**, 084017 (2014).
10. A. Ferreiro and J. Navarro-Salas, *Phys. Rev. D* **97**, 125012 (2018).
11. A. Ferreiro, J. Navarro-Salas and S. Pla, *Phys. Rev. D* **98**, 045015 (2018).
12. J. F. Barbero G., A. Ferreiro, J. Navarro-Salas and E. J. S. Villaseñor, *Phys. Rev. D* **98**, 025016 (2018).
13. P. Beltrán-Palau, J. Navarro-Salas and S. Pla, *Phys. Rev. D* **99** 105008 (2019).
14. F. Sauter, *Z. Phys.* **69**, 742 (1931).
15. R. A. Bertlmann, *Anomalies in Quantum Field Theory*, Oxford University Press, Oxford (2000).

Dynamics of relativistic electrons in non-uniform magnetic fields and its applications in quantum computing and astrophysics

Srishty Aggarwal* and Banibrata Mukhopadhyay

Department of Physics, Indian Institute of Science, Bengalore, Karnataka 560012, India
* E-mail: srishtya@iisc.ac.in

We explore the two-dimensional motion of relativistic electrons when they are trapped in magnetic fields having spatial power-law variation. Its impacts include lifting of degeneracy that emerged in the case of the constant magnetic field, special alignment of Landau levels of spin-up and spin-down electrons depending on whether the magnetic field is increasing or decreasing from the centre, splitting of Landau levels of electrons with zero angular momentum from that of positive one and the change in the equation of state of matter. Landau quantization (LQ) in variable magnetic fields has interdisciplinary applications in a variety of disciplines ranging from condensed matter to quantum information. As examples, we discuss the increase in quantum speed of the electron in presence of spatially increasing magnetic field; and the attainment of super Chandrasekhar mass of white dwarfs by taking into account LQ and Lorentz force simultaneously.

Keywords: Landau quantization; Non-uniform magnetic field; Dirac equation; Chandrasekhar-limit; Quantum speed limit

1. Introduction

Landau Quantization (LQ) is the phenomenon of the quantization of the cyclotron orbits of charged particles in presence of magnetic field. LQ has been widely discussed for uniform magnetic fields both in non-relativistic[1] as well as relativistic[2] cases. It leads to many interesting effects like quantum Hall effect, de Has Van Alphen effect, Shubnikov oscillations, modification to the equation of state (EOS) and change in the neutron drip line. The modified EOS was later proved to be useful in explaining the mass of super Chandrasekhar white dwarfs.[3]

However, a complete uniform magnetic field is an idealistic realization. What if it is non-uniform as in astrophysical systems and plasmas? In white dwarfs, neutron stars and even main sequence stars, the magnetic field varies drastically from centre to surface. Plasma can act as a source of both increasing and decreasing magnetic fields depending on its properties. Even in laboratories, fluctuations in the magnetic field are a common sight. This motivates us to initiate the exploration of the dynamics of a relativistic electron in presence of strictly spatially variable magnetic fields.[4]

We show different arrangements of the energy levels of an electron when it is trapped in variable magnetic fields. Further, we explore its applications in the fields of quantum information by showing an increase in quantum speed of an electron in presence of a spatially increasing magnetic field, and astrophysics, in the magnetized white dwarfs.

2. Solution of Dirac equation in presence of magnetic fields

The Dirac equation in the presence of magnetic field for an electron of mass m_e and charge q $(-e)$ is given by

$$i\hbar \frac{\partial \Psi}{\partial t} = \left[c\boldsymbol{\alpha} \cdot \left(-i\hbar \nabla - \frac{q\mathbf{A}}{c} \right) + \beta m_e c^2 \right] \Psi, \tag{1}$$

where $\boldsymbol{\alpha}$ and β are Dirac matrices, $\mathbf{A}$ is the vector potential, $\hbar$ is the reduced Planck constant and c is the speed of light. For stationary states, we can write

$$\Psi = e^{-i\frac{Et}{\hbar}} \begin{bmatrix} \chi \\ \phi \end{bmatrix}, \tag{2}$$

where ϕ and χ are 2-component spinors.

Therefore, the decoupled equation for χ obtained from Eq. (1) is

$$(E^2 - m_e^2 c^4)\chi = \left[c^2 \left(\pi^2 - \frac{q\hbar}{c} \boldsymbol{\sigma} \cdot \mathbf{B} \right) \right] \chi, \tag{3}$$

where $\boldsymbol{\pi} = -i\hbar \nabla - q\mathbf{A}/c$.

We choose a simple power law variation of the magnetic field in compliance with Maxwell's equations as

$$\mathbf{B} = B_0 \rho^n \hat{z}, \tag{4}$$

in cylindrical coordinates (ρ, ϕ, z). Such a field profile can take into account the uniformity in magnetic field when $n = 0$ as well as an increase and a decrease in fields with respect to radial coordinate with $n > 0$ and $n < 0$ respectively, satisfying other physics intact. Using a gauge freedom for the vector potential $\mathbf{A}$, we choose

$$\mathbf{A} = B_0 \frac{\rho^{n+1}}{n+2} \hat{\phi} = A\hat{\phi}. \tag{5}$$

Let

$$\chi = e^{i\left(m\phi + \frac{p_z}{\hbar} z\right)} R_\pm(\rho). \tag{6}$$

Since the electron is confined to a plane perpendicular to the direction of magnetic field (z-direction), $p_z = 0$. By substituting χ from Eq. (6) into Eq. (3), and dividing it by $m_e^2 c^2$, Eq. (3) becomes

$$\alpha R_\pm(\rho) = -\lambda_e^2 \left[\frac{\partial^2}{\partial \rho^2} + \frac{1}{\rho} \frac{\partial}{\partial \rho} - \frac{m^2}{\rho^2} \right] \tilde{R}_\pm$$

$$+ \left[\left(\frac{kB_0 \rho^{n+1}}{n+2} \right)^2 + k\lambda_e \left(-\frac{2m}{n+2} \pm 1 \right) B_0 \rho^n \right] R_\pm, \tag{7}$$

where α is the eigenvalue of the problem and is equal to $\epsilon^2 - 1$, $\epsilon = E/m_e c^2$, $\lambda_e = \hbar/m_e c$ and $k = e/m_e c^2$. Further, choosing $R_\pm(\rho) = u_\pm(\rho)/\sqrt{\rho}$, the above equation is reduced to

$$\alpha u_\pm = \left(-\lambda_e^2 \frac{\partial^2}{\partial \rho^2} + V_{eff} \right) u_\pm, \tag{8}$$

such that

$$V_{eff} = -\lambda_e^2 \left[\frac{1}{4\rho^2} - \frac{m^2}{\rho^2}\right] + \left(\frac{kB_0\rho^{n+1}}{n+2}\right)^2 + k\lambda_e\left(-\frac{2m}{n+2} \pm 1\right) B_0\rho^n. \quad (9)$$

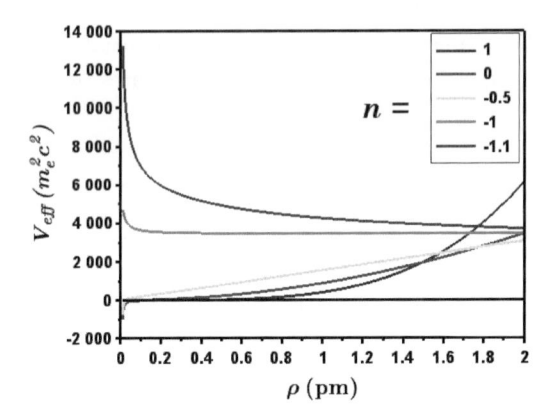

Fig. 1. The variation of effective potential for different n for $B_0 = 10^{15}$ G pm^{-n}. The black horizontal line represents $V_{eff} = 0$. Various potentials at $\rho = 1$ pm from bottom to top represent $n = 1, 0, -0.5, -1$ and -1.1 respectively.

The variation of V_{eff} for different n is shown in Fig. 1. It can be seen that V_{eff} is completely repulsive for n less than or equal to -1, whose solution will depend on the distance from the source (origin of the system) upto which a particle can move. Therefore, the energy eigenvalues for such cases depend upon where we put a hard wall making the system equivalent to confining the electron in a box. However, we do not want to apply any such restrictions on the electron. We, therefore, limit our analysis to the cases with n greater than -1.

We use "Shooting and Matching" method to solve Eq. (8). For computational analysis, we choose ρ and B_0 in the units of picometer (pm) and G pm^{-n} respectively.

For uniform magnetic field, i.e. $n = 0$, the eigenvalue of level ν is given by

$$\alpha_\nu = 2k\lambda_e B_0 \left(\nu + \frac{|m|}{2} - \frac{m}{2} + \frac{1}{2} \pm \frac{1}{2}\right), \quad (10)$$

where 'm' is the azimuthal quantum number.[1] One can easily see from Eq. (10) that ground state eigenvalue (α_0) is 0 and all the other energy levels are doubly degenerate. Also, energies are same for $m \geq 0$, which turn out to be

$$E^2 = p_z^2 c^2 + m_e^2 c^4 \left(1 + 2\nu \frac{B_0}{B_c}\right), \quad (11)$$

where $B_c = m_e^2 c^3 / e\hbar$, the Schwinger limit of pair production.

3. Eigenspectra and dispersion relations

3.1. $m = 0$

Figures 2 and 3 show the eigenspectra for different n, obtained from Eq. (7) by taking $m = 0$. On comparison of the eigenlevels without Zeeman effect (yellow-solid lines in the left) in Fig. 2, it can be observed that the spacing between the eigenlevels increases for $n > 0$, remains same if $n = 0$ and decreases for $n < 0$, from ground to higher levels. It owes to the chosen magnetic field variation in the region. If the magnetic field is spatially increasing, it has low strength near the centre and becomes strong near the outer boundary. Hence, the lower levels have lesser spacing, and the gap between consecutive levels increases for higher levels. The opposite is true for a decaying field profile.

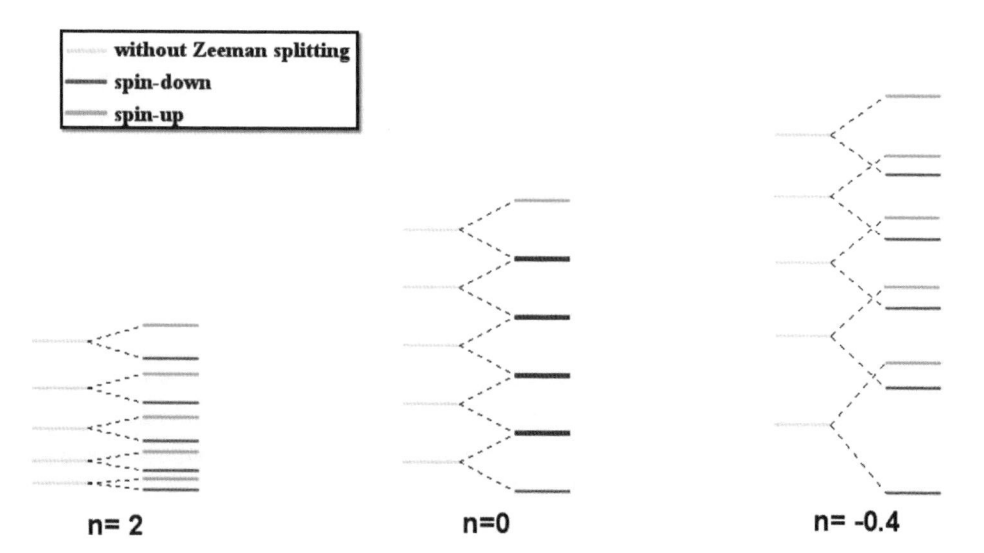

Fig. 2. Comparison of eigenlevels and the splitted states of $+\sigma.B$ and $-\sigma.B$ for $n = 2, 0$ and -0.4.

Breaking of degeneracy that arose in uniform magnetic field takes place for both increasing and decreasing magnetic fields if Zeeman effect is included. However, the alignment of levels for spin-up and spin-down electrons is quite different for these two cases as shown in Fig. 2. While the spin pattern for $n > 0$ is $dududu...$, it becomes $ddudud...$ for $n < 0$ until $n = -0.6$, as can be inferred from Fig. 3. Below -0.6, the spin pattern is highly ambiguous, say for $n = -0.8$, it is $dddudud...$, whereas for $n = -0.9$, it changes to $ddddudud....$ Here, d and u denote the levels for spin-down and spin-up electrons respectively. It is remarkable that the ground level for the spin-down electron always lies at 0 for all n.

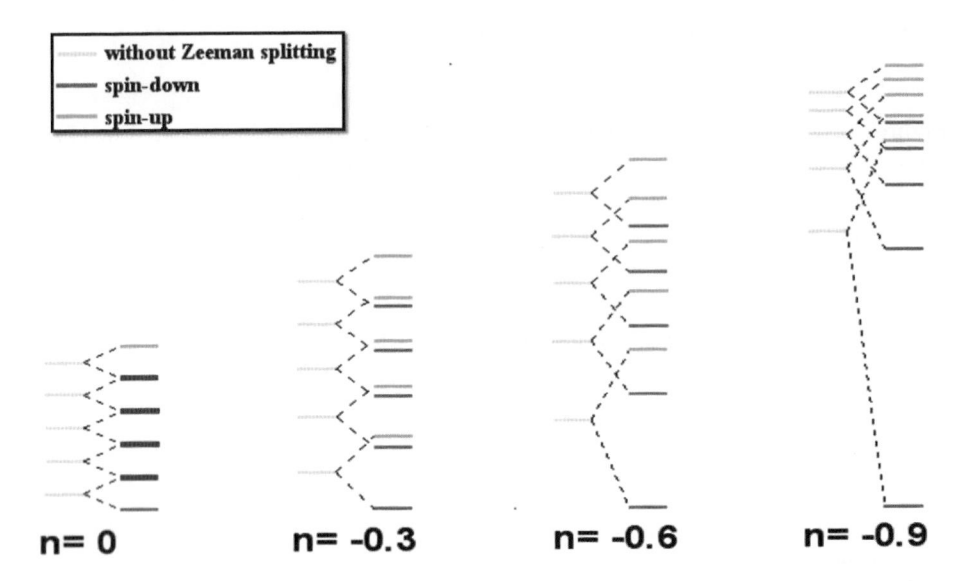

Fig. 3. Comparison of eigenlevels and the splitted states of $+\sigma.B$ and $-\sigma.B$ for $n=0$ and when n is negative.

One can, thus, obtain the desired spacing between the eigenlevels using non-uniform magnetic fields. For example, we can prepare a system with electrons confined to lower levels in a decaying magnetic field, say with $n = -0.8$ or -0.9. Such a system will then have only spin-down electrons due to the availability of lower levels for the same. Thus, we can achieve a single spin system using such variable magnetic fields. Also, a spin-based transition can be observed in presence of increasing magnetic fields, if we restrict the energy of electron between spin-up ground level and spin-down first excited state energies.

Table 1. The values of the constants of Eq. (12) for various n. Here B_0 in Eq. (12) is chosen in the units of 10^{15} G pm^{-n}

n	C_3	C_5
−0.5	195.66	0.484
−0.4	134.63	0.486
−0.3	97	0.488
−0.2	72.5	0.4934
−0.1	56	0.50
0	44.42	0.50
1	10.95	0.5156
2	5.72	0.50
3	3.965	0.51
4	3.15	0.51

We obtain a general expression for the eigenvalue of a level ν for arbitrary n using trial and error method, given by[4]

$$\alpha_{\nu\pm} = C_3 \, B_0^{\frac{2}{n+2}} \, (\nu + C_5)^{\frac{2+2n}{n+2}} \left[1 \pm \frac{C_5}{(\nu + C_5)}\right]. \tag{12}$$

where C_3 and C_5 are constants whose value depends on n. The values of these constants for some n are given in Table 1.

3.2. $m \neq 0$

We compare the eigenvalues between positive m ($m = 1$) and negative m ($m = -1$) with $m = 0$ for different variations in the magnetic fields. When $n = 0$, positive m does not have any impact on the eigenvalues in comparison with $m = 0$, while negative m leads to the increment in energies, as depicted in Fig. 4 as well as can be inferred from Eq. (10). The Fig. 4 shows that for variable magnetic fields, the trend with respect to negative m remains same as that for the uniform one, however, the impact of positive m changes for the varying field. While it leads to an increase in energies for $n > 0$, the energies decrease, if n is negative.

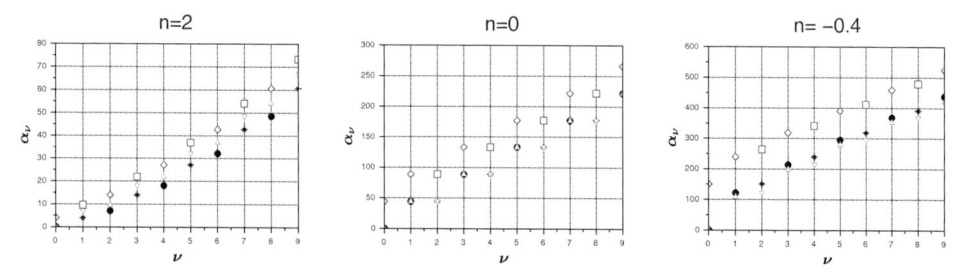

Fig. 4. The variation of eigenvalue with the eigen-index for $m = 0$ with $-\sigma.B$ (black solid circles) and $+\sigma.B$ (black asterisks); $m = +1$ with $-\sigma.B$ (cyan upward triangles) and $+\sigma.B$ (cyan downward triangles); $m = -1$ with $-\sigma.B$ (magenta diamonds) and $+\sigma.B$ (magenta squares), for $n = 2, 0$ and -0.4.

4. Finding ground state energy using variational method

We can find the upper bound of the ground state eigenvalue α_0 using the variational principle,[5] which states that

$$E_{gs} \leq \langle H \rangle, \tag{13}$$

where E_{gs} represents the ground state energy and $\langle H \rangle$ is the expectation value of Hamiltonian.

We choose the ground state wavefunction for both the spins of electron as

$$R_0 = e^{-\frac{KB_0 \rho^{n+1}}{\lambda_e(n+2)^2}}. \tag{14}$$

The normalisation constant (N_0) is given by

$$N_0 = \sqrt{\frac{(n+2)}{\Gamma\left(\frac{2}{n+2}\right)} \left(\frac{2KB_0}{\lambda_e(n+2)^2}\right)^{\frac{2}{n+2}}}, \quad (15)$$

where

$$\Gamma\left(\frac{a}{b}\right) = b \int_0^\infty x^{a-1} e^{-x^b} dx.$$

Hence, the normalised wavefunction $\tilde{R}_0 = N_0 R_0$. Therefore,

$$\tilde{R}_0' = -\rho^{n+1} \frac{KB_0}{\lambda_e(n+2)} \tilde{R}_0, \quad (16)$$

and

$$\tilde{R}_0'' = -(n+1)\rho^n \frac{KB_0}{\lambda_e(n+2)} \tilde{R}_0 + \left(\frac{KB_0 \rho^{n+1}}{\lambda_e(n+2)}\right)^2 \tilde{R}_0. \quad (17)$$

Hence,

$$\alpha_{0Th\pm} = \langle \tilde{R}_0 | \alpha_\pm | \tilde{R}_0 \rangle \quad (18)$$

$$= \frac{KB_0 \lambda_e(1\pm 1)}{\Gamma\left(\frac{2}{n+2}\right)} \left(\frac{2KB_0}{\lambda_e(n+2)^2}\right)^{-\frac{n}{n+2}}. \quad (19)$$

Thus, Eq. (19) provides an upper bound on the ground state energies for spin-down and spin-up electrons. (Eq. 19 can be obtained from Eq. 7).

Table 2. Comparison of analytical and computational α_0 values at different n for $B_0 = 10^{15}$ G pm^{-n}.

n	α_{0Comp+}	α_{0Th+}
−0.5	225.83	256.70084
−0.4	151.124	162.464
−0.3	105.612	109.563
−0.2	76.716	77.840
−0.1	57.55	57.746
0	44.4	44.418
1	8.702	10.090
2	3.969	5.700
3	2.534	4.427
4	1.907	3.953

Note that α_{0Th-} is zero for all n, which is the exact eigenvalue for the ground state of spin-down electron. For spin-up electron, the above expression provides the exact ground state eigenvalue only for the uniform magnetic field, but deviates for the non-uniform one. The comparison of actual α_0 obtained computationally (α_{0Comp+}) and the approximate analytical one obtained in this section (α_{0Th+}) for spin-up electron at $B_0 = 10^{15}$ G pm^{-n} for different n is shown in Table 2. The deviation between the two values increases as one goes away from $n = 0$ in either direction. It is noteworthy that the power-law dependence of α_{0Th} on B_0 in Eq. (19) is $2/(n+2)$ which is same as in Eq. (12), where α for a general ν is obtained using an appropriate ansatz.

5. Applications

In general, LQ in non-uniform magnetic fields can be useful in multiple domains of physics ranging from quantum information to condensed matter systems. Here, we will discuss its applications in quantum information via the increase in quantum speed of an electron and in astrophysics for the super-Chandrasekhar white dwarfs.

5.1. Increase of quantum speed

Quantum speed of a particle is defined as the speed of its transition from one energy level to the other. It has a direct influence on the processing speed of quantum information. The electron levels are equivalent to qubits in quantum information. Thus, if the transition between the levels takes place at higher pace, switching between the qubits will be more rapid, thereby, leading to faster processing of quantum information. Therefore, attaining higher quantum speed is one of the major requirements of the researchers in the field of quantum computation.

Assuming that the initial state of the electron is the superposition of the two consecutive states: the ground and the first excited one, given by

$$\Psi(\rho, 0) = \frac{1}{\sqrt{2}} \left[\psi_0(\rho) + \psi_1(\rho) \right], \tag{20}$$

with $m = 0$, $p_z = 0$ and the respective energies E_0 and E_1. For the transition of an electron from ground state to first excited state, the minimum time of evolution of wavefunction (T_{min}) is evaluated using Mandelstam-Tamm bound[6] as

$$T_{min} = \frac{\pi \hbar}{2 \Delta H}, \tag{21}$$

where

$$\Delta H = \frac{E_1 - E_0}{2}. \tag{22}$$

The radial displacement of electron in time T_{min} is given by

$$\rho_{disp} = 2 \left| \int_0^\infty \rho D_S(\rho) d\rho \right|, \tag{23}$$

where

$$D_s(\rho) = \psi_0^\dagger \, \rho \, \psi_1. \tag{24}$$

Hence, the quantum speed of electron is

$$\tilde{v} = \frac{\rho_{disp}}{T_{min}}, \tag{25}$$

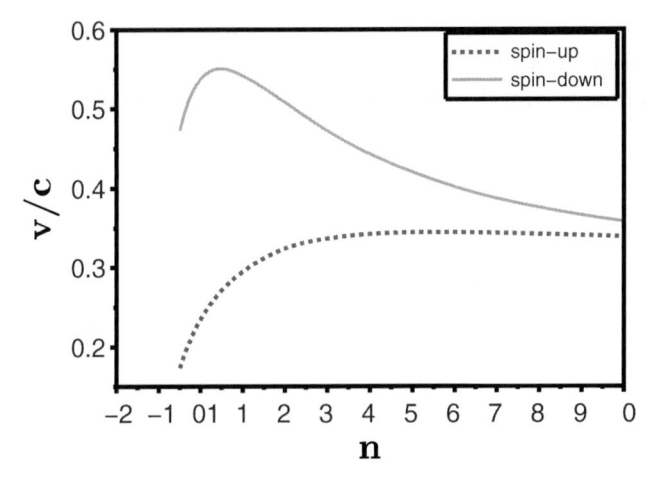

Fig. 5. Variation of quantum speed of spin-up and spin-down electrons for transition from ground state to first excited state with different n at $B_0 = 10^{16}$ G pm^{-n}.

Figure 5 illustrates the variation of the quantum speed of an electron with the change in non-uniformity index of the magnetic field in the relativistic regime. As it can be seen from the figure, the quantum speed of the electron increases with increasing n; reaches the maximum and then begins to decrease. Whereas quantum speed is maximum for $n = 1$ for spin-down electron, n has to be 6 to reach the highest speed for spin-up electron for $B_0 = 10^{16}$ G pm^{-n}. This is associated with the varied alignment of energy levels in non-uniform magnetic fields lifting the degeneracy between $n < 0$ and $n > 0$ as shown in Fig. 2. Therefore, if a spin-up electron is trapped in a magnetic field that is spatially increasing in magnitude even linearly ($n = 1$), then we can achieve a higher speed of transition of the electron as shown in Fig. 5.

5.2. Super-Chandrasekhar white dwarfs

Astrophysical bodies like white dwarfs, neutron stars and magnetars are the natural sites to observe non-uniform magnetic fields, wherein, the difference between the central and the surface magnetic fields lies upto $3 - 4$ orders of magnitude or even higher.

The main impact of LQ in stellar physics is to modify the underlying EOS due to the discretization of energy levels in presence of strong magnetic fields. For a constant magnetic field, the energy levels are degenerate and the spacing between the eigenlevels is constant, but for a variable magnetic field case, the degeneracy breaks down and the spacing between levels is non-uniform, as shown in Figs. 2 and 3, which brings a considerable change in EOS in presence of non-uniform magnetic fields.

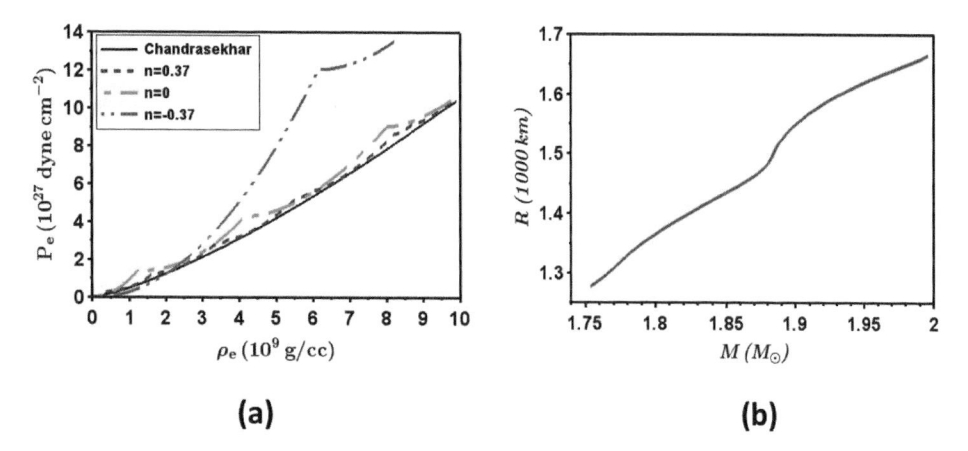

Fig. 6. (a) EOS for different n at $\epsilon_{Fmax} = 17$ for $B_0 = 2 \times 10^{15}$ G pm^{-n}. (b) Mass-radius relation of magnetized white dwarf for the magnetic field profile chosen in Eq. (33).

In a non-uniform magnetic field, the electron number density at zero temperature is given by

$$n_e = \frac{1}{(2\pi)^2 \lambda_e^3} \left(\sum_{\nu=0}^{\nu=\nu_{m-}} \beta_-(\nu) x_{F-}(\nu) + \sum_{\nu=0}^{\nu=\nu_{m+}} \beta_+(\nu) x_{F+}(\nu) \right), \quad (26)$$

where '+' sign and '−' sign indicate spin-up and spin-down respectively,

$$x_{F\pm}(\nu) = \left[\epsilon_F^2 - (1 + \alpha_\pm(\nu)) \right]^{\frac{1}{2}} \quad (27)$$

and

$$\beta_\pm = (\alpha_\pm(\nu+1) - \alpha_\pm(\nu-1))/2. \quad (28)$$

Note that $\nu_{m\pm}$ is the largest integer value of ν such that

$$\alpha_{\nu\pm} \leq \epsilon_F^2 - 1. \quad (29)$$

The pressure of an electron gas at zero temperature is given by

$$P_e = \frac{m_e c^2}{(2\pi)^2 \lambda_e^3} \left(\sum_{\nu=0}^{\nu=\nu_{m-}} \beta_-(\nu)(1+\alpha_-(\nu)) f_2 \left[\frac{x_{F-}(\nu)}{(1+\alpha_-(\nu))^{1/2}} \right] \right.$$
$$\left. + \sum_{\nu=0}^{\nu=\nu_{m+}} \beta_+(\nu)(1+\alpha_+(\nu)) f_2 \left[\frac{x_{F+}(\nu)}{(1+\alpha_+(\nu))^{1/2}} \right] \right), \quad (30)$$

where

$$f_2(z) = \frac{1}{2} \left(z\sqrt{1+z^2} - \ln(z + \sqrt{1+z^2}) \right). \quad (31)$$

Figure 6(a) shows how the EOS changes with n at $B_0 = 2 \times 10^{15}$ G pm^{-n}. For a given ϵ_{Fmax}, the allowed number of levels decreases with decreasing n. With the decrease in number of levels, EOS becomes stiffer and softer in high and low density regimes respectively. Although, the spatially increasing magnetic field is not common in stellar objects, we also show the change in EOS of electron in presence of an increasing magnetic field that may come handy for future explorations.

To probe the effect of LQ and Lorentz force simultaneously in white dwarfs, we choose the following sample magnetic field profile.

$$B = \begin{cases} B_0 \hat{z}, & \text{if } \rho < 850 \text{ km}, \\ B_0 \left(\frac{\rho}{1 \text{ km}}\right)^{-0.37} \hat{z}, & \text{if } 850 \text{ km} \leq \rho \leq 900 \text{ km}, \\ B_0 \left(\frac{\rho}{1 \text{ km}}\right)^{-0.99} \hat{z}, & \text{otherwise}, \end{cases} \quad (32)$$

such that the central and the surface magnetic field are 2×10^{15} G and around 10^{12} G respectively. Also, $(\mathbf{B} \cdot \nabla)\mathbf{B} = 0$ and $\nabla \cdot \mathbf{B} = 0$ for the chosen profile. Therefore, the non-rotating white dwarfs will be spherical in shape. Hence, in spherical polar coordinates with $\theta = \pi/2$, the field profile is given by

$$B = \begin{cases} -B_0 \hat{\theta}, & \text{if } r < 850 \text{ km}, \\ -B_0 \left(\frac{r}{1 \text{ km}}\right)^{-0.37} \hat{\theta}, & \text{if } 850 \text{ km} \leq r \leq 900 \text{ km}, \\ -B_0 \left(\frac{r}{1 \text{ km}}\right)^{-0.99} \hat{\theta}, & \text{otherwise}, \end{cases} \quad (33)$$

The mass and radius of a white dwarf can be obtained by solving

$$\frac{d}{dr}\left(P_e + \frac{B^2}{8\pi}\right) = -\frac{GM(r)(\rho_e + \rho_B)}{r^2}, \quad (34)$$

$$\frac{dM(r)}{dr} = 4\pi r^2 (\rho_e + \rho_B), \quad (35)$$

where ρ_B is the magnetic density, $B^2 = \mathbf{B} \cdot \mathbf{B}$, $\rho_e = n_e m_p \mu_e$, m_p is the mass of proton, μ_e is the mean molecular weight per electron and G is Newton's gravitation constant.

The mass-radius relation, shown in Fig. 6(b), depicts the existence of super-Chandrasekhar mass white dwarfs in presence of central strong magnetic field. Although, here, the surface magnetic field obtained is around 10^{12} G, the results are unaffected even if the surface magnetic field of white dwarfs is lower, say around 10^9 G which is detectable.

Here, for $r < 850$ km, since, magnetic field is uniform, EoS would be Landau quantized for the same magnetic field at $B_0 = 2 \times 10^{15}$ G. For $r \geq 850$ km, the field decays to a lower strength so that Chandrasekhar's non-magnetic EoS suffices. Only at the interface around 850 km, non-uniform field based LQ applies in EoS, but in a very tiny region. Hence practically, for the present example, LQ EOS based on non-uniform field does not play an important role in controlling the dynamics of magnetised white dwarf. However, it helps to account for the whole system including the small zone around 850 km that contains the decay of the magnetic field.

6. Summary

LQ in strictly spatially variable magnetic fields is a new venture on its own. It leads to the different alignment of energy levels of an electron as well as the breaking of spin degeneracy, depending on the variation of magnetic field. Hence, it can be useful in the multitude of fields wherein one can attain the desired spacing and alignment of levels through an appropriate non-uniformity in magnetic fields.

We have explored its application in quantum computing through an increase in quantum speed of electron in spatially increasing magnetic field. We also discuss the increase in stiffness and softenss of EOS at high and low densities in presence of non-uniform magnetic fields as compared to the case of uniform magnetic field (as well as Chandrasekhar EOS). This, we, further, use to understand the properties of magnetized white dwarfs in the small zone of rapidly decaying magnetic field.

References

1. L. D. Landau and E. M. Lifshitz, *Quantum mechanics: Non-Relativistic Theory*, 2nd edn. (Elsevier, Amsterdam, the Netherlands, 1965).
2. P. Strange, *Relativistic Quantum Mechanics* (Cambridge University Press, Cambridge, 1998).
3. U. Das and B. Mukhopadhyay, Strongly magnetized cold degenerate electron gas: Mass-radius relation of the magnetized white dwarf, *Phys. Rev. D* **86**, 042001 (2012).
4. S. Aggarwal, B. Mukhopadhyay and G. Gregori, Relativistic landau quantization in non-uniform magnetic field and its applications to white dwarfs and quantum information, *SciPost Physics* (2021), *accepted for publication*, arXiv:2110.09543.
5. D. J. Griffiths, *Introduction to Quantum Mechanics*, 2nd edn. (Cambridge University Press, Cambridge, 2017).
6. L. Mandelstam and I. Tamm, The energy–time uncertainty relation in non-relativistic quantum mechanics, *Izv. Akad. Nauk SSSR* **9**, 122 (1945).

Validity of the semiclassical approximation in 1+1 electrodynamics: Numerical solutions to the linear response equation

Ian M. Newsome

Department of Physics, Wake Forest University,
Winston-Salem, NC 27109, USA
Email: newsim18@wfu.edu

From previous work,[1] the semiclassical backreaction equation in 1+1 dimensions was solved and a criterion was implemented to assess the validity of the semiclassical approximation in this case. The criterion involves the behavior of solutions to the linear response equation which describes perturbations about solutions to the semiclassical backreaction equation. The linear response equation involves a time integral over a two-point correlation function for the current induced by the quantum field and it is expected that significant growth in this two-point function (and therefore in quantum fluctuations) will result in significant growth in solutions to the linear response equation. It was conjectured for early times that the difference of two nearby solutions to the semiclassical backreaction equation, with similar initial conditions, can act as an approximate solution to the linear response equation. A comparative analysis between the approximate and numerical solutions to the linear response equation, for the critical scale for particle production, will be presented for the case of a massive, quantized spin ½ field in order to determine how robust the approximation method is for representing its solutions.

Keywords: Schwinger effect; semiclassical electrodynamics; linear response; validity.

1. Introduction

The semiclassical approximation has been utilized in a wide range of physical situations where a quantized field evolves in a classical background. The relevant scenario for the following discussion involves the decay of an electric field via the Schwinger effect.[2] The original calculation by Schwinger in 1951 involved a background field calculation in which an electric field E, that is constant in space and time, gives rise to a particle production rate due to vacuum decay. At leading one-loop order the particle production rate is proportional to a factor of $\exp\{-\pi m^2/qE\}$, from which one can define a critical scale for pair production that is $E_{\text{crit}} \sim m^2/q$.

The time evolution of the net electromagnetic field is described by the semiclassical backreaction equation and has been solved for the case of a homogeneous electric field coupled to a massive scalar or a massive spin ½ field in 1+1[3-5] and 3+1[5-7] dimensions. When particles are produced, they accelerate in reaction to the background electric field, creating an electric current. This current produces a counter electric field which initially damps the original background electric field, and at late times the net electric field will oscillate.

Given that the semiclassical electrodynamics model is an approximation to quantum electrodynamics, it must be asked to what extent is this an accurate approximation? Concerning the model presented here, the semiclassical backreaction equation involves an expectation value of the current constructed from quantum fields and for this to be a satisfactory approximation to what one would measure, it is necessary that quantum fluctuations be small.

To summarize the previous work which led to the development of the numerical solution to the linear response equation presented in these proceedings, the main goals in [1] had been to study the details of the particle production process when backreaction effects were taken into account and subsequently to estimate the significance of certain types of quantum fluctuations to investigate the validity of the semiclassical approximation for 1+1 electrodynamics. This included solving the necessary backreaction equations for scalar and spin ½ fields coupled to two different classical source profiles, one which led to an asymptotically constant electric field and the other being the Sauter pulse. To wit, a criterion was implemented to assess the validity of the semiclassical approximation which had been previously applied to the process of preheating in models of chaotic inflation,[8] with an earlier version applied to semiclassical gravity.[9] This criterion involves the behavior of solutions to the linear response equation, which can be derived by perturbing the semiclassical backreaction equation about a background field solution.

In general, the linear response equation is a second order integro-differential equation which can be cumbersome to solve numerically. Therefore a method was developed[8] to approximate solutions to the linear response equation which involves the difference between solutions to the semiclassical backreaction equation with similar initial conditions. For early times, this difference is expected to act as an approximate solution to the linear response equation as long as the exact solution is relatively small.

Subsequently, an effort has been made to directly solve for the numerical solutions to the linear response equation for the case of an asymptotically constant background electric field, initially zero, coupled to a spin ½ field. For the purposes of this proceeding, the numerical solutions to the linear response equation are desired in order to determine how robust the method for approximating its solutions will be. Therefore, a comparative analysis between the numerical solutions to the linear response equation and its approximate solutions described previously will be presented in what follows, with special attention given to the critical scale for particle production.

The structure of this paper is as follows: in Sec. 2 a brief review of the system is discussed including quantization of the spin ½ field, the semiclassical backreaction equation, and the renormalization procedure used. Sec. 3 contains a review of relevant material[1] including the criterion for the validity of the semiclassical approximation with the general and specific forms of the linear response equation presented for the case of a spin ½ field coupled to a background electric field. Also, included is a discussion of the method used to approximate solutions to the linear response equation. In Sec. 4 an analysis of the numerical solutions to the linear response equation is given, with a comparison drawn between its approximate solutions, with an emphasis on the critical scale for significant particle production. Sec. 5 includes a summary of results and discussion thereof.

2. Quantization and Renormalization of a Spin ½ Field

This section describes the model under consideration: a quantized spin ½ field which interacts with a background electric field generated by a prescribed classical source. Analysis is restricted to 1+1 Minkowski spacetime with the assumption that the background electric field is spatially homogeneous in a given reference frame, i.e. $E = E(t)$. Furthermore, the metric signature is chosen to be $(-,+)$ with $c = \hbar = 1$.

The classical action describing a spin ½ field $\psi(t,x)$ coupled to a background electric field is given by

$$S = \int d^2x \left[-\frac{1}{4} F_{\mu\nu} F^{\mu\nu} + A_\mu J_C^\mu + i\bar{\psi}\gamma^\mu D_\mu \psi - m\bar{\psi}\psi \right]. \tag{1}$$

Here $F_{\mu\nu} = \partial_\mu A_\nu - \partial_\nu A_\mu$ is the electromagnetic field strength tensor, m the mass of spin ½ field excitations, $D_\mu = \partial_\mu - iqA_\mu$ the gauge covariant derivative, J_C^μ a classical and conserved external source, and $\bar{\psi} = \psi^\dagger \gamma^0$. The Dirac matrices γ^μ satisfy the following anticommutation relations $\{\gamma^\mu, \gamma^\nu\} = -2\eta^{\mu\nu}$.

Variation of (1) with respect to the vector potential yields the general form of Maxwell's equation

$$-\Box A^\mu + \partial^\mu \partial_\nu A^\nu = J_C^\mu + J_Q^\mu. \tag{2}$$

The classical source and background electric field generated by this source is chosen to be

$$J_C = -\frac{qE_0}{(1+qt)^2}, \quad E_C = -\int J_C \, dt = E_0 \left(\frac{qt}{1+qt} \right), \tag{3}$$

for $t \geq 0$ and $J_C = 0$ for $t < 0$. Note, the term J_C in (3) is the spatial component of J_C^μ. Since the classical current is initially zero, and gives rise to an electric field that is initially zero as well, there is no ambiguity in the choice of vacuum state. The source term J_Q^μ induced by the spin ½ field is given by

$$J_Q^\mu = q\bar{\psi}\gamma^\mu\psi. \tag{4}$$

Variation of (1) with respect to the field $\bar{\psi}$ yields the Dirac equation

$$(i\gamma^\mu D_\mu - m)\psi(t,x) = 0. \tag{5}$$

In what follows, the gauge choice

$$A^\mu = (0, A(t)), \tag{6}$$

will be implemented. Expanding the spin ½ field $\psi(t,x)$ in terms of a complete set of modes yields

$$\psi(t,x) = \int_{-\infty}^{\infty} dk \left[B_k u_k(t,x) + D_k^\dagger v_k(t,x) \right], \tag{7}$$

with $B_k, B_k^\dagger, D_k, D_k^\dagger$ the usual creation and annihilation operators obeying the anticommutation relations $\{B_k, B_{k'}^\dagger\} = \{D_k, D_{k'}^\dagger\} = \delta(k - k')$. Utilizing a particular form for the modes,[10] two independent spinor solutions can be constructed as follows

$$u_k(t,x) = \frac{e^{ikx}}{\sqrt{2\pi}} \begin{pmatrix} h_k^I(t) \\ -h_k^{II}(t) \end{pmatrix}, \quad v_k(t,x) = \frac{e^{-ikx}}{\sqrt{2\pi}} \begin{pmatrix} h_{-k}^{II*}(t) \\ h_{-k}^{I*}(t) \end{pmatrix}. \tag{8}$$

Using the Weyl representation of the Dirac matrices γ^μ

$$\gamma^0 = \begin{pmatrix} 0 & 1 \\ 1 & 0 \end{pmatrix}, \quad \gamma^1 = \begin{pmatrix} 0 & 1 \\ -1 & 0 \end{pmatrix}, \tag{9}$$

the functions $h_k^I(t)$ and $h_k^{II}(t)$ satisfy the mode equations

$$\dot{h}_k^I - i(k - qA)h_k^I - imh_k^{II} = 0, \tag{10a}$$

$$\dot{h}_k^{II} + i(k - qA)h_k^{II} - imh_k^I = 0. \tag{10b}$$

The time evolution of this system is governed by the semiclassical backreaction equation. This can be obtained by replacing J_Q^μ in (2) with its expectation value $\langle J_Q^\mu \rangle$ and then use the gauge choice (6) with (7) to yield

$$\frac{d^2}{dt^2} A(t) = -\frac{d}{dt} E(t) = J_C + \langle J_Q \rangle. \tag{11}$$

Due to the coupling between the classical background electric field and the quantized spin ½ field, charged spin ½ particles will be created. These particles will be accelerated by the background electric field, creating a current which generates a secondary electric field. In the semiclassical approximation, the current created from the accelerated spin ½ particles is given by $\langle J_Q \rangle$. The renormalized expression for $\langle J_Q \rangle$, evaluated in the vacuum state is[1]

$$\langle J_Q \rangle_{\text{ren}} = \frac{q}{2\pi} \int_{-\infty}^{\infty} dk \left[|h_k^I(t)|^2 - |h_k^{II}(t)|^2 + \frac{k}{\omega} - \frac{qm^2}{\omega^3} A(t) \right]. \tag{12}$$

with $\omega^2 = k^2 + m^2$. Here adiabatic regularization was used to eliminate the ultraviolet divergences.[10]

3. Validity Criterion for the Semiclassical Approximation

This section gives a review of relevant material[1] required for the investigation of the solutions to the linear response equation.

Since the current term $\langle J_Q \rangle$, in part, characterizes the quantum particle production process, a natural way to determine the size of quantum fluctuations, compared to other relevant quantities, is to evaluate a two-point correlation function for the current. In general, there are a number of different correlation functions which could be used, but in order to avoid such problems as state-dependent divergences,[11] incompatible results from various renormalization techniques,[12] or covariance issues,[9] it is useful to proceed with a two-point correlation function which emerges naturally from the semiclassical theory itself, namely $\langle [J_Q(t,x), J_Q(t',x')] \rangle$. This two-point function measures the extent to which the value of the current $\langle J_Q \rangle$ at two separate spacetime points commutes, thereby having the interpretation of characterizing the degree to which quantum fluctuations are introduced into the system.

Perturbing the semiclassical backreaction equation yields the linear response equation which contains this two-point correlation function and describes the time evolution of perturbations about a given semiclassical solution. A criterion for the validity of the semiclassical approximation was originally developed for semiclassical gravity[9] and modified for preheating in chaotic inflation.[8] This criterion was applied to semiclassical electrodynamics[1] and states: the semiclassical approximation will break down if any linearized gauge invariant quantity constructed from solutions to the linear response equation with finite non-singular initial data grows rapidly for some period of time. It is important to note this is a necessary, but not sufficient condition for the validity of the semiclassical approximation.

3.1. *The Linear Response Equation*

The linear response equation for semiclassical electrodynamics is found by perturbing the semiclassical backreaction equation about a given solution. From (11) this becomes

$$\frac{d^2}{dt^2} \delta A(t) = -\frac{d}{dt} \delta E(t) = \delta J_C + \delta \langle J_Q \rangle \,. \tag{13}$$

More specifically, the type of perturbation being performed is one that changes the classical current by altering the value of the classical background electric field amplitude E_0 in (3). Thus the term δJ_C is expressed as

$$\delta J_C = -\frac{q}{(1+qt)^2} \delta E_0 \,. \tag{14}$$

In conjunction with the validity criterion stated previously, it is useful to break up the solutions to the semiclassical backreaction equation into the purely classical and quantum pieces

$$E_C = -\int_{t_0}^{t} J_C(t_1)\, dt_1 \,, \tag{15a}$$

$$E_Q = E - E_C \,. \tag{15b}$$

Solutions to the linear response equation can be partitioned in the same way which allows for the statement of the validity criterion to be modified to state that if δE_Q grows rapidly during some time interval, then the semiclassical approximation is not valid.

For the case of a spin ½ field, the renormalized $\delta\langle J_Q \rangle$ term present in (13) can be expressed as[1]

$$\delta\langle J_Q\rangle_{\rm ren} = -\frac{q^2}{\pi}\delta A(t) + i\int_{-\infty}^{\infty} dx' \int_{-\infty}^{t} dt'\, \langle[J_Q(t,x), J_Q(t',x')]\rangle\, \delta A(t')\,, \quad (16)$$

with the relationship

$$\int_{-\infty}^{\infty} dx'\, \langle[J_Q(t,x), J_Q(t',x')]\rangle = \frac{4iq^2}{\pi}\int_{-\infty}^{\infty} dk\, {\rm Im}\left\{h_k^I(t)h_k^{II}(t)h_k^{I*}(t')h_k^{II*}(t')\right\}. \quad (17)$$

Thus (13) takes the specific form

$$\frac{d^2}{dt^2}\delta A(t) = -\frac{q}{(1+qt)^2}\delta E_0 - \frac{q^2}{\pi}\delta A(t)$$
$$-\frac{4q^2}{\pi}\int_{-\infty}^{\infty} dk \int_{-\infty}^{t} dt'\, {\rm Im}\left\{h_k^I(t)h_k^{II}(t)h_k^{I*}(t')h_k^{II*}(t')\right\}\delta A(t')\,. \quad (18)$$

3.2. *Approximate Solutions to the Linear Response Equation*

A technique that was developed to approximate solutions to the linear response equation for the case of homogeneous perturbations[1] involves solving the semiclassical backreaction equation for two solutions whose initial conditions are similar. It is expected that the difference between these two solutions ΔE is an approximate solution to the linear response equation δE, for early times, as long as $\Delta E \approx \delta E$. If the difference does grow large, then the corresponding solution to the linear response equation should grow significantly as well. This would violate the criterion discussed above and thus signal a breakdown in the semiclassical approximation.

A way to measure the relative growth of two solutions E_1 and E_2 to the semiclassical backreaction equation is with the modified relative difference expression[1]

$$R = \frac{|\Delta E|}{|E_1| + |E_2|}\,, \quad \Delta E = E_2 - E_1\,. \quad (19)$$

From the semiclassical backreaction equation, it is clear the difference ΔE will be a solution of the following equation

$$-\frac{d}{dt}\Delta E = \Delta J_C + \Delta\langle J_Q\rangle\,, \quad (20)$$

with the definitions

$$\Delta J_C = J_{C,2} - J_{C,1}\,, \quad \Delta\langle J_Q\rangle = \langle J_{Q,2}\rangle - \langle J_{Q,1}\rangle\,. \quad (21)$$

For ΔE to be an approximate solution to the linear response equation, i.e. $\Delta E \approx \delta E$, it is clear that $\Delta\langle J_Q\rangle \approx \delta\langle J_Q\rangle$ must hold, since one can set $\Delta J_C = \delta J_C$ for all times.

A natural way to measure the growth of the approximate quantum contribution to the finite difference equation ΔE_Q is with a relative difference R_Q given as

$$R_Q = \frac{|\Delta E_Q|}{|E_{Q,1}| + |E_{Q,2}|}, \quad \Delta E_Q = E_{Q,2} - E_{Q,1}. \tag{22}$$

This acts as the gauge invariant quantity constructed from solutions to the linear response equation mentioned in the formal statement for the validity criterion. This difference can be compared to the relative difference R_C between corresponding classical solutions, which does not vary in time. Therefore if R_Q grows rapidly for some period of time, this signals a breakdown in the semiclassical approximation.

In Fig. 1, some results[1] are given for the quantity R_Q for a variety of different particle masses[a]. The most significant effect on the behavior of R_Q is the size of the characteristic dimensionless quantity qE_0/m^2. It is therefore useful to distinguish between three different regimes: (i) $qE_0/m^2 \gg 1$ in which the mass is relatively small compared to the electric field, resulting a large amount of particle production, (ii) $qE_0/m^2 \sim 1$ in which the mass is of the same order as the electric field, resulting in less but still significant particle production, and (iii) $qE_0/m^2 \ll 1$ in which the mass is relatively large compared to the electric field, resulting in very little particle production. The critical case for particle production is defined as $E \sim E_{\text{crit}} = m^2/q$ and therefore the most relevant mass value is $m^2/q^2 = 1$.

As seen in Fig. 1, this particular mass value corresponds to the most rapid growth of R_Q based on the cases considered here, and this implies the most severe breakdown of the semiclassical approximation for this case. However, one can see that R_Q has the least amount of growth in the small mass regime and steadily increases its early time growth as the mass is increased up to the critical case. The conclusion drawn in [1], in the context of the validity criterion put forward, is that the semiclassical approximation is most greatly violated when $qE_0/m^2 \sim 1$ and becomes more accurate as the particle mass is decreased (or increased since quantum fluctuations are expected to diminish due to lack of particle production in the high mass regime).

4. Numerical Solutions to the Linear Response Equation

In this section, an analysis of the numerical solution to the linear response equation for the critical case in which the characteristic quantity $qE_0/m^2 = 1$ is presented. A comparison is then drawn between its approximate and numerical solutions in the context of the validity criterion stated previously.

To arrive at numerical solutions to the linear response equation, one can partition the problem into two parts. The first part involves solving the semiclassical backreaction equation, and the second involves using the output from the

---

[a]This is an aggregate plot built from the results and data presented in [1].

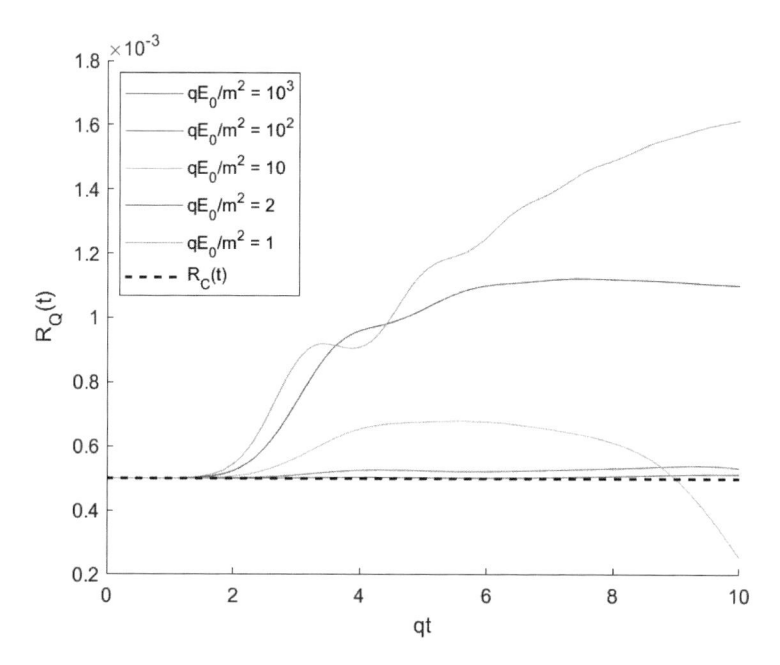

Fig. 1. Results obtained for the quantity R_Q. The values $E_{0,1}/q = 1$ and $E_{0,2}/q = 1 + 10^{-3}$ have been chosen for the solutions which comprise ΔE. The values of the characteristic quantity qE_0/m^2 for each case are shown along with the type of curve for that solution in the legend. Here $R_C(t)$ denotes the relative difference excluding quantum effects.

semiclassical backreaction equation to supply the necessary data for solving the linear response equation. Generating the solutions to the semiclassical backreaction equation involves simultaneously solving a set of three coupled differential equations, namely (10a), (10b), and (11) with (12). The solution output will be the vector potential $A(t)$, and by extension the electric field $E(t)$, and the time dependent spin ½ field modes $h_k^{I,II}(t)$. The quantities needed for solving the linear response equation (18) are the modes $h_k^{I,II}(t)$, which the two-point function in (17) depends on.

4.1. Numerical Details

The $|in\rangle$ state of the time dependent modes $h_k^{I,II}(t)$, prior to the classical source being turned on, is defined as positive frequency plane wave solutions to the mode equation. When the source term is turned on at $qt = 0$ and subsequently $A(t) \neq 0$, the mode solutions are altered by the presence of the background field, specifically $k \to k - qA(t)$. This leads to particle production which is measured, in part, by the quantity $\langle J_Q \rangle$. Since the two-point function $\langle [J_Q(t,x), J_Q(t',x')] \rangle$ depends on these time dependent modes in a non-trivial way, the modification to the mode solutions will induce a non-zero contribution to the two-point function.

It is useful to separate the time dependent modes $h_k^{I,II}(t)$ into their real and imaginary parts

$$h_k^I = \text{Re}\{h_k^I\} + i\,\text{Im}\{h_k^I\}\,, \tag{23a}$$

$$h_k^{II} = \text{Re}\{h_k^{II}\} + i\,\text{Im}\{h_k^{II}\}\,. \tag{23b}$$

From this, the two mode equations defined in (10a) and (10b) now become four mode equations, given as

$$\text{Re}\{\dot{h}_k^I\} + (k - qA)\,\text{Im}\{h_k^I\} + m\,\text{Im}\{h_k^{II}\} = 0\,, \tag{24a}$$

$$\text{Im}\{\dot{h}_k^I\} - (k - qA)\,\text{Re}\{h_k^I\} - m\,\text{Re}\{h_k^{II}\} = 0\,, \tag{24b}$$

$$\text{Re}\{\dot{h}_k^{II}\} - (k - qA)\,\text{Im}\{h_k^{II}\} + m\,\text{Im}\{h_k^I\} = 0\,, \tag{24c}$$

$$\text{Im}\{\dot{h}_k^{II}\} + (k - qA)\,\text{Re}\{h_k^{II}\} - m\,\text{Re}\{h_k^I\} = 0\,. \tag{24d}$$

Furthermore, the quantity $\langle J_Q \rangle$ in (12) can now be expressed in the following way

$$\langle J_Q \rangle_{\text{ren}} = -\frac{q^2}{\pi}A(t) + \frac{q}{2\pi}\int_{-\infty}^{\infty} dk \left[\text{Re}^2\{h_k^I\} + \text{Im}^2\{h_k^I\} - \text{Re}^2\{h_k^{II}\} - \text{Im}^2\{h_k^{II}\} + \frac{k}{\omega} \right]. \tag{25}$$

It is straightforward to now implement a numerical routine which will solve Eqs. (10) and (11).

From (17) it is clear that $\langle [J_Q(t,x), J_Q(t',x')] \rangle$ depends on the modes $h_k^{I,II}(t)$. However, the time integral present in (18) depends on both the current time t and the integration variable t'. In order to make this integral suitable for numerical evaluation, it is convenient to utilize (23a) and (23b) which allows it to be expressed as

$$\int_{-\infty}^{t} dt'\,\text{Im}\{h_k^I(t)h_k^{II}(t)h_k^{I*}(t')h_k^{II*}(t')\}\delta A(t')$$

$$= \left(\text{Im}\{h_k^I(t)\}\text{Im}\{h_k^{II}(t)\} - \text{Re}\{h_k^I(t)\}\text{Re}\{h_k^{II}(t)\} \right)$$

$$\times \int_{-\infty}^{t} dt' \left(\text{Re}\{h_k^{I*}(t')\}\text{Im}\{h_k^{II*}(t')\} + \text{Im}\{h_k^{I*}(t')\}\text{Re}\{h_k^{II*}(t')\} \right) \delta A(t')$$

$$+ \left(\text{Re}\{h_k^I(t)\}\text{Im}\{h_k^{II}(t)\} + \text{Im}\{h_k^I(t)\}\text{Re}\{h_k^{II}(t)\} \right)$$

$$\times \int_{-\infty}^{t} dt' \left(\text{Re}\{h_k^{I*}(t')\}\text{Re}\{h_k^{II*}(t')\} - \text{Im}\{h_k^{I*}(t')\}\text{Im}\{h_k^{II*}(t')\} \right) \delta A(t')\,. \tag{26}$$

Here the inter-dependence of t and t', seen in the product $h_k^I(t)h_k^{II}(t)h_k^{I*}(t')h_k^{II*}(t')$, has been separated out. This allows for the time integral to be computed which then acts as the integrand for the k-integral in (18), which can be computed as well. From this the numerical solutions $\delta A(t)$ and $\delta E(t)$ to the linear response equation can be found.

4.2. Results and Discussion

In what follows, numerical results are presented for the critical case of $qE_0/m^2 = 1$. In Fig. 2, the net electric field $E(t)$ including backreaction is plotted[1] with both the electric field contributions E_C when quantum effects are absent and E_Q generated by only quantum effects, seen in (15b) and (15a). One can see that at early times the net electric field begins to dampen compared to its classical counterpart E_C. This is due to the backreaction of the produced particles, resulting from the coupling of the spin $1/2$ field to the classical background source, causing an increase in the field E_Q.

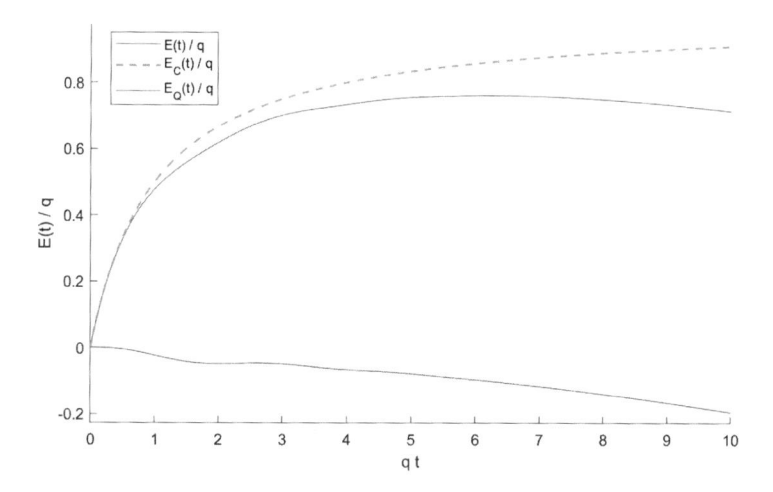

Fig. 2. A plot of the electric field including backreaction. The net electric field $E(t)$ is given by the blue curve, the electric field $E_C(t)$ with no quantum effects present is given by the yellow dashed curve, and the electric field $E_Q(t)$ generated by only quantum effects is given by the red curve.

Numerical solutions to the linear response equation are plotted in Fig. 3. The top plot shows the numerical solution δE to the linear response equation, its approximate solution given by the finite difference between two nearby semiclassical backreaction equation solutions ΔE, and the classical pieces $\delta E_C = \Delta E_C$. The bottom plot shows the purely quantum contributions to both the approximate ΔE_Q and numerical δE_Q solutions to the linear response equation. From (14) the initial value δE_0 was chosen in such a way as to equal the finite difference ΔE at early times, with this value being of order 10^{-3}.

For early times, there appears to be agreement between δE and ΔE, as well as ΔE_Q and δE_Q since the classical contribution dominates due to a lack particle production. However, near the time $qt = 1$ significant deviation between the two begins to occur, as could be measured by $(\delta E - \Delta E)/\delta E$. This deviation and subsequent late time growth in δE is driven by the dependence of $\langle [J_Q(t,x), J_Q(t',x')] \rangle$

on the modes $h_k^{I,II}(t)$, whose positive frequency plane wave solutions are being altered due to the presence of the classical source term $A(t)$ having been switched on and leading to particle production. Since the critical case $qE_0/m^2 = 1$ considered is a threshold case for significant particle production, above which even more particle production will occur, the growth of δE due to $\langle [J_Q(t,x), J_Q(t',x')] \rangle$ is expected.

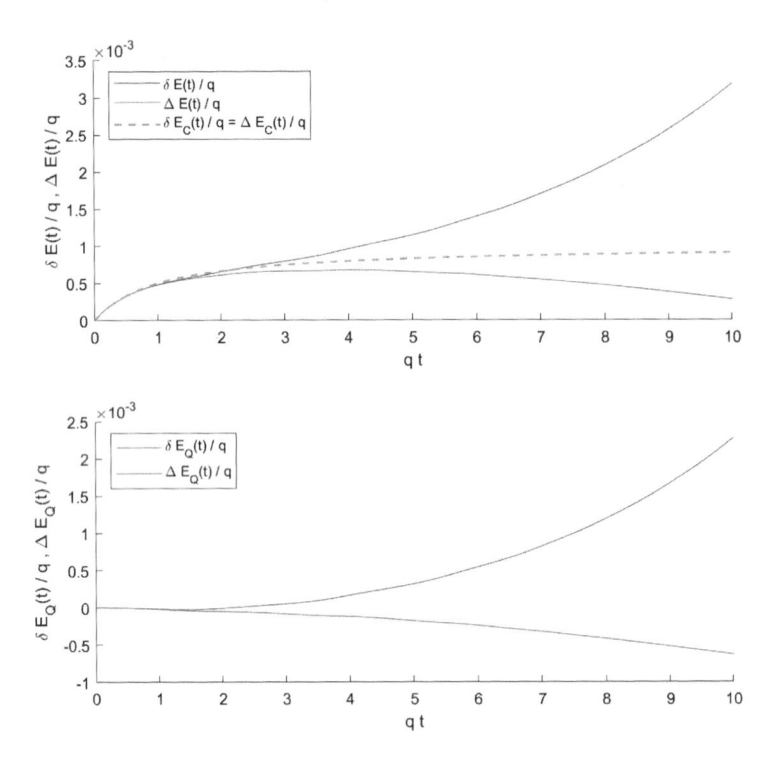

Fig. 3. The top plot shows solutions to the linear response equation, with red and blue curves representing the approximate and numerical solutions ΔE and δE, respectively, with the yellow dashed curve being the classical contribution to the solution. The bottom plot isolates the quantum contribution to the linear response equation, for both the approximate and numerical solutions ΔE_Q and δE_Q. All plots reflect the critical case of $qE_0/m^2 = 1$ and were done with δE_0 and ΔE of order 10^{-3} for early times.

The time $qt = 1$ is also when one begins to notice substantial deviation between the net and classical electric fields, seen in Fig. 2, due to the presence of a nontrivial $\langle J_Q \rangle$ factor in (11) which will grow as more particles are produced. Furthermore, this time is also when one sees substantial growth of R_Q in Fig. 1 for the critical case. It therefore appears that for early times the ΔE is a good approximation to the linear response equation solution δE, and for late times $\delta E \neq \Delta E$. Comparing to the corresponding R_Q behavior, there is a breakdown in the semiclassical approximation based on the validity criterion implemented here. This was the conclusion that was arrived at in [9], and it appears the behavior of the solutions δE as compared with the ΔE validates this conclusion.

5. Conclusions

In previous work,[1] a criterion for the validity of the semiclassical approximation was applied to the case of 1+1 semiclassical electrodynamics which involves the behavior of solutions to the linear response equation. The linear response equation depends, in part, on a two-point correlation function $\langle [J_Q(t,x), J_Q(t',x')] \rangle$, which characterizes the quantum fluctuations introduced through the current $\langle J_Q \rangle$. Numerical solutions to the linear response equation have been obtained for 1+1 semiclassical electrodynamics using a model of the Schwinger effect in which particle production occurs in the presence of a strong, spatially homogeneous, electric field. The particle production, in the context of the system considered here, is a consequence of the coupling between a quantized spin ½ field and a classical, asymptotically constant, background electric field generated by an external source. Since the linear response equation depends on $\langle [J_Q(t,x), J_Q(t',x')] \rangle$, if there is rapid growth in this correlation function for some period of time, then quantum fluctuations must be significant, and will drive the growth of solutions δE to the linear response equation, resulting in a breakdown of the semiclassical approximation.

A previously developed technique to approximate solutions to the linear response equation involves the difference ΔE between two solutions to the semiclassical backreaction equation with similar initial conditions. The behavior of a quantity R_Q built from this difference of semiclassical backreaction equation solutions gives a measure for the validity of the semiclassical approximation. When R_Q grows large over some time, the corresponding linear response equation solution is expected to do so as well.

An analysis comparing the numerical δE and approximate ΔE solutions to the linear response equation has been conducted. At the critical scale, where $qE_0/m^2 \sim 1$, it was found that at early times the quantity ΔE approximated the linear response equation solutions δE quite well. It was only after enough time had passed and significant particle production occurred that the numerical and approximate solutions deviated from one another. Therefore the claim that ΔE adequately approximates solutions to the linear response equation for early times is substantiated in this case. This critical scale was also the case for which the quantity R_Q had its largest growth[1] and therefore was the case considered for the purposes of this proceeding. The significant growth in both δE and R_Q signals a breakdown of the semiclassical approximation based on the validity criterion utilized here.

Regarding future work, the numerical solutions to the linear response equation will be used to further investigate the nature of how quantum fluctuations affect these solutions. More specifically, since the linear response equation involves several factors which dictate the behavior of its solutions, one of which is a term characterizing quantum fluctuations introduced through the particle production process, having the numerical solution will allow one to isolate and investigate its respective contributions in detail.

Acknowledgements

I. M. N. would like thank Silvia Pla for sharing semiclassical backreaction numerical code and data as well as helpful discussions, Eric Grotzke for helpful discussions regarding linear response equation numerical details, Paul R. Anderson for guidance regarding the creation of this manuscript as well as helpful discussions, and Jose Navarro-Salas and Kaitlin Hill for helpful discussions. All numerical work was performed using MATLAB software with special thanks to the Distributed Environment for Academic Computing (DEAC) at Wake Forest University for providing HPC resources which contributed to the research presented in this proceeding.

References

1. S. P. Pla, I. M. Newsome, R. S. Link, P. R. Anderson, and J. Navarro-Salas, Phys. Rev. D **103**, 105003 (2021).
2. J. Schwinger, Phys. Rev. **82**, 664 (1951).
3. Y. Kluger, J. M. Eisenberg, B. Svetitsky, F. Cooper and E. Mottola, Phys. Rev. Lett. **67**, 2427 (1991).
4. Y. Kluger, J. M. Eisenberg, B. Svetitsky, F. Cooper and E. Mottola, Phys. Rev. D **45**, 4659 (1992).
5. Y. Kluger, J. M. Eisenberg, and B. Svetitsky, Int. J. Mod. Phys. E **02**, 333 (1993).
6. N. Tanji, Ann. Phys. (Amsterdam) **324**, 1691 (2009).
7. F. Gelis and N. Tanji, Phys. Rev. D **87**, 125035 (2013).
8. P. R. Anderson, C. Molina-Paris, and D. H. Sanders, Phys. Rev. D **92**, 083522 (2015).
9. P. R. Anderson, C. Molina-Paris, and E. Mottola, Phys. Rev. D **67**, 024026 (2003).
10. A. Ferreiro and J. Navarro-Salas, Phys. Rev. D **97**, 125012 (2018).
11. C.-H. Wu and L. H. Ford, Phys. Rev. D **60**, 104013 (1999).
12. N. G. Phillips and B. L. Hu, Phys. Rev. D **62**, 084017 (2000).

On Kerr black hole perfect MHD processes in Doran coordinates

C. Cherubini

Department of Science and Technology for Humans and the Environment and ICRA,
Campus Bio-Medico University of Rome, Rome, 00128 Italy
and International Center for Relativistic Astrophysics Network-ICRANet,
65122 Pescara, Italy
E-mail: c.cherubini@unicampus.it
www.unicampus.it

S. Filippi

Department of Engineering and ICRA, Campus Bio-Medico University of Rome,
Rome, 00128 Italy
and International Center for Relativistic Astrophysics Network-ICRANet,
65122 Pescara, Italy
E-mail: s.filippi@unicampus.it
www.unicampus.it

A. Loppini

Department of Engineering, Campus Bio-Medico University of Rome, Rome, 00128 Italy
Center for Life Nano- & Neuro-Science, Istituto Italiano di Tecnologia (IIT), Viale Regina
Elena 291, 00161 Roma, Italy
E-mail: a.loppini@unicampus.it
www.unicampus.it

R. Ruffini[*], R. Moradi[†] and Y. Wang[‡]

ICRANet, Piazza della Repubblica 10, Pescara, I–65122, Italy,
ICRA, Dipartimento di Fisica, Sapienza Universita' di Roma, Rome, I–00185, Italy
and INAF, Rome, 00136, Italy
[*]E-mail: ruffini@icra.it
[†]E-mail: rahim.moradi@icranet.org
[‡]E-mail: yu.wang@icranet.org
www.icranet.org

S.S. Xue

ICRANet, Piazza della Repubblica 10, Pescara, I–65122, Italy,
ICRA, Dipartimento di Fisica, Sapienza Universita' di Roma, Rome, I–00185, Italy
E-mail: xue@icra.it
www.icranet.org

Doran horizon penetrating coordinates are adopted to study specific perfect MHD processes around a Kerr black hole, focusing in particular on the physical relevance of selected electrodynamical quantities.

Keywords: Black hole physics, Relativistic MHD, Analytical solutions.

1. Introduction

General Relativity is a non linear theory which couples any physical field to gravitation described in terms of the geometry of space-time. This makes the search of exact or approximate analytical solutions for physical relevant problems an extraordinary task. Nowadays, Numerical Relativity has greatly circumvented such a problem by using the huge computational power available[1] although analytical solutions still remain fundamental to have important physical insights. The 60s and the 70s represented an important moment of rediscovery of Einstein's Theory. At that time, numerical relativity was almost unknown and Mathematical Physics techniques were widely adopted to find exact or approximate solutions. In particular, in the field of Black Holes Physics, the understanding of the electrodynamics and magnetohydrodynamics (MHD) around the recently discovered Kerr rotating black hole solution[2] was central. Due to the aforementioned difficulty associated to the non-linearity of the equations, approximate techniques of perturbative type were applied to this aim as, for instance, in the classical work by Ruffini and Wilson[3] and the one by Damour[4] (RWD) based on the properties of the geodesics in Kerr background studied by Carter.[5] In particular Ruffini and Wilson used a simplified model to describe possible charge separation processes involving the black hole and its magnetosphere. Such a studies have been recently revisited[6] by using coordinates regular on the horizon found decades later by Doran[8] and are here reviewed. Doran's work in particular generalizes classical Painlevé-Gullstrand coordinates for spherical black holes. These coordinates are horizon penetrating and are naturally associated to regular infalling physical observers. They are usually adopted in Numerical Relativity in union with the *excision* technique which allows to extend the computational domain beyond the black hole event horizon, avoiding to impose problematic boundary conditions for the partial differential equations there. Moreover, Painlevé-Gullstrand type coordinates naturally occur in Analogue Gravity in relation with acoustic black holes.[7] Summarizing, what we discuss here is the revisitation of RWD works by using useful coordinates found almost 25 years later. We will show in particular that these coordinates are the most natural ones to describe plasma physics by comoving with the fluid itself.

2. The RWD solution

RWD started from the Kerr metric in Boyer-Lindquist coordinates

$$ds^2 = -\left(1 - \frac{2Mr}{\Sigma}\right)dt^2 - \frac{4aMr\sin^2\theta}{\Sigma}dtd\phi + \frac{\Sigma}{\Delta}dr^2 + \Sigma d\theta^2$$
$$+ \left[r^2 + a^2 + \frac{2Mra^2\sin^2\theta}{\Sigma}\right]\sin^2\theta d\phi^2, \qquad (1)$$

with $\Sigma = r^2 + a^2\cos^2\theta$, $\Delta = r^2 - 2Mr + a^2$, a being the specific angular momentum and M the black hole mass, while the outer event horizon is located at $r_+ = M + \sqrt{M^2 - a^2}$ and Boyer-Lindquist coordinates are singular there. In the test field approximation (no metric back reaction), neglecting pressure gradients in MHD equations as well as magnetic force terms and imposing a perfect plasma condition $F_{\mu\nu}U^\nu = 0$, the fluid must follow the geodesics on Kerr background studied by Carter:

$$U_{\mu;\nu}U^\nu = 0. \qquad (2)$$

In particular in their works, RWD consider $U_\phi = 0$ and $U_t = -1$ at infinity and this implies that U_θ is a constant of motion. The four-velocity geodesic vector is then:

$$U^t = \frac{\Sigma(r^2+a^2) + 2Mra^2\sin^2\theta}{\Sigma\Delta}, \quad U^r = -\frac{[-\Delta U_\theta^2 + 2Mr(r^2+a^2)]^{\frac{1}{2}}}{\Sigma}$$
$$U^\theta = \frac{U_\theta}{\Sigma}, \quad U^\phi = \frac{2MRa}{\Sigma\Delta}. \qquad (3)$$

Finally, requiring overall neutral stationary and axisymmetric configuration, the vector potential A_μ is characterized by the A_ϕ component only. RWD solving the simplified MHD equations found in such a a first approximation the analytical solution:

$$A_\phi = A(\theta_\infty) = A_\phi(\theta, r) \qquad (4)$$

where

$$\theta_\infty = \theta - U_\theta \xi(r) \qquad (5)$$

and

$$\xi(r) = \int_r^\infty \frac{dr'}{\sqrt{-(r'^2 - 2Mr' + a^2)U_\theta^2 + 2Mr'(r'^2 + a^2)}}. \qquad (6)$$

From these relations, one case easily reconstruct the entire Maxwell tensor $F_{\mu\nu}$ and obtain the associated four-current J^μ. Great simplification occur by choosing $U_\theta = 0$ because in such a case it results $A_\phi = F(\theta)$ with F a being an arbitrary function. Specifically, in RWD works it has been assumed the simple form $F(\theta) = A_0|\cos\theta|$ where quantity A_0 is a constant. Concerning Maxwell invariants, for this solution they have these properties:[6]

$$\frac{1}{2}F_{\mu\nu}F^{\mu\nu} = (\mathbf{B}^2 - \mathbf{E}^2) \geq 0, \quad \frac{1}{4}F_{\mu\nu}{}^*F^{\mu\nu} = \mathbf{E}\cdot\mathbf{B} = 0, \qquad (7)$$

so there must exist a frame in which the observer associated to the geodesics four-velocity measures a magnetic field only, while the electric one vanishes in consequence of the perfect plasma condition. In standard perfect MHD physics, both charge density and electric field disappear in a locally comoving (and corotating) plasma frame. This frame is in general not easy to be found analytically,[9] but for the RWD solution however, by using Doran coordinates, we will successfully obtain it, as now discussed.

3. Doran coordinates analysis

The transformation from Boyer-Lindquist (BL) coordinates (t, r, θ, ϕ) to Doran Painlevé-Gullstrand-like (DPG) ones (T, R, Θ, Φ) is:

$$T = t - \int^r f(r)dr, \quad R = r, \quad \Theta = \theta,$$

$$\Phi = \phi - \int^r \frac{a}{r^2 + a^2} f(r)dr, \quad f(r) = -\frac{\sqrt{(2Mr)(r^2 + a^2)}}{\Delta}, \tag{8}$$

so Kerr solution becomes

$$ds^2 = -\left(1 - \frac{2Mr}{\Sigma}\right)dT^2 + 2\sqrt{\frac{2Mr}{r^2 + a^2}}dTdr - \frac{2a(2Mr)}{\Sigma}\sin^2\theta dTd\Phi$$

$$+ \sin^2\theta\left[r^2 + a^2 + \frac{a^2(2Mr)}{\Sigma}\sin^2\theta\right]d\Phi^2 - 2a\sin^2\theta\sqrt{\frac{2Mr}{r^2 + a^2}}drd\Phi$$

$$+ \frac{\Sigma}{r^2 + a^2}dr^2 + \Sigma d\theta^2. \tag{9}$$

In the following, due to some of the coordinates' coincidence, we shall denote R with r and Θ with θ again. Using the coordinates transformation above, the RWD vector potential becomes

$$A_\mu = \left[0, -a\sqrt{\frac{2Mr}{r^2 + a^2}}\frac{F(\theta)}{\Delta}, 0, F(\theta)\right]. \tag{10}$$

with $F(\Theta) \equiv F(\theta) = A_0|\cos\theta|$. Concerning the geodesics, we get

$$U_\mu = \left[-1, -\frac{\sqrt{-\Delta U_\theta^2 + 2Mr(r^2 + a^2)}}{\Delta} + \frac{\sqrt{2Mr(r^2 + a^2)}}{\Delta}, U_\theta, 0\right], \tag{11}$$

which in the case of interest $U_\theta = 0$ case become

$$U_\mu = [-1, 0, 0, 0] \tag{12}$$

$$U^\mu = \left[1, -\frac{\sqrt{(2Mr)(r^2 + a^2)}}{\Sigma}, 0, 0\right]. \tag{13}$$

The four-velocity U^μ above represents the $T = const$ normal geodesic observer. Quantity T is the local proper time of observers in free fall along trajectories characterized by constant θ and Φ. The DPG electromagnetic tensor of the $U_\theta = 0$ RWD solution field has the only non vanishing component, undefined on the equatorial plane, given by:

$$F_{\Phi\theta} = A_{\Phi,\theta} \equiv \frac{dF(\theta)}{d\theta} = -A_0 \sin\theta \frac{|\cos\theta|}{\cos\theta}. \tag{14}$$

Defining the orthonormal locally Lorentzian frame $e^{(a)}{}_\mu$ associated to the DPG normal observer discussed above:

$$e^{(0)}{}_\mu = [-1,0,0,0]\,, \quad e^{(1)}{}_\mu = \left[\sqrt{\frac{2Mr}{\Sigma}}, \sqrt{\frac{\Sigma}{r^2+a^2}}, 0, -\sqrt{\frac{2Mr}{\Sigma}}\,a\sin^2\theta\right]$$
$$e^{(2)}{}_\mu = \left[0,0,\sqrt{\Sigma},0\right]\,, \quad e^{(3)}{}_\mu = \left[0,0,0,\sqrt{r^2+a^2}\sin\theta\right]\,, \quad (15)$$

one can easily show that the Maxwell tensor in the frame $F_{(a)(b)} = e_{(a)}{}^\mu e_{(b)}{}^\mu F_{\mu\nu}$ has the only non vanishing component (giving a magnetic field only):

$$F_{(3)(4)} = -F_{(4)(3)} \equiv B_{(1)} \equiv B_{\hat{r}} = -\frac{A_0}{\sqrt{(r^2+a^2)\Sigma}}\frac{|\cos\theta|}{\cos\theta}\,. \quad (16)$$

Moreover, by computing the charge density $J^\mu U_\mu \equiv J_{(0)} = \rho$ measured by the same observer one easily finds that it vanishes everywhere. As anticipated, we have found the natural frame to describe this perfect MHD problem which is the comoving fluid one. Moreover by using the fact that we have horizon penetrating coordinates, we can follow the fields inside the black hole. In particular it is possible to plot the four current lines for this RWD solution given by the numerical integration of the differential equations set $dx^\alpha/d\lambda = J^\alpha$ with λ parametrising the curves.[6] To note that while in BL coordinates the current lines whirl infinite times around the event horizon without entering inside, in DPG coordinates (we remind that these are naturally associated to comoving observers) the current lines are not whirled and can be continued regularly in the interior of the black hole. Finally, the use of DPG coordinates allows one to obtain elegant expressions for studying the energetics of the RWD solution. Always in the $U_\theta = 0$ case, one can easily compute an important quasi-local quantity i.e. the electromagnetic energy stored outside the event horizon through a $T = const$ cut in space-time as measured by the DPG normal observer. This quantity is given by

$$E_\sigma(U) = \int_\sigma T^{(em)}_{\mu\nu} U^\mu d\sigma^\nu\,. \quad (17)$$

Here σ is a bounded hypersurface which contains a portion of spacetime while U^μ represents the normal observer's four-velocity. In the relation above,

$$\mathcal{E} = T^{(em)}_{\mu\nu} U^\mu U^\nu \equiv \frac{A_0^2}{8\pi(r^2+a^2)\Sigma} \equiv 8\pi\mathcal{F} \geq 0\,, \quad (18)$$

is the local electromagnetic energy density obtained from the $T^{(em)}_{\mu\nu}$ electromagnetic energy-momentum tensor in DPG coordinates, here proportional to the first Maxwell invariant. Assuming the outer boundary of σ being the 2-surface $r = \mathcal{R} = const$, we get the simple relation:

$$E_{(r_+,\mathcal{R})}(U) = \frac{A_0^2}{2a}\left[\arctan\frac{\mathcal{R}}{a} - \arctan\frac{r_+}{a}\right]\,. \quad (19)$$

4. Conclusions

We have shown that the adoption of recent modern tools is extremely useful for revisiting classical studies of the 60s and 70s. We have adopted in particular the most natural object to describe the physics of Ruffini-Wilson and Damour works, represented by Kerr black hole Doran horizon penetrating coordinates with their naturally associated normal observer. We have in particular described plasma physics from the fluid comoving frame and found great simplification for the electrodynamical quantities. The limitation of the analysis here presented however rely on the $U_\theta = 0$ choice which does not allow to obtain possible charge separation processes (charge density is vanishing everywhere in this case in fact), obtained by Ruffini and Wilson by imposing $U_\theta(\theta) = -U_\theta(\pi - \theta) = const$ instead. In order to address such a more complicated problem one should require a further generalization of Doran's work for the $U_\theta \neq 0$ case first. This study is not present in the literature and deserves future studies in order to revisit also the problem of Ruffini and Wilson charge separation.

Acknowledgments

C.C., S.F. and A.L. acknowledge ICRANet and INdAM-GNFM for support.

References

1. T. W. Baumgarte and S. L. Shapiro, *Numerical Relativity: Solving Einstein's Equations on the Computer* (Cambridge University Press 2010)
2. R. P. Kerr, *Phys. Rev. Lett.* **11**, 237 (1963).
3. R. Ruffini and J.R. Wilson, *Phys. Rev. D* **12**, 2959 (1975).
4. T. Damour, *Annals of the New York Academy of Sciences*, **262**, 113 (1975).
5. B. Carter, *Phys. Rev.* **174**, 1559 (1968).
6. C. Cherubini, S. Filippi, A. Loppini, R. Moradi, R. Ruffini, Y. Wang and S-S. Xue, *Phys. Rev. D.*, **97**, 064038 (2018).
7. C. Barcelo, S. Liberati and M. Visser, *Living Rev. Relativ.*, **14**, 3 (2011).
8. C. Doran, *Phys. Rev. D* **61**, 067503 (2000).
9. H. C. Spruit, *arXiv: 1301.5572v3* page 49 (2016).

Tadpole contribution to magnetic photon-graviton conversion

N. Ahmadiniaz

Helmholtz-Zentrum Dresden-Rossendorf, Bautzner Landstraße 400, 01328 Dresden, Germany
E-mail: n.ahmadiniaz@hzdr.de

F. Bastianelli

Dipartimento di Fisica ed Astronomia, Università di Bologna, Via Irnerio 46, I-40126 Bologna, Italy and INFN, Sezione di Bologna, Via Irnerio 46, I-40126 Bologna, Italy
E-mail: bastianelli@bo.infn.it

F. Karbstein

Helmholtz-Institut Jena, Fröbelstieg 3, 07743 Jena, Germany and Theoretisch-Physikalisches Institut, Friedrich-Schiller-Universität Jena, Max-Wien-Platz 1, 07743 Jena, Germany
E-mail: felix.karbstein@uni-jena.de

C. Schubert

Instituto de Física y Matemáticas Universidad Michoacana de San Nicolás de Hidalgo Edificio C-3, Apdo. Postal 2-82 C.P. 58040, Morelia, Michoacán, México
E-mail: christianschubert137@gmail.com

Photon-graviton conversion in a magnetic field is a process that is usually studied at tree level, but the one-loop corrections due to scalars and spinors have also been calculated. Differently from the tree-level process, at one-loop one finds the amplitude to depend on the photon polarization, leading to dichroism. However, previous calculations overlooked a tadpole contribution of the type that was considered to be vanishing in QED for decades but erroneously so, as shown by H. Gies and one of the authors in 2016. Here we compute this missing diagram in closed form, and show that it does not contribute to dichroism.

Keywords: Photon-graviton; tadpole; Einstein-Maxwell

1. Introduction: Photon-graviton conversion

Einstein-Maxwell theory contains a tree-level vertex for photon-graviton conversion in a constant electromagnetic field:

$$\frac{1}{2}\kappa h_{\mu\nu}\left(F^{\mu\alpha}f^{\nu}{}_{\alpha} + f^{\mu}{}_{\alpha}F^{\nu\alpha}\right) - \frac{1}{4}\kappa h^{\mu}_{\mu}F^{\alpha\beta}f_{\alpha\beta}. \quad (1)$$

Here $h_{\mu\nu}$ denotes the graviton, $f_{\mu\nu}$ the photon, $F^{\mu\nu}$ the external field, and κ the gravitational coupling constant.

This interaction leads to photon-graviton oscillations similar to the better-known neutrino or photon-axion oscillations[1-11] (see[12] for a recent application to gravitational waves).

In momentum space, this vertex becomes

$$\Gamma^{(\text{tree})}(k,\varepsilon;F) = \epsilon_{\mu\nu}\varepsilon_\alpha \Pi^{\mu\nu,\alpha}_{(\text{tree})}(k;F), \quad \Pi^{\mu\nu,\alpha}_{(\text{tree})}(k;F) = -\frac{i\kappa}{2}C^{\mu\nu,\alpha} \qquad (2)$$

with

$$C^{\mu\nu,\alpha} = F^{\mu\alpha}k^\nu + F^{\nu\alpha}k^\mu - (F\cdot k)^\mu \delta^{\nu\alpha} - (F\cdot k)^\nu \delta^{\mu\alpha} + (F\cdot k)^\alpha \delta^{\mu\nu}. \qquad (3)$$

Since in a constant field the four-momentum is preserved, k^μ here is the four-momentum of the photon as well as of the graviton.

For the photon polarizations, as is customary we will use the Lorentz frame where **E** and **B** are collinear, and choose the polarization basis $\varepsilon^\alpha_\perp, \varepsilon^\alpha_\parallel$, where $\varepsilon^\alpha_\parallel$ lies in the plane spanned by k and **B** or **E**, and $\varepsilon^\alpha_\perp$ is perpendicular to it. For convenience we construct also the graviton polarization tensor using the same vectors:

$$\varepsilon^{\oplus\mu\nu} = \varepsilon^{\perp\mu}\varepsilon^{\perp\nu} - \varepsilon^{\parallel\mu}\varepsilon^{\parallel\nu}, \quad \varepsilon^{\otimes\mu\nu} = \varepsilon^{\perp\mu}\varepsilon^{\parallel\nu} + \varepsilon^{\parallel\mu}\varepsilon^{\perp\nu}. \qquad (4)$$

From the CP-invariance of Einstein-Maxwell theory one can then derive the following selection rules:

- For a purely magnetic field $\varepsilon^\oplus$ couples only to $\varepsilon^\perp$ and $\varepsilon^\otimes$ only to $\varepsilon^\parallel$.
- For a purely electric field $\varepsilon^\oplus$ couples only to $\varepsilon^\parallel$ and $\varepsilon^\otimes$ only to $\varepsilon^\perp$.

2. One-loop photon-graviton vacuum polarization

In[13,14] the worldline formalism was used along the lines of[15–17] to study the one-loop corrections to this amplitude due to a scalar or spinor loop, see Fig. 1.

Fig. 1. One-loop correction to the photon-graviton amplitude in a constant field.

Here we employ the usual double-line notation for the full propagator in the external electromagnetic field, Fig. 2.

Fig. 2. Full scalar or spinor propagator in a constant field.

These calculations lead to the same type of two-parameter integrals as for the well-studied case of the one-loop photon vacuum polarisation in a constant field.[18–29]

Both the scalar and the spinor-loop amplitudes are UV divergent, but multiplicatively renormalizable. For example, the scalar-loop contribution in dimensional regularization displays the pole

$$\Pi^{\mu\nu,\alpha}_{\text{scal,div}}(k) = \frac{ie^2\kappa}{3(4\pi)^2} \frac{1}{D-4} C^{\mu\nu,\alpha}$$

where $C^{\mu\nu,\alpha}$ is the tree level vertex (3).

For studying the relative importance of the one-loop amplitudes it is useful to normalize them by the tree-level amplitude (the "bar" on Π denotes renormalization)

$$\hat{\Pi}^{Aa}_{\text{scal,spin}}(\hat{\omega}, \hat{B}, \hat{E}) \equiv \frac{\bar{\Pi}^{Aa}_{\text{scal,spin}}(\hat{\omega}, \hat{B}, \hat{E})}{-\frac{i}{2}\kappa C^{Aa}} \tag{5}$$

where $A = \oplus, \otimes$ and $a = \perp, \|$, $\hat{\omega} = \frac{\omega}{m}$, $\hat{B} = \frac{eB}{m^2}$, $\hat{E} = \frac{eE}{m^2}$.

It then becomes obvious that the one-loop amplitudes become quantitatively relevant only for field strengths close to the critical ones $\hat{B}, \hat{E} \approx 1$. Macroscopic fields of this magnitude are known to exist only for the magnetic case, so that we will set $\hat{E} = 0$ in the following. In[14] it was shown that for this purely magnetic case the parameter integrals allow for a straightforward numerical evaluation as long as the photon energy $\hat{\omega}$ is below the pair-creation threshold $\hat{\omega}_{\text{cr}}$,

$$\hat{\omega}^{\oplus\perp}_{\text{cr,scal}} = \hat{\omega}^{\otimes\|}_{\text{cr,scal}} = 2\sqrt{1+\hat{B}},$$
$$\hat{\omega}^{\oplus\perp}_{\text{cr,spin}} = 1 + \sqrt{1+2\hat{B}},$$
$$\hat{\omega}^{\otimes\|}_{\text{cr,spin}} = 2. \tag{6}$$

There also a number of special cases were studied that allow for more explicit representations:

(1) The case of small B and arbitrary ω leads to single - parameter integrals over Airy functions.
(2) In the large B limit one finds a logarithmic growth in the field strength,

$$\hat{\Pi}^{Aa}_{\text{scal}}(\hat{\omega}, \hat{B}) \overset{\hat{B}\to\infty}{\sim} -\frac{\alpha}{12\pi} \ln(\hat{B}), \tag{7}$$

$$\hat{\Pi}^{Aa}_{\text{spin}}(\hat{\omega}, \hat{B}) \overset{\hat{B}\to\infty}{\sim} -\frac{\alpha}{3\pi} \ln(\hat{B}). \tag{8}$$

(3) In the limit of vanishing photon energy the amplitudes can be related to the corresponding one-loop effective Lagrangians:

$$\hat{\Pi}^{\oplus\perp}_{\text{scal,spin}}(\hat{\omega}=0, \hat{B}) = -\frac{2\pi\alpha}{m^4}\left(\frac{1}{\hat{B}}\frac{\partial}{\partial\hat{B}} + \frac{\partial^2}{\partial\hat{B}^2}\right) \mathcal{L}^{\text{EH}}_{\text{scal,spin}}(\hat{B}), \tag{9}$$

$$\hat{\Pi}^{\otimes\|}_{\text{scal,spin}}(\hat{\omega}=0, \hat{B}) = -\frac{4\pi\alpha}{m^4}\frac{1}{\hat{B}}\frac{\partial}{\partial\hat{B}} \mathcal{L}^{\text{EH}}_{\text{scal,spin}}(\hat{B}). \tag{10}$$

Here $\mathcal{L}_{\text{scal,spin}}^{\text{EH}}(\hat{B})$ denotes the one-loop effective Lagrangian in a constant magnetic field, obtained for the spinor QED case by Heisenberg and Euler[30] and for scalar QED by Weisskopf[31]:

$$\mathcal{L}_{\text{scal}}^{\text{EH}}(\hat{B}) = -\frac{m^4}{16\pi^2} \int_0^\infty \frac{d\hat{s}}{\hat{s}^3} e^{-i\hat{s}} \left[\frac{\hat{B}\hat{s}}{\sin(\hat{B}\hat{s})} - \frac{(\hat{B}\hat{s})^2}{6} - 1 \right], \tag{11}$$

$$\mathcal{L}_{\text{spin}}^{\text{EH}}(\hat{B}) = \frac{m^4}{8\pi^2} \int_0^\infty \frac{d\hat{s}}{\hat{s}^3} e^{-i\hat{s}} \left[\frac{\hat{B}\hat{s}}{\tan(\hat{B}\hat{s})} + \frac{(\hat{B}\hat{s})^2}{3} - 1 \right]. \tag{12}$$

3. Dichroism

For realistic parameters, the one-loop corrections turn out to be small compared to the tree-level amplitudes. However, there is also a qualitative difference to the tree-level amplitude. As has been emphasized in,[9] the tree level photon-graviton conversion does, contrary to the better known photon-axion case, not lead to a dichroism effect for photon beams. This is because both photon polarization components have equal conversion rates. This symmetry gets broken by the loop corrections. Although this effect is, of course, tiny and hardly measurable in the near future, an exhaustive analysis by Ahlers et al.[32] has shown that it is still the leading contribution to magnetic dichroism in the standard model (including standard gravity)!

4. Quantum electrodynamics in external fields

In vacuum QED, there is, of course, no one-photon amplitude because of Furry's theorem. In the presence of an external field, however, one-photon tadpole diagrams such as the one in Fig. 3 will in general be nonzero.

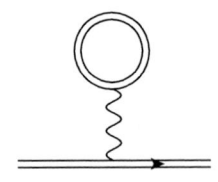

Fig. 3. Full scalar or spinor propagator in a constant field.

If the external field is constant, then the one-photon amplitude Fig. 4 can still be shown to vanish.

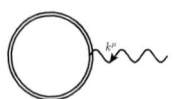

Fig. 4. One photon amplitude in a constant field.

The argument goes as follows:

(1) A constant field emits only photons with zero energy-momentum, thus there is a factor of $\delta(k)$.
(2) Because of gauge invariance, this diagram in a momentum expansion starts with the term linear in momentum.
(3) $\delta(k)k^\mu = 0$.

Since the tadpole vanishes, it has been assumed for decades that also any diagram containing it can be discarded. For example, in the book "Quantum Electrodynamics with Unstable Vacuum" by E.S. Fradkin, D.M. Gitman and S.M. Shvartsman[34] it is stated (on page 225) even more generally that, "*Thus, in the constant and homogeneous external field combined with that of a plane-wave, all the diagrams containing the causal current $\mathcal{J}^\mu(x)$ (i.e., those containing tadpoles having a causal propagator $S^c(x,y)$), are equal to zero.*"

Sometimes also additional arguments have been given; in the book "Effective Lagrangians in Quantum Electrodynamics" by Dittrich and Reuter[33] it is argued that the "handcuff" diagram of Fig. 5 vanishes because of Lorenz invariance.

Fig. 5. Handcuff diagram in a constant field.

However, in 2016 H. Gies and one of the authors[35] noted that such diagrams can give finite values because of the infrared divergence of the connecting photon propagator. In dimensional regularization, the key integral is

$$\int d^D k \, \delta^D(k) \frac{k^\mu k^\nu}{k^2} = \frac{\eta^{\mu\nu}}{D}. \tag{13}$$

Applying this integral to the handcuff diagram one finds a non-vanishing result, which can be expressed in the following simple way in terms of the one-loop Euler-Heisenberg Lagrangian[36]

$$\mathcal{L}_{\text{spin}}^{\text{1PR}} = \frac{1}{2} \frac{\partial \mathcal{L}_{\text{spin}}^{(EH)}}{\partial F^{\mu\nu}} \frac{\partial \mathcal{L}_{\text{spin}}^{(EH)}}{\partial F_{\mu\nu}}$$

(the superscript "1PR" stands for "one-particle reducible"). This adds on to the standard diagram for the two-loop Euler-Heisenberg Lagrangian, studied by V.I. Ritus[39] half a century ago:

$$\mathcal{L}_{\text{spin}}^{(EH)2-\text{loop}} = \quad + \quad \tag{14}$$

Along the same lines, it was found in[37,38] that the one-loop tadpole contribution Fig. 3 to the scalar or spinor propagator in a constant field is also non-vanishing,

and given by
$$S^{\text{1PR}}(p) = \frac{\partial S(p)}{\partial F_{\mu\nu}} \frac{\partial \mathcal{L}^{(EH)}}{\partial F^{\mu\nu}}$$

where $S(p)$ denotes the tree-level propagator in the field.

5. Tadpole contribution to the photon-graviton amplitude

Returning to the photon-graviton amplitude in a constant field, the point of the present talk is that this amplitude, too, has a previously overlooked tadpole contribution, shown in Fig. 6.

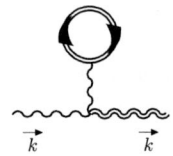

Fig. 6. Tadpole contribution to photon-graviton conversion.

Using the integral (13) it is easy to show that its contribution to the one-loop amplitudes with a scalar or spinor loop can be written as

$$\Gamma^{(\text{tadpole})}_{\text{scal}}(k^\alpha, \varepsilon_\beta; \epsilon_{\mu\nu}; F_{\kappa\lambda}) = -i\frac{\alpha}{8\pi}\kappa\Big(\varepsilon \cdot F \cdot \epsilon \cdot k + \varepsilon \cdot \epsilon \cdot F \cdot k\Big)$$
$$\times \int_0^\infty \frac{dz}{z} e^{-\frac{m^2}{eB}z} \frac{\coth(z) - 1/z}{\sinh(z)}, \quad (15)$$

$$\Gamma^{(\text{tadpole})}_{\text{spin}}(k^\alpha, \varepsilon_\beta; \epsilon_{\mu\nu}; F_{\kappa\lambda}) = i\frac{\alpha}{4\pi}\kappa\Big(\varepsilon \cdot F \cdot \epsilon \cdot k + \varepsilon \cdot \epsilon \cdot F \cdot k\Big)$$
$$\times \int_0^\infty \frac{dz}{z} e^{-\frac{m^2}{eB}z} \frac{\coth(z) - \tanh(z) - 1/z}{\tanh(z)}. \quad (16)$$

Expanding out the tadpole in powers of the external field we see that the leading term, which is linear in the field (Fig. 7), is removed by the photon wave function renormalization.

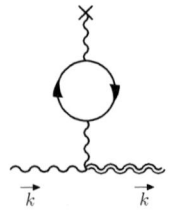

Fig. 7. Expanding the tadpole to lowest order in the field.

This gives the renormalized amplitudes

$$\Gamma^{(\text{tadpole})}_{\text{scal,ren}}(k^\alpha, \varepsilon_\beta; \epsilon_{\mu\nu}; F_{\kappa\lambda}) = -i\frac{\alpha}{8\pi}\kappa\Big(\varepsilon \cdot F \cdot \epsilon \cdot k + \varepsilon \cdot \epsilon \cdot F \cdot k\Big)$$
$$\times \int_0^\infty \frac{dz}{z} e^{-\frac{m^2}{eB}z} \left[\frac{\coth(z) - 1/z}{\sinh(z)} - \frac{1}{3}\right],$$

$$\Gamma^{(\text{tadpole})}_{\text{spin,ren}}(k^\alpha, \varepsilon_\beta; \epsilon_{\mu\nu}; F_{\kappa\lambda}) = i\frac{\alpha}{4\pi}\kappa\Big(\varepsilon \cdot F \cdot \epsilon \cdot k + \varepsilon \cdot \epsilon \cdot F \cdot k\Big)$$
$$\times \int_0^\infty \frac{dz}{z} e^{-\frac{m^2}{eB}z} \left[\frac{\coth(z) - \tanh(z) - 1/z}{\tanh(z)} + \frac{2}{3}\right].$$

6. Comparison with the main diagram

These amplitudes are of a structure similar to what we got from the main diagram Fig. 1 in the limit of low photon energy ω, eqs. (9), (10).

However, they do not contribute to dichroism since the polarizations are still bound up in the tree-level vertex $(\varepsilon \cdot F \cdot \epsilon \cdot k + \varepsilon \cdot \epsilon \cdot F \cdot k)$. Thus the above-mentioned analysis of Ahlers et al.[32] remains unaffected by the presence of the tadpole diagram.

7. Summary and outlook

- We have presented the first example of a non-vanishing diagram in Einstein-Maxwell theory involving a tadpole in a constant field.
- This diagram does not contribute to magnetic dichroism.
- A more quantitative analysis is in progress.
- In the ultra strong-field limit, the tadpoles have been shown even to dominate the (multi-loop) effective action in QED.[40] It would be interesting to extend this analysis to the Einstein-Maxwell case.

References

1. M.E. Gertsenshtein, Sov. Phys. JETP **14** (1962) 84.
2. Ya. B. Zel'dovich and I.D. Novikov, *The structure and evolution of the universe*, Rel. Astrophys. Vol. 2 (1983), Chicago University Press.
3. G.G. Raffelt and L. Stodolsky, Phys. Rev. **D37** (1988) 1237.
4. P. Sikivie, Phys. Rev. Lett. **51** (1983) 1415; erratum-ibid. **52** (1984) 695.
5. D.E. Morris, Phys. Rev. **D34** (1986) 843.
6. H.N. Long, D.V. Soa, and T.A. Tran, Mod. Phys. Lett. **A9** (1994) 3619, astro-ph/9410003.
7. J.C.R. Magueijo, Phys. Rev. **D49** (1994) 671.
8. P. Chen, Phys. Rev. Lett. **74** (1995) 634; erratum-ibid. **74** (1995) 3091.
9. A.N. Cillis and D. Harari, Phys. Rev. **D54** (1996) 4757, astro-ph/9609200.
10. N. Arkani-Hamed, S. Dimopoulos, and G. Dvali, Phys. Lett. **B429** (1998) 263, hep-ph/9803315; Phys. Rev. **D59** (1999) 086004, hep-ph/9807344.
11. C. Deffayet and J.-P. Uzan, Phys. Rev. **D62** (2000) 063507, hep-ph/0002129.

12. A. Ejlli, D. Ejlli, A.M. Cruise, G. Pisano and H. Grote, Eur. Phys. J. C **79** (2019) 1032, arXiv:1908.00232[gr-qc].
13. F. Bastianelli and C. Schubert, JHEP **0502**, 069 (2005), gr-qc/0412095.
14. F. Bastianelli, U. Nucamendi, C. Schubert, and V.M. Villanueva, JHEP **0711** (2007) 099, arXiv:0710.5572.
15. M.J. Strassler, Nucl. Phys. **B 385** (1992) 145.
16. M. Reuter, M.G. Schmidt, and C. Schubert, Ann. Phys. (N.Y.) 259 (1997) 313, hep-th/9610191.
17. C. Schubert, Nucl. Phys. **B 585** (2000) 407, hep-ph/0001288.
18. J.S. Toll, PhD thesis, Princeton Univ., 1952 (unpublished).
19. A. Minguzzi, Nuovo Cim. **6** (1956) 476.
20. R. Baier and P. Breitenlohner, Acta Phys. Austr. **25** (1967) 212; Nuovo Cim. **47** (1967) 261.
21. Z. Bialynicka-Birula and I. Bialynicka-Birula, Phys. Rev. **D 2** (1970) 2341.
22. S.L. Adler, Ann. Phys. (N.Y.) **67** (1971) 599.
23. I.A. Batalin and A.E. Shabad, Zh. Eksp. Teor. Fiz. **60** (1971) 894 [JETP **33** (1971) 483].
24. V.I. Ritus, Ann. Phys. (N.Y.) **69** (1972) 555.
25. W.-Y. Tsai and T. Erber, Phys. Rev. **D 10** (1974) 492; Phys. Rev. **D 12** (1975) 1132.
26. V.N. Baier, V.M. Katkov, and V.M. Strakhovenko, Zh. Eksp. Teor. Fiz. **68** (1975) 405 [JETP **41** (1975) 198].
27. D.B. Melrose and R.J. Stoneham, Nuov. Cim. **32** (1976) 435.
28. W. Dittrich and H. Gies, *Probing the Quantum Vacuum*, Springer 2000.
29. K. Kohri and S. Yamada, Phys. Rev. **D 65**:043006 (2002), astro-ph/0102225.
30. W. Heisenberg and H. Euler, "Folgerungen aus der Diracschen Theorie des Positrons", Z. Phys. **98** (1936) 714.
31. V. Weisskopf, "Über die Elektrodynamik des Vakuums auf Grund der Quantentheorie des Elektrons", Kong. Dans. Vid. Selsk. Math-fys. Medd. XIV No. 6 (1936), reprinted in *Quantum Electrodynamics*, J. Schwinger (Ed.) (Dover, New York, 1958).
32. M. Ahlers, J. Jaeckel and A. Ringwald, Phys. Rev. D **79** 075017 (2009), arXiv:0812.3150 [hep-ph].
33. W. Dittrich and M. Reuter, *Effective Lagrangians in Quantum Electrodynamics*, Springer 1985.
34. E.S. Fradkin, D.M. Gitman, S.M. Shvartsman, *Quantum Electrodynamics with Unstable Vacuum*, Springer 1991.
35. H. Gies and F. Karbstein, *JHEP* **1703** (2017) 108, arXiv:1612.07251 [hep-th].
36. F. Karbstein, *JHEP* **10** (2017) 075, arXiv:1709.03819 [hep-th].
37. J.P. Edwards and C. Schubert, Nucl. Phys. B **923** (2017) 339, arXiv:1704.00482 [hep-th].
38. N. Ahmadiniaz, F. Bastianelli, O. Corradini, J.P. Edwards and C. Schubert, Nucl. Phys. B **924** (2017) 377, arXiv:1704.05040 [hep-th].
39. V.I. Ritus, Zh. Eksp. Teor. Fiz **69** (1975) 1517 [Sov. Phys. JETP **42** (1975) 774].
40. F. Karbstein, Phys. Rev. Lett. **122** (2019) 21, arXiv:1903.06998 [hep-th].

Correspondence of gamma radiation coming from GRBs and magnetars based on the effects of nonlinear vacuum electrodynamics

Tursynbek Yernazarov[1,*], Medeu Abishev[1] and Yerlan Aimuratov[1,2,†]

[1] *Department of Theoretical and Nuclear Physics*
Faculty of Physics and Technology, al-Farabi Kazakh National University
al-Farabi avenue 71, Almaty, 050040, Kazakhstan
E-mail: medeu.abishev@kaznu.kz
yernazarov_tursynbek@live.kaznu.kz

[2] *Fesenkov Astrophysical Institute*
Observatory 23, Kamenskoye Plateau
Almaty, 050020, Kazakhstan
E-mail: aimuratov@aphi.kz

It appears that studying data from the catalogue of Gamma-Ray Bursts (GRBs) can be used to examine the birefringence phenomenon in the magnetosphere of the magnetars. By analysing the data from the McGill Online Magnetar and HEASARC Fermi Burst Catalogues, in this work we studied the angular distances between GRBs and magnetars in projection, we built their distribution map by the end of 2020, and the relative lag time periods of lights coming from GRBs and magnetars. It is confirmed that there are 29 galactic magnetars and their candidates, while the other two are located out of the Milkyway. The maximum separation angle for GRB and Magnetar projectiles was 3.76 degrees (4U0142+61 and GRB110818860), while minimum angular resolution was 0.54 degrees (SGR 1627-41 and GRB090829672). Currently, we discuss the relationship of GRB light intensity by their lag time as it would come after bending in the magnetosphere of the magnetar.

Keywords: Neutron stars; magnetars; light bending; gamma-ray bursts; birefringence.

1. Introduction

Magnetars emit a variety of electromagnetic waves ranging from gamma-ray to radio spectrum. Their bursts last from millisecond to a month.[1] Magnetar's bursts are generated by the powerful magnetic field inside of it. By taking into account the probability of boosting of core circular magnetic field covered by forceful reaction in a protoneutron star coming after a core-collapse supernova the magnetar model was created.[2] Currently there were detected 34 objects that are considered to be magnetars: 10% of them might belong to young neutron star populations.

To the date nearly thousand research articles were published on the topic of magnetars.[1] The first observational reviews on magnetars was carried out by Rea and Esposito, 2011.[3] The leading theoretical review was done by Turolla in 2015.[4] Also, both of observational and theoretical reviews were done by a group of researchers.[5,6]

---
*Doctoral student
†Postdoctoral associate

Historically magnetars were first presented by covering the name "Soft gamma repeaters" (SGR) and "Anomalous X-ray pulsars" (AXP).[1] The primary exposure of magnetar was done by the interplanetary space probes Venera 11 and 12 by detecting the burst activity.[7] The short-term bursts and outbursts, also continuous emissions were described by the sources of the impulsive magnetic field decays. The essential relation of SGRs to AXP was studied. It is believed that future SGRs burst activity might be detected from AXPs.[1]

It was also expected that magnetars might be prolific glitchers, described as unusual increase of rotation spin of a neutron star and they are observed basically in young neutron stars.[8,9] The first estimation of an SGR spin-down was published and the SGR 1806-20 was confirmed of a magnetar model by its sign and magnitude. Also for SGR 1900+14, as the SGR 1806-20, measurements verified that all SGRs are magnetar models.[10]

Contrary possibility of SGRs to be defined as a magnetar model was reviewed by using Einstein's observatory. They discovered a new unusual celestial bright X-ray source located at the center of the magnetar.[11] Then the new unusual celestial bright X-ray source's pulsation was estimated with the period of 3.5 s. (later it was concluded as a second harmonic of a 7-s fundamental).[11] The SGR bursts from two AXPs were explored and this confirmed Thompson and Duncans' (1996) expectations. Futhermore, the SGR bursts are one of the basic features of AXPs and, it is believed that, there is not any difference between them.[12,13]

The first catalogue of observed magnetar models and their complete characteristics were made by Olausen and Kaspi, in 2014.[14] Height scale of the known magnetar was detected to be about 20-30 pc (parsec). This height scale confirmed the magnetars to be young. Majority of magnetars from the catalog were discovered by their X-ray bursts by the sensitive all-sky monitors such as Burst Alert Telescope (BAT) onboard of Swift Gamma-Ray Burst Mission[15] and Gamma-Ray Burst Monitor (GBM)[16] onboard of Fermi Gamma-Ray Space Telescope. As well as magnetars X-ray burst activities they make X-ray pulsation in the period of range of 2-12 s.[1] Primary exploration of magnetars' glitch was carried out by Kaspi et al., 2000. One of the magnetar candidate had an unusual 6-hr period in X-ray with a different pulse and was explored in the source of the supernova remnant RCW 103, 1E 161348-5055. However, this object was considered not to be the magnetar because of their period of the bursts.[17] Another object was expected to be a magnetar by its bursts coupling with one more large X-ray flux outburst. But these bursts had long periods and this might be defined by a fall-back disc that interrupts the primarily fast-rotating neutron star.[18]

Some magnetar characteristics was detected from low-B radio pulsars from the source of SGR0418+5729.[19] The high-B radio pulsars are expected to be the magnetar by the confirmation of the exciting X-ray and soft gamma-rays are bursted by a magnetic field of neutron stars.[20,21] The relationship of magnetars to high-magnetic-field radio pulsars is expected by the research of radio pulsation from magnetars. But the magnetars' radio characters are unlike the common radio pulsars.[22,23]

Gravitational effect to the light bending is crucial in astrophysics. A weak gravitational bending effect causes gravitational lensing phenomenon, also a strong gravitational effect takes place near a compact objects, such as black holes or neutron stars.The gravitational effect of light bending near pulsars is studied by defining the angle of deflection and the flux coming to observer in a symmetrical metric of Schwarcshild.[24]

Non-linear electrodynamic bending angle based on the theory of Heisenberg-Euler and gravitational bending of a ray passing through the magnetosphere of magnetars are defined.[25] Due to this work the bending angle of light passing through the magnetars is about as a radian or 60 degree. Also the gravitational effect on the bending angle on the surface of a magnetar with the radius of about 3 km is up to 4 degree. Thus the polarisation does not effect on the gravitational bending.These non-linear electrodynamics and the gravitational bending are observable by the method of lensing. These non-linear electrodynamics and the gravitational bending are observable by the method of lensing. Additionally, it is proposed that, if the GRB comes from the nearest sources from the magnetars the scattering og light is negligible. Thus the falling of detected emission intensity will not be as deep as in the case of extra galaxies.

It appears that studying the data from the catalogue of Gamma-Ray Bursts (GRBs) can be used to study the birefringence phenomenon in the magnetosphere of the magnetars. By analysing the data from the McGill Online Magnetar and HEASARC Fermi Burst Catalogues, in this work we studied the angular distances between the nearest GRBs and magnetars in projection, built their distribution map as detected by 2020, and the relative lag time periods of lights coming from GRBs and magnetars. Currently, we discuss the relationship of GRB light intensity by their lag time as it would come after bending by the magnetosphere.

2. Methods

The effects of nonlinear electrodynamics of vacuum on the light propagation in dipole magnetic field causes the light to split into two normal modes and they can be detected in time interval of Δt.[26] It is said that the two modes of light coming to the observer can be observed in different years one by another. Initially, we should observe the detected GRBs and magnetars by their spatial distributions.

All the calculations were done in the Phyton programming platform. We downloaded the fits catalogue as a fits file from the website of HEASARC catalogue search (heasarc.gsfc.nasa.gov) in November 2020. By that time there were about 2915 gamma-ray bursts detected by Fermi GBM satellite telescope. Firstly, we defined short(less than 2 seconds) and long(more than 2 seconds) period bursts by the T90(time duration) table. It is confirmed that the long GRB bursts corresponds to core-collapse supernova stars, while the short bursts are the merges of neutron stars.[27] The number of short GRBs were 478 and the long GRBs were 2437 events.

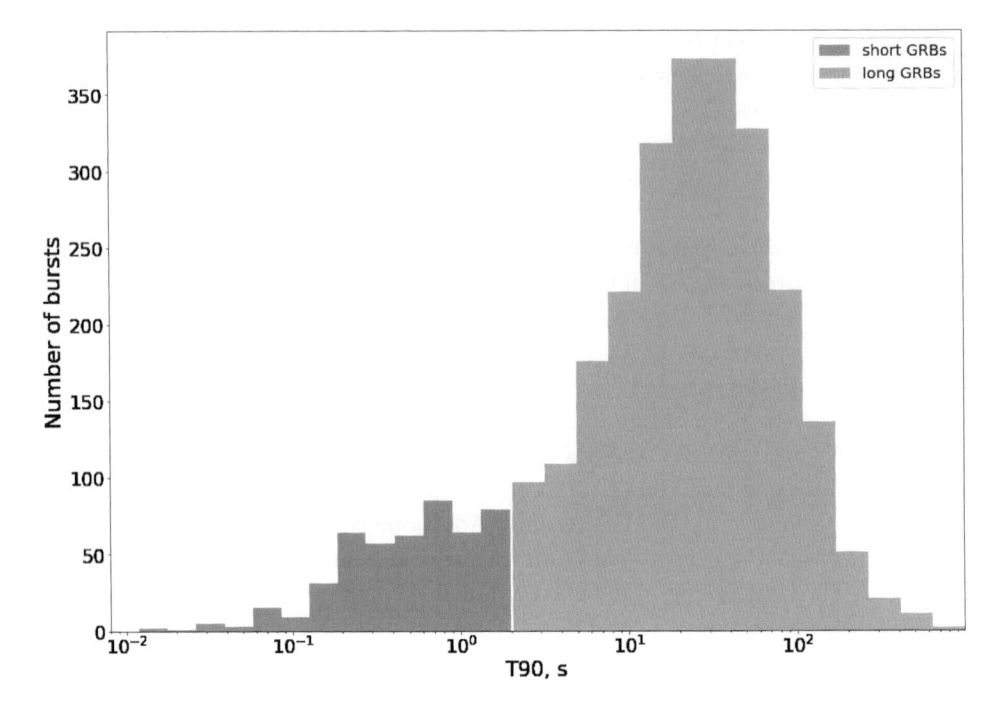

Fig. 1. The histogram of the GRBs by their periods.

In Fig. 1 we build the logarithmic histogram of the number of the bursts by their periods.[28] The minimum period of the short bursts lasted up to 0.008 s, while the maximum period was 1.984 s. Furthermore, the minimum period of the long bursts lasted up to 2.045 s, while the maximum period was 984.084 s. The majority of bursts lay between 10 and 100 s. But other short period bursts have the maximum number corresponds approximately to a second. This results are comparable with the previous works although in size by the order of magnitude.[28] As can be learned from their red shifts the bursts come from different parts of the universe. Let us define their spatial distribution.

Firstly, we took spatial coordinates from catalogue and changed them from the ecliptic into galactic (l,b) values.

We used Aitoff-Hammer projection in order to make the distribution of 2915 bursts on Fig. 2. Marked as red(long) and blue(short) dots these events isotropically distributed, which proves theis extragalactic origin. In previous works the spatial distribution were observed as an object of the definite goals. We use the spatial distribution to study the delay of light within the distribution of the observed magnetars and their candidates.

Nowadays there are 29 galactic and 2 extragalactic magnetars observed; among them there are 26 known magnetars and 5 magnetar candidates.[14] Their distribution

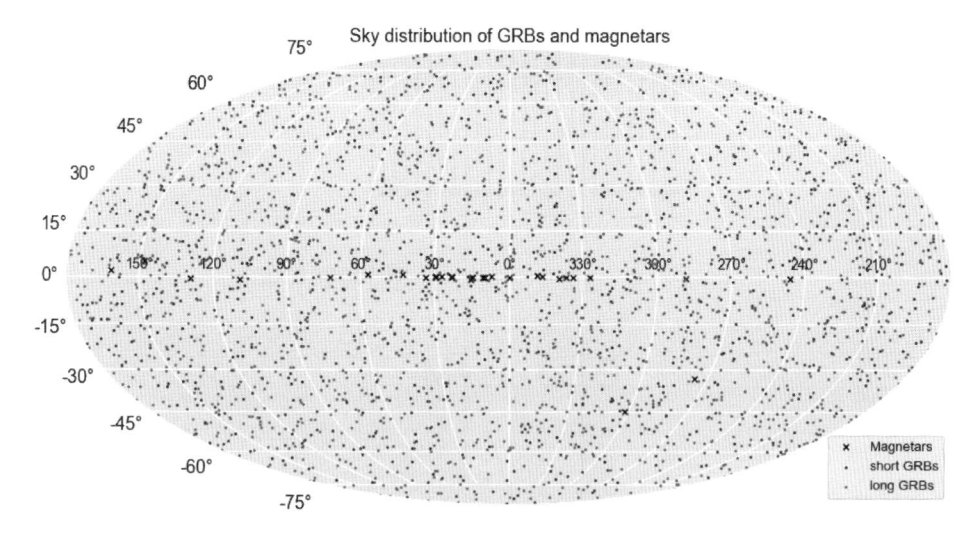

Fig. 2. The sky distribution of GRBs from HEASARC Catalogue as for November, 2020 observed by Fermi's Gamma-ray Burst Monitor (Fermi-GBM).[29]

in the Aitoff-Hammer map are made by using the McGill Online Magnetar catalog and indicated as black crosses in Fig. 2. As for GRBs we changed their coordinates into the galactic coordinates. Indeed, we could present both of the GRB and magnetars in the same map. Most of the magnetars are accumulated along the galactic plane. The other two can be seen out of the Galaxy of Milky-way.

When the light coming from the GRB passes through the magnetosphere of the magnetar it declines to some angle and the light splits into two modes.[30] This phenomena requires first to find out the relation of the spatial coordinates of the GRBs and the magnetars.

In order to illustrate the effect of the light bending we present its schematic view in Fig. 3. The light passing through the magnetars inclines to some θ angle.

If the light coming directly to the observer passes l distance, while the delayed distance is defined as: $\Delta l = (1 - ME \cdot cos\alpha) \cdot GE$. Here, ME is a distance between a magnetar and an observer. GE is a distance between a GRB and the Earth.

The next step is a calculation of the distance between the GRBs and the magnetars in projection. Here we take a magnetar, then we define the distance between this magnetar and the GRBs in order to find the closest pair.

Thus it is a projection distance: angular separation between the magnetar and the GRBs. Firstly, we define the difference of right ascensions of the magnetars and the GRBs, we do the same, as well as for the declination. Secondly, we define the distance between a magnetar and GRBs by the simple formula for triangle: $\Delta D = \sqrt{RA^2 + Dec^2}$.

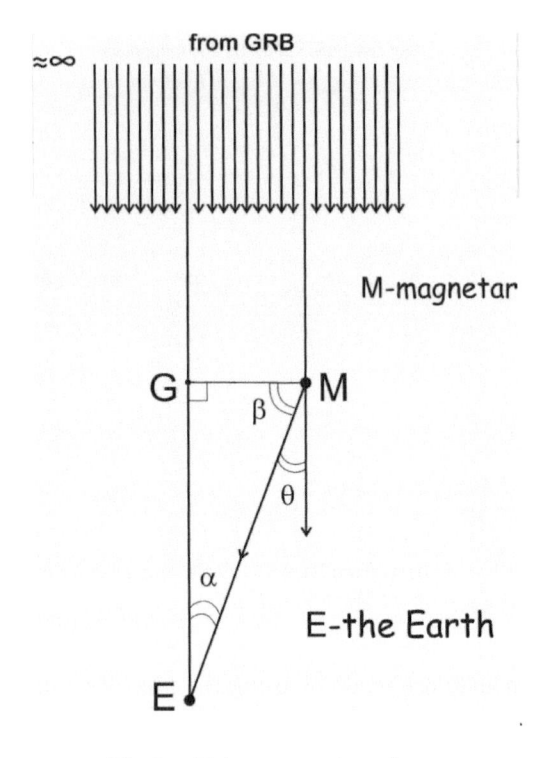

Fig. 3. Light propagation scheme.

We calculated angular distance corresponded to every 31 magnetars. Hence, every magnetars in the map surrounded by 2915 GRBs. The minimum of the angular distance corresponded to the magnetar is defined as the nearest GRB to the magnetar. As in Table 1, α is an angular projection distance for magnetars and GRBs. This results help to define the lag time of light coming to the detector by passing through the magnetar.

Delay of the GRB coming to the Earth can be defined by the distance between the magnetar and the detector. This data can be used from the McGill Online Magnetar Catalog website. We changed the units of parsec to light years and then we calculated the delayed time of light of GRB by dividing the delayed distance by the speed of light. Hopefully, we present the result in Figure 6. Here nan is a unknown data of the distance to a given magnetar. We do not use them in the future. Minimum of lag time corresponds to the magnetar of SGR 0418+5729, while the longest time is for the magnetar of CXOU J010043.1-721134. Futhermore, the errors of the distance to a magnetar should be useful for the calculation of delayed time period of the light.

Table 1. Minimum distance in projection between magnetars and GRBs.

GRB	Magnetar	α	Lagtime, ly
GRB080905570	CXOU J010043.1-721134	2.92347	264.873
GRB110818860	4U 0142+61	3.76798	25.3813
GRB130304658	SGR 0418+5729	1.08932	1.1789
GRB110319628	SGR 0501+4516	1.96316	3.82867
GRB181026540	SGR 0526-66	2.54773	172.803
GRB141102536	1E 1048.1-5937	0.656687	1.92799
GRB170803415	1E 1547.0-5408	3.19981	22.8822
GRB140619490	PSR J1622-4950	2.59277	30.0502
GRB090829672	SGR 1627-41	0.547211	1.63625
GRB190630257	CXOU J164710.2-455216	1.51366	4.43859
GRB120711446	1RXS J170849.0-400910	2.95812	16.5147
GRB140511095	CXOU J171405.7-381031	3.98594	104.138
GRB160819852	SGR J1745-2900	1.05186	4.56176
GRB160819852	SGR 1806-20	1.93754	16.2229
GRB160819852	XTE J1810-197	2.64306	12.1438
GRB160819852	Swift J1818.0-1607	2.13983	10.9169
GRB140627401	Swift J1822.3-1606	1.90291	2.87785
GRB150811849	SGR 1833-0832	1.92805	nan
GRB150811849	Swift J1834.9-0846	1.69774	6.01329
GRB171010792	1E 1841-045	1.49363	9.41957
GRB150705588	3XMM J185246.6+003317	2.4124	20.5231
GRB140723067	SGR 1900+14	1.25032	9.70704
GRB140723067	SGR 1935+2154	3.18331	nan
GRB140723067	1E 2259+586	2.92617	13.6084
GRB120224898	SGR 0755-2933 #	2.38008	nan
GRB171120556	SGR 1801-23 #	1.93446	nan
GRB180517309	SGR 1808-20 #	1.70049	nan
GRB151118554	AX J1818.8-1559 #	1.95134	nan
GRB130404877	AX J1845.0-0258 #	1.94219	15.9261
GRB170511477	SGR 2013+34 #	3.29051	47.3196
GRB151212064	PSR J1846-0258 ##	2.2824	15.5248

3. Summary

By building the distribution of magnetars on galactic map, it is confirmed that there are 29 galactic magnetars and their candidates, while the other two are located out of the Milkyway. The number of GRBs we studied is 2915. The maximum separation angle for GRB and Magnetar projectiles was 3.76 degrees (4U0142+61 and GRB110818860), while minimum angular resolution was 0.54 degrees (SGR1627-41 and GRB090829672). There are five candidates of lag time period for GRBs (GRB130304658, GRB110319628, GRB141102536, GRB090829672, GRB140627401) and corresponding magnetars(SGR 0418+5729, SGR 0501+4516, 1E 1048.1-5937, SGR 1627-41, Swift J1822.3-1606) we expect to study in the future works. We discuss the relationship of GRB light intensity by their lag time as it would come after bending by the magnetosphere. The further steps will include modelling of the front emission from GRBs passing through the magnetosphere of the given magnetar.

References

1. V. M. Kaspi and A. M. Beloborodov, Magnetars, *Annual Review of Astronomy and Astrophysics* **55**, 261 (August 2017).
2. R. C. Duncan and C. Thompson, Formation of Very Strongly Magnetized Neutron Stars: Implications for Gamma-Ray Bursts, *Astrophysical Journal Letters* **392**, p. L9 (June 1992).
3. N. Rea and P. Esposito, Magnetar outbursts: An observational review, *Astrophysics and Space Science Proceedings* **21**, p. 247 (January 2011).
4. R. Turolla, S. Zane and A. L. Watts, Magnetars: The physics behind observations. A review, *Reports on Progress in Physics* **78**, p. 116901 (November 2015).
5. P. M. Woods and C. Thompson, Soft gamma repeaters and anomalous X-ray pulsars: Magnetar candidates, in *Compact stellar X-ray sources*, 2006, pp. 547–586.
6. S. Mereghetti, J. A. Pons and A. Melatos, Magnetars: Properties, Origin and Evolution, *Space Science Reviews* **191**, 315 (October 2015).
7. E. P. Mazets, S. V. Golenetskij and Y. A. Guryan, Soft gamma-ray bursts from the source B1900+14, *Soviet Astronomy Letters* **5**, p. 343 (December 1979).
8. C. Thompson and R. C. Duncan, The soft gamma repeaters as very strongly magnetized neutron stars - I. Radiative mechanism for outbursts, *Monthly Notices of the Royal Astronomical Society* **275**, 255 (July 1995).
9. C. Thompson and R. C. Duncan, The Soft Gamma Repeaters as Very Strongly Magnetized Neutron Stars. II. Quiescent Neutrino, X-Ray, and Alfven Wave Emission, *Astrophysical Journal* **473**, p. 322 (December 1996).
10. C. Kouveliotou, S. Dieters, T. Strohmayer, J. van Paradijs, G. J. Fishman, C. A. Meegan, K. Hurley, J. Kommers, I. Smith, D. Frail and T. Murakami, An X-ray pulsar with a superstrong magnetic field in the soft γ-ray repeater SGR1806 - 20, *Nature* **393**, 235 (May 1998).
11. G. G. Fahlman and P. C. Gregory, An X-ray pulsar in SNR G109.1-1.0, *Nature* **293**, 202 (September 1981).
12. F. P. Gavriil, V. M. Kaspi and P. M. Woods, Magnetar-like X-ray bursts from an anomalous X-ray pulsar, *Nature* **419**, 142 (September 2002).
13. V. M. Kaspi, F. P. Gavriil, P. M. Woods, J. B. Jensen, M. S. E. Roberts and D. Chakrabarty, A Major Soft Gamma Repeater-like Outburst and Rotation Glitch in the No-longer-so-anomalous X-Ray Pulsar 1E 2259+586, *The Astrophysical Journal* **588**, L93 (May 2003).
14. S. A. Olausen and V. M. Kaspi, The McGill Magnetar Catalog, *The Astrophysical Journal* **212**, p. 6 (May 2014).
15. N. Gehrels and Swift, The Swift Gamma-Ray Burst Mission, in *American Astronomical Society Meeting Abstracts*, American Astronomical Society Meeting Abstracts Vol. 205, December 2004.
16. C. Meegan, G. Lichti, P. N. Bhat, E. Bissaldi, M. S. Briggs, V. Connaughton, R. Diehl, G. Fishman, J. Greiner, A. S. Hoover, A. J. van der Horst, A. von Kienlin, R. M. Kippen, C. Kouveliotou, S. McBreen, W. S. Paciesas, R. Preece, H. Steinle, M. S. Wallace, R. B. Wilson and C. Wilson-Hodge, The Fermi Gamma-ray Burst Monitor, *The Astrophysical Journal* **702**, 791 (September 2009).

17. A. De Luca, P. A. Caraveo, S. Mereghetti, A. Tiengo and G. F. Bignami, A Long-Period, Violently Variable X-ray Source in a Young Supernova Remnant, *Science* **313**, 814 (August 2006).
18. A. D'Aì, P. A. Evans, D. N. Burrows, N. P. M. Kuin, D. A. Kann, S. Campana, A. Maselli, P. Romano, G. Cusumano, V. La Parola, S. D. Barthelmy, A. P. Beardmore, S. B. Cenko, M. De Pasquale, N. Gehrels, J. Greiner, J. A. Kennea, S. Klose, A. Melandri, J. A. Nousek, J. P. Osborne, D. M. Palmer, D. Sbarufatti, P. Schady, M. H. Siegel, G. Tagliaferri, R. Yates and S. Zane, Evidence for the magnetar nature of 1E 161348-5055 in RCW 103, *Monthly Notices of the Royal Astronomical Society* **463**, 2394 (December 2016).
19. N. Rea, P. Esposito, R. Turolla, G. L. Israel, S. Zane, L. Stella, S. Mereghetti, A. Tiengo, D. Götz, E. Göğüş and C. Kouveliotou, A Low-Magnetic-Field Soft Gamma Repeater, *Science* **330**, p. 944 (November 2010).
20. V. M. Kaspi and M. A. McLaughlin, Chandra X-Ray Detection of the High Magnetic Field Radio Pulsar PSR J1718-3718, *The Astrophysical Journal* **618**, L41 (January 2005).
21. C. Y. Ng, V. M. Kaspi, R. Dib, S. A. Olausen, P. Scholz, T. Güver, F. Özel, F. P. Gavriil and P. M. Woods, Chandra and RXTE Observations of 1E 1547.0-5408: Comparing the 2008 and 2009 Outbursts, *The Astrophysical Journal* **729**, p. 131 (March 2011).
22. F. Camilo, S. M. Ransom, J. P. Halpern, J. Reynolds, D. J. Helfand, N. Zimmerman and J. Sarkissian, Transient pulsed radio emission from a magnetar, *Nature* **442**, 892 (August 2006).
23. F. Camilo, S. M. Ransom, J. P. Halpern and J. Reynolds, 1E 1547.0-5408: A Radio-emitting Magnetar with a Rotation Period of 2 Seconds, *The Astrophysical Journal* **666**, L93 (September 2007).
24. A. M. Beloborodov, Gravitational Bending of Light Near Compact Objects, *The Astrophysical Journal* **566**, L85 (February 2002).
25. V. I. Denisov, I. P. Denisova and S. I. Svertilov, Nonlinear Electrodynamic Effect of Ray Bending in the Magnetic-Dipole Field, *Physics - Doklady* **46**, 705 (October 2001).
26. M. Abishev, Y. Aimuratov, Y. Aldabergenov, N. Beissen, Z. Bakytzhan and M. Takibayeva, Some astrophysical effects of nonlinear vacuum electrodynamics in the magnetosphere of a pulsar, *Astroparticle Physics* **73**, 8 (January 2016).
27. S. I. Shirokov, A. A. Raikov and Y. V. Baryshev, Spatial Distribution of Gamma-Ray Burst Sources, *Astrophysics* **60**, 484 (December 2017).
28. C. Kouveliotou, C. A. Meegan, G. J. Fishman, N. P. Bhat, M. S. Briggs, T. M. Koshut, W. S. Paciesas and G. N. Pendleton, Identification of Two Classes of Gamma-Ray Bursts, *Astrophysical Journal Letters* **413**, p. L101 (August 1993).
29. A. von Kienlin, C. A. Meegan, W. S. Paciesas, P. N. Bhat, E. Bissaldi, M. S. Briggs, E. Burns, W. H. Cleveland, M. H. Gibby, M. M. Giles, A. Goldstein, R. Hamburg, C. M. Hui, D. Kocevski, B. Mailyan, C. Malacaria, S. Poolakkil, R. D. Preece, O. J. Roberts, P. Veres and C. A. Wilson-Hodge, The Fourth Fermi-GBM Gamma-Ray Burst Catalog: A Decade of Data, *The Astrophysical Journal* **893**, p. 46 (April 2020).
30. M. E. Abishev, S. Toktarbay, N. A. Beissen, F. B. Belissarova, M. K. Khassanov, A. S. Kudussov and A. Z. Abylayeva, Effects of non-linear electrodynamics of vacuum in the magnetic quadrupole field of a pulsar, *Monthly Notices of the Royal Astronomical Society* **481**, 36 (November 2018).

Absorption of massless scalar waves by electrically charged regular black holes

Marco A. A. de Paula[1,*], Luiz C. S. Leite[1,2,†], and Luís C. B. Crispino[1,‡]

[1] *Programa de Pós-Graduação em Física, Universidade Federal do Pará, 66075-110, Belém, Pará, Brazil*
[2] *Campus Altamira, Instituto Federal do Pará, 68377-630, Altamira, Pará, Brazil*
E-mail: marco.paula@icen.ufpa.br
†*E-mail: luiz.leite@ifpa.edu.br*
‡*E-mail: crispino@ufpa.br*

We study the absorption cross section of a massless test scalar field, for arbitrary frequency values, in the background of an Ayón-Beato-García electrically charged regular black hole spacetime. We show that Ayón-Beato-García regular black holes can mimic the absorption properties of Reissner-Nordström black holes in the whole frequency range, for small-to-moderate values of the normalized electric charge.

Keywords: Regular black holes; scalar field; absorption cross section.

1. Introduction

General relativity (GR) is a geometric theory of gravity that over more than one hundred years has successfully passed several experimental tests.[1–3] The observational evidences of GR[4–6] confirm the existence of black holes (BHs). These objects are characterized by a one-way membrane, called the event horizon, and in standard GR they are normally associated to a curvature singularity. Since the known laws of physics break down at such singularities, the standard GR is not able to explain the physics of a BH singular core.

An attempt to avoid the curvature singularity issues are the so-called regular BH (RBH) spacetimes,[7] i.e., singularity-free black hole geometries. The first exact charged RBH solution was proposed in 1998 by Eloy Ayón-Beato and Alberto García (ABG).[8] This solution was based on the minimal coupling between gravity and a nonlinear electrodynamics model, and describes a static and electrically charged RBH. The nonlinear electrodynamics theory can be seen as a possible generalization of Maxwell's linear electrodynamics for strong electromagnetic fields.[9]

In real astrophysical scenarios BHs are surrounded by distributions of matter.[10] Among the bosonic and fermionic distributions of matter, the simplest one is the scalar field, corresponding to spinless particles.[11] It is possible to study how BHs absorb and scatter matter fields as an attempt to better comprehend how BHs interact with their surroundings.[12–17] We present a selection of results for the massless scalar absorption by ABG RBHs, focusing in the possibility of RBHs mimic the absorption properties of standard BHs. More details on this work are presented in a previously published paper (see Ref. 18).

2. Ayón-Beato-García RBH Spacetime

The line element of the ABG solution is given by[8]

$$ds^2 = f(r)dt^2 - f(r)^{-1}dr^2 - r^2\left(d\theta^2 + \sin^2\theta\, d\varphi^2\right), \tag{1}$$

with

$$f(r) = f^{ABG}(r) \equiv 1 - \frac{2Mr^2}{(r^2+Q^2)^{3/2}} + \frac{Q^2 r^2}{(r^2+Q^2)^2}, \tag{2}$$

where M and Q are the mass and the electric charge of the BH, respectively. The asymptotic limits of the metric function are given by

$$\lim_{r\to 0} f^{ABG}(r) \approx f^{\text{de Sitter}}(r) = 1 - \frac{1}{3}\left[\frac{3\left(2|Q|M - Q^2\right)}{Q^4}\right]r^2 \tag{3}$$

and

$$\lim_{r\to\infty} f^{ABG}(r) \approx f^{RN}(r) = 1 - \frac{2M}{r} + \frac{Q^2}{r^2}. \tag{4}$$

The ABG solution describes RBHs when $|Q| \le Q_{\text{ext}} \approx 0.6341 M$. For $|Q| < Q_{\text{ext}}$ we have a Cauchy, r_-, and an event horizon, r_+, given by

$$r_\pm = |Q|\sqrt{\left(\pm\frac{\sqrt{-\frac{9(12s^2-1)}{\sqrt{u(s)}} - 12s^2 - \frac{u(s)}{6} + \frac{9}{2}}}{2\sqrt{6}s} + \frac{\sqrt{u(s)}}{12s} + \frac{1}{4s}\right)^2 - 1}, \tag{5}$$

where $s \equiv |Q|/(2M)$ and

$$u(s) \equiv 6\left(-\frac{4(11s^2-3)s}{\sqrt[3]{g(s)}} + s\sqrt[3]{g(s)} - 4s^2 + \frac{3}{2}\right), \tag{6}$$

$$g(s) \equiv 4(74s^3 + 3\sqrt{3}\sqrt{400s^6 - 112s^4 + 47s^2 - 4} + 9s). \tag{7}$$

On the other hand, $Q = Q_{\text{ext}}$ corresponds to the so-called extreme ABG RBH, for which we have only one horizon; while $Q > Q_{\text{ext}}$ corresponds to a horizonless solution. The regularity of the solution at the core of the geometry is evidenced by the behavior of the scalar invariants presented in Ref. 8, which are all regular there.

3. Absorption of Massless Test Scalar Fields

3.1. *Massless scalar field*

The massless and chargeless test scalar field Φ obeys the Klein-Gordon equation:

$$\nabla_\mu \nabla^\mu \Phi = \frac{1}{\sqrt{-g}}\partial_\mu\left(\sqrt{-g}g^{\mu\nu}\partial_\nu\right)\Phi = 0. \tag{8}$$

We can decompose Φ as

$$\Phi = \sum C_{\omega l} \left(\frac{\psi_{\omega l}(r)}{r} P_l(\cos\theta) e^{-i\omega t} \right), \tag{9}$$

where $C_{\omega l}$ are constant coefficients. The indexes ω and l denote the frequency and the angular momentum of the wave, respectively, $\psi_{\omega l}(r)$ is the radial function and P_l are the Legendre Polynomials.

By inserting Eq. (9) into Eq. (8) we may find the following radial equation

$$\frac{d^2}{dr_\star^2}\psi_{\omega l} + \left[\omega^2 - V_{\text{eff}}(r)\right]\psi_{\omega l} = 0, \tag{10}$$

where $\frac{dr_\star}{dr} \equiv \frac{1}{f(r)}$ is the tortoise coordinate and the effective potential $V_{\text{eff}}(r)$ reads

$$V_{\text{eff}}(r) \equiv f(r)\left[\frac{1}{r}\frac{df(r)}{dr} + \frac{l(l+1)}{r^2}\right]. \tag{11}$$

In Fig. 1 we present the effective potential in the background of ABG RBHs. We note that the peak of the effective potential increases as we consider higher values of the normalized charge $\alpha \equiv Q/Q_{\text{ext}}$, as well as higher values of l; and for the asymptotic limits, we have $\lim_{r_\star \to \pm\infty} V_{\text{eff}}(r_\star) = 0$.

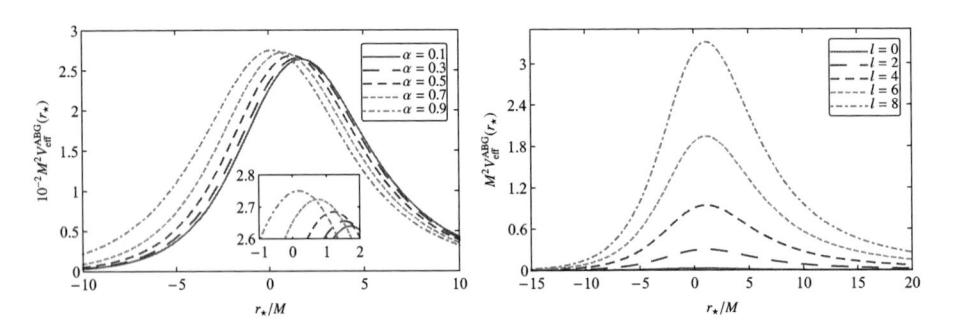

Fig. 1. The effective potential of scalar waves in the background of the ABG RBH, as a function of $r_\star$: (i) with $l = 0$, for different choices of the normalized charge α (left panel); and (ii) for different choices of l, with $\alpha = 0.8$ (right panel). The lower inset in the left panel emphasizes the peaks of the effective potential.

The appropriate boundary conditions are given by plane waves incoming from the infinite null past (the so-called *in modes*), so that the solutions of Eq. (10) reads

$$\psi_{\omega l} \sim \begin{cases} T_{\omega l} e^{-i\omega r_\star}, & r \to r_+ \ (r_\star \to -\infty), \\ e^{-i\omega r_\star} + R_{\omega l} e^{i\omega r_\star}, & r \to \infty \ (r_\star \to \infty), \end{cases} \tag{12}$$

where $T_{\omega l}$ and $R_{\omega l}$ are complex coefficients. By using the conservation of the flux, one can show that the transmission $|T_{\omega l}|^2$ and reflection $|R_{\omega l}|^2$ coefficients satisfy

$$|R_{\omega l}|^2 + |T_{\omega l}|^2 = 1. \tag{13}$$

3.2. Absorption cross section

By using the so-called partial-wave method, we may write the total absorption cross section (ACS) of the massless scalar wave as a sum of partial-waves contributions, given by[19]

$$\sigma = \sum_{l=0}^{\infty} \sigma_l, \qquad (14)$$

where the partial ACS, σ_l, reads

$$\sigma_l = \frac{\pi}{\omega^2}(2l+1)|T_{\omega l}|^2. \qquad (15)$$

There are analytic approximations for the ACS of massless test scalar fields by BHs in the low- and high-frequency regimes. In the low-frequency regime, for stationary BH geometries, the ACS tends to the surface area of the BH event horizon, namely[20,21]

$$A = 4\pi r_+^2. \qquad (16)$$

On the other hand, in the high-frequency regime, the absorption of a massless scalar field is governed by the geometric cross section (GCS) of null geodesics, i.e., $\sigma_{\text{gcs}} = \pi b_c^2$, where b_c is the critical impact parameter. By using the so-called sinc approximation, it is possible to obtain an improvement for the high-frequency approximation, which can be expressed as[22]

$$\sigma_{\text{hf}} = \sigma_{\text{gcs}}\left[1 - 8\pi b_c \Lambda e^{-\pi b_c \Lambda}\text{sinc}\,(2\pi b_c \omega)\right], \qquad (17)$$

where $\text{sinc}(x) \equiv \sin(x)/x$, and Λ is the Lyapunov exponent.[23]

4. Results

4.1. Main features

The numerical method employed to obtain the ACS consists in integrating numerically Eq. (10) from very close to the BH event horizon r_+, up to some radial position very far from the BH, with the boundary conditions in these regions given by Eq. (12).

In Fig. 2 we show the total ACS, normalized by the BH area, for distinct ABG RBHs. We note that, as $\omega \to 0$, the ratio σ/A tends to the unity. Hence, at the low-frequency limit, the numerical result for the ACS tends to the BH area, as expected.

A comparison between the horizon area of ABG and RN BHs is presented in Fig. 3. We see that for fixed values of α, ABG and RN BHs have very similar BH areas.

In Fig. 4 we compare the total ACS obtained numerically with the analytic approximations for the high-frequency regime (see Subsec. 3.2). As we can see, in this frequency regime, the total ACS obtained numerically oscillates around the

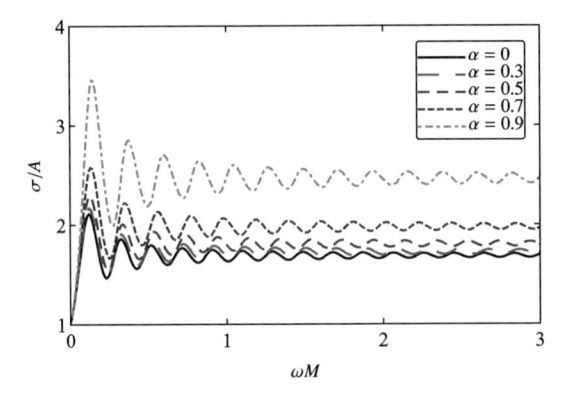

Fig. 2. The total ACS of the scalar wave for distinct ABG RBHs (divided by the BH area), as a function of ωM. We also exhibit, for comparison, the results for the Schwarzschild case ($\alpha = 0$).

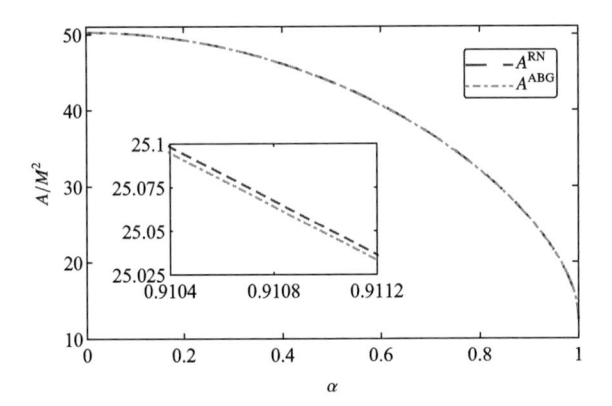

Fig. 3. The surface area of the BH event horizon of ABG and RN BHs, as a function of the normalized charge. The central inset shows the areas of ABG and RN BHs for α between 0.9104 and 0.9116, emphasizing the high similarity between the corresponding areas.

corresponding GCS and the oscillatory profile is very well reproduced by the sinc approximation. These results, combined with the ones for the low-frequency regime (cf. Fig. 2), show that our numerical results are consistent with the analytic approximations available in the literature. We also see that the total ACS of the ABG RBH diminishes as we increase α, so that the wave is more absorbed in the background of small-charge ABG RBH spacetimes. This is in accordance with the fact that the potential barrier raises as we increase α (see Fig. 1).

Examples of partial ACSs in the background of different ABG RBHs are shown in Fig. 5. We observe that the peak of the partial-wave modes diminishes as we consider higher values of the normalized electric charge and the mode $l = 0$ provides the main contributions for the ACS in the low-frequency regime.

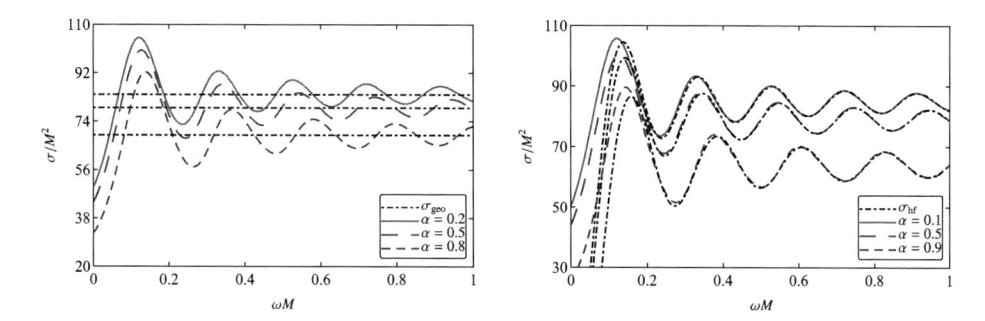

Fig. 4. Comparison of the total ACS (as a function of ωM) of the ABG RBH obtained numerically with: (i) the corresponding GCSs (left panel) and (ii) the corresponding sinc approximation (right panel), considering distinct values of α.

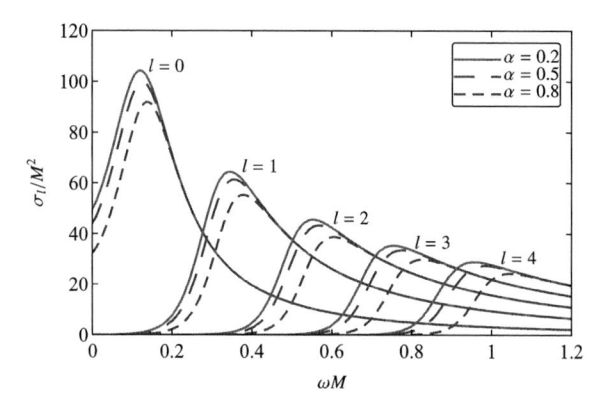

Fig. 5. Partial ACSs of the scalar wave considering different ABG RBHs (distinct values of α), as functions of ωM.

In Fig. 6 we compare the absorption results for ABG and RN BHs, considering two values of α. The total ACS of the ABG RBH is typically larger than the corresponding RN case. However, for small values of α, the total ACS of ABG and RN BH solutions can be very similar for arbitrary values of the frequency. Notice also that the zero-frequency regime of the total ACSs of ABG and RN BHs are very similar, for the same α value. This is in agreement with the behavior of their areas which are very similar for the same choices of α (cf. Fig. 3).

4.2. RBHs as standard BHs mimickers

We can consider the values of $(\alpha^{\text{ABG}}, \alpha^{\text{RN}})$ for which the corresponding GCSs coincide in order to find situations in which the absorption results of ABG and RN BHs are very similar. In Fig. 7 we display such values, which can be found up to $(\alpha^{\text{ABG}}, \alpha^{\text{RN}}) = (1, 0.9161)$.

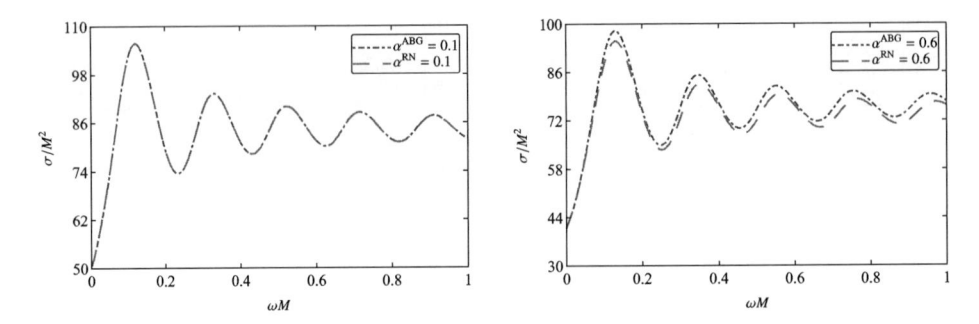

Fig. 6. The total ACSs of ABG and RN BHs as a function of ωM, for $\alpha = 0.1$ (left panel) and for $\alpha = 0.6$ (right panel).

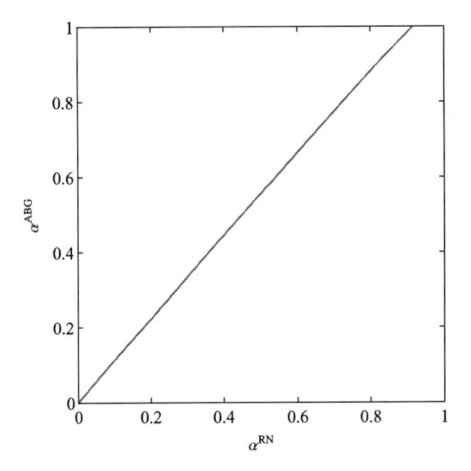

Fig. 7. The values of the normalized charges for which the GCSs of ABG and RN BHs coincide.

In Fig. 8 we exhibit the total ACSs for two pairs of $(\alpha^{ABG}, \alpha^{RN})$, for which the GCSs coincide. For low-to-moderate α values, the total ACSs of the ABG and RN BHs are basically indistinguishable along the whole frequency regime. This contrasts with the absorption results for massless test scalar fields in the Bardeen case,[24] for which the ACSs of Bardeen and RN BH solutions can be very similar only in the high-frequency regime.

We can define a function to estimate the percentual deviation between the BH area of each pair $(\alpha^{ABG}, \alpha^{RN})$, namely

$$A_{\text{dif}} \equiv \frac{A^{RN} - A^{ABG}}{A^{ABG}} 100\%. \tag{18}$$

The smaller the function A_{dif} is, the more similar are the ABG and RN BHs areas. In Table 1 we present the corresponding BH areas, as well as A_{dif}, for several pairs $(\alpha^{ABG}, \alpha^{RN})$ displayed in Fig. 7. As we can see, the function A_{dif} increases with

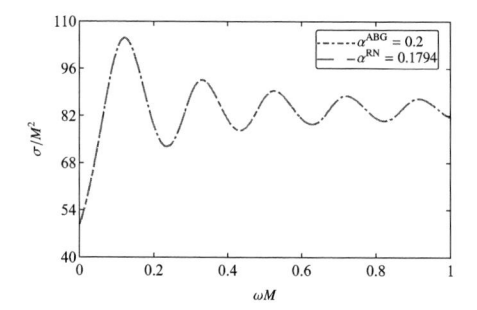

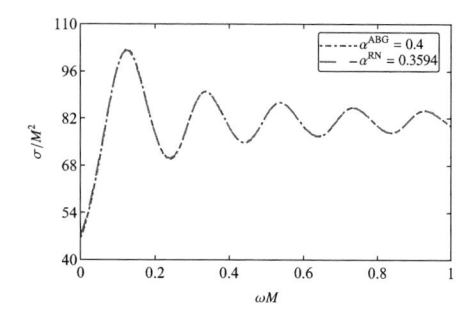

Fig. 8. The total ACS for the pairs $(\alpha^{ABG}, \alpha^{RN}) = (0.2, 0.1794)$ (left panel) and $(\alpha^{ABG}, \alpha^{RN}) = (0.4, 0.3594)$ (right panel). In both cases, the corresponding GCSs coincide.

Table 1. The BH areas and A_{dif} for several pairs $(\alpha^{ABG}, \alpha^{RN})$ shown in Fig. 7.

α^{ABG}	α^{RN}	A^{ABG}/M^2	A^{RN}/M^2	A_{dif}
0.1516	0.1365	49.6831	49.7961	0.2274%
0.182	0.1629	49.425	49.5963	0.3453%
0.2027	0.1815	49.2219	49.4341	0.4309%
0.2852	0.2548	48.189	48.6201	0.8946%
0.318	0.2855	47.6772	48.1951	1.0863%
0.3417	0.3054	47.2708	47.8927	1.3156%
0.4003	0.3608	46.1309	46.9368	1.7469%
0.4707	0.4226	44.4976	45.6667	2.6273%
0.5003	0.4489	43.7207	45.0586	3.0601%

the increase of α. We also note that for an ABG RBH with $\alpha \lesssim 0.5$, we have that $A_{dif} \lesssim 3\%$. Therefore, pairs $(\alpha^{ABG}, \alpha^{RN})$ that satisfy $\sigma_{gcs}^{ABG} = \sigma_{gcs}^{RN}$ correspond to very similar BH areas, as long as we consider only low-to-moderate values of α, implying that the ACSs of ABG and RN BHs are very similar also at the low-frequency regime. This also contrasts with the absorption results for massless test scalar field in the Bardeen case.[24]

5. Final Remarks

We revisited the scalar absorption of massless scalar fields by the first electrically charged ABG RBH solution,[18] presenting a selection of additional results. The height of potential barrier (related to the propagation of massless scalar waves in the background of the ABG RBH) enhances as we increase l or α. The ACSs obtained with our numerical method tend to the corresponding BH area in the low-frequency regime, as expected,[20] and, in this limit, the mode $l = 0$ provides the main contribution to the ACS. We also obtained that the BH areas of ABG and RN BHs are very similar for certain values of α.

The total ACS of the ABG RBH, in the mid-to-high frequency limit, oscillates around the corresponding GCS and the sinc approximation provides excellent results for ACS in this regime. Therefore, considering the results in the low- and high-frequency regime, we conclude that our numerical results for the ACS agree very well with the analytic approximations. We also noted that the ABG RBH total ACS diminishes as we increase α, what is in accordance with the fact that $V_{\text{eff}}(r)$ increases as we increase α. The ABG RBH total ACS is typically larger than the RN one, for the same choice of α, but it is possible to find situations for which the total ACSs of ABG and RN BHs are very similar in the whole frequency range, mainly for small values of α. This similarity shows that it is possible that electrically charged RBHs mimic standard BHs, in what concerns the absorption of massless test scalar fields.

Acknowledgments

We are grateful to Conselho Nacional de Desenvolvimento Científico e Tecnológico (CNPq) and Coordenação de Aperfeiçoamento de Pessoal de Nível Superior (CAPES) – Finance Code 001, from Brazil, for partial financial support. This research has also received funding from the European Union's Horizon 2020 research and innovation programme under the H2020-MSCA-RISE-2017 Grant No. FunFiCO-777740.

References

1. C. M. Will, The Confrontation between General Relativity and Experiment, Living Rev. Relativ. **17**, 4 (2014).
2. L. C. B. Crispino and D. J. Kennefick, A hundred years of the first experimental test of general relativity, Nat. Phys. **115**, 416 (2019).
3. L. C. B. Crispino and S. Paolantonio, The first attempts to measure light deflection by the Sun, Nat. Astron. **4**, 6 (2020).
4. R. Narayan and J. E. McClintock, Observational Evidence for Black Holes, arXiv:1312.6698 [astro-ph.HE].
5. B. P. Abbott et al. [LIGO Scientific Collaboration and Virgo Collaboration], Observation of Gravitational Waves from a Binary Black Hole Merger, Phys. Rev. Lett. **116**, 061102 (2016).
6. The Event Horizon Telescope Collaboration et al., First M87 Event Horizon Telescope Results. I. The Shadow of the Supermassive Black Hole, Atrophys. J. **875**, L1 (2019).
7. J. Bardeen, Non-singular General Relativistic Gravitational Collapse, in *Proceedings of the International Conference GR5* (Tbilisi, Georgia, U.S.S.R., 1968), p. 174.
8. E. Ayón-Beato and A. García, Regular Black Hole in General Relativity Coupled to Nonlinear Electrodynamics, Phys. Rev. Lett. **80**, 5056 (1998).
9. M. Born and L. Infeld, Foundations of the new field theory, Proc. R. Soc. A **144**, 425 (1934).
10. R. Narayan, Black holes in astrophysics, New J. Phys. **7**, 199 (2005).

11. W. Greiner and J. Reinhardt, *Field Quantization* (Springer, Berlim, 1996).
12. J. A. Futterman, F. A. Handler, and R. A. Matzner, *Scattering from Black Holes* (Cambridge University Press, Cambridge, England, 1988).
13. L. C. B. Crispino, S. R. Dolan, and E. S. Oliveira, Scattering of massless scalar waves by Reissner-Nordström black holes, Phys. Rev. D **79**, 0640022 (2009).
14. E. S. Oliveira, L. C. B. Crispino, and A. Higuchi, Equality between gravitational and electromagnetic absorption cross sections of extreme Reissner-Nordstrom black holes, Phys. Rev. D **84**, 084048 (2011).
15. L. C. B. Crispino, S. R. Dolan, A. Higuchi, and E. S. de Oliveira, Inferring black hole charge from backscattered electromagnetic radiation, Phys. Rev. D **90**, 064027 (2014).
16. L. C. B. Crispino, S. R. Dolan, A. Higuchi, and E. S. de Oliveira, Scattering from charged black holes and supergravity, Phys. Rev. D **92**, 084056 (2015).
17. C. L. Benone and L. C. B. Crispino, Superradiance in static black hole spacetimes, Phys. Rev. D **93**, 024028 (2016).
18. M. A. A. Paula, L. C. S. Leite, and L. C. B. Crispino, Electrically charged black holes in linear and non-linear electrodynamics: Geodesic analysis and scalar absorption, Phys. Rev. D **102**, 104033 (2020).
19. W. Unruh, Absorption cross section of small black holes, Phys. Rev. D **14**, 3251 (1976).
20. S. R. Das, G. Gibbons, and S. D. Mathur, Universality of Low Energy Absorption Cross Sections for Black Holes, Phys. Rev. Lett. **78**, 417 (1997).
21. A. Higuchi, Low-frequency Scalar absorption cross sections for stationary black holes, Classical Quantum Gravity **18**, L139 (2001); **19**, 599(A) (2002).
22. Y. Décanini, G. Esposito-Farèse, and A. Folacci, Universality of high-energy absorption cross sections for black holes, Phys. Rev. D **83**, 044032 (2011).
23. V. Cardoso, A. S. Miranda, E. Berti, H. Witek, and V. T. Zanchin, Geodesic stability, Lyapunov exponents, and quasinormal modes, Phys. Rev. D **79**, 064016 (2009).
24. C. F. B. Macedo and L. C. B. Crispino, Absorption of planar massless scalar waves by Bardeen regular black holes, Phys. Rev. D **90**, 064001 (2014).

Modeling Type Ia supernovae with explosions in white dwarfs near and below the Chandrasekhar mass

Friedrich K. Röpke

Zentrum für Astronomie der Universität Heidelberg, Institut für Theoretische Astrophysik and Heidelberger Institut für Theoretische Studien Heidelberg, Germany
E-mail: friedrich.roepke@h-its.org

Florian Lach and Sabrina Gronow

Zentrum für Astronomie der Universität Heidelberg, Astronomisches Recheninstitut and Heidelberger Institut für Theoretische Studien Heidelberg, Germany

Stuart A. Sim and Fionntan P. Callan

Astrophysics Research Center, School of Mathematics and Physics, Queen's University Belfast, Belfast BT7 1NN, Northern Ireland, UK

Christine E. Collins

Astrophysics Research Center, School of Mathematics and Physics, Queen's University Belfast, Belfast BT7 1NN, Northern Ireland, UK and
GSI Helmholtzzentrum für Schwerionenforschung, Darmstadt, Germany

The progenitor evolution and the explosion mechanism of Type Ia supernovae remain unexplained. Nonetheless, substantial progress has been made over the past years with three-dimensional hydrodynamic simulations of different scenarios. Here, we review some recent work pertaining to the leading paradigms of modeling: thermonuclear explosions of white dwarf stars near and below the Chandrasekhar mass limit. We discuss implications of the different explosion channels and their predictions of observables.

Keywords: Type Ia supernovae, thermonuclear explosions, white dwarf stars, numerical simulations

1. Introduction

Despite substantial progress in theoretical modeling and numerical simulations over the past years,[1] our understanding of the physical mechanism of Type Ia supernovae remains incomplete. This has two main reasons. (i) The progenitor systems from which these explosions arise have not been identified, and therefore the initial conditions for the explosion simulations are uncertain. (ii) Modeling the explosion stage itself is a severe multi-scale multi-physics challenge and relies on assumptions and approximations. Some of these approximations could be mitigated with multi-dimensional hydrodynamical simulations. They form a cornerstone of a consistent modeling pipeline that follows a progenitor model over explosion and nucleosynthesis to the formation of observables. By avoiding tunable parameters, such a modeling pipeline facilitates a direct comparison of model predictions with astronomical data.

This allows for conclusions to be drawn on the validity of the assumed progenitor scenarios. In the following, we describe the application of this modeling pipeline to two different explosion scenarios.

2. Explosion models

Ignoring the fascinating but complex and still enigmatic evolution of progenitor systems of Type Ia supernovae, the main question to simulations is how to set up the state of the white dwarf at the onset of explosion. The two fundamental choices, a configuration close to the limit of stability, the Chandrasekhar mass, and a white dwarf below that mass limit, imply different explosion scenarios.[2] The compact structure of a near-Chandrasekhar mass object causes high densities of the material ahead of the thermonuclear burning front[3] if it propagates as a supersonic detonation. The products of such an explosion, almost exclusively iron group elements, are inconsistent with observations of Type Ia supernova. To produce the required intermediate mass elements detected in their spectra, burning has to start out as a subsonic deflagration in a white dwarf close to the Chandrasekhar mass. After some time of pre-expansion of the star, the burning front may turn into a supersonic detonation. In a sub-Chandrasekhar mass white dwarf, in contrast, the densities are lower and allow for the required intermediate-mass elements to be produced in a detonation.

For both scenarios, the actual ignition of the burning remains uncertain and is difficult to resolve in multidimensional hydrodynamic simulations.[4] Therefore, simulations often start out with an assumption on the triggering of the explosive burning.

3. Near-Chandrasekhar mass explosions

Sets of simulations have been carried out to test the impact of initial parameters on the outcome of explosions in near-Chandrasekhar mass white dwarf stars. Testing the ignition configuration[5] revealed that the number and spatial distribution of ignition sparks is the most important parameter for the strength of the deflagration. Few and asymmetrically distributed sparks lead to an incomplete disruption of the white dwarf. With very many ignition kernels (that are less likely to be realized in nature[4,6]), a complete unbinding of the star becomes possible, but the mass of ^{56}Ni produced is too low to explain the brightness of normal Type Ia supernovae. A detonation may form later and enhance the thermonuclear burning,[7] but here we restrict our discussion to cases where the flame propagation remains subsonic throughout.

Pure deflagrations in near-Chandrasekhar mass white dwarfs have been discussed as a model for the subclass of Type Iax supernovae.[8] An open question, however, remains: Can deflagrations in Chandrasekhar-mass white dwarfs cover the entire range of objects in this class, including the very faint events? To explore this, we have carried out an extended systematic study of three-dimensional hydrodynamic explosion simulations[9] varying the distance of single-spark ignitions from the stellar center, but also other parameters such as the central density of the white dwarf at the onset of explosion, its metallicity, its carbon mass fraction, and its rotation state. This suite of models shows that it it well possible to decrease the ^{56}Ni production and thus the brightness of the modeled events to values that would match the faintest members of the Type Iax supernova class. However, inconsistencies were discovered, too. The faint events evolve to quickly in brightness. All models fall onto a strong correlation between the produced ^{56}Ni mass and the total eject mass. This correlation does not match observations and none of the initial parameters was able to perturb it significantly. For the brighter models, however, reasonable matches with observations were found. Previous claims of chemically layered ejecta structures[10] based on the "abundance tomography" method contradict the picture of Type Iax supernovae originating from deflagrations in Chandrasekhar-mass white dwarfs. Because of the intrinsic instabilities of subsonic flame propagation, such a scenario would predict well-mixed ejecta. Recent forward-modeling,[11] however, finds that the predictions of such models may still be consistent with observations.

Improvements in explosion modeling and – in particular – in the treatment of non local thermodynamic equilibrium (NLTE) effects in the radiation transfer calculations are needed to settle the question of whether deflagrations in Chandrasekhar-mass white dwarfs can explain at least the brighter Type Iax supernovae. Given the failure to model the faint events in this framework, it seems possible that not all members of the observationally-defined class of Type Iax supernovae pertain to the same physical explosion mechanism.

4. Sub-Chandrasekhar mass explosions

Explosions of white dwarf stars below the Chandrasekhar mass are an appealing model because they seem to reproduce important observational trends.[12] The question, however, is how such inert objects trigger a detonation. A classical model is that of double detonations: A helium shell is accreted on top of a carbon-oxygen white dwarf. Once massive enough, it triggers a shell detonation that initiates a secondary detonation of the carbon-oxygen core. If the helium shell is not too massive, its products do not strongly impact the observables and the match with data from normal Type Ia supernovae improves.[13–16]

We have recently explored the mechanism of triggering of the secondary core detonation and the impact of the shell detonation products on predicted observables in an extended sequence of three-dimensional hydrodynamic simulations.[17–19] This study identifies different possibilities for the core detonation initiation depending on the mass of the helium shell and the carbon-oxygen core. Although a reasonable match is obtained in the predicted observables with observational data, some shortcomings remain. These include too red spectra and too wide variations of the lightcurve width-luminosity relation with viewing angle. Some of these deficiencies can be attributed to approximations in the treatment of NLTE effects in radiation transport,[16] but the mismatches may also call into question the explosion model itself.

5. Imprints on nucleosynthesis yields

Apart from comparing to optical observables, another approach to discriminate between and assess the validity of Type Ia supernova explosion models is by their imprints on the nucleosynthesis yields.[20] An important difference between near- and sub-Chandrasekhar mass explosion models is the production of manganese.[21] In explosive carbon burning, it can only be produced in (super-)solar ratio to iron if the densities are sufficiently high to allow for normal freeze-out from nuclear statistical equilibrium. This is the case for explosive burning in the cores of Chandrasekhar-mass white dwarfs. Alpha-rich freezeout, as occurring at lower densities in explosions of sub-Chandrasekhar mass objects, destroys the mother nucleus of ^{55}Mn, ^{55}Co, by proton captures. This produces additional ^{56}Ni at the expense of manganese. Therefore, it was concluded that a substantial fraction of Type Ia supernovae has to originate from the Chandrasekhar-mass explosion channel so that these objects can drive the manganese-over-iron trend in galactic chemical evolution towards the solar value. Our new double-detonation sub-Chandrasekhar mass explosion models,[19,20] however, show that additional manganese can be produced in the helium shell detonation. This lowers the fraction of Chandrasekhar-mass models needed to explain the galactic chemical evolution of manganese.

6. Conclusions

Three-dimensional hydrodynamic simulations help to avoid tunable parameters in the modeling of different explosion scenarios for Type Ia supernovae. The optical observables derived from such models via nucleosynthesis postprocessing[22] and radiative transfer calculations can be exposed directly to observational data. For the time being, however, the discriminative power of this approach is insufficient to identify a valid model for normal Type Ia supernovae. All considered scenarios have some advantages and some shortcomings. The reason may simply be that the correct scenario has not yet been found. Sub-Chandrasekhar mass explosions are a promising model, but in the double detonation mechanism they still fail to match some important observational properties of Type Ia supernovae. Similar explosions can, however, also be triggered by mergers of two white dwarfs.[23-26]

A similar situation is encountered with deflagrations in near-Chandrasekhar mass white dwarf stars. While this model looks promising for explaining brighter members of the Type Iax supernova class, its fainter end cannot be reproduced.

To ultimately settle the question of the origin of Type Ia supernovae, constant improvement is required in the explosion modeling as well as in the treatment of radiative transfer predicting the optical observables. Alternative observables that may help to discriminate between models include the nucleosynthesis yields discussed here, but also spectropolarimetry data,[27–29] the search for surviving companion stars in the double degenerate progenitor model[30] and imprints of different explosion scenarios on the forming supernova remnants.[31,32]

Acknowledgments

This work was supported by the Deutsche Forschungsgemeinschaft (DFG, German Research Foundation) – Project-ID 138713538 – SFB 881 ("The Milky Way System", subproject A10), by the ChETEC COST Action (CA16117), and by the National Science Foundation under Grant No. OISE-1927130 (IReNA). FL and FKR acknowledge support by the Klaus Tschira Foundation. FPC acknowledges an STFC studentship and SAS acknowledges funding from STFC Grant Ref: ST/P000312/1. The authors gratefully acknowledge the Gauss Centre for Supercomputing e.V. (www.gauss-centre.eu) for funding this project by providing computing time on the GCS Supercomputer JUWELS[33] at Jülich Supercomputing Centre (JSC). Part of this work was performed using the Cambridge Service for Data Driven Discovery (CSD3), part of which is operated by the University of Cambridge Research Computing on behalf of the STFC DiRAC HPC Facility (www.dirac.ac.uk). The DiRAC component of CSD3 was funded by BEIS capital funding via STFC capital grants ST/P002307/1 and ST/R002452/1 and STFC operations grant ST/R00689X/1. DiRAC is part of the National e-Infrastructure.

References

1. W. Hillebrandt, M. Kromer, F. K. Röpke and A. J. Ruiter, Towards an understanding of type ia supernovae from a synthesis of theory and observations, *Frontiers of Physics* **8**, 116 (April 2013).
2. I. R. Seitenzahl and D. M. Townsley, *Nucleosynthesis in Thermonuclear Supernovae*, in *Handbook of Supernovae*, eds. A. W. Alsabti and P. Murdin 2017, p. 1955.
3. F. K. Röpke, Combustion in thermonuclear supernova explosions, in *Handbook of Supernovae*, eds. A. Alsabti and P. Murdin (Springer, March 2017) pp. 1185–1209.
4. A. Nonaka, A. J. Aspden, M. Zingale, A. S. Almgren, J. B. Bell and S. E. Woosley, High-resolution simulations of convection preceding ignition in Type Ia supernovae using adaptive mesh refinement, *ApJ* **745**, p. 73 (January 2012).
5. M. Fink, M. Kromer, I. R. Seitenzahl, F. Ciaraldi-Schoolmann, F. K. Röpke, S. A. Sim, R. Pakmor, A. J. Ruiter and W. Hillebrandt, Three-dimensional pure deflagration models with nucleosynthesis and synthetic observables for Type Ia supernovae, *MNRAS* **438**, 1762 (February 2014).
6. C. Byrohl, R. Fisher and D. Townsley, The intrinsic stochasticity of the ^{56}ni distribution of single-degenerate near-Chandrasekhar-mass SN Ia, *ApJ* **878**, p. 67 (June 2019).
7. I. R. Seitenzahl, F. Ciaraldi-Schoolmann, F. K. Röpke, M. Fink, W. Hillebrandt, M. Kromer, R. Pakmor, A. J. Ruiter, S. A. Sim and S. Taubenberger, Three-dimensional delayed-detonation models with nucleosynthesis for Type Ia supernovae, *MNRAS* **429**, 1156 (February 2013).

8. S. W. Jha, *Type Iax Supernovae*, in *Handbook of Supernovae*, eds. A. W. Alsabti and P. Murdin 2017, p. 375.
9. F. Lach, F. P. Callan, D. Bubeck, F. K. Roepke, S. A. Sim, M. Schrauth, S. T. Ohlmann and M. Kromer, Type iax supernovae from deflagrations in Chandrasekhar-mass white dwarfs, *arXiv e-prints*, arXiv:2109.02926 (September 2021).
10. B. Barna, T. Szalai, W. E. Kerzendorf, M. Kromer, S. A. Sim, M. R. Magee and B. Leibundgut, Type Iax supernovae as a few-parameter family, *MNRAS* **480**, 3609 (November 2018).
11. M. R. Magee, J. H. Gillanders, K. Maguire, S. A. Sim and F. P. Callan, An analysis of the spectroscopic signatures of layering in the ejecta of type Iax supernovae, *arXiv e-prints*, arXiv:2110.12294 (October 2021).
12. S. A. Sim, F. K. Röpke, W. Hillebrandt, M. Kromer, R. Pakmor, M. Fink, A. J. Ruiter and I. R. Seitenzahl, Detonations in sub-Chandrasekhar-mass C+O white dwarfs, *ApJ* **714**, L52 (May 2010).
13. M. Fink, F. K. Röpke, W. Hillebrandt, I. R. Seitenzahl, S. A. Sim and M. Kromer, Double-detonation sub-Chandrasekhar supernovae: can minimum helium shell masses detonate the core?, *A&A* **514**, p. A53 (May 2010).
14. M. Kromer, S. A. Sim, M. Fink, F. K. Röpke, I. R. Seitenzahl and W. Hillebrandt, Double-detonation Sub-Chandrasekhar Supernovae: Synthetic Observables for Minimum Helium Shell Mass Models, *ApJ* **719**, 1067 (August 2010).
15. D. M. Townsley, B. J. Miles, K. J. Shen and D. Kasen, Double Detonations with Thin, Modestly Enriched Helium Layers can Make Normal Type Ia Supernovae, *ApJ* **878**, p. L38 (June 2019).
16. K. J. Shen, S. Blondin, D. Kasen, L. Dessart, D. M. Townsley, S. Boos and D. J. Hillier, Non-local Thermodynamic Equilibrium Radiative Transfer Simulations of Sub-Chandrasekhar-mass White Dwarf Detonations, *ApJ* **909**, p. L18 (March 2021).
17. S. Gronow, C. Collins, S. T. Ohlmann, R. Pakmor, M. Kromer, I. R. Seitenzahl, S. A. Sim and F. K. Röpke, SNe Ia from double detonations: Impact of core-shell mixing on the carbon ignition mechanism, *A&A* **635**, p. A169 (March 2020).
18. S. Gronow, C. E. Collins, S. A. Sim and F. K. Röpke, Double detonations of sub-M_{Ch} CO white dwarfs: Variations in Type Ia supernovae due to different core and He shell masses, *A&A* **649**, p. A155 (May 2021).
19. S. Gronow, B. Côté, F. Lach, I. R. Seitenzahl, C. E. Collins, S. A. Sim and F. K. Roepke, Metallicity-dependent nucleosynthetic yields of Type Ia supernovae originating from double detonations of sub-M_{Ch} white dwarfs, *arXiv e-prints*, arXiv:2103.14050 (March 2021), submitted to *A&A*.
20. F. Lach, F. K. Roepke, I. R. Seitenzahl, B. Coté, S. Gronow and A. J. Ruiter, Nucleosynthesis imprints from different Type Ia Supernova explosion scenarios and implications for galactic chemical evolution, *A&A* **644**, p. A118 (December 2020).
21. I. R. Seitenzahl, G. Cescutti, F. K. Röpke, A. J. Ruiter and R. Pakmor, Solar abundance of manganese: A case for near chandrasekhar-mass type ia supernova progenitors, *A&A* **559**, p. L5 (November 2013).
22. I. R. Seitenzahl, F. K. Röpke, M. Fink and R. Pakmor, Nucleosynthesis in thermonuclear supernovae with tracers: Convergence and variable mass particles, *MNRAS* **407**, 2297 (October 2010).
23. R. Pakmor, M. Kromer, F. K. Röpke, S. A. Sim, A. J. Ruiter and W. Hillebrandt, Sub-luminous type ia supernovae from the mergers of equal-mass white dwarfs with mass $\sim 0.9 m_\odot$, *Nature* **463**, 61 (January 2010).
24. R. Pakmor, M. Kromer, S. Taubenberger, S. A. Sim, F. K. Röpke and W. Hillebrandt, Normal Type Ia supernovae from violent mergers of white dwarf binaries, *ApJ* **747**, p. L10 (March 2012).

25. R. Pakmor, M. Kromer, S. Taubenberger and V. Springel, Helium-ignited violent mergers as a unified model for normal and rapidly declining type Ia supernovae, *ApJ* **770**, p. L8 (June 2013).
26. K. J. Shen, S. J. Boos, D. M. Townsley and D. Kasen, Multi-Dimensional Radiative Transfer Calculations of Double Detonations of Sub-Chandrasekhar-Mass White Dwarfs, *arXiv e-prints*, arXiv:2108.12435 (August 2021).
27. M. Bulla, S. A. Sim, R. Pakmor, M. Kromer, S. Taubenberger, F. K. Röpke, W. Hillebrandt and I. R. Seitenzahl, Type Ia supernovae from violent mergers of carbon-oxygen white dwarfs: Polarization signatures, *MNRAS* **455**, 1060 (January 2016).
28. M. Bulla, S. A. Sim, M. Kromer, I. R. Seitenzahl, M. Fink, F. Ciaraldi-Schoolmann, F. K. Röpke, W. Hillebrandt, R. Pakmor, A. J. Ruiter and S. Taubenberger, Predicting polarization signatures for double-detonation and delayed-detonation models of Type Ia supernovae, *MNRAS* **462**, 1039 (October 2016).
29. M. Bulla, Z. W. Liu, F. K. Röpke, S. A. Sim, M. Fink, M. Kromer, R. Pakmor and I. R. Seitenzahl, White dwarf deflagrations for Type Iax supernovae: Polarisation signatures from the explosion and companion interaction, *A&A* **635**, p. A179 (March 2020).
30. K. J. Shen, D. Boubert, B. T. Gänsicke, S. W. Jha, J. E. Andrews, L. Chomiuk, R. J. Foley, M. Fraser, M. Gromadzki, J. Guillochon, M. M. Kotze, K. Maguire, M. R. Siebert, N. Smith, J. Strader, C. Badenes, W. E. Kerzendorf, D. Koester, M. Kromer, B. Miles, R. Pakmor, J. Schwab, O. Toloza, S. Toonen, D. M. Townsley and B. J. Williams, Three Hypervelocity White Dwarfs in Gaia DR2: Evidence for Dynamically Driven Double-degenerate Double-detonation Type Ia Supernovae, *ApJ* **865**, p. 15 (September 2018).
31. G. Ferrand, D. C. Warren, M. Ono, S. Nagataki, F. K. Röpke and I. R. Seitenzahl, From Supernova to Supernova Remnant: The Three-dimensional Imprint of a Thermonuclear Explosion, *ApJ* **877**, p. 136 (Jun 2019).
32. G. Ferrand, D. C. Warren, M. Ono, S. Nagataki, F. K. Röpke, I. R. Seitenzahl, F. Lach, H. Iwasaki and T. Sato, From Supernova to Supernova Remnant: Comparison of Thermonuclear Explosion Models, *ApJ* **906**, p. 93 (January 2021).
33. Jülich Supercomputing Centre. (2019). JUWELS: Modular Tier-0/1 Supercomputer at the Jülich Supercomputing Centre. *Journal of Large-Scale Research Facilities* **5**, A171.

Type Ia supernovae and their explosive nucleosynthesis: Constraints on progenitors

Shing-Chi Leung

Department of Mathematics and Physics, SUNY Polytechnic Institute, 100 Seymour Road, Utica, New York 13502, USA
TAPIR, Mailcode 350-17, California Institute of Technology, Pasadena, CA 91125, USA
E-mail: leungs@sunypoly.edu
https://sunypoly.edu/faculty-and-staff/shing-chi-leung.html

Ken'ichi Nomoto

Kavli Institute for the Physics and Mathematics of the Universe (WPI), The University of Tokyo Institutes for Advanced Study, The University of Tokyo, Kashiwa, Chiba 277-8583, Japan
E-mail: nomoto@astron.s.u-tokyo.ac.jp

What the progenitors of Type Ia supernovae (SNe Ia) are, whether they are near-Chandrasekhar mass or sub-Chandrasekhar mass white dwarfs, has been the matter of debate for decades. Various observational hints are supporting both models as the main progenitors. In this paper, we review the explosion physics and the chemical abundance patterns of SNe Ia from these two classes of progenitors. We will discuss how the observational data of SNe Ia, their remnants, the Milky Way Galaxy, and galactic clusters can help us to determine the essential features where numerical models of SNe Ia need to match.

Keywords: Supernova; Hydrodynamics; Nucleosynthesis; Supernova Remnant; Galactic Chemical Evolution

1. Introduction

Type Ia supernovae (SNe Ia) are well-understood as the thermonuclear explosions of carbon-oxygen white dwarfs (CO WDs).[1–3] They produce the majority of iron-peak elements in the galaxy, in particular ^{55}Mn. Their light curves can be standardized for measuring distance in the cosmological scale.[4,5] Understanding their progenitors, the explosion mechanisms and their obseravables are important for understanding the Universe in the larger scale.[6,7] In this review paper, we will explore possible progenitors of SNe Ia, whether they are the explosions of near-Chandrasekhar mass (Ch-mass) WDs or sub-Chandrasekhar mass (subCh-mass) WDs. In Table 1 we tabulate the important features to contrast between the Ch-mass and subCh-mass WDs.

The rise of the two classes of models comes from the diversity of observed SNe Ia. In the literature, a number of explosion models have been proposed to explain the normal and peculiar SNe Ia. For the Ch-mass WD, representative models include the pure turbulent deflagration model (PTD),[8–15] PTD with deflagration-detonation transition,[16–22] gravitationally confined detonation model[23–27] and pulsation reverse detonation models.[28,29] The subCh-mass WD models include the double-detonation model,[30–38] violent merger model[39–42] and WD head-on collision model.[43–45] On top of these, unconventional models such as magnetized WDs,[46] super-Chandrasekhar mass WDs,[47] differentially rotating WDs[48,49] and interaction with dark matter gravity[50,51] have been proposed to explain some unusual SNe Ia.

Table 1. Comparing essential features of Ch-mass and subCh-mass WDs.

	unit	Ch-mass WD	subCh-mass WD
mass	$M_\odot$	$1.30 - \geqslant 1.38$	$0.9 - 1.2$
central density	g cm^{-3}	$10^9 - 10^{10}$	$10^7 - 10^8$
composition		^{12}C+^{16}O+^{22}Ne	core: ^{12}C+^{16}O+^{22}Ne envelope (env): ^{4}He
reaction		subsonic deflagration	supersonic detonation
first site		(near-)center	off-center (He-env)

The study of SNe Ia as explosions of (sub)Ch-mass WDs is often linked to the open question about the progenitors of SNe Ia: the single degenerate (SD) vs. the double degenerate (DD) scenario. The SD scenario means that the primary WD develops its nuclear runaway by mass accretion from its companion star, which can be a slightly evolved main-sequence, a red-giant, or a He-star.[49,52] The DD scenario means that the primary WD triggers the runaway by dynamical interaction with its companion WD.

We remind that the question on whether SNe Ia develop from Ch-mass WDs is not equivalent to arguing SNe Ia mainly develop in the SD scenario. For example, in the SD scenario, when the WD explodes as an SN Ia depends on the mass accretion rate from its companion star and the WD initial mass (see the left panel of Figure 1). A WD having (1) a high mass accretion rate above $\sim 10^{-9}$ $M_\odot$ yr^{-1} or (2) having a low mass accretion rate and a high initial mass > 1.1 $M_\odot$ is likely to develop nuclear runaway in the Ch-mass limit. Otherwise, the WD is more likely to explode as a subCh-mass WD.[53] Similar features have been seen also for WDs in the DD scenario.

To understand why the C-deflagration is associated with the Chandrasekhar mass WD, we show in the right panel of Figure 1 the relative pressure change of the CO-rich matter as a function of the matter density. During the thermonuclear runaway, ^{12}C and ^{16}O burn to form iron-peak elements peaked at ^{56}Ni, releasing an amount of $\sim 10^{18}$ erg g^{-1}. When the density is high ($\sim 10^9$ g cm^{-3}), the electron degeneracy pressure dominates the matter pressure, and the overall pressure becomes insensitive to its temperature. As a result, the relative pressure jump decreases as the matter becomes more degenerate. Without an abrupt pressure jump, the nuclear runaway in the Ch-mass WD may not spontaneously trigger a shock wave and hence no detonation may form. The hot matter may ignite ^{12}C in the nearby cold matter only by thermal conduction.

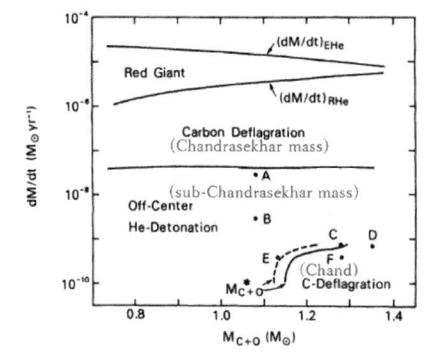

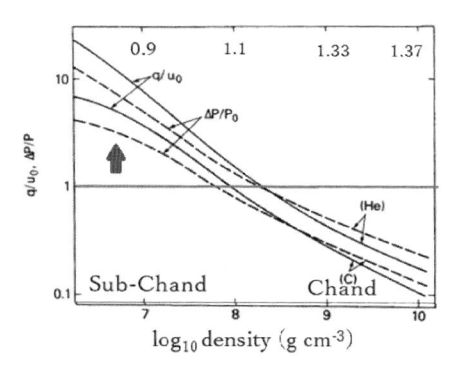

Fig. 1. (left panel) The final fate of the WD in the SD scenario with the mass accretion rate and the initial CO WD mass as parameters (derived and edited from Ref. 53). (right panel) The relative pressure change $\Delta P/P_0$ and relative internal energy change q/u_0 before and after nuclear runaway as a function of the matter density for the He-rich (solid line) and CO-rich (dashed line) matter (Ref. 30). The numbers on the top corresponds to the mass of the WD when the density corresponds to the central density of the WD. The red arrow indicates the relative pressure change of the CO-rich matter.

Unlike the detonation, the subsonic deflagration is subject to hydrodynamical instabilities such as the Rayleigh-Taylor (RT), Kelvin-Helmholtz (KH) and Landau-Derrieus[54–56] instabilities. The analytic model suggests that the buoyancy force can drive the early flame away from the center.[57] In Figure 2 we plot the electron fraction Y_e profile of a canonical PTD model where the deflagration has quenched after the expansion of the WD. The Y_e profile is a useful scalar for tracking how the fluid elements move inside the star. We observe the elongated "mushroom" shape as features of the RT-instabilities and the spiral along and inside the "mushrooms" as features of the KH-instabilities.

However, a WD may not naturally explode if there is only a slow subsonic nuclear flame because the WD expands and quenches the flame before the whole WD is burnt.[8,12] To alleviate this issue, a deflagration-detonation transition[16] and a flame-acceleration scheme[9,58,59] have been proposed for assisting nuclear burning to spread around the entire WD before the WD expands.

2. Typical Type Ia Supernova Explosion

Both the Ch-mass and subCh-mass WD models have their individual strengths and concerns, despite both of them can reproduce the observed features of normal SNe Ia,[60–62] including the Philip's relation.[37,63] For example, the Ch-mass model can produce Mn with an amount consistent with the solar abundance,[64] while the subCh-mass models do not produce a significant amount of Mn. But the DDT mechanism remains a matter of debate whether or not the turbulence is sufficient to pre-condition the CO rich matter.[57,65–69]

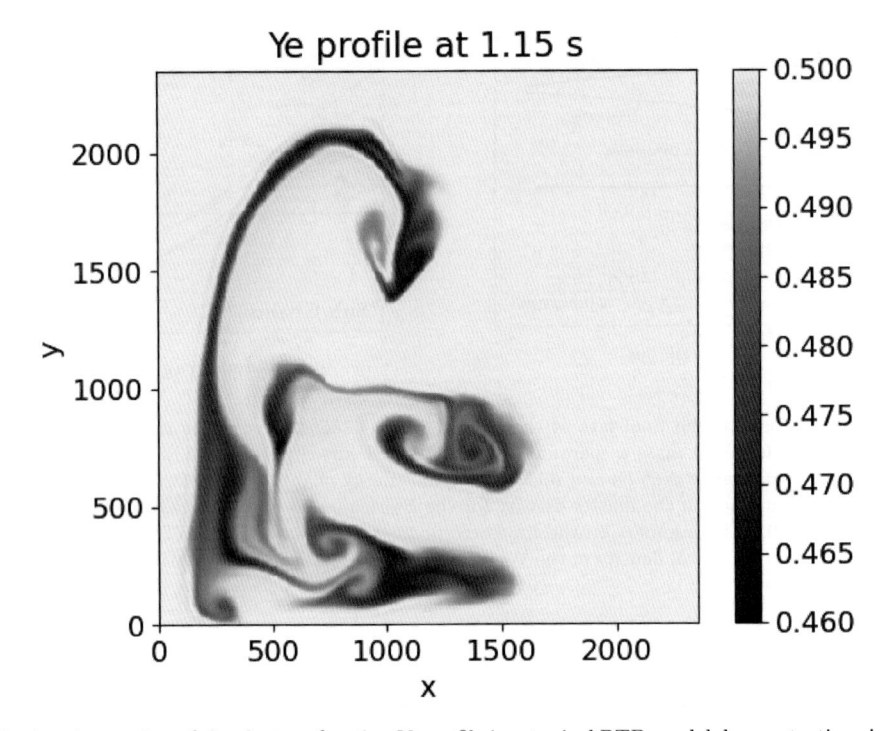

Fig. 2. A snapshot of the electron fraction Y_e profile in a typical PTD model demonstrating simultaneously the Rayleigh-Taylor and Kelvin-Helmholtz instabilities due to interaction of turbulent fluid motion with the deflagration front.

2.1. *Typical Explosion Mechanism of Ch-mass and subCh-mass Models*

We now examine the typical explosion mechanism in both the Ch-mass and subCh-mass WDs. Even though we have described a number of explosion mechanisms in the previous section, in general they are only different by the progenitor or the initial explosion kernel. The underlying mechanism, namely the deflagration and detonation, remains unchanged. Here we examine how the WD explodes accordingly.

In Figures 3 and 4 we plot the temperature profiles of the representative Ch-mass WD explosion using the PTD model with DDT for a WD of 1.37 $M_\odot$, metallicity $Z = 0.02$ and a $c3$ deflagration kernel[22] based on two-dimensional simulations.[70] The WD is burnt by subsonic flame for around 1 s, consuming about $\sim 30\%$ of the CO-rich matter in mass. After that, DDT is assumed to take place and the remaining matter is burnt within ~ 0.1 s. Eventually, the WD undergoes homologous expansion which quenches both deflagration and detonation.

In Figures 5 and 6 we plot similar profiles to Figure 3-4 but for the subCh-mass model with the initial mass 1.10 $M_\odot$, $Z = 0.02$ and a single He-detonation bubble.[35] In the first 1 s, the detonation burns the He-rich matter along the envelope.

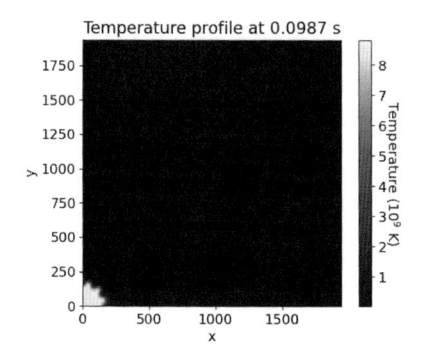

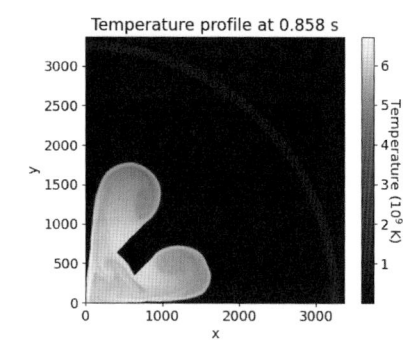

Fig. 3. (left panel) The initial temperature profile of the quadrant cross-section in a typical Ch-mass model using the PTD model with DDT for an initial mass $M = 1.37~M_\odot$, metallicity $Z = 0.02$, and a "three-finger" initial flame kernel.[22] (top right panel) Same as the top left panel when the DDT is assumed to be triggered.

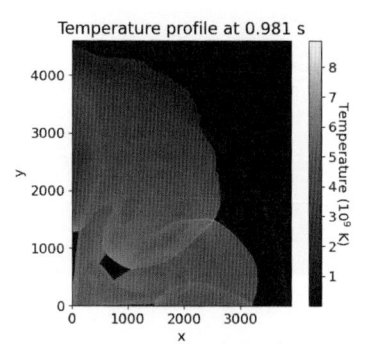

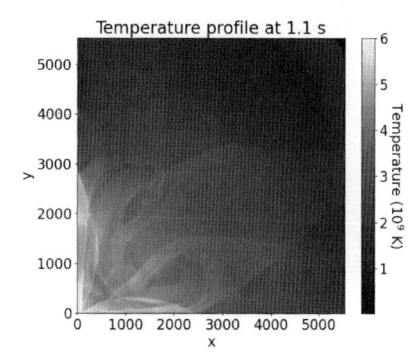

Fig. 4. (left panel) Same as Figure 3 but during the detonation phase. (right panel) Near complete disruption of the WD.

The detonation strength increases during the collision, which creates a shock that penetrates into the CO-core. This creates the C-detonation which later disrupts the entire WD.

2.2. *General Thermodynamical Features*

Typical multi-dimensional SN Ia simulations solve the Eulerian hydrodynamics equations with a simplified nuclear reaction network. To obtain the detailed chemical

Table 2. Major isotopes of iron-peak elements and their corresponding electron fraction.

Isotope	^{54}Fe	^{55}Mn	^{55}Fe	^{55}Fe	^{56}Fe	^{56}Co	^{56}Ni	^{57}Fe	^{58}Ni	^{60}Ni
Ye	0.481	0.454	0.472	0.490	0.464	0.482	0.500	0.456	0.483	0.467

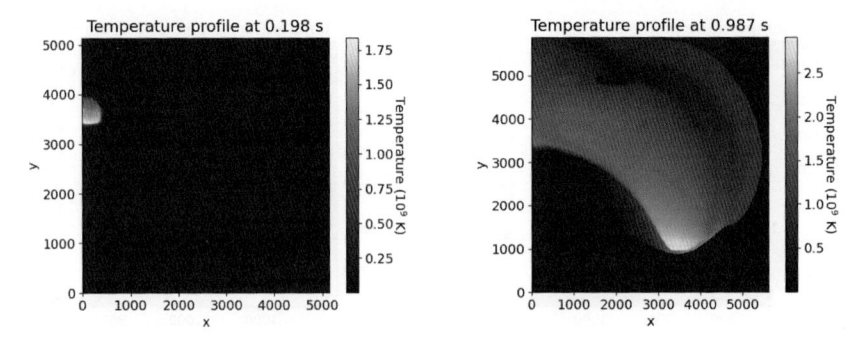

Fig. 5. (left panel) The initial temperature profile of a typical subCh-mass model using the double detonation model with the initial mass $M = 1.10\ M_\odot$, $Z = 0.02$, and a "single bubble" initial detonation kernel.[35] (right panel) Same as the top left panel but during the amplification of the He detonation.

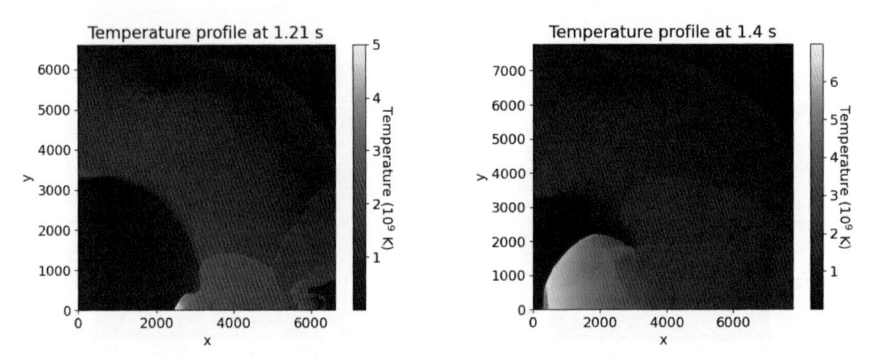

Fig. 6. (left panel) Same as Figure 5 but during the onset of the C-detonation. (right panel) Same as the left panel but during the C-detonation phase.

features of the explosion, a passive tracer particle scheme[71–74] is necessary. This scheme allocates a number of Lagrangian tracers to follow the fluid motion. The notation "passive" means that the tracers do not affect the fluid motion; they only record the thermodynamical condition along their trajectories.

The tracer particles record $(\rho(t), T(t))$ as a Lagrangian fluid packet along its path for reconstructing the exact chemical abundances. For SNe Ia, the trajectory is less convoluted that its peak density and temperature $(\rho_{\text{peak}}, T_{\text{peak}})$ can characterize the typical nucleosynthesis features inside the tracer. We make numerical experiments to show how various nucleosynthesis quantities depend on the parameters $(\rho_{\text{peak}}, T_{\text{peak}})$ parameter space.

We assume that the tracers start from given $(\rho_{\text{peak}}, T_{\text{peak}})$ and then adiabatically expand. The expansion timescale is chosen according to the typical explosion energy 10^{51} erg. The nuclear reactions are computed using the 495-isotope network.[75]

In Figures 7 and 8 we plot the final mean atomic number $\bar{A}$, Y_e, asymptotic mass fraction of ^{55}Mn and ^{56}Fe for tracers under different initial conditions. The region is

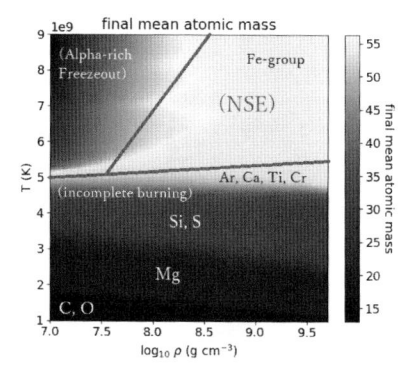

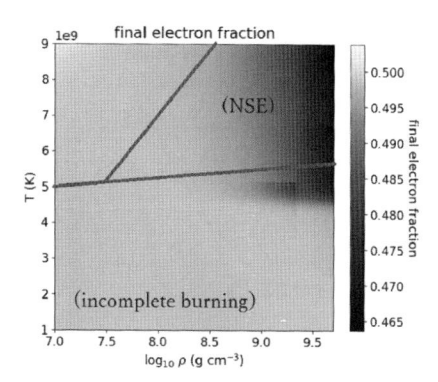

Fig. 7. (left panel) The final mean atomic mass number $\bar{A}$ of the tracer particles starting from different $\rho_{\rm peak}$ and $T_{\rm peak}$ (in units of 10^9 K). (right panel) Same as the left panel, but for the final electron fraction Y_e of the tracer.

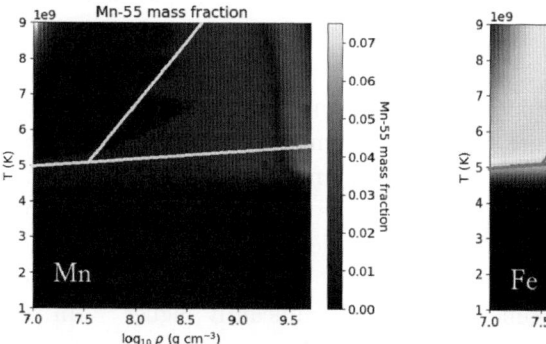

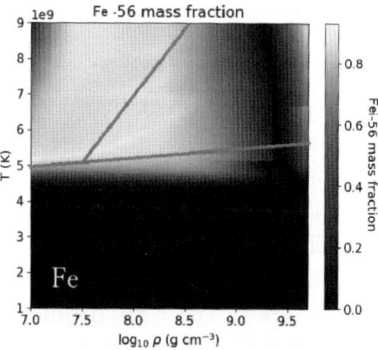

Fig. 8. (left panel) Same as Figure 7, but for the final mass fraction of stable ^{55}Mn. (right panel) Same as the left panel but for the final mass fraction of stable ^{56}Fe.

divided into three regions.[76,77] The low-$\rho_{\rm peak}$ region corresponds to the incomplete Si-burning regime, where the nuclear reaction terminates before reaching Fe-group elements, such as Si, S, Ar and so on. The high-$T_{\rm peak}$ (in units of 10^9 K) and low-$\rho_{\rm peak}$ region corresponds to the α-rich freezeout regime. As the name suggests, the nuclear reaction is confined to be along the α-chain from ^{12}C to ^{56}Ni. The high-$T_{\rm peak}$ and high-$\rho_{\rm peak}$ region corresponds to the nuclear statistical equilibrium (NSE) regime. This regime plays an important role in the Ch-mass WD as it allows isotopes away from the α-chain to form through weak interaction (electron capture).

As the Y_e-profile indicates, the NSE zone is also the region where matter with $Y_e < 0.5$ can be formed. The low Y_e environment is vital for forming the parents of ^{55}Mn (see Table 2 for the representative Y_e for the major neutron-rich isotopes of iron-peak elements). The ^{55}Mn profile also shows that the NSE zone is the primary site for generating a significant amount of stable ^{55}Mn after decay. On the other hand, ^{56}Fe is mostly formed in the α-rich freezeout and NSE ($Y_e \approx 0.5$) regions.

2.3. Thermodynamical Trajectories of SN Ia Models

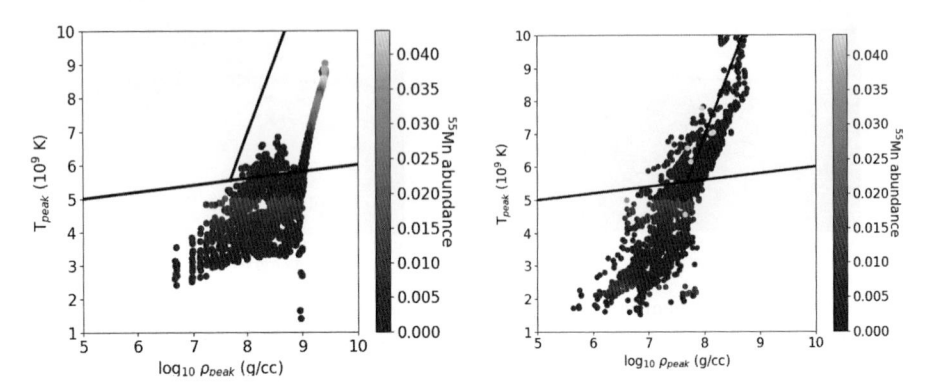

Fig. 9. (left panel) The thermodynamical trajectories of tracer particles of the Ch-mass model with the colour being the asymptotic ^{55}Mn abundance. Same as the left panel but for the subCh-mass model.

Having explored which thermodynamical parameter space is responsible for iron-peak elements, we show in Figure 9 the thermodynamics trajectories of tracers obtained from the typical Ch-mass and subCh-mass models. The chemical abundance of each tracer is directly computed according to its individual (ρ, T) time evolution.

The Ch-mass model (left panel) has two distinctive parts: the high density thin tail and the thick body at low density. At high density ($\rho_{\text{peak}} > 10^9$ g cm^{-3}), the tracers are in the NSE regime and have a significantly higher ^{55}Mn and low fluctuations in T_{peak} for the same ρ_{peak}. These are the tracers burnt by the subsonic deflagration. The absence of shock ensures that nuclear burning does not generate strong acoustic waves. On the other hand, the majority of tracers burnt by the detonation undergo incomplete Si-burning. The aspherical explosion allows tracers with the same initial mass coordinate to be burnt at a range of time. This leads to a wide temperature range for the same ρ_{peak}. There is also a narrow band of tracers for $7 < \log_{10} \rho_{\text{peak}} < 9$ and $T_{\text{peak}} \approx 5 \times 10^9$ K also responsible for synthesizing a small fraction of ^{55}Mn.

The subCh-mass model (right panel) has a uniform structure where the T_{peak} scales with ρ_{peak} with some fluctuations. Only a small part of tracers reaches the NSE regime but their density is not high enough for the ^{55}Mn synthesis. There is also a narrow band of tracers containing ^{55}Mn by the synthesis of ^{55}Co. In general the global ^{55}Mn in the subCh-mass model is lower than that of the Ch-mass model.

2.4. Typical Nucleosynthesis in Ch-mass and subCh-mass Models

Now we have examined the thermodynamical differences between the Ch-mass and subCh-mass WDs. In Figure 10 we compare the qualitative differences in the nucleosynthesis pattern.

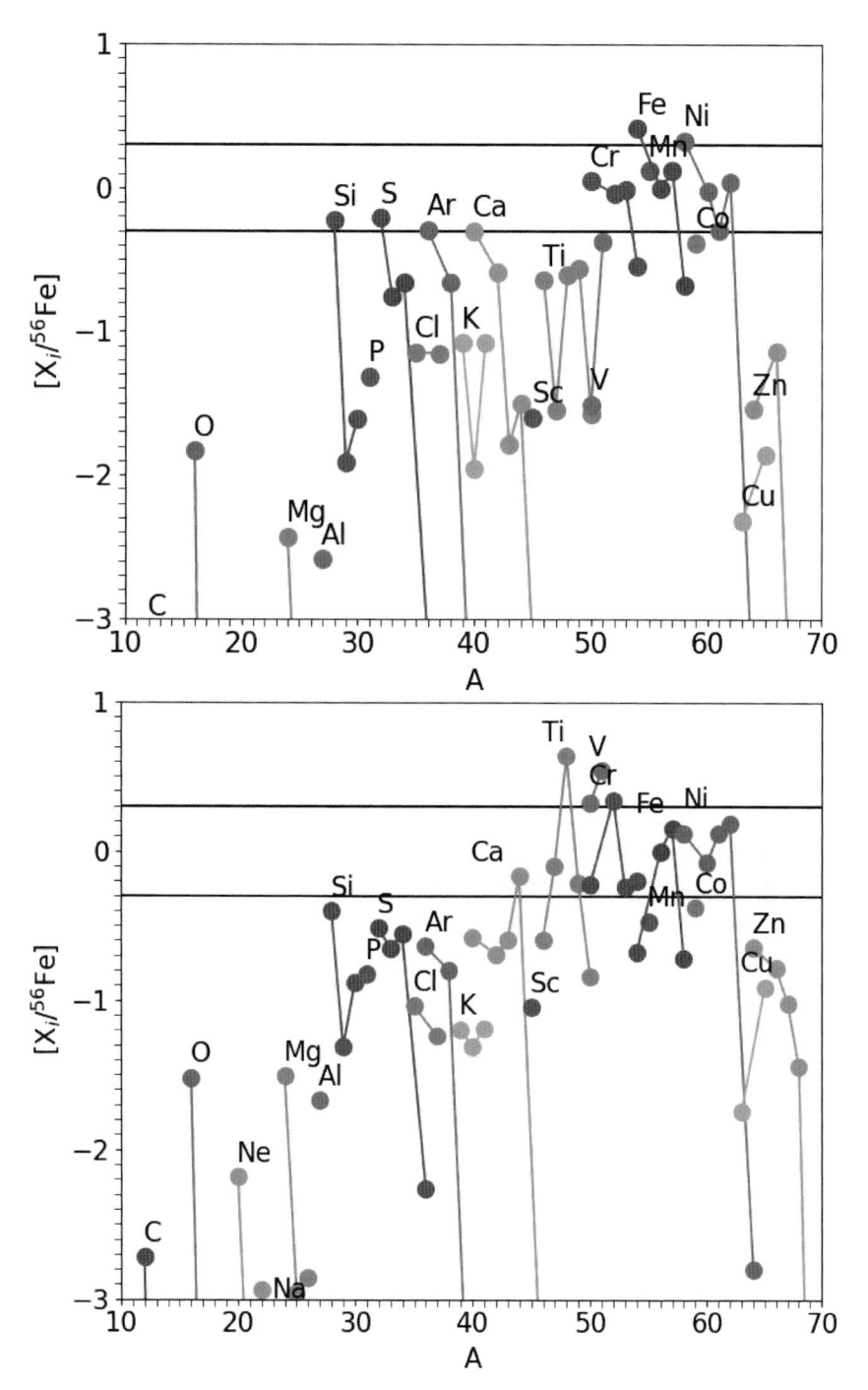

Fig. 10. (top panel) The final chemical abundance pattern of the typical Ch-mass WD[22] assuming the aspherical explosion. (bottom panel) Same as the top panel but for the typical subCh-mass WD.[35] $[X_i/^{56}\text{Fe}] = \log_{10}[(X_i/^{56}\text{Fe}) / (X_i/^{56}\text{Fe})_\odot]$. The two horizontal lines correspond to 50% and 200% of the solar value.

Both Ch-mass and subCh-mass WDs share some common features. They are responsible for the production of intermediate mass elements (IMEs) from Si to Ca, and the iron-peak elements from Ti to Ni. Odd number elements of IMEs are underproduced in SNe Ia. Some individual features allow us to distinguish the two models. (1) The aspherical explosion of the subCh-mass model can lead to signatures of strong Ti, V and Cr. (2) Mn is well-produced in the Ch-mass model but not in the subCh-mass model.

3. Applications of Nucleosynthesis

We have surveyed the major differences of the nucleosynthetic signature between the Ch-mass and subCh-mass WDs. Comparisons with observational data allow us to understand the progenitors of observed SNe Ia, which directly constrains the modeling. We can compare the optical signatures directly (i.e., light curves and spectra) by matching the radiative transfer model with SN Ia data.[41,60] One can also extract the chemical abundances from the spectra, and compare with nucleosynthetic results.[62,78] We shall focus on the latter method here.

3.1. *Supernova Remnant Sagittarius A East*

Within thousand years after the SN explosion, the shock-heated gas remains observable in the X-ray band, where the spectra reveal the metal composition inside the ejecta. Such a technique has been applied to the study of galactic supernova remnants (SNRs) including Tycho,[80] Kepler[81] and N103B.[82]

In Ref. 79 the SNR in Sagittarius A (Sgr A) East (G0.0+0.0) is observed based on the X-ray data taken by the *Chandra* telescope. The observed abundance ratios relative to Fe (with respect to the solar ratios) [Xi/Fe] are shown in Figure 11. The SNR features sub-solar intermediate mass elements (IMEs) and slightly super-solar iron-peak elements (Cr, Mn, and Ni).

The sub-solar IMEs exclude the possibility of associating a core-collapse SN as the origin of this remnant. On the left panel, the abundances of two distinctive classes of models, the subCh-mass and Ch-mass DDT models are plotted. The model uncertainties are shown by the shaded area. The subCh-mass models clearly overproduce the IME. Among the Ch-mass DDT models, the model that produces enough Mn and Ni overproduces Cr and the IME. There is a model whose Cr and Ni are consistent with the data points and IMEs are marginal, but its Mn is too small.

The Ch-mass PTD model (i.e., no DDT) with the initial central density of $\sim 5 \times 10^9$ g cm^{-3} is shown to be compatible with the data (right panel of Figure 11). [Such a high central density is realized in the rotating WD model.[83]] Note that this Ch-mass PTD model can well-explain the observed features of SNe Iax. Thus this object is the first identified SN Iax in the Milky Way Galaxy observed as SNR. This example also shows how the abundance guides us to identify the explosion mechanism.

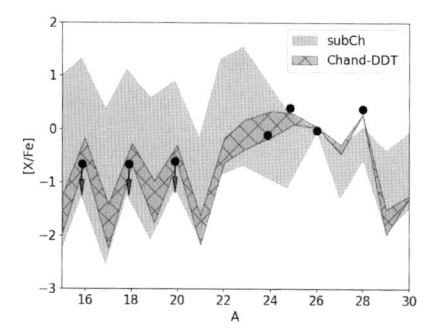

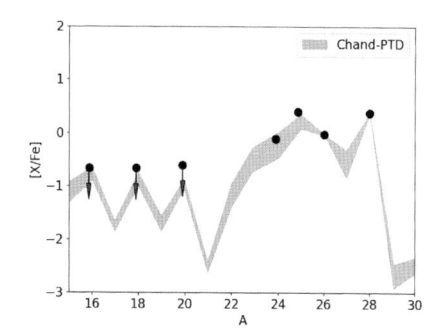

Fig. 11. (left panel) The chemical abundance pattern of the supernova remnant (SNR) Sagittarius A (from Ref. 79) for the data points compared with those of the subCh-mass[35] and Ch-mass DDT[22] models shown by the shaded regions. (right panel) Same as the left panel but for the Ch-mass PTD[15] models.

3.2. Supernova Remnant 3C 397

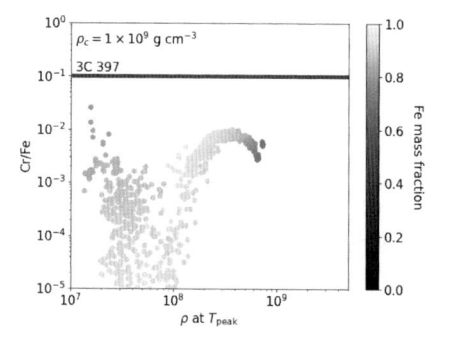

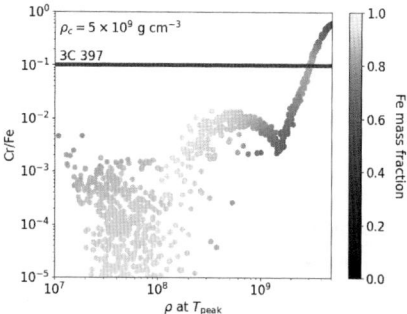

Fig. 12. (left panel) The Cr/Fe distribution of the tracers taken from the Ch-mass model with the initial central density 1×10^9 g cm^{-3}.[22] The color represents the tracer Fe mass fraction. The horizontal line is the measured value in SNR 3C 397 from Ref. 84. (right panel) Same as the left panel but for the model with the initial central density 5×10^9 g cm^{-3}.

The SNR 3C 397 is a nearby object (8 kpc) on the galactic plane. Its close distance allows astronomers to extract the spectra from individual parts similar to Sgr A. This object features a high Mn/Ni ratio, which is a key evidence of the Ch-mass explosion.[85]

In a recent observation using the *XMM-Newton* telescope, the spectra from the South and West hot blobs are measured, which give the constraint on the Cr/Fe mass ratio $\sim 0.106^{+0.011}_{-0.009}$.[84] The high value is used to distinguish the explosion progenitor shown in Figure 12. By comparing the tracer in different Ch-mass models, it becomes clear that the low-mass model ($\rho_c = 1 \times 10^9$ g cm^{-3}) does not have tracers reaching the observed high value. Meanwhile the high density tail in the high-mass model

($\rho_c = 5 \times 10^9$ g cm^{-3}) has tracers crossing the expected value. This provides a strong indication that this object is the explosion of the high-mass Ch-mass WD. This also demonstrates how a precise measurement of element abundance ratios can guide us to select the potential progenitor.

3.3. Milky Way Galaxy

In the last two sections we have shown how the SNR abundance determines its progenitor and the explosion mechanism. While there is no distinctive SNR showing chemical abundances exclusively for subCh-mass WD models, it is possible that a large sample size is needed to understand the distribution of each model. To understand the SN Ia explosion globally, we need the chemical abundances from a larger system, for example, the Milky Way Galaxy. The elements ejected by supernovae become the building block of the next-generation stars.[6] The surface abundance of stars in the solar neighbourhood may thus indicate how much each element is ejected by generations of SNe Ia.

In Ref. 86 the galactic chemical evolution model is computed with supernova abundance patterns taken from literatures. The Mn/Fe evolution is plotted in Figure 13. Two contrasting classes of models are shown, one assuming the pure Ch-mass WD explosion, and the other two assuming pure subCh-mass WD. To reproduce the trend as well as the magnitude of the data, a non-negligible fraction of the Ch-mass WD is necessary.

We remark that the supernova history can be strongly dependent on the galaxy evolution history. Some galaxies (e.g., Sculptor dwarf spheroidal galaxy) have a low Mn/Fe ratio that indicates the dominance of the subCh-mass WD explosion in their evolution histories.[90,91] Meanwhile, some early rise of [Mn/Fe] in this subclass of galaxies can be a result of the Ch-mass SN Iax explosion.[92]

3.4. Perseus Galactic Cluster

The Milky Way Galaxy can provide a detailed reference in how generations of stars contributes to the cosmic metal enrichment. However, large N-body simulations suggest that each galaxy is unique in their evolution history. To understand how each supernova model contributes in the cosmic scale, data from an even larger system is important to average out the statistical fluctuations of individual galaxies.

In Ref. 93 the X-ray spectra of the Perseus Cluster is studied by the *Hitomi* telescope. The highly resolved spectral lines provide the abundance measurement with uncertainties down to $\sim 10\%$. The high precision can distinguish supernova models and mechanisms explicitly. The fitting using SN Ia and CCSN models from literature is shown in Table 3. The best-fit model is found to be the scenario assuming pure Ch-mass WD explosion. If the fraction of the Ch-mass WD is relaxed as a model parameter, the expected Ch-mass WD still contributes about 10 – 40% of the SN Ia population, depending on the exact CCSN models.

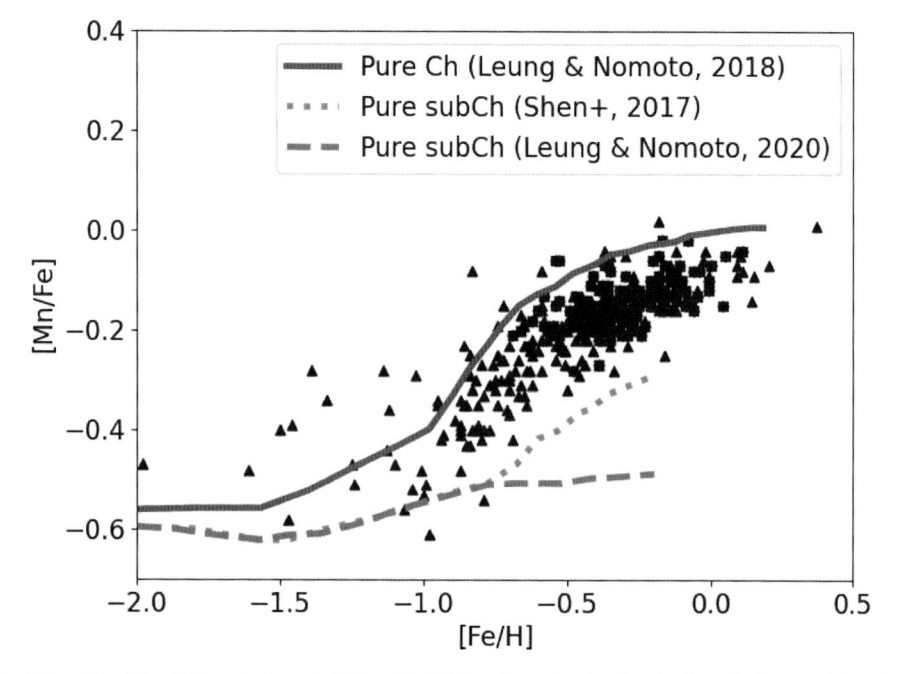

Fig. 13. The [Mn/Fe] against metallicity [Fe/H] for the galactic chemical evolution models taken from Ref. 86. Solid lines come from theoretical models assuming pure Ch-mass and subCh-mass explosion history. Data points are the stellar abundances from the solar neighbourhood.[87–89]

Table 3. Models assuming different stellar and supernova models and their corresponding (Ch-mass) SN Ia rates (data taken from [Ref. 93]).

Model	f_{Ia}	f_{Chand}	χ^2
pure Ch-mass[Ref. 22]+ CCSN[Ref. 94]	0.21 ± 0.02	N/A	11.78
Ch-mass[Ref. 95] + subCh-mass[Ref. 32] + CCSN[94]	0.25 ± 0.06	0.36 ± 0.14	23.96
Ch-mass[Ref. 95] + subCh-mass[Ref. 32] + CCSN[96]	0.38 ± 0.06	0.09 ± 0.09	15.73

4. Conclusion

In this review article we have presented the physical background about the Ch-mass and subCh-mass WD models as the SN Ia explosion progenitors. We discussed the differences in their explosion mechanisms and their associated nucleosynthetic signatures. We have also demonstrated how the chemical abundances of SNRs, Milky Way Galaxy, and galactic clusters can help us distinguish (1) the individual SN explosion scenario and (2) the relative importance of each explosion model.

Nucleosynthesis will remain an important subject in the future supernova study thanks to observational projects such as XRISM (X-Ray Imaging and Spectroscopy Mission). Given the power of resolving spectral lines as its predecessor *Hitomi*, we can anticipate that the high quality spectral data, and hence the precise chemical abundance measurements, will shed light on supernova models to an unprecedented accuracy.

Acknowledgments

S.C.L. thanks the session chairpersons Pilar-Ruiz Lapuente and Robert Fisher for the invitation to the introductory talk in the Marcel Grossmann 16 Meeting. S.C.L acknowledges support by NASA grants HST-AR-15021.001-A and 80NSSC18K1017. K.N. has been supported by the World Premier International Research Center Initiative (WPI Initiative), MEXT, Japan, and JSPS KAKENHI Grant Numbers JP17K05382, JP20K04024, and JP21H04499.

References

1. W. D. Arnett, A Possible Model of Supernovae: Detonation of ^{12}C, *Astrophysics and Space Science* **5**, 180 (October 1969).
2. W. Hillebrandt and J. C. Niemeyer, Type IA Supernova Explosion Models, *Annual Review of Astronomy and Astrophysics* **38**, 191 (January 2000).
3. K. Nomoto and S.-C. Leung, Thermonuclear Explosions of Chandrasekhar Mass White Dwarfs, in *Handbook of Supernovae*, eds. A. W. Alsabti and P. Murdin 2017, p. 1275.
4. A. G. Riess, A. V. Filippenko, P. Challis, A. Clocchiatti, A. Diercks, P. M. Garnavich, R. L. Gilliland, C. J. Hogan, S. Jha, R. P. Kirshner, B. Leibundgut, M. M. Phillips, D. Reiss, B. P. Schmidt, R. A. Schommer, R. C. Smith, J. Spyromilio, C. Stubbs, N. B. Suntzeff and J. Tonry, Observational Evidence from Supernovae for an Accelerating Universe and a Cosmological Constant, *Astronomical Journal* **116**, 1009 (September 1998).
5. S. Perlmutter, G. Aldering, G. Goldhaber, R. A. Knop, P. Nugent, P. G. Castro, S. Deustua, S. Fabbro, A. Goobar, D. E. Groom, I. M. Hook, A. G. Kim, M. Y. Kim, J. C. Lee, N. J. Nunes, R. Pain, C. R. Pennypacker, R. Quimby, C. Lidman, R. S. Ellis, M. Irwin, R. G. McMahon, P. Ruiz-Lapuente, N. Walton, B. Schaefer, B. J. Boyle, A. V. Filippenko, T. Matheson, A. S. Fruchter, N. Panagia, H. J. M. Newberg, W. J. Couch and T. S. C. Project, Measurements of Ω and Λ from 42 High-Redshift Supernovae, *Astrophysical Journal* **517**, 565 (June 1999).
6. F. Matteucci, *The chemical evolution of the Galaxy* 2001.
7. C. Kobayashi, A. I. Karakas and H. Umeda, The evolution of isotope ratios in the Milky Way Galaxy, *Monthly Notices of the Royal Astronomical Society* **414**, 3231 (July 2011).
8. K. Nomoto, D. Sugimoto and S. Neo, Carbon Deflagration Supernova, an Alternative to Carbon Detonation, *Astrophysics and Space Science* **39**, p. L37 (February 1976).
9. K. Nomoto, F. K. Thielemann and K. Yokoi, Accreting white dwarf models for type I supern. III. Carbon deflagration supernovae., *Astrophysical Journal* **286**, 644 (November 1984).
10. E. Livne, Numerical Simulations of the Convective Flame in White Dwarfs, *Astrophysical Journal Letter* **406**, p. L17 (March 1993).
11. M. Reinecke, W. Hillebrandt and J. C. Niemeyer, Thermonuclear explosions of Chandrasekhar-mass C+O white dwarfs, *Astronomy and Astrophysics* **347**, 739 (July 1999).

12. M. Reinecke, W. Hillebrandt and J. C. Niemeyer, Refined numerical models for multidimensional type Ia supernova simulations, *Astronomy and Astrophysics* **386**, 936 (May 2002).
13. F. K. Röpke, W. Hillebrandt, W. Schmidt, J. C. Niemeyer, S. I. Blinnikov and P. A. Mazzali, A Three-Dimensional Deflagration Model for Type Ia Supernovae Compared with Observations, *Astrophysical Journal* **668**, 1132 (October 2007).
14. H. Ma, S. E. Woosley, C. M. Malone, A. Almgren and J. Bell, Carbon Deflagration in Type Ia Supernova. I. Centrally Ignited Models, *Astrophysical Journal* **771**, p. 58 (July 2013).
15. S.-C. Leung and K. Nomoto, Explosive Nucleosynthesis in Near-Chandrasekhar Mass White Dwarf Models for Type Iax Supernovae: Dependence on Model Parameters, *Astrophysical Journal* **900**, p. 54 (September 2020).
16. A. M. Khokhlov, Delayed detonation model for type IA supernovae, *Astronomy and Astrophysics* **245**, 114 (May 1991).
17. H. Yamaoka, K. Nomoto, T. Shigeyama and F.-K. Thielemann, Late Detonation Models for the Type IA Supernovae SN 1991T and SN 1990N, *Astrophysical Journal Letter* **393**, p. L55 (July 1992).
18. K. Iwamoto, F. Brachwitz, K. Nomoto, N. Kishimoto, H. Umeda, W. R. Hix and F.-K. Thielemann, Nucleosynthesis in Chandrasekhar Mass Models for Type IA Supernovae and Constraints on Progenitor Systems and Burning-Front Propagation, *Astrophysical Journal Supplementary* **125**, 439 (December 1999).
19. I. Golombek and J. C. Niemeyer, A model for multidimensional delayed detonations in SN Ia explosions, *Astronomy and Astrophysics* **438**, 611 (August 2005).
20. F. K. Röpke and J. C. Niemeyer, Delayed detonations in full-star models of type Ia supernova explosions, *Astronomy and Astrophysics* **464**, 683 (March 2007).
21. M. Fink, M. Kromer, I. R. Seitenzahl, F. Ciaraldi-Schoolmann, F. K. Röpke, S. A. Sim, R. Pakmor, A. J. Ruiter and W. Hillebrandt, Three-dimensional pure deflagration models with nucleosynthesis and synthetic observables for Type Ia supernovae, *Monthly Notices of the Royal Astronomical Society* **438**, 1762 (February 2014).
22. S.-C. Leung and K. Nomoto, Explosive Nucleosynthesis in Near-Chandrasekhar-mass White Dwarf Models for Type Ia Supernovae: Dependence on Model Parameters, *Astrophysical Journal* **861**, p. 143 (July 2018).
23. T. Plewa, A. C. Calder and D. Q. Lamb, Type Ia Supernova Explosion: Gravitationally Confined Detonation, *Astrophysical Journal Letter* **612**, L37 (September 2004).
24. C. A. Meakin, I. Seitenzahl, D. Townsley, I. Jordan, George C., J. Truran and D. Lamb, Study of the Detonation Phase in the Gravitationally Confined Detonation Model of Type Ia Supernovae, *Astrophysical Journal* **693**, 1188 (March 2009).
25. I. Jordan, G. C., C. Graziani, R. T. Fisher, D. M. Townsley, C. Meakin, K. Weide, L. B. Reid, J. Norris, R. Hudson and D. Q. Lamb, The Detonation Mechanism of the Pulsationally Assisted Gravitationally Confined Detonation Model of Type Ia Supernovae, *Astrophysical Journal* **759**, p. 53 (November 2012).
26. D. García-Senz, R. M. Cabezón, I. Domínguez and F. K. Thielemann, Type Ia Supernovae: Can Coriolis Force Break the Symmetry of the Gravitational Confined Detonation Explosion Mechanism?, *Astrophysical Journal* **819**, p. 132 (March 2016).
27. I. R. Seitenzahl, M. Kromer, S. T. Ohlmann, F. Ciaraldi-Schoolmann, K. Marquardt, M. Fink, W. Hillebrandt, R. Pakmor, F. K. Röpke, A. J. Ruiter, S. A. Sim and S. Taubenberger, Three-dimensional simulations of gravitationally confined detonations compared to observations of SN 1991T, *Astronomy and Astrophysics* **592**, p. A57 (July 2016).

28. E. Bravo, D. García-Senz, R. M. Cabezon and I. Domnguez, Pulsating Reverse Detonation Models of Type Ia Supernovae. I. Detonation Ignition, *Astrophysical Journal* **695**, 1244 (April 2009).
29. E. Bravo, D. García-Senz, R. M. Cabezón and I. Domínguez, Pulsating Reverse Detonation Models of Type Ia Supernovae. II. Explosion, *Astrophysical Journal* **695**, 1257 (April 2009).
30. K. Nomoto, Accreting white dwarf models for type I supernovae. II. Off-center detonation supernovae, *Astrophysical Journal* **257**, 780 (June 1982).
31. M. Fink, F. K. Röpke, W. Hillebrandt, I. R. Seitenzahl, S. A. Sim and M. Kromer, Double-detonation sub-Chandrasekhar supernovae: Can minimum helium shell masses detonate the core?, *Astronomy and Astrophysics* **514**, p. A53 (May 2010).
32. K. J. Shen, D. Kasen, B. J. Miles and D. M. Townsley, Sub-Chandrasekhar-mass White Dwarf Detonations Revisited, *Astrophysical Journal* **854**, p. 52 (February 2018).
33. A. Tanikawa, K. Nomoto and N. Nakasato, Three-dimensional Simulation of Double Detonations in the Double-degenerate Model for Type Ia Supernovae and Interaction of Ejecta with a Surviving White Dwarf Companion, *Astrophysical Journal* **868**, p. 90 (December 2018).
34. A. Tanikawa, K. Nomoto, N. Nakasato and K. Maeda, Double-detonation Models for Type Ia Supernovae: Trigger of Detonation in Companion White Dwarfs and Signatures of Companions' Stripped-off Materials, *Astrophysical Journal* **885**, p. 103 (November 2019).
35. S.-C. Leung and K. Nomoto, Explosive Nucleosynthesis in Sub-Chandrasekhar-mass White Dwarf Models for Type Ia Supernovae: Dependence on Model Parameters, *Astrophysical Journal* **888**, p. 80 (January 2020).
36. A. Polin, P. Nugent and D. Kasen, Nebular Models of Sub-Chandrasekhar Mass Type Ia Supernovae: Clues to the Origin of Ca-rich Transients, *Astrophysical Journal* **906**, p. 65 (January 2021).
37. K. J. Shen, S. Blondin, D. Kasen, L. Dessart, D. M. Townsley, S. Boos and D. J. Hillier, Non-local Thermodynamic Equilibrium Radiative Transfer Simulations of Sub-Chandrasekhar-mass White Dwarf Detonations, *Astrophysical Journal Letter* **909**, p. L18 (March 2021).
38. S. Gronow, C. E. Collins, S. A. Sim and F. K. Röpke, Double detonations of sub-M_{Ch} CO white dwarfs: Variations in Type Ia supernovae due to different core and He shell masses, *Astronomy and Astrophysics* **649**, p. A155 (May 2021).
39. R. Pakmor, S. Hachinger, F. K. Röpke and W. Hillebrandt, Violent mergers of nearly equal-mass white dwarf as progenitors of subluminous Type Ia supernovae, *Astronomy and Astrophysics* **528**, p. A117 (April 2011).
40. R. Pakmor, M. Kromer, S. Taubenberger, S. A. Sim, F. K. Röpke and W. Hillebrandt, Normal Type Ia Supernovae from Violent Mergers of White Dwarf Binaries, *Astrophysical Journal Letter* **747**, p. L10 (March 2012).
41. M. Kromer, R. Pakmor, S. Taubenberger, G. Pignata, M. Fink, F. K. Röpke, I. R. Seitenzahl, S. A. Sim and W. Hillebrandt, SN 2010lp—A Type Ia Supernova from a Violent Merger of Two Carbon-Oxygen White Dwarfs, *Astrophysical Journal Letter* **778**, p. L18 (November 2013).
42. A. Tanikawa, N. Nakasato, Y. Sato, K. Nomoto, K. Maeda and I. Hachisu, Hydrodynamical Evolution of Merging Carbon-Oxygen White Dwarfs: Their Pre-supernova Structure and Observational Counterparts, *Astrophysical Journal* **807**, p. 40 (July 2015).
43. D. García-Senz, R. M. Cabezón, A. Arcones, A. Relaño and F. K. Thielemann, High-resolution simulations of the head-on collision of white dwarfs, *Monthly Notices of the Royal Astronomical Society* **436**, 3413 (December 2013).

44. D. Kushnir, B. Katz, S. Dong, E. Livne and R. Fernández, Head-on Collisions of White Dwarfs in Triple Systems Could Explain Type Ia Supernovae, *Astrophysical Journal Letter* **778**, p. L37 (December 2013).
45. O. Papish and H. B. Perets, Supernovae from Direct Collisions of White Dwarfs and the Role of Helium Shell Ignition, *Astrophysical Journal* **822**, p. 19 (May 2016).
46. U. Das and B. Mukhopadhyay, Maximum mass of stable magnetized highly super-Chandrasekhar white dwarfs: Stable solutions with varying magnetic fields, *Journal of Cosmology and Astroparticle Physics* **2014**, p. 050 (June 2014).
47. Y. Kamiya, M. Tanaka, K. Nomoto, S. I. Blinnikov, E. I. Sorokina and T. Suzuki, Super-Chandrasekhar-mass Light Curve Models for the Highly Luminous Type Ia Supernova 2009dc, *Astrophysical Journal* **756**, p. 191 (September 2012).
48. S. C. Yoon and N. Langer, On the evolution of rapidly rotating massive white dwarfs towards supernovae or collapses, *Astronomy and Astrophysics* **435**, 967 (June 2005).
49. I. Hachisu, M. Kato, H. Saio and K. Nomoto, A Single Degenerate Progenitor Model for Type Ia Supernovae Highly Exceeding the Chandrasekhar Mass Limit, *Astrophysical Journal* **744**, p. 69 (January 2012).
50. S. C. Leung, M. C. Chu and L. M. Lin, Dark Matter Admixed Type Ia Supernovae, *Astrophysical Journal* **812**, p. 110 (October 2015).
51. H.-S. Chan, M.-c. Chu, S.-C. Leung and L.-M. Lin, Delayed Detonation Thermonuclear Supernovae with an Extended Dark Matter Component, *Astrophysical Journal* **914**, p. 138 (June 2021).
52. K. Nomoto and S.-C. Leung, Single Degenerate Models for Type Ia Supernovae: Progenitor's Evolution and Nucleosynthesis Yields, *Space Science Review* **214**, p. 67 (June 2018).
53. K. Nomoto, Accreting white dwarf models for type I supernovae. I - Presupernova evolution and triggering mechanisms, *Astrophysical Journal* **253**, 798 (February 1982).
54. J. C. Niemeyer and W. Hillebrandt, Turbulent Nuclear Flames in Type IA Supernovae, *Astrophysical Journal* **452**, p. 769 (October 1995).
55. J. B. Bell, M. S. Day, C. A. Rendleman, S. E. Woosley and M. Zingale, Direct Numerical Simulations of Type Ia Supernovae Flames. I. The Landau-Darrieus Instability, *Astrophysical Journal* **606**, 1029 (May 2004).
56. J. B. Bell, M. S. Day, C. A. Rendleman, S. E. Woosley and M. Zingale, Direct Numerical Simulations of Type Ia Supernovae Flames. II. The Rayleigh-Taylor Instability, *Astrophysical Journal* **608**, 883 (June 2004).
57. R. Fisher and K. Jumper, Single-degenerate Type Ia Supernovae Are Preferentially Overluminous, *Astrophysical Journal* **805**, p. 150 (June 2015).
58. J. C. Niemeyer and W. Hillebrandt, Microscopic Instabilities of Nuclear Flames in Type IA Supernovae, *Astrophysical Journal* **452**, p. 779 (October 1995).
59. S. E. Woosley, Neutron-rich Nucleosynthesis in Carbon Deflagration Supernovae, *Astrophysical Journal* **476**, 801 (February 1997).
60. O. Graur, D. Zurek, M. M. Shara, A. G. Riess, I. R. Seitenzahl and A. Rest, Late-time Photometry of Type Ia Supernova SN 2012cg Reveals the Radioactive Decay of 57 Co, *Astrophysical Journal* **819**, p. 31 (March 2016).
61. B. J. Shappee, K. Z. Stanek, C. S. Kochanek and P. M. Garnavich, Whimper of a Bang: Documenting the Final Days of the Nearby Type Ia Supernova 2011fe, *Astrophysical Journal* **841**, p. 48 (May 2017).
62. K. Mori, M. A. Famiano, T. Kajino, T. Suzuki, P. M. Garnavich, G. J. Mathews, R. Diehl, S.-C. Leung and K. Nomoto, Nucleosynthesis Constraints on the Explosion Mechanism for Type Ia Supernovae, *Astrophysical Journal* **863**, p. 176 (August 2018).
63. D. Kasen, F. K. Röpke and S. E. Woosley, The diversity of type Ia supernovae from broken symmetries, *Nature* **460**, 869 (August 2009).

64. I. R. Seitenzahl, G. Cescutti, F. K. Röpke, A. J. Ruiter and R. Pakmor, Solar abundance of manganese: A case for near Chandrasekhar-mass Type Ia supernova progenitors, *Astronomy and Astrophysics* **559**, p. L5 (November 2013).
65. A. M. Lisewski, W. Hillebrandt and S. E. Woosley, Constraints on the Delayed Transition to Detonation in Type IA Supernovae, *Astrophysical Journal* **538**, 831 (August 2000).
66. F. K. Röpke, Flame-driven Deflagration-to-Detonation Transitions in Type Ia Supernovae?, *Astrophysical Journal* **668**, 1103 (October 2007).
67. S. E. Woosley, A. R. Kerstein, V. Sankaran, A. J. Aspden and F. K. Röpke, Type Ia Supernovae: Calculations of Turbulent Flames Using the Linear Eddy Model, *Astrophysical Journal* **704**, 255 (October 2009).
68. D. Fenn, T. Plewa and A. Gawryszczak, No double detonations but core carbon ignitions in high-resolution, grid-based simulations of binary white dwarf mergers, *Monthly Notices of the Royal Astronomical Society* **462**, 2486 (November 2016).
69. E. Brooker, T. Plewa and D. Fenn, Type Ia supernovae deflagration-to-detonation transition explosions powered by the Zel'dovich reactivity gradient mechanism, *Monthly Notices of the Royal Astronomical Society* **501**, L23 (January 2021).
70. S. C. Leung, M. C. Chu and L. M. Lin, A new hydrodynamics code for Type Ia supernovae, *Monthly Notices of the Royal Astronomical Society* **454**, 1238 (December 2015).
71. S. Nagataki, T. M. Shimizu and K. Sato, Matter Mixing from Axisymmetric Supernova Explosion, *Astrophysical Journal* **495**, 413 (March 1998).
72. C. Travaglio, W. Hillebrandt, M. Reinecke and F. K. Thielemann, Nucleosynthesis in multi-dimensional SN Ia explosions, *Astronomy and Astrophysics* **425**, 1029 (October 2004).
73. I. R. Seitenzahl, F. K. Röpke, M. Fink and R. Pakmor, Nucleosynthesis in thermonuclear supernovae with tracers: Convergence and variable mass particles, *Monthly Notices of the Royal Astronomical Society* **407**, 2297 (October 2010).
74. D. M. Townsley, B. J. Miles, F. X. Timmes, A. C. Calder and E. F. Brown, A Tracer Method for Computing Type Ia Supernova Yields: Burning Model Calibration, Reconstruction of Thickened Flames, and Verification for Planar Detonations, *Astrophysical Journal Supplementary* **225**, p. 3 (July 2016).
75. F. X. Timmes, Integration of Nuclear Reaction Networks for Stellar Hydrodynamics, *Astrophysical Journal Supplementary* **124**, 241 (September 1999).
76. F. K. Thielemann, K. Nomoto, and K. Yokoi, Explosive nucleosynthesis in carbon deflagration models of Type I supernovae, *Astronomy and Astrophysics* **158**, 17 (April 1986).
77. F. Lach, F. K. Röpke, I. R. Seitenzahl, B. Coté, S. Gronow and A. J. Ruiter, Nucleosynthesis imprints from different Type Ia supernova explosion scenarios and implications for galactic chemical evolution, *Astronomy and Astrophysics* **644**, p. A118 (December 2020).
78. S.-C. Leung, R. Diehl, K. Nomoto and T. Siegert, Exploration of Aspherical Ejecta Properties in Type Ia Supernovae: Progenitor Dependence and Applications to Progenitor Classification, *Astrophysical Journal* **909**, p. 152 (March 2021).
79. P. Zhou, S.-C. Leung, Z. Li, K. Nomoto, J. Vink and Y. Chen, Chemical Abundances in Sgr A East: Evidence for a Type Iax Supernova Remnant, *Astrophysical Journal* **908**, p. 31 (February 2021).
80. S. Park, C. Badenes, K. Mori, R. Kaida, E. Bravo, A. Schenck, K. A. Eriksen, J. P. Hughes, P. O. Slane, D. N. Burrows and J.-J. Lee, A Super-solar Metallicity for the Progenitor of Kepler's Supernova, *Astrophysical Journal Letter* **767**, p. L10 (April 2013).

81. H. Yamaguchi, J. P. Hughes, C. Badenes, E. Bravo, I. R. Seitenzahl, H. Martínez-Rodríguez, S. Park and R. Petre, The Origin of the Iron-rich Knot in Tycho's Supernova Remnant, *Astrophysical Journal* **834**, p. 124 (January 2017).
82. H. Yamaguchi, F. Acero, C.-J. Li and Y.-H. Chu, Discovery of Double-ring Structure in the Supernova Remnant N103B: Evidence for Bipolar Winds from a Type Ia Supernova Progenitor, *Astrophysical Journal Letter* **910**, p. L24 (April 2021).
83. O. G. Benvenuto, J. A. Panei, K. Nomoto, H. Kitamura and I. Hachisu, Final Evolution and Delayed Explosions of Spinning White Dwarfs in Single Degenerate Models for Type Ia Supernovae, *Astrophysical Journal Letter* **809**, p. L6 (August 2015).
84. Y. Ohshiro, H. Yamaguchi, S.-C. Leung, K. Nomoto, T. Sato, T. Tanaka, H. Okon, R. Fisher, R. Petre and B. J. Williams, Discovery of a Highly Neutronized Ejecta Clump in the Type Ia Supernova Remnant 3C 397, *Astrophysical Journal Letter* **913**, p. L34 (June 2021).
85. H. Yamaguchi, C. Badenes, A. R. Foster, E. Bravo, B. J. Williams, K. Maeda, M. Nobukawa, K. A. Eriksen, N. S. Brickhouse, R. Petre and K. Koyama, A Chandrasekhar Mass Progenitor for the Type Ia Supernova Remnant 3C 397 from the Enhanced Abundances of Nickel and Manganese, *Astrophysical Journal Letter* **801**, p. L31 (March 2015).
86. C. Kobayashi, S.-C. Leung and K. Nomoto, New Type Ia Supernova Yields and the Manganese and Nickel Problems in the Milky Way and Dwarf Spheroidal Galaxies, *Astrophysical Journal* **895**, p. 138 (June 2020).
87. B. E. Reddy, J. Tomkin, D. L. Lambert and C. Allende Prieto, The chemical compositions of Galactic disc F and G dwarfs, *Monthly Notices of the Royal Astronomical Society* **340**, 304 (March 2003).
88. B. E. Reddy, D. L. Lambert and C. Allende Prieto, Elemental abundance survey of the Galactic thick disc, *Monthly Notices of the Royal Astronomical Society* **367**, 1329 (April 2006).
89. S. Feltzing, M. Fohlman and T. Bensby, Manganese trends in a sample of thin and thick disk stars. The origin of Mn, *Astronomy and Astrophysics* **467**, 665 (May 2007).
90. E. N. Kirby, J. L. Xie, R. Guo, M. A. C. de los Reyes, M. Bergemann, M. Kovalev, K. J. Shen, A. L. Piro and A. McWilliam, Evidence for Sub-Chandrasekhar Type Ia Supernovae from Stellar Abundances in Dwarf Galaxies, *Astrophysical Journal* **881**, p. 45 (August 2019).
91. M. A. C. de los Reyes, E. N. Kirby, I. R. Seitenzahl and K. J. Shen, Manganese Indicates a Transition from Sub- to Near-Chandrasekhar Type Ia Supernovae in Dwarf Galaxies, *Astrophysical Journal* **891**, p. 85 (March 2020).
92. C. Kobayashi, K. Nomoto and I. Hachisu, Subclasses of Type Ia Supernovae as the Origin of [α/Fe] Ratios in Dwarf Spheroidal Galaxies, *Astrophysical Journal Letter* **804**, p. L24 (May 2015).
93. A. Simionescu, S. Nakashima, H. Yamaguchi, K. Matsushita, F. Mernier, N. Werner, T. Tamura, K. Nomoto, J. de Plaa, S. C. Leung, A. Bamba, E. Bulbul, M. E. Eckart, Y. Ezoe, A. C. Fabian, Y. Fukazawa, L. Gu, Y. Ichinohe, M. N. Ishigaki, J. S. Kaastra, C. Kilbourne, T. Kitayama, M. Leutenegger, M. Loewenstein, Y. Maeda, E. D. Miller, R. F. Mushotzky, H. Noda, C. Pinto, F. S. Porter, S. Safi-Harb, K. Sato, T. Takahashi, S. Ueda and S. Zha, Constraints on the chemical enrichment history of the Perseus Cluster of galaxies from high-resolution X-ray spectroscopy, *Monthly Notices of the Royal Astronomical Society* **483**, 1701 (February 2019).

94. K. Nomoto, C. Kobayashi and N. Tominaga, Nucleosynthesis in Stars and the Chemical Enrichment of Galaxies, *Annual Review of Astronomy and Astrophysics* **51**, 457 (August 2013).
95. I. R. Seitenzahl, F. Ciaraldi-Schoolmann, F. K. Röpke, M. Fink, W. Hillebrandt, M. Kromer, R. Pakmor, A. J. Ruiter, S. A. Sim and S. Taubenberger, Three-dimensional delayed-detonation models with nucleosynthesis for Type Ia supernovae, *Monthly Notices of the Royal Astronomical Society* **429**, 1156 (February 2013).
96. T. Sukhbold, T. Ertl, S. E. Woosley, J. M. Brown and H. T. Janka, Core-collapse Supernovae from 9 to 120 Solar Masses Based on Neutrino-powered Explosions, *Astrophysical Journal* **821**, p. 38 (April 2016).

Charged polarized white dwarfs with finite temperature as a possible source of type Ia supernovae

Sílvia P. Nunes

Departamento de Física, Instituto Tecnológico de Aeronáutica,
12228-900 São José dos Campos, São Paulo, Brazil
E-mail: silviapn@ita.br

José D. V. Arbañil

Departamento de Ciencias, Universidad Privada del Norte,
Avenida el Sol 461 San Juan de Lurigancho, 15434 Lima, Peru

Facultad de Ciencias Físicas, Universidad Nacional Mayor de San Marcos,
Avenida Venezuela s/n Cercado de Lima, 15081 Lima, Peru

Manuel Malheiro

Departamento de Física, Instituto Tecnológico de Aeronáutica,
12228-900 São José dos Campos, São Paulo, Brazil

We investigate the structure of polarized charged white dwarfs with finite temperature as a possible type Ia supernovae source. The white dwarf is modeled considering an isothermal core with central temperature 10^8 [K] and an envelope where the temperature distribution depends on the mass density. Regarding the fluid, we assume that it is composed of nucleons and electrons. The structure of the polarized charged white dwarfs is obtained by solving the Einstein-Maxwell equations with charge densities represented by two Gaussians, forming an electric dipole layer at the stellar surface. We obtain larger and more massive white dwarfs when polarized charge and the Gaussians width are increased. We find that to appreciate effects in the white dwarf's structure, the electric polarized charge must be in the order of 5.0×10^{20}[C]. We obtain a maximum white dwarf mass of around $2.4 M_\odot$ for a polarized charge of 1.5×10^{21}[C]. This mass result can indicate that polarized charged white dwarfs are possible progenitors of superluminous type Ia supernovae. Furthermore, the mass-central density curves we obtain are very similar to the ones reached recently for ultra-magnetized white dwarfs.

Keywords: White dwarfs; charged white dwarfs; type Ia supernovae explosions

Introduction

The mechanisms that increase the mass of a white dwarf (WD) have been extensively studied since supermassive WDs were associated with superluminous Type Ia supernovae (2003fg,[1] 2009dc,[2] 2006gz[3] and 2007if[4]). In what concerns the structure of WDs, in literature, there are works consider magnetic field, rotation, and electric field to explain the increase of such mass. To present considerable effects in the WD structure, recent works[5,6] present magnetic fields are the order of 9×10^{13}[G] and electric field of around 10^{16} [V/cm] .

We investigate charged white dwarfs made up by a non-degenerate fluid with isothermal core with central temperature $T_c = 10^8$[K] and envelope with temperature distribution.[7] Moreover, we assume a charge polarization[8] in the surface of WDs. We obtain very massive white dwarfs which can be the progenitors of Type Ia Supernovae. We note that the polarization generate notable effect in the structure of WDs and it decreases the electric field outside the star.

1. Structure equilibrium equations and boundary conditions

The line element considered to describe a charged WD, in Schwarzschild-like coordinates, is given by

$$ds^2 = -e^\nu dt^2 + e^\lambda dr^2 + r^2 d\theta^2 + r^2 \sin^2\theta d\phi^2, \tag{1}$$

where ν and λ depend on the radial coordinate only. The inclusion of the electromagnetic tensor in the energy-momentum tensor leads to the nonzero Maxwell-Einstein equations:

$$\frac{dq}{dr} = 4\pi \rho_e r^2 e^{\lambda/2}, \tag{2}$$

$$\frac{dm}{dr} = 4\pi\varepsilon^2 + \frac{q}{r}\frac{dq}{dr}, \tag{3}$$

$$\frac{dP}{dr} = -(P+\varepsilon)\left[4\pi r p + \frac{m}{r^2} - \frac{q^2}{r^3}\right]e^\lambda + \frac{q}{4\pi r^4}\frac{dq}{dr}, \tag{4}$$

$$\frac{d\nu}{dr} = -\frac{2}{(p+\varepsilon)}\left[\frac{dP}{dr} - \frac{q}{4\pi r^4}\frac{dq}{dr}\right], \tag{5}$$

with q and m representing respectively the electric charge and the mass within the radius r. The potential metric e^λ is described as

$$e^\lambda = \left[1 - \frac{2m}{r} + \frac{q^2}{r^2}\right]^{-1}. \tag{6}$$

Due to temperature, the white dwarfs are considered to have a partial degeneracy, thus the contribution of electrons in the EoS is related to Fermi-Dirac integrals. Once the temperature distribution is defined,[7] these integrals are solved by using an adaptive quadrature method.[9] Next, we proceed to integrate Eqs. (2)-(5) by using the fourth-order Runge-Kutta method for the uncharged star, i.e., $Q = 0$. For this aim, in the center $r = 0$, it is considered the boundary conditions:

$$m(0) = 0, \quad \varepsilon(0) = \varepsilon_0, \quad \text{and } \nu(0) = \nu_0, \tag{7}$$

and the star's surface is determined at $P(r = R^+) = 0$. This first integration enables us to find the values of the total star mass M and total radius R^+. The location of the second and negative Gaussian at R^- is determined through the relation $R^- = R^+ + \Delta R$, where $\Delta R = 4b$ and $b = 5$[km]. The value of b employed is the smallest necessary to obtain considerable effects on the structure of the white dwarf. Once found the polarized charge, by using the charge density, we integrate again Eqs. (2)-(5) to obtain the charged white dwarf structure. The boundary conditions in Eq. (7) are used together with $q(0) = 0$ and $\rho_e(0) = \rho_{e0}$.

2. Equation of state and charge density profile

Regarding the stellar fluid, we consider that the equation of state is made of by nucleons, electrons, and photons.[10,11] Due to our consideration of very high central temperatures ($T_c = 10^8$ [K]), we neglect the lattice interactions. Thus, the pressure P and energy density ε is depicted by

$$P = P_e + P_N + P_\gamma, \tag{8}$$

$$\varepsilon = \varepsilon_e + \varepsilon_N + \varepsilon_\gamma, \tag{9}$$

where the subindexes e, N and γ represent the electrons, nucleons, and photons contributions, respectively.

We assume that electrons and protons are susceptible to a centrifugal force responsible for accelerating heavy particles away from light ones. Consequently, polarization forms in the stellar envelope. Inspired in Negreiros work,[8] we consider the polarization to be defined with the inclusion of two Gaussians in the charge density:

$$\rho_e = e^{-\lambda/2}\left[k^+\exp\left(-\frac{(r-R^+)^2}{b^2}\right) + k^-\exp\left(-\frac{(r-R^-)^2}{b^2}\right)\right], \tag{10}$$

where r represents the radial coordinate, $b = 5$ [km] is the Gaussian width, and with k^+ and k^- being constants that depend on the global charge neutrality. The R^+ is the radius for the uncharged configuration. Moreover, $R^- = R^+ + \Delta R$, being $\Delta R = 4b$ a fixed value for all the central energy densities.

To obtain k, we solve the integration by considering a total zero charge

$$Q_t = \int_0^\infty e^{\lambda/2} 4\pi r^2 \rho_e dr = 0. \tag{11}$$

By using Eq. (10) in this last relation, we find

$$k^+ = \frac{Q}{8\pi}\left(\frac{\sqrt{\pi}b(R^+)^2}{2} + \frac{\sqrt{\pi}b^3}{4}\right)^{-1}, \tag{12}$$

$$k^- = \frac{-Q}{8\pi}\left(\frac{\sqrt{\pi}b(R^-)^2}{2} + \frac{\sqrt{\pi}b^3}{4}\right)^{-1}. \tag{13}$$

With the intent to better illustrate the stellar charge profile, we present the charge density as a function of radial coordinate in Fig. 1.

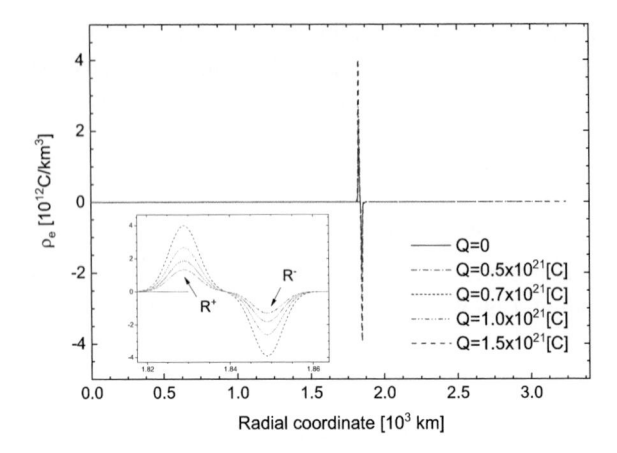

Fig. 1. The charge density as a function of the radial coordinate for a star with central energy density $\varepsilon_c = 10^{10}$ [g cm^{-3}] and several polarized charge values.

3. White dwarf configurations

Consequently to the polarized charge, we find a very high electric field in the stellar envelope and no electric field outside the star (in contrast to previous charge white dwarfs studies[6]). In our calculations, considering a star with central density $\varepsilon_c = 5 \times 10^{10}$ [g/cm^3], we find maximum internal electric fields of around 10^{16} [V/cm]. Under these conditions, the radius is increased in 77% and the mass 63% for $Q = 1.5 \times 10^{21}$ [C]. This electric field induces an increase in the internal star pressure.

The pressure in the stellar interior enhancing due to the charge density was already noticed in previous charge white dwarfs studies.[6] The pressure profile found by Carvalho and collaborators increases with charge and decreases due to self-gravitation. In our work, the neutralization of charge is the main responsible to decrease the stellar charge pressure. Thus, compared to Carvalho's work,[6] the charge density we propose affects more the mass than the radius.

In Fig. 2 we show the mass as a function of central energy density. This figure is important to analyze the relation between polarized charge white dwarfs and Type Ia Supernovae. We can note that for the uncharged sequence, the mass increases with central energy density until it reaches a maximum mass (pink dot) and decreases. This behavior is different for sequences of charged stars. These curves increase mass with central energy density (the same pattern observed for ultra-magnetized white dwarfs[5]). Another important observation in this figure is related to the maximum mass obtained.

For the maximum polarized charge we find maximum masses around $\approx 2.4 M_\odot$ for 1.5×10^{21} [C]. This increase in mass is obtained for the first time for charged white dwarfs with no electric field outside the star, which is the main novelty of this work.

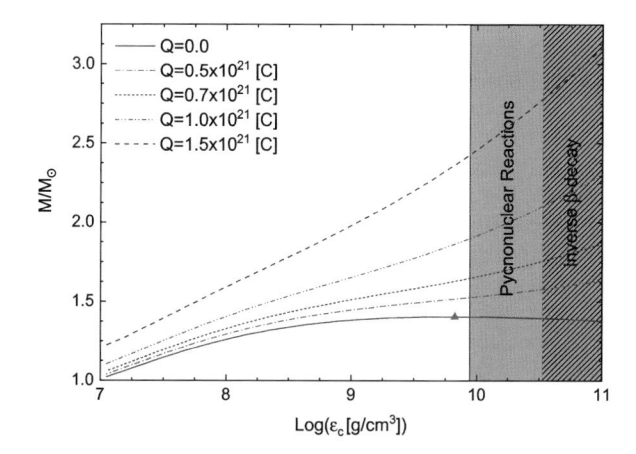

Fig. 2. The mass as a function of the energy density for several sequences of constant polarized charge and $T_c = 10^8$[K].

4. Conclusion

In this work, we investigated the structure of charged hot white dwarfs to associate them with superluminous type Ia supernovae. In what concerns to the stellar fluid, we consider a central temperature of $T_c = 10^8$[K] and a temperature distribution in the envelope.[11] Besides, due to the high central temperature considered, we neglected the particles' interactions. We used Maxwell-Einstein equations to find the structure of these charged polarized white dwarfs. We found that more massive and bigger white dwarfs are found with our predictions.

Our calculations enable the finding of maximum masses around $2.4 M_\odot$ for stable charge white dwarfs configurations. Albeit we reach very high electric fields to obtain these results ($\approx 10^{16}$ [V/cm]), the electric field outside the star is zero. For the first time, isolated charged white dwarfs are obtained with a zero electric field outside.

Acknowledgments

We would like to thank Fundação de Amparo à Pesquisa do Estado de São Paulo (FAPESP), Grant No. 2013/26258 − 4. SPN thanks Conselho Nacional de Desenvolvimento Científico e Tecnológico (CNPq), Grant No. 140863/2017−6 and CAPES for the financial support. JDVA would like to thank the Universidad Privada del Norte and Universidad Nacional Mayor de San Marcos for funding - RR Nº 005753-2021-R/UNMSM under the project number B21131781. MM is grateful to CAPES and CNPq financial support.

References

1. D. A. Howell, M. Sullivan, P. E. Nugent, R. S. Ellis, A. J. Conley, D. Le Borgne, R. G. Carlberg, J. Guy, D. Balam, S. Basa, D. Fouchez, I. M. Hook, E. Y. Hsiao, J. D. Neill, R. Pain, K. M. Perrett and C. J. Pritchet, The type Ia supernova SNLS-03D3bb from a super-Chandrasekhar-mass white dwarf star, *Nature* **443**, 308 (September 2006).
2. S. Taubenberger, S. Benetti, M. Childress, R. Pakmor, S. Hachinger, P. A. Mazzali, V. Stanishev, N. Elias-Rosa, I. Agnoletto, F. Bufano, M. Ergon, A. Harutyunyan, C. Inserra, E. Kankare, M. Kromer, H. Navasardyan, J. Nicolas, A. Pastorello, E. Prosperi, F. Salgado, J. Sollerman, M. Stritzinger, M. Turatto, S. Valenti and W. Hillebrandt, High luminosity, slow ejecta and persistent carbon lines: SN 2009dc challenges thermonuclear explosion scenarios, *MNRAS* **412**, 2735 (April 2011).
3. M. Hicken, P. M. Garnavich, J. L. Prieto, S. Blondin, D. L. DePoy, R. P. Kirshner and J. Parrent, The Luminous and Carbon-rich Supernova 2006gz: A Double Degenerate Merger?, *ApJ* **669**, L17 (November 2007).
4. R. A. Scalzo, G. Aldering, P. Antilogus, C. Aragon, S. Bailey, C. Baltay, S. Bongard, C. Buton, M. Childress, N. Chotard, Y. Copin, H. K. Fakhouri, A. Gal-Yam, E. Gangler, S. Hoyer, M. Kasliwal, S. Loken, P. Nugent, R. Pain, E. Pécontal, R. Pereira, S. Perlmutter, D. Rabinowitz, A. Rau, G. Rigaudier, K. Runge, G. Smadja, C. Tao, R. C. Thomas, B. Weaver and C. Wu, Nearby Supernova Factory Observations of SN 2007if: First Total Mass Measurement of a Super-Chandrasekhar-Mass Progenitor, *ApJ* **713**, 1073 (April 2010).
5. E. Otoniel, B. Franzon, G. A. Carvalho, M. Malheiro, S. Schramm and F. Weber, Strongly Magnetized White Dwarfs and Their Instability Due to Nuclear Processes, *ApJ* **879**, p. 46 (July 2019).
6. G. A. Carvalho, J. D. V. Arbañil, R. M. Marinho and M. Malheiro, White dwarfs with a surface electrical charge distribution: Equilibrium and stability, *European Physical Journal C* **78**, p. 411 (May 2018).
7. A. L. Kritcher, D. C. Swift, T. Döppner, B. Bachmann, L. X. Benedict, G. W. Collins, J. L. DuBois, F. Elsner, G. Fontaine, J. A. Gaffney, S. Hamel, A. Lazicki, W. R. Johnson, N. Kostinski, D. Kraus, M. J. MacDonald, B. Maddox, M. E. Martin, P. Neumayer, A. Nikroo, J. Nilsen, B. A. Remington, D. Saumon, P. A. Sterne, W. Sweet, A. A. Correa, H. D. Whitley, R. W. Falcone and S. H. Glenzer, A measurement of the equation of state of carbon envelopes of white dwarfs, *Nature* **584**, 51 (August 2020).
8. R. Picanço Negreiros, I. N. Mishustin, S. Schramm and F. Weber, Properties of bare strange stars associated with surface electric fields, *Phys. Rev. D* **82**, p. 103010 (November 2010).
9. K. A. Boshkayev, J. A. Rueda, B. A. Zhami, Z. A. Kalymova and G. S. Balgymbekov, Equilibrium structure of white dwarfs at finite temperatures, in *IJMPC*, 2016.
10. F. X. Timmes and D. Arnett, The Accuracy, Consistency, and Speed of Five Equations of State for Stellar Hydrodynamics, *ApJS* **125**, 277 (November 1999).
11. S. P. Nunes, J. D. V. Arbañil and M. Malheiro, The structure and stability of massive hot white dwarfs, *To appear in the Astrophysical Journal*, p. arXiv:2108.08238 (August 2021).

CTCV J2056-3014 and other fast-spinning white dwarfs

C. V. Rodrigues

Divisão de Astrofísica, Instituto Nacional de Pesquisas Espaciais
12227-010, São José dos Campos, SP, Brazil
E-mail: claudia.rodrigues@inpe.br
www.inpe.br

R. Lopes de Oliveira

Departamento de Física, Universidade Federal de Sergipe
Av. Marechal Rondon, S/N, 49100-000 São Cristóvão, SE, Brazil
E-mail: raimundo.lopes@academico.ufs.br
and
Observatório Nacional,
Rua Gal. José Cristino 77, 20921-400, Rio de Janeiro, RJ, Brazil

A. Bruch

Laboratório Nacional de Astrofísica
Rua Estados Unidos, 154, CEP 37504-364, Itajubá, MG, Brazil
E-mail: albert@lna.br

A. S. Oliveira

IP&D, Universidade do Vale do Paraíba, 12244-000, São José dos Campos, SP, Brazil
E-mail: alexandre@univap.br

K. Mukai

CRESST II and X-ray Astrophysics Laboratory, NASA Goddard Space Flight Center
Greenbelt, MD 20771, USA
E-mail: koji.mukai-1@nasa.gov
and
Center for Space Science and Technology, University of Maryland
Baltimore County, 1000 Hilltop Circle, Baltimore, MD 21250, USA

This contribution summarises our recent determination of the spin period of the magnetic white dwarf in CTCV J2056-3014, a cataclysmic variable binary system. Its X-ray and optical emission comes from its magnetic accretion column and is modulated with a 29.6 s period, due to the WD rotation. We briefly discuss this object in the context of other fast-spinning white dwarfs.

Keywords: White dwarfs; Cataclysmic variable stars; X-rays: stars.

1. Introduction

White dwarfs (WDs) are the evolutionary fate of most stars. WDs are composed of degenerated matter and, together with neutrons stars and stellar black holes, constitute the group of compact stellar objects with strong gravitational fields in their neighborhood. The maximum mass that a WD can reach is around 1.4 $M_\odot$, the Chandrasekhar limit. The exact limit depends on many assumptions as the rotation, the magnetic field strength, and the adopted equation of state, which is related to the physical conditions and processes taking place in the stellar interior. Due to the compactness of their degenerated interior, WDs can rotate very rapidly, reaching spin periods as small as a few tens of seconds. WDs also show the largest values of magnetic moments among stellar objects. As stars in general, they are found isolated or in binary systems.

In isolated WDs, high values of mass, spin, and magnetic field seem to appear together. WD 0316-849 is one example of such an extreme WD. It has a magnetic field (B) of around 500 MG, a spin (P_{spin}) of 725 s, and a mass (M_{WD}) equal to 0.86 $M_\odot$ (see Ref. 1 and references therein). ZTF J190132.9+145808.7 has been recently associated with a very massive WD, $M_{WD} > 1.3$ $M_\odot$. Its P_{spin} is 416.4 s and its surface magnetic field is estimated to be in the range 600 – 900 MG.[2] Those WDs are probably originated by mergers - see, for instance, the discussion in Ref. 3. In particular, mergers can produce remnants with high angular momenta.

CVs are binary systems in which a WD accretes matter from the secondary star, a low-mass on the main sequence or slightly evolved that loses material by Roche lobe overflow. The magnetic CVs are those systems in which the WD magnetic field is strong enough to play a role in the dynamics of the accretion flow. If the WD magnetic field is not strong enough to synchronize the WD spin with the orbital period, the system is classified as an intermediate polar.

The optical and X-ray emission of intermediate polars is caused by mass accretion onto the magnetic WD and modulates with the WD spin. It is caused by accretion onto a magnetic WD. This process produces a stand-off shock near the WD surface where gravitational energy is converted to thermal energy. This enhances the gas density and heats it to keV temperatures producing the X-ray emission and the high excitation optical spectrum. The footprint of the accretion structure covers a small area of the WD surface. Therefore, the WD rotation causes a modulation of the emission as seen by the observer.

In this contribution, we outline our recent finding that CTCV J2056-3014, an intermediate polar, harbors a very fast-spinning WD. We also discuss this result in the context of similar objects.

2. CTCV J2056-3014

The optical spectrum of CTCV J2056-3014[4,5] is characterized by a very blue continuum and strong emission lines, including the Bowen complex, indicative of high excitation temperatures. The radial velocity variation of the emission lines indicates an orbital period of 1.76 h.[4] The first indications that CTCV J2056-3014 could be an intermediate polar were the possible association with the X-ray source 1RXS J205652.1−301433 and a photometric modulation of around 15 min.[4] However, this periodic variability was not confirmed by further observations.[6]

Recently, XMM-Newton X-ray observations of CTCV J2056-3014 have revealed a coherent modulation at 29.6098 ± 0.0014 s, also present in the optical emission.[7] This modulation and the X-ray spectrum of CTCV J2056-3014 confirm that the object is an intermediate polar, i.e., an accreting magnetic WD in an asynchronous CV. The fit of its X-ray spectrum provides an accretion mass rate, $\dot{M}$, of about 6×10^{-12} $M_\odot \mathrm{yr}^{-1}$ (Ref. 7).

Most intermediate polars have X-ray luminosities, L_X, of $\sim 10^{33}$ erg s^{-1}. The luminosity of CTCV J2056-3014 is around 100 times smaller (10^{31} erg s^{-1}); a property shared with a very small group of CVs named low-luminosity intermediate polars (LLIPs).[8] It is not clear if the number of LLIPs is small because they are rare objects or because their X-ray faintness hampers their discovery in X-ray surveys. If the true number of LLIPs is high and we are missing them because of observational biases, this class of objects is probably a relevant contributor to the Galactic X-ray background.[8]

3. The fastest spinning WDs

In this section, we enumerate the bona fide fastest spinning WDs, which are all located in compact binary systems. However, for completeness, we also mention some objects that could be WDs with a rapid spin. A summary of selected characteristics of individual objects is shown in Table 1.

There is a debate in the literature if some soft gamma-ray repeaters (SGR) and anomalous X-ray pulsars (AXP), the so-called magnetars, could contain a WD instead of a neutron star.[9,10] For example, the spectral energy distribution from the infrared to the gamma-rays of 4U 0142+61 (P_{spin}= 8.62 s) can be fitted in a scenario of a fast, massive, and magnetic WD.[3] If some magnetars were indeed WDs, they would put strong constraints on the physics of the WD interiors, to cite only one consequence of this hypothesis. In spite of the importance of this subject, those objects are not considered here.

WZ Sge is a short orbital period cataclysmic variable that shows dwarf-nova outbursts with a very long recurrence time (a few decades). The system has intermittent periodical signals at 28.87 s and 28.96 s. One of these periods could be the WD spin period, but it is not a settled question (see Ref. 11 and references therein). We do not consider this system as a confirmed fast-spinning WD, but we list its properties in Table 1.

Another fast-spinning compact object is RX J0648.0-4418, with a P_{spin} of 13.2 s. This object is in a relatively wide binary system, with an orbital period of 1.55 d. However, it is debated if the compact object is a WD or a neutron star.[7,12] In some sense, this object is a link between fast-spinning WDs and magnetars. As for WZ Sge, we do not include it in the list of bona fide fast-spinning WDs, but its properties can be found in Table 1.

AE Aqr was the first discovered fast and magnetic WD, and its peculiar properties prompted many studies.[13] Its WD spins at a 33 s rate. The system is the prototype of a propeller: a system in which the centrifugal force of a magnetic fast-rotating object prevents the accretion from a mass reservoir to reach the object's surface. This is one of the possible accretion-flow configurations in cataclysmic variables. It depends on the WD magnetic field, WD spin, and accretion rate.[14] However, even if part of the material is propelled out of the WD magnetosphere, some material can reach the WD surface. This is probably the case for AE Aqr,[15,16] since its X-ray luminosity is small but not null: $\dot{M} \approx 10^{31}$ erg s^{-1}.[15] The radius of the companion star is twice as large as is expected for its mass, indicating a very inflated object.

V1460 Her is an intermediate polar with a WD that spins at 38.9 s.[17] The companion star is less massive than that of AE Aqr, but it is also significantly inflated. Contrary to AE Aqr, there is an accretion disk in V1460 Her, clearly seen in optical spectra.

At the time of this conference, CTCV J2056-3014 was known as the fastest-spinning WD. However, a faster WD has been recently discovered: LAMOST J024048.51+195226.9, with a spin period of 24.9328 ± 0.0038 s.[18] The system shows strong evidence of an outflow with properties consistent with those expected for a propeller.[19]

4. Discussion and conclusions

Two possible mechanisms for spinning up WDs are mergers and accretion.

The isolated WDs with large values of M_{WD}, B, and P_{spin} are probably produced by mergers. The majority of the most massive WDs have high values of magnetic fields,[1,2,24–26] which indicates that these two properties may have a common origin. Simulations show that double-degenerated mergers can produce WDs with high and stable magnetic fields.[27] From an observational perspective, there is also evidence for mergers. The color-magnitude distribution of a *Gaia* sample of nearby WDs ($d \lesssim 100$ pc) indicates the presence of two populations of WDs, which can be explained if some objects are formed by a merger.[28] Considering objects within 20 pc, the fraction of WDs in binary systems is considerably smaller than the fraction of binary systems composed of two main-sequence objects. This can be explained if a portion of the isolated WDs is formed via mergers.[29] Although mergers can play an important role in producing extreme WDs, the bona fide fastest-rotating WDs are all located in binary systems, specifically cataclysmic variables.

In cataclysmic variables, the rapid WD spin may be the result of the mass transfer. Specifically, the accretion transforms the orbital angular momentum into the rotational angular momentum of the WD. To reach the observed high P_{spin}, high values of $\dot{M}$ are necessary. However, a high mass-transfer rate should produce a high X-ray luminosity, which is not observed in the fast-spinning WDs (see Table 1). Therefore, the current high spin is explained by a previous phase of high mass transfer rate from a secondary star in a thermal time-scale phase. In fact, the

Table 1. Selected properties of the confirmed fastest spinning WDs and related objects.

Object	P_{spin} (s)	Orbital period (h)	M_{sec} ($M_\odot$)	M_{WD} ($M_\odot$)	L_X (erg s^{-1})	Confirmed	Comments	References
LAMOST J024048.51+195226.9	24.9328	7.33	-	-	-	Yes	Propeller	18, 19
CTCV J2056-3014	29.6098	1.76	-	0.56 – 1.38	10^{-31}	Yes	Below the period gap	4, 7, 20
AE Aqr	33	9.88	0.37 ± 0.04	0.63 ± 0.05	10^{-31}	Yes	Inflated secondary; Propeller	21, 21
V1460 Her	38.9	4.99	0.295 ± 0.004	0.869 ± 0.006	-	Yes	Inflated secondary	17
RX J0648.0-4418	13.2	37.2	1.50 ± 0.05	1.28 ± 0.05	10^{-32}	No	WD or neutron star?	22
WZ Sge	28.87 or 28.96	1.36	0.078 – 0.13	0.88 – 1.53	10^{-30}	No	Period is not firmly associated with spin	11, 23

secondary stars in AE Aqr[13] and V1460 Her[17] are twice as large as is expected for their masses, which reinforces the idea of a star slightly out of equilibrium. If the same is true for CTCV J2056-3014 and LAMOST J024048.51+195226.9 cannot be said, because their secondary stars have not yet been directed observed. Along its evolution, a CV evolves to shorter orbital periods. Consequently, the component separation as well as the radius of the secondary star shrink. In particular, the mass of the secondary, M_{sec}, is expected to decrease together with the orbital period. Moreover, above the observed period gap in the orbital period distribution of CVs, the angular-momentum transfer occurs by magnetic braking and produces larger $\dot{M}$ in comparison with objects below the period gap, which should have the angular momentum transfer sustained by gravitational radiation. Interestingly, CTCV J2056-3014 is the only object among the fast-spinning WD below the period gap.

The WDs in CTCV J2056-3014 and AE Aqr are certainly magnetic.[7] The understanding of the origin of the modulation in V1460 Her and LAMOST J024048.51+195226.9 would benefit from X-ray observations, which could reveal the presence of a magnetic WD.

Until recently, AE Aqr occupied an isolated position as the fastest-spinning confirmed WD. In the last years, other fast-spinning WDs have been discovered, all of them in CVs. Although most of them are similar to AE Aqr in the context of CV evolution, CTCV J2056-3014 - the only system with an orbital period below the CV period gap - seems to be a more evolved object. Those new results can help us understanding the physics behind the rapid spin of WDs in CVs and how the WD spin evolves along the CV evolution.

Acknowledgements

The authors thank the organizers for the invitation to present this work at this conference. CVR and RLO acknowledge CNPq – *Conselho Nacional de Desenvolvimento Científico e Tecnológico*, through Grants 303444/2018-5 and 312705/2020-4, respectively.

References

1. S. Bagnulo and J. D. Landstreet, New insight into the magnetism of degenerate stars from the analysis of a volume-limited sample of white dwarfs, *MNRAS* **507**, 5902 (November 2021).
2. I. Caiazzo, K. B. Burdge, J. Fuller, J. Heyl, S. R. Kulkarni, T. A. Prince, H. B. Richer, J. Schwab, I. Andreoni, E. C. Bellm, A. Drake, D. A. Duev, M. J. Graham, G. Helou, A. A. Mahabal, F. J. Masci, R. Smith and M. T. Soumagnac, A highly magnetized and rapidly rotating white dwarf as small as the Moon, *Nature* **595**, 39 (June 2021).
3. S. V. Borges, C. V. Rodrigues, J. G. Coelho, M. Malheiro and M. Castro, A Magnetic White Dwarf Accretion Model for the Anomalous X-Ray Pulsar 4U 0142+61, *The Astrophysical Journal* **895**, p. 26 (May 2020).

4. T. Augusteijn, C. Tappert, T. Dall and J. Maza, Cataclysmic variables from the Calán-Tololo Survey - II. Spectroscopic periods, *MNRAS* **405**, 621 (June 2010).
5. A. S. Oliveira, C. V. Rodrigues, D. Cieslinski, F. J. Jablonski, K. M. G. Silva, L. A. Almeida, A. Rodríguez-Ardila and M. S. Palhares, Exploratory Spectroscopy of Magnetic Cataclysmic Variables Candidates and Other Variable Objects, *The Astronomical Journal* **153**, p. 144 (April 2017).
6. A. Bruch, Photometry of some more neglected bright cataclysmic variables and candidates, *New Astronomy* **58**, 53 (January 2018).
7. R. Lopes de Oliveira, A. Bruch, C. V. Rodrigues, A. S. Oliveira and K. Mukai, CTCV J2056-3014: An X-Ray-faint Intermediate Polar Harboring an Extremely Fast-spinning White Dwarf, *The Astrophysical Journal Letters* **898**, p. L40 (August 2020).
8. M. L. Pretorius and K. Mukai, Constraints on the space density of intermediate polars from the Swift-BAT survey, *MNRAS* **442**, 2580 (August 2014).
9. M. Malheiro, J. A. Rueda and R. Ruffini, SGRs and AXPs as Rotation-Powered Massive White Dwarfs, *Publications of the Astronomical Society of Japan* **64**, p. 56 (June 2012).
10. J. G. Coelho and M. Malheiro, Magnetic dipole moment of soft gamma-ray repeaters and anomalous X-ray pulsars described as massive and magnetic white dwarfs, *Publications of the Astronomical Society of Japan* **66**, p. 14 (February 2014).
11. A. A. Nucita, E. Kuulkers, F. De Paolis, K. Mukai, G. Ingrosso and B. M. T. Maiolo, XMM-Newton and Swift observations of WZ Sagittae: Spectral and timing analysis, *Astronomy & Astrophysics* **566**, p. A121 (June 2014).
12. S. Mereghetti, F. Pintore, T. Rauch, N. La Palombara, P. Esposito, S. Geier, I. Pelisoli, M. Rigoselli, V. Schaffenroth and A. Tiengo, New X-ray observations of the hot subdwarf binary HD 49798/RX J0648.0-4418, *MNRAS* **504**, 920 (June 2021).
13. P. J. Meintjes, A. Odendaal and H. van Heerden, AE Aquarii: A Short Review, *Acta Polytechnica CTU Proceedings* **2**, 86 (January 2015).
14. A. J. Norton, O. W. Butters, T. L. Parker and G. A. Wynn, The Accretion Flows and Evolution of Magnetic Cataclysmic Variables, *The Astrophysical Journal* **672**, 524 (January 2008).
15. T. Kitaguchi, H. An, A. M. Beloborodov, E. V. Gotthelf, T. Hayashi, V. M. Kaspi, V. R. Rana, S. E. Boggs, F. E. Christensen, W. W. Craig, C. J. Hailey, F. A. Harrison, D. Stern and W. W. Zhang, NuSTAR and Swift Observations of the Fast Rotating Magnetized White Dwarf AE Aquarii, *The Astrophysical Journal* **782**, p. 3 (February 2014).
16. C. Rodrigues, K. da Silva, G. Luna, J. Coelho, I. Lima, J. Costa and J. de Araujo, The accretion column of AE Aqr, in *The X-ray Universe 2017*, eds. J.-U. Ness and S. Migliari (ESA, October 2017).
17. R. P. Ashley, T. R. Marsh, E. Breedt, B. T. Gänsicke, A. F. Pala, O. Toloza, P. Chote, J. R. Thorstensen and M. R. Burleigh, V1460 Her: A fast spinning white dwarf accreting from an evolved donor star, *MNRAS* **499**, 149 (November 2020).
18. I. Pelisoli, T. R. Marsh, V. S. Dhillon, E. Breedt, A. J. Brown, M. J. Dyer, M. J. Green, P. Kerry, S. P. Littlefair, S. G. Parsons, D. I. Sahman and J. F. Wild, Found: A rapidly spinning white dwarf in LAMOST J024048.51+195226.9, *arXiv e-prints*, p. arXiv:2108.11396 (August 2021).
19. P. Garnavich, C. Littlefield, R. M. Wagner, J. van Roestel, A. D. Jaodand, P. Szkody and J. R. Thorstensen, Confirmation of a Second Propeller: A High-inclination Twin of AE Aquarii, *The Astrophysical Journal* **917**, p. 22 (August 2021).
20. E. Otoniel, J. G. Coelho, S. P. Nunes, M. Malheiro and F. Weber, Mass limits of the extremely fast-spinning white dwarf CTCV J2056-3014, *arXiv e-prints*, p. arXiv:2010.12441 (October 2020).

21. J. Echevarría, R. C. Smith, R. Costero, S. Zharikov and R. Michel, High-dispersion absorption-line spectroscopy of AE Aqr, *MNRAS* **387**, 1563 (July 2008).
22. S. Mereghetti, A. Tiengo, P. Esposito, N. La Palombara, G. L. Israel and L. Stella, An Ultramassive, Fast-Spinning White Dwarf in a Peculiar Binary System, *Science* **325**, p. 1222 (September 2009).
23. D. Steeghs, S. B. Howell, C. Knigge, B. T. Gänsicke, E. M. Sion and W. F. Welsh, Dynamical Constraints on the Component Masses of the Cataclysmic Variable WZ Sagittae, *The Astrophysical Journal* **667**, 442 (September 2007).
24. M. Nalezyty and J. Madej, A catalogue of isolated massive white dwarfs. Mass distribution of massive star, *Astronomy & Astrophysics* **420**, 507 (June 2004).
25. L. Ferrario, D. de Martino and B. T. Gänsicke, Magnetic White Dwarfs, *Space Science Review* **191**, 111 (October 2015).
26. L. Ferrario, D. Wickramasinghe and A. Kawka, Magnetic fields in isolated and interacting white dwarfs, *Advances in Space Research* **66**, 1025 (September 2020).
27. E. García-Berro, P. Lorén-Aguilar, G. Aznar-Siguán, S. Torres, J. Camacho, L. G. Althaus, A. H. Córsico, B. Külebi and J. Isern, Double Degenerate Mergers as Progenitors of High-field Magnetic White Dwarfs, *The Astrophysical Journal* **749**, p. 25 (April 2012).
28. M. Kilic, N. C. Hambly, P. Bergeron, C. Genest-Beaulieu and N. Rowell, Gaia reveals evidence for merged white dwarfs, *MNRAS* **479**, L113 (September 2018).
29. S. Toonen, M. Hollands, B. T. Gänsicke and T. Boekholt, The binarity of the local white dwarf population, *Astronomy & Astrophysics* **602**, p. A16 (June 2017).

Gravitational waves from fast-spinning white dwarfs

M. F. Sousa* and J. C. N. de Araujo[†]

*Divisão de Astrofísica, Instituto Nacional de Pesquisas Espaciais,
São José dos Campos, SP/12227-010, Brazil*
* E-mail: manoel.sousa@inpe.br
[†] E-mail: jcarlos.dearaujo@inpe.br
www.inpe.br

J. G. Coelho

*Departamento de Física, Universidade Tecnológica Federal do Paraná,
Medianeira, PR/85884-000, Brazil*
E-mail: jazielcoelho@utfpr.edu.br

We discuss some aspects of Sousa et al. [1, 2] concerning two mechanisms of gravitational wave (GW) emission in fast-spinning white dwarfs (WDs): accretion of matter and magnetic deformation. In both cases, the GW emission is generated by an asymmetry around the rotation axis of the star. However, in the first case, the asymmetry is due to the amount of accreted matter in the magnetic poles, while in the second case it is due to the intense magnetic field. We have estimated the GW amplitude and luminosity for three binary systems that have a fast-spinning magnetized WD, namely, AE Aquarii, AR Scorpii and RX J0648.0-4418. In addition, we applied the magnetic deformation mechanism for SGRs/AXPs described as WD pulsars. We found that, for the first mechanism, the systems AE Aquarii and RX J0648.0-4418 can be observed by the space detectors BBO and DECIGO if they have an amount of accreted mass of $\delta m \geq 10^{-5} M_\odot$. For the second mechanism, the three systems studied require that the WD has a magnetic field above $\sim 10^9$ G to emit GWs that can be detected by BBO. Furthermore, we found that some SGRs/AXPs as WD pulsars can be detected by BBO and DECIGO, whereas SGRs/AXPs as highly magnetized neutron stars are far below the sensitivity curves of these detectors.

Keywords: Gravitational Waves; White Dwarfs; Magnetic Field; Rapid Rotation.

1. Introduction

Over the last years, the astrophysical community's interest in highly magnetized white dwarfs (HMWDs) has increased. Recent results of the Sloan Digital Sky Survey (SDSS) have confirmed these white dwarfs (WDs) with surface magnetic fields ranging from 10^6 G up to 10^9 G [see e.g. Refs. 3–5]. Besides their high magnetic fields, most of them have been shown to be massive, and responsible for the high-mass peak at 1 $M_\odot$ of the WD mass distribution.[3,6,7]

Typically, WDs have rotation periods of days or even years. However, recently, a WD pulsar was discovered, called AR Scorpii. This star emits from X-ray to radio wavelengths, pulsing in brightness with a period of 1.97 min.[8] Moreover, other sources have been proposed as candidates of WD pulsars. Specific examples are AE Aquarii with a short rotation period of $P = 33.08$ s[9] and RX J0648.0-4418

(RX J0648, hereafter) that is a massive WD with $M = 1.28 M_\odot$ and with a very fast spin period of $P = 13.2$ s, that belongs to the binary system HD 49798/RX J0648.0-4418.[10] Nevertheless, it is worth mentioning that the nature of RX J0648 is unclear, meaning it is not yet clearly known whether this star is a WD or a neutron star.[11,12]

Recently, from XMM-Newton observations, the authors in Ref. 13 reported that CTCV J2056-3014 is a X-ray-faint intermediate polar harboring an extremely fast-spinning WD with a coherent pulsation of 29.6 s, thus being the fastest confirmed spin in a WD [see also Ref. 14]. Other fast-spinning WDs have been observed more recently. As examples we can cite: V1460 Her, which is an eclipsing cataclysmic variable, with a overluminous K5-type donor star and a WD that rotates with a period of 38.9 s[15] and ZTF J190132.9+145808.7, which is a highly magnetized and rapidly rotating white dwarf, featuring a magnetic field with strengths between 600 MG and 900 MG on its surface, and a stellar radius that is only slightly larger than the radius of the Moon.[16] This WD has a rotation period of 6.94 min which is considered short as this star is an isolated WD.

Notwithstanding, several studies of magnetized and fast-rotating WDs have been done. In particular, we can highlight one involving WD pulsars in an alternative description for Soft Gamma Repeaters (SGRs) and Anomalous X-Ray Pulsars (AXPs) [see e.g. Refs. 17–20]. From this perspective, the process of energy emission released by dipole radiation in a WD can be explained by a canonical spin-powered pulsar model, since they share quite similar aspects.[18,21]

On the other hand, LIGO and Virgo detectors have recently made direct observations of gravitational waves (GWs).[22,23] All these GW detections are within a frequency band ranging from 10 Hz to 1000 Hz, which is the operating band of LIGO and Virgo. Nevertheless, as is well known, there are proposed missions for lower frequencies, such as LISA,[24,25] whose frequency band is of $(10^{-4} - 0.01)$ Hz, BBO[26,27] and DECIGO[28,29] in the frequency band ranging from 0.01 Hz to 10 Hz.

The generation of continuous GWs in different possibilities has already been proposed.[30–34] More recently, in Refs. 1, 2, 35, it has been suggested that rotating magnetized WDs can emit continuous GWs with amplitudes possibly detected by upcoming GW detectors such as LISA, DECIGO and BBO. Here we revisit our two works [Refs. 1, 2], where we investigate two mechanisms of gravitational radiation emission in fast-rotating magnetized WD: matter accretion and magnetic deformation. In both cases, the emission in GW is produced by the asymmetry around the star's rotation axis.

2. Gravitational emission mechanisms

WDs might generate gravitational radiation whether they are not perfectly symmetric around their rotation axis. The huge dipole magnetic field that can make the star become oblate[36] and accretion of matter are two examples where this asymmetry can occur.

2.1. Accretion of matter

The GW emission is shown here for the case of a WD accreting matter via the magnetic poles which do not coincide with the rotation axis of the star. In this scenario, the system's secondary star transfers matter to the WD through an accretion column and accumulates an amount of mass on the magnetic poles.

Thus, we consider a rigid object rotating about a non-major axis (x_1, x_2, x_3) and which has a deformity about one of the major axes (x_1, x_2, x_3), where are positioned the main moments of inertia I_1, I_2 e I_3, respectively.

With this configuration and doing $I_1 = I_2$, the gravitational amplitude and luminosity are given respectively by[37,38]

$$h_{0_{ac}} = \frac{4G}{c^4} \frac{(I_1 - I_3)\omega^2}{r} \sin^2\theta, \quad (1)$$

$$L_{GW_{ac}} = -\frac{2}{5}\frac{G}{c^5}(I_1 - I_3)^2\omega^6 \sin^2\theta(16\sin^2\theta + \cos^2\theta), \quad (2)$$

where, ω is the angular velocity, θ is the angle between the rotation and magnetic dipole axes and r is the distance to the emitting source.

Now, to determine the moments of inertia I_1 and I_3, we consider that the object has an amount of mass accumulated on the x_3' axis. We reduce this system to a large sphere with two smaller spheres of matter on the x_3' axis: one at each of the poles of the larger sphere. This would be equivalent to a WD accreting matter by the two magnetic poles. Therefore, it follows immediately that

$$I_1 = \frac{2}{5}MR^2 + 2\delta m\, R^2,$$

$$I_3 = \frac{2}{5}MR^2 + 2\frac{2}{5}\delta m\, a^2, \quad (3)$$

where M is the mass of the star, R is the radius of the star, δm is the amount of mass accumulated on one magnetic pole and a its radius.

Considering that $R \gg a$ and by substituting these last expressions into Eqs. (1) and (2), one obtains

$$h_{0_{ac}} = \frac{8G}{c^4} \frac{\delta m\, R^2 \omega^2}{r} \sin^2\theta, \quad (4)$$

and

$$L_{GW_{ac}} = -\frac{8}{5}\frac{G}{c^5}\delta m^2 R^4 \omega^6 \sin^2\theta(16\sin^2\theta + \cos^2\theta). \quad (5)$$

Thereby, we find expressions for the gravitational luminosity and the GW amplitude for the case of a WD accumulating mass, which depends on the accreted mass, the distance to the source, the radius of the star and how fast it is rotating.

2.2. Magnetic deformation

This section deals with the deformation of the WD induced by its own huge magnetic field. Due to the combination of magnetic field and rotation, a WD can become triaxial, presenting therefore a triaxial moment of inertia. In order to investigate the effect arising from the magnetic stress on the equilibrium of stars, let us introduce the equatorial ellipticity, defined as[37,38]

$$\epsilon = \frac{I_1 - I_2}{I_3}. \tag{6}$$

where I_1, I_2 and I_3 are main moments of inertia with respect to the (x, y, z) axes, respectively.

If the star rotates around the z-axis, then it will emit monochromatic GWs with a frequency twice the rotation frequency, f_{rot}, with amplitude given by[37,38]

$$h_{0_{df}} = \frac{16\pi^2 G}{c^4} \frac{I_3 f_{rot}^2}{r} \epsilon, \tag{7}$$

and luminosity as follows:

$$L_{GW_{df}} = -\frac{32}{5} \frac{G}{c^5} I_3^2 \epsilon^2 \omega_{rot}^6. \tag{8}$$

On the other hand, recall that the ellipticity of magnetic origin can be written as[39,40]

$$\epsilon = \kappa \frac{B_s^2 R^4}{GM^2}, \tag{9}$$

where, B_s is the magnetic field strength on the star's surface and κ is the distortion parameter, which depends on the magnetic field configuration and equation of state (EoS) of the star.

Now, substituting this last equation into Eqs. (7) and (8) and considering $I_3 = 2MR^2/5$, one immediately obtains that

$$h_{df} = \frac{32\pi^2}{5c^4} \frac{R^6 f_{rot}^2}{rM} \kappa B_s^2, \tag{10}$$

$$L_{GW_{df}} = -\frac{2^{13}\pi^6}{5^3 c^5} \frac{R^{12} f_{rot}^6}{GM^2} \kappa^2 B_s^4. \tag{11}$$

Note that the two equations just above depend on the rotation frequency and the magnetic field strength.

In contrast, the GW amplitude can also be written as a function of the variation of the star's rotation frequency $\dot{f}_{rot}$. In this case, we must consider that a part of the spindown luminosity is converted into GWs. Thus, we can infer an efficiency, η_{df}, for the variation of the rotation frequency as $\dot{f}_{rot} = \eta_{df} \dot{f}_{rot}$, such that $\dot{f}_{rot}$ can be interpreted as the part of $\dot{f}_{rot}$ related to the GW brake. Hence, the GW amplitude can be written as follows

$$h_0^{sd} = \left(\eta_{df} \frac{5}{2} \frac{G}{c^3} \frac{I_3 \dot{f}_{rot}}{r^2 f_{rot}} \right)^{1/2}. \qquad (12)$$

3. Gravitational waves from rapid rotation white dwarfs

3.1. *Accretion of matter*

Considering the scenario of an amount of mass accumulated on the magnetic poles, we apply Eq. (4) for the three binary systems that have fast-spinning WDs: AE Aqr, AR Sco and RX J0648. The parameters for the systems are listed in Table 1.

From Eq. (4), one notes that the amplitude depends on the amount of mass accumulated; however, it is not easy to predict how much matter may have been accreted to WD and how much has been dispersed on its surface. Thus, for this analysis, we assign four values for the mountain of matter for the analyzed systems: $\delta m = (10^{-3} M_\odot, 10^{-4} M_\odot, 10^{-5} M_\odot, 10^{-6} M_\odot)$ [see Refs. 41–43 for details about accretion in WDs]. Besides that, we consider that the angle between the magnetic and rotation axes is $\theta = 30°$.

Table 1. Parameters of 3 binary systems: Period (P), spindown ($\dot{P}$), WD radius (R) and distance to Earth (r).

Systems	P (s)	$\dot{P}$ (10^{-15} s/s)	R (10^8 cm)	r (pc)
AE Aqr[a]	33.08	56.4	7.0	100
AR Sco[b]	118.2	392	7.1	116
RX J0648[c]	13.18	6.0	3.0	650

Note: [a]see 44; [b]see 34; [c]see 45.

Assuming these values for δm and the parameters listed in Table 1, we obtain $h_{0_{ac}}$ for the three systems, which are shown in Figure 1.

With the amplitude estimations, we compare them with the sensitivity curves of the gravitational wave space detectors. This outcome is shown in Figure 2 where we have the sensitivity curve for LISA, BBO and DECIGO with a signal-to-noise ratio (SNR) of 8 and an integration time of $T = 1$ yr. We notice from this figure that AE Aqr and RX J0648 are good candidates to be detected by BBO and DECIGO if they have an accumulated mass of $\delta m \geq 10^{-5} M_\odot$. For the AR Sco system, the gravitational radiation emitted by this process would hardly be able to be detected by the three space instruments. This system would need to have a very high mass mountain of $\sim 10^{-3} M_\odot$ to be above, for example, the sensitivity curve of the BBO detector.

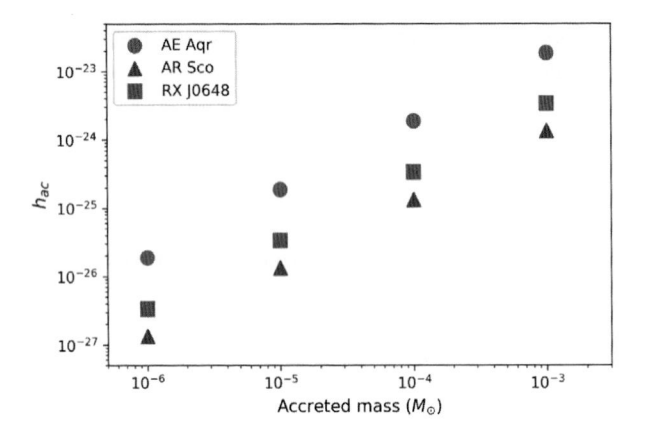

Fig. 1. GW amplitude as a function of accreted mass to AE Aqr, AR Sco and RX J0648.

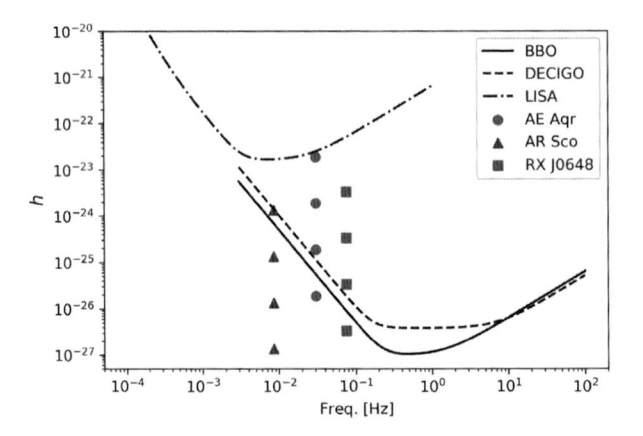

Fig. 2. GW amplitude for AE Aqr, AR Sco and RX J0648 for different values of mass ($10^{-3} M_\odot$, $10^{-4} M_\odot$, $10^{-5} M_\odot$, $10^{-6} M_\odot$, from top to bottom) and the sensitivity curves for LISA, BBO and DECIGO for $SNR = 8$ and integration time of $T = 1$ yr.

Now, we consider the efficiency of this mechanism with respect to the rotational energy rate lost by the systems. To do this, we consider the efficiency of the process ($\eta_{acr} = L_{GW_{acr}}/L_{sd}$) for the four δm's considered above, i.e., how much of the spindown luminosity is converted to gravitational luminosity for every δm (see Table 2). We find that the contribution of gravitational luminosity to the spindown luminosity is irrelevant, since, for the four values of δm adopted, the efficiency $\eta_{acr} \ll 1$. Thereby, the contribution of gravitational luminosity to the spindown luminosity is negligible when we consider this mechanism.

Table 2. The efficiency of the mechanism of GWs due to the amount of mass accumulated at the WD magnetic poles for different values of δm.

AE Aquarii		AR Scorpii		RX J0648	
δm $(M_\odot)$	η_{acr} $(L_{GW_{acr}}/L_{sd})$	δm $(M_\odot)$	η_{acr} $(L_{GW_{acr}}/L_{sd})$	δm $(M_\odot)$	η_{acr} $(L_{GW_{acr}}/L_{sd})$
10^{-3}	1.02×10^{-2}	10^{-3}	3.41×10^{-5}	10^{-3}	0.175
10^{-4}	1.02×10^{-4}	10^{-4}	3.41×10^{-7}	10^{-4}	1.75×10^{-3}
10^{-5}	1.02×10^{-6}	10^{-5}	3.41×10^{-9}	10^{-5}	1.75×10^{-5}
10^{-6}	1.02×10^{-8}	10^{-6}	3.41×10^{-11}	10^{-6}	1.75×10^{-7}

3.2. *Magnetic deformation*

Here, we consider the generation of GWs due to the deformation of the WD structure of the same binary systems (AE Aqr, AR Sco and RX J0648) caused by their own intense magnetic field. For this, we use Eq. (12) to calculate the GW amplitude as a function of the efficiency $\eta_{df} = L_{GW_{def}}/L_{sd}$. The GW amplitudes are shown in Figure 3 as a function of η_{df}, where we use the parameters of Table 1 for all 3 systems.

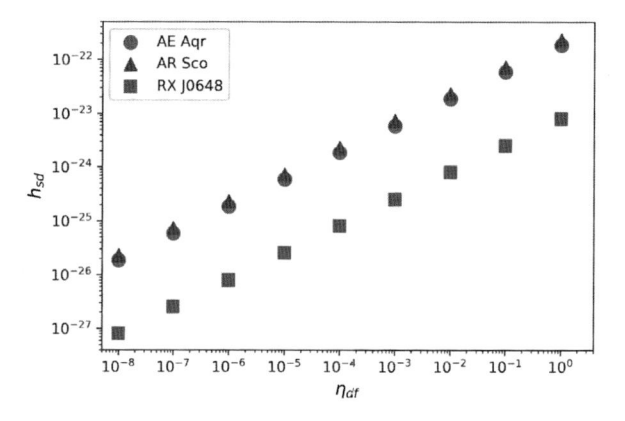

Fig. 3. GW amplitude for different values of efficiency ($\eta_{df} = L_{GW_{def}}/L_{sd}$) to AE Aqr, AR Sco and RX J0648.

From Figure 4, we plot the GW amplitudes inferred in Figure 3, together with sensitivity curves for LISA, BBO and DECIGO for one year of integration time and $SNR = 8$. It is worth noting that all three systems are detectable by BBO and DECIGO as long as AE Aqr has an efficiency $\eta_{df} \geq 10^{-6}$, AR Sco an efficiency $\eta_{df} \geq 10^{-4}$ and RX J0648 an efficiency $\eta_{df} \geq 10^{-5}$. Thus, even if the GWs have a small contribution to the spindown of these systems, they can emit GWs with amplitudes that can be detected by the space antennas.

Nevertheless, it is interesting to know what the value of the magnetic field needed to produce these detectable amplitudes. Thus, we calculate the magnetic

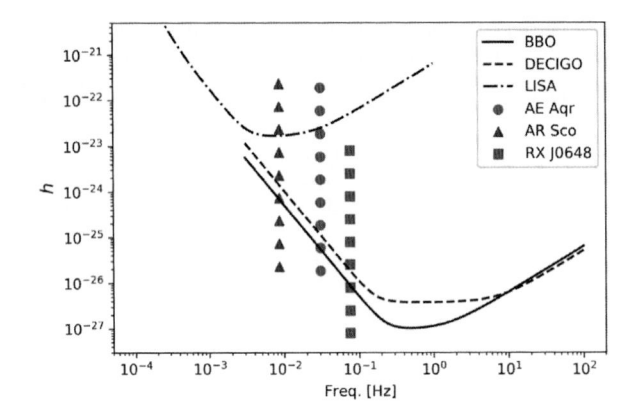

Fig. 4. GW amplitudes as presented in Figure 3 compared to the sensitivity curves of LISA, BBO and DECIGO for $SNR = 8$ and integration time of $T = 1$ year. Here, the efficiency values (1, 10^{-1}, 10^{-2}, 10^{-3}, 10^{-4}, 10^{-5}, 10^{-6}, 10^{-7} and 10^{-8}) are displayed from top to bottom.

field strength so that these sources can be detected by BBO, which is the most sensitive instrument of the three considered in the present work. To do so, we use Eq. (10) together with the minimum efficiency for which each system is detectable by this instrument and we adopted $\kappa \simeq 10$ [see Ref. 46]. Table 3 shows theses results. Notice that the systems must have WDs with high magnetic fields, around $(10^9 - 10^{10})$ G, which are about two orders of magnitude larger than the canonical model of WD pulsars.

In addition, we can further calculate the GW amplitude by considering the upper limit values of the magnetic field strength, B_{dip}, inferred from the canonical model of WD pulsars. Table 4 presents the results of this study. Notice that the amplitudes of the GW shown in this Table is very small to be observed by the space detectors, since they are well below the sensitivities of these detectors. In other words, the space detectors will not be able to detect these sources when considering the upper limit of the magnetic field strength.

Table 3. Minimum efficiency for the sources to be detected by the BBO detector along with the required magnetic field strength.

Minimum efficiency detected by BBO			
Systems	η_{df}	h_{def}	B (G)
AE Aqr	10^{-6}	1.9×10^{-25}	2.8×10^9
AR Sco	10^{-4}	2.3×10^{-24}	3.6×10^{10}
RX J0648	10^{-5}	2.5×10^{-26}	1.6×10^{10}

3.3. *GWs from SGRs/AXPs as fast-spinning WDs*

An alternative model has been proposed for SGRs/AXPs considering they are fast-rotating and magnetized WDs [see e.g. Refs. 17–20 for further details]. From this

Table 4. Elipticity (ϵ), GW amplitude (h_{def}), GW luminosity ($L_{GW_{def}}$) and efficiency of the mechanism (η_{df}) for the upper limit of magnetic field (B_{dip}) of each system.

SYSTEMS	B_{dip} (G)	ϵ	h_{def}	$L_{GW_{def}}$ (erg/s)	η_{df}
AE Aqr	5.0×10^7	5.1×10^{-9}	6.2×10^{-29}	2.13×10^{21}	1.1×10^{-13}
AR Sco	5.0×10^8	5.3×10^{-7}	4.6×10^{-28}	1.25×10^{22}	4.02×10^{-12}
RX J0648	1.0×10^8	2.8×10^{-10}	9.5×10^{-31}	1.33×10^{20}	1.4×10^{-14}

perspective, a canonical spin-powered pulsar model can explain the process of energy emission released by dipole radiation in a WD, since they share quite similar aspects.[21] In addition, these sources could also be candidates for GW emission, since the high magnetic field can deform the star in a non-symmetrical way, thus generating a variation in the quadrupolar moment of the star.

Therefore, we consider in this section that SGRs/AXPs are fast-spinning and magnetized WDs which emit GWs due to the deformation caused by their own intense magnetic field. Thus, using Eq. 10 and adopting $\kappa \simeq 10$, we calculate the GW amplitude for the 23 confirmed SGRs/AXPs[47] [a], considering these objects as a very massive WD. To do so, we assume three values of mass and their corresponding radius, namely, $M_{WD} = 1.4 M_\odot$ ($R_{WD} = 1.0 \times 10^8$ cm), $1.2 M_\odot$ ($R_{WD} = 6.0 \times 10^8$ cm) and $1.0 M_\odot$ ($R_{WD} = 7.5 \times 10^8$ cm) [see Ref. 48 for further details about the mass-radius relation].

After estimating the amplitude, we placed them on the sensitivity curves of the BBO and DECIGO detectors. Figure 5 shows theses results, such that the GW amplitude is presented as a function of frequency for some SGRs/AXPs. In this Figure, the bullets stands for $M_{WD} = 1.2 M_\odot$ and the vertical bars, that crosses the bullets, stands for $1.0 M_\odot \leq M_{WD} \leq 1.4 M_\odot$, from top to bottom.

Notice that some SGRs/AXPs produce GWs with amplitudes that can be detected by BBO and DECIGO. Some of them, for example 1E 1547.0-5408 and SGR 1806-20, could well be detected for the entire mass range considered, while others would be detected depending on how massive they are.

SGRs/AXPs described as WDs generate GW amplitudes much larger than SGRs/AXPs described in the magnetar model where they are neutron stars [see e.g. Refs. 49, 50 for details about magnetar model]. This is because WDs have moments of inertia four orders of magnitude greater than a neutron star. Consequently, the GW amplitudes generated by these sources as neutron stars are far below the sensitivity curves of BBO and DECIGO [see Fig. 6]. Therefore, if these space based instruments detect continuous GWs from these sources, this would corroborate the model of fast spinning and magnetic WDs.

---

[a]For information about the SGRs/AXPs, we refer the reader to the McGill University's online catalog available at: http://www.physics.mcgill.ca/~pulsar/magnetar/main.html

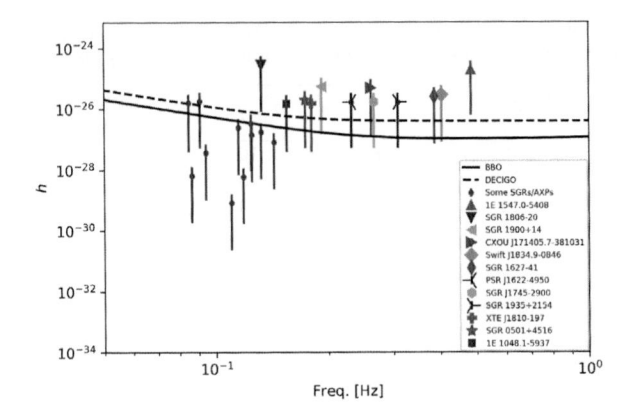

Fig. 5. GW amplitude as a function of frequency for SGRs/AXPs as fast-spinning and magnetized WDs for masses in the interval $1.0 M_\odot \leq M_{WD} \leq 1.4 M_\odot$, represented by the vertical bars, from top to bottom. The bullets stand for $M_{WD} = 1.2 M_\odot$. Also plotted the sensitivity curves for BBO and DECIGO for $SNR = 8$ and integration time $T = 1$ year.

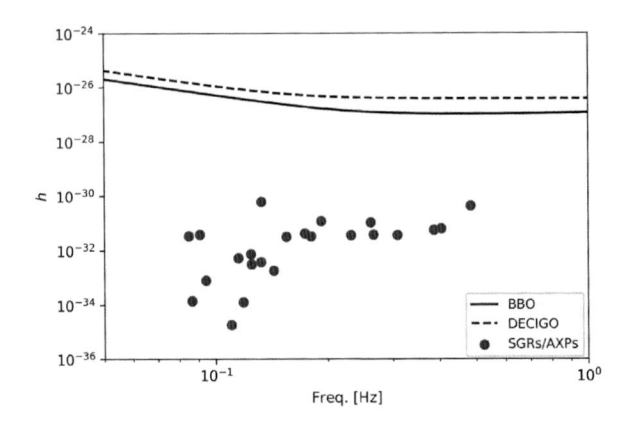

Fig. 6. GW amplitude as a function of frequency for SGRs/AXPs as NSs. Also plotted the sensitivity curves for BBO and DECIGO for $SNR = 8$ and integration time of $T = 1$ year. We consider a NS of $M = 1.4 M_\odot$, radius $R = 10$ km.

4. Final remarks

We investigate two mechanisms - accretion of matter and magnetic deformation - for the production of gravitational waves in fast-spinning WDs. These uncommon WDs have high rotation and huge magnetic fields. Also, these stars are considered in an alternative model to describe SGRs and AXPs, where they are characterized as rotation-powered WD pulsars.

Then, we firstly study the following three binary systems: AE Aqr, AR Sco and RX J0648. For the accretion of matter mechanism, our results show that the AE Aqr and RX J0648 are good candidates for BBO and DECIGO if they have an amount of mass accumulated of $\delta m \geq 10^{-5} M_\odot$, considering 1 year of integration time and $SNR = 8$. In contrast, AR Sco is unlikely to be detected because it is needed a large amount of mass accumulated in the magnetic pole of this WD.

Now, regarding the magnetic deformation mechanism, to emit gravitational radiation with amplitudes that are detectable by BBO, for example, the three binary systems studied require that the WD has a magnetic field above $\sim 10^9$ G. Nevertheless, these WDs are inferred to have magnetic fields with intensity around two orders of magnitude smaller. Moreover, we also conclude that gravitational radiation has an irrelevant contribution to the spindown luminosity of these systems for both mechanism.

Still, taking into account the magnetic deformation mechanism, we investigate the SGRs/AXPs as rotation-powered WD pulsars assigning a mass range $1.0 M_\odot \leq M_{WD} \leq 1.4 M_\odot$ for these objects. We conclude that a possible detection of continuous GWs coming from SGRs/AXPs would be a good indication that could corroborate the WD pulsar model, as for the neutron stars description, they are far below the BBO and DECIGO sensitivity curves.

Acknowledgements

M.F.S. thanks CAPES for the financial support. J.C.N.A. thanks FAPESP (2013/26258-4) and CNPq (308367/2019-7) for partial financial support. J.G.C. is likewise grateful to the support of CNPq (421265/2018-3 and 305369/2018-0), FAPESP Project No. 2015/15897-1, and NAPI (Fenômenos Extremos do Universo) of Fundação de Apoio à Ciência, Tecnologia e Inovação do Paraná.

References

1. M. F. Sousa, J. G. Coelho and J. C. de Araujo, Gravitational waves from fast-spinning white dwarfs, *Monthly Notices of the Royal Astronomical Society* **492**, 5949 (2020).
2. M. F. Sousa, J. G. Coelho and J. C. de Araujo, Gravitational waves from SGRs and AXPs as fast-spinning white dwarfs, *Monthly Notices of the Royal Astronomical Society* **498**, 4426 (2020).
3. B. Külebi, S. Jordan, F. Euchner, B. T. Gänsicke and H. Hirsch, Analysis of hydrogen-rich magnetic white dwarfs detected in the Sloan Digital Sky Survey, *Astronomy and Astrophysics* **506**, 1341 (November 2009).
4. S. O. Kepler, I. Pelisoli, S. Jordan, S. J. Kleinman, D. Koester, B. Külebi, V. Peçanha, B. G. Castanheira, A. Nitta, J. E. S. Costa, D. E. Winget, A. Kanaan and L. Fraga, Magnetic white dwarf stars in the Sloan Digital Sky Survey, *Monthly Notices of the RAS* **429**, 2934 (March 2013).
5. S. O. Kepler, I. Pelisoli, D. Koester, G. Ourique, S. J. Kleinman, A. D. Romero, A. Nitta, D. J. Eisenstein, J. E. S. Costa, B. Külebi, S. Jordan, P. Dufour, P. Giommi and A. Rebassa-Mansergas, New white dwarf stars in the Sloan Digital Sky Survey Data Release 10, *Monthly Notices of the RAS* **446**, 4078 (February 2015).
6. G. D. Schmidt, P. Bergeron, J. Liebert and R. A. Saffer, Two ultramassive white dwarfs found among candidates for magnetic fields, *Astrophysical Journal* **394**, 603 (August 1992).

7. B. Külebi, S. Jordan, E. Nelan, U. Bastian and M. Altmann, Constraints on the origin of the massive, hot, and rapidly rotating magnetic white dwarf RE J 0317-853 from an HST parallax measurement, *Astronomy and Astrophysics* **524**, p. A36 (December 2010).
8. T. R. Marsh, B. T. Gänsicke, S. Hümmerich, F.-J. Hambsch, K. Bernhard, C. Lloyd, E. Breedt, E. R. Stanway, D. T. Steeghs, S. G. Parsons, O. Toloza, M. R. Schreiber, P. G. Jonker, J. van Roestel, T. Kupfer, A. F. Pala, V. S. Dhillon, L. K. Hardy, S. P. Littlefair, A. Aungwerojwit, S. Arjyotha, D. Koester, J. J. Bochinski, C. A. Haswell, P. Frank and P. J. Wheatley, A radio-pulsing white dwarf binary star, *Nature* **537**, 374 (September 2016).
9. Y. Terada, T. Hayashi, M. Ishida, K. Mukai, T. Dotani, S. Okada, R. Nakamura, S. Naik, A. Bamba and K. Makishima, Suzaku Discovery of Hard X-Ray Pulsations from a Rotating Magnetized White Dwarf, AE Aquarii, *Publications of the ASJ* **60**, 387 (April 2008).
10. S. Mereghetti, A. Tiengo, P. Esposito, N. La Palombara, G. L. Israel and L. Stella, An Ultramassive, Fast-Spinning White Dwarf in a Peculiar Binary System, *Science* **325**, p. 1222 (September 2009).
11. S. Mereghetti, F. Pintore, P. Esposito, N. La Palombara, A. Tiengo, G. L. Israel and L. Stella, Discovery of spin-up in the x-ray pulsar companion of the hot subdwarf HD 49798, *Monthly Notices of the Royal Astronomical Society* **458**, 3523 (2016).
12. S. Popov, S. Mereghetti, S. Blinnikov, A. Kuranov and L. Yungelson, A young contracting white dwarf in the peculiar binary HD 49798/RX J0648. 0-4418?, *Monthly Notices of the Royal Astronomical Society* **474**, 2750 (2017).
13. R. Lopes de Oliveira, A. Bruch, C. V. Rodrigues, A. S. Oliveira and K. Mukai, CTCV J2056-3014: An X-Ray-faint Intermediate Polar Harboring an Extremely Fast-spinning White Dwarf, *The Astrophysical Journal Letters* **898**, p. L40 (August 2020).
14. E. Otoniel, J. G. Coelho, M. Malheiro and F. Weber, Mass limits of the extremely fast-spinning white dwarf CTCV J2056-3014, *arXiv e-prints*, p. arXiv:2010.12441 (October 2020).
15. R. P. Ashley, T. R. Marsh, E. Breedt, B. T. Gänsicke, A. F. Pala, O. Toloza, P. Chote, J. R. Thorstensen and M. R. Burleigh, V1460 Her: A fast spinning white dwarf accreting from an evolved donor star, *Monthly Notices of the Royal Astronomical Society* **499**, 149 (September 2020).
16. I. Caiazzo, K. B. Burdge, J. Fuller, J. Heyl, S. Kulkarni, T. A. Prince, H. B. Richer, J. Schwab, I. Andreoni, E. C. Bellm *et al.*, A highly magnetized and rapidly rotating white dwarf as small as the moon, *Nature* **595**, 39 (2021).
17. M. Malheiro, J. A. Rueda and R. Ruffini, SGRs and AXPs as rotation-powered massive white dwarfs, *Publications of the Astronomical Society of Japan* **64**, p. 56 (2012).
18. J. G. Coelho and M. Malheiro, Magnetic dipole moment of soft gamma-ray repeaters and anomalous x-ray pulsars described as massive and magnetic white dwarfs, *Publications of the Astronomical Society of Japan* **66**, p. 14 (2014).
19. R. V. Lobato, M. Malheiro and J. G. Coelho, Magnetars and white dwarf pulsars, *International Journal of Modern Physics D* **25**, p. 1641025 (July 2016).
20. B. Mukhopadhyay and A. R. Rao, Soft gamma-ray repeaters and anomalous X-ray pulsars as highly magnetized white dwarfs, *Journal of Cosmology and Astroparticle Physics* **5**, p. 007 (May 2016).
21. V. V. Usov, Gamma-radiation generation by rotating magnetic white dwarfs, *Pisma v Astronomicheskii Zhurnal* **14**, 606 (1988).
22. B. Abbott, R. Abbott, T. Abbott, S. Abraham, F. Acernese, K. Ackley, C. Adams, R. Adhikari, V. Adya, C. Affeldt *et al.*, Gwtc-1: A gravitational-wave transient catalog

of compact binary mergers observed by ligo and virgo during the first and second observing runs, *Physical Review X* **9**, p. 031040 (2019).
23. R. Abbott, T. Abbott, S. Abraham, F. Acernese, K. Ackley, A. Adams, C. Adams, R. Adhikari, V. Adya, C. Affeldt *et al.*, Gwtc-2: Compact binary coalescences observed by ligo and virgo during the first half of the third observing run, *Physical Review X* **11**, p. 021053 (2021).
24. P. Amaro-Seoane, H. Audley, S. Babak, J. Baker, E. Barausse, P. Bender, E. Berti, P. Binetruy, M. Born, D. Bortoluzzi *et al.*, Laser interferometer space antenna, *arXiv preprint arXiv:1702.00786* (2017).
25. T. Robson, N. J. Cornish and C. Liug, The construction and use of LISA sensitivity curves, *Classical and Quantum Gravity* **36**, p. 105011 (2019).
26. G. M. Harry, P. Fritschel, D. A. Shaddock, W. Folkner and E. S. Phinney, Laser interferometry for the big bang observer, *Classical and Quantum Gravity* **23**, p. 4887 (2006).
27. K. Yagi and N. Seto, Detector configuration of DECIGO/BBO and identification of cosmological neutron-star binaries, *Physical Review D* **83**, p. 044011 (2011).
28. S. Kawamura *et al.*, The japanese space gravitational wave antenna—DECIGO, *Classical and Quantum Gravity* **23**, p. S125 (2006).
29. K. Yagi and N. Seto, Erratum: Detector configuration of DECIGO/BBO and identification of cosmological neutron-star binaries [phys. rev. d 83, 044011 (2011)], *Physical Review D* **95**, p. 109901 (2017).
30. S. Bonazzola and E. Gourgoulhon, Gravitational waves from pulsars: Emission by the magnetic-field-induced distortion, *Astronomy and Astrophysics* **312**, 675 (August 1996).
31. J. C. N. de Araujo, J. G. Coelho and C. A. Costa, Gravitational wave emission by the high braking index pulsar PSR J1640-4631, *Journal of Cosmology and Astroparticle Physics* **2016**, p. 023 (Jul 2016).
32. J. C. N. de Araujo, J. G. Coelho and C. A. Costa, Gravitational Waves from Pulsars and Their Braking Indices: The Role of a Time Dependent Magnetic Ellipticity, *Astrophysical Journal* **831**, p. 35 (Nov 2016).
33. J. C. N. de Araujo, J. G. Coelho and C. A. Costa, Gravitational waves from pulsars in the context of magnetic ellipticity, *European Physical Journal C* **77**, p. 350 (May 2017).
34. B. Franzon and S. Schramm, Ar scorpii and possible gravitational wave radiation from pulsar white dwarfs, *Monthly Notices of the Royal Astronomical Society* **467**, 4484 (2017).
35. S. Kalita and B. Mukhopadhyay, Continuous gravitational wave from magnetized white dwarfs and neutron stars: Possible missions for LISA, DECIGO, BBO, ET detectors, *Monthly Notices of the Royal Astronomical Society*, p. 2346 (Oct 2019).
36. S. Chandrasekhar and E. Fermi, Problems of gravitational stability in the presence of a magnetic field, *The Astrophysical Journal* **118**, 116 (1953).
37. S. L. Shapiro and S. A. Teukolsky, *Black holes, white dwarfs and neutron stars: The physics of compact objects* (John Wiley & Sons, 1983).
38. M. Maggiore, *Gravitational waves: volume 1: Theory and experiments* (OUP Oxford, 2008).
39. K. Konno, T. Obata and Y. Kojima, Flattening modulus of a neutron star by rotation and magnetic field, *Astronomy and Astrophysics* **356**, 234 (April 2000).
40. T. Regimbau and J. A. de Freitas Pacheco, Gravitational wave background from magnetars, *Astronomy and Astrophysics* **447**, 1 (February 2006).

41. W. F. Welsh, K. Horne and R. Gomer, Doppler signatures of Hα flares in AE aquarii, *Monthly Notices of the Royal Astronomical Society* **298**, 285 (1998).
42. B. Warner, *Cataclysmic Variable Stars* (Cambridge University Press, 2003).
43. C. Hellier, *Cataclysmic Variable Stars—How and why they vary* (Springer Science & Business Media, 2001).
44. C.-S. Choi and I. Yi, On the rapid spin-down and low-luminosity pulsed emission from AE aquarii, *The Astrophysical Journal* **538**, 862 (2000).
45. S. Mereghetti, N. La Palombara, A. Tiengo, F. Pizzolato, P. Esposito, P. Woudt, G. Israel and L. Stella, X-ray and optical observations of the unique binary system hd 49798/rx j0648. 0-4418, *The Astrophysical Journal* **737**, p. 51 (2011).
46. V. C. A. Ferraro, On the Equilibrium of Magnetic Stars, *Astrophysical Journal* **119**, p. 407 (March 1954).
47. S. Olausen and V. Kaspi, The mcgill magnetar catalog, *The Astrophysical Journal Supplement Series* **212**, p. 6 (2014).
48. K. Boshkayev, L. Izzo, J. A. Rueda and R. Ruffini, Sgr 0418+5729, swift j1822.3-1606, and 1e 2259+586 as massive fast rotating highly magnetized white dwarfs, *Astronomy and Astrophysics* **555** (05 2013).
49. R. C. Duncan and C. Thompson, Formation of very strongly magnetized neutron stars-implications for gamma-ray bursts, *The Astrophysical Journal* **392**, L9 (1992).
50. V. M. Kaspi and A. M. Beloborodov, Magnetars, *Annual Review of Astronomy and Astrophysics* **55**, 261 (2017).

Highly magnetized white dwarfs: Implications and current status

B. Mukhopadhyay[1,*], M. Bhattacharya[2], A. J. Hackett[3], S. Kalita[1],
D. Karinkuzhi[1] and C. A. Tout[3]

[1] *Department of Physics, Indian Institute of Science, Bangalore 560012, India*
* *E-mail: bm@iisc.ac.in*
[2] *Department of Physics, The Pennsylvania State University,*
University Park, PA 16802, USA
[3] *Institute of Astronomy, University of Cambridge,*
Madingley Road, Cambridge CB3 0HA, UK

Over the last decade or so, we have been developing the possible existence of highly magnetized white dwarfs with analytical stellar structure models. While the primary aim was to explain the nature of the peculiar overluminous type Ia supernovae, later on, these magnetized stars were found to have even wider ranging implications including those for white dwarf pulsars, soft gamma-ray repeaters and anomalous X-ray pulsars, as well as gravitational radiation. In particular, we have explored in detail the mass-radius relations for these magnetized stars and showed that they can be significantly different from the Chandrasekhar predictions which essentially leads to a new super-Chandrasekhar mass-limit. Recently, using the stellar evolution code STARS, we have successfully modelled their formation and cooling evolution directly from the magnetized main sequence progenitor stars. Here we briefly discuss all these findings and conclude with their current status in the scientific community.

Keywords: Conduction; equation of state; magnetic fields; magnetohydrodynamics; opacity; radiative transfer; white dwarfs.

1. Introduction

More than a dozen overluminous Type Ia supernovae (SNe Ia) have already been observed[1,2] which strongly suggest the existence of massive progenitors with masses $M > 2M_\odot$. Although the evolutions of accreting or rapidly differentially rotating white dwarf (WD) binaries have been used to explain such progenitors,[3,4] these models are unable to explain masses up to $2.8M_\odot$ that are inferred from the observations. Highly magnetised super-Chandrasekhar WDs (B-WDs) have been recently proposed as the possible progenitors of these peculiar overluminous SNe Ia. In addition to SNe Ia, B-WDs are also considered as promising candidates for soft gamma-ray repeaters (SGRs) and anomalous X-ray pulsars (AXPs) at lower magnetic fields than neutron star (NS) based magnetar, satisfying their ultraviolet luminosity cut-off.[13]

It has been shown that strong magnetic fields can modify the equation of state (EoS) of electron degenerate matter and yield super-Chandrasekhar WDs,[6–8] irrespective of the rotation rate. Indeed, the observational data from the Sloan Digital Sky Survey (SDSS) suggest that magnetized WDs tend to have larger masses than their non-magnetic counterparts, even though they span the same effective temperature range.[9,10] Inspired by above findings, the effect of strong magnetic fields on the stellar structure, for various field configurations, has been explored for both Newtonian[6] and general relativistic formalisms.[8,11,12]

Magnetized WDs have many important implications apart from their link to peculiar SNe Ia and hence their other properties are worth exploring.[13–15] Recent works[16–19] have shown that B-WDs can be too dim to detect directly, and have also explored[20,21] the ability of rotating B-WDs to generate gravitational radiation which can be detected by the space-based gravitational wave detectors. Furthermore, other additional physics such as modified gravity,[22,23] ungravity effect,[24] effects of net charge,[25,26] lepton number violation[27] and anisotropic pressure[28] have also been explored to show the possible existence of super-Chandrasekhar WDs. Here we discuss the broad implications of these magnetized stars as well as their current status.

2. Origin and evolution of strong magnetic fields

It has been well known that purely poloidally or toroidally dominated fields are both structurally unstable.[29,30] However, it also has been shown that magnetized WDs with toroidally dominated mixed field configuration (along with small poloidal component) are one of the most plausible cases[31] and have approximately spherical shape.[8] Although the surface fields can be observationally inferred, the interior field cannot be directly constrained. Nevertheless, there is a sufficient evidence that the stars exhibit dipolar fields in their outer regions and hence are expected to have stronger interior (toroidally dominated) fields than at the surface. Numerical simulations have indeed shown that central fields of B-WDs can be several orders of magnitude higher than the surface field.[8,14,32]

The evolution of the poloidal and toroidal magnetic field components along with the angular momentum has been modelled recently with the Cambridge stellar evolution code STARS,[32] using advection-diffusion equations coupled to the structural and compositional equations of stars. They have shown that the magnetic field is likely to be dipolar, decaying as an inverse square law for most of the star. Their results also suggest that at the end of main sequence, the star may have toroidally dominated magnetic fields. The left panel of Figure 1 shows the evolution of toroidal field in the stellar interior as a function of radius at the end of main sequence, while the right panel shows the field as a function of the mass coordinate at various times after the helium exhaustion in the core, during the asymptotic giant phase.

Large-scale magnetic fields can be governed in the degenerate core of B-WDs even during the late stages of stellar evolution,[32] and very high fields can develop in these stars based on the conservation of magnetic flux, besides from the dynamo mechanism. Hence, strong fields inside magnetized WDs can also be of fossil origin.[33] This can be understood as follows. While the mass of the WD increases due to accretion, magnetic field is advected into its interior. Consequently, the gravitational

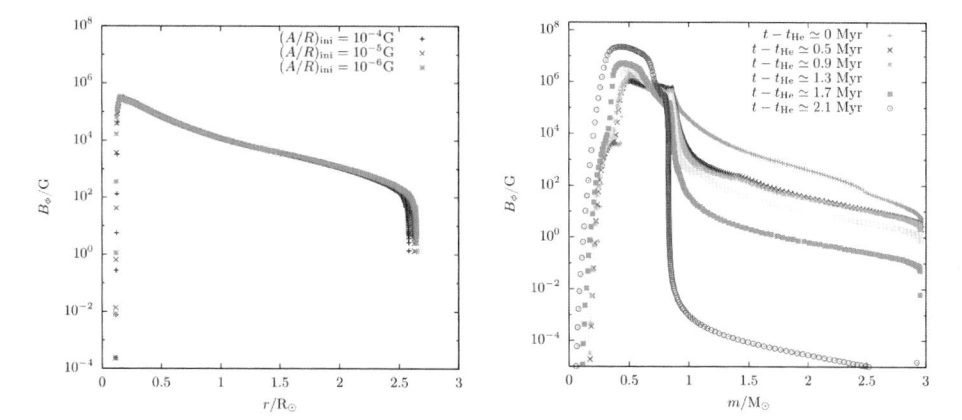

Fig. 1. *Left panel:* Toroidal field in the interior of the star as a function of the radius at the end of the main sequence. *Right panel:* Toroidal field inside the star as a function of the mass coordinate at various times after the helium exhaustion in the core, during the asymptotic giant phase.

power dominates over the degeneracy pressure leading to the contraction of the star. The initial seed magnetic field is then amplified as the total magnetic flux remains conserved. For magnetic field $B \sim 10^8$ G in a star of size $R \sim 10^6$ km, the resultant flux will be $\sim 10^{20}$ G km^2. From flux freezing, for a 1000 km size B-WD, the magnetic field can then grow up to $\sim 10^{14}$ G. Once the field increases, the total outward force further builds up to balance the inward gravitational force and the whole cycle is repeated multiple times. Therefore, the magnetic fields of highly magnetized WDs are likely to be fossil remnants from their main-sequence progenitor stars.

Repeated episodes of accretion and spin-down have also been suggested as a plausible mechanism that can lead to a highly magnetized WD.[14] Here, the entire evolution of the B-WD can be classified in two phases: accretion-powered and rotation-powered. The accretion-powered phase is governed by three conservation laws: linear and angular momenta conservation and conservation of magnetic flux, around the stellar surface, given by

$$l\Omega(t)^2 R(t) = \frac{GM(t)}{R(t)^2},$$

$$I(t)\Omega(t) = \text{constant},$$

$$B_s(t)R(t)^2 = \text{constant}, \tag{1}$$

where l accounts for the dominance of gravitational force over the centrifugal force, hence $l > 1$, I is the stellar moment of inertia and Ω is the angular velocity of the star that includes contribution acquired due to accretion as well. Solving these equations simultaneously gives the time evolution of radius, magnetic field and angular velocity during the accretion phase. Accretion discontinues when

$$-\frac{GM}{R^2} = \frac{1}{\rho}\frac{d}{dr}\left(\frac{B^2}{8\pi}\right)_{r=R} \sim -\frac{B_s^2}{8\pi R \rho}, \tag{2}$$

where ρ is the density of the inner disk edge. If the magnetic field is dipolar, $\dot{\Omega} \propto \Omega^3$ for a fixed magnetic field. Generalizing it to $\dot{\Omega} = k\Omega^n$ with constant k giving for the spin-powered phase, we obtain

$$\Omega = [\Omega_0^{1-n} - k(1-n)(t-t_0)]^{1/1-n}, \qquad (3)$$

$$\text{and } B_s = \sqrt{\frac{5c^3 I k \Omega^{n-m}}{R^6 \sin^2\alpha}}. \qquad (4)$$

Here Ω_0 is the initial angular velocity for the spin-powered phase (once accretion stops) at time $t = t_0$. The value of k is fixed such that B_s can be constrained at $t = t_0$, which is known from the field evolution in the preceding accretion-powered phase. Here $n = m = 3$ corresponds to the dipole field configuration, therefore m represents the deviation from dipolar field, especially for $n = 3$. Figure 2 shows the sample evolutions of angular velocity and magnetic field as functions of stellar mass. In both cases, initially larger Ω with accretion drops significantly during the spin-powered phase, followed by a phase of its increasing trend. At the end of the evolution, the star can be left either as a super-Chandrasekhar WD and/or an SGR/AXP candidate with a higher spin frequency.

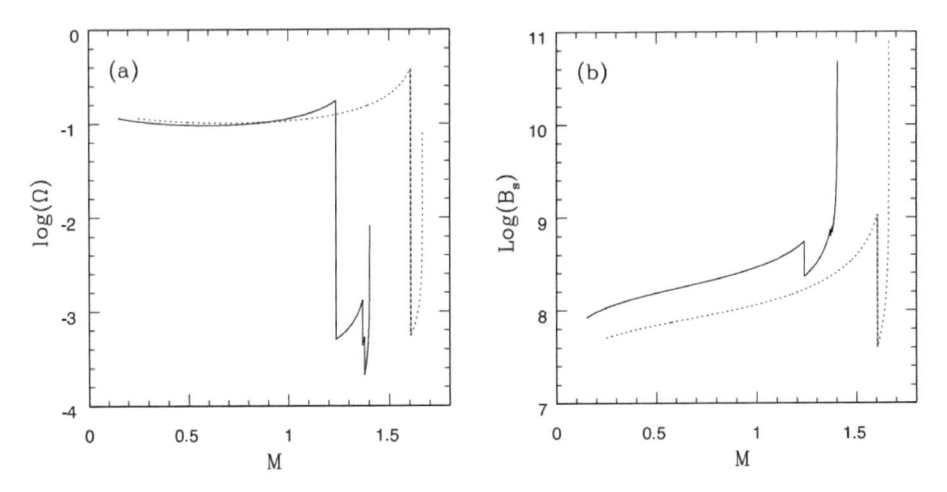

Fig. 2. Time evolution of angular velocity (left) and magnetic field (right) as functions of mass. The solid curves correspond to the case with $n = 3$, $m = 2.7$, $\rho = 0.05\,\text{g cm}^{-3}$, $l = 1.5$ and dotted curves correspond to the case with $n = 3$, $m = 2$, $\rho = 0.1\,\text{g cm}^{-3}$, $l = 2.5$. The other parameters are fixed with $k = 10^{-14}$, $\dot{M} = 10^{-8}\,M_\odot\text{yr}^{-1}$, $\alpha = 10°$ and $R = 10^4\,\text{km}$ at $t = 0$.

3. Rotating magnetized white dwarfs

Although, in nature, WDs are expected to consist of mixed fixed geometry, here we consider toroidally dominated magnetic field cases as they ensure the stability of these stars. It has been shown that toroidally dominated (and purely toroidal) field not only makes the star (slightly) prolate but also increases its equatorial radius.[8,34,35] Figure 3 shows specific cases for toroidal field configuration combined with rotation. In the left panel, as the angular frequency is small, it does not affect the star considerably and results in a marginally prolate star. In contrast, the right panel, due to high angular velocity, exhibits that the low density region is affected more due to rotation than the high density region, resulting in an oblate shaped WD. From the magnetic field strength isocontours shown in the center panel, we can see that the surface magnetic field can decrease up to $\sim 10^9$ G even if the central field is $\sim 10^{14}$ G. For both cases, the magnetic to gravitational energies ratio (ME/GE) as well as kinetic to gravitational energies ratio (KE/GE) are chosen to be $\lesssim 0.1$ to maintain stable equilibrium.[36–38]

We have also considered differentially rotating B-WDs.[8] The angular velocity profile in the XNS code is specified as[39,40]

$$F(\Omega) = A^2(\Omega_c - \Omega) = \frac{R^2(\Omega - \omega)}{\alpha^2 - R^2(\Omega - \omega)^2}, \tag{5}$$

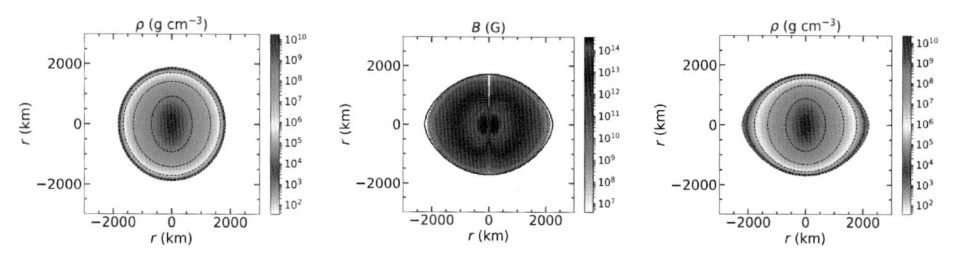

Fig. 3. Density and magnetic field strength isocontours for uniformly rotating B-WDs with toroidal magnetic field are shown in the left and center panels, respectively. The parameters used for both are $\Omega \sim 0.0628\,\text{rad/s}$, $B_{max} \sim 2.7 \times 10^{14}$ G, ME/GE ~ 0.1, KE/GE $\sim 3.6 \times 10^{-6}$. The density isocontours for the $\Omega \sim 3.6537\,\text{rad/s}$, $B_{max} \sim 2.7 \times 10^{14}$ G, ME/GE ~ 0.1, KE/GE $\sim 1.3 \times 10^{-2}$ case is shown in the right panel.

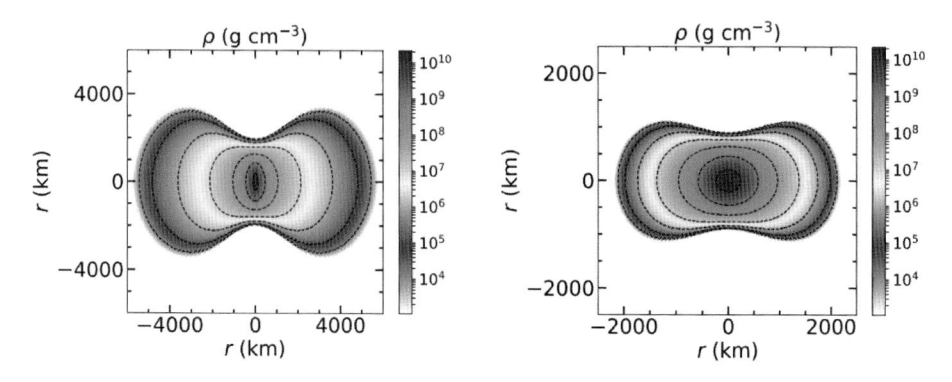

Fig. 4. Density isocontours for differentially rotating magnetized WD is shown. For the left panel, we have toroidal field with $\Omega \sim 0.62\,\text{rad/s}$, $\Omega_c \sim 10.15\,\text{rad/s}$, $B_{max} \sim 3.2 \times 10^{14}$ G, ME/GE ~ 0.14, KE/GE ~ 0.1. For the right panel, we use poloidal field with $\Omega \sim 2.74\,\text{rad/s}$, $\Omega_c \sim 20.30\,\text{rad/s}$, $B_{max} \sim 3.9 \times 10^{11}$ G, ME/GE $\sim 7.8 \times 10^{-8}$, KE/GE ~ 0.14.

where A is a constant that indicates the extent of differential rotation, $R = \psi^2 r \sin\theta$, $\omega = -\beta^\phi$, Ω_c is the angular velocity at the center and ω is the angular velocity at radius r. Figure 4 shows the density isocontours of differentially rotating B-WDs for toroidal field with surface angular velocity $\Omega \sim 0.62\,\mathrm{rad/s}$, $\Omega_c \sim 10.15\,\mathrm{rad/s}$, $B_{max} \sim 3.2 \times 10^{14}$ G, ME/GE ~ 0.14, KE/GE ~ 0.1 (left panel) and poloidal field with $\Omega \sim 2.74\,\mathrm{rad/s}$, $\Omega_c \sim 20.30\,\mathrm{rad/s}$, $B_{max} \sim 3.9 \times 10^{11}$ G, ME/GE $\sim 7.8 \times 10^{-8}$, KE/GE ~ 0.14 (right panel). It can be seen that "polar hollow" structure can form with differential rotation regardless of the specific geometry of the magnetic field.

4. Non-rotating magnetized WDs with finite temperature

Apart from increasing the limiting mass of WDs, strong magnetic fields can also influence the thermal properties such as luminosity, temperature gradient and cooling rate of the star.[16,18,19] In order to model such a WD, the total pressure inside the star is modelled by including the contributions from the degenerate electron gas, ideal gas and magnetic pressures. The interface is defined to be the radius where the contributions from electron degenerate core and outer ideal gas pressures are equal. The presence of strong fields gives rise to additional pressure $P_B = B^2/8\pi$ and density $\rho_B = B^2/8\pi c^2$ inside the magnetized WDs.[41]

Assuming the B-WD to be approximately spherical, the model equations for magnetostatic equilibrium, photon diffusion and mass conservation can be written within a Newtonian framework as

$$\frac{d}{dr}(P_{\mathrm{deg}} + P_{\mathrm{ig}} + P_B) = -\frac{Gm(r)}{r^2}(\rho + \rho_B),$$

$$\frac{dT}{dr} = -\max\left[\frac{3}{4ac}\frac{\kappa\rho}{T^3}\frac{L_r}{4\pi r^2}, \left(1-\frac{1}{\gamma}\right)\frac{T}{P}\frac{dP}{dr}\right],$$

$$\frac{dm}{dr} = 4\pi r^2(\rho + \rho_B). \tag{6}$$

Here we have ignored the magnetic tension terms for radially varying B. In these equations, P_{deg} and $P_{\mathrm{ig}} = \rho k T/\mu m_p$ are the electron degeneracy pressure and hence the ideal gas pressure respectively, ρ is the matter density, T is the temperature, $m(r)$ is the mass enclosed within radius r, κ is the radiative opacity, L_r is the luminosity at radius r, and γ is the adiabatic index of the gas.

The opacity in the surface layers of non-magnetised WD is approximated with the Kramers' formula, $\kappa = \kappa_0 \rho T^{-3.5}$, where $\kappa_0 = 4.34 \times 10^{24} Z(1+X)$ cm^2 g^{-1}, and X and Z are the mass fractions of hydrogen and heavy elements (other than hydrogen and helium) in the stellar interior respectively. To capture the radial variation of the field magnitude within the B-WD, we adopt a profile used extensively to model magnetized NSs and B-WDs,[11,42] given by

$$B\left(\frac{\rho}{\rho_0}\right) = B_s + B_0\left[1 - \exp\left(-\eta\left(\frac{\rho}{\rho_0}\right)^\gamma\right)\right], \tag{7}$$

where B_s is the surface magnetic field, B_0 is a fiducial magnetic field, $\eta = 0.8$ and $\gamma = 0.9$ are dimensionless parameters along with $\rho_0 = 10^9$ g/cm^3 determining how the field decays from the core to the surface. The radial luminosity can be assumed to be constant so that $L_r = L$ as there is no hydrogen burning or other nuclear fusion reactions taking place within the WD core. We solve the differential equations by providing the surface density, mass and surface temperature as the boundary conditions.

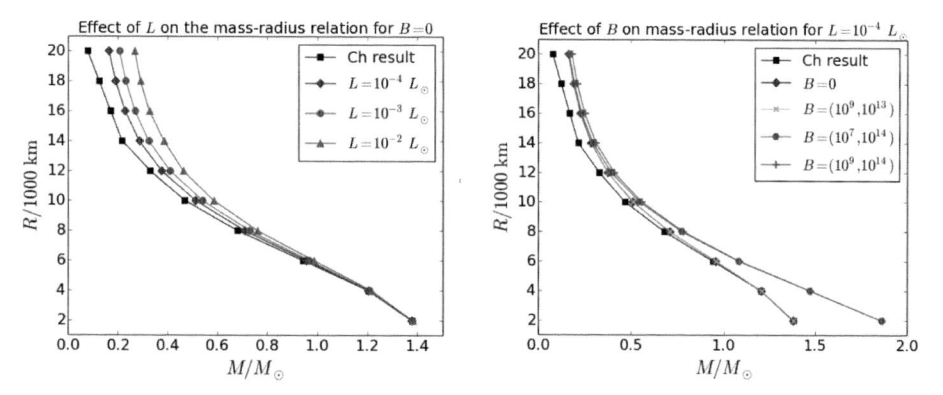

Fig. 5. *Left panel:* The effect of L on the mass–radius relation of non-magnetised WDs is shown for $L = 10^{-4} L_\odot$ (blue diamonds), $L = 10^{-3} L_\odot$ (green circles) and $L = 10^{-2} L_\odot$ (red triangles), along with the Chandrasekhar result (black squares). *Right panel:* The effect of field strength on the mass–radius relation of B-WDs is shown for $B = (B_s, B_0) = (0,0)$ (blue diamonds), $B = (10^9, 10^{13})$ G (orange crosses), $B = (10^7, 10^{14})$ G (green circles) and $B = (10^9, 10^{14})$ G (red pluses), along with the Chandrasekhar result (black squares) for $L = 10^{-4} L_\odot$.

For strong magnetic fields, variation of radiative opacity with B can be modelled as $\kappa = \kappa_B \approx 5.5 \times 10^{31} \rho T^{-1.5} B^{-2}$ cm^2 g^{-1}.[43,44] The field dependent Potekhin's opacity is used instead of Kramers' opacity if $B/10^{12}$ G $\geq T/10^6$ K, which is valid for the strong B cases that we consider here. The left panel of Figure 5 shows the effect of luminosity on the mass-radius relation for non-magnetized WDs compared to Chandrasekhar's results.[45] Although the increase in L leads to progressively higher masses for larger WDs, Chandrasekhar mass limit is retained irrespective of the luminosity. The right panel of Figure 5 shows the effect of magnetic field on the mass-radius relation for B-WDs with $L = 10^{-4} L_\odot$ and compares them with the non-magnetic Chandrasekhar results. It can be seen that the magnetic field affects the mass-radius relation in a manner analogous to increasing L, by shifting the curve towards higher masses for WDs with larger radii. The mass-radius curves for $B_0 \lesssim 10^{13}$ G practically overlap with each other and retain the Chandrasekhar mass limit. However, for strong central fields with $B_0 \sim 10^{14}$ G, super-Chandrasekhar WDs are obtained with masses as high as $\sim 1.9 M_\odot$.

In order to ensure structural stability of a B-WD, an increase in magnetic energy density has to be compensated by a corresponding decrease in the thermal energy and hence the luminosity. This effect is especially prominent for B-WDs with larger radii where the magnetic, thermal and gravitational energies are comparable with each other. We find that a slight decrease in the luminosity for $R \gtrsim 12000$ km WDs leads to masses that are similar to their non-magnetic counterparts. However, the smaller radii B-WDs require a substantial drop in their luminosity (well outside the observable range) and still do not really achieve masses that are similar to the non-magnetized WDs.

5. Effect of cooling evolution and field dissipation

Magnetic fields inside a WD undergo decay by Ohmic dissipation and Hall drift processes with timescales given by[46,47]

$$t_{\rm Ohm} = (7 \times 10^{10}~{\rm yr})\,\rho_{c,6}^{1/3} R_4^{1/2} (\rho_{\rm avg}/\rho_c), \tag{8}$$

$$t_{\rm Hall} = (5 \times 10^{10}~{\rm yr})\,l_8^2 B_{0,14}^{-1} T_{c,7}^2 \rho_{c,10}, \tag{9}$$

where $\rho_{c,n} = \rho_c/10^n$ g cm^{-3}, $R_4 = R/10^4$ km, $T_{c,7} = T_c/10^7$ K, $B_{0,14} = B_0/10^{14}$ G and $l = l_8 \times 10^8$ cm is characteristic length scale of the flux loops through WD outer core. Ohmic decay is the dominant field dissipation process for $B \lesssim 10^{12}$ G, while for $10^{12} \leq B/G \leq 10^{14}$ the decay occurs via Hall drift and for $B \gtrsim 10^{14}$ G, the principal decay mechanism is likely to be ambipolar diffusion.[46] The magnetic field decay in magnetars with surface fields between 10^{14} and 10^{16} G can be solved using

$$\frac{dB}{dt} = -B\left(\frac{1}{t_{\rm Ohm}} + \frac{1}{t_{\rm Amb}} + \frac{1}{t_{\rm Hall}}\right), \tag{10}$$

where $t_{\rm Amb}$ denotes the ambipolar diffusion time scale.

On the other hand, the thermal energy of WDs is radiated away gradually over time in the observed luminosity from the surface layers as the star evolves. The rate at which thermal energy of ions is transported to surface and radiated depends on the specific heat, given by

$$L = -\frac{d}{dt}\int c_v dT = (2 \times 10^6~{\rm erg/s})\,\frac{Am_\mu}{M_\odot}\left(\frac{T}{K}\right)^{7/2}, \tag{11}$$

where $c_v \approx 3k_B/2$ is the specific heat at constant volume. Given an initial L and temperature T_0 at time t_0, final temperature after cooling is given by $(T/K)^{-5/2} - (T_0/K)^{-5/2} = 2.406 \times 10^{-34}~\tau/s$, where $\tau = t - t_0$ is the WD age.

The left panel of Figure 6 shows the effect of B-WD evolution on their mass-radius relations including both magnetic field decay and thermal cooling effects. The luminosities are varied with field strength such that the masses can match those obtained for the non-magnetized WDs. For $B = (B_s, B_0) = (10^9, 10^{14})$ G, although the maximum mass $\sim 1.9\,M_\odot$ shown in the track at small radius turns out to be much larger than the Chandrasekhar limit, we find that it is lowered considerably

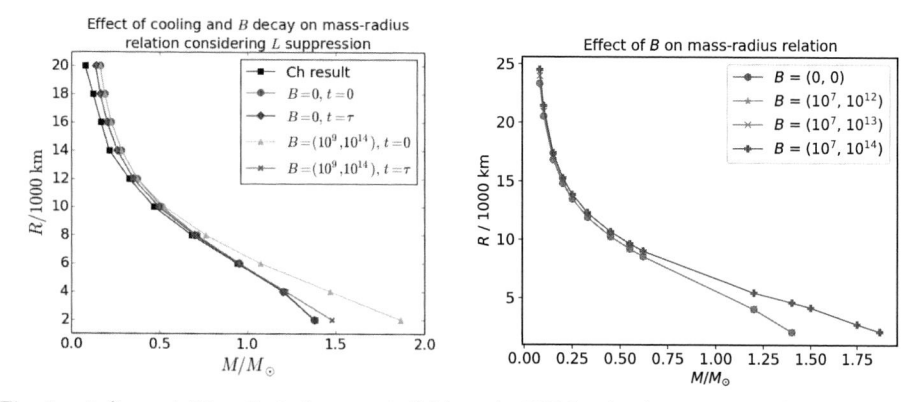

Fig. 6. *Left panel:* The effect of magnetic field on the WD luminosity set to match with the non-magnetised mass–radius relation for the analytical model. The results are shown for $B = (0,0)$ at initial time $t = 0$ (green circles), $B = (0,0)$ at $t = 10$ Gyr (blue diamonds), $B = (10^9, 10^{14})$ G at $t = 0$ (orange triangles) and $B = (10^9, 10^{14})$ G at $t = 10$ Gyr (magenta crosses). *Right panel:* STARS results to show the effect of magnetic field on the mass–radius relation of highly magnetized WDs for $B = (0,0)$ (blue circles), $B = (10^7, 10^{12})$ G (orange stars), $B = (10^7, 10^{13})$ G (green crosses) and $B = (10^7, 10^{14})$ G (red pluses).

to $\sim 1.5\,M_\odot$ primarily as a result of magnetic field decay and also thermal cooling over $t = 10$ Gyr.

Further, we use the STARS stellar evolution code to qualitatively investigate the B-WD mass-radius relationship at different field strengths, with the objective of numerically validating our semi-analytical models. In the right panel of Figure 6, we show the mass-radius relations obtained from STARS. We obtain results that are in good agreement with our analytical formalism and the magnitude of B_0 dictates the shape of the mass-radius curve. In validation of our analytical approach, we have found that the limiting mass $\sim 1.8703\,M_\odot$ obtained with the STARS numerical models is in very good agreement with $M \approx 1.87\,M_\odot$ that is inferred from the semi-analytical calculations for WDs with strong fields $B = (10^{6-9}, 10^{14})$ G. We argue that the young super-Chandrasekhar B-WDs only sustain their large masses up to $\sim 10^5 - 10^6$ yr, and this essentially explains their apparent scarcity even without the difficulty of detection owing to their suppressed luminosities.

6. Continuous gravitational waves from magnetized white dwarfs

The question then remains, how to detect B-WDs directly. Continuous gravitational waves can be among the alternate ways to detect super-Chandrasekhar WD candidates directly. If these B-WDs are rotating with certain angular frequency, then they can efficiently emit gravitational radiation, provided that their magnetic field and rotation axes are not aligned,[48] and these gravitational waves can be detected by upcoming instruments such as LISA, BBO, DECIGO, Einstein Telescope, etc. The dimensionless amplitudes of the two polarizations of the gravitational wave

(GW) at a time t are given by[48,49]

$$h_+ = h_0 \sin\chi \left[\frac{1}{2}\cos i \sin i \cos\chi \cos\Omega t - \frac{1+\cos^2 i}{2}\sin\chi \cos 2\Omega t\right],$$

$$h_\times = h_0 \sin\chi \left[\frac{1}{2}\sin i \cos\chi \sin\Omega t - \cos i \sin\chi \sin 2\Omega t\right], \quad (12)$$

with $h_0 = (-6G/c^4)Q_{z'z'}(\Omega^2/d)$, where $Q_{z'z'}$ is the quadrupole moment of the distorted star, χ is the angle between the rotation axis z' and the body's third principal axis z, i is the angle between the rotation axis of the object and our line of sight. The left panel of Figure 7 shows a schematic diagram of a pulsar with z' being the rotational axis and z the magnetic field axis, where the angle between these two axes is χ. The GW amplitude is

$$h_0 = \frac{4G}{c^4}\frac{\Omega^2 \epsilon I_{xx}}{d}, \quad (13)$$

where $\epsilon = (I_{zz} - I_{xx})/I_{xx}$ is the ellipticity of the body and I_{xx}, I_{yy}, I_{zz} are the principal moments of inertia. Note, we have used the XNS code[50] to simulate the underlying axisymmetric equilibrium configuration of B-WDs in general relativity. Moreover, we assume the distance between the WD and the detector to be 100 pc.

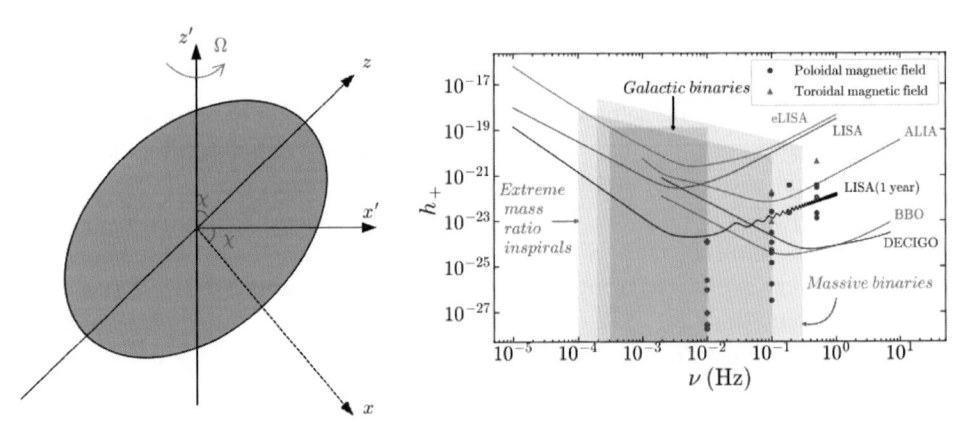

Fig. 7. *Left panel:* Schematic diagram of a B-WD with z' being the rotational axis and z the magnetic axis. *Right panel:* The dimensionless GW amplitudes for WDs are shown as functions of frequency, along with the sensitivity curves of various detectors. Optimum i is chosen for χ at $t = 0$.

Since a pulsating WD can emit both dipole and gravitational radiations simultaneously, it is associated with both dipole and quadrupolar luminosities. The dipole luminosity for an axisymmetric WD is given by[51]

$$L_D = \frac{B_p^2 R_p^6 \Omega^4}{2c^3}\sin^2\chi\, F(x_0), \quad (14)$$

where $x_0 = R_0\Omega/c$, B_p is the magnetic field strength at the pole, R_p is radius of the pole and R_0 is the average WD radius. The function $F(x_0)$ is defined as

$$F(x_0) = \frac{x_0^4}{5(x_0^6 - 3x_0^4 + 36)} + \frac{1}{3(x_0^2 + 1)}. \tag{15}$$

Similarly, the quadrupolar GW luminosity is given by[49]

$$L_{GW} = \frac{2G}{5c^5}(I_{zz} - I_{xx})^2 \Omega^6 \sin^2\chi\,(1 + 15\sin^2\chi). \tag{16}$$

It should be noted that this formula is valid if χ is very small. The total luminosity is due to both dipole and gravitational radiations. Therefore, the changes in Ω and χ with time are dependent on both L_D and L_{GW}. The variations of Ω and χ with respect to time are given by[51]

$$\frac{d(\Omega I_{z'z'})}{dt} = -\frac{2G}{5c^5}(I_{zz} - I_{xx})^2 \Omega^5 \sin^2\chi\,(1 + 15\sin^2\chi) - \frac{B_p^2 R_p^6 \Omega^3}{2c^3}\sin^2\chi\, F(x_0), \tag{17}$$

$$I_{z'z'}\frac{d\chi}{dt} = -\frac{12G}{5c^5}(I_{zz} - I_{xx})^2 \Omega^4 \sin^3\chi\cos\chi - \frac{B_p^2 R_p^6 \Omega^2}{2c^3}\sin\chi\cos\chi\, F(x_0), \tag{18}$$

where $I_{z'z'}$ is the moment of inertia about z'-axis. Equations (17) and (18) need to be solved simultaneously to obtain the timescale over which a WD can radiate.

The right panel of Figure 7 shows the dimensionless GW amplitudes for the WDs as functions of their frequencies, along with the sensitivity curves of various detectors. It can be seen that the isolated WDs may not be detected directly by LISA, but can be detected after integrating the signal to noise ratio S/N for 1 year. As WDs are larger in size compared to NS, they cannot rotate as fast as NS and hence ground-based GW detectors such as LIGO, Virgo and KAGRA are not expected to detect the isolated WDs. These isolated WDs are also free from the noise due to the galactic binaries as well as from the extreme mass ratio inspirals (EMRIs).

7. Summary and conclusions

We have shown that highly magnetized, stable WDs, namely B-WDs, have a variety of implications, including enigmatic peculiar over-luminous SNe Ia. Numerical simulations utilizing the stellar evolution code STARS indicate that the central field in strongly magnetized B-WDs can be toroidally dominated whereas the surface fields are more of dipole nature. The mass $\sim 1.87\,M_\odot$ obtained for these B-WDs from the STARS numerical models, as of now, is totally consistent with the estimates from the analytical stellar structure models for strong fields $B = (10^{6-9}, 10^{14})$ G. These young super-Chandrasekhar B-WDs have suppressed luminosities and are difficult to observe or rare, due to their decaying magnetic fields. We have found that these WDs may not remain super-Chandrasekhar for long i.e. beyond $\sim 10^{5-6}$ year due to decaying field primarily, and indicate rapidly losing pulsar nature and/or low luminosity. However, these stars can be very promising candidates for GW detectors such as LISA (with 1 year integrated S/N) and also for Einstein Telescope and future DECIGO/BBO missions. Therefore, appropriate missions in GW astronomy and otherwise, e.g. radio astronomy, should be planned in order to probe them in the future.

Acknowledgments

B.M. acknowledges a partial support by a project of Department of Science and Technology (DST-SERB) with research Grant No. DSTO/PPH/BMP/1946 (EMR/2017/001226). M.B. acknowledges support from Graduate Continuing Fellowship at the University of Texas, Austin. A.J.H. thanks the Science and Technology Facilities Council (STFC) and the Cambridge Commonwealth, European & International Trust for his doctoral funding. C.A.T. thanks Churchill College for his fellowship.

References

1. D. A. Howell, et al., Nature, 443, 308 (2006).
2. R. A. Scalzo, et al., ApJ, 713, 1073 (2010).
3. I. Hachisu, Ap&SS, 61, 479 (1986).
4. S.-C. Yoon, N. Langer, A&A, 419, 623 (2004).
5. B. Mukhopadhyay, A. R. Rao, JCAP, 05, 007 (2016).
6. U. Das, B. Mukhopadhyay, Phys. Rev. D, 86, 042001 (2012).
7. U. Das, B. Mukhopadhyay, Phys. Rev. Lett., 110, 071102 (2013).
8. S. Subramanian, B. Mukhopadhyay, MNRAS, 454, 752 (2015).
9. K. M. Vanlandingham, et al., AJ, 130, 734 (2005).
10. L. Ferrario, D. Martino, B. Gaensicke, Space Sci. Rev., 191, 111 (2015).
11. U. Das, B. Mukhopadhyay, JCAP, 06, 050 (2014).
12. U. Das, B. Mukhopadhyay, JCAP, 05, 016 (2015).
13. B. Mukhopadhyay, A. R. Rao, JCAP, 05, 007 (2016).
14. B. Mukhopadhyay, A. R. Rao, T. S. Bhatia, MNRAS, 472, 3564 (2017).
15. B. Mukhopadhyay, U. Das, A. R. Rao, S. Subramanian, M. Bhattacharya, S. Mukerjee, T. S. Bhatia, J. Sutradhar, in P.-E. Tremblay, B. Gansicke, T. Marsh, eds, Astronomical Society of the Pacific Conference Series, Vol. 509, 20th European White Dwarf Workshop. Astron. Soc. Pac., San Francisco, p. 401 (2017).
16. M. Bhattacharya, B. Mukhopadhyay, S. Mukerjee, MNRAS, 477, 2705 (2018).
17. M. Bhattacharya, B. Mukhopadhyay, S. Mukerjee, Proceedings of the 21st European Workshop on White Dwarfs, arXiv:1810.07836 (2018).
18. A. Gupta, B. Mukhopadhyay, C. A. Tout, MNRAS, 496, 894 (2020).
19. M. Bhattacharya, A. J. Hackett, A. Gupta, C. A. Tout, B. Mukhopadhyay, arXiv:2106.09736 (2021).
20. S. Kalita, B. Mukhopadhyay, MNRAS, 490, 2692 (2019).
21. S. Kalita, B. Mukhopadhyay, T. Mondal, T. Bulik, ApJ, 896, 69 (2020).
22. S. Banerjee, S. Shankar, T. P. Singh, J. Cosmol. Astropart. Phys., 2017, 004 (2017).
23. B. E. Eslam Panah, H. Liu, Phys. Rev. D, 99, 104074 (2019).

24. O. Bertolami, H. Mariji, Phys. Rev. D, 93, 104046 (2016).
25. H. Liu, X. Zhang, D. Wen, Phys. Rev. D, 89, 104043 (2014).
26. G. A. Carvalho, J. D. V. Arbanil, R. M. Marinho, M. Malheiro, Eur. Phys. J. C, 78, 411 (2018).
27. V. B. Belyaev, P. Ricci, F. Simkovic, J. Adam, M. Tater, E. Truhlik, Nucl. Phys. A, 937, 17 (2015).
28. L. Herrera, W. Barreto, Phys. Rev. D, 87, 087303 (2013).
29. P. Markey, R. J. Tayler, MNRAS, 163, 77 (1973).
30. R. J. Tayler, MNRAS, 161, 365 (1973).
31. D. T. Wickramasinghe, C. A. Tout, L. Ferrario, MNRAS, 437, 675 (2013).
32. L. G. Quentin, C. A.Tout, MNRAS, 477, 2298 (2018).
33. U. Das, B. Mukhopadhyay, A. R. Rao, ApJ, 767, L14 (2013).
34. K. Ioka, M. Sasaki, ApJ, 600, 296 (2004).
35. J. Frieben, L. Rezzolla, MNRAS, 427, 3406 (2012).
36. S. Chandrasekhar, E. Fermi, ApJ, 118, 116 (1953).
37. H. Komatsu, Y. Eriguchi, I. Hachisu, MNRAS, 237, 355 (1989).
38. J. Braithwaite, MNRAS, 397, 763 (2009).
39. N. Stergioulas, Living Reviews in Relativity, 6, 3 (2003).
40. N. Bucciantini, L. Del Zanna, A&A, 528, A101 (2011).
41. M. Sinha, B. Mukhopadhyay, A. Sedrakian, Nucl. Phys. A, 898, 43 (2013).
42. D. Bandyopadhyay, S. Chakrabarty, S. Pal, Phys. Rev. Lett, 79, 2176 (1997).
43. A. Y. Potekhin, D. G. Yakovlev, A&A, 374, 213 (2001).
44. J. Ventura, A. Y. Potekhin, The Neutron Star - Black Hole Connection, Kluwer, Dordrecht (2001).
45. S. Chandrasekhar, MNRAS, 95, 207 (1935).
46. J. S. Heyl, S. R. Kulkarni, ApJ, 506, 61 (1998).
47. A. Cumming, MNRAS, 333, 589 (2002).
48. S. Bonazzola, E. Gourgoulhon, A&A, 312, 675 (1996).
49. M. Zimmermann, E. Szedenits Jr., Phys. Rev. D., 20, 351 (1979).
50. A. G. Pili, N. Bucciantini, L. Del Zanna, MNRAS, 439, 3541 (2014).
51. A. Melatos, MNRAS, 313, 217 (2000).

Electron captures and stability of white dwarfs

N. Chamel* and L. Perot

*Institut d'Astronomie et d'Astrophysique, Université Libre de Bruxelles,
CP-226, 1050 Brussels, Belgium*
E-mail: nicolas.chamel@ulb.be

A. F. Fantina

Grand Accélérateur National d'Ions Lourds (GANIL), CEA/DRF - CNRS/IN2P3, Boulevard Henri Becquerel, 14076 Caen, France

Institut d'Astronomie et d'Astrophysique, CP-226, Boulevard du Triomphe, Université Libre de Bruxelles, 1050 Brussels, Belgium

D. Chatterjee and S. Ghosh

Inter-University Centre for Astronomy and Astrophysics, Post Bag 4, Ganeshkhind, Pune University Campus, Pune, 411007, India

J. Novak and M. Oertel

LUTH, Observatoire de Paris, PSL Research University, CNRS, Université Paris Diderot, Sorbonne Paris Cité, 5 place Jules Janssen, 92195 Meudon, France

Electron captures by atomic nuclei in dense matter are among the most important processes governing the late evolution of stars, limiting in particular the stability of white dwarfs. Despite considerable progress in the determination of the equation of state of dense Coulomb plasmas, the threshold electron Fermi energies are still generally estimated from the corresponding Q values in vacuum. Moreover, most studies have focused on nonmagnetized matter. However, some white dwarfs are endowed with magnetic fields reaching 10^9 G. Even more extreme magnetic fields might exist in super Chandrasekhar white dwarfs, the progenitors of overluminous type Ia supernovae like SN 2006gz and SN 2009dc. The roles of the dense stellar medium and magnetic fields on the onset of electron captures and on the structure of white dwarfs are briefly reviewed. New analytical formulas are derived to evaluate the threshold density for the onset of electron captures for arbitrary magnetic fields. Their influence on the structure of white dwarfs is illustrated by simple analytical formulas and numerical calculations.

Keywords: White dwarf; Chandrasekhar limit; Electron capture; Magnetic field.

1. Introduction

In 1926, the British physicist Ralph Fowler showed that the energy and the pressure of matter in the dense core of a white dwarf remain finite at zero temperature due to quantum mechanics. Considering that electrons are no longer bound to nuclei under such extreme conditions, he derived the equation of state of a degenerate electron Fermi gas.[1] Another British physicist, Edmund Clifton Stoner, calculated the structure of white dwarfs with uniform density in 1929.[2] The same year, Wilhelm Anderson, a physicist at the University of Tartu in Estonia, first stressed the importance of taking into account the relativistic motion of electrons.[3] He showed that the mass of a white dwarf tends to some finite value as the electron concentration increases, namely $M_{\mathrm{And}} \sim 0.69 M_\odot$ assuming an electron fraction $y_e = 0.4$ (with $M_\odot$ the mass of the Sun). Improving Anderson's approximate treatment, Stoner[4] found $M_{\mathrm{St}} \simeq 1.10 M_\odot$. Soon afterwards, the young Indian physicist Subrahmanyan Chandrasekhar solved the hydrostatic equilibrium equations for an ultrarelativistic electron Fermi gas using the theory of polytropes.[5] His numerical result, $M_{\mathrm{Ch}} \simeq 0.91 M_\odot$ (for $y_e = 0.4$), thus differed by less than 20% from that obtained earlier by Stoner, a remarkably close agreement as pointed out by Chandrasekhar himself. A year later, the Russian physicist Lev Landau showed that any degenerate star has a maximum mass, which can be expressed in terms of the fundamental constants as

$$M_{\mathrm{L}} = 3.1 \frac{m_{\mathrm{P}}^3}{m^2} y_e^2, \tag{1}$$

where we have introduced the Planck mass

$$m_{\mathrm{P}} = \sqrt{\frac{\hbar c}{G}}, \tag{2}$$

($\hbar$ is the Planck-Dirac constant, c is the speed of light, G is the constant of gravitation) and m is the average mass per nucleon. Incidentally, such a scaling was already apparent in Stoner's analysis of a uniform density star. Combining his equations (17) and (19b) leads to

$$M_{\mathrm{St}} = \frac{15\sqrt{5\pi}}{16} \frac{m_{\mathrm{P}}^3}{m^2} y_e^2. \tag{3}$$

Landau however did not believe in the physical reality of this limit and even invoked some violation of the laws of quantum mechanics inside massive stars to prevent them from collapsing (see Ref. 6 for a historical perspective on Landau's contribution). As early as 1928, the process by which atoms are crushed at high densities was actually discussed by the Russian physicist Yakov Frenkel.[7] More importantly, he calculated the equation of state of an electron Fermi gas for an arbitrary degree of relativistic motion as well as the correction due to electrostatic interactions between electrons and atomic nuclei. He also studied the conditions for which incompressible "superdense stars" can exist and derived indirectly the mass limit. Correcting for an error in his expression for the gravitational energy[a] and neglecting the electrostatic correction lead to the same result as the one published by Stoner in 1930. Frenkel's pioneer work remained unnoticed during several decades, and is still not very well-known today.[8]

---

[a]The factor 5/3 in his key equation (19a) should read 3/5; this error goes back to his incorrect expression (18) for the gravitational energy.

The analyses of Anderson and Stoner showed that the maximum mass of white dwarfs is only reached asymptotically when the electron concentration tends to infinity and the stellar radius goes to zero. This conclusion was later confirmed by the numerical calculations of Chandrasekhar for more realistic density profiles.[9] However, soon after the discovery of the neutron by James Chadwick in 1932, it was realized that matter becomes predominantly composed of neutrons at high densities.[10,11] In December 1933, during a meeting of the American Physical Society at Stanford, Wilhelm Baade and Fritz Zwicky predicted the existence of *neutron stars* formed from the catastrophic gravitational collapse of stars during supernova explosions.[12] Baade and Zwicky were apparently unaware of the studies about white dwarfs. The connection was first made by Landau[13] and Gamow.[14] At a conference in Paris in 1939, Chandrasekhar also pointed out[15]:

> If the degenerate core attains sufficiently high densities, the protons and electrons will combine to form neutrons. This would cause a sudden diminution of pressure resulting in the collapse of the star to a neutron core.

In 1956, the French physicist Evry Schatzman[16] showed that the central density of white dwarfs is limited by the onset of electron captures by nuclei, implying that the radius of the most massive white dwarfs remains *finite*. Detailed calculations of the structure of white dwarfs taking into account matter neutronization were performed at the end of the 1950s and at the beginning of the 1960s.[17–19] Electron captures are now known to play a key role in the late stages of stellar evolution (see Ref. 20 for a recent review).

Although the electrostatic correction to the equation of state of an electron Fermi gas was calculated long ago[7] (see Ref. 21 and references therein for the latest developments on the equation of state of dense Coulomb plasmas), the threshold electron Fermi energy μ_e for the onset of electron captures by nuclei is still generally estimated from the corresponding Q value in *vacuum*. Moreover, the presence of magnetic fields is usually ignored. However, a significant fraction of white dwarfs have been found[22] to have magnetic fields up to 10^9 G, and potentially much stronger fields may exist in their core.[23] Moreover, it has been recently proposed that very massive so-called super-Chandrasekhar white dwarfs (with a mass $M \gtrsim 2M_\odot$) endowed with extremely strong magnetic fields could be the progenitors of overluminous type Ia supernovae like SN 2006gz and SN 2009dc[24–26] (see also Refs. 27–30). The existence of such stars was actually first studied much earlier by Shul'man,[31] who found that the maximum mass of degenerate stars could be increased by two orders of magnitude if the magnetic field is strongly quantizing.[32,33] However, the stability of such super Chandrasekhar white dwarfs will still be limited by electron captures.[34,35] Detailed calculations of the global structure of these stars taking these processes into account have been carried out in Refs. 36, 37.

In this paper, we review our recent studies of the role of electron-ion interactions and magnetic fields in the onset of electron captures in cold white-dwarf cores.[36,38]

We also present more accurate and more general formulas for the threshold density and pressure, applicable not only to nonmagnetic and strongly magnetized white dwarfs but also to stars with intermediate magnetic field strengths. The impact of electron captures on the global structure of white dwarfs is discussed and new numerical results are presented.

2. Core of white dwarfs with magnetic fields

The core of a white dwarf consists of a dense Coulomb plasma of nuclei in a charge compensating background of relativistic electrons. Apart from carbon and oxygen (the primary ashes of helium burning), the core may contain other nuclei like helium,[39–41] neon and magnesium,[42] or even iron.[43,44] Iron white dwarfs could be formed from the explosive ignition of electron degenerate oxygen-neon-magnesium cores,[45] or from failed detonation supernovae.[46] For simplicity, we assume that the stellar core is made of only one type of nuclei with charge number Z and mass number A (see, e.g. Ref. 38 for the treatment of mixtures). We further suppose that the star has sufficiently cooled down such that thermal effects can be neglected.

Whereas nuclei with number density n_N exert a negligible pressure $P_N = 0$, they contribute to the mass density

$$\rho = n_N M'(A, Z), \tag{4}$$

where $M'(A, Z)$ denotes the ion mass including the rest mass of Z electrons and can be obtained from the experimental *atomic* mass $M(A, Z)$ by subtracting out the binding energy of the atomic electrons (see Eq. (A4) of Ref. 47). In principle, the presence of a magnetic field can have some effect on nuclei.[48,49] However, the change of nuclear masses is negligible even for the strongest magnetic fields of order 10^{15} G expected in super Chandrasekhar white dwarfs.[29,36,50]

To a very good approximation, electrons can be treated as an ideal Fermi gas. In the presence of a magnetic field, the electron motion perpendicular to the field is quantized into Landau-Rabi levels.[51,52] Quantization effects on the equation of state are significant when B exceeds $B_{\rm rel}$, where

$$B_{\rm rel} \equiv \frac{m_e^2 c^3}{e\hbar} \approx 4.4 \times 10^{13} \text{ G}, \tag{5}$$

where m_e is the electron mass and e is the elementary electric charge. The expressions for the energy density $\mathcal{E}_e$ and pressure P_e for arbitrary magnetic field strength can be found in Ref. 53.

The main correction to the ideal electron Fermi gas arises from the electron-ion interactions, as first shown by Frenkel[7] (see e.g. Ref. 53 for a discussion of higher-order corrections). For pointlike ions embedded in a uniform electron gas with number density $n_e = Z n_N$ (from electric charge neutrality), the corresponding energy density is given by (see e.g. Chap. 2 of Ref. 53)

$$\mathcal{E}_L = C_M \left(\frac{4\pi}{3}\right)^{1/3} e^2 n_e^{4/3} Z^{2/3}, \tag{6}$$

where C_M is the Madelung constant. The contribution to the pressure is thus given by

$$P_L = n_e^2 \frac{d(\mathcal{E}_L/n_e)}{dn_e} = \frac{\mathcal{E}_L}{3}. \tag{7}$$

The pressure of the Coulomb plasma finally reads $P = P_e + P_L$.

In the following, we shall consider that ions are arranged in a body-centered cubic lattice since this configuration leads to the lowest energy.[53] In this case, the Madelung constant is given by[54] $C_M = -0.895929255682$. According to the Bohr-van Leeuwen theorem,[55] the electrostatic corrections (6) and (7) are independent of the magnetic field apart from a negligibly small contribution due to quantum zero-point motion of ions about their equilibrium position.[56]

3. Onset of electron captures by nuclei in dense environments

The onset of electron captures by nuclei (A, Z) is formally determined by the same condition irrespective of the magnetic field strength by requiring the constancy of the Gibbs free energy per nucleon at fixed temperature and pressure.[38] The threshold electron Fermi energy is found to first order in the fine-structure constant $\alpha = e^2/(\hbar c)$ from the condition:

$$\gamma_e + C_M \left(\frac{4\pi n_e}{3}\right)^{1/3} \alpha \lambda_e F(Z) = \gamma_e^\beta(A, Z), \tag{8}$$

$$F(Z) \equiv Z^{5/3} - (Z-1)^{5/3} + \frac{1}{3} Z^{2/3}, \tag{9}$$

$$\gamma_e^\beta(A, Z) \equiv -\frac{Q_{\rm EC}(A, Z)}{m_e c^2} + 1, \tag{10}$$

where $\gamma_e \equiv \mu_e/(m_e c^2)$, $\lambda_e = \hbar/(m_e c)$ is the electron Compton wavelength, and we have introduced the Q-value (in vacuum) associated with electron capture by nuclei (A, Z):

$$Q_{\rm EC}(A, Z) = M'(A, Z)c^2 - M'(A, Z-1)c^2. \tag{11}$$

These Q-values can be obtained from the tabulated Q-values of β decay by the following relation:

$$Q_{\rm EC}(A, Z) = -Q_\beta(A, Z-1). \tag{12}$$

In principle, the daughter nucleus may be in an excited state. However, such a transition would occur at a higher density.

In the absence of magnetic fields, the threshold condition (8) can be solved analytically.[57] Recalling that the electron Fermi energy is given by

$$\mu_e = m_e c^2 \sqrt{1 + x_r^2}, \tag{13}$$

where $x_r = \lambda_e k_e$ and $k_e = (3\pi^2 n_e)^{1/3}$ is the electron Fermi wave number, the solution reads

$$x_r^\beta = \gamma_e^\beta \left\{\sqrt{1 - \left[1 - \tilde{F}(Z)^2\right]/(\gamma_e^\beta)^2} - \tilde{F}(Z)\right\}\left[1 - \tilde{F}(Z)^2\right]^{-1}, \quad (14)$$

with

$$\tilde{F}(Z) \equiv C_M \left(\frac{4}{9\pi}\right)^{1/3} \alpha F(Z). \quad (15)$$

The pressure $P_\beta(A, Z)$ at the onset of electron captures is given by

$$P_\beta(A, Z) = \frac{m_e c^2}{8\pi^2 \lambda_e^3}\left[x_r^\beta \left(\frac{2}{3}(x_r^\beta)^2 - 1\right)\sqrt{1 + (x_r^\beta)^2} + \ln(x_r^\beta + \sqrt{1 + (x_r^\beta)^2})\right]$$

$$+ \frac{C_M \alpha}{3}\left(\frac{4}{243\pi^7}\right)^{1/3}(x_r^\beta)^4 \frac{m_e c^2}{\lambda_e^3} Z^{2/3}. \quad (16)$$

The corresponding average mass density is found from Eq. (4) and is given by

$$\rho_\beta(A, Z) = \frac{M'(A, Z)}{Z}\frac{(x_r^\beta)^3}{3\pi^2 \lambda_e^3}. \quad (17)$$

Numerical results are summarized in Table 1 for nuclei expected to be found in the core of white dwarfs, using data from the 2020 Atomic Mass Evaluation.[58] Fundamental constants were taken from NIST CODATA 2018[b]. We have not considered helium since this element is expected to undergo pycnonuclear fusion in white-dwarf cores before capturing electrons.

Table 1. Dimensionless threshold electron Fermi energy $\gamma_e = \mu_e/(m_e c^2)$, mass density ρ_β and pressure P_β for the onset of electron captures by the given nuclei in unmagnetized white dwarfs.

	^{16}O	^{12}C	^{20}Ne	^{24}Mg	^{56}Fe
γ_e	22.0	27.8	15.2	12.2	8.74
ρ_β [g cm^{-3}]	2.06×10^{10}	4.16×10^{10}	6.81×10^9	3.51×10^9	1.37×10^9
P_β [dyn cm^{-2}]	2.73×10^{28}	6.99×10^{28}	6.21×10^{27}	2.56×10^{27}	6.46×10^{26}

In the presence of a magnetic field, the threshold condition (8) must be solved using the following relation between n_e and γ_e:

$$n_e = \frac{2B_\star}{(2\pi)^2 \lambda_e^3}\sum_{\nu=0}^{\nu_{\max}} g_\nu x_e(\nu), \quad (18)$$

$$x_e(\nu) = \sqrt{\gamma_e^2 - 1 - 2\nu B_\star}, \quad (19)$$

---
[b]https://physics.nist.gov/cuu/Constants/index.html

where we have introduced $B_\star \equiv B/B_{\text{rel}}$, and the degeneracy $g_\nu = 1$ for $\nu = 0$ and $g_\nu = 2$ for $\nu \geq 1$. The index $\nu_{\max}$ is the highest integer for which $\gamma_e^2 - 1 - 2\nu_{\max} B_\star \geq 0$, i.e.

$$\nu_{\max} = \left[\frac{\gamma_e^2 - 1}{2B_\star}\right], \tag{20}$$

where $[.]$ denotes the integer part.

In the weakly quantizing regime meaning that many Landau-Rabi levels are populated ($\nu_{\max} \gg 1$), analytical solutions can be found. Remarking that the magnetic field enters explicitly in (8) only through the small electrostatic correction, the threshold electron Fermi energy is still approximately given by the solution in the absence of magnetic fields, namely $\gamma_e \approx \sqrt{1 + (x_r^\beta)^2}$ with x_r^β given by (14). Substituting in Eqs. (18) and (19), using the expansions (41) obtained in Ref. 59 leads to the following estimate for the density marking the onset of electron captures:

$$\rho_\beta(A, Z) \approx \frac{M'(A, Z)}{2\pi^2 Z \lambda_e^3} \left[\frac{2}{3}(\gamma_e^2 - 1)^{3/2} + (2B_\star)^{3/2} \zeta\left(\frac{-1}{2}, \left\{\frac{\gamma_e^2 - 1}{2B_\star}\right\}\right) + \frac{B_\star^2}{6\sqrt{\gamma_e^2 - 1}}\right], \tag{21}$$

where $\zeta(z, q)$ is the Hurwitz zeta function defined by

$$\zeta(z, q) = \sum_{\nu=0}^{+\infty} \frac{1}{(\nu + q)^z} \tag{22}$$

for $\Re(z) > 1$ and by analytic continuation to other $z \neq 1$ (excluding poles $\nu + q = 0$), and $\{.\}$ in the argument denotes the fractional part. The first term in Eq. (21) represents the threshold density in the absence of magnetic field. The second term accounts for magnetic oscillations while the last term is a higher-order correction. The expression for the associated pressure is more involved. Using Eqs. (41), (43) and (44) of Ref. 59 yields[c]

$$P_\beta(A, Z) \approx \frac{m_e c^2}{4\pi^2 \lambda_e^3} \left\{\frac{1}{2}\left(1 - 2B_\star + \frac{2B_\star^2}{3}\right) \log\left(\frac{\gamma_e + \sqrt{2B_\star + \gamma_e^2 - 1}}{1 + \sqrt{2B_\star}}\right)\right.$$
$$-\frac{1}{2}\left(\gamma_e \sqrt{2B_\star + \gamma_e^2 - 1} - \sqrt{2B_\star}\right) + \frac{1}{3}\left(\gamma_e \sqrt{2B_\star + \gamma_e^2 - 1}^3 - \sqrt{2B_\star}^3\right)$$
$$+ B_\star\left(\text{arccosh}\,\gamma_e - \gamma_e \sqrt{\gamma_e^2 - 1}\right) - (2B_\star)^{5/2} \int_0^{+\infty} \frac{\tilde{\zeta}_3(-1/2, q + 1)}{\sqrt{1 + 2B_\star q}} dq$$

---

[c] In the notations of Ref. 59, the electron contribution to the pressure can be directly obtained from the grand potential density by $P_e = -\omega_0^{(\text{mon})} - \omega_0^{(\text{osc})}$. The total pressure is found by adding the electrostatic correction (7) using the expansion for the electron density.

$$+\frac{2}{3}\frac{(2B_\star)^{5/2}}{\gamma_e}\zeta\left(\frac{-3}{2},\left\{\frac{\gamma_e^2-1}{2B_\star}\right\}\right)+\frac{2}{15}\frac{(2B_\star)^{7/2}}{\gamma_e^3}\zeta\left(\frac{-5}{2},\left\{\frac{\gamma_e^2-1}{2B_\star}\right\}\right)$$
$$+\frac{1}{240}\left(\frac{B_\star}{\gamma_e}\right)^4+4B_\star^2\int_0^1 \zeta\left(\frac{-1}{2},q\right)\zeta\left(\frac{1}{2},q+\frac{1}{2B_\star}\right)dq$$
$$+\frac{2}{3}\left(\frac{2}{3\pi}\right)^{1/3}C_M\alpha Z^{2/3}\left[\frac{2}{3}\left(\gamma_e^2-1\right)^{3/2}\right.$$
$$\left.+(2B_\star)^{3/2}\zeta\left(\frac{-1}{2},\left\{\frac{\gamma_e^2-1}{2B_\star}\right\}\right)+\frac{B_\star^2}{6\sqrt{\gamma_e^2-1}}\right]^{4/3}\bigg\}, \quad (23)$$

with

$$\tilde{\zeta}_3(z,q)=\zeta(z,q)-\frac{1}{z-1}q^{-z+1}-\frac{1}{2}q^{-z}-\frac{z}{12}q^{-z-1}. \quad (24)$$

An analytical solution also exists in the strongly quantizing regime whereby electrons are all confined to the lowest Landau-Rabi level ($\nu_{\max}=0$). Introducing

$$\bar{F}(Z,B_\star)\equiv\frac{1}{3}C_M\alpha F(Z)\left(\frac{2B_\star}{3\pi}\right)^{1/3}<0, \quad (25)$$

$$v\equiv\frac{\gamma_e^\beta}{2|\bar{F}(Z,B_\star)|^{3/2}}, \quad (26)$$

the solutions are given by the following formulas[60]:

$$\gamma_e=\begin{cases}8|\bar{F}(Z,B_\star)|^{3/2}\cosh^3\left(\frac{1}{3}\operatorname{arccosh} v\right) & \text{if } v\geq 1,\\ 8|\bar{F}(Z,B_\star)|^{3/2}\cos^3\left(\frac{1}{3}\arccos v\right) & \text{if } 0\leq v<1.\end{cases} \quad (27)$$

The threshold pressure and density are respectively given by:

$$P_\beta(A,Z,B_\star)=\frac{B_\star m_e c^2}{4\pi^2\lambda_e^3}\left[\gamma_e\sqrt{\gamma_e^2-1}-\ln\left(\sqrt{\gamma_e^2-1}+\gamma_e\right)\right.$$
$$\left.+\frac{C_M\alpha}{3}\left(\frac{16B_\star Z^2}{3\pi}\right)^{1/3}(\gamma_e^2-1)^{2/3}\right], \quad (28)$$

$$\rho_\beta(A,Z,B_\star)=\frac{B_\star}{2\pi^2\lambda_e^3}\frac{M'(A,Z)}{Z}\sqrt{\gamma_e^2-1}. \quad (29)$$

Let us recall that Eq. (27) is only valid if all electrons lie in the lowest Landau-Rabi level, i.e. if their Fermi energy does not exceed $\gamma_e=\sqrt{1+2B_\star}\approx\sqrt{2B_\star}$ or equivalently if their density does not exceed $n_e=B_\star^{3/2}/(\sqrt{2}\pi^2\lambda_e^3)$ using Eqs. (18) and (19).

This condition translates into a lower bound for the magnetic field $B_\star \geq B_{\star 1}$. To find $B_{\star 1}$, we substitute the above expressions for γ_e and n_e in Eq. (8). This leads to

$$B_{\star 1} = \frac{(\gamma_e^\beta)^2}{2}\left[1 + \frac{C_M \alpha}{(3\pi)^{1/3}} F(Z)\right]^{-2}. \tag{30}$$

Values for some nuclei are summarized in Table 2. For magnetic field strength $B_\star \lesssim B_{\star 1}$, the threshold condition (8) must be solved numerically.

Table 2. Magnetic field strength in units of $B_{\rm rel}$ above which electrons are confined to the lowest Rabi level when captured by the given nuclei.

^{16}O	^{12}C	^{20}Ne	^{24}Mg	^{56}Fe
240	384	115	74.1	37.8

Full results for different nuclei expected to be found in white-dwarf cores are shown in Figs. 1 and 2. Changes in the occupation of Rabi levels as the magnetic field is increased lead to typical oscillations of the threshold density ρ_β: the onset of electron captures can thus be shifted to either lower or higher density as compared to unmagnetized matter. The lowest value is reached for $B_\star = B_{\star 1}$ and lies about 25% below the threshold density in the absence of magnetic fields irrespective of the composition (this can be easily shown by taking the ratio of Eqs. (29) and (17) using (30) and ignoring all terms in α). In the strongly quantizing regime, ρ_β is unbound from above and increases almost linearly with $B_\star$.

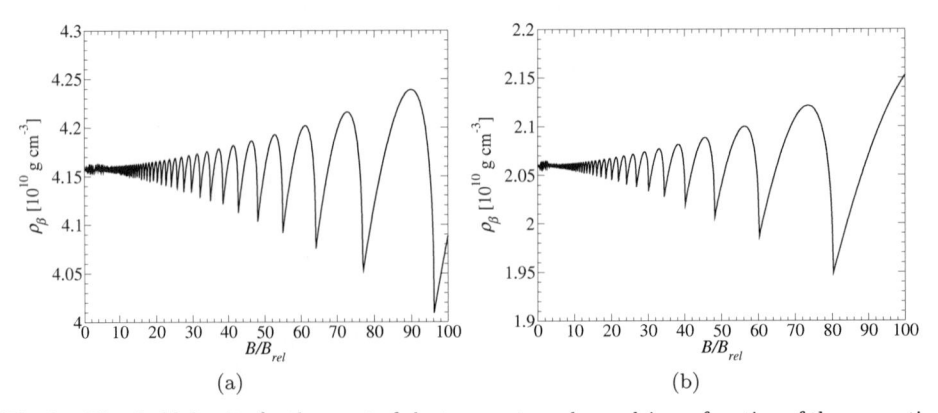

Fig. 1. Threshold density for the onset of electron captures by nuclei as a function of the magnetic field strength in units of the characteristic field (5). (a) Results for ^{12}C. (b) Results for ^{16}O.

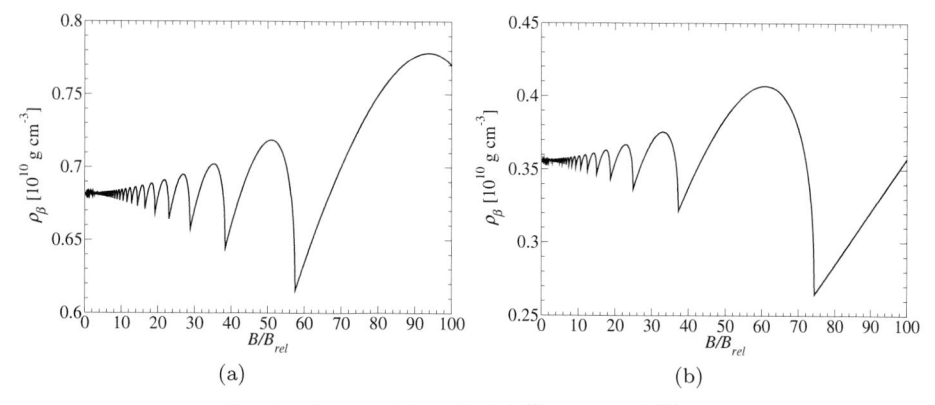

Fig. 2. Same as Fig. 1 for (a) ^{20}Ne and (b) ^{24}Mg.

4. Global structure of white dwarfs

The core of a white dwarf is expected to be surrounded by a helium mantle and an hydrogen envelope. Their contribution to the mass of the star cannot exceed $\sim 1\%$ to avoid a thermonuclear runaway. For simplicity, we will ignore these layers here.

In the model originally considered by Chandrasekhar,[5] the interior of a white dwarf was described using the equation of state of an ideal electron Fermi gas. The composition, assumed to be uniform, was only included throughout the charge neutrality condition. In the ultrarelativistic limit, the resulting equation of state reduces to the polytropic form $P \approx K_0 \rho^{4/3}$ with

$$K_0 = \frac{\hbar c (3\pi^2)^{1/3}}{4} \left(\frac{Z}{M'(A,Z)} \right)^{4/3}. \tag{31}$$

The mass and radius of a white dwarf with central density ρ_c can be deduced from the theory of polytropes[61]

$$M_{\rm Ch} = 4\pi \left(\frac{K_0}{\pi G} \right)^{3/2} \xi_1^2 |\theta'(\xi_1)|, \tag{32}$$

$$R_{\rm Ch} = \sqrt{\frac{K_0}{\pi G}} \frac{\xi_1}{\rho_c^{1/3}} \tag{33}$$

respectively, where $\xi_1 \simeq 6.89685$ and $\xi_1^2 |\theta'(\xi_1)| \simeq 2.01824$. Substituting the expression for K_0 thus yields

$$M_{\rm Ch} = \frac{\sqrt{3\pi}}{2} \xi_1^2 |\theta'(\xi_1)| \frac{m_{\rm P}^3}{m^2} y_e^2 \simeq 3.09798 \frac{m_{\rm P}^3}{m^2} y_e^2, \tag{34}$$

$$R_{\rm Ch} = \frac{\sqrt{3\pi}}{2} \xi_1 \lambda_e \frac{m_{\rm P}}{m} \frac{y_e}{x_{r,c}} \simeq 10.5866 \lambda_e \frac{m_{\rm P}}{m} \frac{y_e}{x_{r,c}}, \tag{35}$$

where
$$m \equiv \frac{M'(A,Z)}{A}, \qquad (36)$$

and $x_{r,c}$ denotes the relativity parameter at the density ρ_c. Equation (34) coincides with the maximum mass because the ultrarelativistic regime is only valid at high densities such that the relativity parameter in the central core of the star satisfies $x_{r,c} \gg 1$. In the limit $x_{r,c} \to +\infty$, the radius $R_{\rm Ch}$ vanishes.

The electrostatic corrections (6) and (7) can be easily taken into account by simply renormalizing the constant K_0 as

$$K = K_0 \left[1 + \alpha \frac{8 C_M}{6} \left(\frac{4}{9\pi} \right)^{1/3} Z^{2/3} \right]. \qquad (37)$$

The mass and radius thus become[d]

$$M = \left[1 + \alpha \frac{8 C_M}{6} \left(\frac{4}{9\pi} \right)^{1/3} Z^{2/3} \right]^{3/2} M_{\rm Ch} < M_{\rm Ch}, \qquad (38)$$

$$R = R_{\rm Ch} \left[1 + \alpha \frac{8 C_M}{6} \left(\frac{4}{9\pi} \right)^{1/3} Z^{2/3} \right]^{1/2} < R_{\rm Ch}. \qquad (39)$$

This shows how the electron-ion interactions lower both the mass and the radius. It can be seen that the radius of the most massive white dwarfs still vanishes in the limit $x_{r,c} \to +\infty$. However, as discussed earlier, nuclei in the white dwarf core will capture electrons as soon as the central density ρ_c exceeds the threshold density ρ_β. The daughter nuclei are generally unstable against a second electron capture. The transition is accompanied by a discontinuous increase of density given by

$$\frac{\Delta \rho}{\rho_\beta} = \frac{Z}{Z-2} \frac{M'(A, Z-2)}{M'(A,Z)} \left[1 + \alpha C_M \left(\frac{4}{9\pi} \right)^{1/3} \left(Z^{2/3} - (Z-2)^{2/3} \right) \frac{\sqrt{1+x_r^2}}{x_r} \right] - 1, \qquad (40)$$

where x_r is given by Eq. (14). The density jump is about 50% for carbon, 33% for oxygen, 25% for neon, 20% for magnesium, and 8.2% for iron.

Because these reactions occur at the same pressure, the adiabatic index defined by

$$\Gamma = \frac{d \log P}{d \log \rho} \qquad (41)$$

therefore vanishes thus making the star unstable. In the limit of ultrarelativistic electrons, the average threshold density and pressure reduce to

$$\rho_\beta(A,Z) \approx \frac{M'(A,Z)}{Z} \frac{\mu_e^\beta(A,Z)^3}{3\pi^2(\hbar c)^3} \left[1 + \alpha C_M \left(\frac{4}{9\pi} \right)^{1/3} F(Z) \right]^{-3}, \qquad (42)$$

---

[d] Such kind of scaling was briefly mentioned in Ref. 19 through an effective mean molecular weight per electron.

$$P_\beta(A, Z) \approx \frac{\mu_e^\beta(A,Z)^4}{12\pi^2(\hbar c)^3}\left[1 + 4C_M\alpha Z^{2/3}\left(\frac{4}{243\pi}\right)^{1/3}\right]\left[1 + \alpha C_M\left(\frac{4}{9\pi}\right)^{1/3}F(Z)\right]^{-4}.$$
(43)

Substituting Eq. (42) in (39) using (35) leads to the following lower bound for the radius of a white dwarf:

$$R_{\min} = \frac{\sqrt{3\pi}}{2}\xi_1\lambda_e\frac{m_P}{m}\frac{y_e}{\gamma_e^\beta(A,Z)}\left[1 + \alpha C_M\left(\frac{4}{9\pi}\right)^{1/3}F(Z)\right]$$

$$\times\left[1 + \alpha\frac{8C_M}{6}\left(\frac{4}{9\pi}\right)^{1/3}Z^{2/3}\right]^{1/2}.$$
(44)

The factors in square brackets account for the electron-ion interactions: the first arises from the shift in the threshold density for the onset of electron captures whereas the second is due to the correction to the equation of state. Both factors lead to a reduction of the radius. Results of Eq. (44) are summarized in Table 3.

Table 3. Minimum radius (in km) of nonmagnetic stable white dwarfs.

^{12}C	^{16}O	^{20}Ne	^{24}Mg	^{56}Fe
958	1209	1743	2168	2791

The mass remains unchanged since it does not depend on the density and is still given by Eq. (38). However, departure from the polytropic equation of state $P = K\rho^{4/3}$ and the fact that the central density ρ_c is finite induce a slight reduction of the maximum mass. Following the perturbative approach described in Chapter 6 of Ref. 62 and based on the minimization of some approximation for the total energy of the star, we find

$$\frac{\delta M}{M} \approx -\frac{k_3}{k_2}\frac{3\pi}{(\gamma_e^\beta)^2}\left(\frac{3}{2\xi_1^4|\theta'(\xi_1)|^2}\right)^{1/3}\left[1 + \alpha\frac{8C_M}{6}\left(\frac{4}{9\pi}\right)^{1/3}Z^{2/3}\right]^{-1}$$

$$\times\left[1 + \alpha C_M\left(\frac{4}{9\pi}\right)^{1/3}F(Z)\right]^2$$
(45)

where $k_2 = 0.639001$ and $k_3 = 0.519723$. Results are summarized in Table 4. The influence of electron captures and electron-ion interactions are all the more important that matter contains heavier elements: whereas the overall reduction of the Chandrasekhar mass M_{Ch} amounts to 3% for carbon, it reaches 13% for iron.

The stability of a white dwarf can be further limited by general relativity, as first shown by Kaplan.[63] The critical density above which the stellar core becomes unstable can be estimated from the minimization of the total energy. Including the electrostatic correction in Eq.(6.10.28) of Ref. 62 we find

$$\rho_{\text{GR}} = \frac{16k_3(k_2)^2}{(3\pi^2)^{2/3}k_4(k_1)^2}\frac{M'(A,Z)^2}{Z^2\lambda_e^3 m_e}\left[1 + \alpha\frac{8C_M}{6}\left(\frac{4}{9\pi}\right)^{1/3}Z^{2/3}\right]^{-2} \text{ g cm}^{-3}, \quad (46)$$

Table 4. Maximum mass (in solar units) of nonmagnetic white dwarfs for an ultra-relativistic electron Fermi gas (first line), with electrostatic correction (second line) and electron captures (third line).

^{12}C	^{16}O	^{20}Ne	^{24}Mg	^{56}Fe
1.456	1.457	1.457	1.458	1.259
1.424	1.418	1.411	1.406	1.184
1.413	1.401	1.377	1.353	1.095

where $k_1 = 1.75579$ and $k_4 = 0.918294$. Because $C_M < 0$, electron-ion interactions thus make the star more stable. We have also solved the Tolman-Oppenheimer-Volkoff[64,65] equations for calculating the whole sequence of white dwarfs in full general relativity. In this way, we have determined more accurately the central (mass-energy) density ρ_{GR} at which $dM/d\rho_{GR} = 0$ marking the onset of instability. The hydrostatic equilibrium equations were integrated from the center of the star up to the point where electrons start to bind to nuclei at the density $\rho_{eip} = ZM'(A,Z)/a_0^3$ with a_0 the Bohr radius. Results are collected in Table 5. The values are systematically lower than those estimated from Eq. (46). Comparing Tables 1 and 5 shows that the central density is limited by general relativity rather than electron captures in carbon white dwarfs. Their mass-density relation is plotted in Fig. 3. The minimum radii and maximum masses of white dwarfs with different composition are indicated in Tables 6 and 7 respectively (note that the mass and radius of carbon white dwarfs at the onset of electron captures are respectively $1.484 M_\odot$ and 855 km). For comparison, results obtained by solving numerically the Newtonian hydrostatic equilibrium equations are also given. Examining Tables 3 and 6 reveals that the polytropic approximation is more reliable for estimating the maximum mass than the minimum radius.

Table 5. Highest density ρ_{GR} (in g cm^{-3}) in nonmagnetic stable white dwarfs in general relativity, as calculated by minimization of the approximate total energy (first line) and by solving the hydrostatic equilibrium equations (second line).

^{16}O	^{12}C	^{20}Ne	^{24}Mg	^{56}Fe
2.73×10^{10}	2.72×10^{10}	2.75×10^{10}	2.76×10^{10}	3.31×10^{10}
2.39×10^{10}	2.40×10^{10}	2.42×10^{10}	2.44×10^{10}	2.93×10^{10}

The influence of a very strong magnetic field on the structure of white dwarfs was studied in Ref. 24 within the theory of polytropes making use of the fact that $P \propto \rho^2$ in the strongly quantizing regime. However, it was soon realized that this assumption is unrealistic and that the influence of the magnetic field itself on the stellar structure cannot be ignored.[27,34,66–68] Moreover, the magnetic-field configuration inside the

Table 6. Minimum radius (in km) of nonmagnetic stable white dwarfs in Newtonian theory (first line) and general relativity (second line).

^{12}C	^{16}O	^{20}Ne	^{24}Mg	^{56}Fe
857.7	1055	1447	1736	2082
1010	1052	1444	1732	2079

Table 7. Maximum mass (in solar units) of nonmagnetic stable white dwarfs in Newtonian theory (first line) and general relativity (second line).

^{12}C	^{16}O	^{20}Ne	^{24}Mg	^{56}Fe
1.414	1.403	1.382	1.363	1.118
1.383	1.378	1.366	1.350	1.111

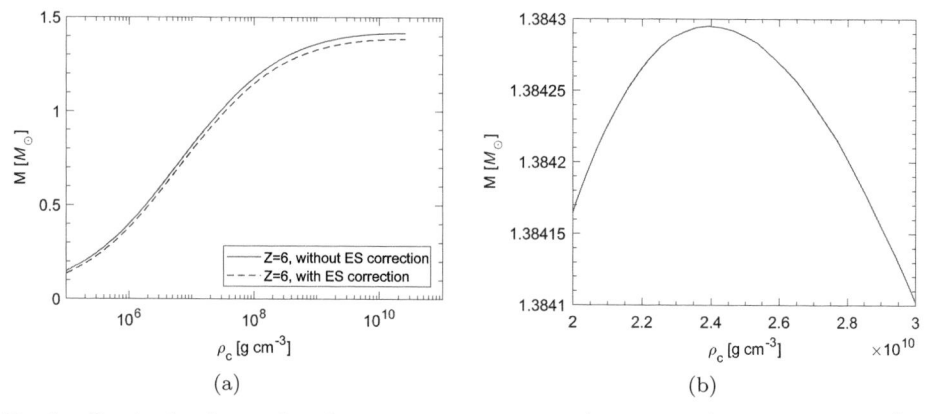

Fig. 3. Gravitational mass in solar masses versus central (mass-energy) density in g cm^{-3} of carbon white dwarfs in general relativity: (a) comparing results with and without electrostatic corrections, (b) closer view of results with electrostatic corrections around the critical point.

star should be calculated from Maxwell's equations consistently with the stellar equilibrium equations. For all these reasons, the structure of magnetic white dwarfs is not easily amenable to a simple analytical treatment.

To study the influence of strong magnetic fields and the role of electron captures in white dwarfs, we have thus computed fully self-consistently numerical solutions of the Einstein-Maxwell equations using the LORENE library,[69] suitably extended to allow for magnetic-field dependent equations of state and magnetization effects.[70] We have found that purely poloidal magnetic fields of order 10^{14} G lead to super Chandrasekhar white dwarfs with a mass $\sim 2M_\odot$. Although such magnetic fields have been found to have a rather small influence on the equation of state, they induce extreme stellar deformations with the most massive white dwarfs adopting a donut-like shape.[36] Similarly to nonmagnetic white dwarfs, electron captures limit the maximum mass and the minimum radius of magnetic white dwarfs, as summarized in Table 8. However, the distortion of the star induced by magnetic fields tends to lower their density. For the most extreme configurations, the maximum density thus lies below the threshold density for the onset of electron captures. The mass-radius relations for magnesium and neon white dwarfs are plotted in Fig. 4.

Table 8. Maximum mass (in solar units) of magnetic white dwarfs, as determined by extreme deformations or electron captures (values in parentheses) for different magnetic moments $\mathcal{M}$ in A m².

$\mathcal{M}$	^{12}C	^{16}O	^{20}Ne	^{24}Mg
10^{33}	1.41 (1.41)	1.41 (1.40)	1.40 (1.38)	1.39 (1.38)
5×10^{33}	1.60 (1.50)	1.59 (1.46)	1.59 (1.41)	1.58 (1.36)
10^{34}	2.00 (1.86)	1.97 (1.67)	1.97 (1.51)	1.96 (1.45)
2×10^{34}	1.99 (1.99)	1.96 (1.96)	1.97 (1.95)	1.95 (1.73)
3×10^{34}	1.96 (1.96)	1.94 (1.94)	1.98 (1.98)	1.97 (1.97)

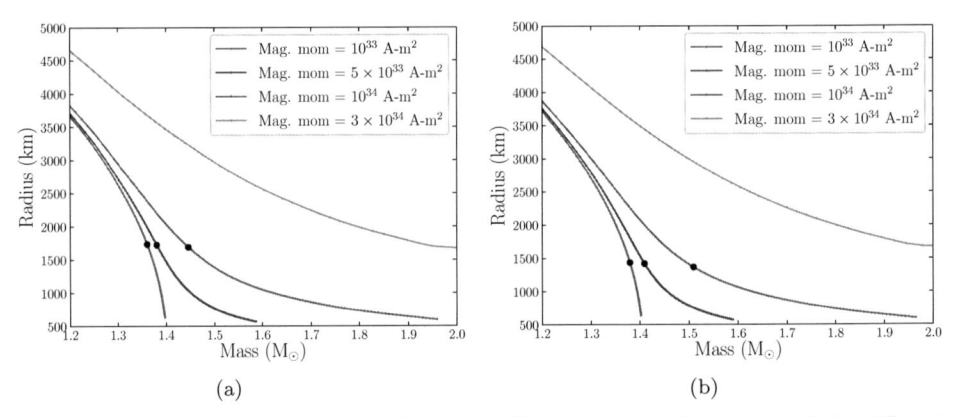

Fig. 4. Radius (in km) versus gravitational mass (in solar units) of white dwarfs for different magnetic moments: (a) for ^{24}Mg, (b) for ^{20}Ne. The onset of electron captures is marked by a filled circle.

The global stability criterion $\partial M/\partial \rho > 0$ still remains valid for magnetic white dwarfs provided the derivatives are evaluated for a fixed magnetic moment $\mathcal{M}$. As shown in Fig. 5, this instability is entirely removed by the presence of strong magnetic fields. In other words, the magnetic field makes the star more stable. In particular, the maximum mass of magnetic white dwarfs made of carbon is not limited by general relativity as their nonmagnetic relatives but by electron captures.

For magnetic white dwarfs to be the progenitors of overluminous type Ia supernova, i.e. to have masses $\sim 2 M_\odot$, their magnetic field must be strong enough. Their minimum observable polar magnetic fields are indicated in Table 9 for different compositions. In all cases, the magnetic dipole moment is 3×10^{34} A m^2.

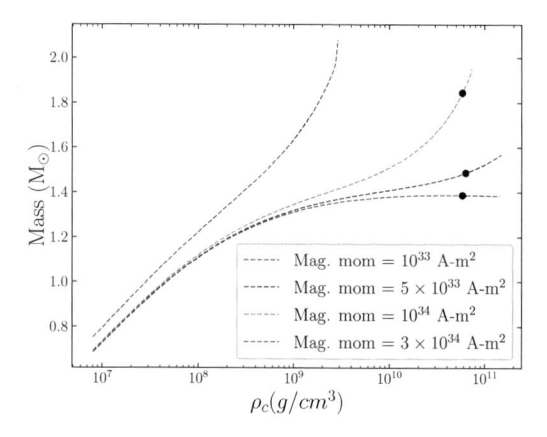

Fig. 5. Gravitational mass (in solar masses) versus central (mass-energy) density in g cm^{-3} of carbon white dwarfs in general relativity with given magnetic moments. The onset of electron captures is marked by a filled circle.

Table 9. Polar magnetic field (in 10^{13} G) of white dwarfs with $\mathcal{M} = 3 \times 10^{34}$ A m^2.

^{12}C	^{16}O	^{20}Ne	^{24}Mg
2.73	2.55	2.89	2.85

5. Conclusions

The stability of white dwarfs is limited by the onset of electron captures by nuclei in their core. We have presented very accurate analytical formulas for calculating the threshold electron Fermi energy, mass density and pressure in cold dense Coulomb plasmas with magnetic fields, taking into account Landau-Rabi quantization of electron motion. In particular, the density exhibits typical quantum oscillations associated with the filling of energy levels. As a consequence, electron captures in magnetic white dwarfs may occur at a lower or higher density than in their non-magnetic relatives depending on the magnetic field strength. The lowest possible density is found to lie about 25% below its value in the absence of magnetic field essentially independently of the composition. On the contrary, the density is not limited from above and increases almost linearly with the magnetic field strength in the strongly quantizing regime.

Taking into account electron-ion interactions using the polytropic approximation $P \approx K\rho^{4/3}$ with K given by Eq. (37), we have explicitly shown how electron captures alter the maximum mass of nonmagnetic white dwarfs and set a lower limit to their radius. We have also solved numerically the hydrostatic equilibrium equations using the full equation of state, both in Newtonian theory and in general relativity. We have found that electron captures reduce the maximum mass of white dwarfs by 3-13% compared to the Chandrasekhar model.

Solving the Einstein-Maxwell equations taking into account the magnetization of dense matter, we have found that white dwarfs with purely poloidal magnetic fields can be significantly more massive than their nonmagnetic relatives. We have also shown that the presence of strong magnetic fields makes the star more stable. The maximum mass of magnetic white dwarfs (including those made of carbon) is thus solely limited by electron captures. In turn, the large stellar deformations induced by the strongest magnetic fields lower the stellar density below the electron capture threshold. White dwarfs with polar magnetic fields exceeding 10^{13} G could thus be massive enough to explain overluminuous type Ia supernova independently of the composition of their core. On the other hand, a purely poloidal magnetic-field configuration is unstable. The magnetic field in super Chandrasekhar white dwarfs is expected to have both poloidal and toroidal components. The question as to whether such stars can exist still remains open.

Although the present study was focused on white dwarfs, it may be also of interest for neutron stars as electron captures by nuclei constituting the outer crust of magnetars may explain their persistent luminosity and outbursts.[71] The general analytical formulas for the threshold density and pressure could thus be applied to determine the precise locations of these reactions.

Acknowledgments

The work of N.C. was financially supported by F.R.S.-FNRS under Grant No. IISN 4.4502.19. L. P. is a FRIA grantee of F.R.S.-FNRS. This work was also supported by COST CA16214 and the CNRS International Research Project "Origine des éléments lourds dans l'univers: Astres Compacts et Nucléosynthèse (ACNu)".

References

1. R. H. Fowler, On dense matter, *MNRAS* **87**, 114 (December 1926).
2. E. C. Stoner, V. the limiting density in white dwarf stars, *Philos. Mag.* **7**, 63 (1929).
3. W. Anderson, Über die Grenzdichte der Materie und der Energie, *Z. Phys.* **56**, 851 (November 1929).
4. E. C. Stoner, Lxxxvii. the equilibrium of dense stars, *Philos. Mag.* **9**, 944 (1930).
5. S. Chandrasekhar, The Maximum Mass of Ideal White Dwarfs, *ApJ* **74**, p. 81 (July 1931).

6. D. G. Yakovlev, P. Haensel, G. Baym and C. Pethick, Lev Landau and the concept of neutron stars, *Physics Uspekhi* **56**, 289 (March 2013).
7. J. Frenkel, Zur wellenmechanischen Theorie der metallischen Leitfähigkeit, *Z. Phys.* **47**, 819 (November 1928).
8. D. G. Yakovlev, The article by Ya I Frenkel' on 'binding forces' and the theory of white dwarfs, *Physics Uspekhi* **37**, 609 (June 1994).
9. S. Chandrasekhar, The highly collapsed configurations of a stellar mass (Second paper), *MNRAS* **95**, 207 (January 1935).
10. T. E. Sterne, The equilibrium theory of the abundance of the elements: A statistical investigation of assemblies in equilibrium in which transmutations occur, *MNRAS* **93**, p. 736 (June 1933).
11. F. Hund, Materie unter sehr hohen Drucken und Temperaturen, *Ergebnisse der exakten Naturwissenschaften* **15**, p. 189 (January 1936).
12. W. Baade and F. Zwicky, Minutes of the stanford meeting, December 15-16, 1933, *Phys. Rev.* **45**, 130 (Jan 1934).
13. L. Landau, Origin of Stellar Energy, *Nature* **141**, 333 (February 1938).
14. G. Gamow, Physical Possibilities of Stellar Evolution, *Phys. Rev.* **55**, 718 (April 1939).
15. S. Chandrasekhar, The White Dwarfs and Their Importance for Theories of Stellar Evolution, in *Conférences du Collège de France, Colloque International d'Astrophysique III, 17-23 Juillet 1939*, 1941.
16. E. Schatzman, Influence of the nucleon-electron equilibrium on the internal structure of white dwarfs, *Astronomiceskij Zhurnal* **33**, p. 800 (1956).
17. E. Schatzman, *White Dwarfs* (North-Holland Publishing Company, 1958).
18. B. K. Harrison, M. Wakano and J. A. Wheeler, Matter-energy at high density: End point of thermonuclear evolution, in *Onzième Conseil de Physique Solvay, Stoops, Brussels*, 1958.
19. T. Hamada and E. E. Salpeter, Models for Zero-Temperature Stars., *ApJ* **134**, p. 683 (November 1961).
20. K. Langanke, G. Martínez-Pinedo and R. G. T. Zegers, Electron capture in stars, *Rep. Prog. Phys.* **84**, p. 066301 (June 2021).
21. A. S. Jermyn, J. Schwab, E. Bauer, F. X. Timmes and A. Y. Potekhin, Skye: A Differentiable Equation of State, *ApJ* **913**, p. 72 (May 2021).
22. L. Ferrario, D. de Martino and B. T. Gänsicke, Magnetic White Dwarfs, *Space Sci. Rev.* **191**, 111 (October 2015).
23. K. Fujisawa, S. Yoshida and Y. Eriguchi, Axisymmetric and stationary structures of magnetized barotropic stars with extremely strong magnetic fields deep inside, *MNRAS* **422**, 434 (May 2012).
24. U. Das and B. Mukhopadhyay, New Mass Limit for White Dwarfs: Super-Chandrasekhar Type Ia Supernova as a New Standard Candle, *Phys. Rev. Lett.* **110**, p. 071102 (February 2013).
25. U. Das and B. Mukhopadhyay, GRMHD formulation of highly super-Chandrasekhar magnetized white dwarfs: Stable configurations of non-spherical white dwarfs, *J. Cosmolol. Astropart. P.* **2015**, p. 016 (May 2015).
26. S. Subramanian and B. Mukhopadhyay, GRMHD formulation of highly super-Chandrasekhar rotating magnetized white dwarfs: Stable configurations of non-spherical white dwarfs, *MNRAS* **454**, 752 (November 2015).
27. P. Bera and D. Bhattacharya, Mass-radius relation of strongly magnetized white dwarfs: Nearly independent of Landau quantization, *MNRAS* **445**, 3951 (December 2014).

28. B. Franzon and S. Schramm, Effects of strong magnetic fields and rotation on white dwarf structure, *Phys. Rev. D* **92**, p. 083006 (October 2015).
29. P. Bera and D. Bhattacharya, Mass-radius relation of strongly magnetized white dwarfs: Dependence on field geometry, GR effects and electrostatic corrections to the EOS, *MNRAS* **456**, 3375 (March 2016).
30. P. Bera and D. Bhattacharya, A perturbation study of axisymmetric strongly magnetic degenerate stars: The case of super-Chandrasekhar white dwarfs, *MNRAS* **465**, 4026 (March 2017).
31. G. A. Shul'Man, Degenerate equilibrium stellar configurations with a frozen-in magnetic field, *Sov. Astron.* **20**, p. 689 (December 1976).
32. G. A. Shulman, Equilibrium Configurations of Degenerate Superstars in the Quantum Limit of a Frozen-In Magnetic Field, *Sov. Astron.* **33**, p. 393 (August 1989).
33. G. A. Shulman, Equilibrium and Stability of Degenerate Stars with a Frozen-In Quantizing Magnetic Field, *Sov. Astron.* **36**, p. 398 (August 1992).
34. N. Chamel, A. F. Fantina and P. J. Davis, Stability of super-Chandrasekhar magnetic white dwarfs, *Phys. Rev. D* **88**, p. 081301 (October 2013).
35. N. Chamel, E. Molter, A. F. Fantina and D. P. Arteaga, Maximum strength of the magnetic field in the core of the most massive white dwarfs, *Phys. Rev. D* **90**, p. 043002 (August 2014).
36. D. Chatterjee, A. F. Fantina, N. Chamel, J. Novak and M. Oertel, On the maximum mass of magnetized white dwarfs, *MNRAS* **469**, 95 (July 2017).
37. E. Otoniel, B. Franzon, G. A. Carvalho, M. Malheiro, S. Schramm and F. Weber, Strongly Magnetized White Dwarfs and Their Instability Due to Nuclear Processes, *ApJ* **879**, p. 46 (July 2019).
38. N. Chamel and A. F. Fantina, Electron capture instability in magnetic and nonmagnetic white dwarfs, *Phys. Rev. D* **92**, p. 023008 (July 2015).
39. G. Nelemans and T. M. Tauris, Formation of undermassive single white dwarfs and the influence of planets on late stellar evolution, *A&A* **335**, L85 (July 1998).
40. J. Liebert, P. Bergeron, D. Eisenstein, H. C. Harris, S. J. Kleinman, A. Nitta and J. Krzesinski, A Helium White Dwarf of Extremely Low Mass, *ApJ* **606**, L147 (May 2004).
41. O. G. Benvenuto and M. A. De Vito, The formation of helium white dwarfs in close binary systems - II, *MNRAS* **362**, 891 (September 2005).
42. K. Nomoto, Evolution of 8-10 solar mass stars toward electron capture supernovae. I - Formation of electron-degenerate O + Ne + Mg cores, *ApJ* **277**, 791 (February 1984).
43. J. A. Panei, L. G. Althaus and O. G. Benvenuto, Mass-radius relations for white dwarf stars of different internal compositions, *A&A* **353**, 970 (January 2000).
44. S. Catalán, I. Ribas, J. Isern and E. García-Berro, WD0433+270: An old Hyades stream member or an Fe-core white dwarf?, *A&A* **477**, 901 (January 2008).
45. J. Isern, R. Canal and J. Labay, The Outcome of Explosive Ignition of ONeMg Cores: Supernovae, Neutron Stars, or "Iron" White Dwarfs?, *ApJ* **372**, p. L83 (May 1991).
46. G. C. Jordan, H. B. Perets, R. T. Fisher and D. R. van Rossum, Failed-detonation Supernovae: Subluminous Low-velocity Ia Supernovae and their Kicked Remnant White Dwarfs with Iron-rich Cores, *ApJ* **761**, p. L23 (December 2012).
47. D. Lunney, J. M. Pearson and C. Thibault, Recent trends in the determination of nuclear masses, *Rev. Mod. Phys.* **75**, 1021 (August 2003).
48. D. Peña Arteaga, M. Grasso, E. Khan and P. Ring, Nuclear structure in strong magnetic fields: Nuclei in the crust of a magnetar, *Phys. Rev. C* **84**, p. 045806 (October 2011).

49. M. Stein, J. Maruhn, A. Sedrakian and P. G. Reinhard, Carbon-oxygen-neon mass nuclei in superstrong magnetic fields, *Phys. Rev. C* **94**, p. 035802 (September 2016).
50. S. Subramanian and B. Mukhopadhyay, GRMHD formulation of highly super-Chandrasekhar rotating magnetized white dwarfs: Stable configurations of non-spherical white dwarfs, *MNRAS* **454**, 752 (November 2015).
51. I. I. Rabi, Das freie Elektron im homogenen Magnetfeld nach der Diracschen Theorie, *Z. Phys.* **49**, 507 (July 1928).
52. L. Landau, Diamagnetismus der Metalle, *Z. Phys.* **64**, 629 (September 1930).
53. P. Haensel, A. Y. Potekhin and D. G. Yakovlev, *Neutron Stars 1: Equation of state and structure* (Springer, 2007).
54. D. A. Baiko, A. Y. Potekhin and D. G. Yakovlev, Thermodynamic functions of harmonic Coulomb crystals, *Phys. Rev. E* **64**, p. 057402 (November 2001).
55. J. H. Van Vleck, *The Theory of Electric and Magnetic Susceptibilities* (Oxford University Press, London, 1932).
56. D. A. Baiko, Coulomb crystals in the magnetic field, *Phys. Rev. E* **80**, p. 046405 (October 2009).
57. N. Chamel and A. F. Fantina, Binary and ternary ionic compounds in the outer crust of a cold nonaccreting neutron star, *Phys. Rev. C* **94**, p. 065802 (Dec 2016).
58. M. Wang, W. J. Huang, F. G. Kondev, G. Audi and S. Naimi, The AME 2020 atomic mass evaluation (II). Tables, graphs and references, *Chin. Phys. C* **45**, p. 030003 (March 2021).
59. C. O. Dib and O. Espinosa, The magnetized electron gas in terms of Hurwitz zeta functions, *Nucl. Phys. B* **612**, 492 (October 2001).
60. N. Chamel and Z. K. Stoyanov, Analytical determination of the structure of the outer crust of a cold nonaccreted neutron star: Extension to strongly quantizing magnetic fields, *Phys. Rev. C* **101**, p. 065802 (June 2020).
61. S. Chandrasekhar, *An Introduction to the Study of Stellar Structure* (Dover, 1957).
62. S. L. Shapiro and S. A. Teukolsky, *Black Holes, White Dwarfs, and Neutron Stars: The Physics of Compact Objects* (John Wiley& Sons, 1983).
63. S. A. Kaplan, Sverkhplotnyè Zvezdy, *Naukovy Zapiski* **15**, 109 (1949).
64. R. C. Tolman, Static Solutions of Einstein's Field Equations for Spheres of Fluid, *Phys. Rev.* **55**, 364 (February 1939).
65. J. R. Oppenheimer and G. M. Volkoff, On Massive Neutron Cores, *Phys. Rev.* **55**, 374 (February 1939).
66. R. Nityananda and S. Konar, Strong constraints on magnetized white dwarfs surpassing the Chandrasekhar mass limit, *Phys. Rev. D* **89**, p. 103017 (May 2014).
67. J. G. Coelho, R. M. Marinho, M. Malheiro, R. Negreiros, D. L. Cáceres, J. A. Rueda and R. Ruffini, Dynamical Instability of White Dwarfs and Breaking of Spherical Symmetry Under the Presence of Extreme Magnetic Fields, *ApJ* **794**, p. 86 (October 2014).
68. D. L. Cáceres, J. A. Rueda and R. Ruffini, On the stability of ultra-magnetized white dwarfs, *J. Korean Phys. Soc.* **65**, 846 (September 2014).
69. E. Gourgoulhon, P. Grandclément, J.-A. Marck, J. Novak and K. Taniguchi, LORENE: Spectral methods differential equations solver (August 2016).
70. D. Chatterjee, T. Elghozi, J. Novak and M. Oertel, Consistent neutron star models with magnetic-field-dependent equations of state, *MNRAS* **447**, 3785 (March 2015).
71. N. Chamel, A. F. Fantina, L. Suleiman, J.-L. Zdunik and P. Haensel, Heating in Magnetar Crusts from Electron Captures, *Universe* **7**, p. 193 (June 2021).

Massive hot white dwarfs: Consequences of finite temperature in the structure and on the onset of instabilities

Sílvia P. Nunes

Departamento de Física, Instituto Tecnológico de Aeronáutica,
12228-900 São José dos Campos, São Paulo, Brazil
E-mail: silviapn@ita.br

José D. V. Arbañil

Departamento de Ciencias, Universidad Privada del Norte,
Avenida el Sol 461 San Juan de Lurigancho, 15434 Lima, Peru

Facultad de Ciencias Físicas, Universidad Nacional Mayor de San Marcos,
Avenida Venezuela s/n Cercado de Lima, 15081 Lima, Peru

Manuel Malheiro

Departamento de Física, Instituto Tecnológico de Aeronáutica,
12228-900 São José dos Campos, São Paulo, Brazil

In this work, we investigate the observable white dwarfs with high-surface gravity in the framework of general relativity. We consider the stellar fluid composed of nucleons and electrons confined in a Wigner-Seitz cell surrounded by free photons. Besides, we implement a temperature depending on the mass density with the presence of an isothermal core. The impact of temperature on the equilibrium and stability of white dwarfs is observed. We compare our results with massive white dwarfs estimated from the Extreme Ultraviolet Explorer Survey and Sloan Digital Sky Survey. We find that the high-surface gravity white dwarfs are well described by our curves with higher central temperatures. Our results suggest that these hot massive stars detected are within the range of white dwarfs with more radial stability. Moreover, we note the radial instability is attained before the pycnonuclear reaction for $T_c \geq 1.0 \times 10^8$[K].

Keywords: White dwarfs; charged white dwarfs; type Ia supernovae explosions

Introduction

Observable white dwarfs' structure has been reported in works using the Extreme Ultraviolet Explorer Survey (EUVE) and Sloan Digital Sky Survey (SDSS).[1–4] Some of these stars have a great surface gravity $(\log(g/g_\odot) \geq 4.4)$ and a high effective temperature $(T_{\rm eff} \gtrsim 10^4 {\rm [K]})$.[1,2] Due to their high surface gravity, it is important to investigate their instabilities against small radial perturbation and pycnonuclear reactions in general relativity scope considering temperature.

The studies concerning instabilities in white dwarfs[5,6] consider a completely degenerate star. To compare results with observable white dwarfs, we include temperature in the model. Thus, following recent white dwarfs models with finite temperature,[7,8] we analyze the structure and stability of hot white dwarf' and compare the results with some observable data. In this article, we detail some conclusions of the previous work.[9]

We study the structure and stability of hot massive white dwarfs and we compare our results with those ones reported by EUVE and SDSS. In addition, we made an instability analysis against the pycnonuclear reactions and radial perturbations. We analyze the stellar fluid by considering nucleons and electrons confined in a Wigner-Seitz cell with surrounding free photons. For this case, the pressure and energy density are respectively considered as following

$$P = P_e + P_N + P_\gamma + P_L, \tag{1}$$
$$\varepsilon = \varepsilon_e + \varepsilon_N + \varepsilon_\gamma + \varepsilon_L, \tag{2}$$

with the subscripts e, N, and γ representing the respective contributions of electrons, nucleons, and photons. Due to the partially degeneracy, the electron contributions are obtained with an adaptive quadrature method.[8]

1. The stellar structure equations and boundary conditions

We consider the unperturbed white dwarf is made of by a perfect fluid, whose energy-momentum tensor is expressed of the form

$$T_{\mu\beta} = (P + \varepsilon) u_\mu u_\beta + P g_{\mu\beta}. \tag{3}$$

The background metric employed to describe the spherically symmetric white dwarf, in Schwarzschild-like coordinates, is given by

$$ds^2 = -e^\nu dt^2 + e^\lambda dr^2 + r^2 d\theta^2 + r^2 \sin^2\theta d\phi^2, \tag{4}$$

where the functions ν and λ dependent on the radial coordinate only. The nonzero Einstein field equation components, for the line element assumed, lead to obtain the stellar structure equations:

$$\frac{dm}{dr} = 4\pi\varepsilon^2, \tag{5}$$

$$\frac{dP}{dr} = -(P + \varepsilon)\left[4\pi r p + \frac{m}{r^2}\right] e^\lambda, \tag{6}$$

$$\frac{d\nu}{dr} = -\frac{2}{(p + \varepsilon)} \frac{dP}{dr}, \tag{7}$$

being m the mass inside the radius r. The potential metric e^λ is described as

$$e^\lambda = \left[1 - \frac{2m}{r}\right]^{-1}. \tag{8}$$

Since we are considering a temperature distribution T dependent on mass density ρ with the presence of an isothermal core, we assume that the parameters T and ρ are related by the equality

$$T/\rho^{2/3} = \text{constant}. \tag{9}$$

The process starts integrating the stellar structure equations from the center ($r = 0$) until the surface of the star ($r = R$). At the center of the star are considered the initial conditions:

$$m(0) = 0, \quad \varepsilon(0) = \varepsilon_0, \text{ and } \nu(0) = \nu_0. \tag{10}$$

The surface of the star is determined at $P(r = R) = 0$.

2. Results

Due to our analysis be restricted to very massive WD, we can use a simple equation for the temperature distribution as Eq. (9). To ensure this affirmation, we compare the mass and radius obtained with the temperature distribution in Eq. (9) and the one found by Kritcher and collaborators[10] which considers a more complete processes as radiation and convection. To analyze massive WDs, we use the temperature distribution stated Eq. (9). By using this relation, we obtain similar masses to those reported by Kritcher's and collaborators[10] for stars near the maximum-mass limit. This is due to the more contribution of the WD mass coming from the degenerate core, which has a constant temperature. The envelope with a different temperature distribution should only modify the stellar radius. In this case, the percentage between the difference obtained by Eq. (9) and Kritcher's envelope, for $g \geq 10^9 [\text{cm s}^{-2}]$, is around 2%.

The surface gravity as a function of radial coordinate is plotted in Fig. 1 for several central temperatures and $M = 1.37 M_\odot$. From the panel, we note that the surface gravity increases with the radial coordinate until it reaches the maximum gravity point, hereafter, gravity decays monotonically with the increment of the radial coordinate.

The change of surface's gravity and total radius of the star with the increment of the central temperature is also observed in Fig. 1. For larger temperature, greater total stellar radius and lower surface's gravity are found. In this sense, WDs with smaller surface gravity -than those ones predicted with the cold catalyzed matter- are expected to have high central temperatures.

The mass against the total radius is shown in Fig. 2 for different values of central temperature. The full triangles in pink over the curves indicate the maximum mass points. The blue dots represent the threshold instability due to pycnonuclear reactions. In addition, in figure, some observational results obtained from the catalogs Nalezyty[2] in green diamond, and in Vennes[1] in brown squares. In all curves of the panel, we note that the mass grows with the surface's gravity until reaches the maximum mass point, thereafter, the mass decreases with the grows of gravity.

In Fig. 2, we observe that the analysis of the pycnonuclear reaction has to be considered for central temperatures below $T_c < 10^8 [\text{K}]$. For central temperatures above $10^8 [\text{K}]$, the secular stability point is reached before the pycnonuclear reaction. It is important to mention that the secular stability point is marked by the maximum mass point.

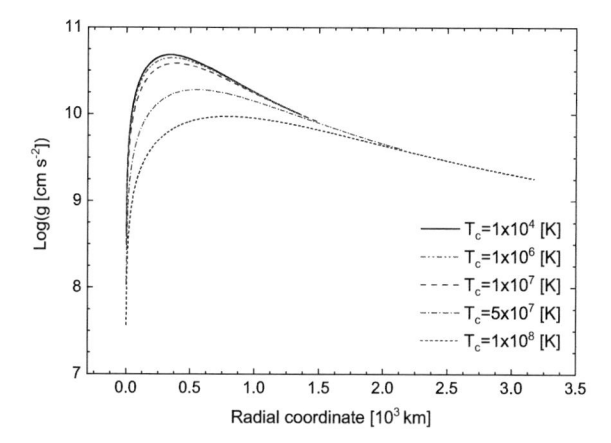

Fig. 1. Surface gravity as a function of radial coordinate for several central temperatures with a fixed $M = 1.37 M_\odot$.

Vennes,[1] and Nalezyty[2] have reported some very massive white dwarfs with very high surface gravity. In Fig. 2, these white dwarfs are matching with the curves of very high central temperatures and are very close to the instabilities thresholds. Indeed, one of them, with a mass of $M = 1.41 M_\odot$ can have a central temperature higher than 10^8[K]. From this, we could understand that these massive white dwarfs could be treated differently. Using the surface gravity and effective temperature reported by Vennes, we could investigate these stars by employing the values of effective temperature and surface gravity. Moreover, considering the general relativity effects, we found that the masses of these stars decrease, thus highlighting the importance of general relativity in the study of massive white dwarfs.

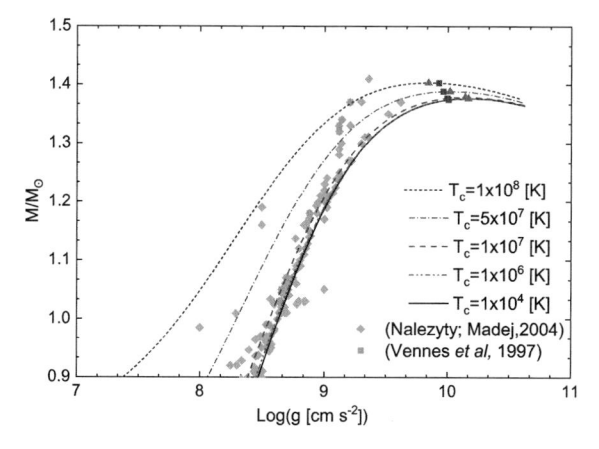

Fig. 2. Mass as a function of surface gravity for several central temperatures. The green diamonds[2] and the brown squares[1] represents observational data.

3. Conclusion

In this work, we investigate the structure and stability of hot white dwarfs. We regard the stellar fluid as composed of nucleons and electrons confined in a Wigner-Seitz cell, with free photons. We consider the temperature profile depending on the mass density with the presence of an isothermal core. We use the stellar structure equations to analyze the equilibrium configurations of white dwarfs and the stability against the pycnonuclear reactions and small radial perturbations.

Comparing our results with observational data, we found that the high masses white dwarfs provided by Vennes[1] could be described by our model. Morevoer, we dicussed about the importance of considering central temperature and general relativity in the study of massive white dwarfs.

Acknowledgments

We would like to thank Fundação de Amparo à Pesquisa do Estado de São Paulo (FAPESP), Grant No. 2013/26258 − 4. SPN thanks Conselho Nacional de Desenvolvimento Científico e Tecnológico (CNPq), Grant No. 140863/2017−6 and CAPES for the financial support. JDVA would like to thank the Universidad Privada del Norte and Universidad Nacional Mayor de San Marcos for funding - RR Nº 005753-2021-R/UNMSM under the project number B21131781. MM is grateful to CAPES and CNPq financial support.

References

1. S. Vennes, P. A. Thejll, R. Génova Galvan and J. Dupuis, Hot White Dwarfs in the Extreme Ultraviolet Explorer Survey. II. Mass Distribution, Space Density, and Population Age, *ApJ* **480**, 714 (May 1997).
2. M. Należyty and J. Madej, A catalogue of isolated massive white dwarfs. Mass distribution of massive star, *Astron. Astrophys.* **420**, 507 (June 2004).
3. D. Koester and S. O. Kepler, Carbon-rich (DQ) white dwarfs in the Sloan Digital Sky Survey, *Astron. Astrophys.* **628**, p. A102 (August 2019).
4. J. Madej, M. Należyty and L. G. Althaus, Mass distribution of DA white dwarfs in the First Data Release of the Sloan Digital Sky Survey, *Astron. Astrophys.* **419**, L5 (May 2004).
5. G. Chanmugam, Radial oscillations of zero-temperature white dwarfs and neutron stars below nuclear densities, *ApJ* **217**, 799 (November 1977).
6. E. Otoniel, B. Franzon, G. A. Carvalho, M. Malheiro, S. Schramm and F. Weber, Strongly Magnetized White Dwarfs and Their Instability Due to Nuclear Processes, *ApJ* **879**, p. 46 (July 2019).
7. S. M. de Carvalho, M. Rotondo, J. A. Rueda and R. Ruffini, Relativistic Feynman-Metropolis-Teller treatment at finite temperatures, *Phys. Rev. C* **89**, p. 015801 (January 2014).
8. K. A. Boshkayev, J. A. Rueda, B. A. Zhami, Z. A. Kalymova and G. S. Balgymbekov, Equilibrium structure of white dwarfs at finite temperatures, in *IJMPC*, 2016.

9. S. P. Nunes, J. D. V. Arbañil and M. Malheiro, The structure and stability of massive hot white dwarfs, *To appear in the Astrophysical Journal*, p. arXiv:2108.08238 (August 2021).
10. A. L. Kritcher, D. C. Swift, T. Döppner, B. Bachmann, L. X. Benedict, G. W. Collins, J. L. DuBois, F. Elsner, G. Fontaine, J. A. Gaffney, S. Hamel, A. Lazicki, W. R. Johnson, N. Kostinski, D. Kraus, M. J. MacDonald, B. Maddox, M. E. Martin, P. Neumayer, A. Nikroo, J. Nilsen, B. A. Remington, D. Saumon, P. A. Sterne, W. Sweet, A. A. Correa, H. D. Whitley, R. W. Falcone and S. H. Glenzer, A measurement of the equation of state of carbon envelopes of white dwarfs, *Nature* **584**, 51 (August 2020).

A study of the infrared emission of SGR/AXPs in a disk scenario and its implications for their origin

Sarah Villanova Borges

Department of Physics, University of Wisconsin-Milwaukee,
1900 E. Kenwood Boulevard, Milwaukee, WI 53211, USA
E-mail: svborges@uwm.edu

Soft Gamma-Ray Repeaters and Anomalous X-ray Pulsars (SGR/AXPs) are widely accepted to be magnetars, isolated neutron star (NS) with a huge decaying magnetic field. They can emit from radio up to hard X-rays, being infrared (IR) one of the most interesting and poorly studied energy ranges. The origin of this IR emission is still controversial, since some authors argue in favor of a magnetospheric emission, whereas others point out to a disk. In this work, we revisit the IR emission of SGR/AXPs in a disk perspective. We find that all SGR/AXPs with IR emission in the K-band are consistent with the presence of an irradiated disk. Even though this finding does not rule out any of the proposed natures, it is a piece of new evidence to confirm the presence of disk around this class. If the disk origin where unambiguously confirmed, this would have important impacts on understanding the origin of SGR/AXPs.

Keywords: Soft Gamma-Ray Repeaters; Anomalous X-ray Pulsars; infrared emission.

1. Introduction

The soft gamma-repeaters/anomalous X-ray pulsars (SGR/AXPs) are observationally characterized by a quiescent soft X-ray with luminosity in the range $10^{29} - 10^{35}$ erg.s^{-1}, period of 2 – 12 s, and spin-down of 10^{-15} to 10^{-10} s.s^{-1} see, e.g.,[24]. Some SGR/AXPs also present emission in other energy ranges, such as radio, optical, infrared (IR), and hard X-rays, as well as soft gamma-ray flares events. SGR/AXPs are widely thought to be magnetars, isolated neutron stars (NSs) emitting by the decay of their ultra-strong magnetic field, in the range of $10^{13} - 10^{15}$ G.[6] There is also alternative models, such as the NS accreting scenario,[36] the white dwarf (WD) pulsar model,[20] and the accreting WD model.[1]

The near-infrared (NIR) emission was confirmed or proposed for a total of 13 SGR/AXPs[15,24,31] and its origin is still debated. For the AXP 4U 0142+61 , the IR emission is well modeled by an irradiated disk, reinforced by an unconfirmed silicate feature around 9.5 μm.[39,40] Nonetheless, the lack of mid-IR emission during the 2007 flare of 1E 1048.1-5937 seems to rule out the presence of a disk in this object.[38] Thus, some authors still argues in favor of an IR magnetospheric emission.[13]

Two classical observational approaches can confirm magnetospheric origin in the IR emission of SGR/AXPs: search for polarization and pulsed emission. High polarization and pulsed fraction are expected for a magnetospheric emission. However, a low pulsed fraction is consistent with both models. Moreover, low polarization discards magnetospheric synchrotron and curvature emission but cannot distinguish between a cyclotron emission and a disk. In this sense, an extensive study of IR polarization and periodic emission can be inconclusive.

For that reason, we suggest a distinct method to determine the IR origin of SGR/AXPs. We propose the search for a correlation between the luminosity in IR and X-rays that can be confronted with the expected correlation for a disk and magnetospheric models. In this sense, the disk could represent the best path to confirm the origin of SGR/AXPs. For instance, if the leftover of a supernova event formed the disk, it probably contains iron, silicon, oxygen, helium, and traces of hydrogen.[17] In this sense, an IR spectroscopy of 4U 0142+61, the magnetar with the brightest quiescent emission, could give essential clues to the origin of the class.

This proceeding aims to study the IR emission of SGR/AXPs and is organized as follows. In Section 2, we present the disk model we have used to fit the data. In section 3, we present the correlation between IR and X-rays. In Section 4, we discuss the consequences of the results for the origin of SGR/AXPs, slow rotating NSs, and the period of Fast Radio Bursts (FRBs). In Section 5, we summarize our findings.

2. An irradiated disk model for isolated neutrons stars

To study the expected correlation between IR and X-rays for an irradiated disk emission, we are going to consider the same irradiated disk model used to fit 4U 0142+61.[39] The emitted flux of a debris disk in a given frequency ν can be expressed by[8,27]:

$$F_{disk} = \frac{2\cos(i)}{D^2} \times \int_{R_{in}}^{R_{out}} B_\nu(T_{irr}(R))RdR; \qquad (1)$$

where, i is the inclination of the disk in respect to the observer, D is the distance to the observer, R is the distance from each infinitesimal part of the disk to the NS, $T_{irr}(R)$ is the debris disk temperature, and B_ν is the emitted spectrum of each element of the disk. Meanwhile T_{irr} is given by[37]:

$$T_{irr}(R) = 25,280 \text{ K } f^{2/7} \left(\frac{L_X}{L_E}\right)^{2/7} \left(\frac{R_\odot}{R}\right)^{3/7}, \qquad (2)$$

where L_E is the Eddington luminosity, $R_\odot$ is the radius of the Sun and the f parameter related with the albedo. Since we expect all SGR/AXPs to have similar temperature and composition, f can be treated as a constant.

With those equations in hand, we can estimate the expected correlation between IR and X-rays luminosity in IR. Calling $x = \frac{h\nu}{kT(R)}$, we have:

$$R \propto x^{7/3} \left(\frac{k}{h\nu}\right)^{7/3} \left(f\frac{L_X}{L_E}\right)^{2/3}; \qquad (3)$$

$$dR \propto x^{4/3} \left(\frac{k}{h\nu}\right)^{7/3} \left(f\frac{L_X}{L_E}\right)^{2/3} dx; \qquad (4)$$

Considering $T_{out} \sim 500$ K and $T_{in} \sim 1500$ K, which is consistent with the temperature range for 4U 0142+61 and also for disk in isolated WDs,[11,39] the flux equation can be approximated to:

$$F_{Ks} \propto \frac{4\pi h \cos i \nu^3}{c^2 d^2} \left((L_X)^{4/3} \left(\frac{k}{h\nu}\right)^{14/3}\right)$$

$$\times \int_{T=500K}^{T=1500K} \frac{x^{11/3} dx}{e^x - 1}, \qquad (5)$$

where all parameters are constant, except for F_{Ks}, $\cos i$, and L_x. If we define the monochromatic luminosity in the Ks-band such as:

$$L_{Ks} = 4\pi D^2 \int_0^\infty F_{Ks} \delta(\nu - \nu_{Ks}) d\nu$$

$$= 4\pi D^2 F_{Ks} \nu_{Ks}, \qquad (6)$$

we find the correlation:

$$L_{Ks} \propto (\cos i) L_{XR}^{1.33}.$$

Since $0 < \cos i < 1$, we expect, at most, one order of magnitude change for a given object. Thus, for a correlation ranging in several orders of magnitude the expected correlation between the monochromatic luminosity in the Ks-band and the bolometric X-rays luminosity is can be simplified to:

$$L_{Ks} \propto L_{XR}^{1.33}. \qquad (7)$$

It is important to highlight that this correlation considers that the disk properties (albedo, inner and outer temperatures of the dusty region) are similar among all objects. Moreover, this correlation discards the contribution of two different mechanisms in the Ks wavelength (such as a non-thermal component along with the disk).

3. A correlation between infrared and X-rays

The search for correlations is a valuable tool to understand the emission mechanism on different energy ranges. For SGR/AXPs, there are a few preliminary studies of the correlation between IR and X-rays. For some outbursts events, an enhancement of the IR emission was proposed.[10,28,30] In others, no correlation has been seen.[29,32,38] Nonetheless, those previous studies were limited since they have only examined the behavior of a single object per time along with the event and did not take into account the hard X-rays.

In this sense, we decide to revisit the possible correlation between IR and X-rays as a tool to confirm the irradiated disk origin. As discussed in sec. 2, if the disk is the main emission mechanics for IR, it is expected a correlation between the X-rays and IR luminosities. To search for such correlation, we chose the IR k_s-band since it is the one with most observations in the magnetar class. For the bolometric X-rays luminosity, we have considered the sum of the luminosity of the 0.5-10 keV (L_s) and 15 - 60 keV (L_H) ranges. All IR and X-rays data are simultaneous or from close dates.

We have used observation from K_s, K' and K bands, considering that the luminosity in all bands is the same (justified since their central wavelengths are extremely close). Nonetheless, we have used the corrected zero-point magnitude for each specific filter. Moreover, not all objects have simultaneous Soft and Hard X-rays observation. When only one is available, the following equation was used to estimate the other[7]:

$$\frac{F_{hard}}{F_{soft}} = (0.59 \pm 0.07) \times (\dot{P}/10^{-11})^{0.51 \pm 0.05} \tag{8}$$

where $\dot{P}$ is the spin-down.

We first check the correlation using both Spearman ($\rho = 0.87$) and Pearson ($p = 0.93$) correlation coefficients, which points out to a strong correlation between the data. To find the best-fit from the data and its goodness, we consider a linear, logarithmic trend and R^2 defined by:

$$R^2 = \frac{\sum_1^n (\hat{y}_i - \bar{y})^2}{\sum_1^n (y_i - \bar{y})^2} \tag{9}$$

where y_i is the data, $\hat{y}_i$ is the fitted result, and $\bar{y}$ is the mean of the data. We use a 1σ error for all fits. Figure 1 shows the best correlation between the luminosity in the K_s-band (L_{Ks}) and X-rays (L_{XR}). The best fit is ($R^2 = 0.87$): $L_{IR} \propto L_S^{1.16 \pm 0.09}$, considering a linear fit without the error-bars (using the python class "stats.linregress") and $L_{IR} \propto L_S^{1.27 \pm 0.09}$ considering the error-bars (using the python class "scipy.odr.ODR"). We have used quiescence and outburst events, and we do not see any discrepancy in results.

For the fit with error bars, the expected slope of an irradiated disk is within the 1σ range, which favors the disk interpretation. Moreover, Fig. 1 considers quiescence/outbursts, and confirmed/candidates indistinctly, which argues in favor of: (i) the same mechanism is possibly responsible for the IR emission in quiescence and outbursts for the majority of objects; (2) candidate emission is possibly correct.

We have also compared the best fit with the IR emission of some few isolated NSs with detected emission in IR: (i) The rotation powered pulsars (RPPs) B0531+21, B0833-45, and B1509-58[12]; (ii) the XDIN RXJ0806.4-4123, and the Central Compact Object (CCO) 1E 161348-5055. We have also included the data from the SGR 1935+2154 in the F140W band. We have not used any of those points in the fit since they are not SGR/AXPs and/or the IR observation is not in the K-band. Even though they were not used in the fit, all but one are in the 90% prediction bound, showing that it is likely that the exact mechanism is responsible for the IR emission in magnetars and other pulsars with IR. This is interesting evidence in favor of a disk: fits using the magnetospheric curvature emission model can reproduce the IR

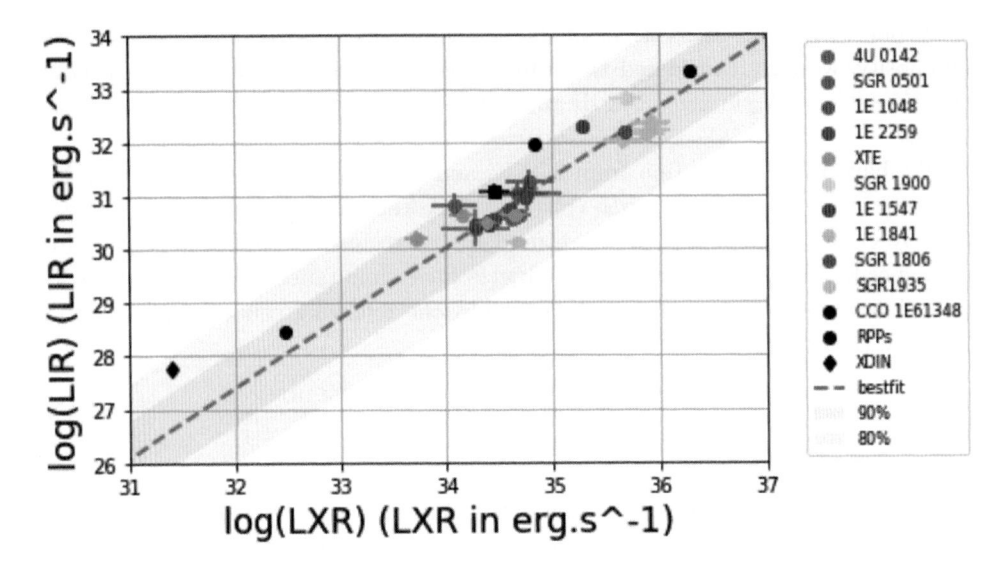

Fig. 1. Best-fit (dotted line) correlation between the luminosity in the Ks band and X-rays. The best-fit was estimated using only magnetars (colored points). The black squares, diamonds, and circles (1E 161348-5055, B0531+21, RXJ0806.4-4123, B0833-45, and B1509-58, respectively) were not used in the best-fit estimate and are only represented for comparison.

luminosity of magnetars using $B \sim 10^{14}$ G.[42] Nonetheless, the highest IR luminosity belongs to Crab Pulsar (B0531+21), a young pulsar with a dipole magnetic field of "only" 7e+12 G.

4. Importance of the disk on magnetars

4.1. *Origin of magnetars*

One of the biggest unanswered questions about magnetars is what are their progenitors. One of the first proposed models relates to massive main-sequence progenitors. A supernova explosion with energy higher than 10^{52} erg/s would enable the formation of such high magnetic fields, since part of the energy would be transferred to the ejecta via the strong magnetic coupling with the proto-neutron star.[35] This high-mass origin is corroborated by the presence of the magnetar CXOU J164710.2 in Westerlund 1, a young star cluster, with 4 Myr, which puts a lower limit in the mass of the progenitor on 40 $M_\odot$.[23]

Nonetheless, this massive origin has encountered some challenges. For instance, the explosion of the associated SNR for magnetars is $< 10^{52}$ erg/s, which put a higher limit on the mass of the progenitor in 20 $M_\odot$.[43] For those small progenitor masses, the formation of high magnetic fields would have to invoke the amplification of a fossil magnetic field.

For this main-sequence scenario, the presence of the disk can be challenging to explain. 1-D simulations have shown that fallback disk in NSs are formed only on very fine-tuned SN events.[26] Nonetheless, if this is this case, an IR spectroscopy (with the to-be-launched James Webb Space Telescope) of 4U 0142+61could confirm the SN origin, since the leftover of a supernova event is expected to contain iron, silicon, oxygen, helium, and traces of hydrogen.[17]

Another possible mechanism, that have been long proposed, is the merger scenario. The merger of compact objects can generate isolated NSs with high magnetic fields and WD+WD, WD+NS, and NS+NS mergers have already been proposed as progenitors of magnetars.[16,18,21] This origin mechanism had gained a lot of attention in the last couple of years for being able to explain the occurrence of Gamma-Ray Bursts[22] and Fast Radio Bursts (FRBs) in a magnetar context.[21]

This merger origin would also be detectable in a IR spectroscopy. For instance, for a CO-WD/CO-WD merger, the disk is formed by the remains of the secondary and contains carbon and oxygen, with traces of other elements such as neon, magnesium, silicon, and nickel.[19] Moreover, the AIC event is expected to produce unusual neutron-rich isotopes.[5]

4.2. *Period of 1E 161348-5055*

The CCO 1E 161348-5055 is one of the most singular NSs: with a period of 6.67 hours, this is the slowest isolated NS known.[4] In the last decade, this curious object gained much attention when magnetar-like bursts activities were detected,[3] which raises a canon explanation evoking an ultra-strong magnetic field (in the order of $\sim 10^{15}$ G) and a fallback to explain how this object's large period came to happen.[9,33,41]

This way, proving that the IR emission of this object is consistent with a disk gives an observational evidence for the disk models explaining period of 1E 161348-5055.

4.3. *Periodicity in Fast Radio Bursts*

Since the discovery of FRB-like events in the SGR 1935+2154,[14] models invoking magnetars have been the focal point in understanding FRBs. In this sense, the presence of the disk in magnetars can emerge as an explanation for long periods in FRB events, such as the 16.35 days observed in the FRB 180916.J0158+65.[2]

In an isolated NS, the most plausible reason for such long period is precession. There are some models that were raised in the last years to explain such motion, with some invoking a disk, such as a forced precession caused by fallback disk,[34] or Lense-Thirring precession of the disk. Thus, proving the presence of the disk gives an extra piece of evidence for those models.

5. Conclusion

We searched for a correlation between IR and X-rays for magnetars and the result is consisted with an irradiated disk. We have also found that the results are consistent the IR emission of some other classes of isolated NSs: RPP, XDINs and CCOs, which suggest a similar IR emission mechanism for all isolated NSs and favors a disk origin for IR. If the presence of such a disk was confirmed, its composition could help determine the origin of magnetars, as well as the long period of 1E 161348-5055 and the two-week-long period of the FRB 180916.J0158+65.

References

1. Borges S. V., Rodrigues C. V., Coelho J. G., Malheiro M., Castro M., 2020, Astrophysical Journal, 895, 26.
2. Chime/Frb Collaboration, Amiri, M., Andersen, B. C. et al., 2020, Nature, 582, 351.
3. D'Aı̀, A., Evans, P. A., Burrows, D. N. et al., 2016, MNRAS, 463, 239D'Aı, A., Evans, P. A., Burrows, D. N. et al., 2016, MNRAS, 463, 2394.
4. De Luca, A., Caraveo, P. A., Mereghetti, S., Tiengo, A. & Bignami, G. F. 2006, Science, 313, 814.
5. Dessart, L., Burrows, A., Ott, C. D. et al., 2006, ApJ, 644, 1063.
6. Duncan, R. C. & Thompson, C. 1992, ApJ Lett., 392, L9.
7. Enoto, T., Shibata, S., Kitaguchi, T. et al., 2017, ApJS, 231, 8.
8. Frank, J., King, A. & Raine, D. J. 2002, Accretion Power in Astrophysics: Third Edition (Cambridge University Press), 398.
9. Ho, W. C. G. & Andersson, N. 2017, MNRAS, 464, L65.
10. Israel, G., Covino, S., Mignani, R. et al., 2005, A&A, 438, L1.
11. Jura, M., Farihi, J. & Zuckerman, B. 2007, ApJ, 663, 1285.
12. Kaplan, D. L. & Moon, D.-S. 2006, ApJ, 644, 1056.
13. Kaspi, V. M. & Beloborodov, A. M. 2017, ARA&A, 55, 261.
14. Kirsten, F., Snelders, M. P., Jenkins, M. et al., 2021, Nature Astronomy, 5, 414.
15. Levan, A., Kouveliotou, C. & Fruchter, A. 2018, ApJ, 854, 161.
16. Levan, A. J., Wynn, G. A., Chapman, R. et al., 2006, MNRAS, 368, L1.
17. Lin, D. N. C., Woosley, S. E. & Bodenheimer, P. H. 1991, Nature, 353, 827.
18. Liu, X. 2020, International Journal of Astronomy and Astrophysics, 10, 28.
19. Loren-Aguilar, P., Isern, J. & Garcıa-Berro, E. 2009, A&A, 500, 11933.
20. Malheiro, M., Rueda, J. A. & Ruffini, R. 2012, PASJ, 64, 56.
21. Margalit, B., Berger, E. & Metzger, B. D. 2019, ApJ, 886, 110.
22. Metzger, B. D., Giannios, D., Thompson, T. A., Bucciantini, N. & Quataert, E. 2011, MNRAS, 413, 2031.
23. Muno, M. P., Clark, J. S., Crowther, P. A. et al., 2006, ApJ Lett., 636, L41.
24. Olausen, S. A. & Kaspi, V. M. 2014, ApJS, 212, 6.
25. Ouyed, R., Leahy, D. & Niebergal, B. 2011, MNRAS, 415, 1590.
26. Perna, R., Duffell, P., Cantiello, M. & MacFadyen, A. I. 2014, ApJ, 781, 119.
27. Perna, R., Hernquist, L. & Narayan, R. 2000, ApJ, 541, 344.
28. Rea, N., Testa, V., Israel, G. L. et al., 2004, A&A, 425, L5.
29. Tam, C. R., Gavriil, F. P., Dib, R. et al., 2008, ApJ, 677, 503.
30. Tam, C. R., Kaspi, V. M., van Kerkwijk, M. H. & Durant, M. 2004, ApJ Lett., 617, L53.
31. Testa, V., Mignani, R. P., Hummel, W., Rea, N. & Israel, G. L.2018, MNRAS, 473, 3180.
32. Testa, V., Rea, N., Mignani, R. P. et al., 2008, A&A, 482, 607.
33. Tong, H., Wang, W., Liu, X. W. & Xu, R. X. 2016, ApJ, 833, 265.

34. Tong, H., Wang, W. & Wang, H.-G. 2020, Research in Astronomy and Astrophysics, 20, 142.
35. Turolla, R., Zane, S. & Watts, A. L. 2015, Reports on Progressin Physics, 78, 116901.
36. van Paradijs, J., Taam, R. E. & van den Heuvel, E. P. J. 1995, A&A, 299, L41.
37. Vrtilek, S. D., Raymond, J. C., Garcia, M. R. et al., 1990, A&A, 235, 162.
38. Wang, Z., Bassa, C., Kaspi, V. M., Bryant, J. J. & Morrell, N. 2008a, ApJ, 679, 1443.
39. Wang, Z., Chakrabarty, D. & Kaplan, D. L. 2006, Nature, 440, 772.
40. Wang, Z., Chakrabarty, D. & Kaplan, D. L. 2008b, in American Institute of Physics Conference Series, Vol. 983, 40 Years of Pulsars: Millisecond Pulsars, Magnetars and More.
41. Xu, K. & Li, X.-D. 2019, ApJ, 877, 138.
42. Zane, S., Nobili, L. & Turolla, R. 2011, Astrophysics and Space Science Proceedings, 21, 329.
43. Zhou, P., Vink, J., Safi-Harb, S. & Miceli, M. 2019, A&A, 629, A51.

Particle acceleration and high energy emission in the white dwarf binaries AE Aquarii and AR Scorpii

P.J. Meintjes[1,*], S.T. Madzime[1], Q. Kaplan[1], H.J van Heerden[1], K.K Singh[1,2], D.A.H. Buckley[1,3], P.A. Woudt[4] and R. Fender[5]

[1] Department of Physics, University of the Free State,
Bloemfontein, 9301, South Africa
*E-mail: MeintjPJ@ufs.ac.za

[2] Astrophysical Sciences Division, Bhabha Atomic Research Center,
Mumbai, 400085, India
E-mail: kksastro@barc.gov.in

[3] South African Astronomical Observatory (SAAO), Observatory, 7925,
Cape Town, South Africa,
E-mail: dibnob@saao.ac.za

[4] Department of Astronomy, University of Cape Town (UCT), Rondebosh,
Cape Town, 7700 South Africa,
E-mail: WoudtPA@ast.uct.ac.za

[5] Department of Physics, University of Oxford, Oxford, OX1 3PU,
United Kingdom
E-mail: Rob.Fender@physics.ox.ac.uk

Here we present results from an in-depth search for pulsed emission from both close binary systems AE Aquarii (AE Aqr) and AR Scorpii (AR Sco) in radio and gamma-ray energies. Both systems were observed recently with the MeerKAT telescope, and combined with this, we utilized the combined 10 year Pass 8 Fermi-LAT dataset to search for pulsed gamma-ray emission from both white dwarfs in these systems. Pulsed emission was detected in MeerKAT data from both these close binary systems at a period that is at, or close to, the spin period of the white dwarf. The search for pulsed gamma-ray emission revealed pulsed emission at the spin period of the white dwarf of AE Aqr after selecting data sets with duration of 2 weeks that show excess emission above the 2 σ significance level. Braking these two-week sets up in 10 minute intervals and stacking the power spectra revealed pulsed emission at both the spin ($P* = 33.08\,\text{s}$) and its associated first harmonic ($P_1 = 16.54\,\text{s}$). A full 10 year analysis of the AR Sco data revealed pulsed emission at the spin period/beat period of the white dwarf, albeit at a lower significance level. Several control analyses were performed to verify the authenticity of the emission in both radio and gamma-rays, which will be discussed in the main text. The results of this study definitely reveal that both white dwarfs in these systems contain a particle accelerator that accelerates charged particles to high energies resulting in associated non-thermal radio and gamma-ray emission.

Keywords: Cataclysmic variable, white dwarf, pulsar, close binary system, particle acceleration, synchrotron radiation, gamma-rays

1. Introduction

Emission of Very High Energy (VHE) gamma-rays from the novalike variable AE Aqr had been reported in the late 1980's early 1990's by two independent groups (e.g. 1–3). These reports showed that AE Aqr display sporadic aperiodic burst-like gamma-ray emission with associated gamma-ray pulsations at, or close to, the spin period of the white dwarf. On occasions the first harmonic of the spin period ($P_1 = 16.54$ s) was also detected.

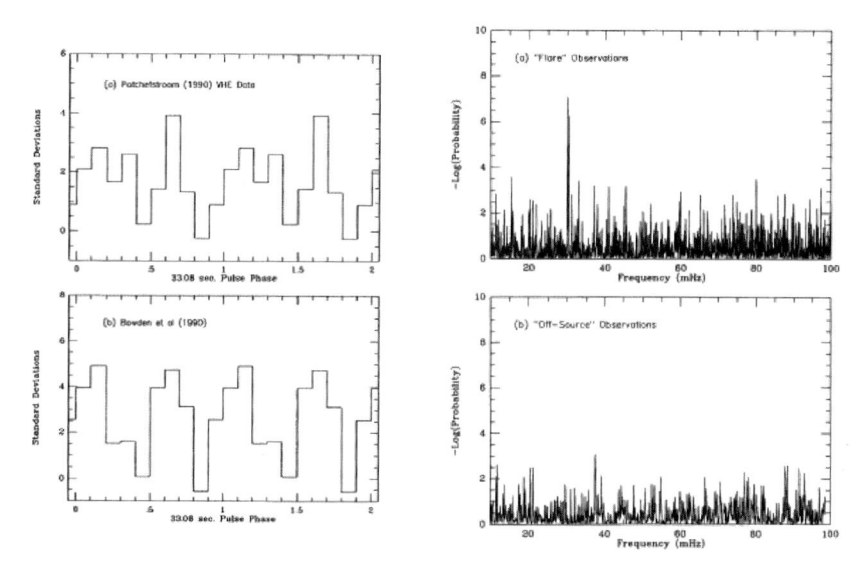

Fig. 1. (a) Pulsed VHE gamma-ray emission detected from AE Aqr at both the 33.08 s and 16.54 s during two contemporaneous burst-like VHE gamma-ray events observed by two independent groups. (b) The top panel represents an incoherently stacked power spectrum of VHE observations made simultaneous with optical flares and show clear indications of pulsed emission at the spin period ($P_* = 33.08$ S) of the white dwarf while the control off-source stacked power spectrum of observations made simultaneously with those above displays a white noise profile without any noticeable pulsed signal at or close to the spin period of the white dwarf of AE Aqr.

These reports have never been confirmed by independent follow-up studies (e.g. 4). However, the cadence in these follow-up studies was significantly poorer than the initial studies. The potential of white dwarfs as possible particle accelerators and gamma-ray sources came under the spotlight again with the discovery of the unique close binary AR Sco. The majority of AR Sco's Spectral Energy Distribution (SED) is the result of non-thermal emission since there is no indication of mass transfer and accretion in this system (e.g. 5). A follow-up study (6) revealed high levels of linear polarization in the optical light, a clear indication of a strong synchrotron component. It was shown (see e.g. 7) that the radio to X-ray SED of AR Sco can be explained by two component synchrotron spectrum produced by a pulsar-like process in the magnetosphere of the white dwarf (optical to X-ray), combined with synchrotron emission in the pumped magnetosphere of the secondary star (radio to infrared). See also (8) for a detailed discussion of the properties of AR Sco.

The evidence of particle acceleration and accompanied non-thermal emission, combined with the availability of the new Fermi-LAT Pass 8 data and the MeerKAT radio telescope array in South Africa, stimulated a new radio and gamma-ray study of these two sources. The paper is constructed as follows: In the following section the results of the radio observations of these two sources will be reported. This will be followed by the results of our Fermi-LAT analysis, after which we will present some conclusions and future prospects.

2. MeerKAT Observations and Results of AE Aqr and AR Sco

Both AE Aqr and AR Sco were observed by the SKA precursor telescope MeerKAT on 25 February 2019 (AE Aqr) and 15-16 June 2020 (AR Sco) respectively. The AE Aqr observation was performed under a ThunderKAT project (e.g.9) while AR Sco was observed under the Director's Discretionary Time (DDT) proposal (DDT-20200615-DB-01).

The L-band (0.9-1.7 GHz) light curves of these observations (see Fig. 2a,b) are presented below. The gaps in the light curves of AE Aqr represent periods when calibration sources were observed. For AR Sco only the last short light curve has been included for illustration purposes since these results are the main focus of another forthcoming publication, i.e Buckley et al. 2021 (in preparation). Both L-band light curves display a significant level of variability from both these sources. Since both these sources are not driven by the direct accretion of mass onto the surface of the white dwarf the variability in the radio band is most probably the result of the interaction between the white dwarf magnetosphere and the propeller ejected matter in the case of AE Aqr, or the secondary star's magnetosphere in the case of AR Sco.

A search for periodicity was conducted for both these sources (see Fig. 3a,b). Here we present the first detection of pulsed emission in the radio band from AE Aqr (see Fig. 3a). Similarly, Fig. 3b shows significant pulsed emission from AR Sco, probably on the beat period between the spin and orbital periods (see 5).

The L-Band spectrum of both these sources reveal a power-law, which may indicate non-thermal synchrotron emission. The exact mechanism driving these pulsations are currently under investigation. The radio flux however displays a non-thermal origin with clear power-law spectral profile in the L-band (see Fig. 4a,b), which may signify a non-thermal synchrotron emission process.

The average L-band flux is also presented on the SED for both AE qr and AR Sco (see Fig. 5a,b).

3. Fermi-LAT gamma-ray emission form AE Aqr and AR Sco

A search was conducted for steady and pulsed gamma-ray emission from both AE Aqr and AR Sco using the upgraded Fermi-LAT Pass 8 dataset. The Pass 8 dataset

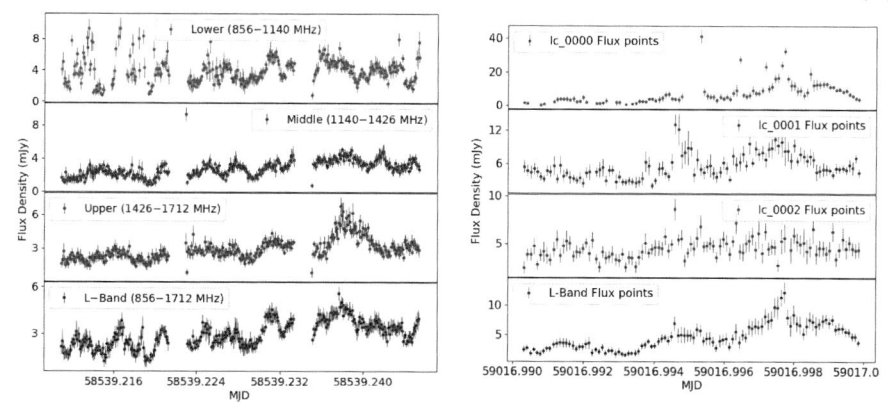

Fig. 2. (a) MeerKAT L-band observation of AE Aqr on 25 February 2019. The light curve was broken up into the lower, middle and upper L-band, with the last light curve representing the total L-Band light curve. The data was binned in 8 second intervals. (b) L-band radio observation of AR Sco performed on 16-17 June 2020. The light curve was broken up in lower, middle and upper L-band, with the last light curve representing the total L-band. The data was binned in 8 second intervals.

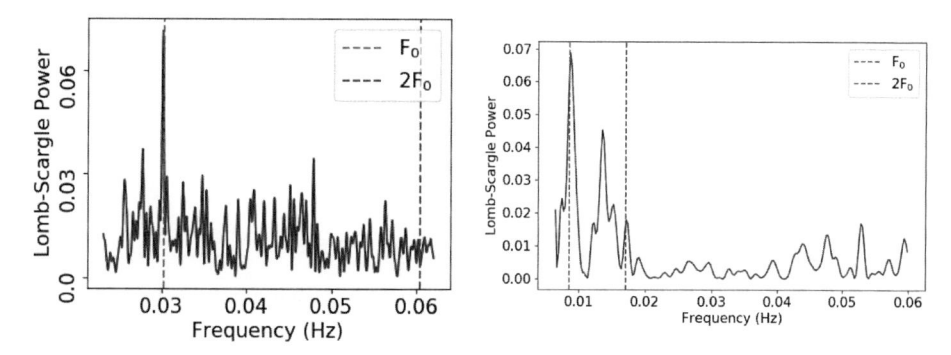

Fig. 3. (a) MeerKAT L-band power spectrum of AE Aqr on 25 February 2019. The power spectrum clearly shows pulsed emission at the spin period of the white dwarf $\nu_\circ = 30.23$ mHz. This is the first report of periodic emission from the white dwarf in AE Aqr in radio. (b) MeerKAT total L-band power spectrum of the short AR Sco observation displayed in Fig. 2b. The power spectrum shows strong pulsed emission close to a beat period between the white dwarf spin period and the orbital period.

is an upgraded version of the earlier versions and allowed for better background estimate, gamma-ray source location and energy determination to name a few.

By utilizing the full 10 year Pass 8 dataset with standard Fermi-tools revealed no steady emission from both these sources. However, when a 10 year light curve was determined for AE Aqr there were sections in the light curve that revealed gamma-ray emission above the 2 sigma significance level. Focusing on these data sections, braking it up in 10 minute sections, each section was searched for period-

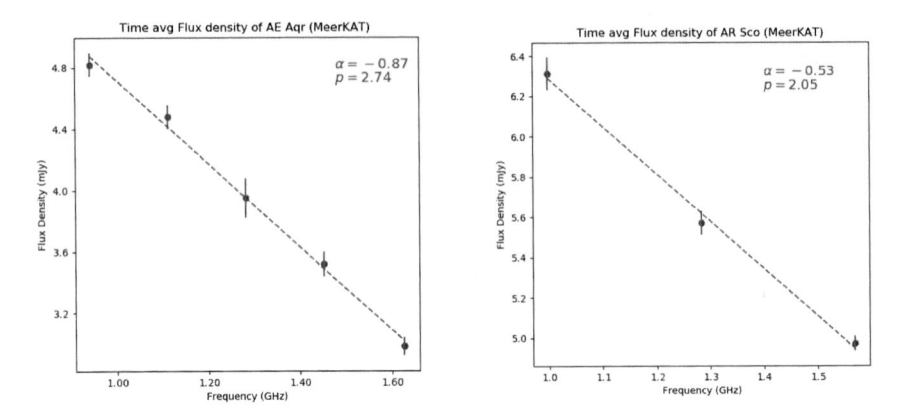

Fig. 4. (a) MeerKAT L-band radio power-law spectrum of AE Aqr. (b) MeerKAT-L-band radio power-law spectrum of AR Sco .

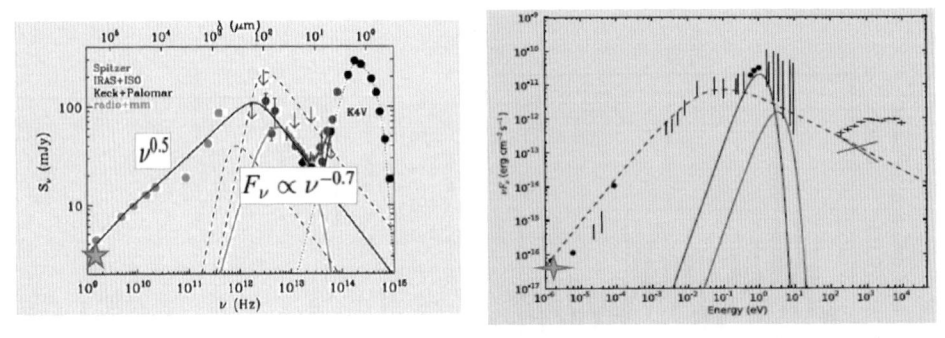

Fig. 5. (a) SED of AE Aqr showing the average MeerKAT L-band flux density (green star) on the SED. Adapted form (10). (b) SED of AR Sco showing the average L-band radio flux density (green cross). Adapted form (11).

icity. The periodograms of these sections all had the same frequency resolution and were then added (stacked) incoherently. These stacked power spectra reveal clear indications of pulsations at both 33.08 s and 16.54 s periods (see Fig. 6a for a few examples). To test whether these pulsations are not spurious we selected regions in the sky consecutively further away from AE Aqr's position in the sky $3° - 15°$ and produced the same power spectra for the same periods. The pulsed power distribution of these were determined and the results displayed in Fig. 6b. Clearly visible is that the power at the 33.08 s and 16.54 s periods deviates from the theoretical white noise distribution for the power spectra produced for data corresponding to AE Aqr's position in the sky, while the distribution of power conforms to a white noise distribution for data sections further away from the source. Fermi-LAT data sections that coincide with optical flares observed with the UFS-Boyden 1.5 m telescope (see Fig. 7a) were selected for periodic analysis. Individual power spectra

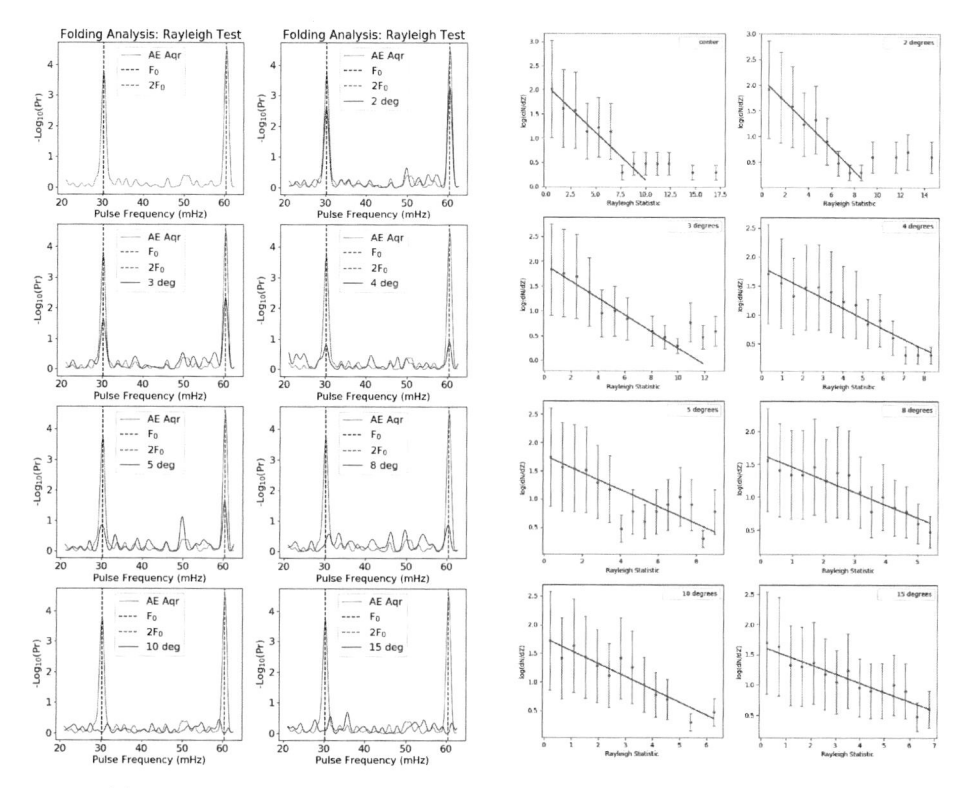

Fig. 6. (a) Example of stacked Fermi power spectra of AE Aqr of epochs showing gamma-ray emission above the 2 sigma significance level. (b) Control analysis showing how the power in the power spectrum return to white noise further away from the source-illustrating that the pulsed power is confined to AE Aqr's position in the sky.

corresponding to flares have been established with the same resolution to enable incoherent stacking (see Fig. 7b). It is clear from Fig. 7b that the gamma-ray periodograms that coincide with enhanced optical activity show clear pulsed emission at a period that corresponds to the spin period of the white dwarf. This result confirms the previously reported pulsed behaviour of VHE emission during optical flares (1, 2).

The unbinned and binned gamma-ray spectra associated with data sections that display a significance above 1σ were produced (see Fig. 8a). Both spectra display a clear power-law profile with photon index $\Gamma \sim 2$. Also shown in Fig. 8a is that the gamma-ray emission seems to be more significant in the lower energy bins. The spectra associated with data sections showing emission above 1σ and 2σ respectively reveal power-law spectra that clearly indicate that AE Aqr may be of interest for more sensitive Air Cherenkov detectors like CTA. It is obvious that when the data sections are selected which reveal gamma-ray emission above the 2σ

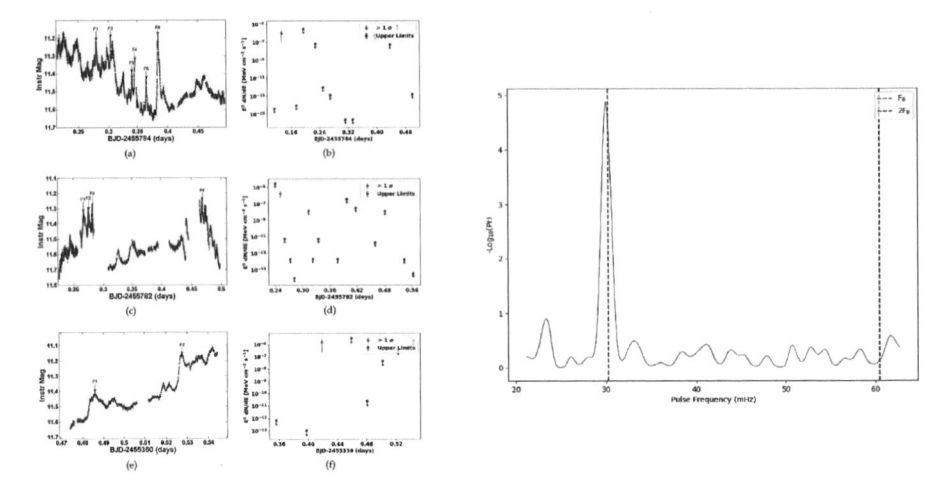

Fig. 7. (a) Optical photometry performed using the UFS-Boyden 1.5 m telescope outside Bloemfontein (South Africa). The gamma-ray data that coincided with optical flares are indicated on the RHS of Fig. 8a. (b) The stacked Fermi-LAT power spectrum of data sections overlapping with optical flares showing clear pulsed emission at or close to the 33.08 s spin period of the white dwarf.

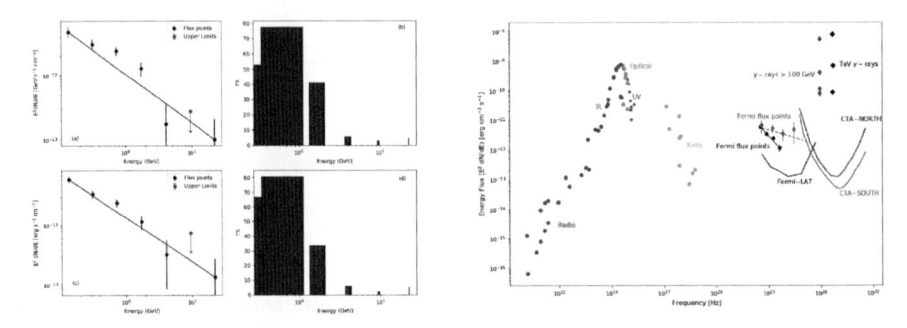

Fig. 8. (a) Gamma-ray spectra for both binned and unbinned analysis, Clearly showing is that the lower energy bins contribute most of the flux. (b) The gamma-ray spectra for quiescence and flare sections of the Fermi-LAT data. It can be seen that the flare sections of the data display spectral hardening which may indicate that AE Aqr may be a source that is of interest for the future Cherenkov Telescope Array (CTA).

level, spectral hardening is observed (see Fig. 8b (red spectrum)), which may result in detectable flux levels during periods of enhanced activity.

The total 10 year Fermi-LAT data of AR Sco was searched for steady gamma-ray emission using the standard Fermi-LAT science tools. No significant steady gamma-ray emission could be distinguished above the 2σ Fermi-LAT threshold (see Fig. 9a). A search for pulsed emission was conducted using the full 10 year Fermi-LAT data. The power spectrum (Fig. 9b) reveals pulsed emission at or close to the spin period of the white dwarf. The period range has been limited to a narrow region around

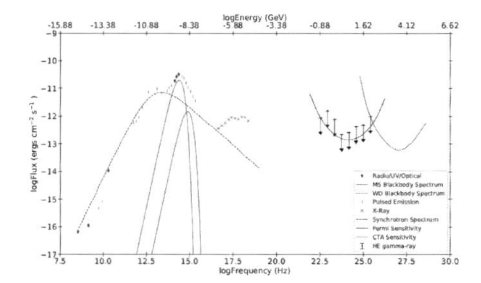

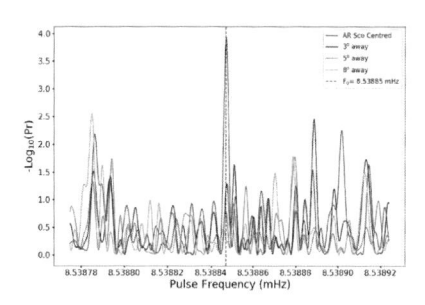

Fig. 9. (a) Gamma-ray spectrum combined with the multi-wavelength SED for AR Sco showing 2 sigma Fermi-LAT upperlimits. (b) The 10 year Fermi-LAT gamma-ray power spectrum revealing pulsations close to the spin period of the white dwarf. Control power spectra at several spatial separations from $3° - 8°$ away from the location of AR Sco does not reveal similar pulsed emission.

the spin period of the white dwarf. To test the validity of these results regions in the sky further away from the position of AR Sco have been selected and the same periodic analysis has been conducted on those sections. These control power spectra correspond to regions in the sky separated from the position of AR Sco between $3°$ - $8°$ are also included in Fig. 9b and show no significant pulsed emission at or close to the spin period of the white dwarf. This may support the notion that low-level pulsed gamma-ray activity may in fact be associated with AR Sco.

4. Discussion

The results from the MeerKAT observations and our analyses of the Fermi-LAT data reveal that both AE Aqr and AR Sco contain a particle accelerator of some sort. For example, the MeerKAT data reveal pulsed emission from AE Aqr at the spin period of the white dwarf. This is the first report of pulsed radio emission from AE Aqr and it makes the white dwarf in this system probably one of the fastest white dwarf radio pulsars. Similarly AR Sco is showing pulsed radio emission at the beat period between the spin and orbital period. This may be the result of the white dwarf's magnetosphere pumping the extended magnetosphere of the secondary star, resulting in particle acceleration and non-thermal synchrotron emission. The Fermi-LAT analysis of both these sources reveal pulsed emission. AE Aqr reveals pulsed emission in gamma-rays that resembles reported emission during flare-like events by two independent groups. A period search on data sections displaying flux above the 2 σ level in both binned and unbinned analyses show clear indications of pulsed emission at or close to the white dwarf spin period and its associated first harmonic. A full 10 year periodic power spectrum of AR Sco reveals pulsed power at or close to the spin period of the white dwarf. For both these sources a control analysis has been performed that validates the authenticity of our detection.

Both these sources are not powered by mass accretion and the majority of the emission is in some or other way related to the spin-down power of the white dwarf.

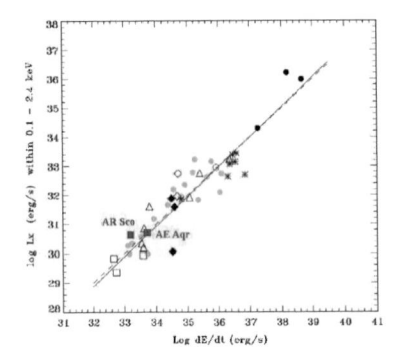

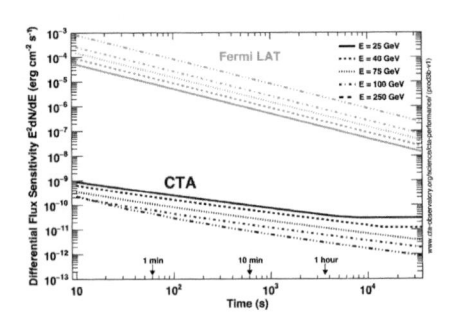

Fig. 10. (a) The X-ray power vs spin-down power of both AE Aqr and AR Sco showing the familiar ratio of X-ray luminosity to spin-down power characteristic of spin-powered neutron stars. Adapted from (12). (b) The most recent 2019 detection threshold comparison between Fermi-LAT and CTA for various observing periods. (**https://www.cta-observatory.org/the-low-end-why-cta-interested-low-energy-gamma-rays**).

Both these sources conform to the well known relation found in rotation powered neutron stars (Fig. 10a), namely that $L_X \sim 10^{-3} L_{s-d}$ (12), meaning that the X-ray emission is not driven by the accretion of mass onto the surface but is driven through a plethora of processes by the spin-down power reservoir. This places both these sources in a unique class. The results that we have presented also show that both these sources provide an opportunity for detection with a new generation of sophisticated ground-based Cherenkov observatories like the Cherenkov Telescope Array (CTA). For example, Fig. 10b shows the latest comparison between the low-energy sensitivity of Fermi-LAT and CTA, which differs slightly form the earlier comparison (13). It is clear that the CTA array will reach the relevant flux levels at energies $\epsilon_\gamma \leq 50$ GeV after observing times of $t_{obs} \sim$ few $\times$ 10^4 s. However, it may be possible to extract a periodic signal after stacking power spectra of shorter observations with similar resolution. The confirmed detection of pulsed gamma-ray emission from both these sources may in fact establish fast rotating highly magnetized white dwarfs in close binaries as a new class of gamma-ray source.

Acknowledgements

The authors thank the organisers of the conference for the invitation to present these results. The authors also acknowledge the Fermi-LAT and MeerKAT collaborations for the gamma-ray and radio data being analysed and presented in this study.

References

1. P.J. Meintjes, et al. 1992, AE Aquarii: An emitter of pulsed gamma-ray emission resembling optical emission during flares, *Astrophysical Journal*, **401**, 325
2. P.J. Meintjes et al. 1994, Simultaneous optical and TeV Gamma-Ray observations of the cataclysmic variable AE Aquarii, *Astrophysical Journal*, **434**, 292

3. C.C.G. Bowden et al. 1992, Sporadic pulsed 350 GeV gamma-ray emission detected from AE Aqr. *Astroparticle Physics* **1**, 47
4. J. Aleksic et al. 2014, MAGIC search for pulsed VHE gamma-ray emission from AE Aquarii in a multiwavelelength context, *Astronomy and Astrophysics*, **568** A109
5. T.R. Marsh et al. 2016, A radio puling white dwarf binary star, *Nature*, **537**, 374
6. D.A.H. Buckley et al. 2017, Polarimetric evidence of a white dwarf pulsar in the binary system AR Scorpii, *Nature Astronomy*, **1**, 0029
7. K.K. Singh, P.J. Meintjes, Q. Kaplan, F.A. Ramamonjisoa & S. Sahayanathan 2020, Modelling the broadband emission from the white dwarf binary system AR Scorpii, *Astroparticle Physics*, 123, 102488
8. K.K. Singh, P.J. Meintjes, K.K. Yadav 2021, Properties of white dwarf in the binary system AR Scorpii and its observed features, *Modern Physics, Lett. A*, 36, 2150096
9. R. Fender, P.A. Woudt et al. 2017, ThundeKAT: The MeerKAT large survey project for image-plane radio transients, In Proceedings of "MeerKAT Science: On the Pathway to the SKA, 25-27 May, 2016, Stellenbosch, South Africa", *Proceedings of Science*, (PoS(MeerKAT2016(013))
10. G, Dubus et al. 2007, Spitzer space telescope observations of the magnetic cataclysmic variable AE Aquarii, *Astrophysical Journal*, **663**, 516
11. J. Takata et al. 2018, A nonthermal pulsed x-ray emission of AR Scorpii, *Astrophysical Journal*, **853**, 106
12. W. Becker and J. Trumpher 1997, The x-ray luminosity of rotation powered neutron stars, *Astronomy and Astrophysics*, **326**, 682
13. S. Funk, J.A. Hinton and the CTA Consortium 2013, Comparison of Fermi-LAT and CTA in the region between 10 to 100 GeV, *Astroparticle Physics*, **43**, 348-355

Study the effects of anisotropy on the highly magnetized white dwarfs

Debabrata Deb

Department of Physics, Indian Institute of Science, Bangalore 560012, India
E-mail: debabratadeb@iisc.ac.in

Banibrata Mukhopadhyay

Department of Physics, Indian Institute of Science, Bangalore 560012, India
E-mail: bm@iisc.ac.in

Fridolin Weber

Department of Physics, San Diego State University, San Diego, CA 92182, USA
Center for Astrophysics and Space Sciences, University of California at San Diego,
La Jolla, CA 92093, USA
E-mail: fweber@sdsu.edu

> The equilibrium configuration of white dwarfs composed of anisotropic fluid distribution in the presence of a strong magnetic field is investigated in this work. By considering a functional form of the anisotropic stress and magnetic field profile, some physical properties of magnetized white dwarfs, such as mass, radius, density, radial and tangential pressures, are derived; their dependency on the anisotropy and central magnetic field is also explored. We show that the orientations of the magnetic field along the radial direction or orthogonal to the radial direction influence the stellar structure and physical properties of white dwarfs significantly. Importantly, we show that ignoring anisotropy governed by the fluid due to its high density in the presence of a strong magnetic field would destabilize the star. Through this work, we can explain the highly massive progenitor for peculiar over-luminous type Ia supernovae, and low massive progenitor for under-luminous type Ia supernovae, which poses a question of considering 1.4 solar mass white dwarf to be related to the standard candle.
>
> *Keywords*: Magnetic fields; white dwarfs; super-Chandrasekhar white dwarf; massive stars

1. Introduction

In a recent article, we have shown that the presence of strong magnetic field, orientations of magnetic field and the combined anisotropy due to both the matter and magnetic field exhibit notable influence on the microscopic and thermodynamic properties of compact stars, viz., neutron stars and strange quark stars. We have also very briefly discussed in their study (hereinafter Paper I) that same effects can be observed for magnetized and anisotropic white dwarfs (WDs) which further may leads to possible violation of Chandrasekhar critical mass limit. Importantly Paper I shows that to achieve hydrostatic stable configuration for the highly magnetized compact stars, it is necessary to consider local pressure anisotropy due to matter besides the anisotropy due to magnetic field. Following Paper I, in the present work we assume two type of magnetic field orientations, such as *radial orientation (RO)* when the magnetic field is directed toward the radial direction and *transverse orientation (TO)* when field is oriented perpendicular to the radial direction (say along θ or ϕ directions). In this work, we investigate in detail the effects of magnetic field strength, their orientations and anisotropy on the highly magnetized WDs and their thermodynamic parameters.

WDs achieve stable stellar configuration via equilibrium of the forces when the inward gravitational pull is counterbalanced by the outward repulsive electron degeneracy pressure. During the accretion of mass from the companion stars when WDs surpass their critical mass limit, immediately a violent explosion triggers, which completely disrupt WDs and releases huge amount of energy of the order $\sim 10^{51}$ erg, known as type Ia supernova (SNIa). The critical mass limit was introduced by Chandrasekhar in his famous works[2,3] where he predicted that the critical mass limit for non-magnetized and non-rotating carbon-oxygen (C-O) WD is 1.4 $M_\odot$ which is known as "Chandrasekhar mass limit" (CML) for WDs.

The standard and specific set of relations among colour, intrinsic luminosity and light-curve width[4,5] make SNIa a perfect candidate for "standard candle" which helps astronomers to measure accurately the distance of the host galaxy. Behind the measurement of cosmological parameters, the disproportional relation between distance and luminosity of SNIa is used as a key technique. In fact, SNIa as a "standard candle" had pivotal role to confirm the accelerated expansion of universe.[6,7] However, the idea of "standard candle" faces a major setback with the recent series of observation of several peculiar over-luminous type Ia supernovae (SNeIa) such as *SN 2003cv*,[8] *SN2007fg*,[9] *SN2009if*[10] and *SN 2013dc*,[11] which are best explained through WDs as a progenitor having mass beyond CML. Howell and collaborators[8] predicted that to explain *SN 2003cv* it requires to power by the radioactive decay of $\sim 1.3 M_\odot$ of ^{56}Ni which further predicts $\sim 2.1 M_\odot$ WD as a progenitor, known as *super-Chandrasekhar progenitor WD* (SCPWD). Later researchers have predicted further massive SCPWD against the overluminous SN 2009if of mass as high as $\sim 2.8 M_\odot$.

To explain these unexpected overluminous SNeIa, researchers suggested two possible conjectures such as (i) explosion of rapidly rotating WDs[8,12,13] and (ii) merger of two massive WDs.[14,15] Chen and Li[22] showed that the differentially rotating and accreting WD can not gain mass more than 1.7 $M_\odot$. On the other hand, further investigations showed that through the double degenerate scenario, it is not possible to explain such a highly massive 2.8 $M_\odot$ SCPWD.[16–21] The results from numerical simulation of massive WD merger suggest that due to off-center carbon burning accreting WD collapses into neutron star.[23,24] Hence, it is evident through the above discussion that the double degenerate scenario conjectures never leads to a SNIa which can explain the massive SCPWDs.

Introducing magnetic model, Mukhopadhyay and collaborators[25,26] are able to explain SCPWDs where they considered Landau levels due to high magnetic field in a plane perpendicular to the magnetic field axis and they[27] are also able to suitably explain $\sim 2.6\ M_\odot$ highly massive SCPWD. In another study, Das and Mukhopadhyay[28] showed that the average magnetic field and related magnetic pressure are significantly low compared to the matter pressure when inside magnetized WDs (hereinafter B-WDs) the strong magnetic field is tangled in a length scale larger than quantum length scale, which however leads to the Landau quantization to matter. The mass-radius relation for B-WDs deviates significantly beyond CML when mass accretion continues as the effective pressure counterbalances the inward gravitational pull.[25, 29] Das and Mukhopadhyay[30] further predicated that it requires a time scale of 2×10^7 years to turn into a super-Chandrasekhar B-WD (SCBWD) for a $0.2\ M_\odot$ accreting WD having surface magnetic field (B_s) 10^9 G. In fact for the last several years, Mukhopadhyay and his group have explored various aspects of SCBWDs through different sophisticated models by considering variation of magnetic field and geometry, Landau quantization, a pure general relativistic effect, differential rotation, deviation from the spherical symmetric stellar configuration and thermal luminosity, etc.[31–38] They also explored the techniques of the possible direct detection of SCBWDs via continuous gravitational wave astronomy by the various upcoming detectors, such as BBO, DECIGO and LISA. The idea of SCBWDs has been further studied and supported by different independent researcher works.[41–47]

Bowers and Liang[48] raised a strong argument against the oversimplified assumption of the isotropic perfect fluid as the constituent matter distribution of compact stars and proposed a modified Tolman-Oppenheimer-Volkoff (TOV) equation,[49, 50] which includes another force raised due to pressure anisotropy, besides the hydrodynamic and gravitational force. They also explored notable effect of local anisotropy due to matter on the different physical properties of the stellar objects, such as density, surface redshift, total mass and radius. Letelier[51] and Bayin[52] pointed out that the possible reason behind this local anisotropy is the presence and mixture of two (or more) fluid within stellar interior. On the other hand, the breaking of spatial rotational symmetry $\mathcal{O}(3)$ due to spontaneous creation of magnetic field instigates pressure anisotropy in the stellar interior.[53–55] Interestingly, during the cooling process of WDs at low temperature, they undergoes a first-order phase transition,[56–58] which is another possible reason for the presence of anisotropy inside the dense plasma. Stevenson[59] introduced a phase diagram through which they predicted that carbon and oxygen remains immiscible when WDs begin to freeze. Later, Garcia and collaborators[60] further explored and confirmed this idea. Nag and Chakrabarty[61] also supported the idea of first-order phase transition during the cooling of WDs through the Bose condensation. In fact, they proposed that "*crystalline normal crustal matter*" is present at the massive WDs core, which is also Bose condensed and similar as the ultra-dense structure of the neutron stars. So, based on the above discussion we are convinced to consider local anisotropy of matter inside WDs.

In this context, it is worth mentioning that though there are several articles[32, 33, 39, 40, 62–71] which study non-spherical magnetized compact stars in general relativity based on the perturbative approach to solve the the Einstein-Maxwell field equations or the numerical techniques (such as Lorene and XNS codes) by considering poloidal or toroidal or mixed field geometries, but they did not include the effects of anisotropy. Although, a recent work[72] has explored the effect of anisotropy on WDs in scalar-tensor (ST) theories of gravity but it did not consider magnetic field. The idea of magnetic field orientations viz. RO and TO was originally coined by Chu et al.[73] In the present study, we explore the combined effects of magnetic field strength, its orientations and anisotropy on the WDs to have a more generalized perspective of the WD stellar interior.

This paper is organized as follows: We discuss the basic mathematical formalism in Section 2. Our results and combined effects of the magnetic field, its orientations and anisotropy on the physical properties of WDs are discussed in Section 3. Finally, we summarise our work and present some concluding remarks in Section 4.

2. Basic mathematical formulation

Mukhopadhyay and group[32,33,39] have shown that the magnetized compact stars which are toroidally dominated approximately retains their spherical symmetric stellar structure. Hence in this work we describe B-WDs by the spherically symmetric spacetime metric given by

$$ds^2 = e^{\nu(r)}dt^2 - e^{\lambda(r)}dr^2 - r^2(d\theta^2 + \sin^2\theta d\phi^2), \tag{1}$$

where we assume that the metric potentials ν and λ are functions of radial coordinate r. We choose $c = G = 1$, where G is Newton's gravitational constant and c is the speed of light.

Now neglecting the effect of the electric field by assuming that inside the B-WDs there are no macroscopic charges, the energy-momentum tensor, which describes anisotropic and magnetized matter distribution, reads

$$T_m^{\mu\nu} = (\rho + p_t)u^\mu u^\nu - p_t g^{\mu\nu} + (p_r - p_t) v^\mu v^\nu$$
$$+ \mathcal{M}B\left(g^{\mu\nu} - u^\mu u^\nu + \frac{B^\mu B^\nu}{B^2}\right) + \frac{B^2}{4\pi}\left(u^\mu u^\nu - \frac{1}{2}g^{\mu\nu}\right) - \frac{B^\mu B^\nu}{4\pi}, \tag{2}$$

where $u^\mu = \delta_0^\mu e^{-\nu(r)/2}$ is a timelike 4-velocity unit vector of fluid and $v^\mu = \delta_1^\mu e^{-\lambda(r)/2}$ is a spacelike unit vector acting along the radial direction. It is noteworthy that these orthogonal vectors satisfy $u^\mu u_\mu = -v^\mu v_\mu = 1$ and $u^\mu v_\mu = 0$. Here, ρ, p_r and p_t are the density, radial pressure and tangential pressure of the matter inside B-WDs. $g_{\mu\nu}$ denotes metric tensor and $\mathcal{M}$ represents magnetization per unit volume. B is the magnetic field strength given by $B^\mu B_\mu = -B^2$. On the other hand, we do not consider the associated magnetization effect since magnetic pressure is one order higher in magnitude compared to the magnetization which has already been predicted by a few articles.[53,74] So in this work the presented numerical results do not include effect of magnetization.

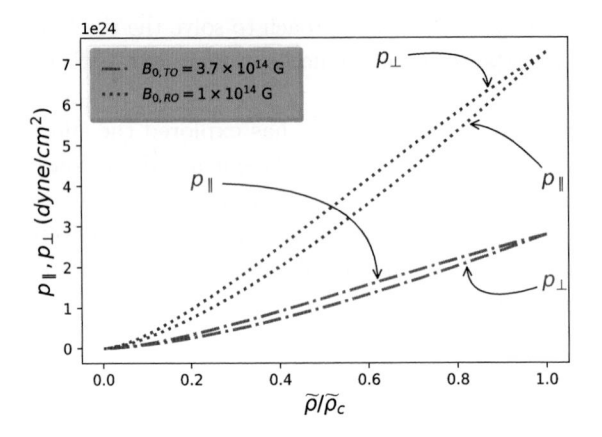

Fig. 1. Variation of parallel pressure ($p_\parallel$) and transverse pressure ($p_\perp$) with the system density ($\tilde{\rho}$) normalized by the central system density ($\tilde{\rho}_c$) for a 1.3 $M_\odot$ magnetized WD candidate.

Now using Eqs. (1) and (2) the conservation of energy-momentum tensor, i.e., $\nabla_\mu T^{\mu\nu} = 0$, leads to the essential stellar structure equations which describe static and anisotropic B-WDs as follows:

$$\frac{dm}{dr} = 4\pi \tilde{\rho} r^2, \tag{3}$$

$$\begin{cases} \dfrac{dp_\parallel}{dr} = -(\tilde{\rho} + p_\parallel) \dfrac{4\pi r^3 p_\parallel + m}{r(r-2m)} + \dfrac{2}{r}\Delta, & \text{for RO,} \\[2mm] \dfrac{dp_\perp}{dr} = -(\tilde{\rho} + p_\perp) \dfrac{4\pi r^3 p_\perp + m}{r(r-2m)} + \dfrac{2}{r}\Delta, & \text{for TO.} \end{cases} \tag{4}$$

where $\tilde{\rho}$ is the system density defined as $\tilde{\rho} = \rho + \frac{B^2}{8\pi}$, $p_\parallel$ and $p_\perp$ are the system pressures, which take the form based on the magnetic field orientations as follows:

$$p_\parallel = \begin{cases} p_r - \dfrac{B^2}{8\pi}, & \text{for RO,} \\[2mm] p_t - \dfrac{B^2}{8\pi}, & \text{for TO.} \end{cases} \tag{5}$$

and (6)

$$p_\perp = \begin{cases} p_t + \dfrac{B^2}{8\pi}, & \text{for RO,} \\[2mm] p_r + \dfrac{B^2}{8\pi}, & \text{for TO.} \end{cases} \tag{7}$$

In Eq. (4), Δ denotes effective anisotropy of the stars and based on the choice of magnetic field orientations it takes the forms as $p_t - p_r + \frac{B^2}{4\pi}$ and $p_t - p_r - \frac{B^2}{8\pi}$ due to RO and TO, respectively. One may get the standard form of TOV equations[48,75] for non-magnetized and anisotropic starts for $B = 0$.

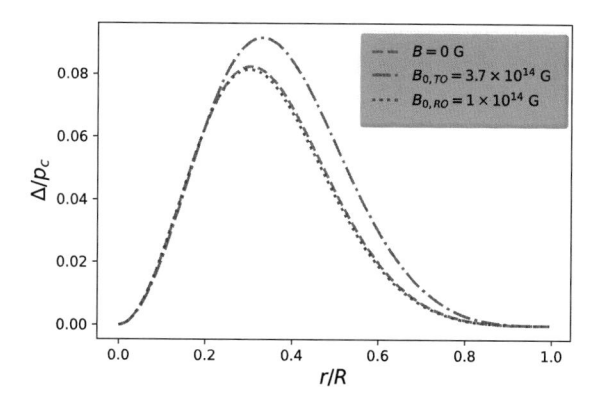

Fig. 2. Variation of anisotropy (Δ) normalized by matter central pressure (p_c) with the radial coordinate r/R for a 1.3 $M_\odot$ magnetized WD candidate.

Bowers and Liang proposed a generalized functional form for the anisotropic stress which has been widely used in different studies. However, since for the present work we require a functional form for anisotropy which includes both the effects of magnetic field strength and magnetic field orientation, we have suitably modified the Bowers-Liang anisotropic form which reads

$$\Delta = \begin{cases} \kappa \dfrac{(\tilde{\rho} + p_\parallel)(\tilde{\rho} + 3p_\parallel)}{(r - 2m)} r^3, & \text{for RO,} \\ \kappa \dfrac{(\tilde{\rho} + p_\perp)(\tilde{\rho} + 3p_\perp)}{(r - 2m)} r^3, & \text{for TO,} \end{cases} \quad (8)$$

where κ is a constant parameter that controls the amount of anisotropy within the star and we use κ maintaining its permissible range, given by $[-\frac{2}{3}, \frac{2}{3}]$.[76] Now, one may notice that if matter anisotropy is not considered, the anisotropic stress become $\sim |B^2|$, which has a finite, non-zero value at the stellar center. Since at the center, the hydrodynamic and gravitational forces are zero, non-zero anisotropic force at the center should trigger instability due to nonequilibrium of the forces. We show this issue can easily be overcome considering combined anisotropy due to both the matter and magnetic field.

Further, to describe matter distribution of WDs we consider equation of state (EoS) proposed by Chandrasekhar which reads

$$p_r = \frac{\pi m_e^4 c^5}{3h^3} \left[x(2x^2 - 3)\sqrt{x^2 + 1} + 3\sinh^{-1} x \right],$$
$$\rho = \frac{8\pi \mu_e m_H (m_e c)^3}{3h^3} x^3, \quad (9)$$

where m_H and m_e denote mass of hydrogen atom and electron, respectively, $\mu_e = 2$ is the mean molecular weight., p_F is the Fermi momentum and $x = p_F/m_e c$. Note that for clarity here we introduce the speed of light c and Planck constant h in their appropriate places. For the present case of C-O WDs we have $\mu_e = 2$. We consider the exterior spacetime is defined by the well-known Schwarzschild exterior spacetime, given by

$$ds^2 = \left(1 - \frac{2M}{r}\right)dt^2 - \frac{1}{\left(1 - \frac{2M}{r}\right)}dr^2 - r^2(d\theta^2 + \sin^2\theta d\phi^2), \tag{10}$$

where M represents total mass of the star.

Both the fossil field of the progenitor star[31,33,77] and dynamo effect[78] ensure stronger magnetic field at the center (B_c), which decreases gradually to reach its minimum value at the surface (B_s). Hence, in this work we consider a density dependent functional form for the magnetic field,[31,36,79,80] which can suitably mimic the spatial dependence of magnetic field strength, given by

$$B(\rho) = B_s + B_0 \left[1 - \exp\left\{-\eta \left(\frac{\rho}{\rho_0}\right)^\gamma\right\}\right], \tag{11}$$

where the η and γ are the dimensionless constants which controls how fast magnetic field strength decays from the center to the surface. In this work we chose $\rho_0 = 10^9$ g/cm^3, $\gamma = 0.9$ and $\eta = 0.2$.[36] We also consider $B_s = 10^9$ G which is consistent with the Sloan Digital Sky Survey.[81]

3. Result and discussion

In this study, we explore that besides magnetic field strength, the magnetic field orientations (such as RO and TO) and combined anisotropy due to matter and field significantly influence the mass-radius curve and physical parameters of B-WDs. Note that to present some basic properties of thermodynamics and anisotropy we consider a 1.3 $M_\odot$ B-WD candidate having surface magnetic field 10^9 G in Figs. 1 and 2. Further, our choices of B_0 for RO and TO are different as they exhibit an asymmetric effect on the stellar mass. In the figures, we put RO and TO in the subscript of B_0 to specify the respective magnetic field orientations. It is also noteworthy that our choice of B_0 is also motivated by the highly massive SCPWDs of peculiar over-luminous SNeIa.

In Fig. 1 we feature combined effects of magnetic field strength and its orientations on the system parallel pressure $p_\parallel$ and transverse pressure $p_\perp$. We find that for TO, as B_0 increases, the slope of the system pressures decreases gradually, whereas, for RO with the increasing B_0, the system pressures become gradually stiffened. This phenomenon is because, as B_0 increases in the TO case, the stellar radius increases, which reduces gravitational force and consequently decreases the hydrodynamic force. However, for increasing B_0 in the RO case, the stellar radius of B-WDs decreases, consequently increasing outward hydrodynamic force to support the increased gravitation force. Importantly, note that at the center the effective anisotropy is zero since $p_\parallel = p_\perp$ at $r = 0$, which reflects consistency of TOV equations. In Fig. 2 we show the profile for system anisotropy Δ which also shows zero anisotropy at the center.

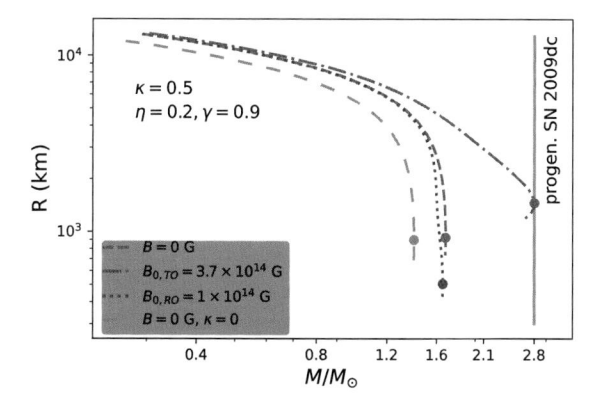

Fig. 3. Variation of the total mass in the units of solar mass ($M/M_\odot$) with the total radius (R) of the stars for varying B_0 and $\kappa = 0.5$. Solid circles represent maximum possible mass for the stars.

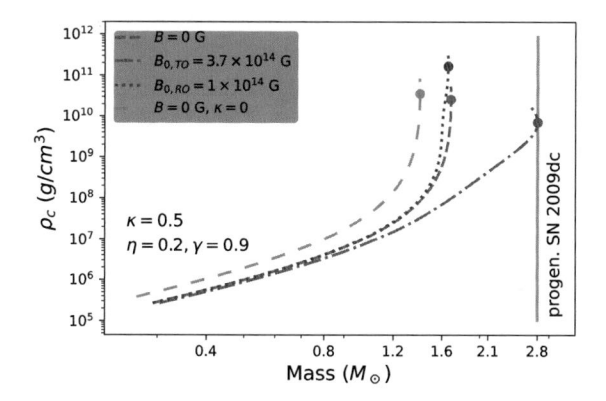

Fig. 4. Variation of $M/M_\odot$ as a function of the matter central density (ρ_c). Solid circles represent maximum possible mass for the stars.

Further, one may note that the maximum magnitude of anisotropy increases with increasing B_0 for the TO case, whereas it decreases for the RO case. We find that for $B_0 = 3.7 \times 10^{14}$ G the maximum magnitude of Δ is $\sim 92\%$ lower compared to the central matter pressure p_c which is insufficient to drive the spherical symmetric stellar structure of B-WDs to non-spherical symmetry.

The total mass and radius (M-R) curve for B-WDs due to different B_0 for both RO and TO is shown in Fig. 3. We find the maximum mass (M_{max}) and the corresponding radius (R_{Mmax}) in TO due to $B_0 = 3.7 \times 10^{14}$ G are 2.8 $M_\odot$ and 1457.24 km, respectively, whereas in RO due to $B_{0,\text{TO}} = 10^{14}$ G they are 1.66 $M_\odot$ and 507.10 km, respectively. In TO due to $B_{0,\text{TO}} = 3.7 \times 10^{14}$ G, M_{max} and R_{Mmax} increase compared to their non-magnetized anisotropic case of $\sim 66\%$ and $\sim 57\%$, respectively, whereas in RO due to $B_{0,\text{RO}} = 10^{14}$ G they decrease to $\sim 2\%$ and $\sim 45\%$, respectively. Only considering local anisotropy due to matter and not

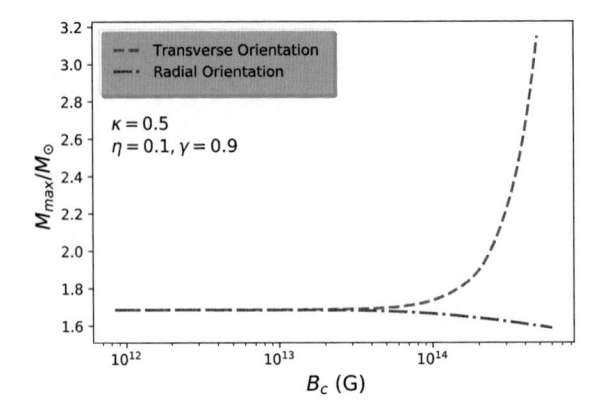

Fig. 5. Variation of $M/M_\odot$ with the central magnetic field (B_c).

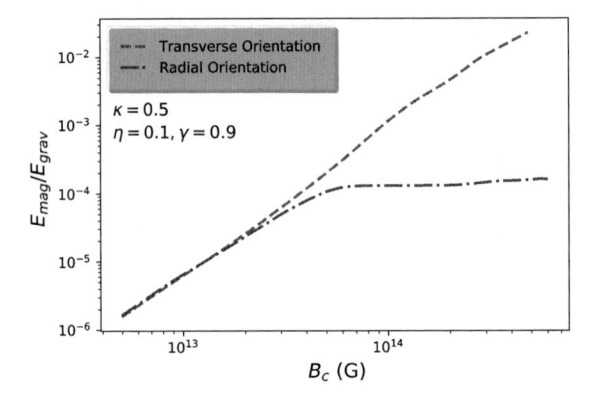

Fig. 6. Variation of the ratio of the magnetic energy (E_{mag}) to the gravitational energy (E_{grav}) with the central magnetic field (B_c).

considering magnetic field through our model one may have 1.81 $M_\odot$ WD having radius 959.63 km which are ∼29% and ∼7%, respectively, higher compared to their values for WD CML. Harrison et al.[82] predicted that for the stability of a spherically symmetric stellar model the M-R relation should be consistent with $dM/d\rho_c > 0$ up to M_{max}. It has been shown in Fig. 4, which confirms stable B-WDs upto maximum limiting mass.

In Fig. 5 we explore the effects of magnetic field orientations on the mass of B-WDs. The effects of magnetic field strength on M_{max} for the TO and RO cases are asymmetric which motivates us to chose different B_0 for different magnetic field orientations. One may find that for a specific set of constant parameter such as $\eta = 0.1$, $\gamma = 0.9$ and $\kappa = 0.5$ the asymmetry of maximum mass for the TO and RO cases due to $B_c = 4 \times 10^{14}$ G is ∼65% which confirms significant effect of

Table 1. Physical parameters of WDs with $\kappa = 0.5$, $\eta = 0.2$ and $\gamma = 0.9$ for different B_0.

Orientation of magnetic field	B_0 (Gauss)	Maximum predicted mass ($M_\odot$)	Corresponding radius (km)	Central magnetic field B_c (Gauss)	Central density $\tilde{\rho}_c$ (gm/cm^3)	Central pressure $\tilde{p}_c$ ($dyne/cm^2$)	$\frac{E_{\mathrm{mag}}}{E_{\mathrm{grav}}}$
Transverse Orientation	3.7×10^{14}	2.80	1457.24	2.538×10^{14}	7.040×10^9	2.809×10^{28}	1.405×10^{-2}
No magnetic Field	-	1.69	926.91	-	2.560×10^{10}	9.865×10^{28}	-
Radial Orientation	10^{14}	1.66	507.10	10^{14}	1.665×10^{11}	1.152×10^{30}	7.227×10^{-5}

magnetic field orientations on B-WDs. Fig. 5 features that for TO (RO) the increase (decrease) of $M_{\max}$ is rapid (slow) with the increase of central magnetic field B_c.

Chandrasekhar and Fermi[83] predicted that for magnetized spherical symmetric stable compact stars it is not sufficient that they are consistent with the inequality $\Gamma > 4/3$ as the strong magnetic field may lead to stellar instability. They further predicted that for the dynamical stability of the magnetized compact stars the necessary condition is $E_{\mathrm{mag}}/|E_{\mathrm{grav}}| \ll 1$, where E_{mag} and $|E_{\mathrm{grav}}|$ denote the magnetic and gravitational potential energies, respectively. In Fig. 6 we present that for both TO and RO due to different B_0, $|E_{\mathrm{grav}}|$ overpowers E_{mag} considerably to achieve dynamical stability of B-WDs.

For the better understanding of the readers, we present the obtained results for the different cases in Table 1. We present the variation of $M_{\max}$, R, B_c, system central density ($\tilde{\rho}_c$), system central pressure ($\tilde{p}_c$) and $E_{\mathrm{mag}}/|E_{\mathrm{grav}}|$ with different B_0 for both TO and RO and non-magnetized cases in Table 1. Note that the presented results in Table. 1 are based on the chosen set of constants such as $\eta = 0.2$, $\gamma = 0.9$ and $\kappa = 0.5$. Clearly, for TO with the increase of B_0, B-WDs become massive, larger in size and less dense compact object, whereas for RO as B_0 increases B-WDs become gradually less massive, smaller in size and highly dense compact object compared to their non-magnetized case.

4. Conclusion

In the present work we explore the combined effects due to magnetic field strength, orientations of magnetic field and effective anisotropy raised due to matter and field on B-WDs. Although anisotropic WDs were studied by Chowdhury and Sarkar,[72] their study was based on the non-magnetised case. On the other hand, Chu et al.[73] explored the effect of magnetic field and their orientation on total mass of compact stars. However, they ignored important effect of anisotropy and did not show effects of magnetic field orientations on the different physical parameters of compact stars. In this work for the first time we have studied the combined effects of magnetic field strength, their orientations and anisotropy on WDs in the strong magnetic field. In conclusion, the two major results of our study on B-WDs are as follows:

(i) We show that to achieve magneto-hydrostatic stability at the stellar center of B-WDs, the effective anisotropy due to matter and magnetic field should be considered.

(ii) With the choice of appropriate set of constant parameters such as κ and B_0 our model can appropriately explain massive progenitors of peculiar over luminous SNeIa as high as 2.8 $M_\odot$, which further raise question regarding the idea of 1.4 $M_\odot$ WDs as the "standard candle".

Acknowledgments

Research of DD is funded by the C.V. Raman Postdoctoral Fellowship (Reg. No. R(IA)CVR-PDF/2020/222) from the Department of Physics, Indian Institute of Science. BM acknowledges partial support by a project of the Department of Science and Technology (DST), India, with Grant No. DSTO/PPH/BMP/1946 (EMR/2017/001226). All computations were performed in open source softwares, and the authors are sincerely thankful to the open source community.

References

1. D. Deb, B. Mukhopadhyay and F. Weber, *accepted for publication in ApJ, arXiv:2108.12436* (2021); Paper I.
2. S. Chandrasekhar, *Astrophys. J.* **74**, 81 (1931).
3. S. Chandrasekhar, *Mon. Not. R. Astron. Soc.* **95**, 207 (1935).
4. M. M. Phillips, *Astrophys. J. Lett.* **413**, L105 (1993).
5. G. Goldhaber, D. E. Groom, A. Kim, G. Aldering, P. Astier, A. Conley, S. E. Deustua, et al. *Astrophys. J.* **558**, 359 (2001).
6. A. G. Riess, A. V. Filippenko, P. Challis, A. Clocchiatti, A. Diercks, P. M. Garnavich, R. L. Gilliland, et al., *Astron. J.* **116**, 1009 (1998).
7. S. Perlmutter, G. Aldering, G. Goldhaber, R. A. Knop, P. Nugent, P. G. Castro, S. Deustua, et al., *Astrophys. J.* **517**, 565 (1999).
8. D. A. Howell, M. Sullivan, P. E. Nugent, R. S. Ellis, A. J. Conley, D. Le Borgne, R. G. Carlberg, et al., *Nature* **443**, 308 (2006).
9. R. A. Scalzo, G. Aldering, P. Antilogus, C. Aragon, S. Bailey, C. Baltay, S. Bongard, et al., *Astrophys. J.* **713**, 1073 (2010).
10. Taubenberger S., Benetti S., Childress M., Pakmor R., Hachinger S., Mazzali P. A., Stanishev V., et al., *Mon. Not. R. Astron. Soc.* **412**, 2735 (2011).
11. Y. Cao, J. Johansson, P. E. Nugent, A. Goobar, J. Nordin, S. R. Kulkarni, S. B. Cenko, et al., Astrophys. J. **823**, 147 (2016)
12. K. Boshkayev, L. Izzo, J. A. Rueda Hernandez and R. Ruffini, *Astron. Astrophys.* **555**, A151 (2013).
13. D. Branch, *Nature* **443**, 283 (2006).
14. I. Iben and A. V. Tutukov, *Astrophys. J., Suppl.* **54**, 335 (1984).
15. M. Hicken, P. M. Garnavich, J. L. Prieto, S. Blondin, D. L. DePoy, R. P. Kirshner and J. Parrent, *Astrophys. J. Lett.* **669**, L17 (2007).
16. K. Nomoto, *Astrophys. J.* **277**, 791 (1984).
17. H. Saio and K. Nomoto, *Astron. Astrophys.* **150**, L21 (1985).
18. K. Nomoto, *Astrophys. J.* **322**, 206 (1987).
19. K. Nomoto and Y. Kondo, *Astrophys. J. Lett.* **367**, L19 (1991).
20. F. X. Timmes, S. E. Woosley and R. E. Taam, *Astrophys. J.* **420**, 348 (1994).
21. H. Saio and K. Nomoto, *Astrophys. J.* **500**, 388 (1998).
22. W.-C. Chen and X.-D. Li, *Astrophys. J.* **702**, 686 (2009).

23. H. Saio and K. Nomoto, *Astrophys. J.* **615**, 444 (2004).
24. R. G. Martin, C. A. Tout and P. Lesaffre, *Mon. Not. R. Astron. Soc.* **373**, 263 (2006).
25. U. Das and B. Mukhopadhyay, *Int. J. Mod. Phys. D* **21**, 1242001 (2012a).
26. A. Kundu and B. Mukhopadhyay, *Mod. Phys. Lett. A* **27**, 1250084 (2012).
27. U. Das and B. Mukhopadhyay, *Phys. Rev. Lett.* **110**, 071102 (2013a).
28. U. Das and B. Mukhopadhyay, *Mod. Phys. Lett. A* **29**, 1450035 (2014a).
29. U. Das and B. Mukhopadhyay, *Phys. Rev. D* **86**, 042001 (2012).
30. U. Das and B. Mukhopadhyay, A. R. Rao, *Astrophys. J. Lett.* **767**, L14 (2013).
31. U. Das and B. Mukhopadhyay, *J. Cosmol. Astropart. Phys.* **2014**, 050 (2014).
32. U. Das and B. Mukhopadhyay, *J. Cosmol. Astropart. Phys.* **2015**, 016 (2015a).
33. S. Subramanian and B. Mukhopadhyay, *Mon. Not. R. Astron. Soc.* **454**, 752 (2015).
34. B. Mukhopadhyay and A. R. Rao, *J. Cosmol. Astropart. Phys.* **2016**, 007 (2016).
35. B. Mukhopadhyay, A. R. Rao and T. S. Bhatia, *Mon. Not. R. Astron. Soc.* **472**, 3564 (2017).
36. M. Bhattacharya and B. Mukhopadhyay, S. Mukerjee, *Mon. Not. R. Astron. Soc.* **477**, 2705 (2018).
37. A. Gupta, B. Mukhopadhyay and C. A. Tout, *Mon. Not. R. Astron. Soc.* **496**, 894 (2020).
38. B. Mukhopadhyay, A. Sarkar and C. A. Tout, *Mon. Not. R. Astron. Soc.* **500**, 763 (2021).
39. S. Kalita and B. Mukhopadhyay, *Mon. Not. R. Astron. Soc.* **490**, 2692 (2019).
40. S. Kalita and B. Mukhopadhyay, T. Mondal, T. Bulik, *Astrophys. J.* **896**, 69 (2020).
41. P. Federbush, T. Luo and J. Smoller, *Arch. Ration. Mech. Anal.* **215**, 611 (2015).
42. B. Franzon and S. Schramm, *Phys. Rev. D* **92**, 083006 (2015).
43. B. Franzon and S. Schramm, *Mon. Not. R. Astron. Soc.* **467**, 4484 (2017).
44. M. Moussa, *Ann. Phys.* **420**, 168263 (2020).
45. H. Shah and K. Sebastian, *Astrophys. J.* **843**, 131 (2017).
46. H. Sotani and T. Tatsumi, *Mon. Not. R. Astron. Soc.* **467**, 1249 (2017).
47. S. K. Roy, S. Mukhopadhyay, J. Lahiri and D. N. Basu, *Phys. Rev. D* **100**, 063008 (2019).
48. R. L. Bowers and E. P. T. Liang, *Astrophys. J.* **188**, 657 (1974).
49. R. C. Tolman, *Phys. Rev.* **55**, 364 (1939).
50. J. R. Oppenheimer and G. M. Volkoff, *Phys. Rev.* **55**, 374 (1939).
51. P. S. Letelier, *Phys. Rev. D* **22**, 807 (1980).
52. S. S. Bayin, *Phys. Rev. D* **26**, 1262 (1982).
53. E. J. Ferrer, V. de La Incera, J. P. Keith, I. Portillo and P. L. Springsteen, *Phys. Rev. C* **82**, 065802 (2010).
54. A. A. Isayev and J. Yang, *Phys. Rev. C* **84**, 065802 (2011).
55. A. A. Isayev and J. Yang, *Phys. Lett. B* **707**, 163 (2012).
56. D. A. Kirzhnits, *Zh. Eksp. Teor. Fiz.* **38**, 503 (1960); *Sov. Phys.—JETP* **11**, 365 (1960).
57. A. A. Abrikosov, *Zh. Eksp. Teor. Fiz.* **39**, 1798 (1960).
58. E. E. Salpeter, *Astrophys. J.* **134**, 669 (1961).
59. D. J. Stevenson, *J. Phys. Colloques* **41**, C2_61 (1980).
60. E. Garcia-Berro, M. Hernanz, R. Mochkovitch and J. Isern, *Astron. Astrophys.* **193**, 141 (1988).
61. N. Nag and S. Chakrabarty, arXiv:astro-ph/0008477 (2000).
62. M. Bocquet, S. Bonazzola, E. Gourgoulhon and J. Novak, *Astron. Astrophys.* **301**, 757 (1995).
63. K. Konno, T. Obata and Y. Kojima, *Astron. Astrophys.* **352**, 211 (1999).

64. C. Y. Cardall, M. Prakash and J. M. Lattimer, *Astrophys. J.* **554**, 322 (2001).
65. K. Ioka and M. Sasaki, *Astrophys. J.* **600**, 296 (2004).
66. A. Oron, *Phys. Rev. D* **66**, 023006 (2002).
67. K. Kiuchi and K. Kotake, *Mon. Not. R. Astron. Soc.* **385**, 1327 (2008).
68. K. Kiuchi, K. Kotake and S. Yoshida, *Astrophys. J.* **698**, 541 (2009).
69. N. Yasutake, K. Kiuchi and K. Kotake, *Mon. Not. R. Astron. Soc.* **401**, 2101 (2010).
70. J. Frieben and L. Rezzolla, *Mon. Not. R. Astron. Soc.* **427**, 3406 (2012).
71. S. Yoshida, K. Kiuchi and M. Shibata, *Phys. Rev. D* **86**, 044012 (2012).
72. S. Chowdhury and T. Sarkar, *Astrophys. J.* **884**, 95 (2019).
73. P.-C. Chu, L.-W. Chen and X. Wang, *Phys. Rev. D* **90**, 063013 (2014).
74. M. Sinha, B. Mukhopadhyay and A. Sedrakian, *Nucl. Phys. A* **898**, 43 (2013).
75. L. Herrera and W. Barreto, *Phys. Rev. D* **88**, 084022 (2013).
76. H. O. Silva, C. F. B. Macedo, E. Berti and L. C. B. Crispino, *Class. Quantum Gravity* **32**, 145008 (2015).
77. K. Fujisawa, S. Yoshida and Y. Eriguchi, *Mon. Not. R. Astron. Soc.* **422**, 434 (2012).
78. A. T. Potter, C. A. Tout, *Mon. Not. R. Astron. Soc.* **402**, 1072 (2010).
79. D. Bandyopadhyay, S. Chakrabarty and Pal S., *Phys. Rev. Lett.* 79 (1997) 2176.
80. D. Bandyopadhyay, S. Pal and S. Chakrabarty, *J. Phys. G* **24**, 1647 (1998).
81. G. D. Schmidt, H. C. Harris, J. Liebert, D. J. Eisenstein, S. F. Anderson, J. Brinkmann, P. B. Hall, et al., *Astrophys. J.* **595**, 1101 (2003).
82. B. K. Harrison, K. S. Thorne, M. Wakano and J. A. Wheeler, *Gravitation Theory and Gravitational Collapse*, Chicago: University of Chicago Press, (1965).
83. S. Chandrasekhar and E. Fermi, *Astrophys. J.* **118**, 116 (1953).

LIST OF PARTICIPANTS

Abbate, Federico	MPI for Radio astronomy	Germany
Abbsi, Kamran	NUST	Pakistan
Abdollahi, Pooya	Isfahan University of Technology	Iran
Abe, Katsuya	Nagoya University	Japan
Abebe, Amare	North-West University	South Africa
Abele, Hartmut	TU Wien	Austria
Abishev, Medeu	Al Farabi Kazakh National Univ.	Kazakhstan
Abreu de Paula, Marco Aurélio	Federal University of Pará	Brazil
Acebron, Ana	Università degli Studi di Milano	Italy
Acharya, Sandeep Kumar	University of Manchester	UK
Addazi, Andrea	Laboratori Nazionali del Gran Sasso	Italy
Adorno, Tiago	Hebei University	China
Afrin, Misba	Jamia Millia Islamia	India
Afshordi, Niayesh	University of Waterloo	Canada
Aggarwal, Srishty	Indian Institute of Science	India
Aghaei, Maryam	Sejong Uiversity & UNIST	South Korea
Aghanim, Nabila	Institut d'Astrophysique Spatiale	France
Aguayo-Ortiz, Alejandro	UNAM	Mexico
Aguilar Ruiz, Edilberto	Instituto de Astronomia, UNAM	Mexico
Ahlgren, Björn	RIKEN iTHEMS and KTH	Japan
Ahmadvand, Moslem	IPM	Iran
Ahumada, Tomas	University of Maryland	USA
Aimuratov, Yerlan	Fesenkov Astrophysical Institute	Kazakhstan
Ajith, Siddarth	University of Virginia	USA
Akhmedov, Emil	MIPT and ITEP	Russia
Alcubierre, Miguel	Inst. de Ciencias Nucleares	Mexico
Alekseev, Georgy	Steklov Mathematical Institute RAS	Russia
Alestas, George	University of Ioannina	Greece
Ali-Haïmoud, Yacine	New York University	USA
Almeida, Ana	CAUP	Portugal
Almheiri, Ahmed	Institute for Advanced Study	USA
Alonso-Bardaji, Asier	UPV/EHU	Spain
Aloy, Miguel ángel	University of Valencia	Spain
Alstein, Paul	Freudenthal Institute	Netherlands
Amati, Lorenzo	INAF - OAS Bologna	Italy
Ambrus, Victor E.	Goethe University	Germany
Amelino-Camelia, Giovanni	Università Federico II di Napoli	Italy
Amendola, Luca	University of Heidelberg	Germany
Anagnostou, Oliver	University of Melbourne	Australia

Anda, Marcelo	Universidad San Francisco de Quito	Ecuador
Anderson, Paul	Wake Forest University	USA
Ando, Masaki	Univ. of Tokyo	Japan
Andrusenko, Svetlana	Bauman Moscow State Technical Univ.	Russia
Ansoldi, Stefano	University of Udine	Italy
Antypas, Dionysios	Johannes Gutenberg-Universität Mainz	Germany
Anzuini, Filippo	The University of Melbourne	Australia
Arcodia, Riccardo	MPI for Extraterrestrial Physics	Germany
Argüelles, Carlos Raúl	Universidad Nacional de La Plata	Argentina
Arkhangelskaja, Irene	National Research Nuclear University	Russia
Arminjon, Mayeul	Univ. Grenoble Alpes & CNRS	France
Arrechea, Julio	Institute of Astrophysics of Andalusia	Spain
Ashtekar, Abhay	Inst. for Gravitation & the Cosmos	USA
Aspelmeyer, Markus	University of Vienna	Austria
Atri, Pikky	ASTRON	Netherlands
Atteia, Jean-Luc	IRAP - CNRS/UPS/CNES	France
Audagnotto, Giulio	Max Planck Institut	Italy
Avgoustidis, Tasos	University of Nottingham	UK
Aviles, Alejandro	Conacyt	Mexico
Ayuso, Ismael	Instituto de Astrofísica de Portugal	Portugal
Babaie, Narges	University of Tehran	Iran
Badaracco, Francesca	UCLouvain	Belgium
Badia, Javier	IACE	Argentina
Bagheri, Mohammad	University of Tehran	Iran
Balbus, Steven	Oxford University	UK
Bamba, Kazuharu	Fukushima University	Japan
Banerjee, Shreya	Friedrich Alexander University	Germany
Barba González, David	Universidad de Salamanca	Spain
Barbato, Felicia	GSSI	Italy
Barca, Gabriele	La Sapienza University of Rome	Italy
Barrau, Aurélien	LPSC CNRS	France
Barreiro, Tiago	IACE	Portugal
Barroso Bellido, Samuel	University of Szczecin	Poland
Bartosch Caminha, Gabriel	Max Planck Institute for Astrophysics	Germany
Baryshev, Andrey	Kapteyn Astronomical Institute	Netherlands
Başaran öz, Işıl	Istanbul University	Turkey
Basquens, Marc	Universidad Carlos III de Madrid	Spain
Basu, Kaustuv	Universität Bonn	Germany
Batrakov, Alexander	MPI for Radio Astronomy	Germany
Battista, Emmanuele	Institute for Theoretical Physics, KIT	Germany
Battistelli, Elia Stefano	Sapienza University of Rome	Italy
Bavarsad, Ehsan	University of Kashan	Iran

Beckwith, Andrew	Chongqing University, physics	China
Beesham, Aroonkumar	University of Zululand	South Africa
Begue, Damien	Bar Ilan University	Israel
Beheshtipour, Banafsheh	AEI	Germany
Bejger, Michał	Nicolaus Copernicus Astronomical Ctr	Poland
Belczynski, Krzysztof	The Polish Academy of Sciences	Poland
Belfiglio, Alessio	University of Camerino	Italy
Belkhadria, Zakaria	Unica - INFN	Italy
Belli, Pierluigi	INFN Roma Tor Vergata	Italy
Bellini, Gianpaolo	University of Milano and INFN	Italy
Bellorin, Jorge	Universidad de Antofagasta	Chile
Bellucci, Stefano	INFN-LNF	Italy
Belonenko, Aleksei	Lomonosov Moscow State University	Russia
Beltrán Palau, Pau	Universitat de València - IFIC (CSIC)	Spain
Beniamini, Paz	Caltech	USA
Benisty, David	University of Cambridge	UK
Berezhiani, Zurab	Univ. L'Aquila and LNGS (Italy)	Italy
Bergamini, Pietro	INAF-OAS	Italy
Bernabei, Rita	University and INFN Roma Tor Vergata	Italy
Bernardini, Elisa	Unipd	Italy
Bernardini, Maria Grazia	INAF - OAB	Italy
Bernardini, Paolo	Universitá del Salento & INFN, Lecce	Italy
Bernuzzi, Sebastiano	FSU Jena	Germany
Berti, Alessio	MPI for Physics	Germany
Berti, Maria	SISSA	Italy
Bhandari, Shivani	CSIRO astronomy and space science	Australia
Bhattacharya, Swastik	BITS Pilani Hyderabad	India
Bhattacharya, Mukul	Virginia Tech, Blacksburg	USA
Bhattacharyya, Soham	AEI Hannover	Germany
Bianchi, Eugenio	Penn State	USA
Bianco, Carlo Luciano	ICRANet	Italy
Bicak, Jiri	Charles University	Czechia
Bihain, Gabriel	Albert Einstein Institute	Germany
Bij, Akanksha	Queen's University	Canada
Bilal, Muhammad	School of Mathematical Sciences	Pakistan
Bini, Donato	CNR	Italy
Biondi, Riccardo	INFN - LNGS	Italy
Birrer, Simon	Stanford University	USA
Bishop, Nigel	Rhodes University	South Africa
Bissaldi, Elisabetta	Politecnico and INFN Bari	Italy
Blair, David	University of Western Australia	Australia
Blanchet, Luc	Institut d'Astrophysique de Paris	France

Blandford, Roger	KIPAC	USA
Blas, Diego	King's College London	UK
Blasi, Simone	VUB	Belgium
Bluemlein, Johannes	DESY	Germany
Bluhm, Robert	Colby College	USA
Bobrick, Alexey	Lund University	Sweden
Boccioli, Luca	University of Notre Dame	USA
Bodmann, Benno	UFRGS	Brazil
Bogush, Igor	Lomonosov Moscow State University	Russia
Bolliet, Boris	Columbia University	USA
Bonavera, Laura	University of Oviedo	Spain
Bondani, Stefano	Università degli studi dell'Insubria	Italy
Bonnaire, Tony	Institut d'Astrophysique Spatiale	France
Bonvin, Camille	University of Geneva	Switzerland
Boos, Jens	William & Mary	USA
Bora, Jyatsnasree	Dibrugarh University	India
Borghi, Nicola	University of Bologna	Italy
Borsevici, Victor	Free International Univ. of Moldova	Moldova
Bose, Nirban	IIT Bombay	India
Boshkayev, Kuantay	Kazakh National University	Kazakhstan
Bošnjak, Željka	Zagreb University - FER	Croatia
Botta, Gioele	University of Warsaw	Italy
Boublil, Shachar Shon	University of Western Australia	Australia
Boudet, Simon	Trento University	Italy
Bozza, Valerio	Università di Salerno, Italy	Italy
Branchesi, Marica	Gran Sasso Science Institute/INFN	Italy
Brandt, William	Penn State University	USA
Brewer, William Dean	Freie Universität Berlin	Germany
Briscese, Fabio	SUSTech	China
Broderick, Avery	Perimeter Institute	Canada
Bromm, Volker	University of Texas at Austin	USA
Bulbul, Esra	MPI for Extraterrestrial Physics	Germany
Buldgen, Gaël	University of Geneva	Switzerland
Burgess, J. Michael	MPE	Germany
Burigana, Carlo	INAF-Istituto di Radioastronomia	Italy
Burns, Eric	Louisiana State University	USA
Burtscher, Annegret	Radboud University Nijmegen	Netherlands
Cabral, Francisco	University of Lisbon	Portugal
Cabrera Rosas, Omar de Jesús	CINVESTAV	Mexico
Caccianiga, Barbara	INFN	Italy
Cai, Yi-Fu	Univ. of Science and Technology of China	China
Calderón, Rodrigo	Université de Montpellier	France

Caleb, Manisha	University of Manchester	UK
Camci, Ugur	Roger Williams University	USA
Cameron, Andrew	Swinburne University of Technology	Australia
Caminata, Alessio	INFN-Genova	Italy
Campion, Stefano	ICRANeT	Italy
Canay, Ezgi	Istanbul Technical University	Turkey
Cantiello, Michele	INAF OAAb	Italy
Capone, Antonio	University La Sapienza and INFN	Italy
Caracciolo, Vincenzo	University of Rome "Tor Vergata"	Italy
Carella, Elisabetta	Università degli Studi di Milano	Italy
Carelli, Giorgio	INFN sezione di Pisa	Italy
Carlin, Julian	The University of Melbourne	Australia
Carmona, Jose Manuel	CAPA/University of Zaragoza	Spain
Carosi, Alessandro	University of Geneva - DPNC	Switzerland
Carvalho, Ana	IA/FCUL	Portugal
Cederbaum, Carla	Tuebingen University	Germany
Célérier, Marie-Noëlle	LUTH Observatoire de Paris	France
Cerruti, Matteo	Université de Paris - APC	France
Cerutti, Benoît	CNRS & Univ. Grenoble Alpes	France
Cervantes-Cota, Jorge L.	ININ (Mexico)	Mexico
Chael, Andrew	Princeton University	USA
Chakraborty, Indranil	Indian Institute of Technology Kharagpur	India
Chakraborty, Sumanta	Indian Ass. for the Cultivation of Science	India
Chakraborty, Srija	Scuola Normale Superiore	Italy
Chamel, Nicolas	Université Libre de Bruxelles	Belgium
Chandra, Koustav	Indian Institute of Technology Bombay	India
Chandran, S. Mahesh	IIT Bombay	India
Chasovnikov, Aristarh	Lomonosov Moscow State University	Russia
Chatziioannou, Katerina	Caltech	USA
Chauvineau, Bertrand	UCA/OCA/Lagrange laboratory	France
Chavanis, Pierre-Henri	Lab. de Physique Theorique de Toulouse	France
Chaves-Montero, Jonas	DIPC	Spain
Chawla, Pragya	McGill University	Canada
Chen, Liang	IHEP	China
Chen, Geoff Chih-Fan	UCLA	USA
Cherubini, Christian	University Campus Bio-Medico of Rome	Italy
Chluba, Jens	JBCA	UK
Chojnacki, Jan	University of Warsaw	Poland
Choudhury, Tirthankar Roy	Natl. Ctr for Radio Astrophys., Pune	India
Christiansen, Øyvind	University of Oslo	Norway
Ciufolini, Ignazio	UNIVERSITY OF SALENTO	Italy
Cleaver, Gerald	Baylor University	USA

Colafranceschi, Eugenia	University of Nottingham	UK
Conceição, Miguel	FCUL; IACE	Portugal
Cong, Wan	University of Waterloo	Canada
Coppi, Bruno	MIT	USA
Cordier, Bertrand	CEA-Saclay	France
Correa, Miguel	University of Notre Dame	USA
Correia, José Ricardo	Universidade do Porto	Portugal
Costa, Filipe	CAMGSD - Universidade de Lisboa	Portugal
Cotsakis, Spiros	Univ. Aegean, Greece	Greece
Crinquand, Benjamin	IPA Grenoble	France
Crispino, Luis	Universidade Federal do Pará	Brazil
Criswell, Alexander	University of Minnesota	USA
Crosta, Mariateresa	INAF-OATo	Italy
Curceanu, Catalina Oana	INFN-LNF	Italy
D'Amico, Giacomo	University of Bergen	Norway
D'Angelo, Annalisa	Universitá di Roma Tor Vergata	Italy
D'Avanzo, Paolo	INAF - OAB	Italy
da Fonseca, Vitor	Inst. of Astrophysics and Space Science	Portugal
da Silva, Antonio	IACE	Portugal
Dafermos, Mihalis	Princeton University	UK
Dahal, Pravin	Macquarie University	Australia
Dainotti, Maria	NAOJ	Japan
Darling, Jeremy	University of Colorado, Boulder	USA
Das, Saurya	University of Lethbridge	Canada
Das, Siddhant	Ludwig-Maximilians-Universitat	Germany
Datta, Sudeb Ranjan	Indian Institute of Science	India
Dayal, Pratika	Kapteyn Astronomical Institute	Netherlands
de Amorim, Erik	Universität zu Köln	Germany
de Cruz, Javier	University of Barcelona	Spain
De Felice Proia, Giuseppina	University of Rome "Tor Vergata"	Italy
De Felice Proia, Valeria	IIS Federico Caffè	Italy
de Mink, Selma	MPI for Astrophysics	Germany
De Mitri, Ivan	GSSI and INFN	Italy
De Paolis, Francesco	University of Salento	Italy
De Rosa, Alessandra	IAPS/INAF	Italy
De Simone, Biagio	Università degli Studi di Salerno	Italy
de Souza Campos, Lissa	University of Pavia	Italy
Deb, Debabrata	Indian Institute of Science	India
Decelle, Aurélien	Universidad Complutense de Madrid	Spain
Del águila, Juan Carlos	I.P.N.	Mexico
Delabrouille, Jacques	CNRS	France
Delband, Masoumeh	Shiraz University	Iran

Delgado, Jorge	University of Aveiro	Portugal
Delhom I Latorre, Adrià	University of Valencia	Spain
DeMille, David	University of Chicago	USA
Deng, Heling	Arizona State University	USA
Dereli-Bégué, Hüsne	Bar-Ilan University	Israel
Dergachev, Vladimir	AEI Hannover	USA
Dev, Bhupal	Washington Univ. in St. Louis	USA
Dhanuka, Ankit	IISER Mohali	India
Di Clemente, Francesco	INFN Ferrara	Italy
Di Giovanni, Fabrizio	Universitat de Valencia	Spain
Di Mauro, Marco	Università di Salerno	Italy
di Niccolo, Cinzia	ICRANet Secretariat	Italy
Di Palma, Irene	Sapienza University of Rome	Italy
Di Valentino, Eleonora	Durham University	UK
Di Virgilio, Angela D. V.	INFN-Pisa	Italy
Díaz Jiménez, Bogar	Universidad Carlos III de Madrid	Spain
Dichiara, Simone	UMD/NASA-GSFC	USA
Dickau, Jonathan	Independent Researcher	USA
Dimakis, Nikolaos	Sichuan University	China
Ding, Chikun	Huaihua University	China
Dorozsmai, Andras	University of Birmingham	UK
dos Anjos, Rita de Cassia	UFPR	Brazil
Douspis, Marian	IAS	France
Drago, Alessandro	University of Ferrara	Italy
Dreissen, Laura	Physikalisch-Technische Bundesanstalt	Germany
Drew, Amelia	University of Cambridge	UK
Droguett, Byron	Universidad de antofagasta	Chile
Dror, Jeff	UC Santa Cruz	USA
Drossel, Barbara	Technische Universität Darmstadt	Germany
Du, Yuchen	University of Virginia	USA
Duarte Lima Junior, Haroldo	Universidade Federal do Pará	Brazil
Ducobu, Ludovic	University of Mons (PhD student)	Belgium
Dumin, Yurii	Sternberg Astronomical Institute	Russia
Dunn, Liam	University of Melbourne	Australia
Dunsby, Peter	University of Cape Town	South Africa
Dupree, Andrea	Harvard & Smithsonian	USA
Durkan, Leanne	University College Dublin	Ireland
Dutta Chowdhury, Dhruba	Yale University	USA
Dutta Roy, Poulami	IIT Kharagpur	India
Dzuba, Vladimir	UNSW Sydney	Australia
Ebrahimi Khuzani, M.	IUT	Iran
Eder, Konstantin	Friedrich-Alexander-Universität	Germany

Efstathiou, George	University of Cambridge	UK
Eiroa, Ernesto F.	IAFE (CONICET-UBA)	Argentina
Elizalde, Emilio	ICE-CSIC and IEEC	Spain
Ellis, David	University of Göttingen	Germany
Elor, Gilly	MITP	Germany
Engel, Kristi	HAWC, University of Maryland	USA
Er, Xinzhong	SWIFAR, Yunnan University	China
Escrivà, Albert	University of Barcelona	Spain
Espinosa-Portalés, Llorenç	Instituto de Física Teórica UAM-CSIC	Spain
Estellés, Héctor	Universitat de les Illes Balears	Spain
Etebar, Sina	Isfahan University of Technology	Iran
Evangelista, Yuri	INAF IAPS	Italy
Famiano, Michael	Western Michigan University	USA
Fanizza, Giuseppe	IA - Lisbon	Portugal
Faraji, Shokoufe	ZARM	Germany
Faraoni, Valerio	Bishop's University	Canada
Farzan, Yasaman	IPM	Iran
Feng, Hua	Tsinghua University	China
Fernandez Uria, Sara	University of the Basque Country	Spain
Feroci, Marco	INAF/IAPS	Italy
Ferreiro, Antonio	University of Valencia/IFIC	Spain
Ferro, Lisa	University of Ferrara	Italy
Fesik, Liudmila	Albert Einstein Institute	Germany
Fialkov, Anastasia	Cambridge University	UK
Field, Scott	University of Massachusetts	USA
Fier, Jared	Baylor Univsersity	USA
Figueroa-Aguirre, Griselda	IAFE (CONICET-UBA)	Argentina
Filippi, Simonetta	Campus Bio-Medico University	Italy
Finster, Felix	Universität Regensburg	Germany
Fishbach, Maya	CIERA/Northwestern University	USA
Fisher, Robert	University of Massachusetts	USA
Flambaum, Victor	University of New South Wales	Australia
Foffa, Stefano	Geneva University	Switzerland
Foley, Ryan	UC Santa Cruz	USA
Fragos, Tassos	University of Geneva	Switzerland
Fraija, Nissim	Instituto de Astronomia, UNAM	Mexico
Franchino-Viñas, Sebastián	Universität Heidelberg	Germany
Franco, Antonio	Università del Salento	Italy
Fraser, Patrick	University of Toronto	Canada
Frati, Maria	Senato della Repubblica	Italy
Frederiks, Dmitry	Ioffe Institute, Saint-Petersburg	Russia
Freedman, Wendy	University of Chicago	USA

Freire, Paulo	MPI for Radio Astronomy	Germany
Fridman, Mitja	University of Lethbridge	Canada
Frisoni, Pietropaolo	Western University	Canada
Frontera, Filippo	Univ. di Ferrara e INAF-OAS Bologna	Italy
Frost, Torben	University of Bremen	Germany
Fruck, Christian	Max-Planck-Institute for Physics	Germany
Frusciante, Noemi	IA/FCUL	Portugal
Fryer, Chris	Los Alamos National Laboratory	USA
Furey, Nichol	Humboldt University	Germany
Gaijan, Mrunali	University of Milan	Italy
Galindo-Uribarri, Salvador	ININ	Mexico
Gallego Cadavid, Alexander	Universidad de Valparaíso	Chile
Gallegos, Omar	Cinvestav-IPN	Mexico
Galtsov, Dmitry	Lomonosov Moscow State University	Russia
Galván, Antonio	Institute of Astronomy, UNAM	Mexico
Gan, Wencong	Baylor University	China
Gangopadhyay, Mayukh	Center For Theoretical Physics, JMI	India
Gao, Dongfeng	IAPMST	China
Gao, Feng	Hamburger Sternwarte	Germany
Garcia-Bellido, Juan	Universidad Autonoma de Madrid	Spain
García-Peláez, David	Universidad Autónoma Metropolitana	Mexico
García-Quismondo, Alejandro	IEM-CSIC	Spain
Gargano, Fabio	INFN	Italy
Garofalo, David	Kennesaw State University	USA
Gasparyan, Sargis	ICRANet-Armenia	Armenia
Gautam, Tasha	MPI For Radioastronomy	Germany
Gautam, Shalabh	IUCAA	India
Gelles, Zachary	Harvard University	USA
Gendre, Bruce	University of Western Australia	Australia
Genzel, Reinhard	MPI for Extraterrestrial Physics	Germany
George, Sandip	Univ. Medical Ctr Groningen	Netherlands
Gervalle, Romain	Institut Denis Poisson	France
Ghezelbash, Masoud	University of Saskatchewan	Canada
Gholizadeh Siahmazgi, S.	Wake Forest University	USA
Gholizadeh, Kasra	—	Iran
Ghosh, Subham	Indian Institute of Science	India
Ghosh, Sushant	University of KwaZulu-Natal	India
Giacomazzo, Bruno	University of Milano-Bicocca	Italy
Giacomelli, Umberto	GSSI - INFN - Univ. di Pisa	Italy
Giannakopoulos, Thanasis	Instituto Superior Técnico, Lisbon	Portugal
Giesel, Kristina	FAU Erlangen-Nürnberg	Germany
Gill, Ramandeep	The Open University of Israel	Israel

Gilman, Daniel	University of Toronto	Canada
Ginat, Barry	Technion - Israel Institute of Technology	Israel
Giovannelli, Franco	INAF-IAPS	Italy
Giovannetti, Eleonora	Università di Roma "La Sapienza"	Italy
Giri, Priyanka	INFN Pisa	Italy
Gitman, Dmitry	P.N. Lebedev Physical Institute	Russia
Gittins, Fabian	University of Southampton	UK
Glushikhina, Maria	Space Research Institute (IKI RAN)	Russia
Gogoi, Dhruba Jyoti	Dibrugarh University	India
Goicoechea, Luis J.	Universidad de Cantabria	Spain
Gomes de Oliveira, Fernanda	LSQM	Germany
Gomes, Pierre Alexandre	Universidade do Estado de Santa Catarina	Brazil
Gómez-Valent, Adrià	Institut für Theoretische Physik	Germany
Goncalves, Tiago	University of Lisbon	Portugal
Good, Michael	Nazarbayev University	Kazakhstan
Gorbatsievich, Alexander	Belarusian State University	Belarus
Gorla, Paolo	INFN-LNGS	Italy
Gottlieb, Ore	Tel Aviv University/CIERA	Israel
Goulart Coelho, Jaziel	UTFPR	Brazil
Gouttenoire, Yann	Tel Aviv University	France
Gralla, Samuel	University of Arizona	USA
Granot, Jonathan	The Open University of Israel	Israel
Grant, Alexander	University of Virginia	USA
Gray, Finnian	Perimeter Institute	Canada
Gregoris, Daniele	Jiangsu University	China
Grillo, Claudio	University of Milan	Italy
Gudmundsson, Jon	Stockholm University	Sweden
Guerrero, Merce	UCM	Spain
Guetta, Dafne	ORT Braude	Israel
Guffanti, Daniele	Johannes Gutenberg-Univ. Mainz	Germany
Guglielmi, Diego	IIS Federico Caffè	Italy
Guinan, Edward	Villanova University	USA
Guo, Minyong	Beijing Normal University	China
Gushima, Yuya	Fukuoka university	Japan
Gwak, Bogeun	Dongguk University	South Korea
Ha, Yuan K.	Temple University	USA
Hackmann, Eva	ZARM, University of Bremen	Germany
Hackstein, Jan	ZARM, University of Bremen	Germany
Haemmerlé, Lionel	Université de Genève	Switzerland
Hafizi, Mimoza	University of Tirana	Albania
Haghani, Zahra	Damghan University	Iran
Hajela, Aprajita	Northwestern University	USA

Hajian, Kamal	HWK institute for advanced study	Iran
Halim, Odysse	INFN Trieste	Italy
Halla, Mourad	ZARM, University of Bremen	Germany
Halzen, Francis	University of Wisconsin- Madison	USA
Hamada, Yu	KEK	Japan
Hamed, Nima	Isfahan University of Technology	Iran
Hammad, Fayçal	Bishop's University	Canada
Hamolli, Lindita	University of Tirana	Albania
Hamuy, Mario	AURA	Chile
Hanauske, Matthias	Goethe University Frankfurt	Germany
Harms, Jan	Gran Sasso Science Institute	Italy
Harper, Graham	University of Colorado Boulder	USA
Harriott, Tina	Mount Saint Vincent University	Canada
Hart, Luke	JBCA, University of Manchester	UK
Harte, Abraham	Dublin City University	Ireland
Hartmann, Angelo	University of Insubria	Italy
Harutyunyan, Gevorg	ICRANet-Armenia	Armenia
Haxton, Wick	University of California, Berkeley	USA
Hayama, Kazuhiro	University of Texas	Japan
Hayes, Fergus	University of Glasgow	UK
He, Hong-Jian	Shanghai Jiao Tong University	China
Heimersheim, Stefan	University of Cambridge	UK
Heinzel, Gerhard	Max Planck Institut Hannover	Germany
Held, Aaron	Imperial College London	UK
Hendi, Seyed Hossein	Shiraz University	Iran
Herdeiro, Carlos	Aveiro University, Portugal	Portugal
Herman, Nicolas	University of Namur	Belgium
Hernanz, Margarita	ICE (CSIC) & IEEC	Spain
Herrera Aguilar, Alfredo	Universidad Autónoma de México	Mexico
Herrmann, Friedrich	Karlsruhe Institute of Technology	Germany
Hidalgo, Carlos	ICF-UNAM	Mexico
Hill, Colin	Columbia Univ./Flatiron Inst.	USA
Himwich, Elizabeth	Harvard University	USA
Hinton, Jim	MPI Kernphysik, Heidelberg	Germany
Hiramatsu, Takashi	Rikkyo Univ.	Japan
Hoang, Vu	University of Texas at San Antonio	USA
Holz, Daniel	University of Chicago	USA
Hoque, SK Jahanur	Charles University	Czechia
Hu, Huanchen	MPI for Radio Astronomy	Germany
Huang, Yong-Feng	Nanjing University	China
Hughes, Scott	MIT	USA
Husa, Sascha	University of the Balearic Islands	Spain

Ianni, Aldo	INFN Gran Sasso Laboratory	Italy
Ibata, Rodrigo	Obs. Astronomique de Strasbourg	France
Ilyas, Amara	Univ. of Science and Technology of China	China
Imtiaz, Batool	Univ. of Science and Technology of China	China
Inomata, Keisuke	University of Chicago, KICP	USA
Islam, Tousif	University of Massachusetts	USA
Israyelyan, Davit	ICRANet-Armenia	Armenia
Ito, Hirotaka	RIKEN	Japan
Iyonaga, Aya	Rikkyo University	Japan
Izzo, Luca	University of Copenhagen	Denmark
Jain, Parul	Indian Institute of Technology	India
Jana, Susmita	IIT BOMBAY	India
Jani, Karan	Vanderbilt University	USA
Jantzen, Robert Theodore	Villanova University	USA
Jawad, Abdul	COMSATS University Islamabad	Pakistan
Jensko, Erik	University College London	UK
Jetzer, Philippe	University of Zurich	Switzerland
Jha, Saurabh	Rutgers University	USA
Jiang, Nan	University of Virginia	USA
Johnson, Joseph P	IIT Bombay	India
Johnson, Michael	Harvard & Smithsonian	USA
Jones, Michael	University of Colorado	USA
Jordana-Mitjans, Nuria	University of Bath	UK
Joshi, Jagdish	Nanjing University China	China
Joudaki, Shahab	University of Waterloo	Canada
Joyce, Meridith	Space Telescope Science Institute	USA
Jullo, Eric	Aix-Marseille Univ/LAM	France
Kaczmarek, Jane	NRC	Canada
Kalinani, Jay Vijay	University of Padova	Italy
Kalita, Surajit	Indian Institute of Science, Bangalore	India
Kamionkowski, Marc	Johns Hopkins University	USA
Kanatchikov, Igor	Quantum Information Center	Poland
Kang, Sunghyun	Sogang University	South Korea
Karas, Vladimír	Astronomical Institute, CAS	Czechia
Kargaltsev, Oleg	The George Washington University	USA
Karinkuzhi, Drisya	Indian Institute of Science	India
Kaspi, Victoria	McGill University	Canada
Kawamura, Seiji	Nagoya University	Japan
Kazanas, Demosthenes	NASA/Goddard Space Flight Center	USA
Kazaras, Demetre	Duke University	USA
Kedia, Atul	University of Notre Dame	USA
Keeley, Ryan	Korea Astr. Space Sci. Inst.	South Korea

Keitel, David	Universitat de les Illes Balears	Spain
Kerin, Alex	University of Melbourne	Australia
Kerr, Roy P.	Canterbury University	New Zealand
Kersting, Magdalena	University of Oslo	Norway
Kerzendorf, Wolfgang	Michigan State University	USA
Khadka, Narayan	Kansas State University	USA
Kharuk, Ivan	INR RAS & MIPT	Russia
Khetan, Nandita	Gran Sasso Science Institute	Italy
Khlopunov, Mikhail	Lomonosov Moscow State University	Russia
Kiessling, Michael	Rutgers University	USA
Kim, Vitaliy	Fesenkov Astrophysical institute	Kazakhstan
Kim, Sang Pyo	Kunsan National University	South Korea
Kim, Sung-Won	Ewha Womans University	South Korea
King, Steven	Physikalisch-Technische Bundesanstalt	Germany
Kirillov, Alexandr	Bauman Moscow State Technical Univ.	Russia
Kisielowski, Marcin	National Centre for Nuclear Research	Poland
Klainerman, Sergiu	Princeton University	USA
Klaoudatou, Ifigeneia	University of the Aegean	Greece
Klinkhamer, Frans R.	Karlsruhe Institute of Technology	Germany
Kobialko, Kirill	Moscow State University	Russia
Kohri, Kaz	KEK	Japan
Kolanowski, Maciej	University of Warsaw	Poland
Kole, Merlin	University of Geneva	Switzerland
Kolekar, Sanved	DAE - Ctr for Excellence in Basic Sci.	India
Komarov, Stanislav	Belarusian State University	Belarus
Kondratyev, Ilya	Space Research Institute RAS	Russia
Konkowski, Deborah	U S Naval Academy	USA
Kontou, Eleni-Alexandra	University of Amsterdam	Netherlands
Konysbayev, Talgar	Al-Farabi Kazakh National Univ.	Kazakhstan
Koo, Hanwool	KASI/UST	South Korea
Korzyński, Mikołaj	Center for Theoretical Physics	Poland
Kosakowski, Daniel	University of Massachusetts	USA
Koshelev, Alexey	universidade da beira interior	Portugal
Kovalev, Yuri	Lebedev Physical Institute	Russia
Kowalski-Glikman, Jerzy	University of Wroclaw	Poland
Kramer, Michael	MPI fuer Radioastronomie	Germany
Kranas, Dimitrios	Louisiana State University	USA
Krichevskiy, Daniil	Bauman Moscow State Technical Univ.	Russia
Krizmanic, John	UMBC/CRESST/NASA/GSFC	USA
Krut, Andreas	ICRANet	Germany
Kubiznak, David	Perimeter Institute	Canada
Kühnel, Florian	LMU Munich	Germany

Kukihara, Moe	Fukuoka University	Japan
Kulitskii, Aleksadr	Lomomosov Moscow state university	Russia
Kumar, Shailesh	Indian Inst. of Information Technology	India
Kunz, Jutta	University of Oldenburg	Germany
Kurmanov, Ergali	Al-Farabi Kazakh National Univ.	Kazakhstan
Kuruvilla, Joseph	Universite Paris-Saclay	France
Kushwaha, Ashu	Indian Institute of Technology Bombay	India
Kutluk, Emine Seyma	METU	Turkey
Kwapisz, Jan	University of Warsaw	Poland
L'Huillier, Benjamin	Sejong University	South Korea
La Mura, Giovanni	LIFEP	Portugal
La Placa, Riccardo	INAF - Osservatorio astronomico di Roma	Italy
Lacchini, Mattia	Università dell'Insubria	Italy
Laemmerzahl, Claus	University of Bremen	Germany
Laguna, Pablo	University of Texas at Austin	USA
Lampe, Bodo	Univ. Hamburg	Germany
Langer, Norbert	Uni Bpnn/MPIfR Bonn	Germany
Lapola, Marcelo	Instituto Tecnológico de Aeronáutica	Brazil
Lappicy, Phillipo	University of Sao Paulo	Brazil
Lapponi, Alessio	UNICAM, University of Camerino.	Italy
Lasky, Paul	Monash University	Australia
Lau, Shu Yan	University of Virginia	USA
Lazzaro, Claudia	Università degli Studi di Padova	Italy
Lebed, Andrei	University of Arizona	USA
Lecian, Orchidea Maria	Sapienza University of Rome	Italy
Ledvinka, Tomáš	Charles University	Czechia
Lee, Yi Shuen Christine	The University of Melbourne	Australia
Lee, Yi Shuen Christine Lee	The University of Melbourne	Australia
LeFloch, Philippe G.	Sorbonne University	France
Lehoucq, Léonard	ENS Paris-Saclay	France
Leibundgut, Bruno	European Southern Observatory	Germany
Leigh, Nathan	Universidad de Concepcion	Chile
Lenart, Aleksander	Jagiellonian University	Poland
Lentz, Erik	Pacific Northwest National Lab	USA
Leung, James	University of Sydney	Australia
Leung, Calvin	MIT	USA
Leung, Shing-Chi	TAPIR, Caltech	USA
Levine, Delina	University of Maryland	USA
Lewandowski, Jerzy	Uniwersytet Warszawski	Poland
Lewicki, Marek	University of Warsaw	Poland
Li, Ang	Xiamen University	China
Li, Benliang	Southwest Jiaotong University	China

Li, Di	National Astronomical Observatories	China
Li, Xiang	Purple Mountain Observatory, CAS	China
Li, Xiangdong	Nanjing University	China
Li, Liang	ICRANet	Italy
Li, Dian-Heng	886910871458	Taiwan
Li, BaoFei	Louisiana state university	USA
Li, Dongzi	California Institute of Technology	USA
Lim, Eugene	King's College London	UK
Lim, Hyun	Los Alamos National Laboratory	USA
Lin, Shin-Ted	Sichuan University	China
Ling, Eric	Rutgers University	USA
Lipunov, Vladimir	Lomonosov Moscow State University, SAI	Russia
Liška, Marek	Charles University	Czechia
List, Meike	DLR	Germany
Liu, Jianglai	SJTU	China
Liu, Lang	Institute of Theoretical Physics, CAS	China
Liu, Ruoyu	Nanjing University	China
Liu, Zike	Nanjing University	China
Liu, Hongguang	FAU Erlangen-Nürnberg	Germany
Lizarraga, Joanes	University of the Basque Country	Spain
Lobanov, Andrei	MPIfR Bonn	Germany
Lobato, Ronaldo	Universidad de los Andes	Brazil
Lobo, Francisco	University of Lisbon	Portugal
Lochan, Kinjalk	IISER Mohali	India
Lockhart, Will	University of Arizona	USA
Longo, Francesco	University of Trieste and INFN, Trieste	Italy
Lopez Eiguren, Asier	Tufts University	USA
López Pérez, Samantha	ICMF	Cuba
López-Caniego, Marcos	Aurora Technology for ESA	Spain
Lopez-Monsalvo, Cesar Simon	Universidad Autonoma Metropolitana	Mexico
Loppini, Alessandro	Università Campus Bio-Medico di Roma	Italy
Lorimer, Duncan	WVU	USA
Lovell, Mark	University of Iceland	Iceland
Lu, Fangjun	IHEP, CAS	China
Lucca, Matteo	ULB	Belgium
Lucchesi, David	INAF/IAPS Tor Vergata	Italy
Lundblad, Nathan	Bates College	USA
Luo, Wentao	USTC	China
Luongo, Orlando	University of Camerino, Physics Division	Italy
Lupsasca, Alex	Princeton University	USA
Lusso, Elisabeta	Università degli Studi di Firenze	Italy
Lutovinov, Alexander	Space Research Institute (IKI)	Russia

Lynch, Morgan	Technion - Israel Institute of Technology	Israel
Lyubarsky, Yuri	Ben-Gurion University	Israel
Macaulay, Ed	University of East Anglia	UK
Mach, Patryk	Jagiellonian University	Poland
Macias, Alfredo	Universidad Autonoma Metropolitana	Mexico
MacLaurin, Colin	University of Queensland	Australia
Maffei, Bruno	IAS, Université Paris-Saclay	France
Magalhães, Renan	Universidade Federal do Pará	Brazil
Mahmoudi, Somayye	Shiraz University, Iran	Iran
Maiorano, Michele	Università del Salento	Italy
Maitra, Chandreyee	MPI for Extraterrestrial Physics	Germany
Majid, Amal	University of the Punjab	Pakistan
Malafarina, Daniele	Nazarbayev University	Kazakhstan
Maldacena, Juan	Institute for Advanced Study	USA
Málek, Tomáš	Institute of Mathematics, CAS	Czechia
Malheiro, Manuel	Instituto Tecnológico de Aeronáutica	Brazil
Malik, Sunil	IIT Bombay and University of Delhi	India
Maltsev, Kiril	University of Heidelberg / HITS	Germany
Malybayev, Algis	Al-Farabi Kazakh National Univ.	Kazakhstan
Maniccia, Giulia	Sapienza University	Italy
Manreza-Paret, Daryel	Universidad de La Habana	Cuba
Marakis, Vassilios	Universität Hildesheim	Germany
Marcantognini, Nicola	University of Camerino	Italy
Margalef, Juan	PSU	USA
Margutti, Raffaella	UC Berkeley	USA
Marrocchesi, Pier Simone	University of Siena and INFN Pisa	Italy
Marsh, David	King's College London	UK
Martins, Carlos	CAUP	Portugal
Martire, Gianni	Applied Physics	USA
Masi, Silvia	Sapienza Università di Roma	Italy
Mastrototaro, Leonardo	Università degli Studi di Salerno	Italy
Mateu-Lucena, Maria Teresa	University of the Balearic Islands	Spain
Mathews, Grant	University of Notre	USA
Matos, Tonatiuh	IPN	Mexico
Mauro, Lorenza	Roma Tre	Italy
Mavromatos, Nikolaos	King's College London	UK
Mayerson, Daniel	IPhT, CEA Saclay	France
McCabe, Christopher	King's College London	UK
McGrew, William	NIST-Boulder	USA
McLaughlin, Andrew	North Carolina Central University	USA
Meda, Paolo	University of Genoa - INFN	Italy
Meintjes, Pieter	University of the Free State	South Africa

Melatos, Andrew	University of Melbourne	Australia
Memmen, Jan-Menno	ZARM	Germany
Mena Marugán, Guillermo A.	IEM, CSIC	Spain
Mendes, Melissa	McGill University	Canada
Menéndez-Pidal, Lucía	University of Nottingham	UK
Meng, Xinhe	Nankai University	China
Meng, Yanzhi	Nanjing University	China
Merafina, Marco	University of Rome La Sapienza	Italy
Merloni, Andrea	MPE	Germany
Messina, Andrea	Sapienza University of Rome & INFN	Italy
Metzger, Brian	Columbia University	USA
Meyers, Patrick	University of Melbourne	Australia
Meynet, Georges	Geneva University	Switzerland
Miceli, Davide	University of Udine & INFN Trieste	Italy
Michilli, Daniele	McGill University	Canada
Michimura, Yuta	University of Tokyo	Japan
Micko, Jakob	Institut Laue-Langevin, TU Wien	Austria
Miedema, Pieter	ASFYON	Netherlands
Mikhailov, Evgeny	Lomonosov Moscow State University	Russia
Miller-Jones, James	ICRAR	Australia
Millhouse, Meg	University of Melbourne	Australia
Mimoso, José Pedro	IACE	Portugal
Minic, Djordje	Virginia Tech	USA
Mirabel, Felix	IAFE & CEA	Argentina
Mirzoyan, Razmik	Max-Planck-Institute for Physics	Germany
Mishra, Tanmaya	University of Florida, Gainesville	USA
Mitsou, Vasiliki	IFIC - Univ. of Valencia and CSIC	Spain
Mitsui, Tadao	Tohoku University	Japan
Modafferi, Luana Michela	Universitat de les Illes Balears	Spain
Mohammadi, Rohoollah	National Science and Technology Museum	Iran
Moiseenko, Sergey	Space Research Institute	Russia
Moita, Miguel	University of Ferrara	Italy
Momtaz, Aidin	Isfahan University of Technology	Iran
Mondal, Tushar	Indian Institute of Science	India
Mooley, Kunal	Caltech	USA
Moradi, Rahim	ICRANet	Italy
Morales, Gibran	IA-UNAM	Mexico
Moreno Pulido, Cristian	University of Barcelona	Spain
Moresco, Michele	University of Bologna	Italy
Mori, Masaki	Ritsumeikan University	Japan
Moriya, Takashi	National Astronomical Observatory	Japan
Moriyama, Kotaro	MIT	USA

Most, Elias Roland	Princeton University	USA
Mueller, Bernhard	Monash University	Australia
Mukherjee, Dipayan	IISER Mohali	India
Mukherjee, Suvodip	University of Amsterdam	Netherlands
Mukhopadhyay, Banibrata	Indian Institute of Science	India
Mumtaz, Saadia	University of the Punjab	Pakistan
Müntinga, Hauke	German Aerospace Center (DLR)	Germany
Murk, Sebastian	Macquarie University, Sydney	Australia
Murshed, Adib	Qavloical Authority	Romania
Myrvold, Wayne	The University of Western Ontario	Canada
Myrzakul, Aizhan	Nazarbayev University	Kazakhstan
Nadal Gisbert, Sergi	University of València-IFIC (CSIC)	Spain
Naddeo, Adele	INFN, Sezione di Napoli	Italy
Naidoo, M	Rhodes University	South Africa
Nakas, Theodoros	University of Ioannina	Greece
Nalewajko, Krzysztof	Nicolaus Copernicus Astronomical Ctr	Poland
Namdar, Mohammadhossein	Isfahan University Of Technology	Iran
Nandra, Kirpal	MPI for extraterrestrial Physics	Germany
Naqvi, Syed	Jagiellonian Universtiy	Poland
Narayan, Ramesh	Harvard University	USA
Narita, Makoto	National Institute of Technology	Japan
Natale, Elisabetta	ICRANet	Italy
Natarajan, Priya	Yale University	USA
Naumov, Dmitry	JINR	Russia
Nava-Callejas, Martin Javier	Instituto de Astronomia - UNAM	Mexico
Navarro-Salas, Jose	University of Valencia-IFIC (CSIC)	Spain
Nenmeli, Vijay	Indian Institute of Technology, Bombay	India
Newsome, Ian	Wake Forest University	USA
Ng, Y. Jack	University of North Carolina	USA
Ni, Wei-Tou	APMST	China
Nickel, Otmar	Bundesdeutsche Arbeitsgemeinschaft	Germany
Nicolas, Nora	IP2I	France
Nielson, Via	University of Michigan	USA
Nimmo, Kenzie	ASTRON/University of Amsterdam	Netherlands
Nomoto, Ken'ichi	The University of Tokyo	Japan
Noui, Karim	IDP Tours & APC Paris	France
Novak, Jan	Technical University of Liberec	Czechia
Novikov, Dmitry	Astro Space Center, Moscow	Russia
Nucita, Achille	University of Salento & INFN	Italy
Nunes, Sílvia	ITA	Brazil
Ó Colgáin, Eoin	Sogang University	South Korea
O'Connor, Brendan	George Washington University	USA

O'Neill, Nicholas	University of Melbourne	Australia
Oates, Samantha	University of Birmingham	UK
Okolow, Andrzej	University of Warsaw	Poland
Olejak, Aleksandra	Nicolaus Copernicus Astronomical Ctr	Poland
Olmedo, Javier	Universidad de Granada	Spain
Olmo, Gonzalo J.	University of Valencia	Spain
Ortolan, Antonello	INFN - LNL	Italy
Osborn, Nicole	Purdue University	USA
Ossowski, Maciej	University of Warsaw	Poland
Özsoy, Ogan	CEICFP	Czechia
Pace, Francesco	Università di Bologna	Italy
Page, Dany	UNAM	Mexico
Pagliara, Giuseppe	University of Ferrara (IT)	Italy
Pagliaro, Gianluca	MPI/AEI	Germany
Pai, Archana	Indian Institute of Technology Bombay	India
Palagiano, Cosimo	Sapienza università di Roma	Italy
Pallavicini, Marco	Università di Genova and INFN Genova	Italy
Palumbo, Daniel	Harvard & Smithsonian	USA
Pannarale, Francesco	Sapienza University of Rome	Italy
Panotopoulos, Grigorios	Universidade de Lisboa	Portugal
Papa, Maria Alessandra	MPI for Gravitational Physics	Germany
Parsotan, Tyler	Oregon State University	USA
Pashentseva, Maria	Lomonosov Moscow State University	Russia
Paulo Bessa Brito, João	Universidade federal do Pará	Brazil
Paynter, James	The University of Melbourne	Australia
Pe'er, Asaf	Bar Ilan University	Israel
Peik, Ekkehard	PTB	Germany
Peng, Wenxi	Institute of High Energy Physics, CAS	China
Pereira, Jonas	Nicolaus Copernicus Astronomical Ctr	Poland
Perez Martinez, Aurora Maria	Universidad de Salamanca	Spain
Perez-Garcia, M. Angeles	University de Salamanca	Spain
Perlick, Volker	ZARM, University of Bremen	Germany
Perlman, Eric	Florida Institute of Technology	USA
Pernas, David	Saturno Interconsult	USA
Perrodin, Delphine	INAF - OAC	Italy
Philipp, Dennis	ZARM, University of Bremen	Germany
Phurailatpam, Hemantakumar	The Chinese University of Hong Kong	India
Pian, Elena	INAF-OAS Bologna	Italy
Piedipalumbo, Ester	University of Naples Federico II	Italy
Pietroni, Silvia	UNISA - Università di Salerno	Italy
Pinfold, James	University of Alberta	Canada
Piran, Tsvi	The Hebrew University	Israel

Pisani, Alice	Princeton University	USA
Pitschmann, Mario	TU Wien	Austria
Pittelli, Antonio	University of Surrey	Italy
Pla Garcia, Silvia	University of Valencia - IFIC	Spain
Planas Llompart, Maria de Lluc	University of the Balearic Islands	Spain
Plavin, Alexander	Lebedev Physical Institute	Russia
Plefka, Jan	Humboldt University Berlin	Germany
Pober, Jonathan	Brown University	USA
Pogosian, Levon	Simon Fraser University	Canada
Pohlig, Michael	Karlsruhe Inst. of Technology	Germany
Polarski, David	Université de Montpellier	France
Polin, Abigail	Carnegie Observatories & Caltech	USA
Poludnenko, Alexei	University of Connecticut	USA
Pombo, Alexandre	Aveiro University	Portugal
Pompa, Tiziana	Liceo Scientifico Galileo Galilei	Italy
Ponti, Gabriele	INAF OAB	Italy
Popkova, Anastasia	University of Western Australia	Australia
Poplawski, Nikodem	University of New Haven	USA
Possenti, Andrea	INAF-OAC	Italy
Pourtsidou, Alkistis	QMUL	UK
Pradler, Josef	Austrian Academy of Sciences	Austria
Prakapenia, Mikalai	ICRANet-Minsk	Belarus
Predehl, Peter	MPI für extraterrestrische Physik	Germany
Pugliese, Daniela	RCTPA	Czechia
Pullin, Jorge	Louisiana State University	USA
Punsly, Brian	ICRANet	USA
Qadir, Asghar	Government college University	Pakistan
Quevedo, Hernando	UNAM	Mexico
Quintero Angulo, Gretel	Universidad de La Habana	Cuba
Quirola, Jonathan	Universidad Catolica de Chile	Chile
Qvarfort, Sofia	Imperial College London	UK
Rafiei Karkevandi, Davood	Isfahan University of Technology	Iran
Rah, Maria	Natl. Astron. Observatories of China	Iran
Rahman, Mostafizur	IIT	India
Rahmani, Elnaz	University of Tehran	Iran
Ramírez Romero, Cupatitzio	Universidad Autónoma de Puebla	Mexico
Ramirez-Baca, Pedro Isaac	Universidad Autonoma de San Luis	Mexico
Ranucci, Gioacchino	INAF – sezione di Milano	Italy
Rastegar Nia, Fatemeh	Alzahra University and ICRANet	Iran
Rastgoo, Saeed	York University	Canada
Rätzel, Dennis	Humboldt Universität zu Berlin	Germany
Ravenni, Andrea	Jodrell Bank Centre for Astrophys.	UK

Re, Alessandra Carlotta	Universita' degli Studi & INFN, Milano	Italy
Reboucas, Marcelo	CBPF	Brazil
Recchia, Sarah	University of Torino, INFN Torino	Italy
Reiber, Thomas	Hildesheim University	Germany
Remazeilles, Mathieu	Jodrell Bank Centre for Astrophys.	UK
Ren, Xin	Univ. of Science and Technology of China	China
Renevey, Cyril	LPSC CNRS	France
Riahi, Rashid	ICRANet Isfahan center, Isfahan	Iran
Ribeiro, Ana Rita	Universidade de Lisboa	Portugal
Ribeiro, Deivid	Columbia University	USA
Ricci, Marco	INFN - Laboratori Nazionali Frascati	Italy
Ricciardi, Lorenzo	University of Strathclyde	Italy
Rick Perche, Tales	Perimeter Institute	Canada
Riess, Adam	Johns Hopkins University	USA
Rincon Ramirez, Monica	Pennsylvania State University	USA
Ripperda, Bart	Princeton Univ. /Flatiron Institute	USA
Robbins, Matthew	University of Waterloo	Canada
Robson, Charles	Tampere University	Finland
Rodrigues De Lima, Rafael	Univ. do Estado de Santa Catarina	Brazil
Rodrigues, Claudia	INPE	Brazil
Rodrigues, Manuel	ONERA	France
Rodriguez-Fernandez, Manuel	Universidad de Guadalajara	Mexico
Roelofs, Freek	Harvard & Smithsonian	USA
Romagnolo, Amedeo	Nicolaus Copernicus Astronomical Ctr	Poland
Romano, Antonio Enea	UDEA/CERN	Colombia
Röpke, Friedrich	Heidelberg University/HITS	Germany
Rosa, João	University of Tartu	Portugal
Rosati, Piero	University of Ferrara	Italy
Rosati, Giacomo	IFT Wroclaw University	Poland
Rossi, Andrea	Istituto Nazionale di Astrofisica	Italy
Rossi, Nicola	INFN LNGS	Italy
Rota, Paolo	Università degli Studi di Salerno	Italy
Roulet, Esteban	CONICET	Argentina
Rovelli, Carlo	AMU University	France
Ruan, Manqi	IHEP	China
Rubiera-Garcia, Diego	Complutense University of Madrid	Spain
Rudenko, Valentin	Sternberg Astronomical Institute	Russia
Rueda Hernandez, Jorge	ICRANet	Italy
Ruep, Maximilian Heinz	University of York, UK	UK
Ruffini, Remo	ICRANet	Italy
Ruggiero, Matteo Luca	Politecnico di Torino and INFN, LNL	Italy
Ruiz Velasco, Edna Loredana	MPI for Nuclear Physics	Germany

Ruiz-Lapuente, Pilar	ICCUB U. Barcelona and IFF (CSIC)	Spain
Rybak, Ivan	IACE	Portugal
Saab, Tarek	University of Florida	USA
Saadatmand, Homa	Tehran University	Iran
Sabido, Miguel	Universidad de Guanajuato	Mexico
Saffer, Alexander	University of Virginia	USA
Safronova, Marianna	University of Delaware	USA
Sahakyan, Narek	ICRANet-Armenia	Armenia
Sahlmann, Hanno	FAU Erlangen-Nürnberg	Germany
Sahoo, Pradyumn	BITS-Pilani, Hyderabad Campus	India
Sahoo, Parbati	University of KwaZulu-Natal	South Africa
Sahota, Harkirat Singh	IISER Mohali	India
Saini, Sahil	Guru Jambheshwar University	India
Sajadmanesh, Sina	EPFL	Switzerland
Sakellariadou, Mairi	King's College London	UK
Saleem, Rabia	COMSATS University Islamabad	Pakistan
Salemi, Francesco	University of Trento and INFN	Italy
Salisbury, Donald	Austin College	USA
Salmon, Sébastien	Université de Genève	Switzerland
Salvati, Laura	IAS, Paris Saclay - CNRS	France
Sanchez, Ariel G.	MPI for Extraterrestrial Physics	Germany
Sanchis-Gual, Nicolas	Universidade de Aveiro	Portugal
Sangwan, Archana	Indian Institute Of Technology	India
Sangwan, Archana	Indian Institute of Technology	India
Santa, Camilo	PhD student	Colombia
Santacruz, Robert	University of New Brunswick	Canada
Santos Pereira, Osvaldo Luiz	Universidade Federal do Rio de Janeiro	Brazil
Santos, Nuno	Técnico Lisboa & Univ. de Aveiro	Portugal
Sapio, Feliciana	Istituto Nazionale di Astrofisica	Italy
Saridakis, Emmanuel	National Observatory of Athens	Greece
Sarkar, Shilpa	Aryabhatta Research Institute	India
Sarkar, Sarben	King's College London	UK
Sartini, Francesco	ENS de Lyon	France
Sarwar, Rafia	Institute of Space Technology	Pakistan
Sato, Yuki	Nagoya University	Japan
Sato, Yuri	Aoyama Gakuin University	Japan
Saurabh, Saurabh	University of Delhi	India
Savelova, Elena	Bauman Moscow State Technical Univ.	Russia
Schaan, Emmanuel	Lawrence Berkeley National Lab	USA
Schiavone, Tiziano	University of Pisa & INFN Pisa	Italy
Scholz, Paul	University of Toronto	Canada
Schubert, Christian	Universidad Michoacana	Mexico

Schüssler, Fabian	IRFU/CEA Paris-Saclay	France
Scott, Susan	The Australian National University	Australia
Scott, Kameron	Baylor University	USA
Sedmik, René	TU Wien	Austria
Seeger, Robert	FAU Erlangen-Nürnberg	Germany
Seglar-Arroyo, Monica	L.A.P.P., Université Savoie Mont-Blanc	France
Sellers, Luke	Univ. of California Santa Barbara	USA
Semerak, Oldrich	Charles University	Czechia
Semrén, Philip	Umeå University	Sweden
Sengo, Ivo	University of Aveiro	Portugal
Serbenta, Julius	Center for Theoretical Physics, PAS	Poland
Serenelli, Aldo	Institute of Space Sciences (ICE, CSIC)	Spain
Serra, Francesco	Scuola Normale Superiore, Pisa	Italy
Seto, Osamu	Hokkaido University	Japan
Shafieloo, Arman	Korea Astron. and Space Sci. Inst.	South Korea
Shahidi, Shahab	Damghan University	Iran
Shakeri, Soroush	ICRANet-Isfahan	Iran
Sharif, Muhammad	University of the Punjab	Pakistan
Sharifian, Mohammad	ICRANet-Isfahan	Iran
Shears, Jeremy	University of Manchester	UK
Shen, Rong-Feng	Sun Yat-Sen University	China
Shen, Ken	UC Berkeley	USA
Shkerin, Andrey	University of Minnesota	USA
Shu, Fu-Wen	Nanchang University	China
Sidharth, Gowtham	vellore institute of technology	India
Sieroka, Norman	University of Bremen	Germany
Sigismondi, Costantino	ICRA Sapienza and ICRANET Pescara	Italy
Silk, Joe	IAP	France
Silva, Hilberto	Inst. Astrofísica e Ciências do Espaço	Portugal
Silvestri, Alessandra	Leiden University	Netherlands
Simão, José Diogo	TPI Jena	Germany
Simpson, Alex	Victoria University of Wellington	New Zealand
Singh, Chandra Bahadur	South-Western Inst. for Astron. Research	China
Singh, Parampreet	Louisiana State University	USA
Skordis, Constantinos	CEICO, Institute of Physics	Czechia
Slagter, Reinoud	ASFYON	Netherlands
Smartt, Stephen	Queen's University Belfast	UK
Smirnov, Oleg	JINR, Dubna	Russia
Sobouti, Yousef	Inst. for Adv. Studies in Basic Sci.	Iran
Soffitta, Paolo	INAF-IAPS	Italy
Sokolenko, Anastasia	Austrian Academy of Sciences	Austria
Solà Peracaula, Joan	Universitat de Barcelona	Spain

Soldateschi, Jacopo	Università degli Studi di Firenze	Italy
Solís López, Jordi	Cinvestav	Mexico
Solon, Mikhail	UCLA	USA
Soltani, Farshid	Western U.	Canada
Sousa, Manoel Felipe	Natl. Inst. for Space Research	Brazil
Spengler, Felix	Universität Tübingen	Germany
Spruit, Hendrik	MPI for Astrophysics	Germany
Sravan Kumar, Korumilli	Tokyo Institute of Technology	Japan
Sreenath, V	Natl. Inst. of Technology Karnataka	India
Srivastava, Manu	IIT Bombay	India
Stadnik, Yevgeny	Kavli IPMU, University of Tokyo	Japan
Staicova, Denitsa	INRNE, BAS	Bulgaria
Starobinsky, Alexei	Landau Institute for Theoretical Physics	Russia
Stathopoulos, Stamatios Ilias	National and Kapodistrian University	Greece
Steele, John	UNSW	Australia
Stefano, Scopel	Sogang University	Italy
Stephan, Preiß	Hildesheim University	Germany
Stephenson, Gary	Seculine Consulting	USA
Stepniczka, Michael	University of Virginia	USA
Strang, Lucy	University of Melbourne	Australia
Stratta, Giulia	INAF/OAS-Bologna	Italy
Straub, Odele	MPI for Extraterrestrial Physics	Germany
Stubbings, Rod	AAVSO	Australia
Stuchlik, Zdenek	Insitute of Physics, Silesian University	Czechia
Suárez Fontanella, Duvier	ICIMAF	Cuba
Suarez Gonzalez, Lismary	ICIMAF	Cuba
Sullivan, Raelyn	The University of British Columbia	Canada
Sun, Ling	The Australian National University	Australia
Suresh, Sandeep	TU Wien	India
Suresh, Jishnu	Institute for Cosmic Ray Research	Japan
Sutton, Patrick	Cardiff University	UK
Suvikranth, Gera	IIT KHARAGPUR	India
Suyu, Sherry	MPI for Astrophysics	Germany
Svarc, Robert	Charles University	Czechia
Svertilov, Sergey	Lomonosov Moscow State University	Russia
Swami, Himanshu	IISER Mohali	India
Szczepanczyk, Marek	University of Florida	USA
't Hooft, Gerard	Utrecht University	Netherlands
T U, Jeevitha	Vellore Inst. of Technology	India
Tahir, Noraiz	Universita Del Salento	Italy
Tahura, Shammi	University of Virginia	USA
Tahvildar-Zadeh, A. Shadi	Rutgers University	USA

Takamoto, Masao	RIKEN	Japan
Takata, Jumpei	Huazhong University	China
Tam, Pak-Hin Thomas	Sun Yat-sen University	China
Tamar, Aditya	Early Career Independent Researcher	India
Tamburini, Matteo	MPI for Nuclear Physics	Germany
Tan, Abraham	National Cheng Kung University	Taiwan
Tanikawa, Ataru	The University of Tokyo	Japan
Tanimura, Hideki	L'Institut d'Astrophysique Spatiale (IAS)	France
Tao, Lian	Institute of High Energy Physics, CAS	China
Tartaglia, Angelo	INAF	Italy
Tashiro, Makoto	Saitama University	Japan
Tauber, Jan	ESA	Netherlands
Tawfik, Abdel Nasser	Egyptian Center for Theoretical Physics	Egypt
Tchekhovskoy, Alexander	Northwestern University	USA
Tedesco, Antonio	University of Salerno	Italy
Teixeira, Elsa	University of Sheffield	UK
Tenorio, Rodrigo	Universitat de les Illes Balears	Spain
Testera, Gemma	INFN Genova (Italy)	Italy
Thomas, Cameron	University of Sheffield	UK
Tiurina, Nataly	Lomonosov Moscow State University	Russia
Tizchang, Seddigheh	Inst. for Research in Fundamental Sci.	Iran
Tluczykont, Martin	University of Hamburg	Germany
Tobar, Michael	The University of Western Australia	Australia
Toda, Yo	Hokkaido University	Japan
Todorinov, Vasil	University of Lethbridge	Canada
Tohuvavohu, Aaron	University of Toronto	Canada
Tokareva, Anna	University of Jyvaskyla	Finland
Toktarbay, Saken	Al-Farabi Kazakh National Univ.	Kazakhstan
Tominaga, Nozomu	NAOJ	Japan
Toprak, Ebru	Rutgers University	USA
Toropina, Olga	Space Research Institute (IKI)	Russia
Torres Sanchez, Victor A.	University of Trento	Italy
Trani, Alessandro	The University of Tokyo	Japan
Tristram, Matthieu	IJClab, CNRS, France	France
Troja, Eleonora	Arizona State University	USA
Trova, Audrey	ZARM, University of Bremen	Germany
Tsujikawa, Shinji	Waseda University	Japan
Tsunetoe, Yuh	Kyoto University	Japan
Tsupko, Oleg	Space Research Institute	Russia
Turundaevskiy, Andrey	SINP MSU	Russia
Turzynski, Krzysztof	University of Warsaw	Poland
Ulmer, Stefan	RIKEN (JP)	Japan

Urena-Lopez, Luis	Universidad de Guanajuato	Mexico
Ursi, Alessandro	INAF-IAPS	Italy
Uzun, Nezihe	Université Claude Bernard Lyon 1	France
V H, Satheeshkumar	UNIRIO	Brazil
V, Gayathri	University of Florida	USA
Vallejo Peña, Sergio Andrés	Universidad De Antioquia	Colombia
van der Walt, Petrus	Rhodes University	South Africa
van Eerten, Hendrik	University of Bath	UK
van Leeuwen, Joeri	ASTRON/U. Amsterdam	Netherlands
van Loon, Jacco	Keele University	UK
van Putten, Maurice	Sejong university	South Korea
Vardanyan, Vazgen	ICRANet-Armenia	Armenia
Vargas, Andrés	The university of Melbourne	Australia
Varo, Valle	Universidad Carlos III de Madrid	Spain
Veitch, John	University of Glasgow	UK
Venkatraman Krishnan, Vivek	MPI for Radio Astronomy	Germany
Vera Garfias, Gabriela Isabel	Universidad Autónoma Metropolitana	Mexico
Verde, Licia	ICREA & ICC Universitat de Barcelona	Spain
Veres, Peter	University of Alabama in Huntsville	USA
Vereshchagin, Gregory	ICRANet	Italy
Vermeulen, Sander	Cardiff University	UK
Verrecchia, Francesco	INAF/OAR, SSDC-ASI	Italy
Veske, Doğa	Columbia University	USA
Vicentini, Silvia	University of Trento	Italy
Vilalta, Ricardo	University of Houston	USA
Villanova Borges, Sarah	University of Wisconsin Milwaukee	USA
Villante, Francesco	University of L'Aquila	Italy
Villaseñor, Eduardo J S	Universidad Carlos III de Madrid	Spain
Vincent, Frederic	CNRS/Paris Observatory/LESIA	France
Virgilli, Enrico	INAF OAS Bologna	Italy
Visser, Matt	Victoria University of Wellington	New Zealand
Vladykina, Polina	Bachelor	Russia
Volkov, Mikhail	University of Tours, France	France
Vollmann, Wolfgang	BAV, AAVSO	Austria
Vorobyeva, Alexandra	RUDN University	Russia
Vyas, Mukesh Kumar	Bar Ilan University, Ramat Gan, Israel	Israel
Wadiasingh, Zorawar	NASA GSFC	USA
Wagner, Jenny	ITP Heidelberg University	Germany
Wallace, John	Bar-Ilan University	Israel
Wands, David	University of Portsmouth	UK
Wang, Fayin	Nanjing University	China
Wang, Xiang-Yu	Nanjing University	China

Wang, Yong-Qiang	Lanzhou University	China
Wang, Yusa	IHEP, CAS, China	China
Wang, Zhiwei	Jilin University	China
Wang, Yu	ICRANet	Italy
Wang, Anzhong	Baylor University	USA
Wardell, Barry	University College Dublin	Ireland
Warren, Don	RIKEN	Japan
Watson, Alan	UNAM	Mexico
Watts, Anna	University of Amsterdam	Netherlands
Weissenborn, Sven	University of Hildesheim	Germany
Weltman, Amanda	University of Cape Town	South Africa
Westerweck, Julian	AEI Hannover	Germany
White, Nicholas	George Washington University	USA
Wicker, Raphaël	IAS	France
Wieland, Wolfgang	IQOQI	Austria
Wielgus, Maciek	Black Hole Initiative at Harvard Univ.	USA
Williams, Jeff	Brandon University	Canada
Williams, Liliya	University of Minnesota	USA
Witzany, Vojtech	University College Dublin	Ireland
Woerner, Lisa	DLR-QT	Germany
Wolz, Anna	University of Virginia	USA
Wondrak, Michael Florian	Goethe-Universität Frankfurt	Germany
Wright, Michael	The Archive Trust for Research	UK
Wu, An-Ming	National Space Program Office	Taiwan
Xavier, Sérgio	Federal University of Pará	Brazil
Xavier, Semin	IIT Bombay	India
Xiong, Shaolin	Institute of High Energy Physics	China
Xu, Fan	Nanjing University	China
Xue, She-Sheng	ICRANet, Sapienza University of Rome	Italy
Yagi, Kent	University of Virginia	USA
Yamamoto, Kohei	Kumamoto University	Japan
Yamazaki, Ryo	Aoyama Gakuin University	Japan
Yan, Sheng-Feng	INFN (Milano), USTC	China
Yan, Zhenyu	Nanjing University	China
Yang, Jun	Nanjing University	China
Yang, Yuanpei	South-Western Inst. for Astron. Research	China
Yasmin, Aqsa	NUST	Pakistan
Ye, Claire	CIERA/Northwestern University	USA
Yefremov, Alexander	RUDN University	Russia
Yeh, Chih-Han	Physikalisch-Technische Bundesanstalt	Germany
Yernazarov, Tursynbek	Al-Farabi Kazakh National Univ.	Kazakhstan
Yildirim, Akin	MPI for Astrophysics	Germany

Yokokura, Yuki	RIKEN	Japan
Yoon, Myungseok	Sangmyung University	South Korea
Young, Samuel	University of Pennsylvania	USA
Yu, Hang	California Institute of Technology	USA
Yuan, Qiang	Purple Mountain Observatory	China
Yuan, Weimin	National Astronomical Observatories	China
Yue, Qian	Tsinghua University	China
Yunis, Rafael Ignacio	ICRANet Pescara	Italy
Zaccagnini, Fabio	University of Rome La Sapienza	Italy
Zahariade, George	Institut de Fisica d'Altes Energies	Spain
Zakharov, Alexander	ITEP, Moscow	Russia
Zamani, Saboura	Golestan University, Iran	Iran
Zaslavskii, Oleg	Kharkov V.N. Karazin Natl. Univ.	Ukraine
Zavatarelli, Sandra	INFN - Sezione di Genova	Italy
Zen Vasconcellos, Cesar A.	ICRANet/UFRGS	Brazil
Zhan, Mingsheng	Wuhan Inst. of Physics and Mathematics	China
Zhang, Binbin	Nanjing University	China
Zhang, Guoqiang	Nanjing University	China
Zhang, Shuang-Nan	Institute of High Energy Physics	China
Zhang, Xuefeng	Sun Yat-sen University	China
Zhang, Yuanhao	AEI Hannover	Germany
Zhang, Cong	University of Warsaw	Poland
Zhang, Bing	University of Nevada, Las Vegas	USA
Zheng, Jiaming	Shanghai Jiao-tong University	China
Zhirkov, Kirill	Moscow State University	Russia
Zhitnitsky, Ariel	University of British Columbia	Canada
Zhou, Hao	Shanghai Jiao Tong University	China
Zhou, Ning	Shanghai Jiao Tong University	China
Zhu, Jinping	Peking University	China
Zhu, Tao	Zhejiang University of Technology	China
Zhu, Sylvia	DESY	Germany
Ziegler, Joshua	University of Texas at Austin	USA
Zuccon, Paolo	Trento University and INFN TIFPA	Italy